Introduction to Management Science with Spreadsheets

Instructor's Edition

William J. Stevenson
Rochester Institute of Technology

Ceyhun Ozgur
Valparaiso University

Boston   Burr Ridge, IL   Dubuque, IA   Madison, WI   New York   San Francisco   St. Louis
Bangkok   Bogotá   Caracas   Kuala Lumpur   Lisbon   London   Madrid   Mexico City
Milan   Montreal   New Delhi   Santiago   Seoul   Singapore   Sydney   Taipei   Toronto

To: Linda, Ann Marie and John
WJS

To: Jan Ozgur
CO

Note to the Instructor

Introduction to Management Science with Spreadsheets offers an introduction to the field of management science using a modern spreadsheet approach. The text presumes a basic background in introductory statistics and some exposure to Excel. The presentation is straightforward and written in a readable, step by step procedural style that will help students develop a conceptual understanding of the concepts. The benefit is accessibility for undergraduate students and success in the course.

The Text

Within each chapter, you will find the following elements developed to help organize and facilitate the learning process.

Chapter Learning Objectives

Each chapter includes a list of learning objectives students should be able to attain upon reading and studying the chapter material. This gives students an overview of what is expected and identifies the goals for learning and understanding the material.

Forecasting

Chapter 2

Learning Objectives

After completing this chapter, you should be able to:
1. Explain the importance of forecasting in organizations.
2. Describe the three major approaches to forecasting.
3. Use a variety of techniques to make forecasts.
4. Measure the accuracy of a forecast over time using various methods.
5. Determine when a forecast can be improved.
6. Discuss the main considerations in selecting a forecasting technique.
7. Utilize Excel to solve various forecasting problems.

Chapter Outline

Introduction, 38
Qualitative Forecasts, 39
Forecasts That Use Time Series Data, 39
Techniques for Averaging, 41
Techniques for Trend, 50
Techniques for Seasonality, 59
Techniques for Cycles, 64
Explanatory Models, 65
Simple Linear Regression, 65
Regression Assumptions, 71
Multiple Regression, 72
Accuracy and Control, 76
Forecast Errors, 77
Summarizing Forecast Accuracy, 77
Monitoring and Controlling the Forecast, 78
Relative Measures of Forecast Accuracy, 79
Using Forecast Information, 84
Selecting a Forecasting Approach, 84
Summary, 86
Glossary, 87
Discussion and Review Questions, 88
Solved Problems, 89
Problems, 91
Chapter 2 Case: Gnomial Functions, Inc., 100

Chapter Outline

Each chapter begins with a list of section topics that are covered in the chapter.

Figures, Tables, and Exhibits

In every chapter, there are many visual elements, including charts, graphs, tables, and spreadsheets to illustrate concepts being applied. These visuals help stimulate student interest and clarify the text explanations.

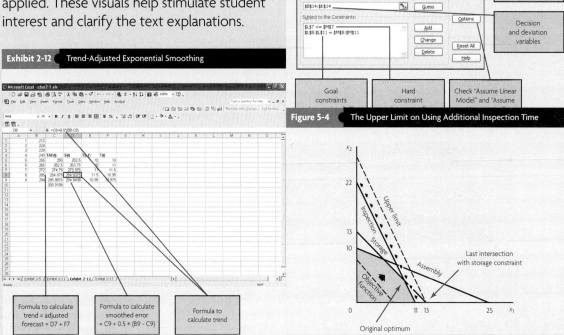

Exhibit 2-12   Trend-Adjusted Exponential Smoothing

Formula to calculate trend = adjusted forecast = D7 + F7

Formula to calculate smoothed error = C9 + 0.5 * (B9 - C9)

Formula to calculate trend

Exhibit 10-2   Excel Solver Parameters Screen for Robinson Chemical Company Goal Programming Problem Considering Only Priority 1 (Minimizing Labor Underutilization) Goal

Objective function

Decision and deviation variables

Goal constraints

Hard constraint

Check "Assume Linear Model" and "Assume

Figure 5-4   The Upper Limit on Using Additional Inspection Time

Upper limit

Inspection

Storage

Objective function

Last intersection with storage constraint

Assembly

Original optimum

> **Example** 8-3

Suppose the manager for the fuel depot wants to determine the minimum spanning tree for the network of storage tanks given in Figure 8-3 and the amount of pipe that will be needed to make the connections.

Let's begin at Node 1. Two arcs are potential connectors with other nodes; one is 13 meters in length and the other is 18 meters. Choose 13 because it is the smaller of the two. Darken that arc and shade in Nodes 1 and 2.

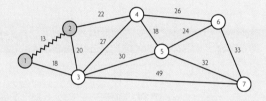

Now compare all possible arcs that could connect the connected nodes of the tree (i.e., Nodes 1 and 2) to another node. The arcs are 18 (Node 1 to Node 3), 20 (Node 2 to Node 3), and 22 (Node 2 to Node 4). Select 18 because it is the smallest, and add Arc 1–3 and Node 3 to the tree or to the set of connected nodes.

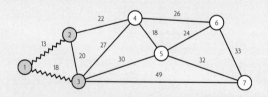

A Modern Management Science Application

Philips Electronics

The 'bullwhip effect' is a phenomenon where the demand variability increases as one moves up a supply chain. In other words, there is less variability in inventory for finished goods than for the individual components that go into those goods.

Philips Electronics Company is the 10th largest electronics company in the world with annual sales over $30 billion and 164,000 employees worldwide. Two subsidiaries of Philips Electronics—Philips Semiconductors (PS) and Philips Optical Storage (POS)—were experiencing problems with the bullwhip effect in managing their supply chain. PS, one of the world's major semiconductor suppliers, has over $5 billion in annual sales and over 33,000 employees. POS develops and builds optical storage products and has only about 9,000 employees. Both companies made a commitment to manage relationships on their supply chains to compensate for the bullwhip effect.

However, this problem could not be solved using existing software. Since POS purchases parts from PS, the companies worked together to reduce the bullwhip effect by developing a collaborative-planning (CP) project to address issues related to the bullwhip effect and the supporting computerized decision support system. The CP project team identified four key

inventories. Since PS is a supplier to POS, Philips must manage one level of inventory at PS and a second level of at POS, making it a two-echelon inventory system.

The production planning process involved integration of medium-level planning with short-term planning to avoid miscommunication among the departments. The short-term planning problem is to decide quantities of each "end-item" to release to the shop floor, while medium-term planning involves demand forecasting and overall aggregate production planning. Integrating the short- and medium-term plans is a matter of synchronizing weekly and daily production planning. There are three production "numbers," or factors, that are driven by these plans:

1. The number of wafers to fabricate.
2. The number of integrated circuits to assemble.
3. The number of integrated circuits to ship to various destinations.

The CP process consists of four "stages":

1. Gather data.
2. Make a decision about supply chain components.
3. Escalate to top management.
4. Deploy and execute decisions.

Excel Screens and Programs

Throughout the text, Excel screenshots are included. Where applicable, dialog and input boxes are shown. In many cases, the text provides both an Excel screenshot along with a grid listing the specific cells and the formulae and functions used to create that screen.

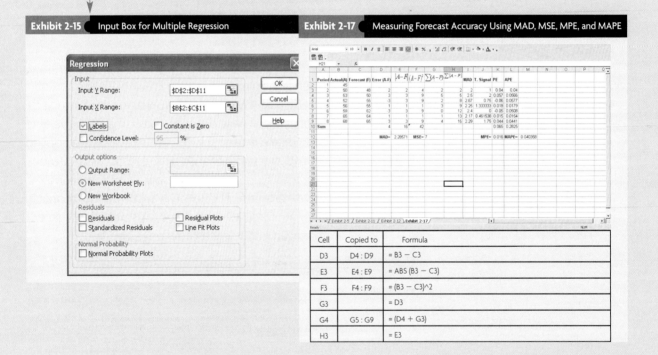

Exhibit 2-15 Input Box for Multiple Regression

Exhibit 2-17 Measuring Forecast Accuracy Using MAD, MSE, MPE, and MAPE

Cell	Copied to	Formula
D3	D4 : D9	= B3 − C3
E3	E4 : E9	= ABS (B3 − C3)
F3	F4 : F9	= (B3 − C3)^2
G3		= D3
G4	G5 : G9	= (D4 + G3)
H3		= E3

End-of-Chapter Resources

For student study and review, the following items are provided at the ends of chapters.

- **Summary.** The summaries provide an overview of the material covered.
- **Glossary.** Key terms are highlighted in the text, and they are listed and defined at the ends of chapters to aid in reviewing.

- **Solved Problems.** A number of representative problems are included with step by step solutions, including graphics.

- **Discussion and Review Questions.** Each chapter has a list of questions for student self review or for discussion.

- **Problems.** Problems give students an opportunity to test their understanding of the chapter material. Problems are included at the ends of chapters.

- **Case.** Every chapter includes a case study for student analysis or group work and discussion in class.

Chapter 6 Case   Sunshine Tomato Inc.

The Sunshine Tomato Soup Shippers produce tomato soup at three West Coast canneries in Bakersfield, Phoenix, and Eugene. The soup is shipped to four regional warehouses. Due to high demand, the company is considering opening a fourth cannery. The company is considering opening up the fourth cannery either at San Diego, San Jose, Los Angeles, or Stockton. The following table shows the cost of shipping a case from each cannery (existing and proposed) to each regional warehouse. The company wishes to ship all of its cannery capacity to the regional warehouses so that monthly transportation cost is minimized.

Source	Seattle, Washington	Los Angeles, California	Denver, Colorado	Dallas, Texas	Maximum Monthly Cannery Capacity
Phoenix, Arizona	$2.80	$0.60	$1.20	$1.50	70,000
Eugene, Oregon	$0.50	$1.20	$2.20	$2.90	80,000
Bakersfield, California	$1.80	$0.40	$1.80	$2.20	90,000
Los Angeles, California	$1.70	$0.75	$1.75	$2.50	110,000
San Diego, California	$1.80	$0.60	$1.60	$2.60	110,000
San Jose, California	$1.40	$0.70	$2.00	$2.40	110,000
Stockton, California	$1.60	$0.80	$1.80	$2.50	110,000
Monthly warehouse demand	80,000	90,000	70,000	100,000	

Discussion questions

1. What is the total transportation cost if each of the four sites should be selected?
2. Which site should be selected to locate the next cannery? Why?
3. State the shipment schedule associated with the selected site.

Summary

This chapter describes two types of problems that lend themselves to solution using linear programming techniques: transportation problems and assignment problems. These problems are part of a larger class of problems known as network flow problems. We will study other network flow problems in Chapter 8. Transportation-type problems, which include standard transportation problems with multiple sources and multiple destinations, and transshipment problems, which include intermediate nodes in addition to multiple sources and multiple destinations, involve the distribution of goods. The assignment-type problems involve the matching or pairing of two sets of items such as jobs and machines, secretaries and reports, lawyers and cases, and so forth. Transportation problems have different costs for different distribution alternatives, while the assignment problems have different cost or time requirements for different pairings. The objective for both types of problems is to identify the transportation or assignment schedule that minimizes total cost or alternatively maximized profits. The manual solution procedures for the transportation and the assignment problems are described in the Chapter 6 Supplement on the CD-ROM. The transshipment problem is also covered in this chapter. It is a variation of the transportation problem. In addition to multiple sources and multiple destinations, the transshipment problem includes multiple intermediate nodes. We show how the model is formulated as an LP model and setup and solved using Excel. The transshipment problem can easily be converted to a transportation problem and solved with the manual approach described in the Chapter 6 Supplement.

For each type of problem, we describe how to formulate it as a linear programming problem. In addition, we provide detailed explanation as to how to solve these problems using Excel and how to interpret the solution provided by Excel.

Glossary

Assignment Problem A problem that requires pairing two sets of items given a set of paired costs or profits in such a way that the total cost (profit) of the pairings is minimized (maximized).

Transportation Problem A distribution-type problem in which supplies of goods that are held at various locations are to be distributed to other receiving locations at minimum cost or maximum profit.

Transshipment Problem A transportation problem in which some locations are used as intermediate shipping points, thereby serving both as origins and as destinations.

Solved Problems

Problem 1

A company ships its products from its two plants to three warehouses. This company wants to minimize total transportation cost of shipment. The cost of shipping one unit from each source (plant) to each destination (warehouse) is given in the following table:

Source	Supply	Destination	Demand
Milwaukee (1)	61	Chicago (1)	50
Cleveland (2)	61	South Bend (2)	55
		Pittsburgh (3)	17

For Instructors

Instructor's Edition

In addition to this introduction to the text, this Instructor's Edition includes brief answers to most even-numbered problems printed in the margin in gold. These do not appear in the student edition. These margin answers are intended to provide quick reference hints for the instructor to use in class, help in choosing problems for assignment, and provide hints to help students in class discussion. The answers to the odd-numbered problems are included in the Answers Appendix in back of both instructor and student editions. Both editions also include the Student CD-ROM.

Instructor's CD-ROM (ISBN: 0073044695)

The Instructor's CD-ROM provides the instructor with a complete Instructor's Solutions Manual in Word format, the complete Test Bank in both Word files and computerized EZ Test format, PowerPoint slides, and text art files.

For Students

Student CD-ROM (ISBN: 0073044687)

The free Student CD-ROM packaged with each copy of the student text and instructor's edition, includes a number of resources for student self study and tools for working the problems in the text. These resources include self quizzes, Excel templates, Excel screencam tutorials, Excel text spreadsheet files, PowerPoint slides, and software—Premium Solver, TreePlan, and Risksim. Four chapter

supplements are also included to extend student learning. These are Chapter 4S: Linear Programming: The Simplex Method; Chapter 6S: Transportation and Assignment Solution Procedures; chapter 7S: Methods of Solving Integer Programming Problems, and Chapter 9S: Mini Review of Differential Arithmetic.

Web Resources

Online Learning Center:
www.mhhe.com/stevensonozgur1e

The Online Learning Center (OLC) is the text Web site with online content for both instructors and students. It provides chapter-by-chapter text-specific resources, including self-grading quizzes, data files, PowerPoint lecture slides, and more.

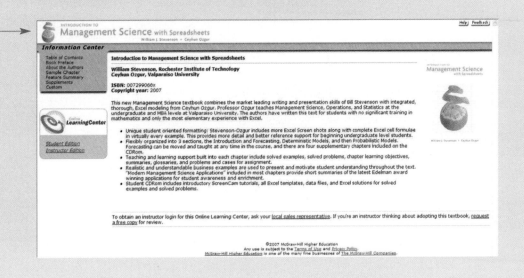

All of the material in the Online Learning Center is also available in portable Web CT, Blackboard, or E-college content "cartridges" provided free to adopters of this text.

PageOut

PageOut is an exclusive McGraw-Hill product that allows instructors to create a professional course Web site in a short time. You simply fill in the template that is provided with course information, click on one of the designs and the Web site is complete. The interactive course syllabus allows you to post content to coincide with your lectures. When students visit the site, they are directed to McGraw-Hill Web content or to your own specific material. The online grade book automatically stores quiz and test grades and allows scores to be posted to the entire class or individually. The discussion board allows for exchanging ideas, questions, or discussion of topics.

Operations Management Center (OMC): www.mhhe.com/pom

The OMC contains links to management science publications and resources, software downloads, learning aids, related Web sites and databases, and McGraw-Hill/Irwin product Web sites, and online courses.

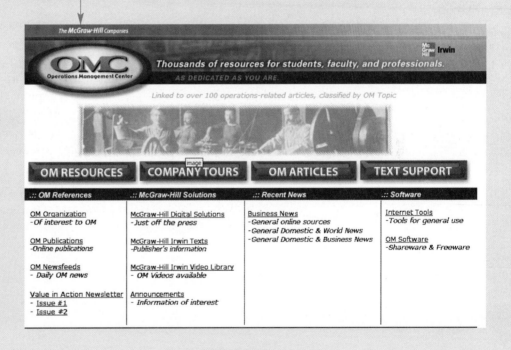

Introduction to Management Science
with Spreadsheets

William J. Stevenson
Rochester Institute of Technology

Ceyhun Ozgur
Valparaiso University

Boston   Burr Ridge, IL   Dubuque, IA   Madison, WI   New York   San Francisco   St. Louis
Bangkok   Bogotá   Caracas   Kuala Lumpur   Lisbon   London   Madrid   Mexico City
Milan   Montreal   New Delhi   Santiago   Seoul   Singapore   Sydney   Taipei   Toronto

To: Linda, Ann Marie and John
WJS

To: Jan Ozgur
CO

McGraw-Hill Irwin

INTRODUCTION TO MANAGEMENT SCIENCE WITH SPREADSHEETS

Published by McGraw-Hill/Irwin, a business unit of The McGraw-Hill Companies, Inc., 1221 Avenue of the Americas, New York, NY, 10020. Copyright © 2007 by The McGraw-Hill Companies, Inc. All rights reserved. No part of this publication may be reproduced or distributed in any form or by any means, or stored in a database or retrieval system, without the prior written consent of The McGraw-Hill Companies, Inc., including, but not limited to, in any network or other electronic storage or transmission, or broadcast for distance learning.

Some ancillaries, including electronic and print components, may not be available to customers outside the United States.

This book is printed on acid-free paper.

1 2 3 4 5 6 7 8 9 0 VNH/VNH 0 9 8 7 6

ISBN-13: 978-0-07-299066-9 (student edition)
ISBN-10: 0-07-299066-X (student edition)
ISBN-13: 978-0-07-321885-4 (instructor's edition)
ISBN-10: 0-07-321885-5 (instructor's edition)

Editorial director: *Stewart Mattson*
Executive editor: *Richard T. Hercher, Jr.*
Senior developmental editor: *Wanda J. Zeman*
Senior marketing manager: *Douglas Reiner*
Marketing coordinator: *Angela Cimarolli*
Senior media producer: *Victor Chiu*
Lead project manager: *Mary Conzachi*
Production supervisor: *Debra R. Sylvester*
Senior designer: *Mary E. Kazak*
Media project manager: *Matthew Perry*
Cover design: *Mary Kazak*
Cover photo: *Sharon Hoogstraten Photography*
Interior design: *Stratton Design*
Typeface: *10/12 Times Roman*
Compositor: *Cenveo*
Printer: *Von Hoffmann Corporation*

Library of Congress Cataloging-in-Publication Data
Stevenson, William J.
    Introduction to management science with spreadsheets / William J. Stevenson, Ceyhun Ozgur.
        p. cm.—(The McGraw-Hill/Irwin series operations and decision sciences)
    Includes index.
    ISBN-13: 978-0-07-299066-9 (student ed. : alk. paper)
    ISBN-10: 0-07-299066-X (student ed. : alk. paper)
    ISBN-13: 978-0-07-321885-4 (instructor's ed. : alk. paper)
    ISBN-10: 0-07-321885-5 (instructor's ed. : alk. paper)
    1. Management science. I. Ozgur, Ceyhun. II. Title.
T56.S82 2007
658—dc22   2005058542

www.mhhe.com

◼◼ Operations and Decision Sciences

Operations Management

Bowersox, Closs, and Cooper, *Supply Chain Logistics Management*, Second Edition

Cachon and Terwiesch, *Matching Supply with Demand: An Introduction to Operations Management*, First Edition

Chase, Jacobs, and Aquilano *Operations Management for Competitive Advantage*, Eleventh Edition

Davis and Heineke, *Operations Management: Integrating Manufacturing and Services*, Fifth Edition

Davis and Heineke, *Managing Services*, First Edition

Finch, *Operations Now: Profitability, Processes, Performance*, Second Edition

Finch, *Interactive Models for Operations and Supply Chain Management*, First Edition

Fitzsimmons and Fitzsimmons, *Service Management*, Fifth Edition

Gehrlein, *Operations Management Cases*, First Edition

Gray and Larson, *Project Management*, Third Edition

Harrison and Samson, *Technology Management*, First Edition

Hill, *Manufacturing Strategy: Text & Cases*, Third Edition

Hopp and Spearman, *Factory Physics*, Second Edition

Jacobs and Whybark, *Why ERP?*, First Edition

Leenders, Johnson, Flynn, and Fearon, *Purchasing and Supply Chain Management*, Thirteenth Edition

Nahmias, *Production and Operations Analysis*, Fifth Edition

Olson, *Introduction to Information Systems Project Management*, Second Edition

Pinto and Parente, *SimProject: A Project Management Simulation for Classroom Instruction*, First Edition

Schroeder, *Operations Management: Contemporary Concepts and Cases*, Third Edition

Seppanen, Kumar, and Chandra, *Process Analysis and Improvement*, First Edition

Simchi-Levi, Kaminsky, and Simchi-Levi, *Designing and Managing the Supply Chain*, Third Edition

Sterman, *Business Dynamics: Systems Thinking and Modeling for Complex World*, First Edition`

Stevenson, *Operations Management*, Eighth Edition

Thomke, *Managing Product and Service Development: Text and Cases*, First Edition

Ulrich and Eppinger, *Product Design and Development*, Third Edition

Vollmann, Berry, Whybark and Jacobs, *Manufacturing Planning & Control for Supply Chain Management*, Fifth Edition

Zipkin, *Foundations of Inventory Management*, First Edition

Business Statistics

Aczel and Sounderpandian, *Complete Business Statistics*, Sixth Edition

ALEKS Corporation, *ALEKS for Business Statistics*, First Edition

Alwan, *Statistical Process Analysis*, First Edition

Bowerman and O'Connell, *Business Statistics in Practice*, Fourth Edition

Bowerman, O'Connell, and Orris, *Essentials of Business Statistics*, First Edition

Cooper and Schindler, *Business Research Methods*, Ninth Edition

Doane, Mathieson, and Tracy, *Visual Statistics*, Second Edition, 2.0

Doane and Seward, *Applied Statistics in Business and Economics*, First Edition

Gitlow, Oppenheim, Oppenheim, and Levine, *Quality Management*, Third Edition

Kutner, Nachtsheim, Neter and Li, *Applied Linear Statistical Models*, Fifth Edition

Kutner, Nachtsheim, and Neter, *Applied Linear Regression Models*, Fourth Edition

Lind, Marchal, and Wathen, *Basic Statistics for Business and Economics*, Fifth Edition

Lind, Marchal, and Wathen, *Statistical Techniques in Business and Economics*, Twelfth Edition

Olson and Shi, *Introduction to Business Data Mining*, First Edition

Orris, *Basic Statistics using Megastat and Excel*, First Edition

Siegel, *Practical Business Statistics*, Fifth Edition

Wilson, Keating, and John Galt Solutions, Inc., *Business Forecasting*, Fifth Edition

Quantitative Methods and Management Science

Hillier and Hillier, *Introduction to Management Science*, Second Edition

Stevenson and Ozgur, *Introduction to Management Science with Spreadsheets*, First Edition

Preface

The material covered in this book is intended as an introduction to the field of management science. The subject matter covers the mainstream management science topics, along with the many practical applications of management science concepts. We include discussion and explanation of the concepts, formulation of problems, and their associated manual and Excel solutions.

The book describes both manual and computer solutions for a variety of management science tools. The purpose of manual solutions is to foster a conceptual understanding of each technique while presenting computer solutions to provide a practical approach to solving real-world problems.

The key areas of application for each topic is described, and appropriate techniques are explained in simple terms, with step-by-step procedures for both manual and computer solutions. There are ample discussions of how to interpret solutions.

Every effort has been made to develop a textbook that is readable and interesting. The writing style is light and informal and assumes that readers have no prior knowledge of the subject matter. The concepts are developed in a logical format, usually beginning with an overview so that readers can immediately see what the discussion will be. Explanations are clear and simple and often intuitive and examples are sprinkled liberally throughout the text.

Solved problems are provided at the end of all chapters . Students use them as a guide for solving the end of chapter problems. Answers are given to most odd numbered problems in the answer appendix.

Prerequisites for being able to understand the material in this book are basic algebra and introductory statistics.

Pedagogical Features

Much attention has been devoted to pedagogy. This book has a number of features designed to enhance learning, including:

1. Every chapter begins with a chapter outline and a list of behavioral objectives. These provide the reader with a topical overview of the chapter and a guide as to what to expect from the chapter. Every chapter includes a summary.
2. There are numerous examples throughout the chapter and a set of solved problems at the end of each chapter that serves as a resource guide for solving problems.
3. The end-of-chapter problems are plentiful. The answers to most odd numbered problems are given in the answer appendix.
4. The writing style is a key feature of this book. It is light and informal and concentrates primarily on key concepts and ideas; it does not spend a lot of time with fine points and minor details. Every effort has been made to present an interesting, readable book.
5. A glossary of key terms is provided at the end of every chapter.

Acknowledgments

We want to thank many contributors to this first edition. The reviewers for this edition made many important ideas and suggestions. While the number of suggestions exceeded the space available, many of the suggestions were incorporated directly, and some could not be incorporated. We recognize all reviewers' suggestions as valuable and important and sincerely appreciated. The list includes the following reviewers:

Kunter Gunasti	St. Francis College
Ahmad Syamil	Arkansas State University
Cem Saydam	University of North Carolina-Charlotte
Peter Shenkin	John Jay College
Abdel-Aziz M. Mohamed	California State-Northridge
Barry A. Wray	University of North Carolina-Wilmington
James C. Ford	SAS
Prakash Mirchandani	University of Pittsburgh
Cyrus K. Motlagh	University of Detroit-Mercy
Alan Chesen	Wright State University
Enrique Zapatero	Norfolk State University
Scott Morris	Southern Nazarene University
Scott Seipel	Middle Tennessee State University
Vinod Lall	Minnesota State University
Brian O'Neil	Clarkson University
Alan Fask	Farleigh Dickinson University
Hassan Hosseini	Thunderbird: Gavin School of International Management

Also thanks to the other contributors: Accuracy checkers: Jacquelynne McLellan, Frostburg State University, and Lawrence Moore, Alleghany College of Maryland; Test Bank and chapter quizzes: P. Sundararaghavan, University of Toledo; Instructor's Manual: Alan Abrahams, University of Pennsylvania, with contributions from Craig Cohen, Russell Woo, Alex Jenner, Ashwin Thapar, Afsheen Ali, and Tiffany Yeh; PowerPoint: Charlie Cook, University of West Alabama; and Excel Templates and Excel Screencam Tutorials: Lee Tangedahl, University of Montana.

The following people helped us in proofreading: Michelle Robinson, State-Farm Insurance Company, Jennifer Worth and Whitney Vogel Valparaiso University. Dr. David Schroeder, Valparaiso University provided invaluable assistance with the Excel solutions. Finally, we would like to thank all the people at McGraw-Hill/Irwin for their efforts and support. It is a pleasure to work with such a competent group of people. Special thanks go to Dick Hercher, Executive Editor; Wanda Zeman, Senior Development Editor; Mary Conzachi, Lead Project Manager; Victor Chiu, Senior Media Technology Producer; Matthew Perry, Media Project Manager; and many others who contributed indirectly.

William J. Stevenson
Ceyhun Ozgur

Contents in Brief

Preface   iv

Part 1   **Introduction to Management Science and Forecasting**   1

1 Introduction to Management Science, Modeling, and Excel Spreadsheets   2

2 Forecasting   36

Part 2   **Deterministic Decision Models**   102

3 Linear Programming: Basic Concepts and Graphical Solution   104

4 Applications and Solutions of Linear Programming   152

4S Linear Programming: The Simplex Method (CD-ROM)   4S-2

5 Linear Programming: Sensitivity Analysis and Duality   206

6 Transportation, Transshipment, and Assignment Problems   274

6S Transportation and Assignment Solution Procedures (CD-ROM)   6S-2

7 Integer Programming   322

7S Methods of Solving Integer Programming Problems (CD-ROM)   7S-2

8 Network Optimization Models   368

9 Nonlinear Programming   422

9S Mini Review of Differential Arithmetic (CD-ROM)   9S-2

10 Multicriteria Decision-Making Models   472

Part 3   **Probabilistic Decision Models**   536

11 Decision Theory   538

12 Markov Analysis   604

13 Waiting-Line Models   658

14 Simulation   722

Appendix A: Answers to Most Odd-Numbered Problems   783
Appendix B: Tables   793
Index   799

Contents

Preface   iv

Part 1 Introduction to Management Science and Forecasting   1

1 Introduction to Management Science, Modeling, and Excel Spreadsheets   2

Introduction   4
    A Problem Focus   4
    Use of a Quantitative Approach   4
Models   6
    Benefits and Risks of Using Models   7
    Assumptions of Models   7
    Deterministic versus Probabilistic Models   8
The Management Science Approach   9
    Problem Definition   9
    Model Construction   10
    Model Analysis   10
    Implementation and Follow-Up   11
The Utilization of Decision Support Systems (DSS) in the Context of Management Science   12
Plan of the Book   13
Role of Computers and Spreadsheets in Management Science   15
Getting Started with Excel   16
Break-Even Analysis   20
    Introduction to Break-Even Analysis   20
    Components of Break-Even Analysis   20
    The Break-Even Point   24
    Assumptions of Break-Even Analysis   24
    Using Excel to Solve the Break-Even Model   25
    Using Excel's Goal Seek to Compute the Break-Even Point   25
    Summary of Break-Even Analysis   27
The Importance and Impact of Management Science   27

Summary   30
Glossary   30
Discussion and Review Questions   31
Problems   32
Chapter 1 Case: Green Daisy Company   34

2 Forecasting   36

Introduction   38
Qualitative Forecasts   39
Forecasts That Use Time Series Data   39
    Techniques for Averaging   41
    Techniques for Trend   50
    Techniques for Seasonality   59
    Techniques for Cycles   64
Explanatory Models   65
    Simple Linear Regression   65
    Regression Assumptions   71
    Multiple Regression   72
Accuracy and Control   76
    Forecast Errors   77
    Summarizing Forecast Accuracy   77
    Monitoring and Controlling the Forecast   78
Relative Measures of Forecast Accuracy   79
Using Forecast Information   84
Selecting a Forecasting Approach   84
Summary   86
Glossary   87
Discussion and Review Questions   88
Solved Problems   89
Problems   91
Chapter 2 Case: Gnomial Functions, Inc.   100

Part 2 Deterministic Decision Models   102

3 Linear Programming: Basic Concepts and Graphical Solution   104

Introduction   106
    Constrained Optimization   106
    Linear Programming   106
    A Simple Example   107

*Successful Implementation of Linear
Programming*   108
*Components and Assumptions of
LP Models*   109
Formulating LP Models   112
Graphical Method   115
Graphing the Model   115
Plotting the Constraints   115
Finding the Optimal Solution   119
The Extreme Point Approach   119
*The Objective Function (Iso-Profit Line)
Approach*   122
A Minimization Example   126
Slack and Surplus   129
Some Special Issues   131
No Feasible Solutions   131
Unbounded Problems   132
Redundant Constraints   133
Multiple Optimal Solutions   134
Summary   134
Glossary   135
Solved Problems   136
Discussion and Review Questions   141
Problems   142
Chapter 3 Case: Son, Ltd.   150

**4   Applications and Solutions of Linear
     Programming**   152
Introduction   154
Product-Mix Problems   154
Problem Formulation   155
*Excel Solution of the Style and Comfort
Furniture Company Example*   157
Diet Problems   163
Blending Problems   164
Marketing Applications   168
Media Selection   168
Marketing Research   172
Financial Applications   176
Financial Planning Problems for Banks   176
Portfolio Selection   179
Production Applications   180
Multiperiod Production Scheduling   181
Workforce Scheduling   183
Make-or-Buy Decisions   185
Agriculture Applications   186
Data Envelopment Analysis   189
Comment about the Use of Excel   192
Other Applications   192
Summary   193

Glossary   194
Solved Problems   195
Discussion and Review Questions   196
Problems   196
Chapter 4 Case: Direct Marketing   204

**4S Linear Programming: The Simplex
     Method** (CD-ROM)   4S-2
Overview of the Simplex Method   4S-4
Finding an Initial Feasible Solution   4S-6
Developing the Initial Simplex Tableau   4S-7
Interpreting the Solution   4S-9
Developing the Second Tableau   4S-10
Interpreting the Second Tableau   4S-16
Developing the Third Tableau   4S-16
Interpreting the Third Tableau   4S-19
Summary of the Simplex Procedure for a
Maximization Problem   4S-20
Mixed Constraints   4S-21
= and ≥ Constraints   4S-21
Solving Maximization Problems That Have
Mixed Constraints   4S-23
Solving Minimization Problems   4S-29
Some Special Issues   4S-32
Unbounded Solutions   4S-32
Degeneracy   4S-33
Multiple Optimal Solutions   4S-34
Infeasibility   4S-35
Summary   4S-36
Glossary   4S-37
Solved Problems   4S-38
Discussion and Review Questions   4S-45
Problems   4S-46

**5   Linear Programming: Sensitivity
     Analysis and Duality**   206
Introduction to Sensitivity Analysis   208
*A Change in the Value of an Objective
Function Coefficient*   209
*A Change in the RHS Value of a
Constraint*   213
Minimization Problems   219
Sensitivity Analysis with Excel   219
Multiple Changes   224
Summary of Sensitivity Analysis   226
Duality   226
Formulating the Dual   227
*Formulating the Dual When the
Primal Has Mixed Constraints*   229
*Comparison of the Primal and Dual
Solutions*   231

Economic Interpretation of the Dual 231
Adding Another Variable 232
Computational Considerations 232
Summary 236
Glossary 237
Solved Problems 238
Discussion and Review Questions 246
Problems 246
Chapter 5 Case: Red Brand Canners 270

6   Transportation, Transshipment, and Assignment Problems 274
Introduction 276
Transportation Problems 276
Formulating the Model 276
Special Cases of Transportation Problems 279
Solving Transportation Problems Using Excel 280
Other Applications 287
Transshipment Problems 287
Aggregate Planning 294
Location Analysis 297
Assignment Problems 298
Linear Programming Formulation of the Assignment Problem 299
Solving the Assignment Problem Using Excel 300
Summary 303
Glossary 303
Solved Problems 303
Discussion and Review Questions 309
Problems 310
Chapter 6 Case: Sunshine Tomato Inc. 321

6S Transportation and Assignment Solution Procedures (CD-ROM) 6S-2
Transportation Problems 6S-4
Formulating the Model 6S-4
Solution of the Transportation Model 6S-4
Overview of the Solution Technique 6S-6
Finding an Initial Feasible Solution 6S-6
Finding an Initial Feasible Solution: The Northwest-Corner Method 6S-7
Finding an Initial Feasible Solution: The Intuitive Approach 6S-8
Finding an Initial Feasible Solution: Vogel's Approximation Method 6S-11
Evaluating a Solution for Optimality 6S-13

Evaluation Using the Stepping-Stone Method 6S-13
Evaluation Using the MODI Method 6S-16
Developing an Improved Solution 6S-18
Special Issues 6S-20
Assignment Problems 6S-24
The Hungarian Method 6S-25
Summary of Procedure 6S-29
Requirements for Use of the Hungarian Method 6S-29
Special Situations 6S-29
Summary 6S-32
Glossary 6S-32
Solved Problems 6S-33
Discussion and Review Questions 6S-42
Problems 6S-43

7   Integer Programming 322
Introduction to Integer Programming 324
Types of Integer Programming Problems 324
Pure-Integer Problems 324
Mixed-Integer Problems 324
0–1 Integer Problems 324
Graphical Representation of Integer Programming Problems 325
Solving Integer Programming Problems Using Excel 326
A Comment about Sensitivity 329
Formulating Integer Programming Problems with 0–1 Constraints 329
Either-Or Alternatives 330
k-Out-of-n Alternatives 330
If-Then Alternatives 330
Either-Or Constraints 331
Variables That Have Minimum Level Requirements 331
Specialized Integer Programming Problems 332
Fixed-Charge Problem 333
Set Covering Problem 336
Knapsack Problem 340
Facility Location Problem 341
Traveling Salesperson Problem 344
Difficulties in Solving Integer Programming Problems 349
Summary 351
Glossary 351
Solved Problems 352
Discussion and Review Questions 356
Problems 357
Chapter 7 Case: Suburban Suntime 365

7S Methods of Solving Integer Programming Problems (CD-ROM)   7S-2

Solving Integer Programming Problems   7S-4
The Branch and Bound Method   7S-5
   A Pure-Integer Problem   7S-6
   Summary of the Branch and Bound
   Method for an All-Integer
   Maximization Problem   7S-13
   Mixed-Integer Problems   7S-14
   Enumeration Method   7S-20
0–1 Problems   7S-20
   Branch and Bound Method   7S-23
A Minimization Problem   7S-25
Summary   7S-26
Glossary   7S-27
Solved Problems   7S-27
Discussion and Review Questions   7S-29
Problems   7S-30

8 Network Optimization Models   368

Introduction   370
The Shortest-Route Problem   371
   The Shortest-Route (Labeling) Algorithm
   (Concept Development)   371
   Summary of Procedure   375
   Linear Programming Formulation of the
   Shortest-Route Problem   376
   Solving the Shortest-Route Problem
   Using Excel   378
The Minimum Spanning Tree Problem   384
   Algorithm for the Minimum Spanning Tree
   Problem (Concept Development)   384
The Maximal Flow Problem   387
   Maximal Flow Algorithm (Concept
   Development)   388
   Demonstration of Reverse Flow   391
   Linear Programming Formulation of the
   Maximal Flow Problem   393
   Comment   400
Summary   401
Glossary   401
Solved Problems   401
Discussion and Review Questions   411
Problems   412
Chapter 8 Case: Furnace County Emergency
Response Routes   420

9 Nonlinear Programming   422

Introduction   424
Models with One Decision Variable   425

   Unconstrained Problem with One
   Decision Variable   425
   Solution of One-Decision-Variable,
   Unconstrained Problem with Excel   429
   Constrained Problem with One
   Decision Variable   433
   Solution of One-Decision-Variable,
   Constrained Problem with Excel   435
Models with Two Decision Variables,
Unconstrained Problem   439
   Solution of Unconstrained Problems
   with Two Decision Variables
   Using Excel   442
Models with Two Decision Variables
and an Equality Constraint
(Lagrange Multipliers)   444
   Interpreting λ   446
   Solution of Problems with Two Decision
   Variables and a Single Equality
   Constraint Using Excel   446
Models with Two Decision Variables and a
Single Inequality Constraint   449
Solution of Problems with Two
Decision Variables and Multiple
Constraints Using Excel   451
Summary   454
Glossary   456
Solved Problems   457
Discussion and Review Questions   466
Problems   466
Chapter 9 Case: Koch International
Incorporated   469

9S Mini Review of Differential Arithmetic (CD-ROM)   9S-2

10 Multicriteria Decision-Making Models   472

Introduction   474
   Goal Programming Versus Linear
   Programming   474
   Deviation Variables   475
Model Formulation   476
   Graphical Solutions   478
Solving Goal Programming Problems
Using Excel   482
   Weighted Goals   490
Analytical Hierarchy Process   493
   Pairwise Comparisons   495
   Normalized Pairwise Comparison
   Matrix   496

Consistency Check for Criteria	496
Analytical Hierarchy Process	
Using Excel	501
Scoring Models	504
The Steps for the Scoring Model	504
Summary	506
Glossary	508
Solved Problems	509
Discussion and Review Questions	523
Problems	525
Chapter 10 Case: Hi-Tech Incorporated	534

Part 3 Probabilistic Decision Models | 536

11 Decision Theory | 538
Introduction	540
List of Alternatives	541
States of Nature	541
Payoffs	541
Degree of Certainty	541
Decision Criterion	542
The Payoff Table	542
Decision Making under Certainty	543
Decision Making under Complete Uncertainty	544
Maximin	544
Maximax	545
Minimax Regret	545
The Hurwicz (Realism) Criterion	547
Equal Likelihood Criterion	548
Using Excel for Decision Making under Complete Uncertainty	549
Decision Making under Risk	552
Expected Monetary Value	552
Expected Opportunity Loss	553
Expected Value of Perfect Information	553
Using Excel for Decision Making under Risk	555
Decision Trees	556
Using TreePlan to Develop Decision Trees with Excel	559
Sequential Decision Tree Analysis with Excel and TreePlan	564
Decision Making with Additional Information	567
Efficiency of Sample Information	570
Computing the Probabilities	571
Computing Revised Probabilities with Excel	573

Sensitivity Analysis	573
Utility	578
Summary	580
Glossary	581
Solved Problems	582
Discussion and Review Questions	594
Problems	595
Chapter 11 Case: MKGP Construction Company	602

12 Markov Analysis | 604
Introduction	606
Transition Probabilities	607
System Behavior	608
Methods of Analysis	609
Tree Diagram	609
Matrix Multiplication	611
Algebraic Solution	614
Using Excel for Markov Analysis	616
Analysis of a 3×3 Matrix	621
Tree Diagram	622
Matrix Multiplication	623
Algebraic Solution	624
Using Excel to Solve Three-State Problems	625
Cyclical, Transient, and Absorbing Systems	630
Analysis of Accounts Receivable	632
Analysis of Absorbing States Using Excel	636
Assumptions	639
Summary	639
Glossary	641
Solved Problems	641
Discussion and Review Questions	649
Problems	650
Chapter 12 Case: Memorial Hospital	657

13 Waiting-Line Models | 658
Introduction	660
Goals of Queuing System Design	660
Elements and Characteristics of Waiting-Line Systems	661
Calling Population	662
Customer Arrivals	662
Poisson Distribution	663
Calculation of Poisson Probability Using Excel	665
The Waiting Line	667
Processing Order	667
Service	667

Exponential Distribution   669
Calculation of Exponential Probability
Using Excel   672
Exit   673

Measures of System Performance   673
   Basic Relationships   674
Queuing Models   676
   Basic Single-Channel (M/M/1) Model   676
   Basic Single-Channel Model with Poisson
   Arrival and Exponential Service Rate
   (M/M/1 Model) with Excel   678
   Multiple-Channel Model (M/M/S)   678
   Multiple-Channel Model with Poisson
   Arrival and Exponential Service Rate
   (M/M/S Model) with Excel   687
   Determining Maximum Length of
   Waiting Lines   687
Cost Considerations   690
Other Queuing Models
(Optional Coverage)   692
   Model Variation I: Poisson Arrival
   Rate with Any ServiceDistribution
   (M/G/1)   692
   Single-Channel Model with Poisson
   Arrival and Any Service Distribution
   (M/G/1 Model) with Excel   693
   Model Variation II: Poisson Arrival
   Rate,Constant Service Time (M/D/1)   695
   Single-Channel Model with Poisson
   Arrival and Constant Service
   Distribution (M/D/1 Model)
   with Excel   695
   Model Variation III: Finite
   Queue Length   696
   Single-Channel Model That Involves a
   Finite Queue Length with Poisson
   Arrival and Exponential Service
   Distribution with Excel   697
   Model Variation IV: Finite Calling
   Population   698
   Single-Channel Model That Involves a
   Finite Calling Population with Poisson
   Arrival and Exponential Service
   Distribution with Excel   700
   Model Variation V: Multiple-Server,
   Priority Servicing Model   702
   Revising Priorities   704
   Utilization of Excel's Goal Seek
   Function   705
The Psychology of Waiting   707

The Value of Waiting Line Models   708
Summary   710
Glossary   711
Solved Problem   711
Discussion and Review Questions   713
Problems   713
Chapter 13 Case: Big Bank   721

14   Simulation   **722**
Introduction   724
Replacement Parts Illustration   725
Types of Simulation   726
   Discrete versus Continuous
   Simulations   726
   Fixed-Interval versus Next-Event
   Simulations   726
   Deterministic versus Probabilistic
   Simulations   727
Steps in Simulation   727
   Defining the Problem and Setting
   Objectives   727
   Developing a Model   729
   Gathering Data   729
   Validating the Model   729
   Designing Experiments   730
   Running Simulations   730
   Analyzing and Interpreting
   the Results   731
The Monte Carlo Method   731
   Simulation Using a Theoretical
   Distribution   735
   The Uniform Distribution   736
   The Exponential Distribution   737
   The Normal Distribution   738
Multiple-Variable Simulations   739
Computer Simulation   742
Computer Simulation Using Excel   742
   Random Number Generation with
   Probability Distributions
   Using Excel   743
   A Discrete Distribution with Two
   Outcomes   746
   A Discrete Distribution with More Than
   Two Outcomes   747
   Simulation of Waiting Lines   749
   Inventory Analysis Using Simulation
   and Excel   752
Scenario Manager   757
Simulation Languages   759
Pseudo-Random Numbers   760

Advantages and Limitations of
Simulation   760
When to Use Simulation   760
Summary   761
Glossary   762
Solved Problems   762
Discussion and Review Questions   769

Problems   770
Chapter 14 Case: Krohler Supermarkets   781

Appendix A: Answers to Most Odd-Numbered
                 Problems   783
Appendix B: Tables   793
Index   799

Introduction to Management Science and Forecasting

Part I begins with an introduction to the field of management science. Chapter 1 discusses the importance of models, the use of the management science approach, which focuses on model development, and then presents the use of break-even analysis, and an introduction on how to use basic Excel functions. The chapter also sets forth the layout of the book, which includes definitions of what is to be covered in each chapter.

Forecasting is covered in Chapter 2 due to its fundamental importance. Given that forecasting affects so many important business activities, including budget planning, hiring, layoffs, production planning and capacity planning, it is important to know how to create reasonably accurate forecasts. Without good forecasting, many of these activities cannot be done correctly. The chapter also points out that it is always impossible to achieve a perfect forecast due to the constant uncertainty existing in the business environment. Fortunately, today, with the help of forecasting research, tools, and technology, we can predict many variables and events with a high level of precision.

Part Outline

Chapter 1   Introduction to Management Science, Modeling, and Excel spreadsheets

Chapter 2   Forecasting

Introduction to Management Science, Modeling, and Excel Spreadsheets

Chapter 1

Learning Objectives

After completing this chapter, you should be able to:

1. Describe the importance of management science.
2. Describe the advantages of a quantitative approach to problem solving.
3. List some of the applications and use of management science models.
4. Discuss the types of models most useful in management science.
5. Demonstrate the basic building blocks and components of Excel.
6. Describe the basic nature and usefulness of break-even analysis.
7. List and briefly explain each of the components of break-even analysis.
8. Solve typical break-even problems manually and with Excel.

Chapter Outline

Introduction, 4
A Problem Focus, 4
Use of a Quantitative Approach, 4

Models, 6
Benefits and Risks of Using Models, 7
Assumptions of Models, 7
Deterministic versus Probabilistic Models, 8

The Management Science Approach, 9
Problem Definition, 9
Model Construction, 10
Model Analysis, 10
Implementation and Follow-Up, 11

The Utilization of Decision Support System (DSS) in the Context of Management Science, 12

Plan of the Book, 13

Role of Computers and Spreadsheets in Management Science, 15

Getting Started with Excel, 16

Break-Even Analysis, 20
Introduction to Break-Even Analysis, 20
Components of Break-Even Analysis, 20
The Break-Even Point, 24
Assumptions of Break-Even Analysis, 24
Using Excel to Solve the Break-Even Model, 25
Using Excel's Goal Seek to Compute the Break-Even Point, 25
Summary of Break-Even Analysis, 27

The Importance and Impact of Management Science, 27

Summary, 30

Glossary, 30

Discussion and Review Questions, 31

Problems, 32

Chapter 1 Case: Green Daisy Company, 34

Management science is the discipline of applying advanced analytical methods to help make better decisions. It is a discipline devoted to solving managerial-type problems using quantitative models. This quantitative approach is widely employed in business. Areas of application include forecasting, capital budgeting, portfolio analysis, capacity planning, scheduling, marketing, inventory management, project management, and production planning.

In this first chapter, some of the basics of management science are covered, including the answers to such questions as: What is management science? Who uses it? Why use a quantitative approach? What are models, and why are they used? What are the different types of models? How are models used? Why are computers important in management science?

◼️ Introduction

Management science uses a logical approach to problem solving. The problem is viewed as the focal point of analysis, and quantitative models are the vehicles by which solutions are obtained.

A Problem Focus

By adopting a problem focus, a decision maker has the advantage of directing attention to the essence of an analysis: to solve a specific problem. The problem in question may pertain to a current condition or it may relate more to the future. An example of a current condition would be customers complaining to the manager of a bank about the amount of time they have to wait in line for a teller. It is hoped that these kinds of problems can be kept to a minimum; a manger cannot be productive if he or she spends very much time putting out fires.

Often, problems result from inadequate planning. Hence, an ideal use of a manager's time, and of management science models, is to plan for the future. An example of that kind of problem would be deciding where to locate a warehouse to minimize future shipping costs. Another example would be choosing a plan for assigning jobs to machines that will minimize the total time needed to complete the jobs. Still other examples include predicting future demand so that intelligent decisions can be made about production levels, workforce levels, capacity, and inventory; selecting the combination of product output quantities that will maximize profits; and identifying appropriate levels of inventory.

Use of a Quantitative Approach

Problem solving can be either qualitative or quantitative. In qualitative problem solving, intuition and subjective judgment are used. Past experience with similar problems is often an important factor in choosing a qualitative approach, as are the complexity and importance of a problem. Managers tend to use a qualitative approach to problem solving when:

1. The problem is fairly simple.
2. The problem is familiar.
3. The costs involved are not great.

Conversely, managers tend to use a quantitative approach when one or more of the following conditions exist

1. The problem is complex.
2. The problem is not familiar.

3. The costs involved are substantial.
4. Enough time is available to analyze the problem.

Generally speaking, decisions based on quantitative analysis tend to be more objective than those based on a purely qualitative analysis. On the other hand, a purely quantitative analysis will include only information that can be quantified. Therefore, the results of models should be followed routinely only for the simplest and best-understood cases; otherwise, the results should be questioned and analyzed. As a general rule, the results of a mathematical analysis should be reviewed by management for reasonableness and feasibility.

The use of quantitative analysis is not new. Quantitative methods of problem solving can be traced back to ancient times. Who would doubt that the great pyramids of Egypt were designed and built using quantitative methods? In similar fashion, the movements and supply requirements of Roman armies, the construction of ancient canals and waterways, and the ancient shipbuilding processes undoubtedly benefited from the use of quantitative methods.

Many of the early uses involved engineering applications. However, there were very few *managerial* applications of mathematical analysis before the Industrial Revolution, particularly with respect to problem solving. Even then, management science as we now know it did not exist.

A key period in the development of the use of the quantitative approach to problem solving came during World War II when teams of scientists were brought together to help solve complex military problems on deploying troops, searching the seas, supplying troops, and so on. These developments were given the name of operations research (OR) because scientists were doing research on managing military operations. The abbreviation for operations research is often used in conjunction with the abbreviation for management science, referring to the discipline as OR/MS. The following two societies publish journals and newsletters dealing with news and the state-of-the-art research and applications of operations research and management science techniques: The Institute for Operations Research and the Management Sciences (**INFORMS**), http://www.informs.org, and Decision Sciences Institute (**DSI**), http://www.decisionsciences.org. After the war, many of the techniques used by the operations researchers were adapted to business applications, and management science began to emerge as a discipline. Previously developed quantitative techniques were added along with newly developed techniques to form an expanding body of knowledge that had important business applications.

One difficulty that early practitioners faced was the burdensome computational requirements that often were required to solve even fairly simple problems. It is not surprising, then, that increasing use of management science has accompanied advances in computer technology, both in hardware and software. Today, access to computers, both mainframe and personal, puts the power of management science within the reach of virtually all managers.

The combination of access to computers and computer codes for solving management problems, continuing developments in management science models, and successful applications have contributed to the respectability of management science as a discipline. Successful applications of management science and new developments in this field are reported regularly in such journals as *Management Science, Decision Sciences, Interfaces,* and *Operations Research.*

Finally, it should be noted that although the field of management science is not entirely quantitative, the preponderance of management science applications fall under the heading of quantitative analysis. For that reason, this book emphasizes applications involving quantitative models.

Models

A **model** is an abstraction of reality. It is a simplified, and often idealized, representation of reality. An equation, an outline, a diagram, and a map are each an example of a model. By its very nature a model is incomplete: A good model will capture the important details of reality without including innumerable minor details that would obscure rather than illuminate. You could think of a model as a selective abstraction because only those details that are considered to be important for the problem at hand are included in the model. For example, suppose the problem involved aerodynamic properties of a new automotive design. Important details that come to mind are weight, shape, size, and height. Unimportant details include color, interior design, type of radio, and so on. Thus, it is important to carefully decide which aspects of reality to include in a model.

Models provide a manager or analyst with an alternative to working directly with reality. This allows the person using the model greater freedom in terms of experimenting with different ideas, controlling certain aspects of the situation, and investigating alternative solutions. It also reduces the cost of mistakes if mistakes can be corrected within the realm of the model.

In practice, models are employed in a variety of ways. **Symbolic models** incorporate numbers and algebraic symbols to represent important aspects of a problem, often in equation form. These numbers and symbols are then manipulated to solve for unknown values of key variables. Moreover, **mathematical models** lend themselves to the computational power inherent in calculators and computers.

Consider this simple mathematical model:

Profit $= 5x$

where

x = pounds of material sold

The number 5 represents the profit per unit of material, and the symbol x represents the quantity of a certain material; profit is the product of the profit per unit and the number of units sold. Thus, if 15 units are sold, the profit is $5(15) = \$75$.

A slightly more complex version of this model is the following:

Profit $= 5x_1 + 8x_2 + 4x_3$

where

x_1 = pounds of material 1 sold
x_2 = pounds of material 2 sold
x_3 = pounds of material 3 sold

Thus, if $x_1 = 10$, $x_2 = 20$, and $x_3 = 30$, the total profit would be

$5(10) + 8(20) + 4(30) = \$330$

Mathematical models are made up of constants and variables; constants are fixed or known quantities not subject to variation, whereas **variables** can take on different values and can be either probabilistic or deterministic. Constants generally are represented by numbers and the variables by letters.

Thus, in the model Profit $= 5x_1 + 8x_2 + 4x_3$, the unit profits (5, 8, and 4) are the constants and the quantities of materials 1, 2, and 3 (i.e., x_1, x_2, and x_3) are the variables. In this example, the variables are **decision variables.** The manager or analyst would want to know what values to set these at (i.e., how much of each material to produce) in order to obtain the highest profit. Decision variables, therefore, are under the control of a decision maker and can be set at a desired level. Another kind of variable that is often encountered is an **uncontrollable variable.** An example would be the weather: Although it is beyond the control of a manager, weather sometimes is a factor that can have some bearing on profits. For instance, a mild, rainy winter can substantially reduce profits at ski resorts. Similarly, rainy weather and flooding can slow down a construction project. Other examples of uncontrollable variables include government decisions (for example, revision of the tax code, pollution regulations), competitors' decisions (e.g., product design, advertising, pricing), and consumer decisions.

Thus, models that are used for problem solving include constants, decision variables, and uncontrollable variables. The challenge for the manager or analyst who is developing a model is to determine the levels of the decision variables that will best serve the goals of the manager, given the constants and uncontrollable variables.

The models used in this book will be a blend of graphical, mathematical, and spreadsheet models: The graphical models will help to illustrate important concepts and help you to develop an intuitive understanding of various models, whereas the mathematical models will enable you to determine solutions for a wide range of problems. The spreadsheet models translate mathematical models to a spreadsheet.

Benefits and Risks of Using Models

Models have numerous benefits for problem solvers, but there also are certain risks for the users. Obviously, the benefits generally must tend to outweigh the risks, or models would not be used.

An important benefit of using a model is that it allows an analyst to strip away many unimportant details of reality and thereby focus attention on a small number of important aspects of a problem. The risk in doing this is that one or more of the important aspects of a problem may be inadvertently left out. If this happens, it is highly unlikely that the analyst will be able to successfully solve the real-world problem using the model.

Another benefit of using quantitative models is that they force the analyst to quantify information. The risk is that nonquantitative information may be down-played or ignored because it is difficult or impossible to include that type of information in a quantitative model.

The third benefit of models is the structure they provide for analyzing a problem in terms of what information is needed and how to organize information. One risk is that an inexperienced analyst may attempt to force a problem to fit the model. In effect, chances of obtaining a good solution would be diminished.

The process of developing a model can generate tremendous insight about reality. Care must be taken, however, so that modeling does not become an end in itself. In fact, it is easy to get carried away with modeling and to end up with a model that is more complex and powerful than what is needed to solve the problem.

Another benefit of models is that they compress time. They usually are also less costly than a real-life situation would be, and they permit users the luxury of experimentation without dangers that would be inherent in a real-life setting. However, due to their abstract nature, models sometimes do not adequately portray relationships that exist in reality. A consequence of this kind of error is that solutions obtained from the model fail under the harsh light of reality. One way to reduce this risk is to give careful consideration to the assumptions on which the model is based.

Assumptions of Models

All models are based on assumptions (that is, conditions that are assumed to exist). Some of these will be technical, such as "the relationship is linear"; others will be operational, such as "the budget is $25,000"; and still others may be political, such as "Marketing will support the proposal."

It is usually wise to write out the assumptions that can be identified before developing the model. This will increase the chances of developing a workable and acceptable model. Moreover, those who are in a position to approve or reject a solution (e.g., manager, customer, potential investor) may want to know what assumptions were made, why they were made, how realistic they are, and so on.

In terms of studying management science, assumptions in the technical category will be most relevant. As each new model is introduced, make note of the assumptions and what impact they have on the model. Recognize that many assumptions simplify; they reduce the complexity that would be inherent in reality. Using simplifying assumptions in practice always involves evaluating the trade-offs: The simpler the model, the easier it will be to understand and use it in order to obtain solutions, but the greater the risk will be that the solutions based on the model will not apply to reality.

Deterministic versus Probabilistic Models

Some models can be used to determine an optimal, or best, solution to a problem, whereas other models are used to predict approximate, or average, future outcomes. The choice between these two kinds of models depends primarily on the *degree of certainty* that can be assigned to the information available to the analyst. **Deterministic models** are used for problems in which information is known with a high degree of certainty. For instance, in a problem involving production times, if the production times are known and are constant (that is, the same time is required for every repetition of the process), a deterministic model could be used to determine an optimal solution to the problem. Conversely, when it cannot be determined precisely what value will occur (usually in the future) a **probabilistic model** that incorporates *probabilities* is appropriate. For example, choosing the size of a warehouse to build depends on how large future demand will be. If, because of contractual commitments from a buyer, a manager knows what demand to plan for, an optimal-size warehouse could be determined. However, such cases are quite rare. Instead, managers usually are faced with situations in which future demand is subject to variability (i.e., it cannot be predicted exactly, but only approximately). Then the goal is to minimize the error in predictions; without complete knowledge, it is virtually impossible to specify an optimal solution.

It should be noted that an optimal solution is generally optimal only in the context of a model and not necessarily in the larger context of reality. This is because all models are simplified versions of reality; that is, they do not and cannot incorporate all of the details and factors that comprise reality. Consequently, it is debatable whether any solution is truly optimal in the purest sense of the word. Therefore, when the term *optimal* is employed in this text, and in management science in general, it refers to the conditions contained in a mathematical model. This is not to say that optimal solutions are unacceptable in reality or that they are not good solutions. On the contrary, such solutions may not only be very good, they also may be much better than solutions generated in less scientific ways. Nonetheless, it would be incorrect to believe that optimal solutions obtained from models will be truly optimal when applied to reality. Because of this, a manager should review all but the most routine solutions before implementing them, and should decide whether to implement the solution as it stands or to first modify it because of some other subjective considerations. In addition, some deterministic models do not result in optimal solutions.

The Management Science Approach

Although management science incorporates quantitative analysis in its approach to problem solving, it would be a mistake to regard management science as merely a collection of techniques. It is as much a *philosophy* of problem solving as it is the use of quantitative methods.

The management science approach is quite similar to the **scientific approach** commonly used in the physical sciences. Both involve a logical sequence that includes careful definition of the problem, use of models, and analysis leading to solution of the problem. The management science approach is outlined in Figure 1-1.

Problem Definition

The first step in problem solving is *careful* problem definition. It is important to resist the temptation to rush through this stage in order to begin working on the model and the solution. Unfortunately, exactly the opposite occurs in many cases. When that happens, the solution is less likely to solve the problem, and it may create additional problems. Furthermore, senior managers may become disillusioned in the process, and they may turn to other, less objective, methods for handling problems.

Good problem definition may involve observing a current situation or process in order to better understand it. Almost always, it is highly desirable to talk with the people who are closely involved (e.g., workers, supervisors, salespeople, staff). Not only do such people usually possess considerable knowledge and insight that enable them to suggest potential solutions, they also are the ones who must live with the solution. By including them in

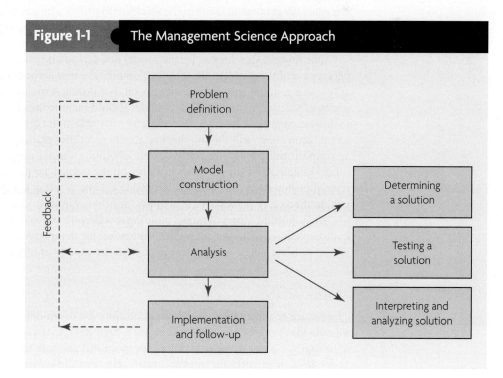

Figure 1-1   The Management Science Approach

the process, they are less likely to resist the solution because they will feel that they contributed to it.

Once the problem has been reasonably defined, it is time to construct a model. However, it is wise to leave room for possible future redefinition of the problem. It is quite common to gain new insights and raise additional questions as modeling progresses. These often lead to refining, or even modifying, the initial problem definition.

Model Construction

The goal of modeling should be to achieve an accurate, yet relatively simple, representation of reality. Hence, the model should reflect the major aspects of the problem as simply as possible. Often, this requires trade-offs because simplicity and accuracy rarely go hand in hand. Therefore, the model builder must decide on an appropriate balance between a model that is highly accurate in its portrayal of reality (and, consequently, complex) and one that is relatively simple. Usually, the more complex the model, the more costly and time-consuming it is to build and the more difficult it is to understand. Conversely, a model that is too simple may not provide an adequate portrayal of reality, thereby decreasing the chances of finding a reasonable solution to the problem. Ideally, a model will enable the analyst or manager to study a problem in a quasi-laboratory environment that will lead to a clearer understanding of the problem and its solution.

Although model building requires abstraction of reality, it is important to obtain accurate information about the problem. This may relate to production times, machine times, or other technical aspects of the problem. In many instances, this information will come from three main sources: the accounting department, those directly involved (for example, managers, other employees), and direct observation. After the model has been constructed, it is generally prudent to confirm the results with people who are more closely involved and to use common sense in evaluating the results before proceeding very far into the analysis stage. This will help to identify any inadequacies in the model.

One mistake that inexperienced model builders often make is failing to take a broad perspective of the problem. That is, they do not take into account other dimensions of reality that a solution may have an impact on. For instance, in dealing with the optimal capacity of a department, the model builder should include the ability to assess the impact that the capacity will have on *other* departments within the organization as well as on external factors (e.g., will the suppliers be able to meet the resulting demands on them?). To accomplish this broad perspective, a model builder should adopt a *systems approach* to model building and should focus not only on the immediate problem but also on the interrelationships that exist within and outside the organization and how these relationships will be affected.

An important aspect of model building is collecting and preparing data. Because information obtained from the data is the foundation for the model, errors or missed information in the data can have a negative impact on the validity of model results.

Model Analysis

The nature of the analysis will depend on the type of model that is used. For instance, models that portray a situation that has a high degree of certainty lend themselves to *algorithms* (a series of steps that are repeated until the best solution is found) that generally help to identify optimal solutions. However, in some instances, no algorithms exist for identifying optimal solutions. Instead, *search techniques* may be used to identify acceptable solutions. In less certain situations, models may be used to identify approximate solutions.

In order to identify optimal or acceptable solutions, the analyst uses a **measure of effectiveness** such as profit, revenue, time, or cost to evaluate alternative solutions. Thus, if profit is the measure of effectiveness, the solution chosen will be the one that is projected to yield the highest profit. The measure of effectiveness that is used usually will come from the objective of the manager who is responsible for solving the problem. If the objective is not obvious or known, it will be necessary to solicit it from the manager or other appropriate person.

After the model is solved successfully, the solution must be tested to make sure that it is logical and the model is appropriate. The use of additional data may be necessary to compare the results obtained with the original data against the results obtained with the new data. At this point, the solution should be reviewed with the managers. In reviewing the solution, the analyst must go over all the assumptions that are used in the model.

Very often, the size of a problem and its computational requirements necessitate using a computer. Consequently, the user of a management science model usually will become involved with examining and interpreting computer output. Therefore, in order to be successful, the manager or other analyst must understand the basics of such techniques as well as how to interpret computer output.

An important part of model analysis, whether done manually or by using a computer, is determining how sensitive a particular solution is to changes in one or more of the constants in the model. This is referred to as **sensitivity analysis.** A manager can use sensitivity analysis to learn if changes in the values of certain constants used in the model will have any effect on the solution and, if so, what that effect would be. One reason for examining possible changes is that the manager has acquired new information indicating that the value of a constant may be different than that used in the model, and the manager wants to know if that will change the results. Another reason for using sensitivity analysis is to answer "What if . . . ?" type questions. For example, a manager may be able to purchase an additional amount of some raw material used in a production process. The question is, would it be profitable to obtain additional amounts of the raw material, and, if so, how much?

Implementation and Follow-Up

Once an appropriate solution has been identified, it must be implemented. This may involve reporting the recommended solution to the appropriate manager (e.g., the manager who requested the analysis) or it may mean making a presentation to senior managers (i.e., selling it to them). Presentations of results based on quantitative models to senior mangers can seem more difficult than the analysis itself. One reason is that these people often ask probing questions. Another is that they have the power to approve or reject the solution. One obstacle that can be encountered is that senior managers may lack quantitative skills. This means that the presenter must explain the model and the results in layman's terms, a feat some find difficult. For these reasons, it is wise to carefully prepare the presentation lest all the work that preceded it be in vain.

Not all solutions will be implemented. Some, of course, will be judged as not solving the problem. Others may be judged as too costly or they may be unacceptable for other reasons. One other reason might be that the goals of management have changed during the problem-solving interval. For instance, a new manager who has different experiences, priorities, and perspectives may have replaced the previous manager. Then too, certain aspects of the problem may have changed (for example, there may be new or different constraints, different legal requirements, new technology, and so on). In some cases, the problem may have corrected itself, or the organization may have decided to abandon that phase of the operation.

If a solution is implemented, it is important to carefully monitor that implementation. One reason for this is to make sure that the recommended solution is applied correctly. Consider the advice of a physician: "Take two every four hours." Unfortunately, the patient takes *four* every *two* hours and ends up in the emergency room. Also, the solution could be implemented correctly but the desired results may not be realized. A reasonable checklist would include questions such as: Were there mistakes in the implementation? Did the analysis support the solution? Was the analysis correct? Were there errors in the model? Was the problem correctly and completely defined?

In some cases, only minor corrections will be needed to achieve the desired results, whereas in other cases, major reworking will be called for. The chances of needing major reworking will be less if each step of the management science process is given careful attention. Continuing feedback at every phase of the process can help uncover inadequacies that can then be corrected, thereby avoiding such pitfalls as working on the wrong problem, working with an incorrect model, using misleading data, and so on. Feedback allows for continual evaluation and corrective action throughout the process.

◼◼ The Utilization of Decision Support Systems (DSS) in the Context of Management Science

A decision support system involves a collection of computerized technologies used to support decision making. DSS is the marriage of the information technology and information systems (IT/IS) field with operations research and management science (OR/MS). The greatest benefit is realized in the context of DSS when IT and OR work together. The DSS framework is described in Figure 1-2. In the data management domain, we organize the information into databases and manage it by software called *database management system* (DBMS). The DBMS interacts with model management systems, which include software packages to solve financial, statistical, and management science problems. These two systems interact and contribute to the intelligence and decision-making capabilities of the entire system. Data management and the model management components contribute to knowledge management, which consists of an expert system that enhances DSS when decision making is rather complex. The knowledge-based subsystem component consists of an intelligence system or systems; it is generally connected with the organizational knowledge base. Knowledge also may be provided through Web servers using a Web development program such as Java. Knowledge-based systems provide the necessary execution of the DSS. Finally, the user communicates with the system through a user interface. It is a good idea to provide graphics in the user interface to make it more effective. The interaction between the user and DSS is crucial to the development of user-friendly and user-oriented DSS models.

Excel is a desirable modeling tool to set up DSS. Excel is not only readily available in both the classroom and the workplace, but it is also relatively easy to learn and use. It is highly functional and extendable and can be integrated with other systems such as Access (Microsoft's database language that has the capability to use information from a variety of formats with a common user interface).

Figure 1-2   **DSS Framework**

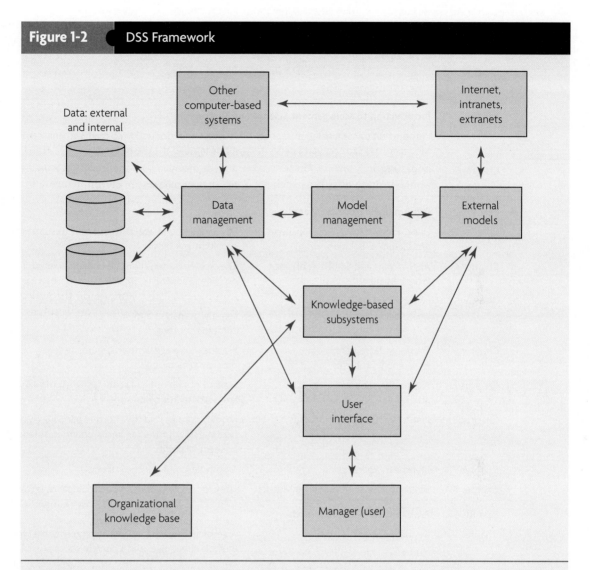

Source: E. Turban, Jay Aronson, and Ting-Peng Liang, *Decision Support Systems and Intelligence Systems*, 7th ed. (Upper Saddle River, NJ: Prentice Hall, 2005), p. 109.

Plan of the Book

The book is organized into three parts. Part I introduces management science and use of spreadsheets and covers forecasting. (*Note:* Forecasting is an "independent" topic and your instructor may cover it at some other time in your course.) Part II covers deterministic decision-making models including linear programming, sensitivity analysis with linear programming, transportation, assignment, transshipment problems, and network, nonlinear, and multicriteria models. Part III introduces probabilistic decision models including decision theory, Markov analysis, waiting line, and simulation models.

Table 1-1 provides a brief overview of the parts and chapters.

Table 1-1	Overview of the book	
Chapter or Part	**Title**	**Brief description**
Part I	**Introduction to Management Science and Forecasting**	
Chapter 1	Introduction to Management Science, Modeling, and Excel Spreadsheets	Provides an introduction to management science, modeling, and the use of Excel
Chapter 2	Forecasting	Provides the decision makers with an improved picture of future occurrences of events
Part II	**Deterministic Decision Models**	
Chapter 3	Linear Programming: Basic Concepts and Graphical Solution	Basic background about LP and how to solve simple LP problems graphically
Chapter 4	Applications and Solutions of Linear Programming	The problem formulation and problem solution are explained and realistic application examples are provided
Chapter 5	Linear Programming: Sensitivity Analysis and Duality	Extension of problem formulation, discussion of sensitivity analysis and duality, how to interpret computer output
Chapter 6	Transportation, Transshipment, and Assignment Problems	Provides coverage of special-purpose linear programming models
Chapter 7	Integer Programming	How to obtain optimal solutions when the variables are restricted to being integer
Chapter 8	Network Optimization Models	Models used to find the shortest path, maximum possible flow, or the minimal amount of distance to connect all points
Chapter 9	Nonlinear Programming	Optimization of nonlinear models
Chapter 10	Multicriteria Decision-Making Models	How to handle problems with multiple objectives
Part III	**Probabilistic Decision Models**	
Chapter 11	Decision Theory	A general approach for handling problems that have multiple alternatives and a discrete set of possible outcomes
Chapter 12	Markov Analysis	Studying the evolution of systems over repeated time periods
Chapter 13	Waiting-Line Models	Analysis of waiting lines
Chapter 14	Simulation	Describes a class of problems used to learn about a real system by experimenting with a model that represents the system
CD-ROM Modules		
Chapter 4	Supplement	Linear Programming: The Simplex Method
Chapter 6	Supplement	Transportation and Assignment Solution Procedures
Chapter 7	Supplement	Methods of Solving Integer Programming Problems
Chapter 9	Supplement	Mini Review of Differential Arithmetic

A Modern Management Science Application: *Hongkong International Terminals*

Hongkong International Terminals (HIT) is the busiest container terminal on the planet. The facility is operated by Hutchison Port Holdings (HPH) and in 2003, HIT handled 20 million 20-foot-equivalent units. HIT receives over 10,000 trucks and 15 vessels every day.

HIT's terminal management system uses Productivity Plus Program (3P), which optimizes the use of resources at the terminal using operations research and management science techniques for such decisions as to how to route container trucks, where to store arriving containers, and when to schedule incoming trucks for container pickup.

In the early 1990s, China's manufacturing expansion created a very high demand for HIT. At the time, HIT also faced tough competition in southern China where labor costs are much cheaper, making the situation difficult. HIT decided to take on the competition on the basis of efficiency and productivity. The terminal initiated 3P, which is a decision support system for optimizing daily operations. It is designed to monitor the movement of containers within the terminal and to organize the movements in an effective, optimized way. There were many implementation issues to overcome for HIT, 3P quickly resulted in a large number of benefits for HIT, including adding additional capacity at low cost. Because of the improved efficiency, HIT began to develop a reputation of being a "catch-up" port. In other words, companies came to rely on HIT in order to regain time they had lost elsewhere in their schedules. Another benefit that resulted from the 3P innovation was environmental. HIT was able to reduce the number of diesel-burning trucks within their transfer business by one-half. In addition, HIT experienced a 30 percent improvement in vessel turnaround time, a 47 percent improvement in vessel operating rate, a 35 percent reduction of material-handling cost, a 15 percent increase in yard crane productivity, and, overall, a 50 percent increase in throughput.

By utilizing a number of management science techniques within 3P, the Hongkong International Terminals was able to exceed expected results. HIT has not only created an additional value to the customers, but also differentiated the company from the competitors in terms of the speed and services that it offers.

Source: K. T. Murty, Y. Wan, J. Liu, M. Tseng, E. Leung, K. Lai, and H. Chiu, "Hongkong International Terminals Gains Elastic Capacity Using a Data-Intensive Decision-Support System," *Interfaces* 35, no. 1 (January–February 2005), pp. 61–75.

Role of Computers and Spreadsheets in Management Science

Computers are an important tool in management science. The use of quantitative models lends itself to computerized solutions. Moreover, the nature of many management science models is such that substantial calculations are required to solve everyday problems.

Until recently, the modeling techniques that will be covered in the remaining chapters of this book were solved using specialized software packages. Even though these packages were effective in solving various management science problems, the students that learned to solve problems with these packages did not own them. Therefore, after completing the course, they did not have the ability to use the packages unless they purchased them. Excel is an application program for Microsoft Office. After many revisions, Microsoft Excel is now capable of solving many of the basic management science problems. Since it is readily available to most students, Excel has become a popular and practical means of solving these problems. Therefore, many colleges have begun to offer spreadsheet based courses. The use of spreadsheets, and specifically Microsoft Excel, has become an important tool in teaching the decision modeling techniques. In this book, we will utilize Excel to teach these modeling techniques. This approach will be beneficial to students by allowing them to improve their proficiency in using Excel while gaining an understanding of the management science techniques in the context of a commonly used program. We will introduce the basic commands and structure of Excel in the next section. In addition, we will discuss various Excel functions and procedures when they are used with respect to a specific decision model.

Consequently, illustration and discussion of computer output using Excel will be covered throughout the book.

It is important to recognize that for instructional purposes, manual solutions are demonstrated in each chapter. These will provide you with a basic understanding of the important concepts related to the various models that are discussed and insights on how the models can be used to generate solutions. Both are important parts to the learning process. Hence, it is important to devote a reasonable amount of time and energy to manual solutions. Once you have mastered the important concepts of a model, you will be in a better position to use and *understand* computer (Excel) input and output.

Since Excel will be utilized extensively throughout the remainder of this text, it is important to understand basic common Excel functions and procedures. Therefore, in the next section an introduction to Excel is presented.

Getting Started with Excel

This section of the chapter contains an explanation of some basic information about the commands and procedures of Excel. It also provides an explanation of how add-ins such as *Solver* and *Data Analysis* can be installed. Spreadsheets provide a relatively easy means of analyzing data and using management science techniques for a wide variety of management problems. A *spreadsheet* allows the analyst to prepare hidden equations that perform calculations on a given data set. The main document in Excel used to store and analyze data is called a *workbook*. A workbook can consist of multiple *worksheets*. The worksheets can be used to analyze and manipulate data. Excel provides the means for the analyst to work with multiple worksheets simultaneously.

Once Excel has been installed, the user can start the program by clicking on **Start | Programs | Microsoft Excel,** by clicking on the Microsoft Excel icon on the Office toolbar, or by double-clicking on any Excel workbook that already exists on the computer. If the user starts Excel without opening an existing workbook, Excel will automatically create an empty workbook.

Description of a Worksheet A worksheet consists of rows and columns, as shown in Exhibit 1-1. Columns are labeled with letters A, B, C, and so forth, and rows are identified with numbers 1, 2, 3, and so on. The intersection of a row and a column is defined as a *cell,* which provides the basic means of data storage for Excel. Each cell's reference, based on the column and row numbers, is displayed in the cell reference towards the upper left corner of the worksheet. Different types of data can be stored, including numbers, labels, text, formulas, dates, and times. Not only can the user make use of the vertical and horizontal scroll bars and the mouse to navigate between cells, but the user also can use **Edit | Go to** on the menu bar to allow more flexibility of movement between cells.

Toolbars consist of icons that provide shortcuts to various tasks. The standard and formatting toolbars will be displayed automatically by default. The standard toolbar includes shortcuts to many simple tasks. When the mouse is placed over the icon, Excel will show the name of the task. The formatting toolbar includes the shortcuts to many commonly used formatting tasks such as alignment and font size. Other toolbars can be viewed and made accessible by clicking **View | Toolbars** and then selecting the desired toolbar.

Using Worksheets To enter data or information into a worksheet, simply click on the cell and then enter the data. By pressing Enter, the data will be inserted into the cell and the next cell (row) will be selected automatically. The user can select *adjacent cells* by clicking on the first cell in the sequence of cells. Then, by holding the Shift key and clicking on the last cell to be selected, all cells between these two cells will be selected. The same task also can be performed

Exhibit 1-1   **Excel Worksheet**

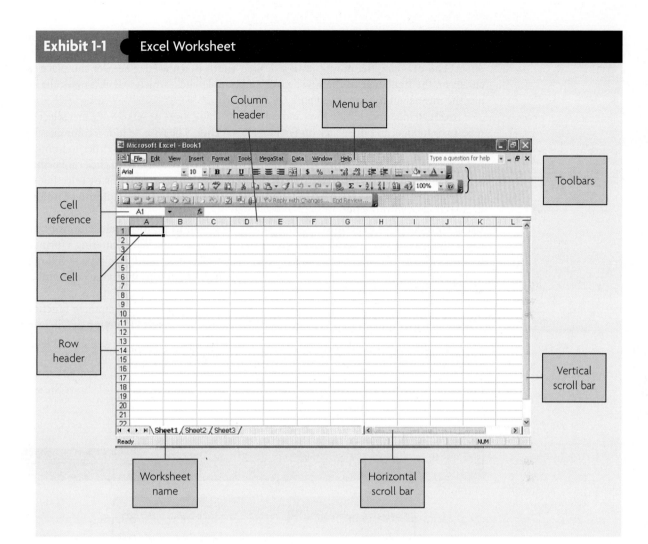

by clicking the first cell, holding the left mouse button down, and dragging it until all of the desired cells have been selected. Clicking on the row or column header will enable the user to select an *entire row or column*. If you want to select more than one row or column, then simply click on the row or column to start the rows or columns to be selected and hold the left mouse button down. Drag it until all of the desired rows or columns have been selected.

If you want to edit or modify existing data that have already been entered, double-click on the cell to be edited. To clear data, first select the cells that need to be cleared, then press the Delete button. If you want to insert a new row, click on the row header and hit **Insert | Row** and a new row will be added above the chosen row. If you want to insert a new column, click on the column header and select **Insert | Column.** A new column will then be added to the left of the selected column. To delete rows and columns, you simply select the row(s) or column(s) to be deleted, right-click with the mouse in the highlighted area, and then select **Delete.**

Changing the width of a column can be accomplished by placing the cursor on the right edge of the column header (the cursor will change to a cross with arrows to the right and to the left) and dragging the mouse until a desired width is achieved. By placing the cursor on the right edge of the column header, the user can double-click to adjust the width of the column to the largest entry in the column.

Changing the row height can be accomplished by placing the cursor on the bottom edge of the row header (the cursor will change to a cross with arrows pointing up and down) and dragging the mouse until a desired width is achieved. The user can place the cursor on the right edge of the row header and double-click, which will automatically adjust the row height to the highest entry in a given row.

Excel can hide and unhide rows and columns. To hide a row or set of rows, first select the rows to be hidden, and then click on **Format | Row | Hide.** Likewise, to hide a column, select the columns to be hidden and then click on **Format | Column | Hide.** In order to unhide a hidden row, first select the rows before and after the hidden row and then click on **Format | Row | Unhide.** A similar process is used to unhide a column or columns by selecting the columns before and after the hidden columns and clicking on **Format | Column | Unhide.**

Using Formulas and Functions Formulas will allow you to perform calculations on the worksheet data. A formula must start with an "equal to" (=) sign. When entering a formula, first click on the cell where you want the formula to take effect, and then type = followed by the formula. A formula can consist of mathematical operations involving cell numbers or references. After typing in a formula, press enter to perform the calculations.

There are functions or formulas automatically built in to Excel. Using these functions will save the user time from preparing formulas. If you click **Insert | Function,** it will bring up a menu window as shown Exhibit 1-2, which shows a list of functions available in Excel. The various subset categories can be viewed by clicking the down arrow on the "Or select a category" box (second box in Exhibit 1-2). When a function is selected, a syntax for that function is provided at the bottom of the window. For example, Exhibit 1-2 shows the syntax for the AVERAGE function.

Exhibit 1-2 **Functions Screen**

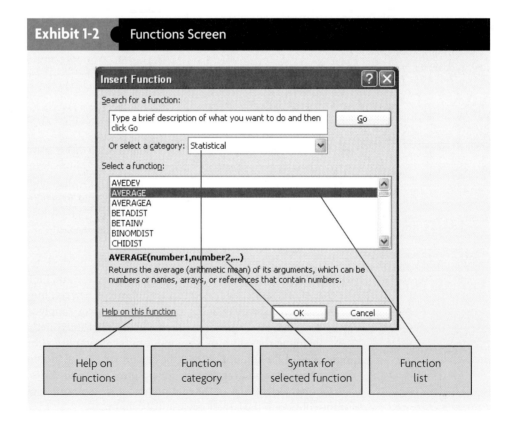

There are many errors that could occur with the use of functions and formulas. The user should use the Help command in case of an error to determine why an error occurred and consequently to remedy the problem.

Printing Worksheets   If you wish to print the entire worksheet, then click on **File | Print** or select the Print icon located on the toolbar. However, if you only wish to print a certain portion of the output, first select the desired section of the worksheet, then click **Print | Print Area | Set Print Area.** Before printing a worksheet or output from a worksheet, you may want to ensure that the printed document will look as desired by utilizing the print preview option found by clicking on **Print | Print Preview.**

Installing and Enabling Excel Add-ins   Excel add-ins are special programs designed to perform specific tasks. Throughout the textbook we will utilize two of these add-ins: **Solver** and **Data Analysis.** In recent versions of Excel, both Solver and Data Analysis are available options. However, the standard default installation of Excel will only install Data Analysis and not Solver. In order to check to see if both Solver and Data Analysis have been activated, you will need to click on **Tools.** If you see both Solver and Data Analysis as options, then both add-ins have been enabled. However, if you don't see an active add-in for Solver or Data Analysis, then you need to enable them by clicking on **Tools | Add-ins.** Doing this will bring up a display menu with a list of all add-ins. If the add-in is enabled, there will be a check by its name. If there is no check mark by Solver or Data Analysis' Analysis ToolPak and Analysis ToolPak-VBA, then they will need to be checked. After checking the Solver or Data Analysis, you need to go back and click on **Tools** to make sure the two add-ins have been activated. However, once these add-ins are activated, then you do not need to check them as they will be available each time you start Excel. See Exhibit 1-3 for the menu of available add-ins.

As we go through the various chapters, we will explain how to utilize different options with Excel. We recommend obtaining the following book to learn details and

---

Exhibit 1-3   Add-in Options

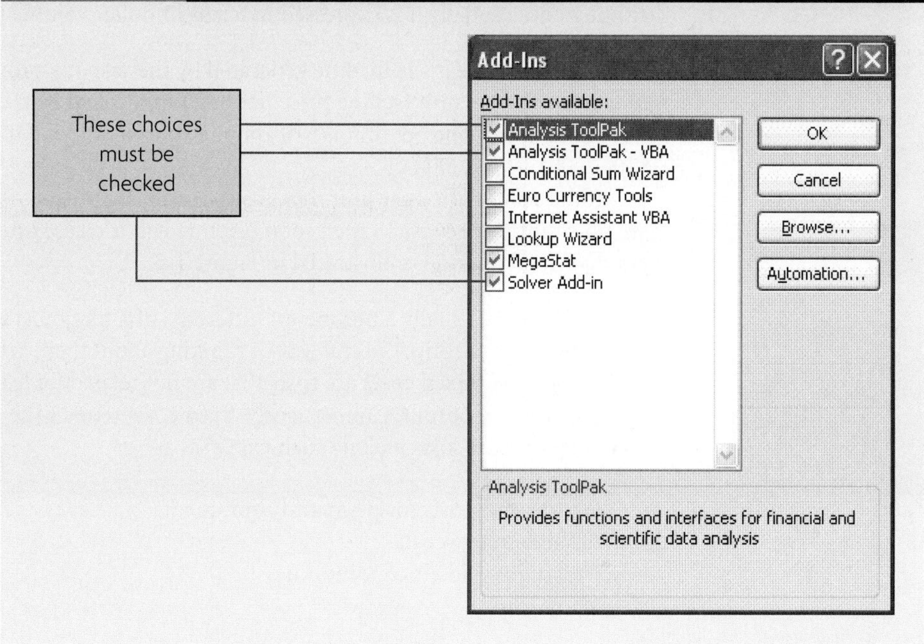

intricacies about Excel: *Excel 2003 Bible* by John Walkenbach published by Wiley Publishing Inc, 2003.

Break-Even Analysis

Introduction to Break-Even Analysis

One of the simplest quantitative models used by managers is the break-even model. Break-even analysis, which is sometimes referred to as cost-volume analysis, is concerned with the interrelationship of costs, volume (quantity of output or sales), and profit. Break-even analysis provides managers with answers to questions such as

1. What profit can be expected if sales are 6,000 units this month?
2. Would it be profitable to produce this product if annual demand is 50,000 units?
3. How many units must be sold in order to cover costs?
4. What costs will result if 3,000 units are made?

The basic relationship that underlies break-even analysis is summarized by the following formula:

Profit = Total revenue − Total cost   (1-1)

We can see from this equation that profit will be positive if total revenue exceeds total cost, and negative (a loss) if total cost exceeds total revenue. If total revenue and total cost are equal, profit will be zero; the organization will just "break even."

Components of Break-Even Analysis

In order to understand break-even analysis, it is necessary to understand the components of the analysis: volume, revenue, and cost.

Volume **Volume** is the level of output of a machine, department, or organization, or the quantity of sales. Generally, it is expressed as the *number of units* that are produced or sold, although occasionally it is expressed in terms of dollar volume (e.g., sales of $32,000).

Revenue **Revenue** is the income generated by the sale of a product. **Total revenue** is equal to the revenue per unit (selling price per unit) multiplied by the number of units (volume) sold. Thus, if revenue per unit is $10 and the volume sold is 2,000 units, the total revenue is $10(2,000) = $20,000.

If the selling price per unit remains the same regardless of the number sold (i.e., there are no quantity discounts), then total revenue will increase linearly as volume increases. A graph of total revenue is illustrated in Figure 1-3.

Costs There are usually a number of different costs that must be taken into account in order to determine profit. A useful way of thinking about them is by classifying them either as *fixed* or *variable*. **Fixed costs** are costs that are not related (at least within reasonable limits) to the volume of output. Consequently, fixed costs remain the same regardless of volume. Examples of fixed costs include such expenses as

- Rent/leasing costs for plant and equipment.
- Administrative costs.
- Heat, light, and air conditioning.
- Maintenance.

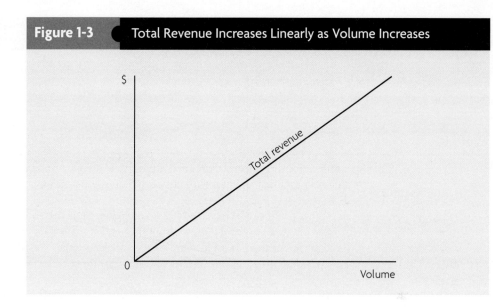

Figure 1-3   Total Revenue Increases Linearly as Volume Increases

- Janitorial services.
- Insurance.
- Depreciation on plant and equipment.

Fixed costs are the sum of these and other costs that do not vary with level of output. Figure 1-4 illustrates fixed costs.

Variable costs are expenses that vary with volume; each unit produced requires certain inputs (e.g., material) that add to the cost. Typical examples of variable costs include such expenses as

- Raw materials and purchased parts.
- Direct labor.
- Packaging and shipping costs.

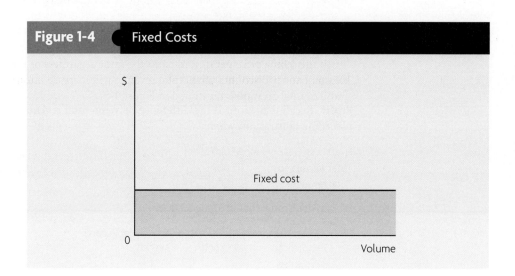

Figure 1-4   Fixed Costs

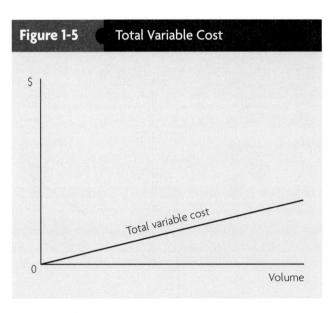

Figure 1-5   Total Variable Cost

Total variable cost is equal to the product of variable cost per unit and the volume that is produced. Thus, if the variable cost per unit is $5 and the volume is 2,000 units, the total variable cost is $5(2,000) = $10,000. Total variable cost is illustrated in Figure 1-5.

Total cost is the sum of fixed cost and total variable cost. Thus, if fixed cost *for the period during which the 2,000 units were produced* was $7,000, then total cost (*TC*) would be

$$TC = \$7,000 + \$5(2,000) = \$17,000$$

The computation of total cost is summarized by the following formula:

$$TC = F + VQ \tag{1-2}$$

where

F = fixed cost assigned
V = variable cost per unit
Q = volume or quantity

Total cost is illustrated in Figure 1-6.

Profit   Recall that profit is the difference between total revenue and total cost. Using the preceding illustrations where

Fixed cost   = $7,000
Total variable cost   = $10,000
Total revenue   = $20,000

we can determine that profit is $3,000:

$$\text{Profit} = \text{Total revenue} - (\text{Fixed cost} + \text{Total variable cost}) \tag{1-3}$$
$$= \$20,000 \qquad - (\$7,000 \quad + \$10,000)$$
$$= \quad \$3,000$$

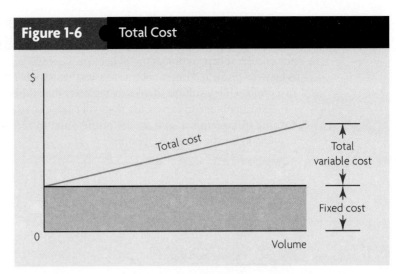

Figure 1-6 — Total Cost

We can write Equation 1-3 in a slightly different form in order to clearly indicate how each of the components is included in the computation of profit:

$$\text{Profit} = RQ - (F + VQ) \tag{1-4}$$

where

R = revenue per unit
Q = quantity or volume
V = variable cost per unit
F = fixed cost assigned

Figure 1-7 incorporates total revenue and total cost on the same graph. Note that profit is the vertical difference between the total revenue line and the total cost line for any given volume. Moreover, notice that if total cost exceeds total revenue, there is a loss (negative profit). If total cost and total revenue are equal, profit is zero. The volume or quantity at which that occurs is called the break-even point (BEP).

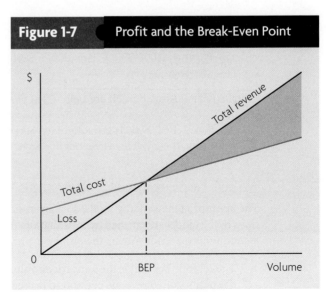

Figure 1-7 — Profit and the Break-Even Point

The Break-Even Point

The **break-even point** (**BEP**) is the volume for which total revenue and total cost are equal. Knowledge of that volume is useful because it reveals to management where the dividing line is between profit and loss; a volume of sales that is higher than the break-even point will result in a profit, while a volume of sales that is lower than the break-even point will result in a loss.

We can obtain an expression that will enable us to calculate the break-even quantity by turning to Equation 1-4. If we set profit equal to zero and then solve for Q, we have an expression for the break-even point:

$$RQ = F + VQ$$
$$RQ - VQ = F$$
$$Q(R - V) = F \qquad\qquad (1\text{-}5)$$
$$Q_{BEP} = \frac{F}{R - V}$$

Example 1-1

Given this information on costs and revenue:

$F = \$60{,}000$
$V = \$20$ per unit
$R = \$30$ per unit

determine each of the following:

a. Profit (loss) at a volume of 5,000 units.
b. Profit (loss) at a volume of 10,000 units.
c. The break-even point.

Solution

$\text{Profit} = RQ - (F + VQ)$

a. $Q = 5{,}000$ units.

$\text{Profit} = \$30(5{,}000) - [\$60{,}000 + \$20(5{,}000)] = -\$10{,}000$

Hence, there is a loss of \$10,000; total cost exceeds total revenue by that amount.

b. $Q = 10{,}000$ units.

$\text{Profit} = \$30(10{,}000) - [\$60{,}000 + \$20(10{,}000)] = \$40{,}000$

c. $Q_{BEP} = \dfrac{F}{R - V} = \dfrac{\$60{,}000}{\$30 \text{ per unit} - \$20 \text{ per unit}} = 6{,}000 \text{ units}$

Hence, if 6,000 units are sold, revenues will just cover costs; if a smaller quantity is sold, there will be a loss, but if a larger quantity is sold, there will be a profit.

Assumptions of Break-Even Analysis

The appropriateness of any model in a given situation depends on how well the assumptions of the model are satisfied by the situation. In the case of the break-even model, the key assumptions made for solving the problems presented in this book are

1. The revenue per unit is the same for all volumes. This would not be the case if quantity discounts caused revenue per unit to decrease as the quantity sold increased.

2. The variable cost per unit is the same for all volumes. This would not be the case if learning was a factor, so that the labor cost per unit decreased as the level of production increased.

3. Fixed cost is the same for all levels of volume. This would not be the case if a volume was called for that exceeded current capacity, so that additional capacity at a different fixed cost had to be added.

4. Only one product is involved. This is a simplifying assumption that avoids having to combine revenues and costs for multiple items.

5. All output is sold. This means that the volume used to compute total revenue is the same as the volume used to compute total variable cost. If this assumption is not met, we must be careful to use each volume as appropriate in computing profit.

6. All relevant costs have been accounted for, and have been correctly assigned to either the fixed cost category or the variable cost category.

Using Excel to Solve the Break-Even Model

In this section, we will re-solve Example 1-1 by utilizing Excel. To solve the break-even model, first we must prepare a spreadsheet with headings that identify model parameters and variables. Once the model variables and parameters are identified, then the appropriate mathematical formulas are entered into appropriate cells. Exhibit 1-4 shows the spreadsheet for the Example 1-1. Note that cell C10 contains the formula for the break-even volume while cell C12 contains the total cost formula and cell C14 contains the formula for total profit or total loss. This is a simple demonstration of modeling using Excel. As we cover more complicated models in the upcoming chapters, we will have the opportunity to demonstrate other aspects and features of Excel in the context to modeling management science techniques.

Using Excel's Goal Seek to Compute the Break-Even Point

Even though the previous analysis of the break-even point with Excel is very simple, we can utilize Excel to automatically calculate the break-even point by using Excel's **Goal Seek** feature. Using this feature allows us to state a goal or target for a certain cell and also specify the cell that must be automatically changed to achieve this goal. In the case of break-even analysis, we indicate the number of units necessary so that the profit is zero. The results of **Goal Seek** are displayed in Exhibits 1-5 and 1-6.

Exhibit 1-5 shows how the **Goal Seek** function is implemented with Excel. First, we activate the Goal Seek feature in Excel by clicking on **Tools | Goal Seek** from the Excel menu. This brings up the Excel **Goal Seek** input window displayed in Exhibit 1-5. On this screen, we first specify cell C16 in Exhibit 1-4 (total profit) as the "set value" cell. In doing the Goal Seek, we simply need to eliminate the formula in cell C10 and instead indicate a value of 0. In the "To value" box, we specify a value of zero, indicating the break-even point or zero profit. In the "By changing cells" box we indicate cell C10, which contains the number of units made. When we click OK, it brings up the **Goal Seek** Status window (output screen) shown in Exhibit 1-6. This screen indicates that the goal of 0 profit (break-even) has been achieved. We also can indicate different profit values in the "To value" box to see the number of units needed to achieve that level of profit. For example, if we indicate a total profit of $2,000 in the "To value" box and run the Goal Seek program again, it will give an answer that we need to sell 6,200 units in cell C10 to achieve a profit of $2,000 in cell C16.

Exhibit 1-4	Break-Even Analysis

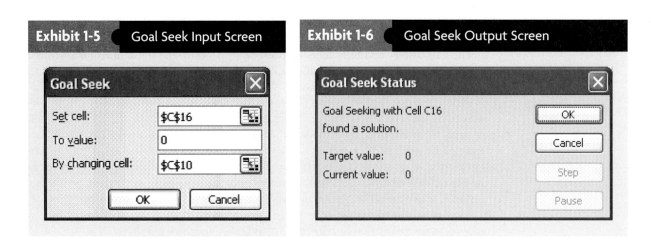

Cell	Formula
C10	$= C4/(C8 - C6)$
C12	$= C4 + (C6 * C10)$
C14	$= C8 * C10$
C16	$= C8 * C10 - (C4 + C10 * C6)$

Exhibit 1-5	Goal Seek Input Screen

Goal Seek

Set cell: $C$16

To value: 0

By changing cell: $C$10

OK   Cancel

Exhibit 1-6	Goal Seek Output Screen

Goal Seek Status

Goal Seeking with Cell C16
found a solution.

Target value: 0
Current value: 0

OK
Cancel
Step
Pause

A Modern Management Science Application: *Lucent Technologies*

Lucent Technologies is in the business of designing software that drives modern communications networks. Lucent Technologies is supported by Bell Labs Research and Development. Lucent provides services in mobile, optical, software, data, and voice networking technologies. The mission of Lucent is to find new revenue-generating opportunities for its customers, particularly by enabling them to deploy and better manage their networks. Lucent's customer base includes communications service providers, governments, and companies around the world.

Inventory Requirements Planning (IRP) is a decision support system (DSS) Lucent utilizes to determine its inventory buffers (safety stock) for parts. The IRP begins by measuring the deviation of actual supply from planned supply and actual demand from planned demand. Lucent depends on the IRP system for routine material planning and for associating inventory levels recommended to the drivers of inventory for both individual items and product families. When inventory requirements change over time, the IRP system assists managers in understanding the reason for the change. For example, there might be a change in the measurement of forecast accuracy. IRP computes the variability of demand and the variability of supply. Based on these variabilities, IRP is able to distinguish between common causes (variation not attributable to any special cause) and assignable causes (variation that can be linked to a specific reason or event). As the company can then decrease the variability in demand as supply decreases, they also are able to reduce safety stock.

Lucent uses the IRP system at a number of manufacturing plants to determine inventory levels and inform managers of their possible causes of higher-than-desired inventory. IRP is completely integrated with the firm's material and production planning systems, and the model parameters are determined from the company ERP system. The IRP system improved Lucent's operation metrics in terms of better forecast accuracy and higher supplier quality as well as improving financial metrics.

Source: A. Bangash, R. Bollapragada, R. Klein, N. Raman, H. Schulman, and D. Smith, "Inventory Requirements Planning at Lucent Technologies," *Interfaces* 34, no. 5 (September–October 2004), pp. 342–52.

Summary of Break-Even Analysis

Break-even analysis focuses on the interrelationship among cost, revenue, volume of sales, and profit. It is useful to managers in a number of ways, but particularly in helping to identify the level of sales for which total revenue will cover total cost. More generally, break-even formulas can be used to answer "What if . . . ?" questions related to selection of a level of volume of output and/or sales.

The Importance and Impact of Management Science

Management science techniques are widely used in today's businesses. A number of surveys have revealed the extent of usage and the importance assigned to the usefulness of management science tools by managers.

The results show that techniques such as linear programming and simulation are used very often, and that these two techniques are ranked the highest in terms of their usefulness. Moreover, most of the techniques are widely used.

Experience suggests that these techniques are being increasingly integrated into the managerial decision process. And increasingly, computers and statistical analysis are being used at all levels of organizations.

The implication of these results is that quantitative tools and computers are becoming increasingly important factors in decision making, so that it behooves decision makers to be well grounded in understanding and using them.

Management science has made a profound difference in many organizations around the globe. There have been many successful applications of management science that have been published in literature. Table 1-2 summarizes some of the successful applications of

Table 1-2	Successful Applications of Management Science		
Organization	**Explanation of the Application**	**Literature Citation**	**Savings or Added Revenue**
Dell Computers	Inventory decisions in Dell's supply chain	*Interfaces*, May–June 2004	Reduction of inventory by 40%, improvement in inventory turn by 67%
Texas Children's Hospital	Developing contract optimization	*Interfaces*, January–February 2004	$6 million per year
UPS	Design of service networks for delivering express packages	*Interfaces*, January–February 2004	$87 million per year
General Electric	GE's energy rentals business automates its credit assessment process	*Interfaces*, September–October 2003	Savings of 60% of the cost per credit decision
Workers' Compensation of British Columbia	Early detection of high-risk claims at the Workers' Compensation Board of British Columbia	*Interfaces*, July–August 2003	$4.7 million per year
Federal Reserve Bank	Models for improving team productivity at the Federal Reserve Bank	*Interfaces*, March–April 2003	$1 million per year
Canadian Pacific Railway	Optimization of the routing and classification plan for railcar scheduling	*Interfaces*, January–February 2003	$170 million per year
Continental Airlines	Developing crew scheduling and crew recovery decision support system	*Interfaces*, January–February 2003	$40 million per year
Chipita International Inc.	Systems analysis speeds up Chipita's food-processing line	*Interfaces*, May–June 2002	$1 million per year

Company	Application	Source	Savings/Revenue
Merrill Lynch	Pricing analysis for Merrill Lynch Integrated Choice	*Interfaces*, January–February 2002	$40 million per year
Hewlett-Packard	Optimization of supply chain network analysis, including inventory optimization	*Interfaces*, January–February 2002	$130 million per year
Hewlett-Packard	Designing an assembly line to improve production methods	*Interfaces*, January–February 1998	$280 million additional revenue per year
Procter & Gamble	Designing production and distribution systems	*Interfaces*, January–February 1997	$200 million per year
Taco Bell	Scheduling of employees to improve customer service and minimize cost	*Interfaces*, January–February 1997	$750 million per year
Delta Airlines	Assignment of airplanes to flights	*Interfaces*, January–February 1994	$100 million per year
New York City Police Department	Devising a process to reduce waiting times between when an individual is arrested and when he/she is arraigned	*Interfaces*, January–February 1993	$9.5 million per year
AT&T	Developing a computerized system for business customer call centers	*Interfaces*, January–February 1993	$750 million per year
American Airlines	Developing a crew scheduling system to maximize service and minimize cost	*Interfaces*, January–February 1992	$500 million additional revenue per year
IBM	Inventory management of spare parts	*Interfaces*, January–February 1990	$250 million less in inventory per year
San Francisco Police Department	Scheduling police patrol	*Interfaces*, January–February 1989	$11 million per year

management science. These have been selected from numerous applications published in *Interfaces* journal.

To consider a specific view of the value and impact of management science and operations research, take it from Robert C. Wright, vice chairman and executive officer, General Electric, and chairman and CEO, National Broadcasting Company:

> Operations research and management science techniques have given us a significant competitive advantage during the "Up Front Market." All the hard work and creativity that went into this project definitely has paid off. In fact, these new systems have an impact on over $50 million in annual revenues and have greatly boosted the productivity of the NBC sales staff. Thanks to GE's corporate research and development center, our network sales organization has seen firsthand how operations research methodologies can revolutionize how we work. We will continue to deploy these technologies across all functions as we grow and improve our business. [**Source:** INFORMS Web site, http://www.orchampions.org.]

Summary

Management science is the discipline devoted to the solution of management problems using a scientific approach. The focus is on problem solving using quantitative models. The approach is to define the problem, construct a model that reflects the important aspects of the problem, analyze the model to identify an appropriate solution to the problem, implement the solution, and check to see that the problem has been solved.

The core of management science is the scientific approach to problem solving. An important part of this is the use of quantitative models. Models are abstractions of reality: Ideally, a model will capture the important aspects of a situation without including all of the minor details that would increase complexity and thereby reduce the chances of finding a solution to the problem.

There are a variety of model types that are employed in decision-making environments; management science models fall under the heading of symbolic models (that is, numbers and symbols are used to form mathematical models). Using these models tends to be a more objective approach than using qualitative models, although in symbolic models the more important qualitative aspects of a problem may be ignored. Furthermore, quantitative models enable users to take advantage of the tremendous computational abilities of computers and calculators.

Glossary

Break-Even Point (BEP) The volume of sales for which total revenue equals total cost; profit is zero at the break-even point.

Decision Variable A variable whose value can be set by a decision maker; the purpose of modeling is to determine appropriate values for decision variables.

Deterministic Model A model in which all numerical values are known with certainty.

DSI Decision Sciences Institute (http://www.decisionsciences.org).

Fixed Costs Costs that do not vary with the level of output or sales. An example would be monthly rent on a facility.

INFORMS Institute for Operations Research and the Management Science (http://www.informs.org).

Management Science A discipline devoted to the use of quantitative models for solving managerial-type problems.

Mathematical Model A symbolic model; uses numbers and symbols.

Measure of Effectiveness A basis for evaluating the desirability of a particular solution. Common measures include profits, costs, and revenues.

Model A selective abstraction of reality.

Probabilistic Model A model that incorporates probability to reflect inherent randomness in certain variables.

Revenue Income received from sale of a product or service.

Scientific Approach A logical approach to problem solving that includes defining the problem, constructing a model, analyzing the model, solving, and implementing the solution.

Sensitivity Analysis Determining the degree to which possible changes in various model dimensions will affect the result of model analysis.

Symbolic Model A model that uses numbers and algebraic symbols to represent selected aspects of reality.

Total Revenue Revenue per unit multiplied by number of units sold.

Total Variable Cost Variable cost per unit multiplied by the number of units produced.

Uncontrollable Variable A variable that influences the results of a model but cannot be controlled by the analyst.

Variable A portion of a model that can take on different values (e.g., the speed of a vehicle, the number of newspapers sold per day).

Variable Costs Costs associated with producing units of a product (e.g., typewriters) that are related to the number of units produced. Typical examples are labor and material costs.

Volume The quantity of units produced and/or sold.

◼ Discussion and Review Questions

1. Explain what is meant by the term *management science*.
2. Suppose you have just been hired by a small firm. Ater being on the job for a few weeks, you realize that most problem solving is done on an informal basis—quantitative models are not being used. You share your reservations about this with your manager, and after a certain amount of discussion, your manager asks you to outline your reasoning on why the firm should adopt a more quantitative approach to problem solving. What would the main points of your response be?
3. Suppose that senior management has asked you to give a presentation that will enlighten them on the use of models for problem solving. Specifically, they want to know what a model is, what types of models there are, how models can lead to good solutions, and any potential pitfalls to be aware of. Outline your presentation.
4. You are faced with making a choice between two models. One is a fairly simple model that will provide an approximate answer to the problem; the other is a much more complex model that can be expected to provide a much more precise answer to the problem.
   a.   Under what circumstances would you choose the simple model?
   b.   Under what circumstances would the more sophisticated model be your choice?
5. Briefly describe the management science approach to problem solving.
6. Briefly describe the symbolic model type and give an example.
7. Contrast deterministic and probabilistic models, and indicate the conditions under which each type would be appropriate.
8. How would you respond to a student who says, "Why should I have to study management science? My major is marketing."

9. Suppose that after a considerable amount of time and effort, the solution obtained from a model is not implemented.
   a. List some possible reasons for this.
   b. Would you say that the time and effort was, therefore, probably wasted? Explain your answer.

10. What does the phrase "modeling can become an end in itself" mean? Is this necessarily bad?

11. Why might a solution that is optimal in a model not be optimal in reality? How might the gap be closed? What risks might there be in attempting to close the gap?

12. How and why are computers an integral part of management science?

▌ Problems

1. The Exxoff Corporation produces an automotive lubricant that is sold to wholesale distributors for $25 a case. Fixed costs are $80,000 and variable costs are $15 per case.
   a. What profit or loss would result if 4,000 cases are sold?
   b. What profit or loss would result if 10,000 cases are sold?
   c. What is the break-even volume in cases?

2. The Greene Daisy Company offers a spring tune-up service for power lawn mowers at a price of $24.95. Labor and supplies cost an average of $10 per tune-up, and overhead charged to the operation is $5,000 a month. Determine:

   a. BEP = 334.45 tune-ups
   b. Profit = $606.25

   a. The monthly volume needed to break even.
   b. The profit that would result if 375 tune-ups are performed per month.

3. A company that produces cleaning products is considering a proposal to begin production of a new detergent that would cost $1 a bottle to make and distribute, and retail for $2.19 a bottle. Fixed cost for the operation would be $3,000 a week. Assume that all output can be sold.
   a. What would the total cost, total revenue, and profit (or loss) be for a weekly volume of 10,000 bottles?
   b. What is the break-even volume?

4. Fast-Lube operates a chain of shops that offer a 20-minute oil change and lubrication service for passenger cars and light trucks. The shops have an overhead of $1,000 per day. Labor and materials cost $5 per job, and customers are charged $19.95 for the service. Determine:

   a. BEP = 66.89 jobs
   b. P = −476.75 (loss of $476.75)
   c. BEP = 69.56 or 70 jobs

   a. The number of jobs per day that a shop needs in order to cover all of its costs.
   b. The profit or loss that would result if 35 cars were serviced in a day.
   c. Suppose two workers work together in a shop and each receives $20 a day in pay and benefits plus $1 per job, customers are still charged 19.95, and material costs $3 per job. What is the break-even volume for the shop? (Hint: $20 per employee is a fixed cost.)

5. Schmaltz, Ltd., produces a variety of specialty beverages. One of its products is made in a separate facility for which monthly rent, administrative costs, and equipment leasing is $80,000. The facility has a monthly capacity of 50,000 cases of the specialty beverage. Eight workers handle production and shipping. Each receives salary and fringe benefits of $2,500 per month. Packaging and distribution costs are $.30 per case, and ingredients cost $1.10 per case. The product is sold for $5.89 a case. Determine the following:
   a. The profit or loss on sales of 40,000 cases.
   b. The break-even volume. Hint: note carefully which costs are truly variable.
   c. The profit or loss that would result from sales of 60,000 cases.

6. Lamb, Stew is a fledgling catering firm that serves the meat-and-potato segment of the market. The co-owners want to expand their successful operations to include a neighboring town. After investigating their options, they have narrowed their choices to two. One option is to have a capacity of 10 events per month. This would result in a cost of $1,600 a month plus a cost of $250 per event. The other option would have a capacity of 20 events per month, a cost of $3,200 a month, and a cost of $200 per event. The firm would charge $450 for each event.

   a. Determine the break-even volume for each option.
   b. What profit (or loss) would each option produce if monthly demand is 10 events?
   c. If monthly demand is 14 events, which option would yield the greater profit?

7. The construction firm of Smagglewhetsy & Kid must decide whether to continue to perform payroll functions in-house or to subcontract those services. In-house costs are $2,000 a month plus $30 per employee. The same services can be performed by a contractor for $50 per employee plus a monthly service fee of $1,200.

   a. If the construction firm has 30 employees, which option would provide the lower cost?
   b. Suppose the firm is undergoing an expansion, adding two new employees to its payroll each month. At this rate, in how many months should the firm consider doing its own payroll?

8. The law firm of Smith, Jones, and Greene provides accounting services for some of its clients. The person who handles this service and her secretary cost the firm an average of $80,000 a year in salary and benefits. Clients are charged a fixed rate of $300 a year for these services, and the firm is billed $50 per client for computer time, postage, and supplies. Now, a local accounting firm has offered to provide comparable service for a fee of $600 per client.

   a. What profit or loss would the firm realize if 354 clients use its accounting service each year?
   b. Assuming 300 clients a year, would the law firm be better off using its own staff, or using the outside accounting firm?
   c. At what level of client usage would the two alternatives produce the same profit?

9. A firm plans to begin production of a new appliance. The manager must decide whether to purchase the motors for the appliance from a vendor to be sold at $7 each or to produce them in-house. Either of the two processes could be used for production. Purchasing the motor from a vendor would have an annual fixed cost of $160,000 and variable cost of $5 per unit, while the in-house production would have an annual fixed cost of $190,000 and a variable cost of $4 per unit.

   a. What is the break-even point if we use an outside vendor?
   b. What is the break-even point if we produce the motor in-house?
   c. Determine the range of annual volume for which each alternative would be the best.

10. A manager must decide how many machines of a certain type of purchase. Each machine can process 100 customers per hour. Purchasing one machine will result in a fixed cost of $2,000 per day while purchasing two machines will result in a fixed cost of $3,800 per day. Variable cost will be $20 per customer and revenue will be $45 per customer.

   a. Determine the break-even point for one machine.
   b. Determine the break-even point for two machines.
   c. If estimated demand is 90 to 120 customers per hour, how many machines should be purchased?

◼◗ Chapter 1 Case   Green Daisy Company

The manager of Green Daisy Inc. is in the process of deciding whether to make or buy carburetors for its power lawn mowers. If Green Daisy decides to manufacture the carburetor, it could utilize one of two manufacturing processes. The first process would entail a variable cost of $17 per unit and an annual fixed cost of $200,000, while the second process would entail variable cost of $14 per unit and an annual fixed cost of $240,000. The manager knows of three vendors who are capable and willing to provide the carburetor. Vendor A charges $20 per unit for any volume up to 30,000 units and cannot supply Green Daisy's need for volume above 30,000 units due to its capacity restrictions. Vendor B offers a price of $22 per unit for a demand of 1,000 units or less and $18 per unit for each unit above the 1,000 units. Vendor C's price is $21 per unit for the first 1,000 units and $19 per unit for any additional units. The manager is unsure about what the demand is going to be for power lawnmowers. If the demand is forecasted to be 10,000, 20,000, 28,000, or 60,000 units, which alternative would be best from a cost standpoint? What is the break-even volume of internal process 1, if we use the best price external option? What is the break-even volume of internal process 2 if we use the best price external option? Determine the range for which each alternative is best.

Forecasting

Learning Objectives

After completing this chapter, you should be able to:

1. Explain the importance of forecasting in organizations.
2. Describe the three major approaches to forecasting.
3. Use a variety of techniques to make forecasts.
4. Measure the accuracy of a forecast over time using various methods.
5. Determine when a forecast can be improved.
6. Discuss the main considerations in selecting a forecasting technique.
7. Utilize Excel to solve various forecasting problems.

Chapter Outline

Introduction, 38

Qualitative Forecasts, 39

Forecasts That Use Time Series Data, 39
Techniques for Averaging, 41
Techniques for Trend, 50
Techniques for Seasonality, 59
Techniques for Cycles, 64

Explanatory Models, 65
Simple Linear Regression, 65
Regression Assumptions, 71
Multiple Regression, 72

Accuracy and Control, 76
Forecast Errors, 77
Summarizing Forecast Accuracy, 77
Monitoring and Controlling the Forecast, 78

Relative Measures of Forecast Accuracy, 79

Using Forecast Information, 84
Selecting a Forecasting Approach, 84

Summary, 86

Glossary, 87

Discussion and Review Questions, 88

Solved Problems, 89

Problems, 91

Chapter 2 Case: Gnomial Functions, Inc., 100

◼️ Introduction

Planning and implementing decisions are tasks performed by virtually all decision makers. Sometimes these tasks are carried out smoothly and successfully, with very satisfactory consequences. But sometimes they are not. Very often, the degree of success is dependent on the amount of uncertainty surrounding some future event. If there is considerable uncertainty, it is much more difficult to formulate plans that will produce the desired results than when there is little or no uncertainty involved. Forecasts are important because they can help to reduce some of the uncertainty. That is, forecasts provide decision makers with an improved picture of probable future events and, thereby, enable decision makers to plan accordingly. For example, if a forecast indicates that an organization can expect an increase in demand for its products or services, plans may focus on the best way to meet those increases. Conversely, a forecast of decreasing demand may trigger attempts to overcome this by pricing strategy, advertising, or design improvements.

In fact, forecasts are vital inputs for almost all planning processes. Forecasts are used for *planning the system* (e.g., product and service design, process design, capacity planning, and equipment investment decisions) as well as for *planning the use of the system* (e.g., advertising, production and inventory planning and scheduling, purchasing commitments, planning the size of the workforce, budgeting, and cost estimation).

Forecasts have the potential to greatly affect the success or failure of an organization's plans. Good forecasts can enable an organization to take advantage of future opportunities; poor forecasts can result in missed opportunities, inefficient operations, customer dissatisfaction, and costs associated with attempts to compensate for inappropriate actions or failure to act.

Good forecasts are more likely to result using this process:

1. Determine the purpose of the forecast. This will generally govern the amount of resources that can be justified for developing and maintaining the forecast.
2. Determine the time horizon. Some techniques work better in the short term, others for intermediate-range applications, and still others work better for the long range.
3. Select an appropriate technique.
4. Identify the necessary data, and gather it if necessary. Special-purpose forecasts may require special collection efforts, whereas more repetitive forecasting requires ongoing, routine data collection.
5. Make the forecast.
6. Monitor forecast errors in order to determine if the forecast is performing adequately. If it is not, take appropriate corrective action.

It is important to recognize that *all* forecasts have the tendency to be inaccurate; there is no technique in existence that will provide perfect forecasts outside of the carefully controlled conditions that are possible in a laboratory. In the real world, the important question is not, "Will the forecast be perfect?" but rather, "How far off might the forecasts be?"

There are many different forecasting techniques from which to choose. For purposes of discussion, the techniques described in this chapter are arranged into three categories: qualitative techniques, times series techniques, and explanatory models. Qualitative techniques are those that rely on judgment and experience. Time series techniques involve smoothing historical data and projecting past experience into the future. There is no attempt in time series models to explain certain patterns in historical data. Rather, the assumption is that future experience will be similar to past experience. Explanatory models involve identifying one or more variables whose values can be used to predict future experience. The presumption is that a logical relationship exists between the variables that can be expressed mathematically.

This chapter describes forecasting methods under each of these three categories, beginning with qualitative models. That is followed by a discussion of accuracy, which includes measuring and evaluating forecast accuracy. The chapter ends with a brief discussion of factors that should be considered when selecting a forecasting technique.

Qualitative Forecasts

Qualitative forecasts are based on judgment and/or opinion rather than on the analysis of "hard" data, such as weekly sales figures. Sometimes qualitative techniques are used because there is not enough time to gather and analyze data (e.g., an emergency situation calling for immediate action), whereas other times data may be nonexistent (e.g., for a new product or service), and still other times existing data may be obsolete (e.g., due to changing conditions such as consumers' buying behaviors or the introduction of a technological breakthrough by a competitor).

Among the advantages of qualitative forecasting techniques are that such forecasts can be made quickly and permit inclusion of "soft" factors (i.e., those that are difficult to quantify) that are ordinarily excluded by quantitative techniques. This might include hunches and intuition as well as insight acquired over a lengthy period of time. Conversely, qualitative forecasts may suffer from personal biases, confusion of desired results with probable results, and overly optimistic or pessimistic attitudes.

Inputs for qualitative forecasts can be obtained from a variety of sources, including consumers, salespeople, managers and executives. These sources can be utilized in a number of ways to generate qualitative forecasts. *Consumer surveys* involve questioning consumers on their future buying plans, likes, and dislikes. We can obtain valuable information from the *sales force* that could be used to modify forecasts. *Executive opinion* can be used when executives from finance, marketing, production, and other parts of the organization come together to prepare a forecast. *Delphi technique* could enable the executives to reach a consensus by employing a series of questionnaires that are answered anonymously by executives or managers. The successive questionnaires supplement information based on previous questionnaires. This iterative process attempts to achieve consensus.

Qualitative forecasting approaches are important for a number of different reasons. Speed in making a forecast sometimes is a factor in choosing a qualitative approach over a quantitative one, especially if data acquisition for a quantitative approach will be time-consuming. The ability to incorporate experience and judgment are sometimes given as important reasons for using qualitative methods. However, the two are not necessarily mutually exclusive; quantitative forecasts can be modified by users in order to incorporate judgment and experience. Thus, qualitative reasoning can be used to supplement (and, hopefully, improve) quantitative forecasts.

Forecasts That Use Time Series Data

Time series data are historical values of a variable that have been recorded at periodic intervals (e.g., daily demand, weekly sales, quarterly revenues, annual demand). Forecasting techniques that use time series data typically involve the assumption that past experience reflects probable future experience (i.e., the past movements or *patterns* in the data will persist into the future).

Some of the most commonly observed patterns in historical data are trends, seasonal variations, and cyclical variations. **Trends** are long-term upward or downward movements; **seasonal variations** are recurring movements often related to regular variations in climate or time of day; and **cyclical variations** are long-term up and down movements in data. They are wavelike variations of more than one year related to economic and political conditions. Identifying and using these patterns to forecast is sometimes difficult because of the presence of random and irregular variations in the data. **Random variations,** the net result of a large number of minor factors, are almost always present in time series data. **Irregular variations** are the result of unusual factors (e.g., severe weather conditions that disrupt supply or demand, equipment breakdowns, fire). When possible, irregular variations should be identified and their effects removed from the data because they tend to distort it.

Figure 2-1 illustrates the different possible patterns that might be observed in time series data. These patterns might exist separately or in combinations. For example, Figure 2-2 illustrates data that include both seasonality and trend.

| Figure 2-1 | Examples of Simple Patterns Sometimes Found in Time Series Data |

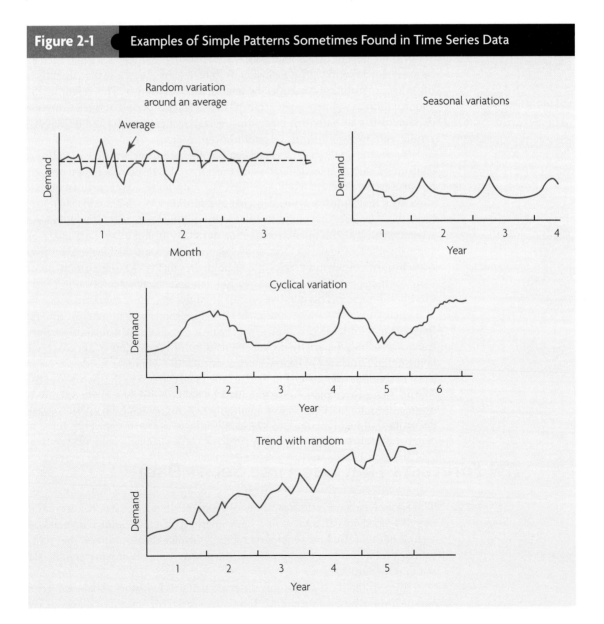

Figure 2-2 • Data with Trend and Seasonal Variations

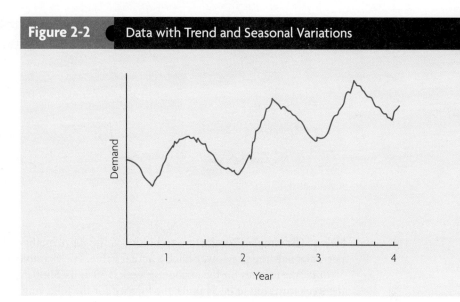

Selecting a technique to use with time series data requires some knowledge of what pattern or patterns a series tends to exhibit. For that reason, it is a good idea to *plot the data* before selecting a technique, especially since certain techniques perform better on trends, whereas others work best with seasonality or cycles, and still others work best when a series varies around an average.

When working with time series data, a distinction should be made between "demand" and "sales." Because stockouts (shortages) sometimes artificially constrain sales, unless it can be established that stockouts have not occurred, demand rather than sales data should be used for forecasting. It should be noted that sales figures may be much easier to obtain than demand, and in some cases demand figures either may be quite difficult to determine or may require a system designed specifically to collect the necessary data.

Techniques for Averaging

Averaging techniques generate a forecast that reflects recent values of a time series (e.g., the average value over the last several periods). These techniques work best when a series tends to vary around an average, although they can handle step changes or *gradual* changes in the level of the series. A forecast based on an average tends to exhibit less variability than the original data because the averaging smooths out some of the up/down movements in the series (see Figure 2-3). This can be advantageous because many of these movements merely reflect random variability rather than a true change in level, or trend, in the series. Moreover, because response to change in expected demand often can represent considerable cost (e.g., changes in production rate, changes in the size of a workforce, inventory changes, etc.), it can be desirable to avoid reacting to minor variations. In effect, minor variations are treated as random variations, whereas larger variations are viewed as more likely to reflect "real" changes, although these, too, are smoothed to a certain degree.

We examine three techniques for averaging in this section:

1. Naive forecasts.
2. Moving averages.
3. Exponential smoothing.

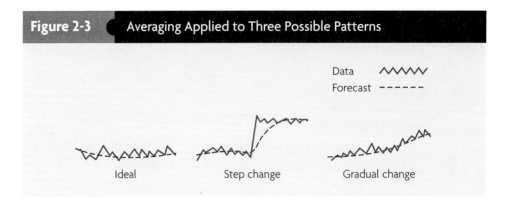

Figure 2-3   Averaging Applied to Three Possible Patterns

Ideal   Step change   Gradual change

Naive   The simplest forecasting technique is the *naive* method. A **naive forecast** for any period equals the previous period's actual value. For example, if demand last week was 50 units, the forecast for the upcoming week is 50 units. Similarly, if demand in the upcoming week turns out to be 54 units, the forecast for the following week would be 54 units.

Although at first glance the naive approach may appear *too* simplistic, nonetheless, it is a legitimate forecasting tool. Consider the advantages: It has virtually no cost, it is quick and easy to prepare a forecast because data analysis is nonexistent, and it is easy for users to understand. The main objections to this method is its inability to provide highly accurate forecasts and its inability to forecast more than one period into the future. However, if resulting accuracy is acceptable, this approach deserves serious consideration. Moreover, even if other forecasting techniques offer better accuracy, they will almost always involve a greater cost. The accuracy of a naive forecast can serve as a *standard of comparison* against which to judge the cost and accuracy of other techniques. Hence, managers must answer the question: Is the increased accuracy of another method worth the additional resources required to achieve that accuracy?

The naive concept also can be applied to a series that exhibits seasonality or trend. For example, if monthly sales exhibit a seasonal pattern, demand for the current December can be based on demand from the preceding December, demand for January can be based on demand from the preceding January, and so on. Similarly, if trend is present, the increase (or decrease) from this period's actual demand to the period's demand can be estimated as the same as the change observed between the last two periods. For instance, if June's demand is 90 units higher than May's demand, a naive forecast that allowed for trend would be June's actual demand plus an additional 90 units. Then, if July's demand was only 85 greater than June's, August's forecast would be July's actual plus 85 units.

Moving Averages   One weakness of the naive method is that it causes the forecast to *trace* the actual data, with a lag of one period; it does not smooth at all. But by expanding the amount of historical data a forecast is based on, this difficulty can be overcome. A **moving average forecast** uses a number of the most recent actual data values in generating a forecast. The moving average forecast can be computed using the following equation:

$$MA_n = \frac{\sum_{i=1}^{n} A_i}{n} \tag{2-1}$$

where

n = the number of periods in the moving average
A_i = actual demand value in period i

For example. MA_3 would imply a three-period moving average.

Example 2-1

Compute a three-period moving average forecast given demand for shopping carts for the last five periods:

Period	Demand	Moving Total	Moving Average
1	40		
2	44		
3	36	120	40
4	42	122	40.67
5	40	118	39.33[a]

$$^a MA_3 = \frac{36 + 42 + 40}{3} = \frac{118}{3} = 39.33$$

If actual demand in period 6 turns out to be 41, the moving average forecast for Period 7 would be

$$MA_3 = \frac{42 + 40 + 41}{3} = 41.00.$$

Note that in a moving average, as each new actual value becomes available, the forecast is updated by adding the newest value and dropping the oldest and then recomputing the average. Consequently, the forecast "moves" by reflecting only the most recent values.

The *moving total* column gives the sum of the *n* most current values from which the average will be computed. It is relatively simple to update the moving total: Subtract the oldest value from the newest value, and add that amount to the moving total for each update.

Figure 2-4 illustrates a three-period moving average forecast plotted against actual demand over 31 periods. Note how the moving average forecast lags the actual values and how smooth the forecasted values are compared to the actual values.

The moving average can incorporate as many data points as desired, beginning with the latest value and working backward. Hence, a 10-period moving average forecast would be the average of the latest 10 actual values. In selecting the number of periods to include in a moving average, the decision maker must take into account that the number of data points in the average determines its sensitivity to each new data point: The fewer the data points in an average, the more responsive the average tends to be, as depicted in Figure 2-5. Hence, if responsiveness is important, a moving average with relatively few data points should be used. This will permit quick adjustment to, say, a step change in the data, but it will also cause the forecast to be somewhat responsive, even to random variations. Conversely, moving averages based on more data points will smooth more but be less responsive to "real" changes. Hence, the decision maker must weigh the cost of responding more slowly to changes in the data against the cost of responding to what might simply be random variations.

The advantages of a moving average forecast are that it is easy to compute and easy to understand. A disadvantage is that all values in the average are weighted equally. Hence, in a 10-period moving average, each value is given a weight of 1/m; the oldest value is given the *same* weight as the most recent value. Decreasing the number of values in the average will increase the weight of more recent values, but this will be at the expense of losing potential information from less recent values.

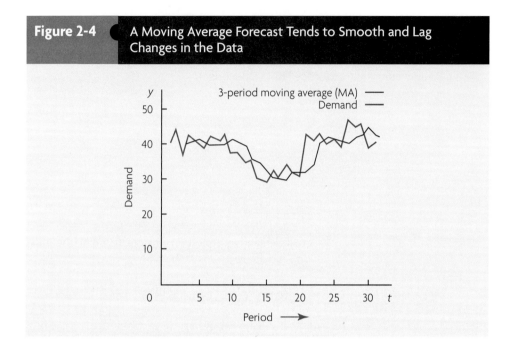

Figure 2-4 • A Moving Average Forecast Tends to Smooth and Lag Changes in the Data

Weighted Moving Averages A weighted moving average is very similar to a simple moving average, except that it assigns unequal weights to each observation. It assigns more weight to the most recent value in a time series. In a time-series, the weights are generally assigned in ascending order with the oldest period having the lowest weight, while the most recent period has the largest weight. For instance, when utilizing a three-period moving average, the most recent value might be assigned a weight of 0.50, the next most recent value may be assigned a weight of 0.30 and the oldest value may be assigned a weight of 0.20. The sum of the weights must add up to 1.0 (0.50 + 0.30 + 0.20 = 1.0) and we cannot assign a negative weight. The weight for period i is designated as w_i.

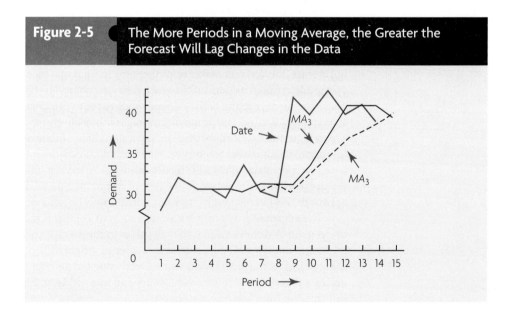

Figure 2-5 • The More Periods in a Moving Average, the Greater the Forecast Will Lag Changes in the Data

Example 2-2

Given the following demand data:

a. Calculate a four-period weighted moving average for week 6, where $w_4 = .45$, $w_3 = .25$, $w_2 = 0.20$, and $w_1 = 0.10$.
b. If the actual demand for period 6 is 44, forecast the demand for week 7.

Week	Demand
1	38
2	40
3	44
4	46
5	42

Solution

a. $F_6 = (0.45)(42) + (0.25)(46) + (0.20)(44) + (0.10)(40) = 43.2$
b. $F_7 = (0.45)(44) + (0.25)(42) + (0.20)(46) + (0.10)(44) = 43.9$

Note that in preparing the four-period moving average, four weights are used. The weights sum to one and weights are arranged in increasing order from the oldest period to the most recent period. In addition, the most recent four periods' demand values are used to prepare the forecast for week 6 and week 7.

The weighted moving average may be preferred over the simple moving average because it is more indicative of the most recent demand values as compared to the simple moving average. However, the weights are arbitrarily selected and we can use a trial-and-error approach to choose a weighting scheme that minimizes the average forecasting error, where forecast error is defined as the difference between actual and forecasted demand in a given period i $(A_i - F_i)$. If the data set involves a trend, then neither simple moving average nor weighted moving average should be used because the forecasted values will lag behind the trend. If there is trend, we should utilize a linear regression or trend-adjusted exponential smoothing.

Moving Averages with Excel Excel can be utilized to determine the moving averages very easily. The user would simply select **Tools | Data Analysis | Moving averages** to trigger the use of the moving averages module with Excel. Exhibit 2-1 shows the data presented in Figure 2-7 in column A, and the resulting three-period moving average forecasts in column B. In generating these forecasts, after selecting the moving average module, the screen shown in Exhibit 2-2 appears. On this screen, the user needs to specify the input range and the output range. When the cursor is in the Input Range box, the user would specify this range by placing the cursor on the first cell of the data set (A2) and dragging the cursor all the way to the cell containing the last data value (A12). Since it is a three-period moving average, the interval should be set at 3. Output range can be specified by placing the cursor in the Output Range box. Since you want to place the forecasted demand one week ahead of the most recent period included in the moving average, specify this range by placing the cursor in cell B3 instead of cell B2 and dragging the cursor all the way to the cell B13 (one row after the last observation in the data set). As an option, the user can chart the moving average values against the actual data by checking the Chart Output box. Note that in cells B2, B3, and B4 there is no numerical value; instead "#N/A" appears. This occurs because the moving average

Exhibit 2-1 Moving Average Input and Output

Microsoft Excel - wrksht2-14

A15 — weights

	A	B	C
1	**Actual demand**	**3 per. Simple moving average**	**3 period weighted moving average**
2	42	#N/A	
3	40	#N/A	
4	43	#N/A	
5	40	41.667	41.9
6	41	41.000	40.9
7	39	41.333	41.1
8	46	40.000	39.8
9	44	42.000	42.9
10	45	43.000	43.6
11	38	45.000	44.9
12	40	42.333	41.3
13		41.000	40.4
14	Totals		
15	**weights**		
16	W_1	0.2	
17	W_1	0.3	
18	W_1	0.5	
19			

Cell	Copied to	Formula
C5	C6 : C13	= SUMPRODUCT (A2 : A4, $B $16 : $B $18)
B5	B6 : B13	= AVERAGE (A2 : A4)

Exhibit 2-2 Moving Average Preparation Screen

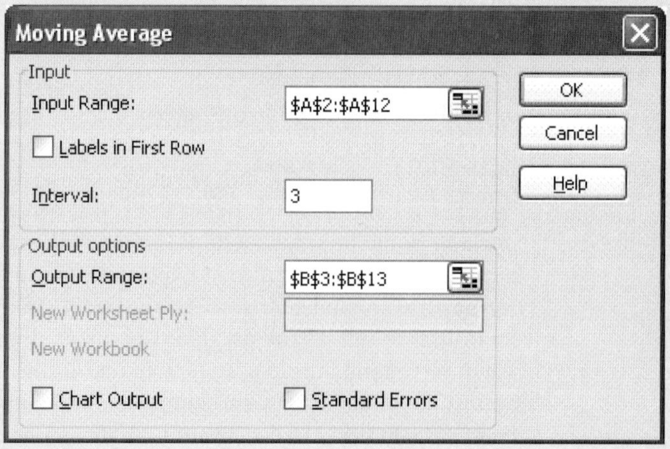
Moving Average
Input
Input Range:
$A$2:$A$12
Labels in First Row
Interval:
3
Output options
Output Range:
$B$3:$B$13
New Worksheet Ply:
New Workbook
Chart Output
Standard Errors
OK
Cancel
Help

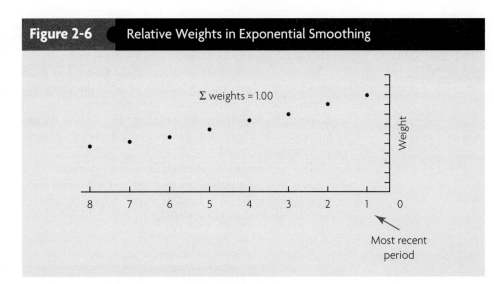

Figure 2-6   Relative Weights in Exponential Smoothing

method cannot compute values for those cells. When the moving average method computes the average, it simply records the average one period ahead of the last period included in the average; therefore, when it computes the average of periods 1, 2, and 3 in cells A2, A3, and A4, it records the resulting average in cell B5, leaving cells B2, B3, and B4 without a numerical value.

The weighted moving average values are displayed in column C of Exhibit 2-1. The values in this column are obtained by using the SUMPRODUCT command. In order to obtain the value given in cell C5, three actual demand values given in cells A2, A3, and A4 are multiplied by the weights in cells B16, B17, and B18. The SUMPRODUCT command not only multiplies the respective actual demand values by the weights, but also sums the multiplied values.

Exponential Smoothing   Exponential smoothing is an averaging technique that reduces these difficulties. In addition, the weights given to previous values are not equal; instead, they decrease with the age of the data, as illustrated in Figure 2-6.

The exponentially smoothed forecast can be computed using this formula:

$$F_t = F_{t-1} + \alpha(A_{t-1} - F_{t-1}) \qquad\qquad (2\text{-}2)$$

where

F_t = the forecast for Period t
F_{t-1} = the forecast for Period $t-1$
α = smoothing constant (Greek alpha)
A_{t-1} = actual demand or sales for Period $t-1$

The **smoothing constant, α,** represents a percentage of the forecast error. Each new forecast is equal to the previous forecast plus a percentage of the previous error. For example, suppose the previous forecast was 100 units, actual demand was 90 units, and $\alpha = .10$. The new forecast would be computed as follows:

$$F_t = 100 + .10(90 - 100) = 99$$

Then, if the next actual demand turns out to be 102, the next forecast would be

$$F_t = 99 + .10(102 - 99) = 99.3$$

A number of different approaches can be used to obtain a *starting forecast* (e.g., average first several periods, subjective estimate). For simplicity, use the first actual as the forecast for the following period and then begin the exponential smoothing.

The sensitivity of forecast adjustment to error is determined by the smoothing constant, alpha. The closer its value is to zero, the slower the forecast will be to adjust to forecast errors (i.e., the greater the smoothing). Conversely, the closer the value of alpha is to 1.00, the greater the sensitivity and the less the smoothing. This is illustrated in Figure 2-7. In Figure 2-7, the error is calculated by simply subtracting the forecast from the actual demand.

Selecting a smoothing constant is, basically, a matter of judgment or trial and error. The goal is to select a smoothing constant that will balance the benefits of smoothing random variations with the benefits of responding to real changes if, and when, they occur. Commonly used values range from .05 to .50.

Figure 2-7	A Small Value of α Will Smooth More Than a Larger Value				
		$\alpha = .10$		$\alpha = .40$	
Period	**Actual Demand**	**Forecast**	**Error**	**Forecast**	**Error**
1	42	—	—	—	—
2	40	42	−2	42	−2
3	43	41.8	1.2	41.2	1.8
4	40	41.92	−1.92	41.92	−1.92
5	41	41.73	−0.73	41.15	−0.15
6	39	41.66	−2.66	41.09	−2.09
7	46	41.39	4.61	40.25	5.75
8	44	41.85	2.15	42.55	1.45
9	45	42.07	2.93	43.13	1.87
10	38	42.36	−4.36	43.88	−5.88
11	40	41.92	−1.92	41.53	−1.53
12		41.73		40.92	

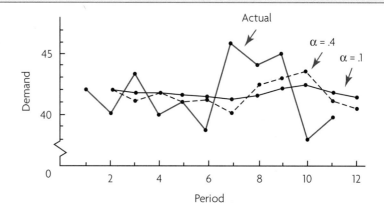

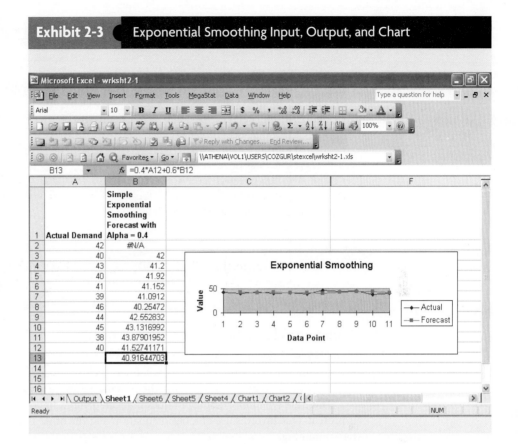

Exhibit 2-3   Exponential Smoothing Input, Output, and Chart

Some computer packages include a feature that permits automatic modification of the smoothing constant if the forecast errors become unacceptably large.

Exponential smoothing is one of the most widely used techniques in forecasting, partly because of its minimal data storage requirements and ease of calculation and partly because of the ease with which the weighting scheme can be altered (i.e., by simply changing the value of α).

The use of a computer software package such as Excel can be very useful in determining the value of α that minimizes the average forecast error.

Exponential Smoothing with Excel   Using Excel to determine the exponentially smoothed forecast is a very convenient way of utilizing computer software to obtain forecasts. The user would simply select **Tools | Data Analysis | Exponential Smoothing** to trigger the use of the exponential smoothing module with Excel. Exhibit 2-3 shows the data presented in Figure 2-7 in column A, and the resulting exponentially smoothed forecasts in column B. In generating these forecasts, after selecting the exponential smoothing module, the screen shown in Exhibit 2-4 appears. On this screen, the user would specify the input range and the output range in the same way it was described for moving averages. In addition, the user would specify the damping factor, which is $1 - \alpha$. If we want to see on a graph how the actual time series compares with the exponentially smoothed series, we can check the Chart Output box. The resulting graph is provided in Exhibit 2-3. In Exhibit 2-4, the range of output will be from cell B2 to cell B13. We also can use the Goal Seek command in Excel to determine the optimal value of α that will minimize the average forecast error. We do this by specifying α in the "Changing Cells" box that minimizes the average forecast error in the "Target Cell" box.

Exhibit 2-4	Exponential Smoothing Preparation Wizard

Exponential Smoothing ☒

Input

Input Range: $A$2:$A$12

Damping factor: 0.6

☐ Labels

OK

Cancel

Help

Output options

Output Range: $B$2:$B$13

New Worksheet Ply:

New Workbook

☐ Chart Output   ☐ Standard Errors

Techniques for Trend

Trend is a persistent upward or downward movement in a time series. The trend may be linear or nonlinear. The discussion here will focus exclusively on linear trends because linear trends are fairly common and because they are the easiest to work with.

There are two important techniques that can be used to develop forecasts when trend is present. One involves use of a trend equation and the other is an extension of exponential smoothing.

Trend Equation   A *linear trend equation* has the form

$$y_t = a + b_t \qquad (2\text{-}3)$$

where

t = a specified number of time periods from $t = 0$
y_t = the forecast for Period t
a = value of y_t at $t = 0$
b = slope of the line

The model used in this chapter is called a simple linear regression model. To define the relationship between Y and t, the user needs to know the value of the coefficients a and b, which are estimates of α and β. α and β represent population parameters, which are almost always unknown. α is the y intercept (the expected value of the dependent variable when t is zero); β is the slope and indicates the amount of change in Y per unit of change in t. Our task is to find the straight line that provides the best possible fit through the data points. The best fit can be defined as the line that minimizes the sum of the squared differences between the actual data points and their respective forecasted values. The technique that produces this line is called the linear trend equation or the regression line.

For example, consider the trend equation $y_t = 45 + 5t$. The value of y_t when $t = 0$ is 45, and the slope of the line is 5, which means that the value of y_t will increase by five units for each one unit increase in t. If $t = 10$, the forecast, y_t, is $45 + 5(10) = 95$ units. The equation can be plotted by finding two points on the line. One can be found by substituting some value of t into the equation (e.g., $t = 10$) and then solving for y_t. The other is a (i.e., y_t at $t = 0$). Plotting those two points and drawing a line through them will yield a graph of the linear trend line.

Table 2-1			Values of Σt, t^2, and Σt^2				
n	Σt	t^2	Σt^2	n	Σt	t^2	Σt^2
1	1	1	1	11	66	121	506
2	3	4	5	12	78	144	650
3	6	9	14	13	91	169	819
4	10	16	30	14	105	196	1,015
5	15	25	55	15	120	225	1,240
6	21	36	91	16	136	256	1,496
7	28	49	140	17	153	289	1,785
8	36	64	204	18	171	324	2,109
9	45	81	285	19	190	361	2,470
10	55	100	385	20	210	400	2,870

The coefficients of the line, a and b, can be computed from historical data using these two equations:

$$b = \frac{n\Sigma ty - \Sigma t\Sigma y}{n\Sigma t^2 - (\Sigma t)^2}$$

(2-4)

$$a = \frac{\Sigma y - b\Sigma t}{n}$$

where

n = the number of periods
y = a value of the time series

Manual computation of the coefficients of a trend line can be simplified by use of Table 2-1, which lists values of Σt, t^2, and Σt^2 for up to 20 ($n = 20$) periods.

Example 2-3

Monthly demand for Dan's Doughnuts over the past nine months for trays (six dozen per tray) of sugar doughnuts was

Mar	112
Apr	125
May	120
Jun	133
Jul	136
Aug	146
Sept	140
Oct	155
Nov	152

1. Plot the data to determine if a linear trend equation is appropriate.
2. Obtain a trend equation.
3. Forecast demand for the next two months.

Solution

1. The data seem to show an upward, roughly linear trend:

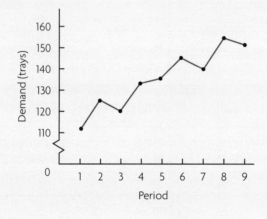

2.

Month	t	y	ty
Mar	1	112	112
Apr	2	125	250
May	3	120	360
Jun	4	133	532
Jul	5	136	680
Aug	6	146	876
Sep	7	140	980
Oct	8	155	1,240
Nov	9	152	1,368
		1,219	6,398

From Table 2-1, for $n = 9$, $\Sigma t = 45$ and $\Sigma t^2 = 285$. Using Equation 2-4, we find

$$b = \frac{9(6,398) - 45(1,219)}{9(285) - 45(45)} = \frac{2,727}{540} = 5.05$$

$$a = \frac{1,219 - 5.05(45)}{9} = 110.19$$

The resulting equation is $y_t = 110.19 = 5.05t$.

3. The next two months represent $t = 10$ and $t = 11$. Hence:

$$y_{Dec} = 110.19 + 5.05(10) = 160.69$$
$$y_{Jan} = 110.19 + 5.05(11) = 165.74$$

Owner Dan T. may decide to round these forecasts to the nearest full tray.

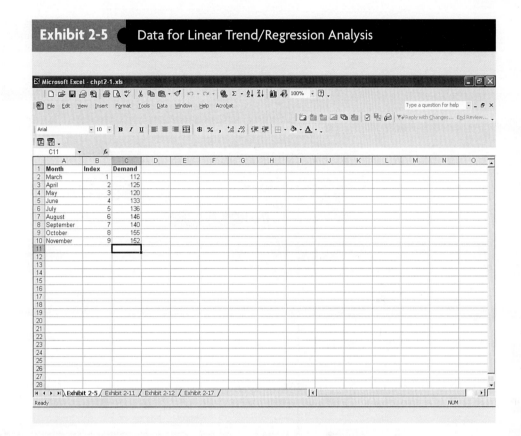

Exhibit 2-5   Data for Linear Trend/Regression Analysis

Estimating Trend with Excel   Excel has built-in features to estimate trend. In this section, we will use the data from Example 2-2, Dan's Doughnuts, to illustrate how Excel can be used to estimate linear trend. Exhibit 2-5 shows the input worksheet. This worksheet consists of three columns. The first column includes the labels for each month, while the second column is the coding for the time series for each month (1, 2, 3, 4, 5 . . . 9). Whenever we are given a data set such as the demand information given in Example 2-2, it is a good idea to draw a scatter plot to ensure that the linear model is appropriate. By choosing **Insert | Chart,** you can obtain the Chart Wizard in Exhibit 2-6 and select **XY (Scatter),** which lets Excel know that a scatter plot will be drawn. The next screen is shown in Exhibit 2.7, which establishes the data range for the scatter plot. The data range is specified by placing the cursor on the first cell of the data set (B2) for *t* (time coded) values and dragging the cursor all the way to the cell containing the last data value of demand (C10). In other words, the data set from B2 to B10 and C2 to C10 in Exhibit 2-5 would be selected.

After completing Exhibit 2-7, Excel will bring up Exhibit 2-8, which provides labels for both axes and a title for the chart along with options dealing with gridlines, legends, and labels. In this chart, we have named the chart "Doughnut demand" and labeled the X axis "Month" and the Y axis "Demand." After completing Exhibit 2-8 by clicking on "Next," the chart in Exhibit 2-9 is drawn. Since the chart appears to show a linear relationship between time and demand, you can proceed with the calculation of the linear trend equation using Excel. Clicking on **Tools | Data Analysis | Regression** will bring up Exhibit 2-10. In this

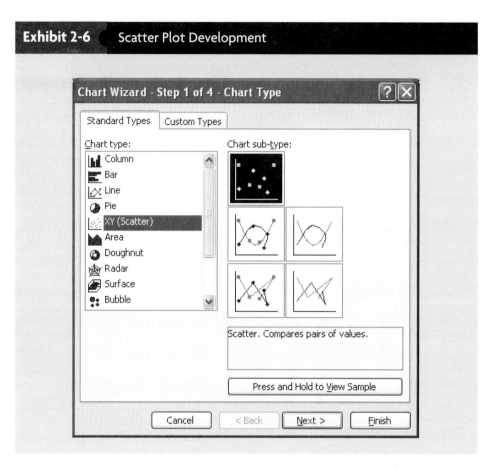

Exhibit 2-6 Scatter Plot Development

exhibit, you need to specify the input range for the dependent variable (C2 to C10) and the input range for the independent variable (time periods) (B2 to B10). This screen also provides options regarding assumptions of linear regression (i.e., residuals), which will be discussed later in the chapter. After completing this screen, by specifying the output to be included in a new worksheet ply, the output report in Exhibit 2-11 is created. Note that intercept value (a) is 110.19 and the slope value (b) is 5.05. The output includes various regression statistics including r^2 (coefficient of determination; shown as R square in Excel). In this problem, $r^2 = .90422$, which means that 90.42 percent of the variation in demand can be explained by the regression equation. The standard error (standard error of estimate) is 4.812, which is the standard deviation of the data points around the regression line. Multiple R, or the correlation coefficient, which is .951, shows the strength of the relationship between time and demand.

The ANOVA table also shows the strength of the relationship between the independent and dependent variables. The higher the value of F in the ANOVA table, or the lower the p-value (significance of F statistic), represents a stronger linear trend equation. However, if we want to obtain a quick and nondetailed regression output, choose **Chart Wizard,** choose the scatter diagram, and specify the data range (dependent and independent variable data ranges; for our example, cells B2:C10). After obtaining the scatter plot on the screen, click **Chart** from the toolbar menu and choose **Add Trend Line.** Another screen entitled "Add Trend Line" will appear. On this screen, click on **Options** check the "Display Equation On Chart" and Display

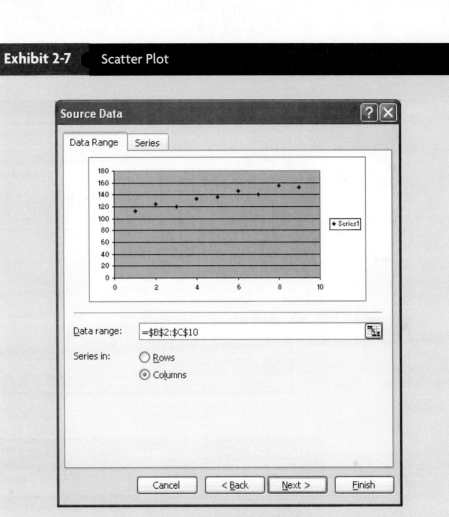

Exhibit 2-7 Scatter Plot

R^2 on Chart, boxes, and click OK. The scatter plot will now include the regression equation and the value of r^2.

Trend-Adjusted Exponential Smoothing A variation of simple exponential smoothing can be used when a time series includes trend. It is called *trend-adjusted* exponential smoothing, or sometimes referred to *double* exponential smoothing, to differentiate it from simple exponential smoothing, which is only appropriate when data vary around an average or have step or ramp changes. If a series exhibits trend, and simple smoothing is used on it, the forecasts will all *lag* the trend. For example, if the data are increasing, each forecast will be too low. Conversely, decreasing data will result in forecasts that are too high. Again, plotting the data can indicate when trend-adjusted smoothing would be preferable to simple exponential smoothing.

The trend-adjusted forecast (TAF) is comprised of two elements: a smoothed error and a trend factor:

$$TAF_{t+1} = S_t + T_t \tag{2-5}$$

where

S_t = smoothed error
T_t = current trend estimate

Exhibit 2-8 Scatter Plot Titles, Axes, and Labels

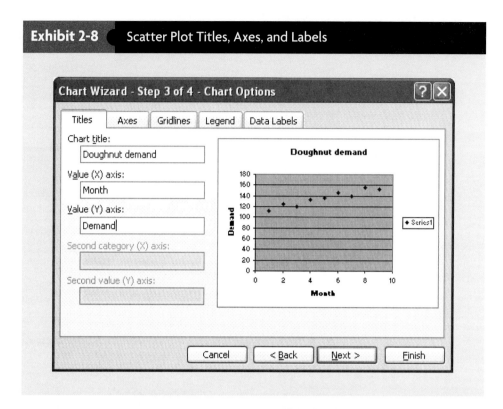

Exhibit 2-9 Scatter Diagram

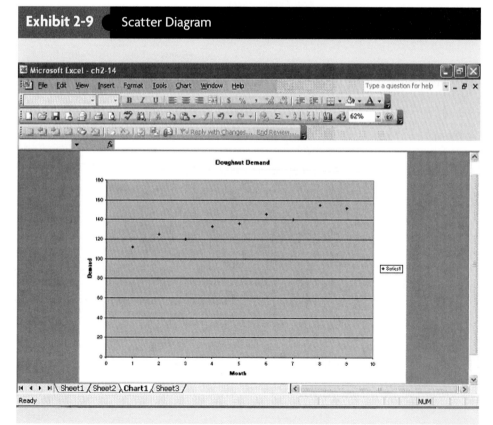

Exhibit 2-10   Regression Input Range

Regression

Input

Input Y Range: $C$2:$C$10

Input X Range: $B$2:$B$10

☐ Labels   ☐ Constant is Zero
☐ Confidence Level: 95   %

OK
Cancel
Help

Output options

○ Output Range:
⦿ New Worksheet Ply:
○ New Workbook

Residuals
☐ Residuals   ☐ Residual Plots
☐ Standardized Residuals   ☐ Line Fit Plots

Normal Probability
☐ Normal Probability Plots

Exhibit 2-11   Regression Output

Microsoft Excel - chpt2-1.xls

File Edit View Insert Format Tools Data Window Help Acrobat

Type a question for help

Arial   ▼ 10 ▼ B I U

C5   ▼   fx

	A	B	C	D	E	F	G	H	I	J	K	L	M
1	SUMMARY OUTPUT												
2													
3	*Regression Statistics*												
4	Multiple R	0.9509076											
5	R Square	0.9042252											
6	Adjusted R Square	0.8905431											
7	Standard Error	4.8117746											
8	Observations	9											
9													
10	ANOVA												
11		df	SS	MS	F	Significance F							
12	Regression	1	1530.15	1530.15	66.0881	8.226E-05							
13	Residual	7	162.0722222	23.1532									
14	Total	8	1692.222222										
15													
16		Coefficients	Standard Error	t Stat	P-value	Lower 95%	Upper 95%	Lower 95.0%	Upper 95.0%				
17	Intercept	110.19444	3.495673188	31.5231	8.4E-09	101.9285	118.460392	101.928497	118.460392				
18	X Variable 1	5.05	0.621197427	8.12946	8.2E-05	3.5811025	6.51889745	3.58110255	6.51889745				
19													
20													

Exhibit 2-5 **Exhibit 2-11** Exhibit 2-12 Exhibit 2-17

Ready   NUM

and

$$S_t = \text{TAF}_t + \alpha_1(A_t - \text{TAF}_t)$$
$$T_t = T_{t-1} + \alpha_2(\text{TAF}_t - \text{TAF}_{t-1} - T_{t-1})$$

where α_1 and α_2 are smoothing constants.

In order to use this method, one must select values of α_1 and α_2 (usually through trial and error) and make a starting forecast and an estimate of trend.

Suppose a manager estimates a trend of +10 units, based on observed changes in the first four data points, and uses a starting forecast of 250, $\alpha_1 = .5$, and $\alpha_2 = .4$. If the next actual value is 255, the TAF for the following period would be computed in this manner:

$$S_t = 250 + .5(255 - 250) = 252.5$$
$$T_t = 10 + .4(0)^*$$

*Since this is the initial forecast, no previous error is available, so a value of zero is used.

$$\text{TAF} = S_t + T_t = 252.5 + 10 = 262.5$$

If the next actual value is 265, the next TAF would be

$$S_t = 262.5 + .5(265 - 262.5) = 263.75$$
$$T_t = 10 + .4(262.5 - 250 - 10) = 11.00$$
$$\text{TAF} = 263.75 + 11.00 = 274.75$$

These values are the first few values in the following example.

Example 2-4

After plotting demand for four periods, the aforementioned manager has concluded that a trend-adjusted exponential smoothing model would be appropriate to predict future demand. Calculations are shown for the next five periods. The initial estimate of trend is based on the net change of 28 for the *three* periods from 1 to 4, for an average of approximately +10 units.

	t period	A_t Actual
Model development	1	212
	2	224
	3	229
	4	240

		TAF_t	$\text{TAF}_t + \alpha_1(A_t - \text{TAF}_t) = S_t$	$T_{t-1} + \alpha_2(\text{TAF}_t - \text{TAF}_{t-1} - T_{t-1}) = T_t$
	5	255	250*	250 + .5(255 − 250) = 252.5	10 + .4(0) = 10
	6	265	262.5	262.5 + .5(265 − 262.5) = 263.75	10 + .4(262.5 − 250 − 10) = 11.00
Model Test	7	272	274.75	274.75 + .5(272 − 274.75) = 273.37	11.00 + .4(274.75 − 262.5 − 11.00) = 11.50
	8	285	284.87	284.87 + .5(285 − 284.87) = 284.94	11.50 + .4(284.87 − 274.75 − 11.50) = 10.95
	9	294	295.89	295.89 + .5(294 − 295.89) = 294.95	10.95 + .4(295.89 − 284.87 − 10.95) = 10.98
Next forecast	10	305.93			

*Estimated by the manager.

A plot of the actual data and predicted values is shown below.

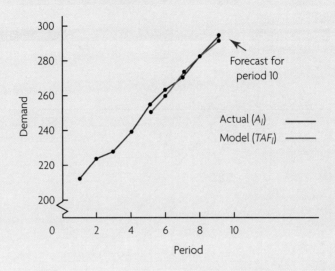

In choosing smoothing constants, it is usually prudent to use an α_1 of .5 if the trend is apt to change or if the initial estimate is uncertain because this will enable fairly rapid adjustment as opposed to values of α_1 that are closer to zero.

Compared to a linear trend line, trend-adjusted exponential smoothing is a more flexible technique because it can handle changes in trend more readily. A linear trend line would have to be recomputed periodically in order to accomplish the same flexibility. On the other hand, the linear trend line can be used to forecast more than simply one period ahead, whereas exponential smoothing cannot.

Trend-Adjusted Exponential Smoothing Using Excel Even though Excel does not have a built-in feature or a module to determine trend-adjusted exponential smoothing, it is relatively easy to prepare a worksheet to determine the trend-adjusted forecasts. The data from Example 2-3 is used to prepare the worksheet in Exhibit 2-12. The formulas to calculate trend T_t, smoothed error S_t, and the trend-adjusted forecast TAF_t values are given in Exhibit 2-12. Note that you are able to obtain exactly the same answers using Excel as we did in Example 2-3.

Techniques for Seasonality

Seasonal variations in time series data are regularly repeating upward or downward movements in series values that can be tied to recurring events. Familiar examples of seasonality relate to weather variations (e.g., sales of winter and summer sports equipment) and vacations or holidays (e.g., airline travel, greeting card sales, visitors at tourist and resort centers). Seasonality often is used to refer to regular annual variations. However, the term *seasonal variation* also is applied to daily, weekly, monthly, and other regularly recurring patterns in data. For example, rush-hour traffic occurs twice a day: in the morning and in the late afternoon. Theaters and restaurants often find weekly demand patterns, with demand higher later in the week than earlier. Banks may experience daily seasonal variations (heavier traffic during the noon hour and just before closing), weekly variations (heavier toward the end of the week), and monthly variations (heaviest around the end of the month because of social security checks, payrolls, and welfare checks being cashed or deposited). Mail volume; sales

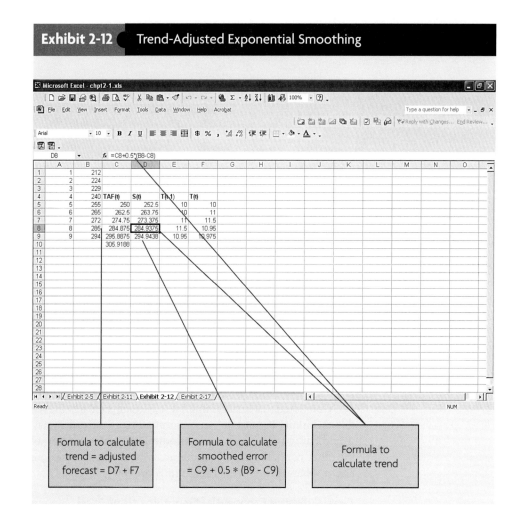

Exhibit 2-12   Trend-Adjusted Exponential Smoothing

Formula to calculate trend = adjusted forecast = D7 + F7

Formula to calculate smoothed error = C9 + 0.5 * (B9 - C9)

Formula to calculate trend

of toys, beer, automobiles, and turkeys; highway usage; hotel registrations; and gardening are common examples of activities that show seasonal variations.

Seasonality in data is expressed relative to the *overage* value of a time series (i.e., to the value if seasonality were not present). Most often, seasonal variations are stated as *percentages* of the series average at a particular point in time. For example, the **seasonal relative** for November for toy sales may be 1.20, or 120 percent. This tells us that November toy sales are 20 percent *above* average. If the seasonal relative for March is .92, this means that March sales are 92 percent of average, or 8 percent *below* the average if seasonality were not present. Thus, a seasonal relative reflects the amount by which a value differs from the expected average for that time period.

Knowledge of seasonal variations is an important factor in planning and scheduling in many retail businesses. Moreover, seasonality can be an important factor in capacity planning for systems that must be designed to handle peak loads (e.g., public transportation, electric power plants, highways and bridges, and so on). Knowledge of the extent of seasonality in a time series can enable one to *remove* seasonality from the data (i.e., to "seasonally adjust" data) in order to discern other movement, or lack of movement, in the series. Thus,

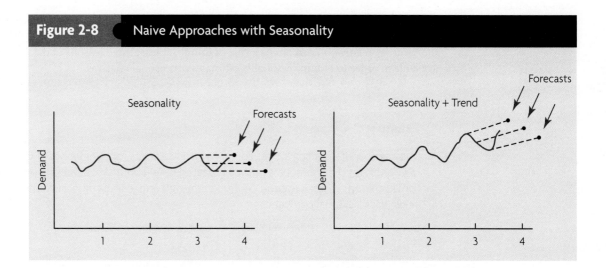

Figure 2-8   Naive Approaches with Seasonality

we frequently read or hear about "seasonally adjusted unemployment" and "seasonally adjusted personal income."

The simplest seasonal model is a variation of the naive technique described for averages. Instead of using the last *period's* actual demand as the forecast amount, the seasonal naive model uses last *season's* actual amount for the forecast. Hence, our forecast of theater attendance this Friday evening would equal last Friday's attendance using the seasonal naive model, and November toy sales in one year might be estimated based on toy sales in November of the preceding year. If trend and seasonal variations are present, the naive model might be: last season's demand plus 10 percent, or whatever increase or decrease is appropriate. (See Figure 2-8.)

Again, the naive approach either can be used as such or can serve as a standard of comparison against which other, more-refined techniques can be judged.

Centered Moving Average   A commonly used method for representing the trend portion of a time series involves a **centered moving average.** Computations are identical to a moving average *forecast,* as are the resulting values. However, the values are *not projected* as in a forecast, but, instead, they are *positioned in the middle* of the periods used to compute the moving average. The implication is that the average is most representative of that point in the series. For example, suppose we have the following time series data:

Period	Demand	Three-Period Centered Average
1	40	
2	46	42.67
3	42	

$$\text{Average} = \frac{40 + 46 + 42}{3} = 42.67$$

A three-period average is 42.67. As a centered average, it would be positioned at Period 2; the average is most representative of the series at that point. The *ratio* of demand at Period 2 to this centered average at Period 2 is an estimate of the seasonal relative at that point.

Because the ratio is 46/42.46 = 1.08, the series is about 8 percent above average at this point. In order to achieve a reasonable estimate of seasonality for any season (e.g., Friday attendance at a theater), it is usually necessary to compute seasonal ratios for a number of seasons and then average these ratios. For instance, in the case of theater attendance, average the relatives of five or six Fridays for the Friday relative, average five or six Saturdays for the Saturday relative, and so on. As a rule of thumb, at least three seasons of data should be available in order to obtain reasonable estimates of seasonal relatives.

Example 2-5

The manager of a parking lot has computed daily relatives for the number of cars per day for his lot. The computations are repeated here (about three weeks are shown for illustration). A seven-period centered moving average is used because there are seven days (seasons) per week.

Day	Volume	Moving Total	Centered MA_7	Volume/MA
Tues	67			
Wed	75			
Thur	82			
Fri	98		71.86	98/71.86 = 1.36 (Friday)
Sat	90		70.86	90/70.86 = 1.27
Sun	36		70.57	36/70.57 = 0.51
Mon	55	503 ÷ 7 =	71.00	55/71.00 = 0.77 (Monday)
Tues	60	496 ÷ 7 =	71.14	60/71.14 = 0.84
Wed	73	494 etc.	70.57	73/70.57 = 1.03
Thur	85	497 .	71.14	85/71.14 = 1.19
Fri	99	498 .	70.71	99/70.71 = 1.40 (Friday)
Sat	86	494 .	71.29	86/71.29 = 1.21
Sun	40	498	71.71	40/71.71 = 0.56
Mon	52	495	72.00	52/72.00 = 0.72 (Monday)
Tues	64	499	71.57	64/71.57 = 0.89
Wed	76	502	71.86	76/71.86 = 1.06
Thur	87	504	72.43	87/72.43 = 1.20
Fri	96	501	72.14	96/72.14 = 1.33 (Friday)
Sat	88	503	73.00	88/73.00 = 1.21
Sun	44	507	73.57	44/73.57 = 0.60
Mon	50	505	72.71	50/72.71 = 0.69 (Monday)
Tues	70	511		
Wed	80	515		
Thur	81	509		

The estimated Friday relative is (136 + 140 + 133)/3 = 136 Relative for other days can be computed in a similar manner. For example, the estimated Monday relative is (0.77 + 0.72 + 0.69)/3 = 0.73

The number of periods used in a centered moving average is equal to the number of data points between seasons. Hence, with monthly data, a 12-period moving average would be used. When the number of periods is even instead of odd, as in the preceding example, one additional step is needed because the middle of an even set falls *between* two periods. The additional step involves taking a centered 2-period moving average of the even-numbered centered moving average, which results in averages that "line up" with data points and, hence, permit determination of seasonal ratios.

| **Figure 2-9** | A Centered Moving Average Closely Tracks the Data |

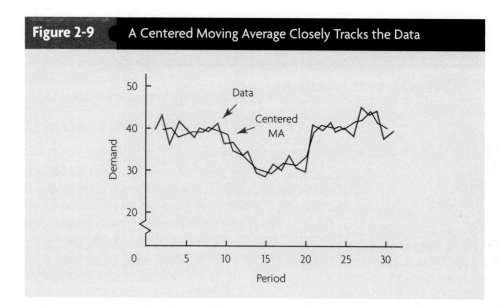

The reason that a centered moving average is used to obtain representative values is that because it "looks forward" and it "looks backward" by virtue of its centered position, it is able to closely follow data movements, regardless of whether they involve trends, cycles, or random variability alone. Figure 2-9 illustrates how a centered moving average closely tracks data that have moderate variability.

Seasonal Relatives with Excel   Excel does not have a special feature or a module to calculate the seasonal relatives; however, it is easy to create a worksheet to determine the seasonal relatives. Exhibit 2-13 shows the worksheet that first calculates the moving totals, then calculates the centered moving averages, and finally calculates the seasonal relative values with the help of very simple equations. Note that after creating the first moving total equation, it is copied to the remainder of the column by dragging it. Dragging is also utilized in calculating the centered moving average as well as the seasonal relative values.

If both trend and seasonality appear in a series, each component can be determined separately, as described previously, and then combined to obtain a forecast.

Example 2-6

A furniture manufacturer wants to predict quarterly demand for a certain loveseat for Periods 15 and 16, which happen to be the second and third quarters of a particular year. The series consists of both trend and seasonality. The trend portion of demand can be projected using the equation $y_t = 124 + 7.5t$. Quarter relatives are $Q_1 = 1.20$, $Q_2 = 1.10$, $Q_3 = .75$, and $Q_4 = .95$. Use this information to predict demand for Periods 15 and 16.

Solution

The trend values at $t = 15$ and $t = 16$ are

$$y_{15} = 124 + 7.5(15) = 236.5$$
$$y_{16} = 124 + 7.5(16) = 244.0$$

Multiplying the trend value by the appropriate quarter relative will yield a forecast that includes both trend and seasonality. Since we are told that $t = 15$ is a second quarter and $t = 16$ a third quarter, the forecasts are

Period 15   236.5(1.10) = 260.15
Period 16   244.0(0.75) = 183.00

Techniques for Cycles

When cycles (up and down movements similar to seasonal variations, but of longer duration, say, two to six years between peaks) occur in time series data, they often are so irregular that it is difficult or impossible to project them from past data because turning points are difficult to identify. A short moving average or a naive approach may be of some value, although both will produce forecasts that lag cyclical movements by one or several periods.

Exhibit 2-13   Seasonal Relative Computations

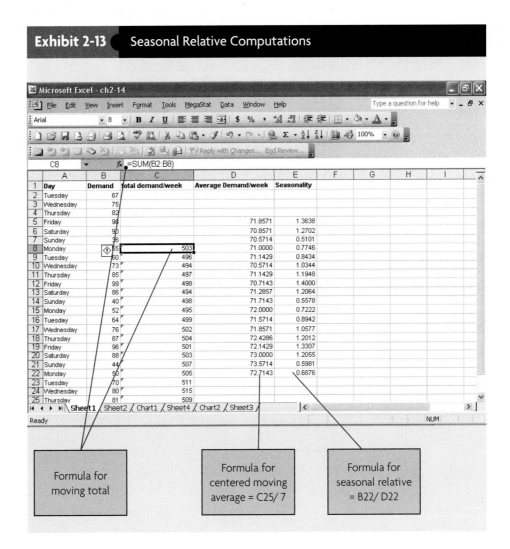

The most commonly used approach to predict cyclical behavior is explanatory: Search for another variable that relates to, and leads, the variable of interest. For example, the number of permissions for housing starts (permits to build houses) in a given month often is an indicator of demand for certain products and services a few months later that are directly tied to construction of new homes (e.g., landscaping, sales of washers and dryers, sales of carpeting and furniture, new demands for shopping, transportation, schools, etc.). Thus, if an organization is able to establish a high correlation between such a *leading* variable (i.e., changes in the variable precede changes in the variable of interest), an equation that describes the relationship can be developed that will enable forecasts to be made. It is important that there be a persistent relationship between the two variables. Moreover, the higher the correlation, the better the chances that the forecast will be on target.

Explanatory Models

Explanatory forecasting models incorporate one or more variables that are *related* to the variable of interest and, therefore, they can be used to predict future values of that variable. The most widely used explanatory models in forecasting are called *regression models*, and the discussion here will concentrate on them, with particular emphasis on simple linear regression models.

Simple Linear Regression

A simple linear regression model consists of two variables that are thought to be related. One of these is the variable to be forecasted, and it is referred to as the *dependent* variable; its value "depends" on (is a function of) the value of another variable. The other variable, which will be used to "explain" or predict the value of the dependent variable, is referred to as an *independent* variable. In order to make a forecast, the two variables must be expressed in a linear equation of the form

$$y = a + bx \tag{2-6}$$

where

y = the dependent variable
x = the independent variable
a = value of y when $x = 0$
b = slope of the line

Trend analysis is just a special form of regression analysis where the independent variable (x) is set as the time (t).

For example, the marketing manager of a paper products company has developed the following equation to predict demand for paper towels (dependent variable) based on the amount of television advertising (independent variable) during the same week;

$$y = 3.57 + 3.78x$$

where

x = television advertising in millions of dollars in preceding week
y = sales of paper towels in millions of dollars

Thus, the marketing manager must feel that advertising expenditure is a major factor in determining sales of this product. According to the equation, if advertising expenditure is $1.0 (million), sales will be about $3.57 + 3.78(1.0) = \$7.35$ (million).

In order to successfully use this approach, it is necessary to be able to

1. Identify an appropriate independent variable or variables.
2. Obtain a sample of at least 10 observations (strongly suggested).
3. Develop an equation.
4. Identify any restrictions on predictions.
5. Measure accuracy in a given forecast.

To begin with, selecting the explanatory variable requires some knowledge of factors that might *logically* be related to the variable of interest. For example, the miles per gallon that a car gets would seem to be somewhat related to its weight; the yield from a home garden may depend on the amount of fertilizer used; and the cost of a textbook may depend on the number of pages it has. If two variables seem related (e.g., changes in one appear to be related to changes in the other), but no reasonable explanation for the relationship can be found, the relationship may simply be due to chance and, therefore, it would be highly unreliable. If it is decided that *more than one* explanatory variable are important, then *multiple regression analysis* is required. This topic will be considered after simple regression analysis is discussed.

Once an independent variable has been identified, it will be necessary to obtain enough observations to construct a model. (One rule of thumb is to observe at least 10.) These can come from historical data or can be observations taken specifically for the purpose of estimating the relationship. The observations represent *paired values*. That is, for each observation of the dependent variable, there must be a corresponding value for the independent variable.

Consider, for example, 10 paired observations about sales and advertising (all figures are in millions of dollars) given in Table 2-2. The data can be plotted on a graph to

Table 2-2	Data for Regression Problem	
Observation	Advertising Expenditure, x	Sales, y
1	$1.1	$7
2	1.4	8
3	1.4	10
4	2.0	10
5	0.9	7
6	1.6	10
7	2.0	11
8	1.7	11
9	1.2	9
10	0.8	6

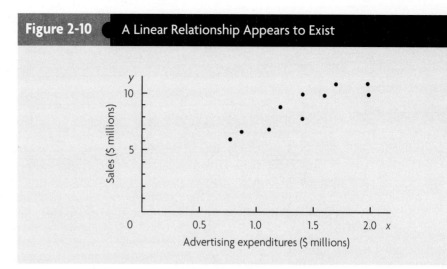

Figure 2-10   A Linear Relationship Appears to Exist

determine if a linear relationship is appropriate (see Figure 2-10). It appears that a linear relationship would reasonably represent the data, if we allow for some variability around a straight line.

The next step is to determine the one line that best fits these points. The line is called a *least squares* regression line because the method used to compute the coefficients of the equation is designed to minimize the sum of the *squared* vertical deviations of points from the line. The equations used for this are essentially the same as those used to compute a linear trend line, except that x replaces t in the equations. Thus:

$$b = \frac{n\sum xy - \sum x \sum y}{n\sum x^2 - (\sum x)^2}$$

$$a = \frac{\sum y - b\sum x}{n} = y - bx$$

(2-7)

where

n = number of observations

The necessary summations needed to compute these regression coefficients are obtained in Table 2-3, along with the $\sum y^2$, which will be used later.

The regression equation can be used to predict a value of y for a given value of x. However, the equation is valid only for values of x that lie within the range of the original x values (which was .8 to 2.0). We have no knowledge of whether the relationship holds beyond that range of values. In fact, if predictions are required for x values outside this range, additional observations should be made, taking care to obtain measurements of y for values of x at desired points.

An indication of how well the line fits the points can be obtained by computing the *correlation coefficient,* which measures the strength of the relationship between the two variables. It can be calculated using this equation:

$$r = \frac{n\sum xy - \sum x \sum y}{\sqrt{n(\sum x^2) - (\sum x)^2} \times \sqrt{n(\sum y^2) - (\sum y)^2}}$$

(2-8)

Table 2-3		Calculations for Regression Coefficients			
Observation	x	y	xy	x^2	y^2
1	1.1	7	7.7	1.21	49
2	1.4	8	11.2	1.96	64
3	1.4	10	14.0	1.96	100
4	2.0	10	20.0	4.00	100
5	0.9	7	6.3	0.81	49
6	1.6	10	16.0	2.56	100
7	2.0	11	22.0	4.00	121
8	1.7	11	18.7	2.89	121
9	1.2	9	10.8	1.44	81
10	0.8	6	4.8	0.64	36
	14.1	89	131.5	21.47	821 (Used later)

$$b = \frac{10(131.5) - 14.1(89)}{10(21.47) - 14.1(14.1)} = \frac{60.1}{15.89} = 3.78$$

$$a = \frac{89 - 3.782(14.1)}{10} = 3.57$$

$$r = \frac{(10)(131.5) - (14.1)(89)}{\sqrt{10(21.47) - (14.1)^2}\sqrt{10(821) - (89)^2}} = \frac{60.1}{67.78} = .887.$$

Thus, the equation is $y = 3.57 + 3.78x$. See Figure 2-11.

For the data shown in Table 2-3, the correlation is +.887. Note that the sign of the correlation is the same as the sign of the slope of the line. Correlation can range from −1.00 (perfect negative relationship) to +1.00 (perfect positive relationship). A positive correlation implies that the lowest values of x generally are paired with the lowest values of y and the highest x and y values are paired. Conversely, a negative correlation implies low x values are paired with high y values and vice versa. A correlation coefficient that is close to zero implies that points do not tend to line up but, instead, tend to scatter randomly.

The square of the correlation coefficient, the coefficient of determination or r^2, can be used as a measure of goodness of fit; the closer the value is to 1.00, the better the fit. If $r^2 = 1.00$, the fit is perfect—all points fall on the line. For the advertising data, $r^2 = .787$. This tells us that about 79 percent of the sum of the squared deviations of y values around the mean of the y values can be eliminated by taking the relationship between x and y into account. We say that the independent variable "explains" 79 percent of the variation. Evidently, 21 percent of the variation cannot be explained by x. This is probably due to other factors that have not been included in our model. More shall be said on that matter very shortly.

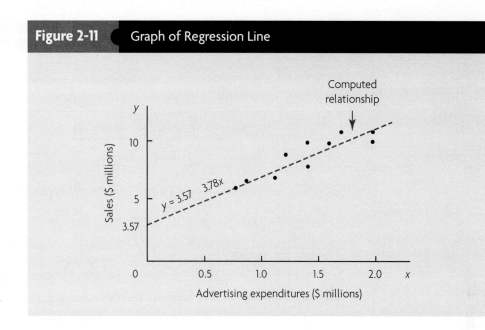

Figure 2-11   Graph of Regression Line

There are a number of important questions that must be answered if a regression equation is to be used for forecasting. The major ones are

1.   Is the relationship significant (i.e., more than could be expected by chance)?
2.   How accurate will a particular forecast probably be?

These and other questions depend in part on the extent to which the points scatter around the regression line. This is measured by the *standard error of estimate, s_e,* which is computed using the equation

$$s_e = \sqrt{\frac{\Sigma y^2 - a\,\Sigma y - b\,\Sigma xy}{n - 2}} \tag{2-9}$$

The reason that 2 is subtracted from n in the denominator is because two degrees of freedom are lost for estimating two population parameters α and β with estimates a and b. For the data in Table 2-3 we have

$$s_e = \sqrt{\frac{821 - 3.57(89) - 3.78(131.5)}{10 - 2}} = .880$$

If the value of r^2 is less than, say, .40, the computed relationship will not be strong enough to yield acceptable forecast accuracy. To test for the existence of relationship (i.e., that the true slope is nonzero), compute the ratio

$$t_{test} = \frac{b}{s_b} \tag{2-10}$$

where

b = slope of regression line and s_b = standard error of the slope

$$s_b = s_e \sqrt{\frac{1}{x^2 - [(x)^2/n]}}$$

Table 2-4	Selected Values of $t_{.025}$ for $n-2$ Degrees of Freedom (df)		
df	**t**	**df**	**t**
8	2.31	15	2.13
9	2.26	16	2.12
10	2.23	17	2.11
11	2.20	18	2.10
12	2.18	19	2.09
13	2.16	20	2.09
14	2.15		

Using the values computed in Table 2-3, and this value of s_e, we find

$$s_b = .880\sqrt{\frac{1}{(21.47)^2 - [14.1]\,(14.1)/10}} = .880\sqrt{.629} = .698$$

$$t_{\text{test}} = \frac{3.78}{.698} = 5.42$$

This value can be compared to the appropriate value from Table 2-4. For df $= 8$, that table value of t is 2.31. If the t_{test} value is greater than the table value, as it is in this case, it can be concluded that the relationship is significant (i.e., probably not due to chance alone). Thus, the computed equation can be used to make predictions.

The next question is: How accurate will a given prediction be? One approach to the answer is to use the regression equation to compute the *expected* value of the dependent variable for a selected, or *given*, value of x and then construct a 95 percent confidence interval around that expected value. That is:

$$y \pm t\, s_{\text{reg}} \tag{2-11}$$

where

$y = a + bx$
t = appropriate value from Table 2-4

$$s_{\text{reg}} = s_e\sqrt{1 + \frac{1}{n} + \frac{(x_g - x)^2}{\Sigma x^2 - [(\Sigma x)^2/n]}}$$

x_g = value of x being used in the regression equation to predict y

Say $x_g = 1.3$. From Table 2-3, $\bar{x} = 14.1/10 = 1.41$ Then:

$$s_{\text{reg}} = .880\sqrt{1 + \frac{1}{10} + \frac{(1.3 - 1.41)^2}{21.47 - [14.1(14.1)/10]}} = .880\sqrt{1.108} = .926$$

The significance of this last equation is that the variability of a forecast based on a simple linear regression model depends on the amount of scatter around the regression line

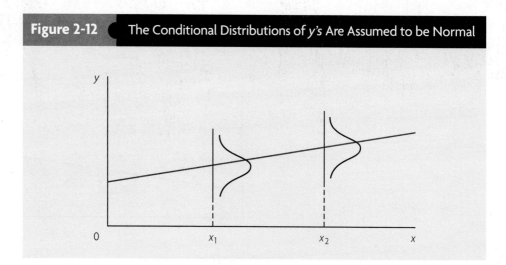

Figure 2-12   The Conditional Distributions of y's Are Assumed to be Normal

(as reflected by s_e) and the extent to which the desired value of x varies from the mean of the x values. For the case where $x_g = 1.3$, a 95 percent confidence interval for the predicted value of y is

$y = a + bx = 3.57 + 3.78(1.3) = 8.48$
95 percent interval $= 8.48 \pm 2.31(.926) = 8.48 \pm 2.14$, or 6.34 to 10.62

Thus, if advertising expenditure is $1,300,000, expected sales would be $8,480,000, and the marketing manager could place a 95 percent confidence interval around that amount that ranges from $6,340,000 to $10,620,000.

Regression Assumptions

There are a number of assumptions that underlie the use of linear regression. If all are not reasonably satisfied, using the regression equation as a forecasting tool may be inappropriate. Briefly, the major assumptions are

1. *Normality.* For any given value of x, there is a distribution of possible y values that has a mean equal to the expected value (i.e., $y = a + bx$) and the distribution is normal. (See Figure 2-12.) These are called *conditional distributions*. This assumption usually is satisfied if the points cluster around the line.
2. *Homoscedasticity.* The conditional distributions for all values of x have the same dispersion (i.e., the scatter of points around the line is the same for all sections of the line). This often can be judged visually. An example of a case that does not satisfy this assumption is presented in Figure 2-13. Uniform scatter is called *homoscedasticity*.
3. *Linearity.* The requirement of uniform scatter also means that there should not be any patterns around the line (e.g., cycles, as illustrated in Figure 2-14). The existence of such a pattern implies that the model is incomplete. For example, squared and cubed terms may be needed to adequately describe the relationship (e.g., $y = 12 + x + 2.4x^2 - 1.3x^3$).
4. *Independence.* Values of y should not be correlated over time. If they are, it may be more appropriate to use a time series model. This can be checked by plotting y values in the order of observation (e.g., June sales, July sales, August sales).

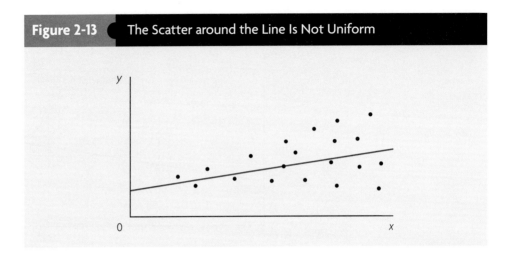

Figure 2-13　The Scatter around the Line Is Not Uniform

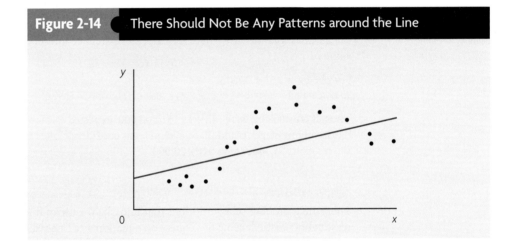

Figure 2-14　There Should Not Be Any Patterns around the Line

Explanatory Models with Excel The advertising example given earlier will be used here to demonstrate how Excel can be utilized to run an explanatory model. Exhibit 2-14 is the Excel output of the advertising problem. Note that the regression equation is $y = 3.57 + 3.78x$. The standard error of estimate, which is the standard deviation of the data points around the regression line, is .88. The coefficient of determination $r^2 = .79$ means that 79 percent of the variation of the sales values is explained by the advertising values. The format of the Excel output is identical to the format of the output that is shown in Exhibit 2-11.

Multiple Regression

In certain situations, an explanatory model with one predictor variable will not provide an acceptable level of accuracy for forecasts. For instance, in Table 2-4, advertising expenditures were used to predict sales. The resulting coefficient of determination was .787, which meant that the unexplained variation (i.e., the variation in sales that could not be explained by variations in advertising expenditure) was about 21 percent. Management may desire a smaller unexplained variation, thereby achieving greater accuracy in forecasts. An increased value of r^2 can be attained by incorporating other explanatory variables in the model. For example,

Exhibit 2-14	Linear Regression-Explanatory Model Output

Microsoft Excel - ch2-14

File   Edit   View   Insert   Format   Tools   MegaStat   Data   Window   Help

B18   fx   3.78225298930145

	A	B	C	D	E	F	G	H	I
1	SUMMARY OUTPUT								
2									
3	*Regression Statistics*								
4	Multiple R	0.88687743							
5	R Square	0.78655157							
6	Adjusted R Square	0.75987052							
7	Standard Error	0.878113							
8	Observations	10							
9									
10	ANOVA								
11		*df*	*SS*	*MS*	*F*	*Significance F*			
12	Regression	1	22.73134047	22.73134	29.47978	0.000623689			
13	Residual	8	6.168659534	0.771082					
14	Total	9	28.9						
15									
16		*Coefficients*	*Standard Error*	*t Stat*	*P-value*	*Lower 95%*	*Upper 95%*	*Lower 95.0%*	*Upper 95.0%*
17	Intercept	3.56702329	1.020714961	3.494632	0.0081429	1.213250365	5.920796	1.213250365	5.9207962
18	X Variable 1	3.78225299	0.696608001	5.429528	0.0006237	2.175872059	5.388634	2.175872059	5.38863392
19									
20									
21									

Sheet6 / Sheet5 / Sheet1 / Sheet2 / Chart1 / Sheet4 / Chart2 / S

Ready   NUM

one might suspect that *unit price* of a product would have some influence on sales: Sales usually are inversely related to price. One additional variable may provide the desired increase in r^2, such as unit price, or other variables may need to be investigated. In each case, the question of adding more variables to the model is whether the added r^2 achieved is worth the increase in costs (of data collection, analysis, etc.). Thus, the simple regression model, $y = a + bx$, is replaced by the multiple regression model, say, with two explanatory variables:

$$y = a + b_1x_1 + b_2x_2 \tag{2-12}$$

where

b_i = reflects the change in y for a one-unit change in x_i

     Suppose an analyst collected price data for the preceding example just in case the simple linear regression model proved unsatisfactory. Those values are shown in Table 2-5, along with the original values.

     A computer analysis of the data in Table 2-5 produced the following multiple regression equation:

$$y = 15.2 + 2.41x_1 - 0.465x_2$$

Everything else being constant, a \$1 increase in unit price is expected to result in a \$465,000 decrease in sales, and a \$1 increase in advertising expenditures is expected to result in a \$2.41 million increase in sales.

     In addition, r^2 for the data was .875, leaving only about 12 percent unexplained variation; compared to the original analysis, which had $r^2 = .787$ and an unexplained variation of about 21 percent.

Table 2-5	Expansion of Data Used in Simple Regression Section		
Observation	Advertising Expenditure, x_1	Price per Unit, x_2	Sales, y
1	$1.1	$22	$7
2	1.4	22	8
3	1.4	19	10
4	2.0	21	10
5	0.9	23	7
6	1.6	20	10
7	2.0	18	11
8	1.7	19	11
9	1.2	22	9
10	0.8	22	6

At this point, management must decide if the level of explained variation is acceptable. If it is not, an effort should be made to identify other possible predictor variables and to determine if they can improve the relationship. Now, it may turn out that although there are many other variables that have a logical relationship to sales of the product in question, none has a major influence on sales, so that inclusion of other variables may not improve the relationship. Then again, some of the other variables may be closely correlated with either advertising expenditures or with price, and for that reason they would add little or nothing in terms of reducing the unexplained variation. Furthermore, the cost of developing and using a model is often a function of the number of explaining variables being used: The greater the number of variables, the greater the cost. Consequently, a decision must be made about whether the cost to achieve a certain level of explained variation is worth the increased accuracy.

As you might guess, much more can be said about multiple regression. However, such a discussion is beyond the scope of this text. For those who are interested, there are many statistics textbooks that provide the necessary details. There are, however, a few points that can be mentioned to enrich the limited discussion here. Most solutions to multiple regression forecasting problems are obtained using a computer package such as Excel, SAS (Statistical Analysis System), and SPSS (Statistical Package for the Social Sciences). It will be instructive to consider a typical Excel computer output in order to understand how such output is interpreted (see Exhibit 2-16.)

Since there are two independent variables as opposed to one, they must be entered into a worksheet in adjacent columns when executing the multiple regression model with Excel. In our example, we have entered advertising expenditures in column 1 and price per unit in column 2. In order to execute the multiple regression model, you click on **Tools | Data Analysis | Regression.** At this point, an input box as shown in Exhibit 2-15 will appear. In specifying the input range for Y, place the cursor in cell D2 and drag it through cell D11. In

| Exhibit 2-15 | Input Box for Multiple Regression |

specifying the input range for the independent variables (X), you place the cursor in cell B2 and drag it through cell C11. Before you close the window, make sure the Labels box is checked.

In addition to the regression equation, the output from a typical multiple regression computer run includes information on the strength of the relationship (as measured by R^2) and whether or not each of the explanatory variables contributes to the relationship.

In Exhibit 2-16, three variables are listed. Intercept is a in the equation $y = a + b_1x_1 + b_2x_2$; it is the value of y when both x_1 and x_2 are equal to zero. The coefficients are the values a, b_1, and b_2 in the equation. The standard deviation of the coefficients indicates a measure of chance variability for each coefficient. A rule of thumb is to compare the p-values, for each variable against $\alpha = .05$. A **p-value** is a measure of how likely sample results are if the variable in question is not making a significant contribution toward the prediction of sales. For example, the p-value of .023782 for x_1 (advertising expenditures) is the probability of observing test statistic values of at least as large or extreme as the t value of 2.876. In other words, if the variable in question is making a contribution toward the prediction of sales, then the p-value would be unusually small. The p-values are generally compared against a most commonly used value of $\alpha = .05$. If the p-value is less than .05, then it can be concluded that the test statistic (calculated value of t, which is equal to 2.876 in our example) is indeed different than the hypothesized value of the test statistic t value ($t.05/2, n-k-1 = t.025, 10-2-1 = 2.365$). Since the p-value is very small, that is, .023782 is less than .05, we have strong evidence that the variable in question is making a valid contribution to the regression model and, thus, should be retained. Note that the t-ratio for each variable and the associated p-value are given in Exhibit 2-16 and in each case, the p-value is less than .05. Hence, we can conclude that each is useful in predicting values of y. Had one of the p-values been greater

Exhibit 2-16 Multiple Regression Output with Excel

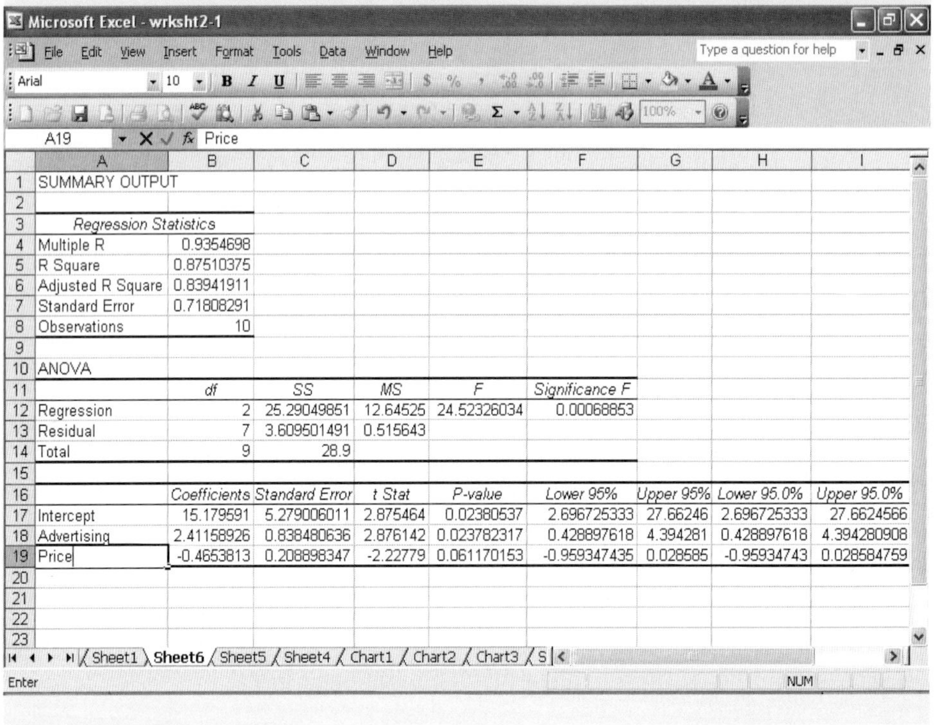

Microsoft Excel - wrksht2-1

File   Edit   View   Insert   Format   Tools   Data   Window   Help

A19   Price

	A	B	C	D	E	F	G	H	I
1	SUMMARY OUTPUT								
2									
3	*Regression Statistics*								
4	Multiple R	0.9354698							
5	R Square	0.87510375							
6	Adjusted R Square	0.83941911							
7	Standard Error	0.71808291							
8	Observations	10							
9									
10	ANOVA								
11		*df*	*SS*	*MS*	*F*	*Significance F*			
12	Regression	2	25.29049851	12.64525	24.52326034	0.00068853			
13	Residual	7	3.609501491	0.515643					
14	Total	9	28.9						
15									
16		*Coefficients*	*Standard Error*	*t Stat*	*P-value*	*Lower 95%*	*Upper 95%*	*Lower 95.0%*	*Upper 95.0%*
17	Intercept	15.179591	5.279006011	2.875464	0.02380537	2.696725333	27.66246	2.696725333	27.6624566
18	Advertising	2.41158926	0.838480636	2.876142	0.023782317	0.428897618	4.394281	0.428897618	4.394280908
19	Price	-0.4653813	0.208898347	-2.22779	0.061170153	-0.959347435	0.028585	-0.95934743	0.028584759
20									
21									
22									
23									

Sheet1 Sheet6 Sheet5 Sheet4 Chart1 Chart2 Chart3 S

than .05, we would have concluded that it did not contribute information to explaining the relationship, and we would eliminate it from the regression analysis. This can easily be done by excluding the variable with the *p*-value greater than .05 and running the regression model again.

Exhibit 2-16 also lists a value for *R*-squared. The value of *R*-squared (.875) indicates the percent of explained variation. The standard error of estimate (.718), which is the standard deviation of *y* around the regression line, can be used to determine the probable accuracy of predictions obtained using the analysis.

Accuracy and Control

Accuracy and control of forecasts are a vital aspect of forecasting. To begin with, the complex nature of most real-world variables makes it almost impossible to correctly predict future values of those variables on a regular basis. Consequently, it is essential to include an indication of the extent to which the forecast might deviate from the value of the variable that actually occurs, along with the forecast itself. This will provide the forecast user with a better perspective on how far off a forecast might be.

Moreover, because some techniques will provide more accuracy than others in a given situation, in choosing among different techniques, the decision maker needs a measure of accuracy that can be used as a basis for comparison.

Finally, some forecasting applications involve a series of forecasts (e.g., weekly revenues), whereas others involve a single forecast that will be used for a one-time decision (e.g., deciding on the size of a power plant). When periodic forecasts are made, it is important to monitor forecast errors in order to determine if the errors are within reasonable bounds. If they are not, it is necessary to take corrective action. This involves controlling the forecast.

Forecast Errors

Forecast error is the difference between the value that occurs and the value that was predicted for a given time period. Hence, Error = Actual − Forecast:

$$e_t = A_t - F_t \tag{2-13}$$

Positive errors result when the forecast is too *low* and negative errors result when the forecast is too *high*. For example, if actual demand for a week is 100 units, while forecasted demand was 90 units, the forecast was too low: the error is $100 - 90 = +10$.

There are a variety of possible reasons for forecast errors. Among the primary sources of forecast errors are the following:

1.   The model may be inadequate due to (*a*) the omission of an important variable, (*b*) a change or shift in the variable that the model cannot deal with (e.g., sudden appearance of a trend or cycle), or (*c*) the appearance of a new variable (e.g., new competitor).
2.   Irregular variations due to severe weather or other natural phenomena, temporary shortages or breakdowns, catastrophes, or similar events may occur.
3.   The forecasting technique may be used incorrectly or the results may be misinterpreted.
4.   There are random variations in the data. Randomness is the inherent variation that remains in the data after all causes of variation have been accounted for.

A forecast is generally deemed to perform adequately when the errors exhibit only random variations. Hence, the key to judging when to reexamine the validity of a particular forecasting technique is whether forecast errors are random. If they are not random, an investigation must be made to determine which of the other sources of errors are present and to correct the problem.

Summarizing Forecast Accuracy

Evaluating and controlling forecast accuracy requires the use of one or more summary measures of forecast errors. Two measures commonly used for these purposes are the mean absolute deviation and the mean squared error.

The **mean absolute deviation (MAD)** measures the average forecast error over a number of periods, without regard to the sign of the error: For computation, all errors are treated as positive. The **mean squared error (MSE)** is the average squared error experienced over a number of periods. The following formulas are used in their computation:

$$\text{MAD} = \frac{\Sigma |e|}{n} = \frac{\Sigma |A - F|}{n} \tag{2-14}$$

$$\text{MSE} = \frac{\Sigma e^2}{n - 1} = \frac{\Sigma (A - F)^2}{n - 1} \tag{2-15}$$

The MSE is a variance, and the $n - 1$ in its denominator is used instead of n for essentially the same reason that $n - 1$ is used to compute a *sample* standard deviation.

The basic difference between the two summary measures of accuracy is that the MSE, by using the square of each error, tends to emphasize large errors more than the MAD measure does. The computation of each summary measure is illustrated in Example 2-7.

Example 2-7

Calculate MAD and MSE for the following data.

Period	Demand A	Forecast F	Error $A - F$	$\|A - F\|$	$(A - F)^2$
1	45	—	—	—	—
2	50	48	+2	2	4
3	53	50	+3	3	9
4	52	55	−3	3	9
5	56	55	+1	1	1
6	59	62	−3	3	9
7	65	64	+1	1	1
8	68	65	+3	3	9
Totals			**+4**	**16**	**42**

MAD and MSE are relatively easy to compute using the following equations

$$\text{MAD} = \frac{\Sigma |A - F|}{n} = \frac{16}{7} = 2.286$$

$$\text{MSE} = \frac{\Sigma (A - F)^2}{n - 1} = \frac{42}{6} = 7$$

A manager can use either measure to compare the relative accuracies of alternative forecasts. For instance, suppose a manager must decide on which of three smoothing constants to use for exponential smoothing. The manager could use historical data to test each of the smoothing constants, and by using either MAD or MSE, select the one that yields the best accuracy. Suppose the manager focuses on MAD, with these results:

Alternative	MAD
#1	26.3
#2	18.2
#3	37.0

Because Alternative #2 has the best accuracy (smallest MAD), the manager probably would decide to use that alternative rather than either of the others. Of course, the manager may decide that none of these alternatives provides an acceptable degree of accuracy. Subsequently, an attempt might be made to identify another alternative that would provide an acceptable level of accuracy.

Monitoring and Controlling the Forecast

In order to control a forecast, it is necessary to monitor the forecast errors over a period of time. The purpose of such monitoring is to attempt to distinguish between random errors, which are inherent and cannot be eliminated, and nonrandom errors, which can be eliminated (e.g., by modifying a technique, improving data collection or analysis, or switching to another technique). Thus, monitoring the forecast errors is intended to answer the question: "Is it time to reexamine the validity of the forecasting technique being used?"

In order to develop a better understanding of the forecast accuracy measures, first we must understand the nature of the forecast errors. There are two types of forecast errors. The first type of error is called the forecast bias, where the direction of the error is the primary consideration. If the value of the error is negative, then we can conclude that the forecasting method overestimated sales, demand, or whatever is being predicted. If the value of the error is positive, then we can conclude that the forecasting method underestimated sales or demand because in calculating the error term, we always subtract the forecasted value from the actual value.

When we sum the error terms, if there is no bias, positive and negative error terms will cancel each other out and the mean forecast error (MFE) is given in Equation 2-16.

$$\text{MFE} = \frac{\sum A_i - F_i}{n},\qquad(2\text{-}16)$$

will be zero. As pointed out above, negative MFE is an indication of overestimation and positive MFE is an indication of underestimation. Upper and lower bounds or *limits* are determined, which serve as a standard against which forecast errors can be judged: They indicate a range of *random* variability. Thus, points falling within that range are suggestive of random variability, whereas points falling outside that range are suggestive of the presence of nonrandomness. This concept is illustrated in Figure 2-15. However, if the positive and negative error values tend to cancel each other out and the MFE value is zero or near zero, then we can conclude that the forecasting method does not result in bias (underestimation or overestimation). Even if there is no significant bias, it is possible that the forecasting method is not giving acceptable results due to overall error.

Two somewhat similar methods are commonly used to monitor overall forecast errors, one involving MAD and the other involving MSE.

Relative Measures of Forecast Accuracy

Relative methods of measuring accuracy use percentages in determining the accuracy of forecasts. Multiple accuracy measures may be needed to evaluate both forecast bias and the overall forecast accuracy. Relative measures are generally considered to be desirable because percentages are easy to interpret.

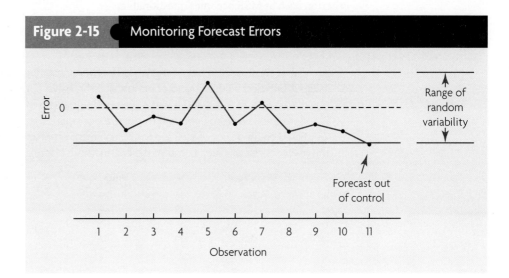

Figure 2-15   Monitoring Forecast Errors

The relative forecast accuracy measures that we will discuss in the remaining portion of this section are

1.   Mean percentage error
2.   Mean absolute percentage error

Mean percentage error (MPE) measures the forecast bias while **mean absolute percentage error (MAPE)** measure overall forecast accuracy. In calculating MPE, as with any other forecast bias measure, negative and positive error terms offset each other. Therefore, for given time series data, MPE ≤ MAPE.

Before stating the equations for MPE and MAPE, first we need to define percentage error. The percentage error (PE) for given time series data measures the percentage point deviation of the forecasted value from the actual value. The equations for PE in period i, MPE, and MAPE are given below in equations 2-17, 2-18, and 2-19, respectively.

$$PE_i = \left(\frac{A_i - F_i}{A_i}\right)(100) \tag{2-17}$$

$$MPE = \frac{\sum_{i=1}^{n} PE_i}{n} \tag{2-18}$$

$$MAPE = \frac{\sum_{i=1}^{n} |PE_i|}{n} \tag{2-19}$$

where

A_i = the actual value from period i
F_i = the forecasted (estimated) value from period i

Both MPE and MAPE are more intuitive and easier to understand and interpret than most of the other measures because 4 percent has far more meaning to the user than MSE of 224. The utilization of MSE as a criterion in determining the accuracy of forecasts has some drawbacks. One of the drawbacks is that, in many cases, it is not appropriate to compare MSE values obtained from different forecasting models because different methods use different ways of obtaining the forecasted values. Thus, comparison of methods using a single criterion such as MSE becomes questionable.

Example 2-8

An analyst must decide between two different forecasting techniques for weekly sales of bicycles: a linear trend equation and the naive approach. The linear trend equation is $y_i = 12 + 2x_i$, and it was developed using data from periods 1 through 10. Based on the data from periods 11 through 20, calculate the MPE and MAPE.

Based on the values of MPE and MAPE, comment on which of the two methods has the greater overall accuracy. Compare the two methods in terms of the forecast bias.

T	Units Sold	T	Units Sold
11	25	16	39
12	28	17	48
13	34	18	50
14	40	19	47
15	44	20	54

Solution

Percentage Error Calculations Using the Naive Method

Period	Actual	Forecast	Error	PE_i	$|PE_i|$
11	25	—	—	—	—
12	28	25	3	.1071	.1071
13	34	28	6	.1765	.1765
14	40	34	6	.15	.15
15	44	40	4	.0909	.0909
16	39	44	−5	−.1282	.1282
17	48	39	9	.1875	.1875
18	50	48	2	.04	.04
19	47	50	−3	−.0638	.0638
20	54	47	7	.1296	.1296

$$\sum PE_i = .6895 \qquad MPE = \frac{.6895}{9} = 7.66\%$$

$$\sum |PE_i| = 1.0735 \qquad MAPE = \frac{1.0735}{9} = 11.93\%$$

Percentage Error Calculations Using the Linear Regression Equation

Period	Actual	Forecast	Error	PE_i	$|PE_i|$
11	25	34	−9	−.36	.36
12	28	36	−8	−.2857	.2857
13	34	38	−4	−.1176	.1176
14	40	40	0	0	0
15	44	42	2	.0455	.0455
16	39	44	−5	−.1282	.1282
17	48	46	2	.0417	.0417
18	50	48	2	.04	.04
19	47	50	−3	−.0638	.0638
20	54	52	2	.037	.037

$$\sum PE_i = -.7911 \qquad MPE = \frac{-.7911}{10} = -7.91\%$$

$$\sum |PE_i| = 1.1195 \qquad MAPE = \frac{1.1195}{10} = 11.12\%$$

Since the MAPE values for the two methods are approximately equal, the overall accuracy of the two methods is about the same. Both methods are predicting approximately 11 percent away from the actual.

Since the MPE is −7.91 percent for the linear trend equation, the trend equation is overestimating sales by 7.91 percent. On the other hand, since the MPE is positive for the naive forecasting method, it is underestimating the sales by 7.66 percent. In order to decide between the two methods in this situation, we have to compare the consequences and the cost of overestimation with the consequences and the cost of underestimation. If the cost of underestimation is less than the cost of overestimation, then the linear trend equation should be selected. However, if the cost of overestimation is less than the cost of underestimation, then the naive method should be used.

The cost of overestimation involves the cost of carrying excess inventories, while cost of underestimation includes the cost of shortages, backordering, and lost sales.

Tracking Signal   A popular method for monitoring bias in forecast errors is the **tracking signal.** This is the ratio of cumulative forecast error at any point in time to the corresponding MAD at that point in time. Thus, the formula for computing the tracking signal for a period is

$$\text{Tracking signal} = \text{T.S.}_t = \frac{\Sigma(A - F)_t}{\text{MAD}_t} \qquad (2\text{-}20)$$

For example, using the data and calculations for Example 2-7, the tracking signal for Period 8 is $4/2.286 = 1.75$. Such a small value would be suggestive of random variation. In practice, values that range from ± 4 to ± 7 are used as action limits. A value of a tracking signal that is beyond the action limits would suggest the need for corrective action. Generally, a manager or analyst will set limits based on experience with the variable in question as well as on the relative costs of falsely concluding the errors are unacceptable when they are not.

It is a good idea to use a value for the MAD that is current because it will tend to reflect the latest behavior of errors. This can be accomplished by using a limited number of only the most recent errors (e.g., the last seven or so) in computing the MAD. Another alternative is to update the value of MAD with exponential smoothing using the formula

$$\text{MAD}_t = \text{MAD}_{t-1} + \alpha(|e|_{t-1} - \text{MAD}_{t-1}) \qquad (2\text{-}21)$$

A decision must be made regarding the number of periods to include in the average. The greater the number of data points used to compute MAD, the lower the response rate of the updated MAD, and vice versa. The choice of rate of response is largely a matter of experience with a particular series and costs of misjudging what is happening.

Example 2-9

A tracking signal is used to monitor the forecast errors. An initial MAD is computed using the first five errors.

t Period	Error	Cumulative Error	$|e_t|$	5-Period Moving Cumulative $|e|$	MAD_t	Tracking Signal
1	−5	−5	5	5		
2	7	+2	7	12		
3	2	+4	2	14		
4	4	+8	4	18		
5	−2	+6	2	20	4.00*	1.5
6	0	+6	0	20	3.0	2.0
7	−3	+3	3	23	2.2	1.364
8	6	+9	6	29	3.0	3.0
9	−8	+1	8	37	3.8	.263
10	1	+2	1	38	3.6	.556

*Computed using MAD $= \Sigma|e|/5$ for first living periods, and all of the remaining MAD values are computed using a 5-period moving average.

Even though the tracking signal is reasonably small in every period (compared to limits of, say, ± 4), due to six consecutive positive tracking signal values, the forecasting method may be underestimating demand. Therefore, the analyst should consider adjusting the forecasts upwards.

Calculation of MAD, MSE, Tracking Signal, MPE, and MAPE Using Excel   Exhibit 2-17 demonstrates the utilization of Excel to calculate MAD, MSE, the tracking signal, MPE, and MAPE using the data from Example 2-7. Again, there is no built-in feature or module to calculate MAD, MSE, the tracking signal, MPE, or MAPE. However, creating the formulas is relatively easy and they are shown in Exhibit 2-17. MSE values are easily computed by squaring

Exhibit 2-17	Measuring Forecast Accuracy Using MAD, MSE, MPE, and MAPE

H21

	A	B	C	D	E	F	G	H	I	J	K	L	M	N	O
1	Period	Actual(A)	Forecast (F)	Error (A-F)	$\lvert A-F\rvert$	$(A-F)^2$	$\sum(A-F)$	$\sum\lvert A-F\rvert$	MAD	T. Signal	PE	APE			
2	1	45													
3	2	50	48	2	2	4	2	2	2	1	0.04	0.04			
4	3	53	50	3	3	9	5	5	2.5	2	0.057	0.0566			
5	4	52	55	-3	3	9	2	8	2.67	0.75	-0.06	0.0577			
6	5	56	55	1	1	1	3	9	2.25	1.333333	0.018	0.0179			
7	6	59	62	-3	3	9	0	12	2.4	0	-0.05	0.0508			
8	7	65	64	1	1	1	1	13	2.17	0.461538	0.015	0.0154			
9	8	68	65	3	3	9	4	16	2.29	1.75	0.044	0.0441			
10	Sum			4	16	42					0.065	0.2825			
11															
12				MAD=	2.28571	MSE=	7			MPE=	0.016	MAPE=	0.040358		

Cell	Copied to	Formula
D3	D4 : D9	= B3 − C3
E3	E4 : E9	= ABS (B3 − C3)
F3	F4 : F9	= (B3 − C3)^2
G3		= D3
G4	G5 : G9	= (D4 + G3)
H3		= E3
H4	H5 : H9	= E4 + H3
I4		= H4 / 2
I5		= H5 / 3
J3	J4 : J9	= G3 / I3
K3	K4 : K9	= D3 / B3
L3	L4 : L9	= ABS (D3 / B3)
E12		= AVERAGE (E3 : E9)
G12		= SUM (F3 : F9) (COUNT (F3 : F9) − 1)
K12		= AVERAGE (K3 : K9)
M12		= AVERAGE (L3 : L9)

the error terms and averaging those squared values, as shown in cell G12. MAD values are computed by taking the absolute value of the error terms and averaging those values, as shown in cell E12. Tracking signal values in column J are computed by taking the running sum of forecast errors given in column G and dividing it by MAD in column I. The formula for cell percentage error (PE) terms is calculated in column K. For instance, in cell K3, we take the error term given in cell D3 and divide it by the actual demand in cell B3. Thus, the formula for cell K3 is =D3/B3. After the computation of the percentage error terms in column K, we average those values in cell K12 to determine MPE. Absolute percentage error (APE) terms are calculated in column L. For instance, the formula in cell L3 is =ABS(D3/B3). In other words, these values are computed in a very similar way to PE. The only difference is that the absolute value of the percentage error is taken using the =ABS(*argument*) Excel function. The formulas for all the cells are given at the bottom of Exhibit 2-17.

Using Forecast Information

Organizations may regard the information provided by forecasts in either a *reactive* or a *proactive* manner. A reactive approach views forecast values as probable descriptions of future demand, and it attempts to respond to meet that demand (e.g., build up inventories, work overtime, retrain workers, scale down operations, lay off workers). Conversely, a proactive approach attempts to influence or create demand (e.g., through advertising, pricing policy, product and service innovation).

A reactive approach is usually associated with forecasts that use historical data, and a proactive approach is usually associated with explanatory models. Nonetheless, a manager who is confronted with an unfavorable forecast based on historical data may decide to adopt a proactive approach toward the future. However, in order to effectively do that, some sort of explanatory model must be used because time series models do not include a mechanism for incorporating explanatory variables.

Qualitative forecasts can sometimes be helpful. For example, a **Delphi** questionnaire can be designed to elicit ideas for the best way to *create* demand, or it can be designed to elicit ideas on how to *respond to* a probable future event.

Selecting a Forecasting Approach

Successful forecasting begins with careful thought about the choice of a forecasting approach. This section outlines the major considerations in making that choice.

The *importance of the forecast* is a prime consideration because it will give some indication of the resources that could be devoted to preparing the forecast and the degree of accuracy that is necessary. Essentially, the importance of the forecast is determined by the *use* to which the forecast will be put. Is the purpose of the forecast to obtain rough estimates, or will the forecast be used to develop very detailed plans? To what extent might profits and/or opportunity costs be affected? Is there a risk that plans based on forecasts will result in errors that are costly or difficult to overcome?

The *cost* of developing a forecast is an obvious factor, although the cost factor should be weighed against the potential benefits of a particular technique. For example, a relatively costly forecasting technique might be justifiable because of the importance of obtaining a good forecast.

Perhaps, the most obvious factor is the expected *accuracy* of a forecast. However, the person selecting a forecasting approach must strike a balance between cost and accuracy because the highest accuracy usually, but not always, is delivered by approaches that lend to highest cost the most.

The *planning horizon* is usually a consideration, for two reasons. One is that some techniques lend themselves more to long-term forecasts (e.g., trend analysis), whereas others perform best, or are limited to, short-term forecasts (e.g., averaging techniques). The other involves the time necessary to prepare a forecast: Some techniques require more time and effort than others. Consequently, if a forecast is needed almost immediately, certain techniques will be ruled out at the start because they cannot be developed during the required time frame.

The *resources* (computer software, data collection, and interpretation, and other expertise) that are required vary considerably among the different forecasting approaches, so it is important to match requirement with available resources.

A factor that is often overlooked is the *user* or *users*. Users are the ones who will make the forecast operational. It is important to consider the level of sophistication of the users and then to select an approach that corresponds to that level. The danger in selecting a technique that is beyond the level of the user's sophistication is that users may tend to mistrust the forecast and they may modify the forecast to suit their own needs or perceptions. Further, forecasts typically have certain assumptions that underlie their use. Highly sophisticated techniques tend to embody assumptions that are beyond the ability of users to appreciate them: Users either may fail to check to see that assumptions are met or they may not grasp the importance of certain assumptions. Because of such factors, they may employ a technique incorrectly and, subsequently, lose faith in the model after getting burned a few times. A good rule is to *choose the simplest technique that gives acceptable results.* It also is prudent to include users in the selection process, whenever possible, to increase their confidence about the approach. Finally, in cases in which it is decided that a certain technique is best, even though the technique is somewhat beyond the level of user sophistication, it is important that a quantitative analyst who is familiar with the technique present it to users so that it appears trustworthy. This analyst also can alert users to potential dangers of the technique and can explain how to spot troubles and what action should be taken if troubles arise.

Finally, if historical data are available, it can be exceedingly informative to *plot the data;* trend, seasonal, or cyclical patterns tend to be much more apparent when data are graphed.

Table 2-6 presents a comparison of forecast types according to frequency, degree of management involvement, cost, and level of aggregation.

Table 2-6	Comparison of Types of Forecasts		
	Type		
Factor	**Short Range**	**Intermediate Range**	**Long Range**
Frequency	Often	Occasional	Infrequent
Techniques	Averaging Projection Regression Judgment	Projection Seasonal Regression Judgment	Regression Judgment
Degree of management Involvement	Low	Moderate	High
Cost per forecast	Low	Moderate	Moderate to high
Level of aggregation	Item	Product family	Product family Total output

◆ A Modern Management Science Application

ABC Worldwide Dosimetry Service helps companies detect and report radioactive exposure. (ABC is a fictitious name used to protect the confidentiality of the company and its clients.) The company provides this service by leasing thermoluminescent badges that record radioactive exposure over a given time period, called a *recording cycle*. As the recording cycle ends, ABC sends refurbished or new badges to the customer, and at the same time, it is the responsibility of the customer to send the used badges back to ABC for measurement of the radioactivity.

When ABC does not have enough badges, it notifies the customer that it does not have sufficient badges and orders new inventory. ABC also informs the customer to keep on using the old badges until the new ones arrive.

The authors were able to devise an integrated planning system made up of three modules: (1) forecasting module, (2) planned ordering module, and (3) optimal ordering module.

The forecasting module is designed to forecast demand for customized badges and also predict how fast the old badges will be returned. The model also predicts the percent of non-defective badges returned to ABC. The forecasting module classifies customers into three groups corresponding to their recording cycle of one, three, or six months. Historical data are used to predict demand for the three customer groups. The forecasting module uses the seasonal decomposition method to estimate the seasonal effect. According to the historical data, the forecasting module estimates the seasonal effect very well and provides accurate forecasts for all three customer groups.

The planned order module determines how many new badges ABC should order to meet target customer service levels. ABC needs to order new badges because the return rates of the badges used by the company are not known with certainty. The company calculates the optimal ordering quantity by using a mixed-integer programming formulation (topic of Chapter 7).

Finally, the authors used this information to develop a decision support system (DSS) for ABC. The DSS assists the managers of ABC to understand demand and return forecasting, and the DSS also reports planned order quantity and optimal order quantity.

It is not only important that the DSS be easily understood, but also that the system be easy to operate and allow users to perform what-if analysis.

Using the authors' integrated approach, ABC was able to reduce the level of inventory by 17.7 percent and reduce the cost by $820,000 within a six-month period. The methods used by ABC integrate various management science methods for managing refurbished product with uncertain demand.

The integration of methods in the refurbished product industry is the first of its kind but holds promise for other possible "integrated" solutions to challenging problems.

Source: M. Bayiz and C. S. Tang, "An Integrated Planning System for Managing the Refurbishment of Thermoluminescent Badges," *Interfaces* 34, no. 5 (September–October 2004), pp. 383–93.

▶ Summary

Decision makers rely on forecasts to reduce uncertainty about the future. For this reason, forecasts play a vital role in planning.

Decision makers have a wide variety of forecasting models to choose from. These can be classified as qualitative, quantitative, and explanatory models. The qualitative models use judgment and experience; the quantitative models simply extend past experience, as reflected by movements of a series over time, into the future; and explanatory models incorporate one or more variables whose movements are related to movements of the variable of interest and, hence, serve as predictor variables. Table 2-7 provides a summary of the forecasting techniques discussed in the chapter and more advanced techniques not covered in this book.

Measuring forecast error and controlling errors are important aspects of forecasting because forecast errors provide feedback about how well a forecast is performing. The errors may be either random or some combination of random and correctable variation. The purpose of controlling the forecast is to distinguish between these two types in order to know when to take corrective action.

Choosing a forecasting technique depends on the purpose of the forecast, the desired accuracy, the cost, previous experience, sophistication of users, and planning horizon.

Table 2-7	Forecasting Approaches
Approaches	**Brief Description**
Qualitative Models	
Judgmental methods	
Consumer surveys	Questioning consumers on future plans
Sales force composites	Joint estimates obtained from salespeople
Executive opinion	Finance, marketing, and manufacturing managers join to prepare forecast
Delphi technique	Series of questionnaires answered anonymously by managers and staff; successive questionnaires are based on information obtained from previous surveys
Market research	Collect data to test hypotheses about the market and make decisions about possible product introductions, and tastes and preferences about customers
Quantitative Models	
Box-Jenkins technique	Complicated but accurate technique that fits models to the time series data using Bayesian posterior distribution
Focus forecasting	Uses easy-to-understand rules to project past data into the future; it validates use of the rules by measuring forecast errors
Times series	
Naive	Next value in a series will equal the previous value
Moving averages	Forecast is based on an average of recent values
Econometric models	Describe economic relationships by a series of dependent equations
Exponential smoothing	Sophisticated form of averaging
Trend	Trend equation used to forecast
Explanatory Models	
Simple regression	Values of one variable are used to predict values of another variable
Multiple regression	Two or more variables are used to predict values of another variable

 # Glossary

Centered Moving Average A moving average with values positioned at the center of the data that each average is derived from.

Cyclical Variations Semi-regular variations in time series data that occur at intervals that are longer than a year.

Delphi Technique Uses a series of anonymous questionnaires in an attempt to achieve a consensus forecast.

Explanatory Forecasting Model A model that uses predictor variables to "explain" values of a dependent variable.

Exponential Smoothing A weighted average technique used to smooth time series data.

Irregular Variations The result of unusual factors such as severe weather conditions, equipment breakdowns, or fire.

MAD (Mean Absolute Deviation) The average magnitude of forecast error.

MAPE (Mean Absolute Percentage Error) Determines the absolute average percentage error from the actual value and measures the overall accuracy of the forecasting method.

Moving Average Forecast A forecast based on the average of the most recent values (e.g., last 3, last 4) of a time series.

MPE (Mean Percentage Error) Determines the average percentage error from the actual value and measures the forecast bias.

MSE (Mean Squared Error) The average of the squares of forecast errors (uses $n-1$ instead of n in computing the average).

Naive Forecasts Forecasts based on the last value in a time series (e.g., last period's demand, the change between the last two periods, demand for the same season the last time around).

p-Value A measure of how likely sample results are if the variable in question is assumed not to be making a significant contribution toward the prediction of sales.

Random Variation No predictable pattern of variation.

Seasonal Relatives Relative deviation from the average or trend.

Seasonal Variation Variability in time series data that can be attributed to events related to weather, cultural, or other regularly occurring events.

Smoothing Constant (α) Percentage of forecast error that is used to update the forecast in exponential smoothing.

Time Series A time-ordered sequence of observations.

Tracking Signal A technique for monitoring forecast error based on cumulative forecast error.

Trend A long-term movement in time series data, often linear, but not necessarily.

◗▶ Discussion and Review Questions

1. What are the main advantages of quantitative techniques over qualitative techniques of forecasting? Discuss the limitations of quantitative techniques.
2. Discuss the consequences of poor forecasts.
3. Discuss the purpose of tracking signals, MPE, and MAPE. Compare the purposes of MPE and MAPE.
4. Compare the use of MAD and MSE in evaluating forecasts.
5. How does the value of α used in exponential smoothing affect the responsiveness of the forecasts?
6. Discuss the advantages of exponential smoothing over moving averages.
7. In a given firm, who needs to be involved in preparing the forecasts?
8. Compare stable (smoothed) forecasts and responsive (naive) forecasts.
9. Compare the term *sales* with the term *demand*.
10. The regression equation to predict demand based on inches of newspaper advertising is $y = 25 + 3x_i$. Provide a managerial interpretation of the y-intercept and slope for this equation.

Solved Problems

Problem 1

For each of these data sets, plot the data, then suggest an appropriate forecasting technique:

Period	1	2	3	4	5	6	7	8	9	10	11
Set #1	64	63	65	69	68	72	76	73	76	79	79
Set #2	79	83	86	82	91	86	80	85	79	88	78

Solution

The plots are:

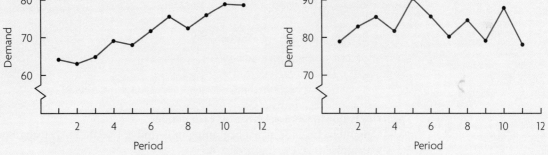

The plot of Set #1 indicates a trend is present. Appropriate techniques include a linear trend line and trend-adjusted exponential smoothing. The plot of Set #2 seems to show variation around an average. Appropriate techniques include a moving average and exponential smoothing.

Problem 2

Given this time series, make a forecast for Period 5 using each of these techniques:

Period	1	2	3	4
Demand	15	13	17	19

a. Naive.
b. A three-period moving average.
c. Exponential smoothing with alpha equal to .20.

Solution

a. The naive forecast for Period 5 is equal to the actual demand for Period 4. Hence, the naive forecast is 19.

b. A three-period moving average forecast is equal to the average of the three preceding demands. Hence, this forecast is

$$MA_3 = \frac{13 + 17 + 19}{3} = 16.33$$

c. An exponential smoothing forecast incorporates historical data into a forecast. In order for this to occur, we begin with data prior to the point of the forecast. In this instance, we can begin by using the first actual demand as a forecast for Period 2, then continue through forecasts for Periods 3 and 4 before developing the forecast for Period 5. The exponential forecast is

$$F_{next} = F_{last} + \alpha(\text{Last actual} - F_{last})$$

Using Period 1 demand of 15 as the forecast for Period 2, we have

Period 3	15 + .20(13 − 15) = 14.6
Period 4	14.6 + .20(17 − 14.6) = 15.08
Period 5	15.08 + .20(19 − 15.08) = 15.86

Problem 3

Given these data on predicted and actual demand for 10 periods:

Period	Demand	Predicted
1	145	142
2	144	145
3	146	146
4	158	146
5	151	150
6	148	150
7	155	149
8	142	151
9	152	147
10	144	150

a. Determine the forecast error for each period.
b. Compute a tracking signal beginning in Period 5. Update MAD using Equation 2-21 with alpha = .3. Use limits of ± 4.
c. Based on the preceding analyses, what can you conclude about how well the forecast is performing?

Solution

Answers to a and b are given below.

Period	D Demand	F Forecast	D − F Error	Cum. Error	Absolute Error	Cum. Abs. Error	MAD	Tracking Signal
1	145	142	+3	+3	3	3		
2	144	145	−1	+2	1	4		$\left[\dfrac{\text{Cum. Error}}{\text{MAD}}\right]$
3	145	146	0	+2	0	4		
4	158	146	+12	+14	12	16		
5	151	150	+1	+15	1	17	17 ÷ 5 = 3.40	4.41
6	148	150	−2	+13	2		3.40 + .3(2 − 3.40) = 2.98	4.36
7	155	149	+6	+19	6		2.98 + .3(6 − 2.98) = 3.89	4.88
8	142	151	−9	+10	9		3.89 + .3(9 − 3.89) = 5.42	1.85
9	152	147	+5	+15	5		5.42 + .3(5 − 5.42) = 5.29	2.84
10	144	150	−6	+9	6		5.29 + .3(6 − 5.29) = 5.50	1.64

Note that all tracking signal values are within ±5 limits.

c. The forecast errors were evaluated using a tracking signal. In all instances, the results fall within acceptable limits, and a plot of errors revealed a possible downward trend. Consequently, we can conclude that the forecast is performing inadequately and corrective action to forecasts must be taken.

Problems

1. The number of bushels of apples sold at a roadside fruit stand over a 12-day period were as follows:

Day	Number Sold	Day	Number Sold
1	25	7	35
2	31	8	32
3	29	9	38
4	33	10	40
5	34	11	37
6	37	12	32

a. If a two-period moving average had been used to forecast sales, what would the daily forecasts have been starting with the forecast for Day 3?

b. If a four-period moving average had been used, determine what the forecasts would have been for each day, starting with Day 5.

c. Use a three-period weighted moving average with $w_1 = .2$, $w_2 = .3$, and $w_3 = .5$ and forecast sales for the seventh and eighth days.

d. Plot the original data and each set of forecasts on the same graph. Which forecast has the greater tendency to smooth? Which forecast has the better ability to respond quickly to changes?

e. What does use of the term *sales* instead of the term *demand* imply?

2. If exponential smoothing with $\alpha = .4$ had been used to forecast daily sales for apples in the preceding problem, determine what the daily forecasts would have been. Then, plot the original data, the exponential forecasts, and a set of naive forecasts on the same graph. Based on a *visual* comparison, can you say that the naive would have been more accurate or less accurate than the exponential smoothing method, or would they have been about the same?

Ex. smoothing
Day 12 = 37.08,
Ex. smoothing
Day 13 = 35.05;
Naive Day 12 = 37,
Naive Day 13 = 32.
Graph given in the
Instructor's Manual

3. A jeweler wants to forecast sales of one-carat diamond rings. Sales data for the previous 15 weeks have been obtained:

Week	1	2	3	4	5	6	7	8	9	10	11	12	13	14	15
Sales	25	19	24	28	30	35	32	36	34	30	32	25	29	32	30

a. Develop a series of forecasts, beginning in Week 4, that would have resulted if a three-period moving average forecast had been used.

b. Using a starting forecast for Week 4 of 23 rings, develop the forecasts that would have resulted if an exponential smoothing model with $\alpha = .20$ had been used.

4. An electrical contractor's records during the last five weeks indicate the number of job requests:

Week	1	2	3	4	5
Requests	20	22	18	21	22

Predict the number of requests for Week 6 using each of these methods:

a. Naive.

b. A four-period moving average.

c. A four-period weighted moving average with $w_1 = .1$, $w_2 = .2$, $w_3 = .3$, and $w_4 = .4$.

d. Exponential smoothing with $\alpha = .30$.

e. Determine the forecast using the naive method for Weeks 2 through 5 and compute MAPE and MPE values.

a. Week 6 forecast = 22
b. Week 6 forecast = 20.75
c. F_6 = 20.9
d. Week 6 forecast = 20.72

e. MPE = .01425
   MAPE = .125361

5. Sales of waterbeds at a specialty store during the past seven weeks were

Week	1	2	3	4	5	6	7
Number sold	26	24	29	33	32	37	36

a. Use two different, but appropriate methods to predict the number of units that will be sold during Week 8. Explain why these methods are appropriate.

b. If actual sales during the next five weeks turn out to be 40, 45, 44, 50, and 53, which of the two methods would have provided a better forecast? Explain what probably occurred based on a comparison of the new data with the original data.

6. A gift shop in a tourist center is open on weekends (Friday, Saturday, and Sunday). The owner-manger hopes to improve scheduling of part-time employees by determining seasonal relatives for each of these days. Data on recent activity at the store (sales transactions per day) have been tabulated and are shown below. Develop seasonal relatives for the shop.

$\bar{x}$: Fri = 0.79;
Sat = 1.34;
Sun = 0.87

	Week					
	#1	#2	#3	#4	#5	#6
Friday	149	154	152	150	159	163
Saturday	250	255	260	268	273	276
Sunday	166	162	171	173	176	183

7. Use a naive trend approach to predict sales transactions for the gift shop in the previous problem for the following week

8. An analyst must decide between two different forecasting techniques, a linear trend equation and the naive approach. The linear trend equation is $y_t = 124 + 2t$, and it was developed using data from Periods 1 through 10. Based on data for Periods 11 through 20 as shown, which of these two methods has the greater accuracy? The data are for daily sales of trail bikes.

$\text{MAD}_{naive} = 4$
$\text{MSE}_{naive} = 25.25$
$\text{MAD}_{trend} = 2.3$
$\text{MSE}_{trend} = 10.11$

t	Units Sold	t	Units Sold
11	147	16	152
12	148	17	155
13	151	18	157
14	145	19	160
15	155	20	165

9. Terri Trendy, the manager of a fashionable restaurant that is open Wednesday through Saturday, has commented that the restaurant does about 30 percent of its business on Friday night, 35 percent on Saturday night, and 20 percent on Thursday night. What seasonal relatives would describe this situation?

10. A pharmacist has been monitoring sales of Quick, an over-the-counter pain reliever. Daily sales during the last 15 days were

Answer in the Instructor's Manual (IM)

Day	1	2	3	4	5	6	7	8	9	10	11	12	13	14	15
Number sold	36	38	42	44	48	49	50	49	52	48	52	55	54	56	57

Without doing any calculations, which method would you suggest using to predict future sales; a linear trend equation or trend-adjusted exponential smoothing? Why?

11. If you now learn that on some of the days in the previous problem the store ran out of the pain reliever in question, would that knowledge cause you any concern? Explain.

12. Assume that the data in Problem 10 refer to demand rather than sales. Using trend-adjusted smoothing with an initial forecast of 50 for Week 8, an initial trend estimate of 2, and $\alpha_1 = \alpha_2 = .30$, develop forecasts for Days 9 through 16. What is the MSE for the eight forecasts for which there are actual data?

Forecast Day 15 = 57.60;
Forecast Day 16 = 58.43;
MSE = 6.13

13. A quality control analyst has kept a record of the defective rate of a process he has been trying to improve during a period of about four weeks. The following data (percentages) were recorded:

	Week			
	1	2	3	4
Monday	10.2	9.4	8.4	7.8
Tuesday	8.2	7.3	7.0	6.5
Wednesday	7.2	6.8	6.3	5.0
Thursday	6.8	6.0	5.4	4.8
Friday	9.4	9.0	8.2	7.1

a. Determine daily relatives for the defective rate.
b. Compute a linear trend equation for the defective rate.
c. Use your answers from the preceding two parts to predict the defective rate for each day of Week 5.

14. A TV repair shop located near a large hospital provides rental TVs to hospital patients. According to shop invoices, the number of TVs rented out per day for the last 12 days were

Day	Rentals	Day	Rentals
Sunday	14	Sunday	18
Monday	17	Monday	20
Tuesday	18	Tuesday	13
Wednesday	10	Wednesday	16
Thursday	15	Thursday	16
Friday	16		
Saturday	14		

Naive 2nd Thursday = 16
Exp. Smoothing 2nd
Thursday = 15.7
MSE_{naive} = 18.2
$MSE_{exp. Smoothing}$ = 9.7

Which approach, naive or exponential smoothing with alpha = .2, would have produced the greater accuracy had it been used for forecasting? Use a starting forecast of 14 for the first Monday for exponential smoothing.

15. An automobile dealer wants to forecast demand for a certain model car for the first week in March using the following data from recent sales:

January	Sales	February	Sales
Week 1	42	Week 1	32
2	38	2	28
3	38	3	26
4	34	4	25

a. Make the forecast on the basis of a linear trend equation.
b. Use trend-adjusted smoothing to make the forecast. Use an average of the first two weeks for the third week forecast to start, and an initial trend estimate of -3. Also, use $\alpha_1 = .2$ and $\alpha_2 = 3$

16. A commuter airline operates five days a week. The general manager of the company wants to determine seasonal relatives for passenger traffic. She has compiled the following data:

Mon = 1.0743
Tue = 0.8724
Wed = 0.9362
Thur = 0.9469
Fri = 1.1666

	Week				
	#1	#2	#3	#4	#5
Monday	212	219	215	218	210
Tuesday	175	180	170	176	174
Wednesday	180	190	194	184	190
Thursday	190	186	188	194	190
Friday	231	225	246	232	240

Estimate daily relatives for passenger traffic.

17. A farming cooperative manager wants to estimate quarterly relatives for grain shipments, based on the data shown here (quantities are in metric tons):

	Quarter			
Year	1	2	3	4
1	200	250	210	340
2	210	252	212	360
3	215	260	220	358
4	225	272	233	372
5	232	284	240	381

Determine quarter relatives. (Hint: Use a centered four-period moving average initially; then a centered, two-period moving average of the four-period moving average.)

Q_5 forecast = $262,800;
Q_6 forecast = $234,000
Q_7 forecast = $174,300
Q_8 forecast = $290,400

18. The vice president of operations for a frozen food company estimates quarterly earnings using a model that has both a seasonal component and a trend component. The seasonal relatives used are $Q_1 = 1.2$, $Q_2 = 1.0$, $Q_3 = .7$, and $Q_4 = 1.1$. The trend equation is $y_t = \$144{,}000 + \$15{,}000t$, where $t = 0$ in the last quarter of last year. Predict earnings for each quarter of *next* year (not *this* year) using this information.

19. Determine an appropriate linear trend equation based on the historical data shown, and forecast the next two values of the series.

Month	Units Demanded
March	445
April	461
May	489
June	505
July	530
August	544

20. For each of the following data sets, decide if a linear egression model would be appropriate for predictive purposes. If you feel such a model is acceptable, determine the least squares equation for the line.

a. x	y	b. x	y	c. x	y
7	34	20	160	72	88
9	60	120	75	90	80
3	30	80	125	65	75
3	65	130	80	35	110
6	60	160	90	55	95
6	35	180	80	64	90
12	70	200	70	82	70
15	70	100	100	40	98
16	75	40	155	65	80
2	50	120	80	85	110
14	65	125	60	40	60
4	55				
5	30				

$y_t = 159 - .53x$
$R^2 = -727$

21. A production manager has collected data on job times. She wants to learn if there is any relationship between the production time per piece and the number of pieces in a job. The following data were collected from shop records:

Job	Time (minutes per piece)	Number of Pieces
1	3.1 min.	15
2	1.1	75
3	2.2	45
4	1.6	62
5	2.5	40
6	1.5	70
7	4.2	12
8	1.8	50
9	1.0	90
10	3.4	18
11	2.8	32

    a.   Which variable is the independent variable in this situation?
    b.   Plot the data on a graph. Does it appear that a linear relationship exists?
    c.   Develop a regression equation for the relationship. What does the slope imply.
    d.   Over what range of values can the regression equation be used for predictive purposes? Explain.

22. The managing partner of a chain of dry cleaning stores wants to determine how the volume of suits the chain cleans in a week relates to the price charged. Records on prices and volume have been kept, and the data have been reproduced here:

Week	Price	Volume (thousands of suits)
1	$2.20	2.3
2	2.10	2.4
3	2.30	1.9
4	2.20	1.8
5	2.20	2.0
6	2.30	2.2
7	2.00	2.5
8	2.15	2.3
9	2.25	2.1
10	2.30	1.8

No linear relationship

For what reasons would you not recommend using simple linear regression to predict the volume of suits based on the price charged per suit?

23. A financial planner wants to develop a linear regression model that he can use to evaluate clients' portfolios. He has collected relevant data on 20 clients, and he has used Excel to analyze the data. The Excel output is summarized in the following information:

$$y = 470.4 + 25.1x \quad \text{where} \quad x = \text{beginning portfolio value}$$
$$s_e = 4.30 \qquad\qquad\qquad\qquad y = \text{portfolio value 2 years later}$$
$$s_b = 6.21$$
$$r = +.924$$

    a.   Is the relationship significant? Explain.
    b.   How well does the regression equation "fit" the data? Explain.
    c.   If the planner determines that s_{reg} for a certain new client's portfolio of 9.8 is 3.70, develop a 95 percent confidence interval for the dependent variable and interpret your answer.

24. An appliance manufacturer wants to know if there is a relationship between percentage change in disposable personal income (DPI), which is reported quarterly by the

government, and the percentage change in gross orders during the following quarter for appliances sold by the manufacturer. An analyst has obtained data for the past 10 quarters:

Quarter	Percent Change, DPI	Percent Change In Orders (following quarter)
1	−2.3	−2.5
2	−1.5	1.0
3	2.8	7.4
4	0.5	2.6
5	4.6	8.5
6	−1.0	1.0
7	0.7	1.4
8	5.2	3.4
9	−2.5	−0.5
10	1.7	1.8

a. $r = .817$; $r^2 = .668$; r^2 seems fairly strong

b. $y = 1.59 + .998x$

c. $t_{test} = 4.01$, relationship is significant

d. −1.04 to 8.72

a. Compute the correlation coefficient for these data. Is the correlation strong enough, in your opinion, to base a predictive linear model on it? Explain.
b. Develop a linear regression equation for the data. Which is the dependent variable?
c. Test the relationship for significance. What can you conclude?
d. Develop a 95 percent confidence interval for percent change in orders when the percent change in DPI for the preceding quarter is 2.0.

25. A company gives a standardized test to all of its new recruits. At the end of the first year of employment, each of these people is given a performance rating. Test scores and performance ratings for a randomly selected sample of recruits yielded these values:

Person	Test Score	Performance Rating
1	78	6.7
2	112	9.4
3	95	9.1
4	82	8.8
5	104	9.5
6	84	8.6
7	89	9.0
8	110	9.8
9	93	9.1
10	95	9.2
11	86	7.7
12	90	9.2
13	107	9.6

a. Develop a linear regression equation for these data.
b. What percent of the performance rating variability can be explained by test scores?
c. Is the relationship between these two measures significant?
d. Determine a 95 percent confidence interval for the predicted performance rating an employee will receive, given the employee had a test score of 86.

Answer given in the IM.

26. Under what conditions might a manager choose to use a multiple regression model for forecasting rather than a simple regression model? What trade-offs might influence the decision one way or the other? Explain.

27. Analyst Anita Anton has gathered sales data on Fax machines in preparation for developing a multiple regression predictive model. The computer printout is reproduced

below, where X1 = unit price of product, X2 = store location (miles from the home office), and X3 = unit price of main competitor.

VARIABLE	COEFFICIENT	STD. DEV. OF COEF.	T-RATIO
X0	68.45	14.70	4.656
X1	−8.20	2.63	−3.118
X2	2.04	1.23	1.659
X3	−4.56	1.95	−2.338

   a. Write the apparent regression equation.
   b. Are all of the variables valid predictors? Explain.

28. Using his new computer, the manager of a small business has obtained the following printout for an explanatory forecasting model.

VARIABLE	COEFFICIENT	STD. DEV. OF COEF.
X0	217.92	44.42
X1	12.30	3.15
X2	20.14	13.45
X3	−4.45	1.02
	R-SQUARED = 92.71 PERCENT	

a. $y = 217.92 + 12.20\,x_1 +$
     $20.14x_2 − 4.45x_3$
b. 7.3 percent
c. x_1 and x_3
d. $y = 254.415$

   a. Write the apparent regression equation.
   b. What percent of variation is unexplained?
   c. Which variables are valid predictors? Explain.
   d. Use the original regression model and predict demand for the case where X1 = 5.4, X2 = .79, and X3 = 10.3

29. Suppose you have collected the following data and must now do a multiple regression analysis.

Period	Demand	Advertising	Unit Price
1	140	23	34
2	163	25	33
3	152	25	33
4	158	25	32
5	168	28	31
6	174	28	31
7	170	28	30
8	181	30	30
9	177	30	31
10	183	30	31
11	189	30	30
12	189	32	29

   a. Using Excel, obtain the regression equation and other relevant statistics to predict demand on the basis of advertising and unit price. Are both price and advertising valid predictors? Explain.
   b. Make Period an "explanatory" variable and include it in the analysts. Rerun the problem using Period as the third independent variable. Which variables are valid predictors? Explain.
   c. What percent of variation is unexplained?
   d. What model would be best to predict demand?

30. The manager of a computer store has been using a certain forecasting model to predict sales of personal computers, and he has monitored forecast errors during the past 13 weeks, with these results:

Week	Error (rounded)	Week	Error (rounded)
1	+3	8	−2
2	+5	9	−3
3	−4	10	+1
4	+1	11	−6
5	+2	12	−4
6	0	13	−4
7	−3		

Possible downward trend of the TS values

Is the forecasting model performing adequately in terms of errors? Explain why or why not, using tracking signal.

31. A small, private university has been using an exponential smoothing model to predict applications for certain programs for the past 12 semesters, with forecast errors as shown below:

Semester	1	2	3	4	5	6	7	8	9	10	11	12
Actual	201	205	190	210	214	187	180	184	195	190	182	173
Forecast	190	210	200	195	210	208	182	182	188	192	188	180

a. Use the first four periods to computer MAD, then update in with exponential smoothing using $\alpha = .40$.

b. Develop a tracking signal starting in the fifth period. If limits of (4 are used, is the forecast tracking properly?

32. The credit manager of a bank has been forecasting mortgage applications using a moving average model. Results for the previous 16 weeks were

Week	1	2	3	4	5	6	7	8	9	10	11	12	13	14	15	16
Error	+6	−2	−1	+5	−4	+7	−5	−5	+4	+3	+4	−2	−2	+5	−5	0

a. MAD Week 15 = 4.36; MAD Week 16 = 2.18

b. All tracking signals within limits of ±4

a. Compute MAD for the first six weeks, then update it using exponential smoothing with $\alpha = .5$.

b. Begin a tracking signal in Week 7. Using limits of ± 4, is the forecast working properly? Explain.

33. A textbook publishing company has compiled data on total annual sales of its business texts for the preceding nine years:

Year	1	2	3	4	5	6	7	8	9
Sales (000)	40.2	44.5	48.0	52.3	55.8	57.1	62.4	69.0	73.7

a. Using a simple linear regression model, forecast textbook sales for each of the next five years.

b. Prepare a tracking signal for the forecast using the original data.

c. Suppose actual sales for the next five years turn out as follows:

Years	10	11	12	13	14
Sales (000)	77.2	82.1	87.8	90.6	98.9

Is the forecast performing adequately? Explain.

34. The owner of a catering company wants to use exponential smoothing to forecast demand for the catering service. These historical values reflect recent experience:

a. For $\alpha = .10$, MAD = 1.673, MSE = 4.79;

Week	1	2	3	4	5	6	7	8	9	10	11	12	13	14
Demand	8	10	10	12	9	7	8	7	9	10	13	12	11	10

For $\alpha = .30$, MAD = 1.80, MSE = 4.67

b. Average TS ($\alpha = .1$) = 4.20

Average TS ($\alpha = .3$) 2.53, choose $\alpha = .3$

c. Week 15 demand = 10.54

$e = -2.54$

d. See the IM

e. $F_{14} = 11.65$

$F_{15} = 10.65$

a.   Use the first half of the data to develop a model. Choose between a smoothing constant of .10 and one of .30.

b.   Test your choice of a smoothing constant on the remainder of the data, using tracking signal.

c.   Forecast the expected demand for Week 15.

d.   If actual demand turns out to be 8, is the forecast in control? Forecast the demand for the following week. If actual demand turns out to be 13, is the forecast in control? Explain.

e.   Compute the three-period weighted moving average with $w_1 = .2$, $w_2 = .25$, and $w_3 = .55$ for the 14th and 15th weeks.

35. The owner of a flower shop has been using a certain forecasting model to predict weekly demand for long-stemmed red roses. Forecast errors during the last 20 weeks were

Week	Error	Week	Error
1	+3	11	+1
2	−4	12	−4
3	−1	13	0
4	−2	14	+3
5	+4	15	+2
6	+2	16	−4
7	−6	17	−3
8	+4	18	+5
9	+1	19	−1
10	+7	20	−2

Compute the MAD for the first five weeks and begin a tracking signal in Week 6, updating MAD with alpha = .3. Is the forecast working properly? Explain. Use limits of ±4 for the tracking signal.

36. Consider the following example where two different forecasting techniques (FC$_1$ and FC$_2$) were used to forecast demand for cases of bottled water. Actual demand and the two sets of forecasts are as follows. Calculate MPE and MAPE values.

Time Period	Actual Demand	Forecasted Demand 1 (FC$_1$)	Forecasted Demand 2 (FC$_2$)
1	68	66	66
2	75	68	68
3	70	72	70
4	74	71	72
5	69	72	74
6	72	70	76
7	80	71	78
8	78	74	80

a. MPE$_1$ = 3.54%, MPE$_2$ = .264%

b. MAPE$_1$ = 5.34%, MAPE$_2$ = 4.1%

c. $F_8 = 75.7$, $F_9 = 78.2$

d. $e_8 = 2.3$

a.   Compute MPE for both sets of forecasts. Which of the two forecasting methods has a higher forecast bias? Explain.

b.   Compute the MAPE for the two sets of forecasts. Which of the two forecasting methods provides higher overall accuracy with this data set

c.   Compute the forecasted demand for the eighth and ninth time period using a three-period weighted moving average with $w_1 = .1$, $w_2 = .4$, and $w_3 = .5$.

d.   What is the forecast error for Period 8 based on your answer to part C.

Chapter 2 Case   Gnomial Functions, Inc.

Gnomial Functions, Inc. (GFI), is a medium-sized consulting firm in San Francisco that specializes in developing various forecasts of product demand, sales, consumption, or other information for its clients. To a lesser degree, it has also developed ongoing models for internal use by client companies. When contacted by a potential client, GFI usually establishes a basic agreement with the firm's top management that sets out the general goals of the end product, primary contact personnel in both firms, and an outline of the project's overall scope (including any necessary time constraints for intermediate and final completion and a rough price estimate for the contract). Following this step, a team of GFI personnel is assembled to determine the most appropriate forecasting technique and to develop a more-detailed work program to be used as the basis for final contract negotiations. This team, which may vary in size according to the scope of the project and the client's needs, will perform the tasks established in the work program in conjunction with any personnel from the client firm who would be included in the team.

Recently, GFI has been contacted by a rapidly growing regional firm that manufactures, sells, and installs active solar water-heating equipment for commercial and residential applications. DynaSol Industries has seen its sales increase by more than 200 percent during the last 18 months and wishes to obtain a reliable estimate of its sales during the next 18 months. The company management expected that sales should increase substantially because of competing energy costs, tax-credit availability, and fundamental shifts in the attitudes of the regional population toward so-called exotic solar systems. They also faced increasing competition within the burgeoning market. This situation requires major strategic

Table 2-8

Month	DynaSol Industries Sales (units)	Sales ($000)	Regional Market Sales (units)	Sales ($000)
September	24	$44.736	223	$396.048
October	28	52.192	228	404.928
November	31	59.517	230	408.480
December	32	61.437	231	422.564
January	30	57.998	229	418.905
February	35	67.197	235	429.881
March	39	78.621	240	439.027
April	40	80.637	265	484.759
May	43	86.684	281	529.449
June	47	94.748	298	561.479
July	51	110.009	314	680.332
August	54	116.480	354	747.596
September	59	127.265	389	809.095
October	62	137.748	421	931.401
November	67	148.857	466	1,001.356
December	69	153.300	501	1,057.320
January	74	161.121	529	1,057.320*
February	79	172.007	573	1,145.264

*The company is using December's results for the market sales for January because market sales data for January could not be collected.

decisions concerning the company's future. At the time when GFI was contacted, DynaSol had almost reached the manufacturing capacity of its present facility and, if it were to continue growing with the market, would have to expand either by relocating to a new facility entirely or by developing a second manufacturing location. Each involved certain known costs and each had its own advantages and disadvantages. The major unknown, as far as management was concerned, was the growth of the overall market for this type of product and how large a share the company would be able to capture.

Table 2-8 contains the preliminary information available to GFI on DynaSol's past sales.

Discussion Questions

1. Given the information available and your knowledge of different forecasting techniques, your role as a team member is to develop a recommendation for utilizing a specific forecasting technique in the subsequent study. The final contract negotiations are pending, so it is essential that you take into account the advantages and disadvantages of your preferred technique as they would apply to the problem at hand and point out any additional information you would like to have.

2. Assume that you are a member of DynaSol's small marketing department and the contract negotiations with GFI have fallen through irrevocably. The company's top management has decided to use your expertise to develop a forecast for the next six months (and perhaps for the six-month period following that one as well) because it must have some information on which to base a decision to expand its operations. Develop such a forecast and note, for the benefit of top management, any reservations or qualifications you feel are vital to its understanding and use of the information.

Sources: James A. Fitzsimmons and Robert S. Sullivan. *Service Operations Management* (New York: McGraw-Hill, 1982). "
© 1982 by McGraw-Hill, Inc.

Part 2

Deterministic Decision Models

The chapters in Part II cover deterministic models. In a deterministic model the inputs or variables not controlled by the decision maker are assumed to be known with certainty and not able to vary. Thus deterministic models can be used when all events or variables are known with certainty, in contrast to probabilistic models where variable values must be estimated.

Chapters 3, 4, and 5 and the Chapter 4 Supplement focus on one of the most widely used and most powerful tools of management science: *linear programming*. The coverage includes formulation of problems, the use of the simplex method, and discussion of business applications and Excel solutions.

Chapter 6 and Chapter 6 Supplement cover transportation, assignment, and transshipment problems. These optimization models are applied in a wide range of businesses to solve shipping, transportation, and logistics problems. They take into account such things as allocating or assigning tasks or jobs, analyzing multiple transportation options to maximize results or revenue as well as minimizing costs. In chapter 6, linear programming formulations as well as the Excel Solution of these problems are shown. The chapter 6 supplement explains the special purpose algorithms used to solve transportation and assignment problems.

Chapter 7 and Chapter 7 Supplement cover integer programming, a special case of linear programming in which only integer values are used. Chapter 7 covers the formulation of the problem and the Excel solution, while chapter 7 supplement demonstrates solution of an integer programming problem using a popular technique called branch and bound.

Chapter 8 covers three network models, namely: shortest route, minimal spanning tree and maximal flow. The importance and relevance of these models, their business applications, and linear programming formulation are discussed. Also, the Excel solutions to the shortest route and maximal flow models are provided.

In Chapter 9, we investigate situations in which the objective function and/or one or more constraints are nonlinear. (Chapters 3–8 assumes the solution is 'linear'.) The chapter shows not only the importance and relevance of nonlinear programming to business applications, but also provides Excel solutions to numerous applied business problems.

Chapter 10 discusses multi-criteria models, which should be utilized whenever more than one criterion needs to be considered in order to arrive at the best decision. Three different multi-criteria models are discussed in chapter 10, Goal Programming, the Analytical Hierarchy Process, and Scoring Models.

Part Outline

Chapter 3 Linear Programming: Basic Concepts and Graphical Solution
Chapter 4 Applications and Solutions of Linear Programming
Chapter 5 Linear Programming: Sensitivity Analysis and Duality
Chapter 6 Transportation, Transshipment, and Assignment Problems
Chapter 7 Integer Programming
Chapter 8 Network Optimization Models
Chapter 9 Nonlinear Programming
Chapter 10 Multi-Criteria Decision-Making Models

Linear Programming: Basic Concepts and Graphical Solution

Learning Objectives

After completing this chapter, you should be able to:

1. Explain what is meant by the terms *constrained optimization* and *linear programming*.
2. List the components and the assumptions of linear programming and briefly explain each.
3. Name and describe at least three successful applications of linear programming.
4. Identify the type of problems that can be solved using linear programming.
5. Formulate simple linear programming models.
6. Identify LP problems that are amenable to graphical solutions.
7. Explain these terms: *optimal solution, feasible solution space, corner point, redundant constraint slack,* and *surplus*.
8. Solve two-variable LP problems graphically and interpret your answers.
9. Identify problems that have multiple solutions, problems that have no feasible solutions, unbounded problems, and problems with redundant constraints.

Chapter Outline

Introduction, 106
Constrained Optimization, 106
Linear Programming, 106
A Simple Example, 107
Successful Implementations of
   Linear Programming, 108
Components and Assumptions
   of LP Models, 109

Formulating LP Models, 112

Graphical Method, 115
Graphing the Model, 115
Plotting the Constraints, 115

**Finding the Optimal
Solution, 119**
The Extreme Points
   Approach, 119
The Objective Function (Iso-
   Profit Line) Approach, 122

A Minimization Example, 126

Slack and Surplus, 129

Some Special Issues, 131
No Feasible Solutions, 131
Unbounded Problems, 132
Redundant Constraints, 133
Multiple Optimal Solutions, 134

Summary, 134

Glossary, 135

Solved Problems, 136

**Discussion and Review
Questions, 141**

Problems, 142

Chapter 3 Case: Son, Ltd., 150

◼️ Introduction

Linear programming is at the heart of many extensive optimization systems that have been used to solve thousands of problems in fields as wide ranging as airline scheduling to portfolio management on Wall Street. The fundamental question these can answer is "how do we get the most out" when we only have limited resources to put in. The major airlines have to decide what flight schedules yield the highest revenue and keep the costs the lowest. These airlines have thousands of costs to consider, and thousands of decisions that "constrain" their total return. They must have enough planes at each location to start the daily flight schedule, they all must be fueled, crewed up, and ready to fly. At the same time, even for the most popular and profitable routes, they are "constrained" from just sending their whole fleet of planes to service that particularly high-profit route. American, Delta, United, and others all have optimization software built into their scheduling systems that use linear programming. Similarly, networks such as the global telephone network, utility providers, and private firms with widespread logistics needs also utilize optimization techniques such as linear programming to allocate resources in order to maximize output subject to the limitations and constraints of their system.

The purpose of this chapter is to provide you with an introduction to linear programming models. Emphasis is placed on familiarization with terminology, problem recognition, model formulation, and examples of applications of linear programming. The chapter is designed to help you to develop three very important skills:

1. The ability to *recognize* problems that can be solved using LP models.
2. The ability to set up, or *formulate,* an LP model in mathematical terms.
3. The ability to *solve* LP problems using the graphical method.

Constrained Optimization

A commonly encountered form of decision making involves situations in which the set of acceptable solutions is somehow restricted. The restrictions may be imposed internally or externally. For example, an internal restriction might be the amount of raw material that a department has available to produce its products. This would impose a limit on the amount of product that could be produced. Other internal restrictions can include availability of labor time, machine time, technical requirements (for example, drying times, curing times), and budgets. An external restriction might be labor regulations (e.g., safety equipment, training requirements, overtime) that limit the options open to decision makers.

The restrictions are referred to as *constraints* for purposes of linear programming. The goal in linear programming is to find the best solution given the constraints imposed by the problem; hence, the term **constrained optimization.**

Linear Programming

In 1947, George Dantzig developed the use of linear algebra for determining solutions to problems that involved the optimal allocation of scarce resources. In spite of numerous potential applications in business, response to this new technique was low, primarily because of the substantial computational burden it required. Subsequent advances that were made during the last five decades in computer technology and related computer software have removed the computational burden. This has led to widespread use of linear programming in business.

Although computers often are used to solve linear programming problems, computer programming is not required to obtain computer solutions: Preprogrammed packages are used to input the problem. The *programming* aspect of linear programming refers to the use of *algorithms*. An **algorithm** is a well-defined sequence of steps that will lead to a solution. The term *linear* refers to straight-line relationships. **Linear programming** (LP) models are based on linear relationships. Taken as a whole, the term linear programming (LP) refers to a family of mathematical techniques that can be used to find solutions to constrained optimization problems. LP problems can be solved using different techniques. These techniques include the **graphical method** (demonstrated later in this chapter, but limited to two variables), **simplex method,** and **Karmakar's method.** Karmakar's method is an interior method while the simplex method is an exterior method. The simplex method is explained and demonstrated in the CD-ROM, in the Chapter 4 supplement.

A Simple Example

A linear programming model is a mathematical statement of a problem, written in a form that lends itself to solution using standard solution techniques. However, at this point, lets consider a verbal model of this in order to see the framework of LP models. When formulating a model, it can be helpful to think of the problem in words before attempting to describe it in mathematical terms. This is illustrated in the following example.

Example 3-1

Suppose a manager wants to know how much of each of three products (call them product A, product B, and product C) he should tell his production department to produce in order to maximize the profit obtained from those products. He knows that he must take into account the fact that the department has limited amounts of labor time, material, and machine time available to produce these items. The manager wants at least 40 units of product B to be produced, and exactly 30 units of product C. He also recognizes that the resulting quantities cannot be less than zero.

A verbal model of this would be:

Maximize profit on products A, B, and C.

   subject to (i.e., satisfying) the following requirements:

The labor hours used cannot exceed the available labor hours.
The amount of materials used cannot exceed the amount of materials available.
The machine time used cannot exceed the available machine time.
Produce at least 40 units of product B.
Produce exactly 30 units of product C.
The quantities produced cannot be less than zero.

Now, suppose that the manager, using additional information not shown here, has formulated a mathematical model of this problem. The model would look something like this:

x_1 = the number of units of product A to produce
x_2 = the number of units of product B to produce
x_3 = the number of units of product C to produce

maximize $8x_1 + 3x_2 + 4x_3$

subject to

Labor	$1x_1 + 1x_2 + 1x_3 \leq 200$ hours
Material	$2x_1 + 1x_2 + 2x_3 \leq 80$ lbs.
Machine	$4x_1 + 2x_2 + 2x_3 \leq 50$ minutes
Product B	$x_2 \geq 40$ units
Product C	$x_3 = 30$ units
	$x_1, x_2, x_3 \geq 0$

This is the general form of a linear programming model. Once such a model has been formulated, it can be solved to determine the optimal quantities of each product (i.e., the quantities to produce in order to maximize profit). For now, we are only concerned with understanding and formulating linear programming models. Solution techniques are described in the following sections of this chapter.

Now, before we turn our attention to model formulation, let us first consider two very important aspects of linear programming models: Their structure and the assumptions they are based on.

Successful Implementation of Linear Programming

Linear programming has been successfully implemented in business throughout the years. Table 3-1 summarizes some of the successful applications of linear programming published in *Interfaces*.

In addition to the applications listed in Table 3-1, there are a variety of successful applications of LP in different fields. These include the diet problem, portfolio optimization, crew scheduling, manufacturing transportation, telecommunications, media selection for advertising, and many more. Examples for many of the above-mentioned applications and some other ones are provided in Chapters 4 and 6.

| **Table 3-1** | Successful Applications of Linear Programming Published in *Interfaces* | | |
Year	Journal Volume/Number	Company	Type of Application
2004	34/4	Continental Airlines	Pilot planning and training
2004	34/2	LKAB's Kiruna Mine	Efficient production scheduling
2004	34/1	Nu-kote's	Spreadsheet modeling for planning shipments of finished goods
2002	32/1	Jan de Witt Company	Production planning and trade of Lilly Flowers
2002	32/1	NBC	Revenue and productivity management
2001	31/6	The Kellog Company	Production, inventory, and distribution optimization
2000	30/6	Quebec Ministry of Natural Resources	Understanding the wood-fiber market

Table 3-2	Characteristics of LP Models

Components
1. Objective
2. Decision variables
3. Constraints   } Model structure
4. Parameters
5. Nonnegativity

Assumptions
1. Proportionality
2. Additivity   } Model validity
3. Divisibility
4. Certainty

Components and Assumptions of LP Models

The components of linear programming models provide the *structure* of the models. The assumptions of linear programming models relate to model validity; they prescribe the conditions under which the models are valid. A list of the components and assumptions of LP models is given in Table 3-2. These are explained in detail in the following two sections. Knowledge of the components and the assumptions of LP models is essential to the formulation of valid models.

Components of LP Models   The *objective* in problem solving is the criterion by which all decisions are evaluated. As such, it provides the focus for problem solving.

In linear programming models, a single, *quantifiable* objective must be specified by the decision maker. For example, the objective might relate to profits, *or* costs, *or* market share, but to only *one* of these. Moreover, because we are dealing with optimization, the objective will be either maximization or minimization. Hence, every LP problem will be either a maximization (max) problem or a minimization (min) problem. Maximization problems often involve profit, revenue, market share, or return on investment, whereas minimization problems often involve cost, time, or distance. Once the objective is specified, it becomes the measure of effectiveness against which alternate solutions are judged. For example, the optimal solution will be the one that yields the highest profit or the one that provides the lowest cost. In our example, each unit of product A will yield a profit of $8, each unit of product B will yield a profit of $3, and so on. However, if the revenue is $8 per unit for each product A and the cost is $4 per unit, the profit per unit for product A is $8 − $4 = $4.

The decision maker can control the value of the objective, which is achieved through choices in the levels of **decision variables.** Decision variables represent choices available to a decision maker, usually with respect to the amount or *quantity* of either an input to a process or an output from a process. For instance, a problem may involve maximizing the profit obtained from the sale of three products, each with its own unit profit (i.e., profit per unit). If we assume that all the output can be sold, the problem facing the decision maker is to determine how much of each product to produce in order to obtain the greatest profit. In terms of the LP model, the decision variables represent those unknown quantities.

The ability of a decision maker to select values of the decision variables in LP is subject to certain restrictions or limits. These can come from a variety of sources. The restrictions may reflect availabilities of resources (e.g., raw materials, labor time, machine time, work space, or storage space), legal or contractual requirements (e.g., product or work standards) or technological requirements (e.g., necessary compressive strength or tensile strength), or they may reflect other limits based on forecasts, customer orders, company policies, and so on. In an LP model, the restrictions are referred to as **constraints.** Only solutions that satisfy all constraints in a model are acceptable. These are referred to as **feasible solutions**. The **optimal solution** is the feasible solution that yields the best value of the objective (e.g., the maximum profit, the minimum cost).

An LP model consists of a mathematical statement of the objective, called the **objective function,** and a set of mathematical statements of the restrictions (the *constraints*). In the objective function, note that the units of all the coefficients multiplied by the units of the corresponding variable must be the same (e.g., all in dollars, all in hours). The objective function and the constraints consist of symbols that represent the decision variables (for example, x_1, x_2, x_3) and numerical values called **parameters.** The parameters are fixed values that specify the impact that one unit of each decision variable will have on the objective and on any constraint it pertains to. For example, if the profit per unit on product 1 is $4, the 4 is a parameter. Similarly, if each unit of product 1 requires 1.5 hours of labor, the 1.5 is a parameter. And, if there are 200 hours of labor available, the 200 is also a parameter.

Generally speaking, a constraint has four elements:

1. A right-hand-side (RHS) quantity that specifies the limit for that constraint. It must be a constant, not a variable.
2. An algebraic sign that indicates whether the limit is an upper bound ($\leq$), a lower bound ($\geq$), or an equality ($=$) that must be met exactly.
3. The decision variables to which the constraint applies.
4. The impact that one unit of each decision variable will have on the right-hand-side quantity of the constraint.

The constraints in this LP model illustrate three inequality/equality relationships: greater than or equal to ($\geq$), less than or equal to ($\leq$), and equal to ($=$). The $\geq$ type of constraint imposes a minimum limit that is acceptable. Examples include "employees must work a minimum of six hours per shift," and "the cottage cheese must contain at least 4 percent butterfat." The $\leq$ type of constraint sets an upper limit that is not to be exceeded. Often such limits pertain to the amount of some resource that will be available. Other examples include an upper limit on demand, technological limits, and managerial preferences. The $=$ type of constraint is the most specific of the three types. Whereas the other two types can be satisfied by a *range* of values (for example, ≤ 30 can be satisfied by any value from 0 to 30), an equality constraint must be met *exactly*. Therefore, the constraint $x_1 = 30$ means that the only acceptable value of x_1 is 30.

Consider the first constraint in the example. The right-hand side quantity is 200 hours, and the $\leq$ sign tells us that this is an upper limit on the availability of labor time. The left side of the inequality reveals that each of the three products requires some labor time: product A requires 1 hour per unit, product B requires 1 hour per unit, and product C requires 1 hour per unit.

The second constraint pertains to the availability of raw material: 80 lbs. are available. Hence, this constraint is also an upper bound. The third constraint pertains to the availability of machine hours. It is an upper limit, and all three products require it. The fourth constraint indicates that the only acceptable value of product B must be at least 40 units, whereas the fifth constraint indicates that the only acceptable value of product C is 30 units, which provides a lower bound. Last statement indicates that negative quantities for the decision variables are not acceptable.

It is a common practice to write constraints in such a way that the variables are on the left side of the expression while a numerical value is placed on the right side of the expression. For example, the expression $x_1 \geq x_2$, would be written as $x_1 - x_2 \geq 0$.

The last set of constraints, arranged on a single line, are the nonnegativity constraints. They specify that no variable will be allowed to take on a negative value. The non-negativity constraints typically apply in an LP model, whether they are explicitly stated or not.

The **nonnegativity constraint** requirement is that negative values of variables are unrealistic and, therefore, will not be considered in any potential solutions; only positive values and zero will be allowed. For instance, in a problem involving the number of houses to construct, an answer of -2 would imply that two houses that have already been constructed should be torn down! Consider another negative solution that requires preparing -3 apple pies. Neither of these makes sense. For that reason, the nonnegativity requirement is inherent in LP models.[1]

Assumptions of LP Models   Table 3-2 lists four basic assumptions of LP models:

1. Proportionality (linearity).
2. Additivity.
3. Divisibility.
4. Certainty.

The **proportionality** (Linearity) assumption is that each decision variable have a *linear* impact in the objective function and in each constraint in which it appears. This means, for example, that if the profit of x_1 is \$4 per unit, that same figure must hold regardless of the quantity of x_1: It must be true over the entire range of possible values of x_1. This also applies to each of the constraints: It is required that the same coefficient (for example, 2 lb. per unit) apply over the entire range of possible values of the decision variable.

In terms of a mathematical model, a function or equation is linear when the variables included are all to the power 1 (that is, not squared, cubed, square root, etc.) and no products (e.g., x_1x_2) appear. Thus, this constraint is linear:

$2x_1 + x_2 = 40$

These constraints are not linear:

$2x_1^2 + x_2 \leq 40$ (x_1 is squared)
$2x_1 + x_1x_2 \leq 40$ (the second term is a product of variables)

The **additivity** assumption requires that terms of the objective function be additive (e.g., the total profit must equal the sum of the profits from each decision variable) and the terms of each constraint be additive (e.g., the total amount of resource used must equal the sum of the resources used by each of the decision variables).

The **divisibility** assumption pertains to potential values of decision variables. It is assumed that noninteger values are acceptable. For instance, $x_1 = 3.5$ is presumed to be an acceptable value. If a problem concerns the quantity of sugar to mix in a recipe, 3.5 pounds would be acceptable. However, if the problem concerns the optimal number of houses to construct, 3.5 does not appear to be acceptable. Instead, that type of problem would seem to require strictly integer solutions. In such cases, *integer programming* methods should be

---

[1]In the strictest sense, nonnegativity is not a theoretical requirement, although certain LP algorithms do require it. However, such unrestricted variables ordinarily would not be found in business applications. For that reason, the discussion here treats nonnegativity as a requirement of LP models.

used, which are discussed in a later chapter. It should be noted, however, that some obvious integer-type situations can be handled under the assumption of divisibility. For instance, suppose 3.5 is determined to be the optimal number of television sets to produce per hour. This would result in 7 sets every two hours, which would be acceptable. Another possibility exists when the items are relatively inexpensive (e.g., nuts, bolts, nails, or small pieces of plastic). For example, a model might yield an optimal solution of 210.33 units to be produced. That quantity could easily be rounded to 210 units, and it would still result in a solution that probably is within a few pennies of equaling the (unattainable) optimal value of the objective function.

Thus, the divisibility assumption allows noninteger values to be acceptable. We have seen that in the strictest sense this holds only if the variables are measured on a continuous scale (such as time, distance, weight, volume, etc.), but that in certain cases, little harm is done if the items are measured on a discrete basis (i.e., by counting, such as number of cars, number of television sets, and number of tables).

The **certainty** assumption involves two aspects of LP models. One aspect relates to the model parameters (i.e., the numerical values). It is assumed that these values are known and constant. For instance, if $2x_1$ appears in a labor constraint with hours as the unit of measure, it is assumed that each unit of x_1 will require exactly 2 hours of labor. If the right-hand side of the constraint is 300 labor hours, it is assumed that this quantity will remain at 300. In practice, production times and other parameters may not be truly constant. Therefore, the model builder must make an assessment as to the degree to which the certainty requirement is met. Small departures may not have a significant effect on the model; large departures almost surely will.

Certainty has another aspect in LP models. It is the assumption that all relevant constraints have been identified and represented in the model. For example, if there is a limit on the demand for some item, that limit should be recorded as a constraint (e.g., $x_1 \leq 100$).

Formulating LP Models

Once a problem has been defined, the attention of the analyst shifts to formulating a model. Just as it is important to carefully define a problem, it is important to carefully formulate the model that will be used to solve the problem. Linear programming algorithms (solution techniques) are widely used and understood, and computer software packages such as Excel are readily available for solving LP problems. Consequently, *obtaining* solutions is not the real issue. In fact, the ease with which solutions can be obtained may tempt an analyst or decision maker to rush through the formulation phase in order to get a quick idea of what the solution will look like. Too often, though, the analyst fails to check that all constraints have been accounted for and have been correctly formulated. This is unfortunate because if a model is ill-structured, it can easily lead to poor decisions.

Formulating linear programming models involves the following steps:

1. Define the decision variables.
2. Determine the objective function.
3. Identify the constraints.
4. Determine appropriate values for parameters and determine whether an upper limit, lower limit, or equality is called for.
5. Use this information to build a model.
6. Validate the model.

In practice, the first step is usually straightforward. In many cases, the decision variables are obvious; in others, a brief discussion with the appropriate manager is necessary. However, identifying the constraints and then determining appropriate values for the parameters can require considerable time and effort on the part of the analyst. Potential sources of information include historical records, interviews with managers and staff, and data collection. Obtaining parameters for the objective function is usually not difficult; accounting records or personnel can generally provide that information. Once the information about constraints and parameters has been obtained, constructing an appropriate model becomes the focus. This can be both demanding and time-consuming, especially for large problems. Validating the model will involve a critical review of the output, perhaps under a variety of inputs, in order to decide if the results are reasonable. This typically involves checking with people who are familiar with the situation (managers and staff) about the reasonableness of the results.

Example 3-2

The Server Problem

General description A firm that assembles computers and computer equipment is about to start production of two new Web server models. Each type of model will require assembly time, inspection time, and storage space. The amounts of each of these resources that can be devoted to the production of the servers is limited. The manager of the firm would like to determine the quantity of each model to produce in order to maximize the profit generated by sales of these servers.

Additional information In order to develop a suitable model of the problem, the manager has met with design and manufacturing personnel. As a result of those meetings, the manager has obtained the following information:

	Type 1	Type 2
Profit per unit	$60	$50
Assembly time per unit	4 hours	10 hours
Inspection time per unit	2 hours	1 hour
Storage space per unit	3 cubic feet	3 cubic feet

The manager also has acquired information on the availability of company resources. These (daily) amounts are:

Resource	Amount Available
Assembly time	100 hours
Inspection time	22 hours
Storage space	39 cubic feet

The manager also met with the firm's marketing manager and learned that demand for the servers was such that whatever combination of these two models of servers is produced, all of the output can be sold.

In determining whether the problem can be solved using linear programming, we can first note that there are *restrictions* on assembly time, inspection time, and storage space. We also can note that the manager has an *objective*, which is to maximize profit. Thus, it would appear that this is a *constrained optimization* problem.

In terms of meeting the assumptions, it would appear that the relationships are *linear:* The contribution to profit per unit of each server and the time and storage space per unit of each are the same regardless of the quantity produced. Therefore, the total impact of each server on the profit and each constraint is a linear function of the quantity of that variable. There may be a question of *divisibility* because, presumably, only whole servers will be sold. However, because this is a recurring process (i.e., the servers will be produced daily: therefore, a noninteger solution such as 3.5 servers per day will result in 7 servers every other day), this does not seem to pose a problem. The question of *certainty* cannot be explored here; in practice, the manager could be questioned to determine if there are any other possible constraints and whether the values shown for assembly times, and so forth, are known with certainty. For the purposes of discussion, we will assume certainty. Lastly, the assumption of *nonnegativity* seems justified; negative values for production quantities would not make sense.

Because we have concluded that linear programming is appropriate, let us now turn our attention to constructing a model of the server problem. First, we must define the decision variables. Based on the statement, "The manager . . . would like to determine the quantity of each server to produce," the decision variables are the quantities of each type of server. Thus:

x_1 = quantity of server model 1 to produce
x_2 = quantity of server model 2 to produce

Next, we can formulate the objective function. The profit per unit of server model 1 is listed as $60, and the profit per unit of server model 2 is listed as $50, so the appropriate objective function is

maximize $Z = 60x_1 + 50x_2$

where Z is the value of the objective-function, given values of x_1 and x_2.

Now for the constraints. There are three resources with limited availability: assembly time, inspection time, and storage space. The fact that availability is limited means that these constraints will all be $\leq$ constraints. Suppose we begin with the assembly constraint. The server model 1 requires 4 hours of assembly time per unit, whereas the server model 2 requires 10 hours of assembly time per unit. Therefore, with a limit of 100 hours available, the assembly constraint is

$4x_1 + 10x_2 \leq 100$ hours

Similarly, each unit of server model 1 requires 2 hours of inspection time, and each unit of server model 2 requires 1 hour of inspection time. With 22 hours available, the inspection constraint is

$2x_1 + x_2 \leq 22$

The storage constraint is determined in a similar manner. It is

$3x_1 + 3x_2 \leq 39$

There are no other system or individual constraints. The nonnegativity constraints are

$x_1, x_2 \geq 0$

In summary, the mathematical model of the microcomputer problem is

x_1 = quantity of server model 1 to produce
x_2 = quantity of server model 2 to produce

maximize $Z = 60x_1 + 50x_2$

subject to

Assembly $4x_1 + 10x_2 \leq 100$ hours
Inspection $2x_1 + 1x_2 \leq 22$ hours
Storage $3x_1 + 3x_2 \leq 39$ cubic feet
                  $x_1, x_2 \geq 0$

After covering the basic concepts associated with LP and learning about formulating basic LP problems, we can discuss how to solve simple problems with two variables using the graphical method.

Graphical Method

Graphical linear programming is a relatively straightforward method for determining the optimal solution to certain linear programming problems. In practical terms, this method can be used only to solve problems that involve two decision variables. However, most linear programming applications involve situations that have more than two decision variables, so graphical linear programming methods cannot be used to solve them. Even so, much can be gained from studying the graphical approach, particularly in terms of the insight it generates about important concepts of models and solutions. Graphical methods provide a visual portrayal of many important concepts. Moreover, they provide a framework for intuitive explanations of other LP techniques that are covered in later chapters. Viewed from this perspective, graphical LP is a valuable learning tool.

In order to demonstrate the graphical method, the server problem that was formulated earlier in the chapter will be solved. The model is

x_1 = quantity of server model 1 to produce per day
x_2 = quantity of server model 2 to produce per day
maximize $z = 60x_1 + 50x_2$

subject to

Assembly $4x_1 + 10x_2 \leq 100$ hours
Inspection $2x_1 + 1x_2 \leq 22$ hours
Storage $3x_1 + 3x_2 \leq 39$ cubic feet
                  $x_1, x_2 \geq 0$

Graphing the Model

The first step in the graphic method is to graph the model. The graphical approach consists of the following steps:

1. Plot each of the constraints.
2. Determine the region or area that contains all of the points that satisfy the entire *set* of constraints.
3. Determine the optimal solution.

Let's examine each of these steps as we solve the server problem.

Plotting the Constraints

We begin by plotting the nonnegativity constraints, as shown in Figure 3-1. For purposes of illustration, the area of feasibility for these two constraints (i.e., the area that satisfies both

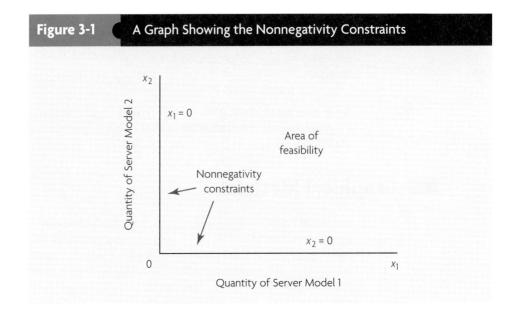

Figure 3-1 A Graph Showing the Nonnegativity Constraints

constraints) has been shaded in. However, as a general rule, the shading would be done after all constraints have been plotted.

The procedure for graphing each of the remaining constraints relies on the fact that a straight line can be plotted if any two points on that line can be identified. Of course, the constraints in this problem are all inequalities rather than lines. As such, they describe a region or area that will satisfy them. However, the boundary of that area of feasibility is represented by the equal portion of the less-than-or-equal-to constraint. Recognizing this, we can deal with the task of graphing a constraint in two parts. First, treat the constraint as an equality and plot the straight line that is the boundary of the feasible region; then, shade in the feasible region.

Consider the assembly time constraint:

$$4x_1 + 10x_2 \leq 100$$

Removing the inequality portion of the constraint produces this straight line:

$$4x_1 + 10x_2 = 100$$

There are a number of different ways to determine the coordinates of two points on the line. Perhaps the easiest two points to identify and work with are the points where the line intersects each axis (i.e., where $x_1 = 0$ and where $x_2 = 0$). We can solve for those points, first by setting $x_2 = 0$ and solving for x_1, and then setting $x_1 = 0$ and solving for x_2. Thus with $x_2 = 0$, we find

$$4x_1 + 10(0) = 100$$

Solving, we find that $4x_1 = 100$, so $x_1 = 25$ when $x_2 = 0$. Similarly, we can solve the equation for x_2 when $x_1 = 0$:

$$4(0) + 10x_2 = 100$$

Solving for x_2, we find $x_2 = 10$ when $x_1 = 0$.

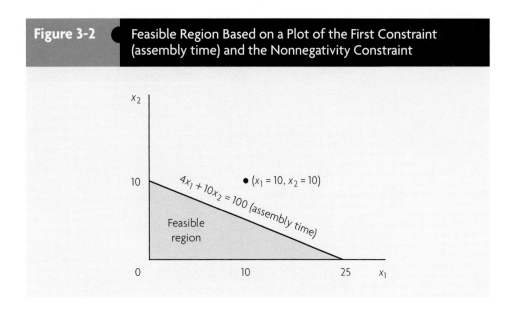

Figure 3-2   Feasible Region Based on a Plot of the First Constraint (assembly time) and the Nonnegativity Constraint

Thus, we have two points: $x_1 = 0$, $x_2 = 10$, and $x_1 = 25$, $x_2 = 0$. We can now add this line to our graph of the nonnegativity constraints by connecting these two points (see Figure 3-2).

Next we must determine which side of the line represents points that are less than 100. To do this, we can select a test point that is not on the line, and we can substitute the x_1 and x_2 values of that point into the left side of the equation of the line. If the result is less than 100, this tells us that all points on that side of the line are less than the value of the line (e.g., 100). Conversely, if the result is greater than 100, this indicates that the other side of the line represents the set of points that will yield values that are less than 100. A relatively simple test point to use is the origin (i.e., $x_1 = 0$, $x_2 = 0$) if both constraint coefficients are positive. Substituting these values into the equation yields:

$4(0) + 10(0) = 0$

Obviously this is less than 100. Hence, the side of the line closest to the origin represents the "less than" area.

The feasible region for this constraint and the nonnegativity constraints then becomes the shaded portion shown in Figure 3-2.

For the sake of illustration, suppose we try one other point, say $x_1 = 10$, $x_{2} = 10$. Substituting these values into the assembly constraint yields

$4(10) + 10(10) = 140$

Clearly this is greater than 100. Therefore, all points on this side of the line are greater than 100 (see Figure 3-2). However, if one of the constraint coefficients is negative, then we would substitute a value of x_1 slightly larger and slightly smaller than its value of the x_1 axis and determine which one is less than the right-hand-side value of the constraint.

Continuing with the problem, we can add the two remaining constraints to the graph. For the inspection constraint:

1. Convert the constraint into the equation of a straight line by replacing the inequality sign with an equality sign:

   $2x_1 + 1x_2 \leq 22$ becomes $2x_1 + 1x_2 = 22$

Figure 3-3 A Completed Graph of the Server Problem Showing the Assembly and Inspection Constraints and the Feasible Solution Space

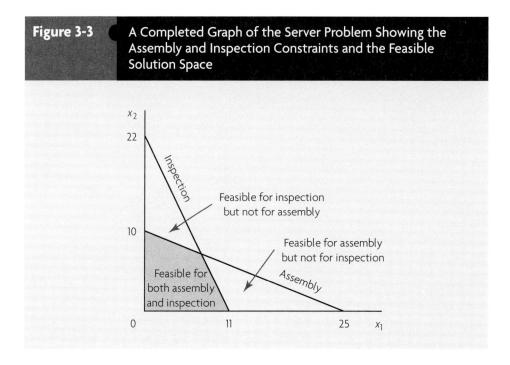

2. Set x_1 equal to zero and solve for x_2:

   $2(0) + 1x_2 = 22$

   Solving, we find $x_2 = 22$. Thus, the line will intersect the x_2 axis as 22.

3. Next, set x_2 equal to zero and solve for x_1:

   $2x_1 + 1(0) = 22$

   Solving, we find $x_1 = 11$. Thus, the other end of the line will intersect the x_1 axis at 11.

4. Add the line to the graph (see Figure 3-3).

5. Note that the area of feasibility for this constraint is below the line (see Figure 3-3). Again the area of feasibility at this point is shaded in for illustration, although when graphing problems, it is more practical to refrain from shading in the feasible region until all constraint lines have been drawn. However, because constraints are plotted one at a time, using a small arrow for each to indicate the direction of feasibility can be helpful.

The storage constraint is handled in the same manner:

1. Convert it into an equality:

   $3x_1 + 3x_2 = 39$

2. Set x_1 equal to zero and solve for x_2:

   $3(0) + 3x_2 = 39$

   Solving, $x_2 = 13$. Thus, $x_2 = 13$ when $x_1 = 0$.

3. Set x_2 equal to zero and solve for x_1:

   $3x_1 + 3(0) = 39$

   Solving, $x_1 = 13$, Thus, $x_1 = 13$ when $x_2 = 0$.

Figure 3-4	Completed Graph of the Server Problem Showing All of the Constraints and the Feasible Solution Space

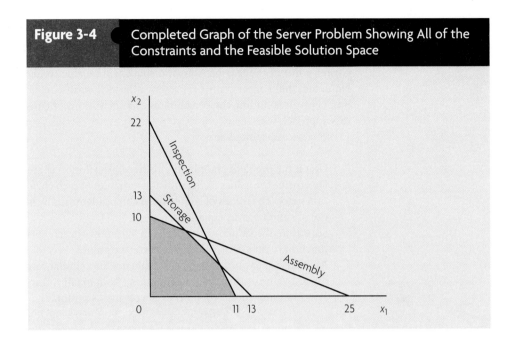

4. Add the line to the graph (see Figure 3-4).
5. Determine the feasible solution space—the area that satisfies all of the constraints—and shade it in (see Figure 3-4). The region that satisfies all constraints is called the **Feasible solution space.**

Finding the Optimal Solution

Once the constraints have been graphed and the area of feasibility has been identified, it is possible to obtain the optimal solution to the problem. Two different approaches to obtaining the solution will be demonstrated. One involves examining points at the edge of the feasible solution space where constraints meet, and the other involves graphing the objective function. The extreme point approach will be demonstrated first.

The Extreme Point Approach

The **extreme point** approach involves finding the coordinates of each corner point that borders the feasible solution space and then determining which corner point provides the best value of the objective function (i.e., the highest value for a maximization problem or the lowest value for a minimization problem). An important mathematical theorem provides the rationale for this approach: The **extreme point theorem** states that if a problem has an optimal solution, at least one optimal solution will occur at a corner point of the feasible solution space. Note that not every problem has an optimal solution; for example, some do not have a feasible solution space. Also note that the extreme point theorem does not exclude the occurrence of an optimal solution somewhere else on the border of the feasible solution space (solutions will *only* occur on the border, never at an internal point of the feasible solution space). In fact, problems that have *multiple* optimal solutions will have solutions that occur at points along a border of the feasible solution space *as well as* at a corner point. In other words, an optimal solution to *every* LP problem that has an optimal solution will occur at a corner point. Therefore, an approach that examines every corner point of the feasible solution space will be able to identify the optimal solution. Note, too, that corner points represent *intersections* of constraints; so finding the corner points involves finding the coordinates of intersections of constraints. Let us now see how this approach works.

The necessary steps are

1. Graph the problem and identify the feasible solution space.
2. Determine the values of the decision variables at each corner point of the feasible solution space. The values of some points can be identified by inspection; others require the use of simultaneous equations.
3. Substitute the values of the decision variables at each corner point into the objective function to obtain its value at each corner point.
4. After all corner points have been evaluated in a similar fashion, select the one with the highest value of the objective function (for a maximization problem) or lowest value (for a minimization problem) as the optimal solution.

We can use the extreme point approach to verify the optimal solution for the server problem that will be obtained in the next section using the objective function approach.

The extreme point solution can be obtained by following the steps outlined above. Figure 3-5 repeats the graph of the problem that was constructed previously in Figure 3-4, with each of the extreme points now labeled for discussion purposes. Note that 0,0 is included as an extreme point, even though it will not yield any profit because both decision variables are equal to zero.

Figure 3-5 ⬤ **Graph of Server Problem with Extreme Points of the Feasible Solution Space Indicated**

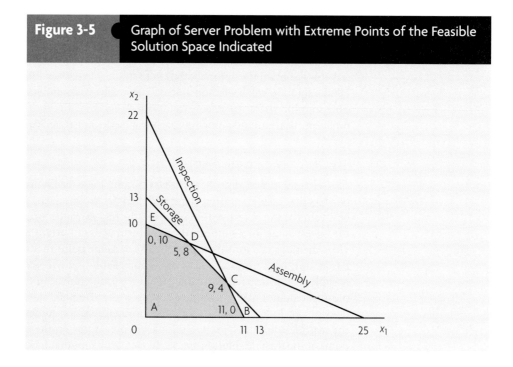

Table 3-3			Extreme Point Solutions for the Server Problem	
	Coordinates			**Value of the**
Point	x_1	x_2	**How Determined**	**Objective Function**
A	0	0	Inspection	$60(0) + $50(0) = $0
B	11	0	Inspection	$60(11) + $50(0) = $660
C	9	4	Simultaneous equations	$60(9) + $50(4) = $740 (largest)
D	5	8	Simultaneous equations	$60(5) + $50(8) = $700
E	0	10	Inspection	$60(0) + $50(10) = $500

Table 3-3 summarizes the approach used to obtain each point and its profit.

Note that the coordinates of points A, B, and E were determined by inspection. The coordinates of the origin are obvious. In addition, the x_1 intercept of the inspection constraint and the x_2 intercept of the assembly constraint were known by having determined them in the course of plotting the constraints. The coordinates of point C and point D can be determined by the solution of simultaneous equations. Using point D to illustrate, we can solve simultaneously for the intersection of the assembly and storage lines because the assembly constraint intersects the inspection constraint at point D (see Figure 3-5)

Assembly $4x_1 + 10x_2 = 100$
Storage $3x_1 + 3x_2 = 39$

As usual, there are a number of ways for obtaining a common solution to this set of equations. One way would be to multiply each coefficient of the assembly constraint by 3/4 thereby resulting in a new x_1 coefficient of 3, which would lead to the elimination of x_1. Thus:

$$\frac{3}{4}(4x_1 + 10x_2 = 100) = 3x_1 + 7.5x_2 = 75$$

Subtracting the storage line from this new line results in one equation with x_2 the only variable:

New $3x_1 + 7.5x_2 = 75$
Storage $-(3x_1 + 3x_2 = 39)$
             $\overline{\qquad\quad 4.5x_2 = 36}$ Solving, $x_2 = 8$

By substituting $x_2 = 8$ into either of the original lines, or the new line, the value of x_1 at intersection D can be determined. If the original assembly equation is used, we find

$4x_1 + 10(8) = 100$

Solving, $x_1 = 5$. Hence, the coordinates of point D are $x_1 = 5$ and $x_2 = 8$.

At point C, the values of x_1 and x_2, are calculated in a similar fashion by simultaneously solving the inspection and storage equations.

The profit at each corner point can be computed by substituting the coordinates of the point into the objective function. Point C ($x_1 = 9$, $x_2 = 4$) represents the optimal solution because it yields the largest profit for the extreme points (see Table 3-3).

The Objective Function (Iso-Profit Line) Approach

The objective function approach avoids the need to determine the coordinates of all of the corner points of the feasible solution space. Instead, this approach directly identifies the optimal corner point, so only the coordinates of the optimal point need to be determined. It accomplishes this by adding the objective function to the graph and then using it to determine which point is optimal. Let's see how the objective function approach works.

The first step is to plot the objective function. Plotting an objective function line involves the same logic as plotting a constraint line: Determine where the line intersects each axis. Recall that the objective function for the server problem is

$$60x_1 + 50x_2$$

Now, this is not an equation because it does not include an equal sign. We can get around this by simply setting it equal to some quantity. Any quantity will do, although one that is evenly divisible by both coefficients and one that falls in the feasible region is desirable.

Suppose we decide to set the objective function equal to 300. That is,

$$60x_1 + 50x_2 = 300$$

We can now plot the line of our graph. As before, we can determine the x_1 and x_2 intercepts of the line by setting one of the two variables equal to zero, solving for the other, and then reversing the process. Thus, with $x_1 = 0$, we have

$$60(0) + 50x_2 = 300$$

Solving, we find $x_2 = 6$. Similarly, with $x_2 = 0$, we have

$$60x_1 + 50(0) = 300$$

Solving, we find $x_1 = 5$. This line is plotted in Figure 3-6.

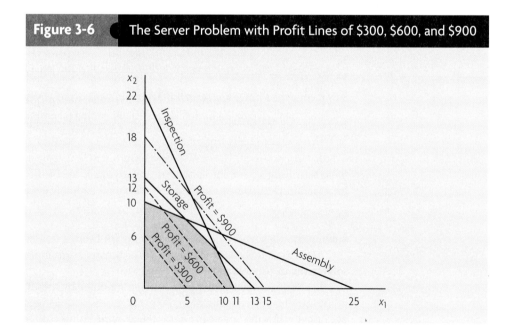

Figure 3-6   The Server Problem with Profit Lines of $300, $600, and $900

The profit line can be interpreted in the following way. Every point on the line (i.e., every combination of x_1 and x_2 that lies on the line) will provide a profit of $300. We can see from the graph many combinations that are both on the $300 profit line and within the feasible solution space. In fact, considering noninteger as well as integer solutions, the possibilities are infinite.

Suppose we now consider another line, say the $600 line. To do this, we set the objective function equal to this amount. Thus,

$$60x_1 + 50x_2 = 600$$

Solving for the x_1 and x_2 intercepts yields these two points:

x_1 Intercept	x_2 Intercept
$x_1 = 10$	$x_1 = 0$
$x_2 = 0$	$x_2 = 12$

This line is also plotted in Figure 3-6, along with the previous $300 line for purposes of comparison.

Two things are evident in Figure 3-6 regarding the profit lines. One is that the $600 line is *farther* from the origin than the $300 line; the other is that the two lines are *parallel*. These parallel lines are referred to as *iso-profit lines*. The lines are parallel because they both have the same slope. The slope is not affected by the right side of the equation. Rather, it is determined solely by the coefficients 60 and 50. It would be correct to conclude that regardless of the quantity we select for the value of the objective function, the resulting line will be parallel to these two lines. Moreover, if the amount is greater than 600, the line will be even farther away from the origin than the $600 line. If the value is less than 300, the line will be closer to the origin than the $300 line. And if the value is between 300 and 600, the line will fall between the $300 and $600 lines.

Also in Figure 3-6 a third profit line, one with the profit equal to $900, is shown along with the previous two profit lines. As expected, it is parallel to the other two, and even farther away from the origin. However, the line does not touch the feasible solution space at all. Consequently, there is no feasible combination of x_1 and x_2 that will yield that amount of profit. Evidently, the maximum possible profit is an amount between $600 and $900, which we can see by referring to Figure 3-6. We could continue to select profit lines in this manner, and, eventually, we could determine an amount that would yield the greatest profit. However, there is a much simpler alternative. We can plot just one line, say the $300 line. We know that all other lines will be parallel to it. Consequently, by moving this one line parallel to itself we can represent other profit lines. We also know that as we move away from the origin, the profits get larger. What we want to know is how far the line can be moved out from the origin and still be touching the feasible solution space, and the values of the decision variables at that point of greatest profit (i.e., the optimal solution). We can locate this point on the graph by placing a straight edge along the $300 line (or any other convenient line) and sliding it away from the origin, being careful to keep it parallel to the $300 line. This approach is also illustrated in Figure 3-7.

Once we have determined where the optimal solution is in the feasible solution space, we must determine what the values of the decision variables are at that point. Then, we can use that information to compute the profit for that combination.

Note that the optimal solution is at the intersection of the inspection boundary and the storage boundary (see Figure 3-7). The last point touched in the feasible region as we move

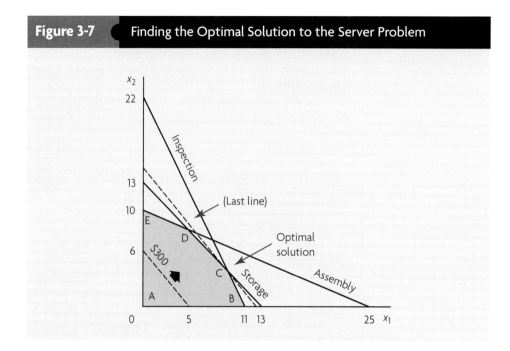

Figure 3-7   Finding the Optimal Solution to the Server Problem

the profit line parallel to itself is given by point C. In other words, the optimal combination of x_1 and x_2 must satisfy both boundary (equality) conditions. We can determine those values by solving the two equations *simultaneously*. The equations are

Inspection $2x_1 + 1x_2 = 22$
Storage $3x_1 + 3x_2 = 39$

The idea behind solving two **simultaneous equations** is to algebraically eliminate one of the unknown variables (i.e., to obtain an equation with a single unknown). This can be accomplished by multiplying the constants of one of the equations by a fixed amount and then adding (or subtracting) the modified equation from the other. (Occasionally, it is easier to multiply each equation by a fixed quantity.) For example, we can eliminate x_2 by multiplying the inspection equation by 3 and then subtracting the storage equation from the modified inspection equation. Thus,

$3(2x_1 + 1x_2 = 22)$ becomes $6x_1 + 3x_2 = 66$

Subtracting the storage equation from this produces

$$\begin{array}{r} 6x_1 + 3x_2 = 66 \\ -(3x_1 + 3x_2 = 39) \\ \hline 3x_1 + 0x_2 = 27 \end{array}$$

Solving the resulting equation yields $x_1 = 9$. The value of x_2 can be found by substituting $x_1 = 9$ into either of the original equations or the modified inspection equation. Suppose we use the original inspection equation. We have

$2(9) + 1x_2 = 22$

Solving, we find $x_2 = 4$.

Hence, the optimal solution to the server problem is to produce nine model 1 servers and four model 2 servers per day. We can substitute these values into the objective function to find the optimal profit. Thus,

$60(9) + $50(4) = $740

Hence, the last line—the one that would last touch the feasible solution space as we moved away from the origin parallel to the $300 profit line—would be the line where profit equaled $740.

In this problem, the optimal values for both decision variables are integers. Now this will not always be the case—one or both of the decision variables may turn out to be non-integer. In some situations noninteger values would be of little consequence. This would be the case if the decision variables were measured on a continuous scale, such as the amount of water, sand, sugar, fuel oil, time, or distance needed for optimality, or if the contribution per unit (profit, cost, etc.) were small, as would be the case with the number of nails or ball bearings to make. In some cases, the answer would simply be rounded down (maximization problems) or up (minimization problems) with very little impact on the objective function. In this chapter and the following two chapters, it will be assumed that noninteger answers are acceptable as such. Chapter 7 on integer programming will discuss how to obtain optimal integer solutions.

Note that the solution to this problem occurred where two constraint lines intersected. These intersections are called **corner points,** or *extreme points,* of the feasible solution space. The optimal solution to an LP problem will always occur at a corner point because as the objective function line is moved in the direction that will improve its value (e.g., away from the origin in a maximization problem), it will last touch one of these intersections of constraints. This is the **fundamental theorem of LP.** (In fact, this is the basis for the extreme point approach to finding the optimal solution that was demonstrated in the previous section.)

Let's review the procedure for finding the optimal solution using the objective function approach:

1. Graph the constraints.
2. Identify the feasible solution space.
3. Set the objective function equal to some amount that is divisible by each of the objective function coefficients. This will yield integer values for the x_1 and x_2 intercepts and, thereby, simplify plotting the line. Often, the product of the two objective function coefficients will provide a satisfactory line. Ideally, the line selected will cross the feasible solution space close to the optimal point, in which case it would not be necessary to slide a straight edge: The optimal solution can be readily identified visually. In some cases, sliding the ruler or straight edge parallel to itself will not provide a clear answer as to which point in the feasible region in the last point touched as we move the profit line parallel to itself. Then we need to determine the value of the objective function (Z) for all the competing extreme points and select the one with the highest value of Z for a maximization problem. However, the process described above can only be utilized for relatively small two-variable problems. It is highly inefficient to try to utilize it for large problems (problems with more than six constraints).
4. After identifying the optimal point, determine which two constraints intersect there. Solve their equations simultaneously to obtain the values of the decision variables at the optimum.
5. Substitute the values obtained in the previous step into the objective function to determine the value of the objective function at the optimum.

Figure 3-8   A Comparison of Maximization and Minimization Problems

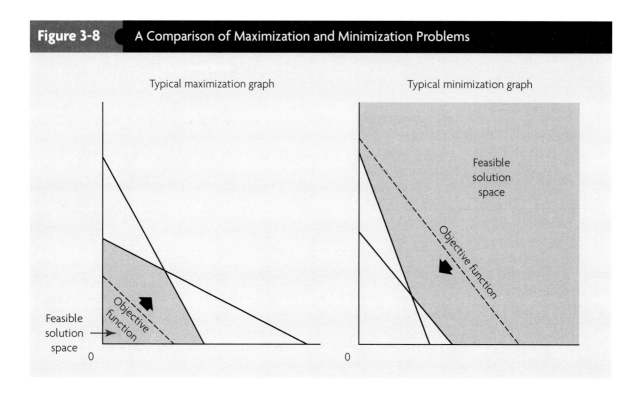

Typical maximization graph

Typical minimization graph

Feasible
solution
space

Objective
function

Feasible
solution
space ⟶

Objective
function

0

0

A Minimization Example

Graphical solutions to minimization problems are very similar to solutions to maximization problems. There are a few differences that will be highlighted in this section. The main difference is that the optimum is the point that has the smallest possible value of the objective function, instead of the largest. Also, at least one of the constraints must be a $\geq$ constraint. In some instance, all constraints will be greater-than-or-equal-to constraints. These contrasts are illustrated in Figure 3-8.

Example 3-3

Determine the values of decision variables x_1 and x_2 that will yield the minimum cost in the following problem. Solve using the objective function approach.

minimize $Z = .10x_1 + .07x_2$

subject to

Constraint 1	$6x_1 + 2x_2 \geq 18$
Constraint 2	$8x_1 + 10x_2 \geq 40$
Constraint 3	$x_2 \geq 1$
	$x_1 \text{ and } x_2 \geq 0$

Figure 3-9   Graphing the Feasible Region and Using the Objective Function to Find the Optimum for Example 3-3

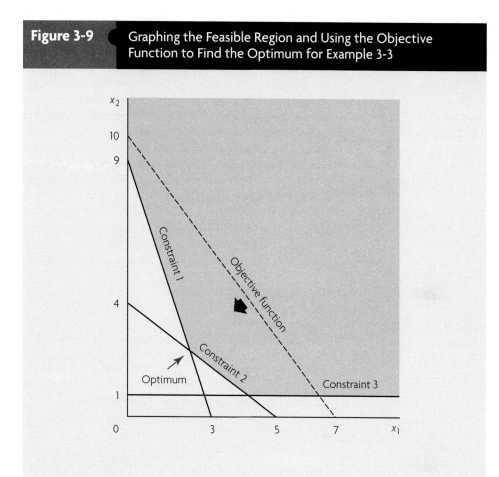

Solution

Graph the constraints using this procedure:

1. Treat each constraint as an equality.
2. For the first two constraints, find the x_1 intercept by setting x_2 equal to 0 and solving for x_1, and then find the x_2 intercept by setting x_1 equal to 0 and solving for x_2. For the third constraint, x_2 is simply equal to 1.
3. Plot these constraints.

Shade in the feasible solution space. (See Figure 3-9.)

Using the objective function approach, we would next plot the objective function on the graph. To do so, we must select an amount to set the objective function equal to. The product of the two cost coefficients is .10(.07) = .007, which would have an x_1 intercept of .07 and an x_2 intercept of .10. Unfortunately, these intercepts are so close to the origin that they will not provide a good indication of the objective function. Suppose we increase our cost function by a factor of 100, to .70. This results in an objective function of

$$.10x_1 + .07x_2 = .70$$

The x_1 intercept would now be 7 and the x_2 intercept would be 10. This line is much more acceptable because it crosses the feasible solution space in the region close to what we now perceive as the optimal solution. (See Figure 3-9.)

Because the solution is at the intersection of constraints 1 and 2, we can solve these two equations simultaneously to determine the optimal values of x_1 and x_2. As before, the approach is to multiply the constants in one equation by some amount that will cause one of the two variables to drop out when the modified equation is added to, or subtracted from, the other. In this case, the coefficient of x_2 in the second constraint is 5 times the value of the x_2 coefficient in the first constraint, so multiplying the first equation by 5 and then subtracting the second from the first equation will eliminate x_2. Thus,

$$5(6x_1 + 2x_2 = 18) \qquad \text{becomes} \qquad 30x_1 + 10x_2 = 90$$

Subtracting the second constraint equation from this yields

$$\begin{array}{r} 30x_1 + 10x_2 = 90 \\ -(8x_1 + 10x_2 = 40) \\ \hline 22x_1 \quad\quad = 50 \end{array}$$

Solving, we find $x_1 = 2.27$. Substituting this value into either of the two original constraint equations or the modified first equation will yield a value of $x_2 = 2.19$. For example, using the modified equation, we find

$$30(2.27) + 10x_2 = 90.$$

Then, $10x_2 = 90 - 30(2.27)$, or $10x_2 = 21.9$. Solving, $x_2 = 21.9/10 = 2.19$.

The optimum value of the objective function (i.e., the minimum cost) is determined by substituting these values into the objective function:

$$Z = \$.10(2.27) + \$.07(2.19) = \$.38$$

Example 3-4

Solve the preceding problem using the extreme point approach.

Solution

The extreme points can be determined either by inspection of Figure 3-9 or from simultaneous equations. The results are summarized in Table 3-4.

The minimum value of the objective function is $.38, which occurs when $x_1 = 2.27$ and $x_2 = 2.19$. This agrees with the solution found in Example 3-3 using the objective function approach.

Table 3-4		Summary of Extreme Point Analysis for Example 3-4	
Extreme Point		**How**	**Value of the**
x_1	x_2	**Determined**	**Objective Function**
0	9	Inspection (see Figure 3-9)	\$.10(0) + \$.07(9) = \$.63
5	0	Inspection (see Figure 3-9)	\$.10(5) + \$.07(0) = \$.50
2.27	2.19	Simultaneous equations (see Example 3-3)	\$10(2.27) + \$07(2.19) = \$.38

Slack and Surplus

The primary goal of a decision maker who is using linear programming is to determine the optimal solution to a problem. However, it also can be useful for the decision maker to know of any *slack* or *surplus* that will occur when the optimal solution is achieved.

Slack relates to a $\leq$ constraint; it is the amount of a constraint that is *unused* by a solution. For example, if one constraint in a problem is that labor $\leq$ 100 hours, and the solution requires the use of 90 hours of labor, then we can say that the labor constraint has a slack of 10 hours. Thus, slack is the amount by which the left-hand side of a $\leq$ constraint is less than the right-hand side of the constraint.

Surplus relates to a $\geq$ constraint; it is the amount by which a constraint is *exceeded* by a solution. For example, if a constraint requires that the number of units of product A that are made be $\geq$ 10, and a solution results in 12 units being produced, we can say that there is a surplus of 2 units. Thus, surplus is the amount by which the left-hand side of a $\geq$ constraint exceeds the right-hand side.

Determination of slack and surplus is straightforward. First, note whether the constraint in the question is a $\leq$ constraint or a $\geq$ constraint. (By definition, = constraints never have slack or surplus because the left side of these constraints must always equal to the right side.) Next, substitute the optimal values of the decision variables into the left-hand side of the constraint and solve. Then, compare the resulting value to the right-hand side of the constraint. The difference between the two is the amount of slack (for a $\leq$ constraint) or surplus (for a $\geq$ constraint).

For example, suppose that we have the constraint $2x_1 + 3x_2 \leq 50$, and that $x_1 = 4$ and $x_2 = 5$. Because this is a $\leq$ constraint, we know that slack rather than surplus is relevant. Substituting the values of x_1 and x_1 into the left side of the constraint, we obtain

$2(4) + 3(5) = 23.$

This is 27 less than the right-hand-side value. Hence, slack = 27.

Now, suppose we have the constraint $4x_1 + 2x_2 \geq 10$, and $x_1 = 3$ and $x_2 = 1$. Because this is a $\geq$ constraint, we know that surplus is involved. Substituting the values of x_1 and x_2 into the left-hand side, we obtain

$4(3) + 2(1) = 14.$

This exceeds the right-hand-side value of 10 by 4. Hence, surplus = 4.

Table 3-5	Computing the Amount of Slack for the Optimal Solution to the Server Problem		
Constraint	Amount Used with $x_1 = 9$ and $x_2 = 4$	Originally Available	Amount of Slack (Available − Used)
Assembly	$4(9) + 10(4) = 76$	100	$100 - 76 = 24$ hours
Inspection	$2(9) + 1(4) = 22$	22	$22 - 22 = 0$ hours
Storage	$3(9) + 3(4) = 39$	39	$39 - 39 = 0$ cubic feet

Table 3-5 illustrates the computations for the server problem. Because every constraint was of the $\leq$ variety, only slack is relevant.

Notice that slack is equal to zero for two of the constraints. This is not unexpected. In fact, in *every* problem, at least one, and usually two, of the constraints will have slack or surplus equal to zero. This is because the solution is *on* those constraint lines. (Recall that the solution to an LP model is at one of the corner points, which is an intersection of constraints, meaning the solution is on those constraints.) A constraint that the optimal solution is on is referred to as a **binding constraint,** meaning that it limits, or binds, the solution. And because the solution is on a binding constraint, it will have slack = 0 (if it is a $\leq$ constraint) or surplus = 0 (if it is a $\geq$ constraint). Moreover, it isn't necessary to calculate slack or surplus for the binding constraints; once they have been identified, it follows that slack or surplus (whichever is appropriate) is equal to zero.

For instance, go back to Figure 3-7. Point C (9,4) is optimum. Notice that the optimal solution is on both the Inspection and Storage constraints. That is why they both have slack = 0. Conversely, the optimal solution is less than (beneath) the Assembly constraint, meaning that some of the assembly time is unused by the solution. Consequently, there is some slack for assembly time. (Note: Although it is possible to determine constraints that have zero slack or zero surplus directly from the graph, and to identify constraints that have nonzero slack or surplus, it is *not* possible to determine the amount of slack or surplus from the graph. That has to be done by substituting the optimal values into the nonbinding constraints and solving).

Knowledge of unused capacity can be useful for planning. A manager may be able to use the remaining assembly time for other products, or, perhaps, to schedule equipment maintenance, safety seminars, training sessions, or other activities. In still another vein, it may be profitable to consider the acquisition of additional amounts of the two other resources to allow for greater use of the assembly resource and, thereby, to increase profits by increasing the size of the feasible solution space.

Slack can potentially exist in a $\leq$ constraint. Moreover, it can be useful to represent slack in a constraint. This is accomplished using a *slack variable, s,* which carries a subscript that denotes which constraint it applies to. For instance, s_1 refers to the amount of slack in the first constraint, s_2 to the amount of slack in the second constraint, and so on. When slack variables are added to the constraints, they are no longer inequalities because the slack variable accounts for any difference between the left- and right-hand sides of the expression. Hence, once slack variables are added to the constraints, they become *equalities.* Furthermore, every variable in a model must be represented in the objective function. However, since slack does not provide any real contribution to the objective, each slack variable is assigned a coefficient of zero in the objective function. With slack variables included, the server problem would appear as follows:

maximize $60x_1 + 50x_2 + 0s_1 + 0s_2 + 0s_3$

subject to

Assembly	$4x_1 + 10x_2 + s_1$	$= 100$
Inspection	$2x_1 + 1x_2 \quad\quad + s_2$	$= 22$
Storage	$3x_1 + 3x_2 \quad\quad\quad\quad + s_3$	$= 39$

$$\text{All variables} \geq 0$$

Note that all variables, including slack variables, must be nonnegative.

When all of the constraints are written as equalities, the linear program is said to be in **standard form.**

Since surplus is defined as the amount by which the left-hand side of a constraint exceeds the right-hand side, subtracting the difference between the left-hand side and the right-hand side of the constraint can represent surplus in a constraint. Also, surplus variables must be accounted for in the objective function. As with slack variables, this is done by using a coefficient of zero for each surplus variable. For the problem illustrated in Example 3-3, the addition of surplus variables produced the following standard form of the linear programming problem.

Min $Z = .10x_1 + .07x_2 + 0s_1 + 0s_2 + 0s_3$

subject to

$$6x_1 + 2x_2 - s_1 \quad\quad\quad = 18$$
$$8x_1 + 10x_2 \quad\quad - s_2 \quad\quad = 40$$
$$x_2 \quad\quad\quad - s_3 = 1$$
$$\text{All variables} \geq 0$$

The reader should be advised that in real applications of LP, we do not convert LP problems to standard from because virtually all commercial software accept $\leq$, $=$ and $\geq$ constraints and do not require the analyst to convert LP problems into standard form.

Some Special Issues

This section points out some special issues that may arise during the formulation or solution of LP problems. These issues are

1. Problems that have no feasible solutions.
2. Unbounded problems.
3. Redundancy in constraints.
4. Problems that have multiple optimal solutions.

No Feasible Solutions

It is possible to formulate a problem for which it is impossible to satisfy the set of all constraints. This situation sometimes occurs in problems that have a mix of greater-than-or-equal-to constraints and less-than-or-equal-to constraints, where in order to satisfy one of

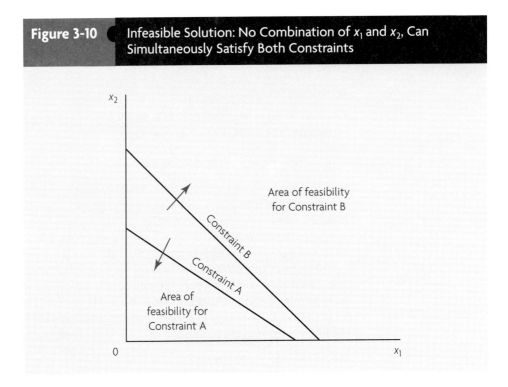

Figure 3-10 Infeasible Solution: No Combination of x_1 and x_2, Can Simultaneously Satisfy Both Constraints

the constraints, another constraint must be violated. Consider the graph in Figure 3-10, where constraint A places an upper bound on feasible solutions and constraint B places a lower bound on feasible solutions. Since the two constraints to not touch or overlap, there is no combination of decision variable values that can satisfy both constraints at the same time.

Sometimes it happens that the problem has been formulated incorrectly (e.g., a constraint coefficient is incorrect, an inequality has the wrong direction). Therefore, when this situation occurs, the first step is to check for one of those errors. If it turns out that the formulation is correct, the manager or analyst might decide to revise some constraint(s), say, by obtaining additional scarce resources, or loosening restrictions. The manager might decide that some constraints are more important than others and might focus on the important ones. Chapter 10 includes a discussion of *goal programming*, which might be of some use in such instances.

Unbounded Problems

An unbounded problem exists when the value of the objective function can be increased without limit. A graphical example of this is shown in Figure 3-11. This difficulty is usually due to either incorrectly maximizing when the real goal is to minimize an objective function or using greater-than-or-equal-to constraints when less-than-or-equal-to constraints are called for. Although the latter error also may occur in a minimization problem, the problem will not be unbounded because of the nonnegativity constraints (i.e., the resulting solution will be 0, 0). Again, checking equalities or rethinking the problem statement may resolve the problem. The latter case may uncover another constraint that should have been included in the original statement of the problem.

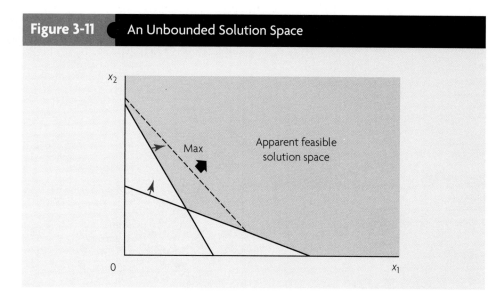

Figure 3-11   An Unbounded Solution Space

Redundant Constraints

In some cases, a constraint does not form a unique boundary of the feasible solution space. Such a constraint is called a **redundant constraint.** This constraint is illustrated in Figure 3-12. Note that a constraint is redundant if its removal would not alter the feasible solution space.

When a problem has a redundant constraint, at least one of the other constraints in the problem is more restrictive than the redundant constraint.

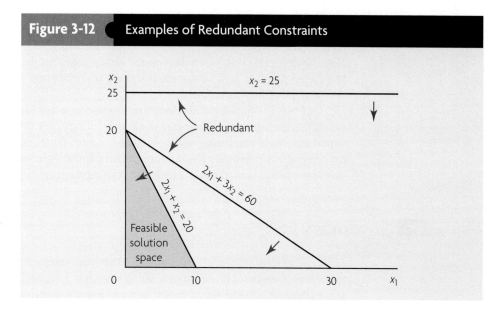

Figure 3-12   Examples of Redundant Constraints

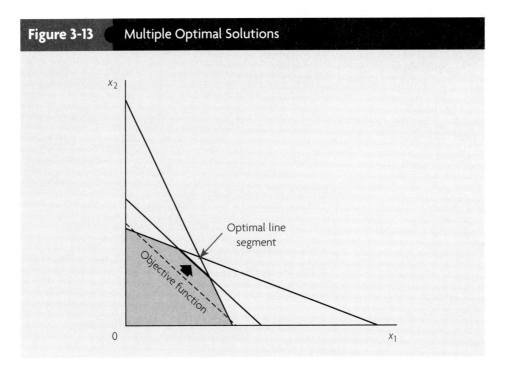

Figure 3-13   Multiple Optimal Solutions

Multiple Optimal Solutions

Most linear programming problems have a single optimal solution. However, in some instances, a problem will have multiple optimal solutions, which is to say that different combinations of values of the decision variables will yield the same optimal value for the objective function.

Figure 3-13 illustrates how this happens in a two-variable problem. We can see that the objective function is *parallel* to a portion of the boundary of the feasible solution space. Because of this, it ends up last touching an entire segment of the boundary (constraint line). Hence, every combination of x_1 and x_2 on this line will yield the same (optimal) solution. Note, however, that this does not refute the earlier statement that the solution will always be at a corner point. In fact, we can see that there are two corner points that are optimal, one at either end of the line segment.

One benefit of having multiple optimal solutions in that for other (perhaps qualitative) reasons, a manager may prefer one of these solutions over the others, even though each would achieve the same value of the objective function. Furthermore, if noninteger solutions are acceptable, the manager has infinite optimal solutions to choose from. In practical terms, one of the two corner points is usually chosen because of ease in identifying those values.

◗ Summary

Linear programming models are used to find optimal solutions to constrained optimization problems. In order for linear programming models to be used, the problems must involve a single objective, a linear objective function, and linear constraints and have known and constant numerical values.

Linear programming models are composed of decision variables and numerical values that are arranged into an objective function and a set of constraints. The constraints are restrictions that can pertain to any decision variable or to a combination of decision variables. In general, variables are not allowed to have negative values. These restrictions are referred to as nonnegativity constraints.

This chapter illustrates how to formulate simple LP problems. This chapter also shows how two-variable linear programming problems can be approached using graphical techniques. Sometimes, the solution can be read directly from the graph, but usually it must be found algebraically using simultaneous equations.

The graphical technique can only handle problems involving two variables; therefore, its value as a general tool for solving LP models is rather limited. Nonetheless, as a vehicle for illustrating important concepts related to LP models and solutions, it is invaluable.

The chapter illustrates the solution of both maximization and minimization problems. In addition, the calculating of slack and surplus is demonstrated. Also, certain special issues that sometimes arise, including problems that have no feasible solutions, unbounded problems, problems with multiple optimal solutions, and redundant constraints, are discussed.

◗ Glossary

Additivity A requirement of LP models that both the terms of the objective function and the terms of the constraints be additive.

Algorithm A solution technique; a sequence of steps that will lead to a solution.

Binding Constraints Constraints whose intersection determines the optimal solution to a problem.

Certainty A requirement that LP model parameters are known and constant.

Constrained Optimization Finding the optimal solution to a problem given that certain constraints must be satisfied by the solution.

Constraint A restriction that must be satisfied by a solution.

Corner Point An extreme point of the feasible solution space; an intersection of two or more constraints that touches the feasible solution space.

Decision Variable A variable that is under the control of the decision maker.

Divisibility The assumption of LP models that noninteger values are acceptable solutions for decision variables.

Extreme Point *See* Corner Point.

Extreme Point Theorem If an LP problem has an optimal solution, at least one optimal solution will occur at a corner point of the feasible solution space.

Feasible Solution Any solution that satisfies all of a problem's constraints.

Feasible Solution Space Determined by the set of constraints of a problem, it contains all feasible solutions to an LP problem, including the optimal solutions.

Fundamental Theorem of LP If there is a solution to an LP problem, at least one optimal solution will occur at a corner point of the feasible solution space.

Graphical Method Method for determining the optimal solution to LP problems with two decision variables that involve visual portrayal of the LP concepts.

Karmakar's Method Interior method of solution to LP problems where the optimal solution is obtained by moving through the interior of the feasible solution space.

Linear Programming A family of mathematical techniques that can be used for constrained optimization problems with linear relationships.

Nonnegativity Constraints Variables are not allowed to have negative values.

Objective Function A mathematical expression that incorporates the contribution per unit of each variable.

Optimal Solution A combination of decision variable amounts that yields the best possible value of the objective function and satisfies all constraints. There may be multiple combinations of decision variables that yield that same best value of the objective function.

Parameters Numerical values that appear in the objective function and constraints; assumed known and constant in LP models.

Proportionality A requirement of LP models that the impact or contribution of every decision variable in the objective function, and each constraint in which it appears, be linear.

Redundant Constraint A constraint that does not form a unique part of the boundary of the feasible solution space.

Simplex Method An exterior, algebraic method for solving any size (i.e. large number of decision variables) LP problem where the optimal solution is obtained by moving from corner point to another corner point.

Simultaneous Equations Solving a set of two equations *simultaneously* for the values of the decision variables that will satisfy both equations.

Slack The amount of scarce resource of capacity that will be unused by a given feasible solution to an LP problem.

Standard Form A linear program in which all constraints are written as equalities, including slack and surplus variables.

Surplus The amount by which a $\geq$ constraint is exceeded by a given solution to an LP problem.

Solved Problems

Problem 1

A toy manufacturer makes three versions of a toy robot. The first version requires 10 minutes each for fabrication and packaging and 2 pounds of plastic, the second version requires 12 minutes for fabrication and packaging and 3 pounds of plastic, and the third version requires 15 minutes for fabrication and packaging and 4 pounds of plastic. There are 8 hours of fabrication and packaging time available and 200 pounds of plastic available for the next production cycle. The unit profits are \$1 for each Version 1, \$5 for each Version 2, and \$6 for each Version 3. A minimum of 10 units of each version of robot must be made to fill previous orders.

Formulate an LP model that will determine the optimal production quantities for profit maximization.

Solution

a. Identify the decision variables:

x_1 = number of Version 1 robots
x_2 = number of Version 2 robots
x_3 = number of Version 3 robots

b. Identify the constraints by name:

Fabrication and packaging time
Quantity of plastic
Quantity of Version 1 robots (minimum of 10)
Quantity of Version 2 robots (minimum of 10)
Quantity of Version 3 robots (minimum of 10)

c.   Write the objective function:

maximize $\quad 1x_1 + 5x_2 + 6x_3$

d.   Write the constraints:
Note that fabrication and packaging times are given in minutes per unit but that available time is given in hours. It is necessary that both sides of a constraint have the same units. This can be accomplished by converting 8 hours to 480 minutes.
The constraints are:

Fabrication and packaging	$10x_1 + 12x_2 + 15x_3 \leq 480$ minutes
Plastic	$2x_1 + 3x_2 + 4x_3 \leq 200$ pounds
Version 1	$x_1 \qquad\qquad \geq 10$ robots
Version 2	$\qquad x_2 \qquad \geq 10$ robots
Version 3	$\qquad\qquad x_3 \geq 10$ robots
	$x_1, x_2,$ and $x_3 \geq 0$

Problem 2

Given this LP model:

maximize $\quad 10x_1 + x_2$

subject to

A $\quad 3x_1 + 2x_2 \leq 12$
B $\quad 2x_1 + 2x_2 \leq 16$
C $\quad x_1 - x_2 \leq 2$
$\quad x_1, x_2 \geq 0$

a.   Graph the model.
b.   Find the optimal point on the graph using the objective function method.
c.   Use simultaneous equations to determine the optimal values of x_1 and x_2.
d.   Determine the amount of slack for each constraint.

Solution

a.   Plot each constraint by first setting one variable equal to zero and solving for the other, and then setting the other variable equal to zero and solving for the first. Then, connect those two points with a straight line. The last constraint is a bit different than the majority of constraints you will encounter in this chapter due to the negative value. Even so, we still follow the same procedure in determining the x_1 and x_2 intercept: The result is that the x_2 intercept is -2, and the x_1 intercept is $+2$.
After all of the constraints have been plotted, shade in the feasible solution space. To determine which side of the third constraint represents less than 2, substitute 0.0 into the constraint.
The plot is shown in Figure 3-14.

b.   The objective function can be plotted by first setting it equal to the product of the x_1 and x_2 coefficients (10) and solving for the x_1 and x_2 intercepts. The objective function is shown in Figure 3-14 with the dotted line. It is apparent that the optimum point occurs at the intersection of constraint lines A and C.

c.   The intersection of A and C is found as follows:

A $\quad 3x_1 + x_2 = 12$
C $\quad \underline{x_1 - x_2 = 2}$
$\quad 4x_1 \qquad = 14 \quad$ subtracting,

Solving, $x_1 = 3.5$.

Substituting $x_1 = 3.5$ into either of the constraints and solving for x_2 yields $x_2 = 1.5$. Then the optimal value of the objective function is found by substituting these values into the objective function: $10(3.5) + 1.5 = 36.5$.

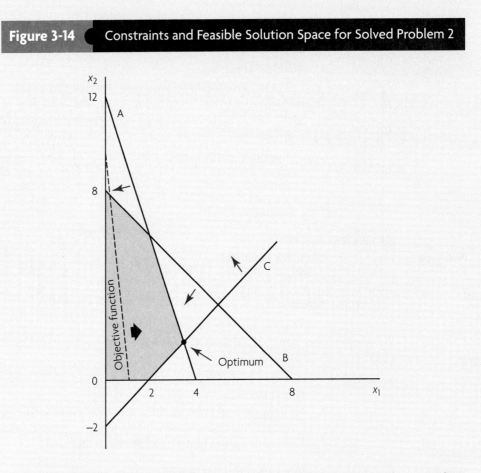

Figure 3-14 Constraints and Feasible Solution Space for Solved Problem 2

d. There is no slack for the two constraints whose intersection determines the optimal so-lution because any point *on* the line means the left and right sides of the constraint expression are *equal*. For constraint B, we can determine the amount of slack by sub-stituting in the optimal values of x_1 and x_2 and solving:

$$2(3.5) + 2(1.5) = 10$$

The slack is the original value minus this amount. Thus, slack equals $16 - 10 = 6$.

Problem 3

Given this LP model:

minimize $3x_1 + 4x_2$

subject to

A	$6x_1 + 1x_2 \geq 120$
B	$4x_1 + 4x_2 \geq 320$
C	$3x_1 + 5x_2 \geq 300$
	$x_1, x_2 \geq 0$

a. Graph the model.
b. Determine the optimal point on the graph using the objective function method.
c. Use simultaneous equations to determine the optimal values of x_1 and x_2, and then find the minimum cost.
d. Determine the amount of slack or surplus for each constraint.

Figure 3-15   A Graph of Solved Problem 3

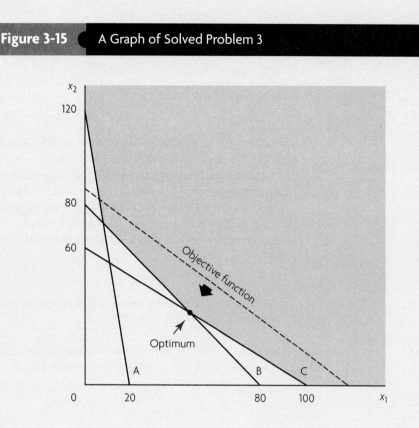

Solution

a. To plot the model, for each constraint:
    (1) Make the constraint an equality.
    (2) Alternately set one of the variables equal to zero and solve for the other. For example, for the first constraint, setting $x_1 = 0$ and solving for x_2, we find $x_2 = 120$; setting $x_2 = 0$ and solving for x_1, we find $x_1 = 20$. Thus, we have two points: $x_1 = 0$, $x_2 = 120$, and $x_1 = 20$, $x_2 = 0$.
    (3) Mark the points on the graph and connect with a straight line. Label the line (i.e., A).
    (4) After all constraints have been plotted, identify and shade in the feasible solution space. (See Figure 3-15.)

b. To plot the objective function, set it equal to any value, usually some multiple of the product of the x_1 and x_2 coefficients (i.e., 12), and then solve for the x_1 and x_2 intercepts in the same way as with a constraint. Connect the intercepts with a straight (dashed) line (see Figure 3-15). The objective function line was plotted using $3x_1 + 4x_2 = 360$.

c. The optimal solution is at the intersection of lines B and C. Solving these simultaneously, we find

    B $4x_1 + 4x_2 = 320$
    C $3x_1 + 5x_2 = 300$

Multiplying the B equation by 5 and the C equation by 4 and then subtracting the modified C equation from the modified B equation will cause the x_2 term to drop out:

    B′ $20x_1 + 20x_2 = 1{,}600$
    C′ $\dfrac{12x_1 + 20x_2 = 1{,}200}{}$
            $8x_1 \qquad\quad = \quad 400$

Solving, $x_1 = 50$. Substituting $x_1 = 50$ into either of the original equations or the modified equations will permit determination of x_2. For instance, using the original B:

$$4(50) + 4x_2 = 320$$

Multiplying and rearranging terms, we have

$$4x_2 = 120.$$

Thus, $x_2 = 30$. The minimum cost is found by substituting the optimal values into the objective function: $3(50) + 4(30) = 270$.

d. The term *slack* pertains to $\leq$ constraints; *surplus* pertains to $\geq$ constraints. Because the constraints in this problem are of the $\geq$ variety, *surplus* is the appropriate term.

Because the intersection of constrains B and C determines the optimal solution (i.e., they are binding constraints), they have no surplus. (You can verify this by substituting the optimal values into these two constraints.) For constraint A, substitution yields

$$6(50) + 1(30) = 330$$

Because this *exceeds* the minimum requirement of 120 by 210 (i.e., $330 - 120 = 210$), the surplus is 210.

Problem 4

Solve the following problem for the optimal values of the decision variables and the objective function. Then answer the questions about slack and surplus.

$$\text{maximize} \quad 5x_1 + 8x_2$$

subject to

#1	$3x_1 + 12x_2 \geq 36$	
#2	$11x_1 + 3x_2 \geq 33$	
#3	$2x_1 + 2x_2 \leq 16$	
	$x_1, x_2 \geq 0$	

a. Do any of the constraints have surplus? If so, which one(s) and how much surplus?
b. Do any of the constraints have slack? If so, which one(s), and how much slack?

Solution

Notice that this problem involves *mixed constraints*. That is, the first two constraints are greater-than-or-equal-to constraints and the third is a less-than-or-equal-to constraint. This can lead to incorrectly identifying the feasible solution space if we are not careful. To avoid this possibility, it can be helpful to place arrows at the ends of the constraint lines on the graph to show which direction is feasible. (See Figure 3-16.)

Adding the objective function line to the graph reveals the optimal solution is at the point where constraints #2 and #3 intersect. Using simultaneous equations, we can determine that the optimal values are $x_1 = 1.2$ and $x_2 = 6.8$. Substituting these values into the objective function and solving yields an optimal profit value of 60.4.

a. The only type of constraint that can have surplus is a $\geq$ constraint. Constraints #1 and #2 are this type. However, the optimal solution is at the intersection of #2 and #3. Because the solution point is on #2, its surplus is zero. The solution is not on #1, so it has surplus. We can determine the amount by substituting the optimal values of x_1 and x_2 into the left side of that constraint and comparing the result to the right side. The difference is the amount of surplus. Thus,

$$\text{#1:} \qquad 3(1.2) + 12(6.8) = 85.2$$

Figure 3-16   Graph for Solved Problem 4

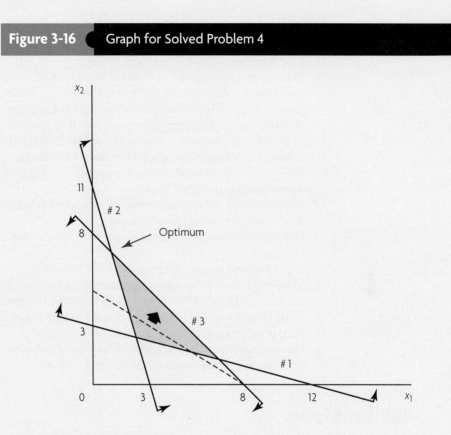

The right-hand-side value is 36. The difference (surplus) is

$$85.2 - 36 = 49.2.$$

b. Only $\leq$ constraints can have slack. Constraint #3 is such a constraint. However, the optimal point is on this constraint, so its slack equals zero. We can also determine this by substituting the optimal values of x_1 and x_2 into the left-hand side of constraint #3 and comparing the result to the right-hand-side value of this constraint. Thus,

#3: $2(1.2) + 2(6.8) = 16$

This equals the right-hand-side value, indicating that slack is zero.

◗ Discussion and Review Questions

1. What are the key advantages of using linear programming as a decision-making tool?
2. What are the assumptions of linear programming problems? Briefly explain each assumption.
3. What are the components of LP models? Briefly discuss each component.
4. What are the three signs for constraints in formulating a linear programming problem?
5. List the steps in formulating a linear programming problem.

6. Describe how an LP problem formulation can be converted into standard form.
7. List the steps in using the graphical approach to obtain an optimal solution to a linear programming problem.
8. In using the graphical approach, the optimal solution can be found by using two methods. Describe the methods in finding the optimal solution using the graphical approach. What are the differences between the two approaches?
9. Describe slack and surplus and explain how they can be determined.
10. Explain how an infeasible solution can be identified on an LP graph.
11. Explain how an unbounded solution can be identified on an LP graph.
12. Does having an unbounded solution space always result in an unbounded solution for a maximization problem? Explain.
13. Using the graphical approach, under what condition is it possible for an LP problem to have more than one optimal solution?
14. Develop two less-than-or-equal-to constraints such that one of them is a redundant constraint.
15. Explain what is meant by the term *binding constraint*?
16. In solving a linear programming problem, the condition of infeasibility occurred. What are some of the factors we should check to resolve this problem.
17. What is the impact of removing a nonredundant constraint from a linear programming problem on the graphical solution?
18. Discuss the similarities and differences in using the graphical approach to solving LP between maximization and minimization problems.

Problems

1. A furniture company produces a variety of products. One department specializes in wood tables, chairs, and bookcases. These are made using three resources: labor, wood, and machine time. The department has 60 hours of labor available each day, 16 hours of machine time, and 400 board feet of wood. A consultant has developed a linear programming model for the department:

x_1 = quantity of tables
x_2 = quantity of chairs
x_3 = quantity of bookcases

maximize $40x_1 + 30x_2 + 45x_3$ (profit)

subject to

Labor	$2x_1 + 1x_2 + 2.5x_3 \leq 60$ hours
Machine	$.8x_1 + .6x_2 + 1.0x_3 \leq 16$ hours
Wood	$30x_1 + 20x_2 + 30x_3 \leq 400$ board-feet
Tables	$x_1 \qquad\qquad\qquad \geq 10$ board-feet

$$x_1, x_2, x_3 \geq 0$$

Answer these questions posed by department manager Barbara Brady:
a. What is the main purpose of the model?
b. What are the decision variables?
c. What are the system constraints (name them)?
d. What is the meaning of the number 2.5 in the labor constraint?

e. Explain what is meant by $x_1 \geq 10$.

f. What does the term $40x_1$ in the objective function represent?

2. The Stone Company produces three sizes of window fans: small, medium, and large. The manager has formulated an LP model for fan production:

maximize $\quad 6x_1 + 8x_2 + 5x_3$ (profit)

subject to

Labor	$3x_1 + 4x_2 + 5x_3 \leq 160$ hours
Metal	$1x_1 + 2x_2 + 3x_3 \leq 100$ pounds
Plastic	$2x_1 + 2x_2 + 2x_3 \leq 110$ pounds
Large fan	$x_3 \geq 18$

$$x_1, x_2, x_3 \geq 0$$

Briefly explain or define each of these parts of the model:

a. $x_1, x_2,$ and x_3.

b. The 6 in the objective function.

c. The product of the 8 and x_2 in the objective function.

d. The terms *labor, metal,* and *plastic.*

e. The 5 in the labor constraint.

f. The 160 hours.

g. $x_3 \geq 18$.

h. The product of 5 and x_3 in the labor constraint.

i. $x_1, x_2, x_3 \geq 0$.

j. What two key questions can be answered using this model?

[margin answers]

a. Quantity of different types of fans produced.

b. Profit per unit on small window fan.

c. Amount of profit on small window fans.

d. Constraints.

e. Amount of labor per one small window fan.

f. Total amount of labor needed for production of small window fan.

g. At least 18 large window fans must be produced.

h. Amount of labor for production of large fan.

i. Nonnegativity constraints.

j. Maximum profit and amount of production for each fan.

3. A confectionary company produces two sizes of its popular dark chocolate bars: a 3.5-ounce size and a 6-ounce size. The 3.5-ounce bar costs $.22 to make and sells for $.35, whereas the 6-ounce bar costs $.40 to make and sells for $.55. The company has 15,000 ounces of chocolate in stock, and the manager wants to use it all on the next production run. In addition, the manager has specified that a minimum of 1,000 of the 3.5-ounce bars and 1,200 of the 6-ounce bars should be made.

a. What are the decision variables in this problem?

b. What are the constraints?

c. Formulate a linear programming model that will enable the manager to determine how many of each size bar to produce in order to satisfy the conditions specified with maximum profit.

4. The Mantell Company makes softballs and baseballs. In order to make each type of ball, leather, nylon, wood chips, and machine time and labor are needed. The requirements for each item and the resources available are shown in the following table:

Item	Softball	Baseball	Available
Leather	6	4	6,000 ounces
Nylon	8	3	5,000 yards
Wood chips	10	2	5,000 ounces
Labor	3	2	3,600 minutes
Machine	1	1	2,000 minutes

Softballs sell for $17 each, and baseballs sell for $15 each. Formulate a linear programming model that can be used to determine the number of each type of ball to produce in order to maximize revenue.

[margin answer]

Max $17x_1 + 15x_2$

s.t. $\quad 6x_1 + 4x_2 \leq 6,000$

$\qquad 8x_1 + 3x_2 \leq 5,000$

$\qquad 10x_1 + 2x_2 \leq 5,000$

$\qquad 3x_1 + 2x_2 \leq 3,600$

$\qquad x_1 + x_2 \leq 2,000$

$\qquad x_1, x_2 \geq 0$

5. Given this linear programming model:

$$\text{maximize} \quad Z = 10x_1 + 16x_2 \quad \text{(profit)}$$

subject to

$$
\begin{array}{lll}
A & 8x_1 + 20x_2 \le 120 \\
B & 25x_1 + 20x_2 \le 200 \\
& x_1, x_2 \ge 0
\end{array}
$$

a. Graph the constraints.
b. Shade in the feasible solution space.
c. Plot the objective function and determine the optimal point on the graph.
d. Use simultaneous equations to determine the optimal values of the decision variables and the maximum value of the objective function.
e. What would the optimal values be if the objective function had been $6x_1 + 3x_2$?

See the IM.

6. For the preceding problem, determine the coordinates of each feasible corner point using the original objective function. Then, determine the profit at each of those corner points. Use that information to identify the optimal solution.

7. The manager of a construction project has formulated this LP model:

$$\text{maximize} \quad Z = 25x_1 + 30x_2 \quad \text{(profit)}$$

subject to

$$
\begin{array}{lll}
\text{Time} & 20x_1 + 15x_2 \le 1{,}200 \text{ hours} \\
\text{Materials} & 8x_1 + 12x_2 \le 600 \text{ tons} \\
& x_1, x_2 \ge 0
\end{array}
$$

a. Graph the model.
b. Determine the optimal values of the decision variables using the objective function approach. What is the maximum profit?

$x_1 = 45, x_2 = 20,$
$Z = 1{,}725$

8. For the previous problem, use the extreme point approach to determine the optimal solution.

9. The manager of a warehouse has developed this LP model:

$$\text{maximize} \quad Z = 50x_1 + 30x_2 \quad \text{(revenue)}$$

subject to

$$
\begin{array}{lll}
\text{Time} & 15x_1 + 12x_2 \le 900 \text{ minutes} \\
\text{Space} & 8x_1 + 16x_2 \le 800 \text{ square feet} \\
& x_1 \qquad\quad \ge 40 \text{ units} \\
& x_1, x_2 \ge 0
\end{array}
$$

a. Graph the constraints and shade in the feasible solution space.
b. Determine the optimal solution and maximum revenue.

$x_1 = 40, x_2 = 25,$
$Z = 2{,}450$

10. Answer the questions of the previous problem with this modification: Assume the objective function is $30x_1 + 50x_2$. (The manager had the coefficients of the objective function reversed.)

11. The owner of a telephone subscription service specializes in taking orders for two magazines, x_1 and x_2. She has formulated the following model that describes the unit contributions to profits and the use of scarce resources involved:

$$\text{maximize} \quad Z = .60x_1 + .90x_2$$

subject to

Telephone	$8x_1 + 12x_2 \leq 480$ minutes per day
Paperwork	$10x_1 + 6x_2 \leq 480$ minutes per day
	$x_1 \qquad\qquad \geq 20$
	$x_1, x_2 \geq 0$

a. Is there a unique optimal solution?
b. What is the maximum profit?
c. Can you find an optimal solution for which both decision variables are integer?

12. The manager of a food processing plant that specializes in potato chips has developed an LP model to reflect processing times.

x_1 = boxes of regular chips
x_2 = boxes of crinkle cut chips

maximize $Z = .40x_1 + .30x_2$ (profit)

subject to

Cutting	$3.6x_1 + .8x_2 \leq 144$ minutes
Frying	$3.2x_1 + 1.6x_2 \leq 160$ minutes
Packing	$4.8x_1 + 7.2x_2 \leq 576$ seconds
Crinkle	$x_2 \leq 80$ boxes
Crinkle	$x_2 \geq 20$ boxes
	$x_1, x_2 \geq 0$

a. *x₁ = 15, x₂ = 70, Z = 27*

a. Determine the combination of boxes of the two types of chips that will maximize profits.
b. Is any constraint redundant? Explain briefly.

b. *x₂ ≤ 80; it does not form a unique boundary of the feasible solution space*

13. For the previous problem, determine each of the following:
a. The amount of each resource that will be used.
b. The amount of slack for each resource.
c. The special condition that would exist if the profit for crinkle cut chips dropped to $.20 per box. (Hint: Plot the revised constraint on your graph.)

a. *x₁ = qty. of mid-sized cars*
x₂ = qty of compact cars.
Max z = 500 x₁ + 400 x₂
s.t.   8x₁ + 8x₂ ≤ 720
x₁   ≥ 10
x₁ ≤ 50
x₂ ≥ 10
x₂ ≤ 60

b. *x₁ = 50, x₂ = 40, Z = $41,000*

14. A manager of an automobile dealership must decide how many cars to order for the end of the model year. Midsize cars yield an average profit of $500 each, and compact cars yield an average of $400 each. Either type of car will cost the dealership $8,000 each and no more than $720,000 can be invested. The manager wants at least 10 of each type of car but no more than 50 of the midsized cars and no more than 60 of the compact cars.
a. Formulate the linear programming model of this problem.
b. Solve for the optimal quantities of each type of car and the optimal value of the objective function.

15. Given this model:

minimize $Z = 4x_1 + 2x_2$ (cost)

subject to

A	$16x_1 + 5x_2 \geq 80$
B	$18x_1 + 15x_2 \geq 180$
C	$24x_1 + 45x_2 \geq 360$
	$x_1 \geq 0, x_2 \geq 0$

a. Solve for the values of x_1 and x_2 that will minimize cost.
b. Which restriction is exceeded by the optimal solution to the model? By how much?

16. Given this model:

$$\text{minimize} \quad Z = 20x_1 + 30x_2 \quad \text{(cost)}$$

subject to

Town	$6x_1 + x_2 \geq 12$
Country	$7x_1 + 7x_2 \geq 49$
State	$3x_1 + 11x_2 \geq 33$
	$x_1, x_2 \geq 0$

a. $x_1 = 5.5, x_2 = 1.5,$
$Z = 155$
b. Town = 22.5,
County = 0, State = 0

    a. Find the optimal values of x_1 and x_2 and the minimum cost.
    b. Determine the amount of surplus associated with each constraint.

17. The manager of a health store has formulated the following LP model, which describes parameters for a new product:

$$\text{minimize} \quad Z = 2.40x_1 + 1.50x_2 \quad \text{(cost)}$$

subject to

Vitamin A	$10x_1 + 6x_2 \geq 1{,}200$ mg
Vitamin B_1	$10x_1 + 30x_2 \geq 1{,}800$ mg
	$x_1, x_2 \geq 0$

    a. Determine the optimal solution.
    b. What is the minimum cost at the optimum?

18. The new manager of a food processing plant hopes to reduce costs by using linear programming to determine the optimal amounts of two ingredients it uses, x_1 and x_2. The manager has constructed this model:

$$\text{minimize} \quad Z = .40x_1 + .40x_2$$

subject to

Protein	$3x_1 + 5x_2 \geq 30$ grams
Carbohydrates	$6x_1 + 4x_2 \geq 48$ grams
	$x_1, x_2 \geq 0$

a. $x_1 = 6.67, x_2 = 3.0$
b. $Z = \$3.47$

    a. Determine the optimal solution.
    b. Compute the minimum cost for the optimal solution.

19. There is a single optimal solution to Problem 18. However, if the objective function had been parallel to one of the constraints, there would have been two equally optimal solutions. If the cost of x_2 remains at $.40, what cost of x_1 would cause the objective function to be parallel to the carbohydrate constraint? Explain how you determined this.

20. Graph this problem and briefly explain why it cannot be solved:

$$\text{maximize} \quad Z = 2.20x_1 + 2.35x_2$$

subject to

Feasible regions of the
constraints have no points
in common

A	$6x_1 + 9x_2 \geq 108$
B	$3x_1 + 5x_2 \leq 45$
	$x_1, x_2 \geq 0$

21. Given this linear programming problem:

$$\text{maximize} \quad Z = 5x_1 + 3x_2$$

subject to

$$1 \quad 7x_1 + 4x_2 \geq 84$$
$$2 \quad 5x_1 + 8x_2 \geq 80$$
$$x_1, x_2 \geq 0$$

a. Graph the problem.
b. Why is it impossible to obtain an optimal solution for the problem?
c. Can you suggest two different possible errors that might have occurred in formulating the problem that prevent a solution?

22. Explain why the following linear programming problem cannot be solved for an optimal solution.

minimize $Z = 7x_1 + 3x_2$

There is no feasible
solution space

subject to

$$1 \quad 6x_1 + 8x_2 \leq 48$$
$$2 \quad 4x_1 + 3x_2 \geq 24$$
$$3 \quad x_2 \geq 5$$
$$x_1, x_2 \geq 0$$

23. Explain why the following linear programming formulation is probably in error:

minimize $Z = 30x_1 + 33x_2$

subject to

$$1 \quad 15x_1 + 18x_2 \leq 90$$
$$2 \quad 20x_1 + 12x_2 \leq 120$$
$$x_1, x_2 \geq 0$$

24. A wood products firm uses leftover time at the end of each week to make goods for stock. Currently, there are two products on the list of items that are produced for stock: a chopping board and a knife holder. Both items require three operations: cutting, gluing, and finishing. The manager of the firm has collected the following data on these products:

Item	Profit per Unit	Cutting	Gluing	Finishing
		Time per Unit (minutes)		
Chopping board	$2	1.4	5	12
Knife holder	$6	.8	13	3

a. Max $Z = 2x_1 + 6x_2$
  s.t. $1.4x_1 + .8x_2 \leq 56$
        $5x_1 + 13x_2 \leq 650$
        $12x_1 + 3x_2 \leq 360$
        $x_1, x_2 \geq 0$
b. $x_1 = 0, x_2 = 50,$
   $Z = 300$
c. Cutting, 16 min;
   Finishing, 210 min.

The manager has also determined that during each week 56 minutes are available for cutting, 650 minutes are available for gluing, and 360 minutes are available for finishing.
a. Formulate this problem as a linear programming model.
b. Determine the optimal quantities of the decision variables.
c. Which resources are not completely used by your solution? How much of each resource is unused?

25. The manager of an inspection department has been asked to help reduce a backlog of safety devices that must be inspected. There are two types of safety devices: one for construction workers and one for window washers. The manager will be permitted to select any combination of items because new testing equipment will soon be available that will handle the remaining items. However, in the short run, the manager has been asked to help generate revenue. The revenue for each construction device is $60, and

the revenue for each window-washing device is $40. The manager has obtained data on the necessary inspection operations, which are

Operation	Time per Unit (minutes) Construction	Window Washing	Total Time Available (minutes)
Test #1	¾	⅓	75
Test #2	¼	½	50
Test #3	½	¼	40

a. Formulate this problem as a linear programming model.
b. Determine the optimum values of the decision variables and the revenue that will result.
c. Which testing operations will have slack time? How much?
d. Is any constraint redundant? Which one? Why?

26. A dietician has been asked by the athletic director of a university to develop a snack that athletes can use in their training programs. The dietician intends to mix two separate products together to make the snack. The following information has been obtained by the dietician:

Nutrient	Minimum Amount Required (grams)	Contribution per Ounce (grams) Product A	Product B
Carbohydrates	20	2	5
Protein	12	6	1
Calories	450	90	50

a. Min $Z = .2x_1 + .1x_2$
s.t. $2x_1 + 5x_2 \geq 20$
$6x_1 + x_2 \geq 12$
$90x_1 + 50x_2 \geq 450$
$x_1, x_2 \geq 0$
b. Product A = .7143,
Product B = 7.7143,
Z = .9143
c. Yes, carbohydrates—20 grams

Product A costs $.20 per ounce and Product B costs $.10 per ounce
a. Formulate this problem as a linear programming model.
b. Determine the optimal quantities of the two products for cost minimization. What is the cost per snack?
c. Are any requirements exceeded? If so, which ones, and by how much?

27. The manager of the deli section of a grocery superstore has just learned that the department has 112 pounds of mayonnaise, of which 70 pounds is approaching its expiration date and must be used. In order to use up the mayonnaise, the manager has decided to prepare two items: a ham spread and a deli spread. Each pan of the ham spread will require 1.4 pounds of the mayonnaise and each pan of the deli spread will require 1.0 pound. The manager has received an order for 10 pans of ham spread and 8 pans of the deli spread. In addition, the manager has decided to have at least 10 pans of each spread available for sale. Both spreads will cost $3 per pan to make, but ham spread yields revenue of $5 per pan and deli spread yields $7 per pan.
a. Formulate this problem as a linear programming model.
b. Determine the solution that will minimize cost.
c. Determine the solution that will maximize profit.

28. A production manager is faced with the question of how to allocate the manufacturing of a microwave oven between his own company and a subcontractor because neither firm can handle the demand alone. Fabrication costs are $10 per unit within the company and $20 per unit from the subcontractor; assembly costs are $8 per unit within the company and $5 from the subcontractor; and inspection costs are $3 per unit within the company and $1 per unit from the subcontractor. The company

a. See the IM
b. $x_1 = 1,818.18,$
  $x_2 = 5,090.9,$
  $Z = \$414,546$
c. $s_1 = 0, s_2 = 0, s_3 = 1,455$

a. $x_1 = 0, x_2 = 1,500,$
  $Z = \$22,500$
b. Leather, 0 ounces;
  Nylon, 500 yards;
  Wood Chips, 7,000
  ounces; Labor,
  600 minutes;
  Machine, 500 minutes
c. Labor and Machine
  constraints

has a budget of $120,000 for fabrication, $40,000 for assembly, and $12,000 for inspection. The contribution to profits is $60 per unit regardless of which firm does the work.

a. Formulate this problem as a linear programming model.
b. What is the optimal solution? How much profit will it yield?
c. How much of the total budget will be unused by the optimal solution?

29. Determine the optimal solution and value of the objective function for Problem 3.
30. (Refer to Problem 4.)
  a. What are the optimal values of the decision variables and the objective function?
  b. What is the amount of slack for each resource?
  c. Which constraints are redundant?
31. An accountant has developed the following LP model:

  maximize $Z = 4.0A + 3.6B$ (revenue)

  subject to

$$1\ \ 11A + 5B \geq 55$$
$$2\ \ 3A + 4B \leq 36$$
$$3\ \ 4A - 9B \leq 0$$
$$A, B \geq 0$$

  a. Determine the optimal quantities of variables A and B and the maximum revenue.
  b. For the optimal solution, determine the slack or surplus that would result for each constraint.
  c. Are any constraints redundant? Explain.

32. Given this LP model:

  maximize $Z = x_1 + 5x_2$

  subject to

$$x_1 + 3x_2 \leq 12$$
$$3x_1 + 4x_2 = 24$$
$$x_1 \leq 6$$
$$x_1, x_2 \geq 0$$

a. $x_1 = 4.8, x_2 = 2.4$
b. $Z = 16.8$
c. No

  a. Determine the optimal values of the decision variables.
  b. Compute the optimal value of the objective function.
  c. Is any constraint redundant? If so, which one?

33. Tom Smith is the manager of a discount store. He wants to maximize the total revenue from two furniture items; a bedroom set and a living room set. It is important that the showroom space of 40,000 square feet be *completely* filled with these sets, some of which will be in crates. Nonetheless, the manager wants to give the impression that the store is overstocked on these items. The bedroom sets will occupy an average of 400 square feet each, and the living room sets will occupy an average of 500 square feet each. The manager estimates that it requires approximately 14 minutes to unload a bedroom set and 7 minutes to unload a living room set. There are 980 minutes available for the unloading. The living room sets will produce a revenue of $500 each, and the bedroom sets will produce a

revenue of $1,000 each. The manager also has decided that a minimum of 20 living room sets should be ordered.

   a.   What question is to be answered by linear programming?

   b.   Formulate the problem in a linear programming format.

   c.   Determine the optimal solution.

34. A real estate broker is responsible for selling homes in a new development. There will be two types of floor plans: Model I and Model II. Each Model I will require .6 acre of land, and each Model II will require 1.0 acre of land. Twelve acres of land are available. The broker already has orders for three Model I and three Model II homes, and the contractor has requested that no more than 10 Model I homes be sold because of other circumstances. The broker also operates a tree nursery and wants to use at least 81 maple trees to landscape the development. Each Model I and Model II home will receive nine maple trees. The broker estimates it will cost $300,000 to sell each Model I home and $400,000 to sell each Model II home.

   a.   What question can be answered using linear programming?

   b.   Formulate this problem in an LP format.

   c.   Determine the optimal solution graphically.

   d.   If the broker had estimated a cost of $600 to sell each Model I and $400 to sell each Model II, what solution would be optimal?

a. Answer in the IM.

b. Min $Z = 300,000x_1 + 400,000x_2$

s.t $.6x_1 + 1x_2 \le 12$

$\quad x_1 \ge 3$

$\quad x_1 \le 10$

$\quad\quad x_2 \ge 3$

$\quad 9x_1 + 9x_2 \ge 81$

$\quad x_1, x_2 \ge 0$

c. $x_1 = 3, x_2 = 6,$

$\quad Z = 4,200,000$

◼◗ Chapter 3 Case Son, Ltd.

Son, Ltd., manufactures a variety of chemical products used by photoprocessors. Son was recently bought out by a conglomerate, and managers of the two organizations have been working together to improve the efficiency of Son's operations.

    Managers have been asked to adhere to weekly operating budgets and to develop operating plans using quantitative methods whenever possible. The manager of one department has been given a weekly operating budget of $11,980 for production of three chemical products, which for convenience shall be referred to as Q, R, and W. The budget is intended to pay for direct labor and materials. Processing requirements for the three products, on a per unit basis, are

Product	Labor (hours)	Material A (pounds)	Material B (pounds)
Q	5	2	1
R	4	2	—
W	2	1/2	2

The company has a contractual obligation for 85 units of Product R per week.

    Material A costs $4 per pounds, as does Material B. Labor costs $8 an hour.

    Product Q sells for $122 a unit, Product R sells for $115 a unit, and Product W sells for $76 a unit.

    The manager is considering a number of different proposals regarding the quantity of each product to produce. The manager is primarily interested in maximizing contribution. Moreover, the manager wants to know how much labor will be needed, as well as the amount of each material to purchase.

Required

Prepare a report that addresses the following issues:

1. The optimal quantities of products and the necessary quantities of labor and materials.
2. One proposal is to make equal amounts of the products. What amount of each will maximize contribution, and what quantities of labor and materials will be needed? How much less will total contribution be if this proposal is adopted?
3. How would you formulate the constraint for Material A if it was determined that there is a 5 percent waste factor for Material A and equal quantities of each product are required?

Applications and Solutions of Linear Programming

Learning Objectives

After completing this chapter, you should be able to:

1. Formulate linear programming problems with different objectives.
2. Set up constraints that have unique structures.
3. Translate statements into constraint formulas.
4. Utilize Excel to solve a variety of linear programming problems.
5. Interpret the Excel output of linear programming problems.
6. Make managerial conclusions based on computer (Excel) output.
7. Explain at least two applications of linear programming.

Chapter Outline

Introduction, 154

Product-Mix Problems, 154
Problem Formulation, 155
Excel Solution of the Style and Comfort Furniture Company Example, 157

Diet Problems, 163

Blending Problems, 164

Marketing Applications, 168
Media Selection, 168
Marketing Research, 172

Financial Applications, 176
Financial Planning Problems for Banks, 176
Portfolio Selection, 179

Production Applications, 180
Multiperiod Production Scheduling, 181

Workforce Scheduling, 183
Make-or-Buy Decisions, 185

Agriculture Applications, 186

Data Envelopment Analysis, 189

Comment about the Use of Excel, 192

Other Applications, 192

Summary, 193

Glossary, 194

Solved Problems, 195

Discussion and Review Questions, 196

Problems, 196

Chapter 4 Case: Direct Marketing, 204

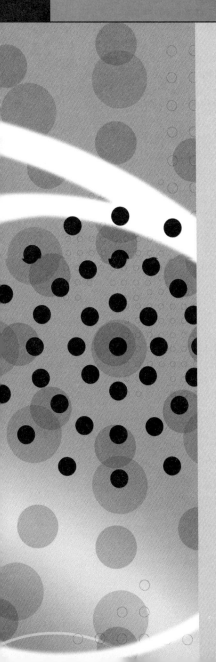

◼ Introduction

There are a wide range of problems that lend themselves to solution by linear programming techniques. This section briefly describes some of those problem types. The discussion is not meant to be all-inclusive. Rather, its purpose is to give you a sense of the importance of LP techniques for managerial decision making and the apparent diversity of situations to which linear programming can be applied.

In Chapter 3, we formulated some basic linear programming problems. In this chapter, we will expand our discussion of problem formulation and illustrate a variety of linear programming applications to show that linear programming is a flexible decision-making tool that can assist the decision maker in a wide variety of circumstances. In order to show the richness and variety of applications involving linear programming problems, we will present applications from marketing, production agriculture, and finance areas as well as formulate and solve a diet problem. In our discussion of these applications, first and foremost we emphasize accurate modeling of the real-world problem. Linear programming models always involve simplification of the real-world problem. In formulating a model, some of the assumptions of linear programming (additivity, divisibility, certainty, and proportionality) may be violated. In those cases, it may still be worthwhile to use linear programming provided that we understand the shortcomings of the model, test the model under different circumstances, and perform sensitivity analysis to see how the model reacts to the changes in the value of variables.

A critical question to answer is the degree of simplification in using a linear programming model to solve a real-world problem. In making this decision, we need to weigh the potential gains from developing a more complicated model against the potential losses of not including a real-world complication. Although the model should reflect the real-world situation, incorporating every aspect of the problem could add unnecessary complications to the model. On the other hand, if the model is not simplified enough, either it cannot be formulated or it will unnecessarily increase the formulation and/or solution time. The analysts may disagree on how much simplification is necessary. The degree of simplification is generally based on judgment and experience of the analyst. We will start demonstrating the utility of linear programming models by showing a variety of applications. First we will demonstrate a product-mix problem.

◼ Product-Mix Problems

Organizations often produce similar products or offer similar services that use the same resources (for example, labor, equipment, time, materials). Because of limits in the amounts of these resources that are available during any time period, a decision must be made concerning how much of each product to produce, or service to make available, during the time period that will be consistent with the goals of the organization. The basic question that can be answered using linear programming is what mix of output (or service) will maximize profit (revenue, etc.) given the availability of scarce resources?

The server problem presented in Chapter 3 is an example of a **product-mix problem.** In this section, we will give another example of a product-mix problem.

Example 4-1

Product-Mix Example
The Style and Comfort Furniture Manufacturing Company wishes to determine its production schedule for the next quarter. The company produces four types of

furniture, including sofas, love seats, recliners, and coffee tables. The profit contribution from selling one sofa is $120, one love seat is $105, one recliner is $150, and one coffee table is $73. The quarterly production budget is set at $180,000. Each unit of a sofa, love seat, recliner, and coffee table costs $400, $300, $500, and $150, respectively. The sales forecasts indicate that the potential sales volume is limited to 200 units of sofas, 150 units of love seats, 100 units of recliners, and 400 units of coffee tables. There are an aggregate of 800 machine hours available and 1,200 labor hours available. Table 4-1 summarizes the number of machine hours and the number of labor hours required per unit of each product.

Table 4-1   Per Unit Machine and Labor Hour Required for Each Product

Product	Machine Hours/Unit	Labor Hours/Unit
Sofa	2.0	2.5
Love seat	1.0	2.0
Recliner	2.2	3.0
Coffee table	.75	1.0

The management also imposed the following policy constraints:

1. At least 40 percent of all production costs must be incurred for the sofas.
2. At least 25 percent of all production costs must be allocated to the recliners.
3. There must be at least 30 love seats manufactured.

Problem Formulation

In formulating this problem, first we need to define the decision variables. If we define the quantity of the product produced as x_i, we will have the following variable definitions:

x_1 = number of sofas produced
x_2 = number of love seats produced
x_3 = number of recliners produced
x_4 = number of coffee tables produced

After defining the decision variables, we need to state the objective function. Since the amount of profit margin for producing each type of furniture is given, we can establish this as a maximization problem with the profit margin values as the objective function coefficients. Therefore, the objective function can be stated as follows:

maximize $Z = 120x_1 + 105x_2 + 150x_3 + 73x_4$

Once the objective function is determined, then we can determine the constraint equations. For our example, we know that we are constrained by the $180,000 provided in the budget. Therefore, for the budget limit of $180,000, we formulate the constraint equation by multiplying each variable by the production cost per unit of each product. For example, since the cost of producing a sofa is $400, we have $400x_1$ for the sofas. Therefore, the left-hand side of the budget constraint becomes

$400x_1 + 300x_2 + 500x_3 + 150x_4$

The sum of the above calculation must be less than or equal to the total production budget; thus, the budget constraint is

$$400x_1 + 300x_2 + 500x_3 + 150x_4 \leq 180,000 \tag{1}$$

Note that the above relationship is expressed as an inequality. In other words, it is not a requirement that the entire budget be consumed. Next we will formulate the sales volume limitation constraints. Based on the sales forecast, the production of the products will be limited to the upper bounds given in the problem. Since there is an upper bound for each product, we have the following four sales volume constraints:

$$x_1 \leq 200 \tag{2}$$
$$x_2 \leq 150 \tag{3}$$
$$x_3 \leq 100 \tag{4}$$
$$x_4 \leq 400 \tag{5}$$

It is typical for the forecasted sales values to represent an upper bound or maximum production quantities to define a range of feasible values.

Next, we need to consider the capacity of the machine hours as well as the capacity of the labor hours. Since there are 800 machine hours available, the value of 800 constitutes the right-hand side of the less than or equal to constraint for the machine hours capacity. The sum of the per unit machine hour requirements multiplied by their respective variable constitutes the left-hand side of the inequality. The resulting inequality is presented below:

$$2x_1 + 1x_2 + 2.2x_3 + .75x_4 \leq 800 \qquad \text{(machine hour capacity constraint)} \tag{6}$$

The labor hour capacity constraint is constructed in a similar fashion:

$$2.5x_1 + 2x_2 + 3x_3 + 1x_4 \leq 1200 \qquad \text{(labor hour capacity constraint)} \tag{7}$$

Finally we will formulate the three management-imposed policy constraints.

Policy 1: At Least 40 Percent of All Production Costs Must Be Incurred for the Sofas   In formulating this constraint, we place the sofa variable x_1 multiplied by its unit production cost on the left side of the inequality. The wording "at least" implies a lower bound or a minimum production requirement; therefore, the sign of the inequality is greater than or equal to ($\geq$). On the right-hand side of the constraint, we have 40 percent of total production cost. Since the total production cost is given by $400x_1 + 300x_2 + 500x_3 + 150x_4$, 40 percent of total production costs is given by $.40(400x_1 + 300x_2 + 500x_3 + 150x_4)$. This results in the following inequality:

$$400x_1 \geq .40(400x_1 + 300x_2 + 500x_3 + 150x_4)$$

Note that on the right-hand side of the inequality, 40 percent is not multiplied by the $180,000 of production budget because not all of the budget will necessarily be spent. Rearranging this inequality to eliminate all of the variables from the right-hand side of the inequality gives us the following inequality:

$$240x_1 - 120x_2 - 200x_3 - 60x_4 \geq 0 \tag{8}$$

Policy 2: At Least 25 Percent of All Production Costs Must Be Allocated to Recliners
Similarly, in formulating this constraint, we place the dining room table variable x_3 multiplied by its unit production cost on the left-hand side of the inequality. Again, the wording

"at least" implies a lower bound; therefore, the sign on the inequality is greater than or equal to ($\geq$). On the right-hand side of the constraint, we have 25 percent of total production cost. Since the total production cost is given by $400x_1 + 300x_2 + 500x_3 + 150x_4$, 25 percent of total production cost is given by $.25(400x_1 + 300x_2 + 500x_3 + 150x_4)$. This results in the following inequality:

$$500x_3 \geq .25(400x_1 + 300x_2 + 500x_3 + 150x_4)$$

Rearranging this inequality to eliminate all of the variables from the right-hand side of the inequality gives us the following inequality:

$$-100x_1 - 75x_2 + 375x_3 - 37.5x_4 \geq 0 \tag{9}$$

Policy 3: There Must Be At Least 30 Love Seats Manufactured The minimum production quantity (lower bound) of the love seats (variable X_2) constraint can be written as follows:

$$x_2 \geq 30 \tag{10}$$

Since the value of 30 is a minimum production quantity, the sign of the inequality is greater than or equal to.

We have now formulated the entire problem with the exception of nonnegativity constraints. Let's summarize the completed formulation for the Style of Comfort Furniture manufacturing company example:

x_1 = number of sofas produced
x_2 = number of love seats produced
x_3 = number of recliners produced
x_4 = number of coffee tables produced

maximize $Z = 120x_1 + 80x_2 + 150x_3 + 40x_4$

subject to

$$
\begin{array}{llr}
400x_1 + 300x_2 + 500x_3 + 150x_4 \leq 180{,}000 & \text{(budget constraint)} & (1) \\
\qquad\qquad x_1 \qquad\qquad\qquad \leq 250 & & (2) \\
\qquad\qquad\qquad x_2 \qquad\qquad \leq 300 & \text{(sales volume constraints)} & (3) \\
\qquad\qquad\qquad\qquad x_3 \qquad \leq 200 & & (4) \\
\qquad\qquad\qquad\qquad\qquad x_4 \leq 600 & & (5) \\
2x_1 + 1x_2 + 2.5x_3 + .75x_4 \leq 800 & \text{(machine hour constraint)} & (6) \\
2.5x_1 + 2x_2 + 3x_3 + 1x_4 \leq 1{,}200 & \text{(labor hour constraint)} & (7) \\
240x_1 - 120x_2 - 200x_3 - 60x_4 \geq 0 & \text{(sofa production cost)} & (8) \\
-100x_1 - 75x_2 + 375x_3 - 37.5x_4 \geq 0 & \text{(recliner cost)} & (9) \\
\qquad\qquad\qquad x_2 \qquad\qquad \geq 30 & \text{(minimum love seat production)} & (10) \\
x_1, x_2, x_3, x_4 \geq 0 & \text{(nonnegativity constraint)} &
\end{array}
$$

Excel Solution of the Style and Comfort Furniture Company Example

We need to answer two questions to begin the process of utilizing Excel to formulate a linear programming model for this problem:

1. What are the decisions to be made? This question translates into the question of what are the values of the decision variables or the production quantities of each of the products?
2. How do we measure the total performance of the company in regards to this decision? This question can be answered by the total profit per month for all four products.

Exhibit 4-1 Input Screen for the Style and Comfort Furniture Company Problem

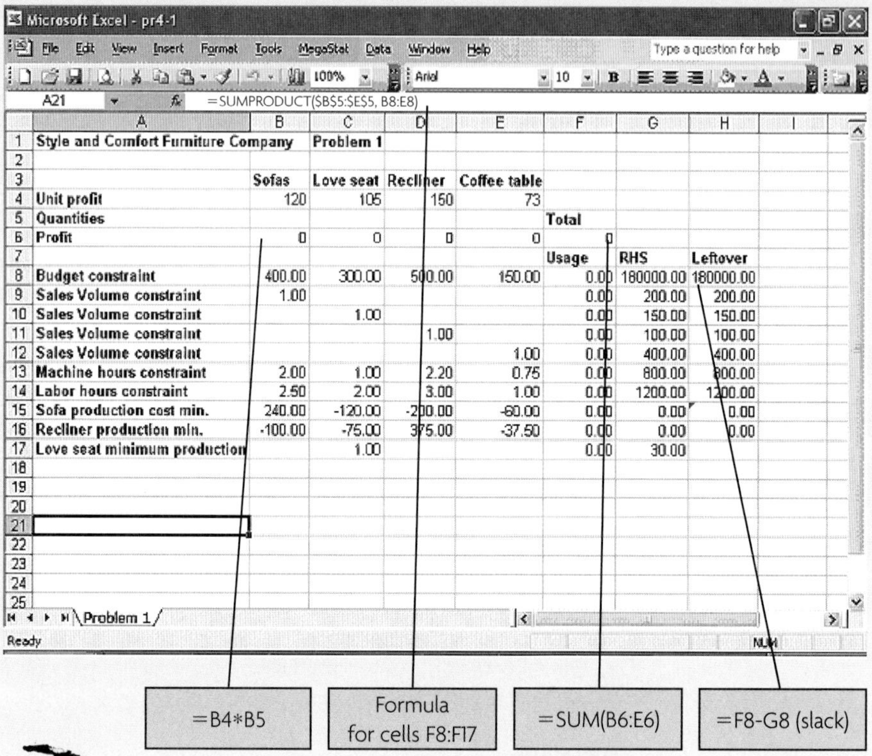

	A	B	C	D	E	F	G	H
1	Style and Comfort Furniture Company		Problem 1					
2								
3		Sofas	Love seat	Recliner	Coffee table			
4	Unit profit	120	105	150	73			
5	Quantities					Total		
6	Profit	0	0	0	0	0		
7						Usage	RHS	Leftover
8	Budget constraint	400.00	300.00	500.00	150.00	0.00	180000.00	180000.00
9	Sales Volume constraint	1.00				0.00	200.00	200.00
10	Sales Volume constraint		1.00			0.00	150.00	150.00
11	Sales Volume constraint			1.00		0.00	100.00	100.00
12	Sales Volume constraint				1.00	0.00	400.00	400.00
13	Machine hours constraint	2.00	1.00	2.20	0.75	0.00	800.00	800.00
14	Labor hours constraint	2.50	2.00	3.00	1.00	0.00	1200.00	1200.00
15	Sofa production cost min.	240.00	-120.00	-200.00	-60.00	0.00	0.00	0.00
16	Recliner production min.	-100.00	-75.00	375.00	-37.50	0.00	0.00	0.00
17	Love seat minimum production		1.00			0.00	30.00	

The Excel spreadsheet associated with this problem is shown in Exhibit 4-1. When the Excel spreadsheet is first made available, we should start by setting up the headings and labels. Column A is designated as the column that contains all of the labels for each of the constraints and the objective function coefficients. Columns B, C, D, and E are earmarked for each variable (sofas, love seats, recliners, and coffee tables, respectively). The variable labels are in cells B3, C3, D3, and E3. Immediately below the variable labels, we have three rows (4, 5, and 6) designated by unit profit, quantity, and profit, respectively. The unit profit values in row 4 are coming from the objective function, while the quantities, called the *output cells*, are the decision variable values that Solver will provide after solving the model. The profit values are obtained by multiplying the unit profit values in row 4 by the quantity values (output cells) in row 5. For example, cell B6 contains the equation =B4*B5, which is the multiplication of the unit profit (B4) by the quantity of the decision variable (B5). The formulas for cells C6, D6, and E6 are very similar to the formula for cell B6. For example, for cell C6, the formula is =C4*C5.

Rows 8 through 17 list the constraints of the model. When the model constraints are listed, the signs of the constraints are temporarily ignored. In addition, nonnegativity constraints are not explicitly stated. In listing the model constraints, we need an extra column that will show the value of the left-hand side of each constraint once Solver has determined the values of the decision variables. This column is designated as column F and is labeled as "Usage." In the usage column, we utilize the SUMPRODUCT function, which will sum up the product of each of the individual terms in two different ranges provided that the two ranges have the same number of rows or columns included. For example, for cell F8, we have the equation =SUMPRODUCT ($B$5:$E$5,B8:E8). In order to determine the value of cell F8, this function will multiply the value in cell B5 by the value in cell B8 and multiply the value in cell C5 by the value in cell C8, and so on. Once all four terms are multiplied, then all four product terms are summed to obtain the value of cell F8. The values in column G indicate the right-hand-side (RHS) values of each of the constraints. The values in column H represent the difference between the left-hand side and the right-hand side of the inequality or equality sign. For a less-than-or-equal-to resource constraint, column H values are a convenient way of showing the unused resources. Since F8 provides the total for the left-hand side of the equation and G8 is the value of the right-hand side of the constraint equation, =F8-G8 is the correct formula for cell H8.

The overall performance of the model measured by the total profit is stated in cell F6. This total profit value is calculated by summing the values in rows B6 through E6; therefore, the equation in cell F6 is =SUM(B6:E6). Since cell B6 represents the portion of the profit attributable to sofas, cell C6 represents the portion of the profit attributable to love seats, and so on, summing these profit values will yield the total profit for the linear programming model given in cell F6.

Recall earlier we had stated that we ignored the signs of the constraint coefficients in setting up the spreadsheet for this problem. Once we complete the data entry and the equations for various cells discussed above, we are now ready to execute the Solver. When we start executing the Solver, among other things, we need to specify the signs of the constraints. We click on **Tool | Solver,** and the Solver dialog box given in Exhibit 4-2 appears.

In executing Solver, we need to specify exactly where each component of the model is located on the spreadsheet. We have two options. (1) manually enter the appropriate information in the Solver dialog box or (2) click on the appropriate cells, which in turn will automatically identify the specific components of the model in the Solver dialog box. We would recommend the clicking option because it is faster and will save time, especially in solving large problems. The first information requested by the Solver dialog box is to complete the "Set Target Cell" box. The *target cell* contains the value of the objective function, which measures the overall performance of the model. In our spreadsheet, given in Exhibit 4-1, this

Exhibit 4-2   Solver Dialog Box

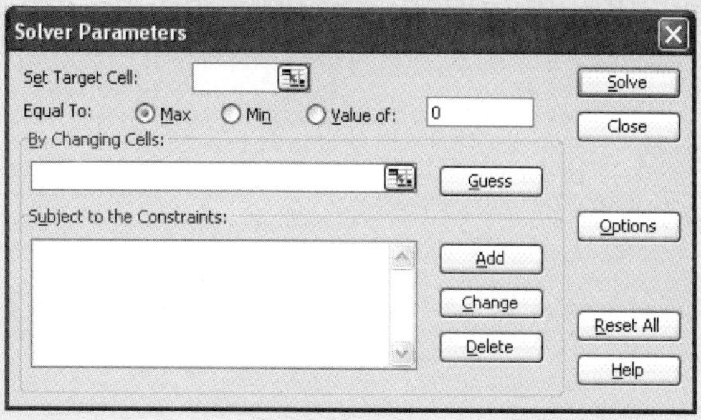

Exhibit 4-3   Add Constraint Dialog Box

Add Constraint

Cell Reference: Constraint:

$F$8:$F$14   <=   =$G$8:$G$14

OK   Cancel   Add   Help

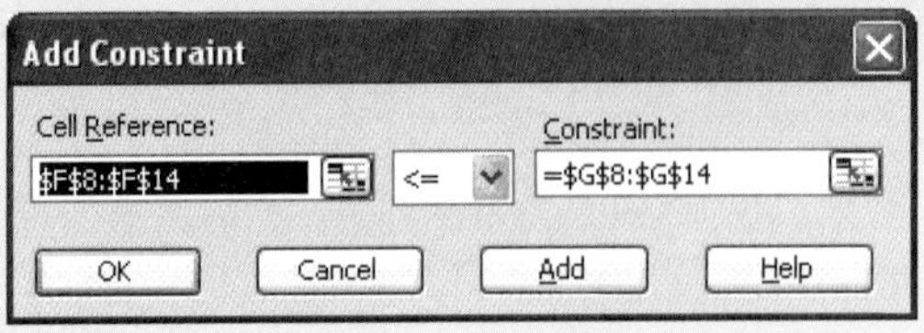

particular value is specified in cell F6. The objective is to either minimize or maximize the target cell. Therefore, in the second line of the dialog box, we have the option of choosing "Max," "Min," or "value of," of course, in this problem we choose "Max." The dialog box next requests that we specify the decision variables in the text box labeled "By Changing Cells." Since the output cells (decision variables) are located in cells B5, C5, D5, and E5, click on cell B5 and drag it through cell E5.

Since the cells associated with the decision variables, the objective function, and the total profit have been specified, next we specify the constraints by clicking on the "Add" button of the Solver dialog box. After clicking the "Add" button, the "Add Constraint" dialog box given in Exhibit 4-3 will appear.

In the "Add Constraint" dialog box, we click on the "Cell Reference" box and then click cell F8 and drag it through cell F14. For the sign box, we choose the less-than-or-equal-to sign ($\leq$). Similar to what we did with the "Cell Reference" box, we click in the "Constraint box" and then click cell G8 and drag it through G14. Since the first seven constraints are $\leq$ types, we have just specified all of the constraints in rows 8 through 14. We click on the "Add" button again to specify the 8th, 9th, and 10th constraints, which are all greater-than-or-equal-to types. The 8th, 9th, and 10th constraints are specified in rows 15 through 17. Therefore, after clicking on the "Add" button, we click in the "Cell Reference" box and then click on cell F15 and drag it through cell F17 to specify the left-hand side of the constraints. We choose the $\leq$ sign, click in the Constraint box, and then click cell G15 and drag it through G17 to indicate the right side of the three $\geq$ constraints. We have now completed the specification of the problem in the Solver dialog box (see Exhibit 4-4).

Exhibit 4-4   Completed Solver Dialog Box

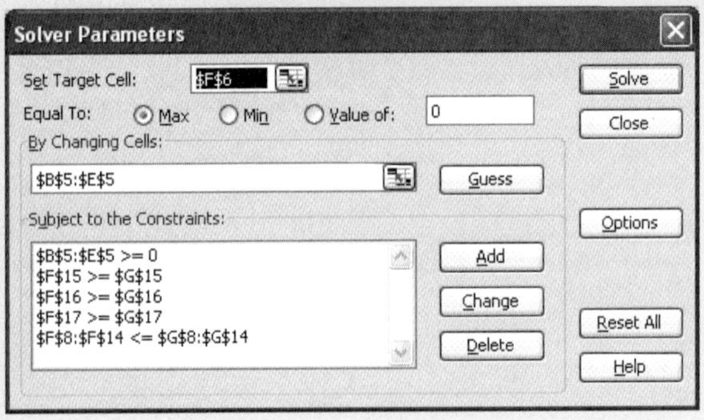

Solver Parameters

Set Target Cell: $F$6   Solve

Equal To: ⊙ Max   ○ Min   ○ Value of: 0   Close

By Changing Cells:

$B$5:$E$5   Guess

Subject to the Constraints: Options

$B$5:$E$5 >= 0   Add
$F$15 >= $G$15
$F$16 >= $G$16   Change
$F$17 >= $G$17
$F$8:$F$14 <= $G$8:$G$14   Reset All

Delete

Help

Exhibit 4-5   Solver Options Dialog Box

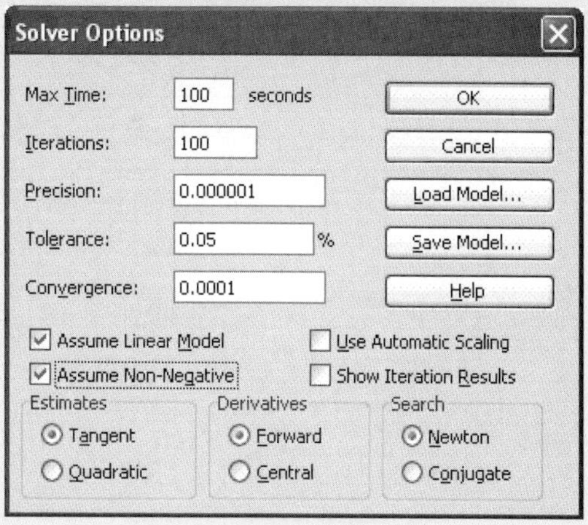

However, before asking Solver to solve this linear programming problem, we need to check to make sure that the right options have been specified. Therefore, clicking on the "Options" button will bring up the Options dialog box shown in Exhibit 4-5. This box allows the user to specify a number of options about how the problem will be solved. As shown in Exhibit 4-5, make sure that the options "Assume Linear Model" and "Assume Non-Negative" are checked. Checking these boxes will ensure that the problem solved is a linear programming problem, as opposed to nonlinear programming, with all decision variables being subject to nonnegativity constraints. $x_1, x_2, x_3, x_4 \geq 0$ (nonnegativity constraints) do not have to be specified as Excel will automatically take them into account if "Assume Non-Negative" is checked. With respect to the remaining options presented in the Solver Options dialog box, simply choose the default options. Clicking on the "OK" button will return you to the Solver Parameters dialog box. At this point we are ready to solve the problem. Clicking on the "Solve" button will solve the problem and bring up the Solver Results dialog box shown in Exhibit 4-6.

If the Solver Results dialog box, as shown in Exhibit 4-6, has the message "Solver found a solution. All constraints and optimality conditions are satisfied." This means that an optimal

Exhibit 4-6   Solver Results Dialog Box

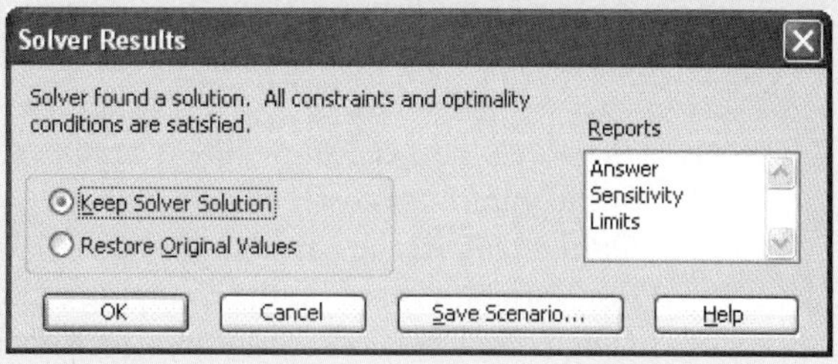

Exhibit 4-7	Output Screen for the Style and Comfort Furniture Company Problem

Microsoft Excel - pr4-1

F6   fx =SUM(B6:E6)

	A	B	C	D	E	F	G	H	I
1	Style and Comfort Furniture Company		Problem 1						
2									
3		Sofas	Love seat	Recliners	Coffee table				
4	Unit profit	120	105	150	73				
5	Quantities	168.041	30	84.02062	332.09622	Total			
6	Profit	20164.9	3150	12603.09	24243.0241	60161.07			
7						Usage	RHS	Leftover	
8	Budget constraint	400.00	300.00	500.00	150.00	168041.24	180000.00	11958.76	
9	Sales Volume constraint	1.00				168.04	200.00	31.96	
10	Sales Volume constraint		1.00			30.00	150.00	120.00	
11	Sales Volume constraint			1.00		84.02	100.00	15.98	
12	Sales Volume constraint				1.00	332.10	400.00	67.90	
13	Machine hours constraint	2.00	1.00	2.20	0.75	800.00	800.00	0.00	
14	Labor hours constraint	2.50	2.00	3.00	1.00	1064.26	1200.00	135.74	
15	Sofa production cost min.	240.00	-120.00	-200.00	-60.00	0.00	0.00	0.00	
16	Recliners production min.	-100.00	-75.00	375.00	-37.50	0.00	0.00	0.00	
17	Love seat minimum production		1.00			30.00	30.00		
18									

Problem 1

Ready   NUM

solution has been found. However, if the formulation does not lead to an optimal or feasible solution, then the Solver Results dialog box will state: "Solver could not find a feasible solution" or "The Set Cell values do not converge."

After solving the problem, Solver will change the values of the decision variables (quantities) from blanks to the optimal values, as shown in Exhibit 4-7. According to Exhibit 4-7, the Style and Comfort Manufacturing Company should produce the following: 168.04 sofas (cell B5), 30 love seats (cell C5), 84.02 recliners (cell D5), and 332.09 coffee tables (cell E5) for a total profit of $60,161.07 (cell F6). Column H, labeled Leftovers, shows the difference between the left and right-hand side of each constraint. For example, in cell H8 there is a value of 11,959. Since row 8 is the row associated with the budget constraint, the interpretation of this value would be that $11,959 of the total budget has not been spent. At this point, it may be a good idea to change some of the profit or constraint coefficients and run Solver again to see how sensitive the solution is to the changes in the parameters.

In summarizing Solver usage, there are three types of cells:

1. *Target cell.* This cell shows the overall performance measure (i.e., the maximum profit or the minimum cost).
2. *Output cells.* As the name suggests, these cells show the output or quantity of the decision variables based on the changing cells.
3. *Data cells.* These cells simply show the data of the problem (constraint coefficients, objective function coefficients, and right-hand-side constraints).

If the furniture company routinely makes such production decisions on a daily or weekly basis, a computer code should be written that uses the LP model with an easy-to-use user interface to allow the user to change the model parameters. The code should be able to call Excel Solver to determine the optimal solution. This type of decision support system (DSS) helps the managers who are not experts in management science to easily use such LP models over and over again.

Diet Problems

Diet problems usually involve the mixing of raw materials or other ingredients to obtain an end product that has certain characteristics. For instance, food processors and dieticians generally are concerned with meeting dietary needs in food products. There may be specific requirements pertaining to nutrients, calories, sodium content, and so on. The general question to be answered by linear programming is: What mix of inputs (e.g., different food types) will achieve the desired results for the least cost? The following example illustrates this type of problem.

Example 4-2

A cereal manufacturer is investigating the possibility of introducing a new cereal. It would be composed of wheat, rice, and corn flakes. The cost per ounce and dietary requirements are shown in Table 4-2.

Table 4-2   Cost per Ounce and Dietary Requirements for Diet Problem

	Wheat	Rice	Corn	Requirements per 12-Ounce Box
Protein (grams per ounce)	4	2	2	At least 27 grams
Carbohydrates (grams per ounce)	20	25	21	At least 240 grams
Calories per ounce	90	110	100	No more than 1.260 calories
Cost per ounce	$.03	.05	.02	

Formulate an LP model for this problem that will determine the optimal quantities of wheat, rice, and corn per box that will achieve the requirements at minimum most.

Solution
Variable definitions

x_1 = ounces of wheat per box
x_2 = ounces of rice per box
x_3 = ounces of corn per box

The decision variables involve the different types of food. Since the data are given in grams per ounce, the decision variables are ounces of food type per box.

The objective function for this problem is a minimization type, since we are attempting to minimize cost.

In order to formulate the constraints for this problem, we evaluate the table given above and decide that there should be three constraints: one for protein, one for carbohydrates, and one for calories. The signs of all these three constraints should be greater than or equal to because "requirements" indicate the minimum amount (lower bound) necessary for each constraint. For example, for the protein constraint, each ounce of wheat has 4 grams of protein, each ounce of rice has 2 grams of protein, and each ounce of corn has 2 grams of protein. The total value for protein from all three food types must be at least 27 grams or exceed it. Therefore, we can set this constraint as $4x_1 + 2x_2 + 2x_3 \geq 27$. Utilizing the same logic for the remaining two constraints, the final formulation of this problem is as follows:

minimize $\quad Z = .03x_1 + .05x_2 + .02x_3$

subject to

Protein	$4x_1 + 2x_2 + 2x_3 \geq$	27 grams
Carbohydrates	$20x_1 + 25x_2 + 21x_3 \geq$	240 grams
Calories	$90x_1 + 110x_2 + 100x_3 \leq$	1,260 calories
Box size	$x_1 + x_2 + x_3 =$	12 ounces

$$x_1, x_2, \text{ and } x_3 \geq 0$$

Note the box size constraint, which is needed to assure that the quantities of inputs per box equal the box size.

Solution to diet problem

$x_1 = 1.5 \quad$ (ounces of wheat per box)
$x_3 = 10.5 \quad$ (ounces of corn per box)
$z = \$0.26 \quad$ (minimum cost per box)

Blending Problems

Blending problems are very similar to diet problems. In fact, diet and blending problems could be lumped into the same category. Strictly speaking, though, blending problems have an additional requirement: to achieve a mix that has a specific consistency, as illustrated in the next example.

Example 4-3

Formulate the appropriate model for the following blending problem: The sugar content of three juices—orange, banana, and pineapple—is 10, 15, and 20 percent, respectively. How many quarts of each must be mixed together to achieve one gallon (four quarts) that has a sugar content of at least 17 percent to minimize cost? The cost per quart is 20 cents for orange juice, 30 cents for banana juice, and 40 cents for pineapple juice.

Solution
Variable definitions

O = quantity of orange juice in quarts
B = quantity of banana juice in quarts
P = quantity of pineapple juice in quarts

In setting up the constraints for this problem, first we need to consider the sugar content of the three juices. Since the sugar content of the juice mix must exceed 17 percent, mixing orange juice with banana juice will not be sufficient because the sugar content of orange juice and banana juice is 10 percent and 15 percent, respectively. Even though it is the most costly, we need to mix pineapple juice (which has a sugar content of 20 percent) to achieve a minimum of 17 percent sugar content. The left-hand side of the sugar content constraint is stated as what the sugar content of each juice is: $.10O + .15B + .20P$. The right-hand side of the constraint provides the minimum sugar content requirement, which is 17 per-cent. Therefore, the right-hand side of the constraint is $.17(O + B + P)$. The sign of this constraint must be $\geq$ to ensure that we meet the minimum sugar content requirement. This constraint can be written as

$$.10O + .15B + .20P \geq .17\,(O + B + P)$$

Since the profit is stated on a per-quart basis and variables are defined as "quan-tity of *type of* juice in quarts," the second constraint should indicate the number of quarts mixed. Since the juice has to be exactly 4 quarts, then the constraint is written as $O + B + P = 4$. The final formulation of this problem is summarized below:

minimize $Z = .20O + .30B + .40P$

subject to

Sugar content $.10O + .15B + .20P \geq .17(O + B + P)$
Total amount $O + \quad B + \quad P = 4$ quarts

The sugar constraint must be rewritten so that the decision variables are on the left-hand side and the constant is on the right-hand side. Thus, expanding the right-hand-side results in

$$.10O + .15B + .20P \geq .17O + .17B + .17P$$

Then, subtracting the right-hand-side amounts from both sides gives us

$$-.07O - .2B + .03P \geq 0$$

Solution to blending problem

O = 1.2 quarts   (quantity of orange juice)
P = 2.8 quarts   (quantity of pineapple juice)
Z = \$1.36   (minimum total cost of the blended juice per gallon)

Linear programming formulation of blending problems is also commonly used in blending oil or gasoline. This type of application also can be illustrated with the following example.

Example 4-4

TUNACO Oil Company produces three grades of gasoline (regular, premium, and super) by blending three types of crude oil. All three types of crude oil contain two important ingredients (X and Y) required to produce the three gasoline grades. The percentage of these ingredients differs in each type of crude oil. These percentages are given in the following table.

	Crude Oil Type		
	1	2	3
Ingredient X	40	20	55
Ingredient Y	35	30	60

Cost of each type of crude oil is $0.80, $0.60, and $0.40 per gallon for crude oil types 1, 2, and 3, respectively.

Each gallon of regular gasoline must contain at least 35 percent of ingredient X. Each gallon of premium gasoline can contain at most 45 percent of ingredient Y. Each gallon of super gasoline can contain at most 40 percent of ingredient Y.

Daily demand for regular, premium, and super grades of gasoline is 400,000, 150,000, and 150,000 gallons, respectively.

Daily production quantities are 350,000 gallons for crude oil 1; 250,000 gallons for crude oil 2; and 200,000 for crude oil 3. How many gallons of each type of crude oil should be used in the three grades of gasoline to satisfy demand at minimum cost?

Solution

First, we must define the variables by using a double script notation.

Let X_{ij} = amount of crude oil i used in gasoline type j

where

$i = 1, 2, 3$ 1 = crude oil type 1, 2 = crude oil type 2, 3 = crude oil type 3.
$j = 1, 2, 3$ 1 = regular, 2 = premium, 3 = super

For example, x_{21} = amount of crude oil 2 used in regular gasoline.

The objective function, which involves the minimization of total cost, can be stated as follows:

$$\text{minimize } Z = 8x_{11} + .8x_{12} + .8x_{13} + .6x_{21} + .6x_{22} + .6x_{23} + .4x_{31} + .4x_{32} + .4x_{33}$$

We can begin to formulate the constraints of this problem by determining the production quantities of each type of crude oil.

$x_{11} + x_{12} + x_{13} = 350{,}000$ gallons   (production of crude oil 1)
$x_{21} + x_{22} + x_{23} = 250{,}000$ gallons   (production of crude oil 2)
$x_{31} + x_{32} + x_{33} = 200{,}000$ gallons   (production of crude oil 3)

Note that in formulating each of the above production constraints, the subscript i remains constant, while the subscript j changes. For example, x_{11}, x_{12}, x_{13} indicates the production of crude oil 1 used in all three types of gasoline. The sign of these production constraints can be set up as $\leq$ or $=$.

The demand quantities for each gasoline type is given by the following constraints:

$x_{11} + x_{21} + x_{31} \geq 400{,}000$ gallons   (demand for regular gasoline)
$x_{12} + x_{22} + x_{32} \geq 150{,}000$ gallons   (demand for premium gasoline)
$x_{13} + x_{23} + x_{33} \geq 150{,}000$ gallons   (demand for super gasoline)

Note that in formulating each of the above demand constraints, the opposite of the production constraints occurs: the subscript j remains constant, while the subscript i varies. For example, x_{12}, x_{22}, x_{32} indicates the demand for premium gasoline using all three types of crude oil. The sign of these demand constraints can be specified as $\geq$ or $=$. If these constraints were inadvertently specified as $\leq$, the solution quantities of all decision variables would be forced to equal zero since the objective of the problem is to minimize cost.

Now, we must formulate the percentage mix constraints. The constraint that each gallon of regular gasoline must contain at least 35 percent of ingredient X can be formulated as follows:

$$0.4x_{11} + 0.2x_{21} + .55x_{31} \geq .35(x_{11} + x_{21} + x_{31}).$$

The left-hand side of the inequality shows the total amount of ingredient X provided by all three types of crude oil in regular gasoline. The right-hand side of the inequality, indicates that the regular gasoline must contain at least (due to the greater-than-or-equal-to sign) 35 percent ingredient X. Rearranging this constraint to move all of the variable values to the left of the inequality so that the right-hand side of the constraint is a numerical value results in the following inequality.

$$.05x_{11} - .15x_{21} + .20x_{31} \geq 0$$

Likewise, the constraint that each gallon of premium gasoline must contain at most 45 percent of ingredient Y can be written as

$$.35x_{12} + .30x_{22} + .60x_{32} \leq .45(x_{12} + x_{22} + x_{32})$$

The left-hand side of the inequality shows the total amount of ingredient Y in premium gasoline. The right-hand side of the inequality, due to the less-than-or-equal-to sign indicates that premium gasoline must contain at most 45 percent of ingredient Y. Rearranging this constraint to move all of the variable values to the left-hand side of the inequality results in the following:

$$-.10x_{12} - .15x_{22} + .15x_{32} \leq 0$$

Similarly, the constraint that each gallon of super gasoline can contain at most 40 percent of ingredient Y can be written as follows:

$$.35x_{13} + .30x_{23} + .60x_{33} \leq .40(x_{13} + x_{23} + x_{33})$$

Rearranging this constraint results in the following:

$$-.05x_{13} - .10x_{23} + .20x_{33} \leq 0$$

The linear programming formulation of the TUNACO Oil Company problem can be summarized as follows:

x_{ij} = amount of crude oil i used in gasoline type j, where i = crude oil type 1, 2, 3, where $j = 1$ = regular gasoline, $j = 2$ = premium gasoline, $j = 3$ = super gasoline

minimize $Z = .8x_{11} + .8x_{12} + .8x_{13} + .6x_{21} + .6x_{22} + .6x_{23} + .4x_{31} + .4x_{32} + .4x_{33}$

subject to

$$x_{11} + x_{12} + x_{13} = 350{,}000 \text{ gallons} \qquad \text{(production of crude oil 1)}$$
$$x_{21} + x_{22} + x_{23} = 250{,}000 \text{ gallons} \qquad \text{(production of crude oil 2)}$$
$$x_{31} + x_{32} + x_{33} = 200{,}000 \text{ gallons} \qquad \text{(production of crude oil 3)}$$
$$x_{11} + x_{21} + x_{31} \geq 400{,}000 \text{ gallons} \qquad \text{(demand for regular gasoline)}$$
$$x_{12} + x_{22} + x_{32} \geq 150{,}000 \text{ gallons} \qquad \text{(demand for premium gasoline)}$$
$$x_{13} + x_{23} + x_{33} \geq 150{,}000 \text{ gallons} \qquad \text{(demand for super gasoline)}$$
$$\left. \begin{array}{l} -.05x_{11} - .15x_{21} + .20x_{31} \geq 0 \\ -.10x_{12} - .15x_{22} + .15x_{32} \leq 0 \\ -.05x_{13} - .10x_{23} + .20x_{33} \leq 0 \end{array} \right\} \quad \text{(ingredient constraints)}$$

$$x_{ij} \geq 0 \text{ for all } i, j \text{ combinations}$$

Solution to TUNACO Oil Company problem

$$x_{11} = 200{,}000 \qquad \text{(amount of crude oil 1 used in regular gasoline)}$$
$$x_{13} = 150{,}000 \qquad \text{(amount of crude oil 1 used in super gasoline)}$$
$$x_{21} = 100{,}000 \qquad \text{(amount of crude oil 2 used in regular gasoline)}$$
$$x_{22} = 150{,}000 \qquad \text{(amount of crude oil 2 used in premium gasoline)}$$
$$x_{31} = 200{,}000 \qquad \text{(amount of crude oil 3 used in regular gasoline)}$$
$$Z = \$510{,}000.00 \qquad \text{(minimum total cost)}$$

Marketing Applications

There are many applications of linear programming in marketing. These include

1. Media selection (how to allocate an advertising budget among different media of advertising).
2. Determination of the optimal assignment of salespeople that work for the company among the sales territories. In this scenario, there are various territories that need to be covered by a sales force where the sales force have different capabilities.
3. Marketing research study in which the objective is to determine the best number of interviews, mailings, or phone calls, given a number of client-specified constraints and the cost considerations.

Media Selection

Media selection problems using linear programming can assist marketing managers in deciding how to allocate a fixed advertising budget among the different media such as television, newspapers, radio, and direct mail. In media selection problems, the objective could be the maximization of profit based on different media usages. However, it is difficult, or somewhat unrealistic, to model a situation to maximize profit based on different media usages because it is very difficult to put dollars and cents to the usage of a certain advertising medium. Therefore, instead of maximizing profit, in media selection problems, the objective is generally to maximize audience exposure. There are generally restrictions on how much each medium can be used. These restrictions are based on overall advertising budget and the cost to utilize a certain medium, company policy, contractual requirements, and others. The following example demonstrates the use of linear programming in conjunction with the media selection problem.

Example 4-5

The Long Last Appliance Sales Company is in the business of selling appliances such as microwave ovens, traditional ovens, refrigerators, dishwashers, washers, dryers, and the like. The company has stores in the greater Chicagoland area and has a monthly advertising budget of $90,000. Among its options are radio advertising, advertising in the cable TV channels, newspaper advertising, and direct-mail advertising. A 30-second advertising spot on the local cable channel costs $1,800, a 30-second radio ad costs $350, a half-page ad in the local newspaper costs $700, and a single mailing of direct-mail insertion for the entire region costs $1,200 per mailing.

The number of potential buying customers reached per advertising medium usage is as follows:

Radio	7,000
TV	50,000
Newspaper	18,000
Direct mail	34,000

Due to company restrictions and availability of media, the maximum number of usages of each medium is limited to the following:

Radio	35
TV	25
Newspaper	30
Direct mail	18

The management of the company has met and decided that in order to ensure a balanced utilization of different types of media and to portray a positive image of the company, at least 10 percent of the advertisements must be on TV. No more than 40 percent of the advertisements can be on radio. The cost of advertising allocated to TV and direct mail cannot exceed 60 percent of the total advertising budget.

What is the optimal allocation of the budget among the four media? What is the total maximum audience contact?

Formulation
Variable definitions

x_1 = Number of radio ads
x_2 = Number of television ads
x_3 = Number of newspaper ads
x_4 = Number of direct-mail ads

The objective function

Maximize $Z = 7{,}000x_1 + 50{,}000x_2 + 18{,}000x_3 + 34{,}000x_4$

The constraints

$$350x_1 + 1{,}800x_2 + 700x_3 + 1{,}200x_4 \leq 90{,}000 \qquad \text{(budget constraint)} \qquad (1)$$

$$
\left.
\begin{aligned}
x_1 &\leq 35 \\
x_2 &\leq 25 \\
x_3 &\leq 30 \\
x_4 &\leq 18
\end{aligned}
\right\} \quad \text{(maximum exposure constraints)}
\qquad
\begin{aligned}
&(2) \\
&(3) \\
&(4) \\
&(5)
\end{aligned}
$$

$$x_2 \geq .10(x_1 + x_2 + x_3 + x_4) \qquad \text{(10\% minimum TV ads)}$$
$$x_1 \leq .40(x_1 + x_2 + x_3 + x_4) \qquad \text{(40\% maximum radio ads)}$$

Since the right-hand side of the constraints must be a numeric value, the two constraints given above can be rewritten as follows so that the problem can be solved using Excel:

$$-.10x_1 + .9x_2 - .1x_3 - .1x_4 \geq 0 \qquad (6)$$
$$-.6x_1 - .4x_2 - .4x_3 - .4x_4 \leq 0 \qquad (7)$$

The cost of television and direct-mail ads cannot exceed 60 percent of the total advertising budget. This can be written as

$$1{,}800x_2 + 1{,}200x_4 \leq .6(90{,}000) \qquad (8)$$
$$x_1, x_2, x_3, x_4 \geq 0 \qquad \text{(nonnegativity constraint)}$$

Solution
Solving this problem with Excel results in the following:

$$
\begin{aligned}
x_1 &= 25.71 &&\text{(number of radio advertisements)} \\
x_2 &= 21.33 &&\text{(number of TV advertisements)} \\
x_3 &= 30 &&\text{(number of newspaper advertisements)} \\
x_4 &= 18 &&\text{(number of direct-mail advertisements)}
\end{aligned}
$$

$$Z = 2{,}398{,}667 \qquad \text{(total number of potential customers reached)}$$

The results for the Long Last Appliance Sales Company problem is given in Exhibit 4-8. Note that the number of radio and TV advertisements are not integers. We have a couple of options when the number of advertisements results in a nonintger value. First, we could simply round the values down and use 25 for x_1 and 21 for x_2. However, when we round down the noninteger values to integer values, we run the risk that the solution may turn out to be infeasible. The consequences and the magnitude of infeasibility increase as the noninteger value of the decision variable decreases. Second, we could negotiate with the radio station an ad that is only 71 percent as long as the regular ad at a proportional cost ($x_1 = 25.71$). Likewise with the local television station, we could negotiate an ad that is only 33 percent of the regular 30-second ad ($x_2 = 21.33$). Therefore, instead of a 30-second TV advertisement, an advertisement that is only one-third as, or 10 seconds, long would be utilized at a proportional cost. Of course another option is to impose an integer restriction on the variables, which we will cover in the integer programming chapter of the book (Chapter 7).

The model results can be summarized by the reports generated from Excel. When we are running Solver to solve a linear programming problem, and click on

Exhibit 4-8 Output Screen for the Long Last Appliance Sales Company

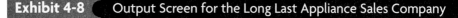

	Radio	TV	Newspaper	Direct-Mail			
1 Long Last Appliance Sales Company							
2							
3	Radio	TV	Newspaper	Direct-Mail			
4 # of customers reached per advertisement	7000.00	50000.00	18000.0	34000.0			
5 # od advertisments	25.71	21.33	30.0	18.0	Total		
6 Total number of customers reached	180000.0	1066666.67	540000.0	612000.0	2398666.67		
7					Usage	Limits	Leftover
8 Budget constraint	350.00	1800.00	700.0	1200.0	90000.00	90000	0
9 Maximum exposure constraint	1.00				25.71	35	9
10 Maximum exposure constraint		1.00			21.33	25	4
11 Maximum exposure constraint			1.0		30.00	30	0
12 Maximum exposure constraint				1.0	18.00	18	0
13 10% min. TV advertisement constraint	-0.10	0.90	-0.1	-0.1	11.83	0	-12
14 40% max. radio advertisement constraint	0.60	-0.40	-0.4	-0.4	-12.30	0	12
15 50% restriction (combined cost of TV and DM)		1800.00		1200.0	60000.00	60000	0

Cell reference: H8 =G8-F8

Callout boxes: =B4*B5   =SUM(B6:E6)   =G8-F8

=SUMPRODUCT($B$5:$E$5,B8:E8)

"Solve," an intermediate screen will appear. The screen is entitled Solver Results and it provides the user with the option of selecting several reports. The most important report that provides the basic solution and the optimal values of the decision variables is the Answer Report, shown in Exhibit 4-9.

The Answer Report starts with the value of the target cell, which provides the value of the maximum profit or minimum cost found by the linear programming procedure. In the second section of the Answer Report, labeled "Adjustable Cells," the optimal values of the decision variables are reported. In the third section of the Answer Report, entitled "Constraints," a summary information regarding the constraints of the problem is given. For example, row 15 of the Answer Report deals with the budget constraint. It shows that the budget constraint is a binding constraint, which means that all of the $90,000 in the advertising budget is spent. However, row 12 of the Answer Report is associated with the 10 percent minimum TV advertisement constraint. The total number of advertisements using all media available to the firm is 95.05; 10 percent of this value is 9.505. In other words, the number of TV advertisements must be at least 9.505. Since the optimal number of TV advertisements is 21.3333, subtracting 9.505 from 21.3333 provides the cell value of 11.82857. Since this value is not

Exhibit 4-9   Excel Answer Report for the Long Last Appliance Sales Company

	Microsoft Excel - pr4-5						
	File Edit View Insert Format Tools MegaStat Data Window Help						Type a question for help

	A	B	C	D	E	F	G
1	Target Cell (Max)						
2	Cell	Name	Original Value	Final Value			
3	$F$6	Total number of customers reached Total	2398666.667	2398666.667			
4	Adjustable Cells						
5	Cell	Name	Original Value	Final Value			
6	$B$5	# of advertisements Radio	25.71428571	25.71428571			
7	$C$5	# of advertisements TV	21.33333333	21.33333333			
8	$D$5	# of advertisements Newspaper	30	30			
9	$E$5	# of advertisements Direct-Mail	18	18			
10	Constraints						
11	Cell	Name	Cell Value	Formula	Status	Slack	
12	$F$13	10% min. TV advertisement constraint Usage	11.82857143	$F$13>=$G$13	Not Binding	11.82857143	
13	$F$14	40% max. radio advertisement constraint Usage	-12.3047619	$F$14<=$G$14	Not Binding	12.3047619	
14	$F$15	50% restriction (combined cost of TV and direct-mail) Usage	60000	$F$15<=$G$15	Binding	0	
15	$F$6	Budget constraint Usage	90000	$F$6<=$G$6	Binding	0	
16	$F$9	Maximum exposure constraint Usage	25.71428571	$F$9<=$G$9	Not Binding	9.285714286	
17	$F$10	Maximum exposure constraint Usage	21.33333333	$F$10<=$G$10	Not Binding	3.666666667	
18	$F$11	Maximum exposure constraint Usage	30	$F$11<=$G$11	Binding	0	
19	$F$12	Maximum exposure constraint Usage	18	$F$12<=$G$12	Binding	0	
20	$B$5	# of advertisements Radio	25.71428571	$B$5>=0	Not Binding	25.71428571	
21	$C$5	# of advertisements TV	21.33333333	$C$5>=0	Not Binding	21.33333333	
22	$D$5	# of advertisements Newspaper	30	$D$5>=0	Not Binding	30	
23	$E$5	# of advertisements Direct-Mail	18	$E$5>=0	Not Binding	18	

Sensitivity Report 1 \ Answer Report 2 / Problem 5 /

exactly equal to 9.505, the constraint is not binding and we exceed the minimum number of TV advertisements by the cell value of 11.82857.

Marketing Research

Companies conduct **marketing research** to determine company strategy, product planning, and forecasting product demand by learning about consumer characteristics, spending/buying tendencies, and consumer preferences toward products. Typically, marketing research firms meet with the client company and determine its needs in consumer buying tendencies and its preferences toward products. Based on the client company's needs, the marketing research firm goes through the following stages of marketing research study development:

1. Design study.
2. Conduct marketing survey.
3. Analyze data and obtain results.
4. Make recommendations based on the results.

In designing the study, the marketing research firm, in consultation with the client company, may establish a target number of respondents to be reached by the market survey being designed. After establishing the target number of respondents, the goal of the marketing research company is to conduct a survey to reach the target number of respondents at minimum cost. Let us look at an example.

Example 4-6

Market Facts Inc. is a marketing research firm that works with client companies to determine consumer reaction toward various products and services. A client company requested that Market Facts investigate the consumer reaction to a recently developed electronic device. Market Facts and the client company agreed that a combination of telephone interviews and direct-mail questionnaires would be used to obtain the information from different type of households.

The households are divided into six categories:

1. Households containing a single person under 40 years old and without children under 18 years of age.
2. Households containing married people under 40 years old and without children under 18 years of age.
3. Households containing single parents with children under 18 years of age.
4. Households containing married families with children under 18 years of age.
5. Households containing single people over 40 years old without children under 18 years of age.
6. Households containing married people over 40 years old without children under 18 years of age.

The client company has requested that the total people contacted via direct mail and phone interviews be 50,000. There can be no more than 2,000 phone interviews and no more than 48,000 mail-in questionnaires. The cost of a direct-mail questionnaire, including the cost of a self-stamped, mail-back envelope, is $1.00 for a household without children under 18 years of age and $1.50 for households with children. The cost of the phone interview also differs depending on whether the household contains children less than 18 years of age and if it contains a married couple. The interview costs more for the households with children because the interviewer has to ask more questions. The cost of a phone interview of a household with a married couple with children is $15. The cost of a phone interview of a household containing single adults under 40 years old without children is $10; for married adults under 40 years old without children, it is $11. The cost of a phone interview of a household with a single person over 40 years old without children is $7. The cost of a phone interview of a household with a married couple over 40 years old without children is $9. The cost of a phone interview of a household with a single parent with children is $12. Discussions between Market Facts and the client company has resulted in the following restrictions:

1. At least 60 percent of the phone interviews must be conducted to households with children.
2. At least 50 percent of the direct-mail questionnaires must be mailed to households with children.
3. No more than 30 percent of the phone interviews and mail-in questionnaires can be conducted at households with single people.
4. At least 25 percent of the phone interviews and mail-in questionnaires must be conducted to households that contain married couples.

How many phone interviews will be conducted with different types of households, and how many direct-mail questionnaires will be mailed to different types of households to minimize the total cost of this market survey?

In formulating this problem, we must define the decision variables using the following double subscripted notation:

x_{ij} = number of phone interviews or questionnaires used to reach household type j

where

$i = 1, 2$ 1 = phone interview, 2 = mail-in questionnaire
$j = 1, 2, 3, 4, 5, 6$ (j represents the six household categories defined earlier)

Based on the above definitions of the decision variables, the objective function can be written as

minimize $Z = 10x_{11} + 11x_{12} + 12x_{13} + 15x_{14} + 7x_{15} + 9x_{16} + 1x_{21} + 1x_{22} + 1.5x_{23} + 1.5x_{24} + 1x_{25} + 1x_{26}$

We can begin to write the constraints for this problem by considering the target values of advertising. Since the target number of phone interviews is 2,000 and the target number of mail-in questionnaires is 48,000, the two constraints can be written as follows:

$x_{11} + x_{12} + x_{13} + x_{14} + x_{15} + x_{16} = 2,000$ (target number of phone interviews)
$x_{21} + x_{22} + x_{23} + x_{24} + x_{25} + x_{26} = 48,000$ (target number of mail-in questionnaires)

Note that in each of the constraints, the value of subscript i remains constant, while the value of j varies from 1 to 6, representing all six types of households defined earlier. We do not need a constraint that includes the combined phone interview and direct-mail target in one constraint since we accounted for them in separate constraints. In addition, if we erroneously use a less-than-or-equal-to sign instead of an equal to sign, the values of all decision variables will assume zero at the optimal solution.

At least 60 percent of the phone interviews must be conducted to households with children.

$x_{13} + x_{14} \geq .60(x_{11} + x_{12} + x_{13} + x_{14} + x_{15} + x_{16})$

The left-hand side of the inequality represents the variables of those phone interviews conducted at households with children, while the right-hand side of the constraint shows the 60 percent of all phone interviews. The above constraint can be put, into the form for computer implementation by moving all the variables to the left-hand side of the constraint, leaving only the numerical value of zero on the right-hand side:

$-.60x_{11} - .60x_{12} + .40x_{13} + .40x_{14} - .60x_{15} - .60x_{16} \geq 0$

At least 50 percent of the direct-mail questionnaires must be mailed to households with children, a restriction that can be written as follow:

$x_{23} + x_{24} \geq .50(x_{21} + x_{22} + x_{23} + x_{24} + x_{25} + x_{26})$

The left-hand side of the inequality includes all of the variables of those mail-in questionnaires sent to households with children, while the right-hand side of the constraint shows the 50 percent of all mail-in questionnaires. This constraint also can be put into computer-implementation-ready form by moving all of the decision variables from the right-hand side of the constraint to the left-hand side. This results in the following inequality:

$$-.50x_{21} - .50x_{22} + .50x_{23} + .50x_{24} - .50x_{25} - .50x_{26} \geq 0$$

No more than 30 percent of the phone interviews and mail-in questionnaires can be conducted to households with single people. There are two separate constraints to be written: one for phone interviews and one for mail-in questionnaires. First we will write the phone interview constraint, then it will be easy to duplicate that for the mail-in questionnaires.

$$x_{11} + x_{13} + x_{15} \leq .30(x_{11} + x_{12} + x_{13} + x_{14} + x_{15} + x_{16}) \qquad \text{(30\% single people phone interview restriction).}$$

The left-hand side of the inequality indicates the variables of all of the phone interviews conducted with single people, while the right-hand side of the inequality shows 30 percent of all phone interviews. Rewriting this equation results in the following inequality:

$$.70x_{11} - .30x_{12} + .70x_{13} - .30x_{14} + .70x_{15} - .30x_{16} \leq 0$$

Similar logic can be applied to mail-in questionnaires.

$$x_{21} + x_{23} + x_{25} \leq .30(x_{21} + x_{22} + x_{23} + x_{24} + x_{25} + x_{26}) \qquad \text{(30\% single people mail-in questionnaire restriction).}$$

Rewriting this equation results in the following inequality:

$$.70x_{21} - .30x_{22} + .70x_{23} - .30x_{24} + .70x_{25} - .30x_{26} \leq 0$$

At least 25 percent of the phone interviews and mail-in questionnaires must be conducted to households that contain married couples. These are two separate constraints to be written: one for phone interviews and one for mail-in questionnaires. First we will write the phone interview constraint, then it will be easy to duplicate that for the mail-in questionnaires.

$$x_{12} + x_{14} + x_{16} \geq .25(x_{11} + x_{12} + x_{13} + x_{14} + x_{15} + x_{16})$$

Rewriting this equation results in the following inequality:

$$-.25x_{11} + .75x_{12} - .25x_{13} + .75x_{14} - .25x_{15} + .75x_{16} \geq 0$$

Applying the same logic to mail-in questionnaire variables results in the following inequality:

$$x_{22} + x_{24} + x_{26} \geq .25(x_{21} + x_{22} + x_{23} + x_{24} + x_{25} + x_{26})$$

Rewriting this equation results in the following inequality:

$$-.25x_{21} + .75x_{22} - .25x_{23} + .75x_{24} - .25x_{25} + .75x_{26} \geq 0$$

We can summarize the linear programming formulation of this problem as follows:

x_{ij} = number of phone interviews or questionnaires used to reach household type j

where

$i = 1, 2 \qquad 1 = $ phone interview, $2 = $ mail-in questionnaire
$j = 1, 2, 3, 4, 5, 6 \qquad (j$ represents the six household categories defined earlier)

minimize $Z = 10x_{11} + 11x_{12} + 12x_{13} + 15x_{14} + 7x_{15} + 9x_{16} + 1x_{21} + 1x_{22} + 1.5x_{23} + 1.5x_{24} + 1x_{25} + 1x_{26}$

Subject to:

$x_{11} + x_{12} + x_{13} + x_{14} + x_{15} + x_{16} = 2{,}000$ (target number of phone interviews)

$x_{21} + x_{22} + x_{23} + x_{24} + x_{25} + x_{26} = 48{,}000$ (target number of mail-in questionnaires)

$-.60x_{11} - .60x_{12} + .40x_{13} + .40x_{14} - .60x_{15} - .60x_{16} \geq 0$

$-.50x_{21} - .50x_{22} + .50x_{23} + .50x_{24} - .50x_{25} - .50x_{26} \geq 0$

$.70x_{11} - .30x_{12} + .70x_{13} - .30x_{14} + .70x_{15} - .30x_{16} \leq 0$

$.70x_{21} - .30x_{22} + .70x_{23} - .30x_{24} + .70x_{25} - .30x_{26} \leq 0$

$-.25x_{11} + .75x_{12} - .25x_{13} + .75x_{14} - .25x_{15} + .75x_{16} \geq 0$

$-.25x_{21} + .75x_{22} - .25x_{23} + .75x_{24} - .25x_{25} + .75x_{26} \geq 0$

$x_{ij} \geq 0$ for all i, j combinations

Solution

$x_{13} = 600$ (number of phone interviews completed with households containing single parents with children under 18 years of age)

$x_{14} = 600$ (number of phone interviews completed with households containing married families with children under 18 years of age)

$x_{16} = 800$ (number of phone interviews completed with households containing married people over 40 years old without children under 18 years of age)

$x_{22} = 24{,}000$ (number of mail-in questionnaires completed with households containing married people under 40 years old without children under 18 years of age)

$x_{23} = 14{,}400$ (number of mail-in questionnaires completed with households containing single parents with children under 18 years of age)

$x_{24} = 9{,}600$ (number of mail-in questionnaires completed with households containing married families with children under 18 years of age)

$Z = \$83{,}400$

◼ Financial Applications

Linear programming has many applications in finance. These applications range from financial planning for banks to portfolio selection. In the next sections, we will first provide an example of how banks can utilize linear programming in planning their finances; then we will illustrate a portfolio selection example.

Financial Planning Problems for Banks

Linear programming can be very beneficial in banking. In banking one of the important decisions that bankers make involves how a bank wants to allocate its funds among the various types of loans and investment securities. Decisions are based on maximizing annual rate of return subject to state and federal regulations, and bank policies and restrictions. Consider the following **financial planning** example.

Example 4-7

First American Bank issues five types of loans. In addition, to diversify its portfolio, and to minimize risk, the bank invests in risk-free securities. The loans and the risk-free securities with their annual rate of return are given in Table 4-3.

Table 4-3   Rates of Return for Financial Planning Problem

Type of Loan or Security	Annual Rate of Return (%)
Home mortgage (first)	6
Home mortgage (second)	8
Commercial loan	11
Automobile loan	9
Home improvement loan	10
Risk-free securities	4

The bank's objective is to maximize the annual rate of return on investments subject to the following policies, restrictions, and regulations:

1. The bank has $90 million in available funds.
2. Risk-free securities must contain at least 10 percent of the total funds available for investments.
3. Home improvement loans cannot exceed $8,000,000.
4. The investment in mortgage loans must be at least 60 percent of all the funds invested in loans.
5. The investment in first mortgage loans must be at least twice as much as the investment in second mortgage loans.
6. Home improvement loans cannot exceed 40 percent of the funds invested in first mortgage loans.
7. Automobile loans and home improvement loans together may not exceed the commercial loans.
8. Commercial loans cannot exceed 50 percent of the total funds invested in mortgage loans.

First we must define the decision variables:

x_1 = dollars invested in first home mortgage loans
x_2 = dollars invested in second home mortgage loans
x_3 = dollars invested in commercial loans
x_4 = dollars invested in automobile loans
x_5 = dollars invested in home improvement loans
x_6 = dollars invested in risk-free securities

The objective function can be stated as follows:

maximize $Z = .06x_1 + .08x_2 + .11x_3 + .09x_4 + .10x_5 + .04x_6$

This objective function is subject to the following constraints. First we state the budget constraint:

$$x_1 + x_2 + x_3 + x_4 + x_5 + x_6 = 90,000,000 \tag{1}$$

Note that by using the equality sign, we force the entire budget to be spent.

The minimum funds invested in risk-free securities to control risk can be stated as follows:

$$x_6 \geq .10 \, (90,000,000)$$

or

$$x_6 \geq 9,000,000 \tag{2}$$

The constraint "Home improvement loans cannot exceed $8,000,000" can be stated as follows:

$$x_5 \leq 8,000,000 \tag{3}$$

The investment in mortgage loans must be at least 60 percent of all the funds invested in loans.

$$x_1 + x_2 \geq .6(x_1 + x_2 + x_3 + x_4 + x_5)$$

Note that we did not state the right-hand-side of the constraint as 54,000,000 or 60 percent of the total budget value of 90,000,000 because investment in risk-free securities is not included in the restriction.

x_1 and x_2 are decision variables that involve the mortgage loans; x_1 through x_5 are funds invested in all loans. Since investment in mortgage loans must "at least" be equal to 60 percent of the funds invested in all loans, we must utilize the greater than or equal to sign as follows: $x_1 + x_2 \geq .60(x_1 + x_2 + x_3 + x_4 + x_5)$. After converting it into computer-implementation-ready form by moving all of the variable values to the left-hand side of the inequality, the inequality takes the following form:

$$.40x_1 + .40x_2 - .60x_3 - 60x_4 - .60x_5 \geq 0 \tag{4}$$

The investment in first mortgage loans must be at least twice as much as the investment in second mortgage loans. This constraint can be set up so that we must invest at least twice as much funds in the first mortgage loans as we do in the second mortgage loans. This can be stated as $x_1 \geq 2x_2$, and after converting,

$$x_1 - 2x_2 \geq 0 \tag{5}$$

Home improvement loans cannot exceed 40 percent of the funds invested in first mortgage loans. This constraint can be stated as $x_5 \leq .40x_1$. The left-hand side of the inequality is the variable home improvement loans and the right side of the inequality is 40 percent of the first home mortgage loans. After converting, the inequality is stated as follows:

$$-.4x_1 + x_5 \leq 0 \tag{6}$$

Automobile loans and home improvement loans together may not exceed the commercial loans; this can be stated as $x_4 + x_5 \leq x_3$, and after rewriting,

$$-x_3 + x_4 + x_5 \leq 0 \tag{7}$$

Commercial loans cannot exceed 50 percent of the total funds invested in mortgage loans: $x_3 \leq .50 (x_1 + x_2)$, and after rewriting,

$$-.50x_1 - .50x_2 + x_3 \leq 0 \tag{8}$$

The linear programming formulation of the bank financial problem can be summarized as follows:

Let
x_1 = dollars invested in first home mortgage loans
x_2 = dollars invested in second home mortgage loans
x_3 = dollars invested in commercial loans
x_4 = dollars invested in automobile loans
x_5 = dollars invested in home improvement loans
x_6 = dollars invested in risk free securities

maximize $Z = .06x_1 + .08x_2 + .11x_3 + .09x_4 + .10x_5 + .04x_6$

subject to:

$$x_1 + x_2 + x_3 + x_4 + x_5 + x_6 = 90{,}000{,}000 \qquad \text{(budget constraint)} \qquad (1)$$
$$x_6 \geq 9{,}000{,}000 \qquad (2)$$
$$x_5 \leq 8{,}000{,}000 \qquad (3)$$
$$.40x_1 + .40x_2 - .60x_3 - .60x_4 - .60x_5 \geq 0 \qquad (4)$$
$$x_1 - 2x_2 \geq 0 \qquad (5)$$
$$-.4x_1 + x_5 \leq 0 \qquad (6)$$
$$-x_3 + x_4 + x_5 \leq 0 \qquad (7)$$
$$-.50x_1 - .50x_2 + x_3 \leq 0 \qquad (8)$$
$$x_1, x_2, x_3, x_4, x_5, x_6 \geq 0 \qquad \text{(nonnegativity constraint)}$$

Solution

$x_1 = 32{,}400{,}000$	(dollars invested in first home mortgage loans)
$x_2 = 16{,}200{,}000$	(dollars invested in second home mortgage loans)
$x_3 = 24{,}300{,}000$	(dollars invested in commercial loans)
$x_4 = 99{,}999.27$	(dollars invested in automobile loans)
$x_5 = 8{,}000{,}000$	(dollars invested in home improvement loans)
$x_6 = 9{,}000{,}000$	(dollars invested in risk-free securities)
$Z = \$7{,}082{,}000.00$	(profit over the investment of \$90,000,000)

Portfolio Selection

Portfolio selection problems generally involve allocating a fixed dollar amount (e.g., $100,000) among a variety of investments such as bonds, stocks, real estate, and so on. Usually the goal is to maximize income or total return. The problems take on an added dimension when certain other requirements are specified (for instance, no more than 40 percent of the portfolio can be invested in bonds). The next example illustrates this kind of problem.

Example 4-8

A conservative investor has $100,000 to invest. The investor has decided to use three vehicles for generating income: municipal bonds, a certificate of deposit (CD), and a money market account. After reading a financial newsletter, the investor has also identified several additional restrictions on the investments:

1. No more than 40 percent of the investment should be in bonds.
2. The proportion allocated to the money market account should be at least double the amount in the CD.

The annual return will be 8 percent for bonds, 9 percent for the CD, and 7 percent for the money market account. Assume the entire amount will be invested.

Formulate the LP model for this problem, ignoring any transaction costs and the potential for different investment lives. Assume that the investor wants to maximize the total annual return.

Solution

$x_1 =$ amount invested in bonds
$x_2 =$ amount invested in the CD
$x_3 =$ amount invested in the money market account

The annual return from each investment is the product of the rate of return and the amount invested. Thus, the objective function is

maximize $Z = .08x_1 + .09x_2 + .07x_3$

The requirement that no more than 40 percent be in bonds produces this constraint:

$x_1 \leq .40(\$100.000)$, which becomes $x_1 \leq \$40,000$

The requirement that the proportion invested in the money market account be at least double the amount in the CD leads to: $x_3 \geq 2x_2$. Then, subtracting $2x_2$ from both sides gives us $x_3 - 2x_2 \geq 0$, which can be rearranged so that x_2 comes before x_3: $-2x_2 + x_3 \geq 0$. Finally, the investor must recognize that the amounts invested in bonds, the CD, and the money market account must equal \$100,000. This gives us

$x_1 + x_2 + x_3 = \$100,000$ (budget constraint)

In sum, the model is:

maximize $.08x_1 + .09x_2 + .07x_3$

subject to

Amount in bonds	x_1	$\leq \$40,000$
Money/CD	$-2x_2 + x_3 \geq 0$	
Investment	$x_1 + x_2 + x_3 = \$100,000$	
	$x_1, x_2,$ and $x_3 \geq 0$	

Solution to portfolio problem

$x_1 = \$40,000$ (amount invested in bonds)
$x_2 = \$20,000$ (amount invested in CD)
$x_3 = \$40,000$ (amount invested in the money market account)
$Z = \$7,800$ (profit over the investment of \$100,000)

Note: If the problem had stated that the investor did not necessarily want to invest the entire \$100,000, the investment constraint would have been a less-than-or-equal-to constraint:

$x_1 + x_2 + x_3 = \$100,000$

In addition, the bond constraint would be affected because the amount in bonds is related to the amount invested. The bond constraint would have been

$x_t \leq .40(x_1 + x_2 + x_3)$

which would be rearrange to

$.60x_1 - .40x_2 - .40x_3 \leq 0$

■ Production Applications

There are numerous applications of linear programming in production management. This chapter will demonstrate three distinct types of applications that involve manufacturing: production scheduling, workforce scheduling, and make-or-buy decisions.

Multiperiod Production Scheduling

The first of the applications is multiperiod **production scheduling.** When the demand for the product varies across different time periods, linear programming can be used to determine a production schedule of a product over several production periods. Consider the following example.

Example 4-9

Morton and Monson Inc. is a small manufacturer of parts for the aerospace industry. The production capacity for the next four months is given as follows:

Production Capacity in Units

Month	Regular Production	Overtime Production
January	3,000	500
February	2,000	400
March	3,000	600
April	3,500	800

The regular cost of production is $500 per unit and the cost of overtime production is $150 per unit in addition to the regular cost of production. The company can utilize inventories to reduce fluctuations in production, but carrying one unit of inventory costs the company $40 per unit per month. Currently there are no units in inventory. However, the company wants to maintain a minimum safety stock of 100 units of inventory during the months of January, February, and March. The estimated demand for the next four months is as follows:

Month	January	February	March	April
Demand	2,800	3,000	3,500	3,000

The production manager is in the process of preparing a four-month production schedule. What is the schedule that minimizes total cost, if the company wants to have 300 units in inventory at the end of April?

First, we define the decision variables as follows:

$i = 1, 2, 3, 4$ $1 =$ January, $2 =$ February, $3 =$ March, $4 =$ April,
$x_i =$ quantity produced in month i on a regular time basis for $i = 1, 2, 3, 4$
$y_i =$ quantity produced in month i on overtime for $i = 1, 2, 3, 4$
$l_i =$ quantity in inventory at the end of month i for $i = 1, 2, 3, 4$

The objective function and the constraints for this problem can be stated as follows:

minimize $Z = 500(x_1 + x_2 + x_3 + x_4) + 650(y_1 + y_2 + y_3 + y_4) + 40(l_1 + l_2 + l_3 + l_4)$

subject to:

$$
\left.\begin{array}{l}
x_1 \leq 3,000 \\
x_2 \leq 2,000 \\
x_3 \leq 3,000 \\
x_4 \leq 3,500
\end{array}\right\} \quad \text{(regular time production constraint for each month)}
$$

$$y_1 \leq 500$$
$$y_2 \leq 400$$
$$y_3 \leq 600$$
$$y_4 \leq 800$$

(overtime production constraint for each month)

The total production (regular + overtime) minus what we carry in inventory must equal the demand for a particular month. These constraints result in the following transition equalities:

$$x_1 + y_1 - l_1 = 2,800$$
$$x_2 + y_2 - l_2 = 3,000$$
$$x_3 + y_3 - l_3 = 3,500$$
$$x_4 + y_4 - l_4 = 3,000$$

The inventory constraints can be formulated as follows:

$$l_1 \geq 100$$
$$l_2 \geq 100$$
$$l_3 \geq 100$$
$$l_4 = 300$$

The addition of the following nonnegativity constraint completes the formulation of this problem.

All $x_i, y_i, l_i \geq 0$ for $i = 1, 2, 3, 4$

In summary, the formulation of this problem is as follows:

minimize $Z = 500x_1 + 500x_2 + 500x_3 + 500x_4 + 650y_1 + 650y_2 + 650y_3 + 650y_4$
$$40l_1 + 40l_2 + 40l_3 + 40l_4$$

subject to:

$$x_1 \leq 3,000$$
$$x_2 \leq 2,000$$
$$x_3 \leq 3,000$$
$$x_4 \leq 3,500$$

(regular time production constraint for each month)

$$y_1 \leq 500$$
$$y_2 \leq 400$$
$$y_3 \leq 600$$
$$y_4 \leq 800$$

(overtime production constraint for each month)

$$x_1 + y_1 - l_1 = 2,800$$
$$x_2 + y_2 - l_2 = 3,000$$
$$x_3 + y_3 - l_3 = 3,500$$
$$x_4 + y_4 - l_4 = 3,000$$

(transition constraints)

$$l_1 \geq 100$$
$$l_2 \geq 100$$
$$l_3 \geq 100$$

(minimum inventory investment for the first three quarters)

$$l_4 = 300$$ (ending inventory constraint for the month of April)

All $x_i, y_i, l_i \geq 0$ for $i = 1, 2, 3, 4$

Solution

$x_1 = 2,900$ (quantity produced in January on a regular time basis)
$x_2 = 2,000$ (quantity produced in February on a regular time basis)
$x_3 = 3,000$ (quantity produced in March on a regular time basis)
$x_4 = 3,300$ (quantity produced in April on a regular time basis)
$y_2 = 400$ (quantity produced in February on overtime)
$y_3 = 600$ (quantity produced in March on overtime)
$I_1 = 100$ (quantity in inventory at the end of January)
$I_2 = 100$ (quantity in inventory at the end of February)
$I_3 = 100$ (quantity in inventory at the end of March)
$I_4 = 300$ (quantity in inventory at the end of April)
$Z = \$6,274,000$

Workforce Scheduling

Linear programming can be extremely helpful in scheduling personnel, that is, **workforce scheduling.** Lets consider the following hospital example. Linear programming can be used to determine the best set of assignments of workers subject to demand and company-imposed restrictions to minimize the cost of making those assignments. Let's consider the following example.

Example 4-10

Lincoln General Hospital is trying to determine the nursing schedule of the pediatric department. The nursing staff consists of full-time nurses who work eight-hour shifts and part-time nurses who work four-hour shifts. The supervisor of nurses divides the day into six four-hour periods. In each period, a different level of demand (number of cases to be treated) is expected, which requires different numbers of nurses to be hired. The required number of nurses for each time period is given in Table 4-4.

Table 4-4   Staffing Requirements for Workforce Scheduling Problem

$i =$ Time Period Index	Time Period	Required Number of Nurses
1	7–11 a.m.	7
2	11 a.m.–3 p.m.	9
3	3–7 p.m.	12
4	7–11 p.m.	5
5	11 p.m.–3 a.m.	4
6	3–7 a.m.	3

It is also required that there must be at least two full-time nurses at each time period and the number of part-time nurses cannot exceed the number of full-time nurses in any time period. The full-time nurses get paid $160 per shift, while the part-time nurses get paid $50 per shift. The normal shifts can begin at the start of any of the four-hour periods.

The decision variables can be defined as

x_i = number of full-time nurses scheduled during time period i for i = 1, 2, 3, 4, 5, 6 as defined in Table 4-4.

y_i = number of part-time nurses scheduled during time period i for i = 1, 2, 3, 4, 5, 6 as defined in Table 4-4.

The objective function for this problem can be written as

minimize $Z = 160(x_1 + x_2 + x_3 + x_4 + x_5 + x_6) + 50(y_1 + y_2 + y_3 + y_4 + y_5 + y_6)$

In writing the constraints for this problem, there must be a constraint for each time period, as specified below.

$$x_1 + x_6 + y_1 \geq 7 \qquad \text{(constraint for nurses starting at 7 a.m.)}$$
$$x_1 + x_2 + y_2 \geq 9 \qquad \text{(constraint for nurses starting at 11 a.m.)}$$
$$x_2 + x_3 + y_3 \geq 12 \qquad \text{(constraint for nurses starting at 3 p.m.)}$$
$$x_3 + x_4 + y_4 \geq 5 \qquad \text{(constraint for nurses starting at 7 p.m.)}$$
$$x_4 + x_5 + y_5 \geq 4 \qquad \text{(constraint for nurses starting at 11 p.m.)}$$
$$x_5 + x_6 + y_6 \geq 3 \qquad \text{(constraint for nurses starting at 3 a.m.)}$$

$$x_1 \geq 2$$
$$x_2 \geq 2$$
$$x_3 \geq 2$$
$$x_4 \geq 2 \qquad \text{(there must be at least two full-time nurses during any period)}$$
$$x_5 \geq 2$$
$$x_6 \geq 2$$

$$x_1 + x_6 \geq y_1$$
$$x_1 + x_2 \geq y_2$$
$$x_2 + x_3 \geq y_3 \qquad \text{(the number of full-time nurses must be greater than that}$$
$$x_3 + x_4 \geq y_4 \qquad \text{of part-time workers)}$$
$$x_4 + x_5 \geq y_5$$
$$x_5 + x_6 \geq y_6$$

$x_i \geq 0, y_i \geq 0$ for all i (nonnegativity constraint)

Solution

$x_1 = 2$ (number of full-time nurses scheduled from 7–11 a.m.)
$x_2 = 3$ (number of full-time nurses scheduled from 11 a.m.–3 p.m.)
$x_3 = 3$ (number of full-time nurses scheduled from 3–7 p.m.)
$x_4 = 2$ (number of full-time nurses scheduled from 7–11 p.m.)
$x_5 = 2$ (number of full-time nurses scheduled from 11 p.m.–3 a.m.)
$x_6 = 2$ (number of full-time nurses scheduled from 3–7 a.m.)
$y_1 = 3$ (number of part-time nurses scheduled from 7–11 a.m.)
$y_2 = 4$ (number of part-time nurses scheduled from 11 a.m.–3 p.m.)
$y_3 = 6$ (number of part-time nurses scheduled from 3–7 p.m.)
$Z = \$2,890.00$ (total minimum cost associated with scheduling of nurses in pediatrics)

Make-or-Buy Decisions

In production management, production managers are often faced with a **make-or-buy decision**, that is, the decision of either producing a part or purchasing the part from a supplier. Linear programming can be a helpful tool in assisting managers to decide when to produce and when to purchase. Let us consider an example.

Example 4-11

The T & L Manufacturing Company produces parts X, Y, and Q. The next month's demand for parts X, Y, and Q are 3,000, 5,000 and 4,000 units, respectively. Even though T & L would like to manufacture all of the units demanded, it is concerned that it does not have the necessary production capacity to make all of the components. Therefore, the company is considering hiring a local supplier of these parts. The production and purchasing cost of parts X, Y, and Q are given in Table 4-5.

Table 4-5   Production and Purchasing Cost of All Parts

Component	Production Cost per Unit	Purchasing Cost per Unit
X	$2.20	$3.00
Y	$1.50	$2.80
Q	$1.20	$2.20

All parts must go through plating and heat-treating processes. The production time requirements per unit of parts X, Y, and Z for the plating and heat-treating processes and capacity are given in Table 4-6.

Table 4-6   Production Time Requirements and Capacity of Process

Processes	Part X	Part Y	Part Q	Total Hours Available
Plating	.2	.3	.10	1,500
Heat treating	.1	.2	.05	1,000

Determine the optimal production and buying schedule for parts X, Y, and Q.

First we define the decision variables. Since we have to decide between buying and making, we have to define two types of variables: manufacturing variables and purchasing variables.

M_i = number of units of production of product i
P_i = number of units purchased of product i

where

$i = X, Y, Q$

The objective function can be written as

minimize $Z = 2.2M_X + 1.5M_Y + 1.2M_Q + 3P_X + 2.8P_Y + 2.2P_Q$

This objective function is subject to the following constraints. First, we must account for demand for each product.

$$\left.\begin{array}{l} M_X + P_X = 3,000 \\ M_Y + P_Y = 5,000 \\ M_Q + P_Q = 4,000 \end{array}\right\} \quad \text{(demand constraint for each product)}$$

Now, we need to state the capacity of the plating and heat-treating processes.

$.20M_X + .30M_Y + .10M_Q \leq 1{,}500$ hours   (capacity of plating department)
$.10M_X + .20M_Y + .05M_Q \leq 1{,}000$ hours   (capacity of heat-treating department)
All M_i and all $P_i \geq 0$ for $i = X, Y, Q$

Solutions

$M_Y = 3{,}667$ (number of units of production of part Y)
$M_Q = 4{,}000$ (number of units of production of part Q)
$P_X = 3{,}000$ (number of units purchased of part X)
$P_Y = 1{,}333$ (number of units purchased of part Y)
$Z = \$23{,}033.33$ (maximum profit)

Agriculture Applications

Linear programming has many useful applications in the agriculture sector. The following example demonstrates one such useful application. **Agricultural** applications involve determining the best set of crops to plant on given farmland given demand constraints, land and cultivation, and fertilizer considerations.

Example 4-12

A farm owner in Des Moines, Iowa, is interested in determining how to divide the farmland among four different types of crops. The farmer owns two farms in separate locations and has decided to plant the following four types of crops in these farms: corn, wheat, bean, and cotton. The first farm consists of 1,450 acres of land, while the second farm consists of 850 acres of land. Any of the four crops may be planted on either farm. However, after a survey of the land, based on the characteristics of the farmlands, Table 4-7 shows the maximum acreage restrictions the farmer has placed for each crop.

Table 4-7   Maximum Acreage Restrictions for Agricultural Problem

	Crop			
Farm	**Corn**	**Wheat**	**Bean**	**Cotton**
Farm 1	550	450	350	400
Farm 2	250	300	200	350

The profit per acre for each crop is estimated as follows:

Crop	**Profit/Acre**
Corn	$500
Wheat	$400
Bean	$300
Cotton	$350

In determining the optimal cultivation of land, the farmer has to account for the cost of fertilizer estimated for each acre of land. Due to the different terrain and soil, the two farms have different costs of fertilizers per acre.

Farm	Cost of Fertilizer/Acre
Farm 1	$100
Farm 2	$70

Seasonal demand for the four crops is given in Table 4-8.

Table 4-8   Seasonal Demand for the Four Crops

Crop	Seasonal Demand (acres' worth)
Corn	450
Wheat	550
Bean	400
Cotton	600

The farmer has a storage facility that can store 100 acres' worth of the excess supply of different types of crops. In addition, the farmer wants to ensure that total wheat and bean cultivation must be proportionally equal to the maximum acreage restriction of both farms. In other words, the farm owner wants the same proportion of wheat and beans in both farms. The farmer's objective is to determine how much of each crop to plant on each farm in order to maximize profit and satisfy seasonal demand.

First, we can use the double subscripted notation and define variables as follows: Let x_{ij} = number of acres in farm i planted with crop j. In defining the objective function, first we must specify all of the profit values for each crop in each farm and then we must subtract the cost of the fertilizers for each farm. This procedure results in the following:

maximize $Z = 500x_{11} + 400x_{12} + 300x_{13} + 350x_{14} + 500x_{21} + 400x_{22} + 300x_{23} + 350x_{24} - 100x_{11} - 100x_{12} - 100x_{13} - 100x_{14} - 70x_{21} - 70x_{22} - 70x_{23} - 70x_{24}$

After performing the arithmetic operations and collecting the same terms together, the objective function can be rewritten as

maximize $Z = 400x_{11} + 300x_{12} + 200x_{13} + 250x_{14} + 430x_{21} + 330x_{22} + 230x_{23} + 280x_{24}$

We can begin to write the constraints for this problem by considering the maximum acreage available in each farm:

$x_{11} + x_{12} + x_{13} + x_{14} \leq 1,450$ (capacity of farm 1)
$x_{21} + x_{22} + x_{23} + x_{24} \leq 850$ (capacity of farm 2)

We can continue writing the constraints by stating the maximum acreage of each farm suitable for a certain type of crop. This requires individual less-than-or-equal-to constraints for each farm–crop combination.

$x_{11} \leq 550$
$x_{12} \leq 450$
$x_{13} \leq 350$
$x_{14} \leq 400$
$x_{21} \leq 250$ (maximum acreage suitable in each farm for each crop)
$x_{22} \leq 300$
$x_{23} \leq 200$
$x_{24} \leq 350$

Since the farmer can store the excess capacity, we can write the demand constraints as greater than or equal to. The demand constraints can be written as follows:

$x_{11} + x_{21} \geq 450$ (total demand for corn)
$x_{12} + x_{22} \geq 550$ (total demand for wheat)
$x_{13} + x_{23} \geq 400$ (total demand for beans)
$x_{14} + x_{24} \geq 600$ (total demand for cotton)

Since we can store 100 acres of crops above the level of demand, we need to add a constraint that restricts the amount of storage. Adding the demand quantities, we get a total acreage of 2,000. Since we have the capacity to store up to 100 units of any crop, we add the following constraint:

$x_{11} + x_{12} + x_{13} + x_{14} + x_{21} + x_{22} + x_{23} + x_{24} \leq 2,100$

In other words, the farmer cannot exceed farming more than 2,100 acres (100 more than demanded) total for the crops.

Finally, we need to consider the proportionality constraints. Since the owner wants the same proportion of the maximum acreage for wheat and beans cultivated, we need to set up the proportionality constraints as follows. First, in stating the proportion of the maximum acreage cultivated for wheat, it is $(x_{12} + x_{22})/(450 + 300)$, or $(x_{12} + x_{22})/750$.

Stating the proportion of the maximum acreage cultivated for beans, it is $(x_{13} + x_{23})/(350 + 200) = (x_{13} + x_{23})/550$. Since the two proportions must be equal, the constraint can be written as follows:

$(x_{12} + x_{22})/750 = (x_{13} + x_{23})/550$

We can rewrite this constraint by multiplying both sides of the equality by (550)(750). The resulting equation is $550(x_{12} + x_{22}) = 750(x_{13} + x_{23})$. Simplifying this equation,

$550x_{12} + 550x_{22} - 750x_{13} - 750x_{23} = 0$

The linear programming formulation of the entire problem is given by

maximize $Z = 400x_{11} + 300x_{12} + 200x_{13} + 250x_{14} + 430x_{21} + 330x_{22} + 230x_{23} + 280x_{24}$

subject to

$x_{11} + x_{12} + x_{13} + x_{14} \leq 1,450$ (capacity of farm 1)
$x_{21} + x_{22} + x_{23} + x_{24} \leq 850$ (capacity of farm 2)

$x_{11} \leq 550$
$x_{12} \leq 450$
$x_{13} \leq 350$
$x_{14} \leq 400$ (Maximum acreage suitable in each farm for each crop)
$x_{21} \leq 250$
$x_{22} \leq 300$
$x_{23} \leq 200$
$x_{24} \leq 350$

$x_{11} + x_{21} \geq 450$ (total demand for corn)
$x_{12} + x_{22} \geq 550$ (total demand for wheat)
$x_{13} + x_{23} \geq 400$ (total demand for beans)
$x_{14} + x_{24} \geq 600$ (total demand for cotton)
$x_{11} + x_{12} + x_{13} + x_{14} + x_{21} + x_{22} + x_{23} + x_{24} \leq 2,100$
$550x_{12} + 550x_{22} - 750x_{13} - 750x_{23} = 0$ (proportionality constraint)

$x_{ij} \geq 0$ for all i, j combinations, where x_{ij} = number of acreas of crop j cultivated in farm i

Solution

$x_{11} = 296.667$	(acres of corn planted on farm 1)
$x_{12} = 250$	(acres of wheat planted on farm 1)
$x_{13} = 350$	(acres of beans planted on farm 1)
$x_{14} = 353.333$	(acres of cotton planted on farm 1)
$x_{21} = 250$	(acres of corn planted on farm 2)
$x_{22} = 300$	(acres of wheat planted on farm 2)
$x_{23} = 53.333$	(acres of beans planted on farm 2)
$x_{24} = 246.667$	(acres of cotton planted on farm 2)
$Z = \$639,833.4$	(total maximum profit)

Data Envelopment Analysis

Managers are often interested in comparing the efficiency of various sections or departments within a company. **Data envelopment analysis (DEA)** is an application of linear programming that is used to make comparisons. DEA is used to measure the relative efficiency of the departments within an organization or relative efficiencies of two different organizations. DEA has been applied in various industries including fast food restaurants, hospitals, schools, and banks. Measuring the efficiency of departments within the same organization is difficult because the departments have multiple input measures (number of workers, cost of labor, cost of machine operations, pay scale for employees, and cost of advertising) and multiple output measures (profit, sales, and market share). In applying DEA, we first have to define the efficiency of a department or an organization so that we can compare the efficiencies of different departments or different organizations.

Let e_i = efficiency of unit i
wo_j = weight j applied to outputs
wi_j = weight j applied to input
O_{ij} = value of department i based on output j
I_{ij} = value of department i based on input j
k = number of output variables
w = number of input variables

Efficiency of unit i can be computed using the following equation.

$$e_i = \frac{\sum_{i=1}^{k} O_{ij} wo_{ij}}{\sum_{j=1}^{w} I_{ij} wi_j} \tag{4-1}$$

In DEA, executing the linear programming problem will provide us with values of the decision variables, which are the weights wo_j and wi_j.

In DEA we solve a separate linear programming problem for each department, where the objective is to maximize the weighted sum of the units output. In other words, the objective can be stated as follows:

$$\text{Max} \sum_{j=1}^{k} O_{ij} wo_{ij} \tag{4-2}$$

This objective is subject to the constraint that the department's efficiency cannot exceed 100 percent. Therefore, the weighted sum of the department's outputs cannot exceed the weighted sum of the department's inputs. In other words,

$$\sum_{j=1}^{k} O_{ij} wo_{ij} - \sum_{j=1}^{w} I_{ij} wi_j \leq 0 \tag{4-3}$$

In order to ensure that we have a bounded solution, the sum of the weighted inputs for the department under consideration must equal 1. This requirement is given in equation (4-4).

$$\sum_{j=1}^{w} I_{ij} wi_j = 1 \tag{4-4}$$

This constraint also will ensure that the efficiency score for the outputs cannot exceed 1, or 100 percent.

When implementing DEA, the output variables are like profit or sales, where more is better, and the input variables are cost or number of employees, where less is better.

Example 4-13

A consumer advocacy group would like to evaluate the efficiency of three airline companies with respect to several criteria that are important to consumers. The three companies are Beta, Unified, and Southeast.

The output measures are identified as average minutes late arriving, number of luggage losses per 10,000 customers, waiting time for check-in, friendliness, and quality of air service (result of a questionnaire that measured this output on a 100-point scale). The input measures were labor cost per day, number of flights per day, and overhead cost per day. Table 4-9 summarizes the results.

Table 4-9   Analysis of Airline Efficiency

	Airline Companies		
	Beta	Unified	Southeast
Input Measures			
Labor cost per day (i_1)	$8,000,000	$10,000,000	$6,000,000
Overhead cost per day (i_2)	$2,500,000	$3,000,000	2,000,000
Number of flights per day (i_3)	300	400	200
Output Measures			
Average minutes late arriving (o_1)	−15	−20	−7
Number of luggage losses per 10,000 (o_2)	−10	−15	−5
Waiting time for check-in (o_3)	−10	−20	−5
Friendliness/quality of air service (o_4)	85	80	95

Note that a minus sign is included for the first three output measures: the higher the value, the better the measure. In other words, if average minutes late are −15, the airplanes are late an average of 15 minutes. Note that positive values for these three measures are impossible.

Use DEA and determine the relative efficiency of the three airline companies.

Solution
First we need to formulate the problem for Beta.

The decision variables are

wo_1 = weight associated with average minutes late arriving
wo_2 = weight associated with the number of luggage lost per 10,000
wo_3 = weight associated with waiting time for check-in
wo_4 = weight associated with friendliness/quality of air service
wi_1 = weight associated with labor cost per day
wi_2 = weight associated with overhead cost per day
wi_3 = weight associated with the number of flights per day

Second, the objective function can be stated as follows:

maximize $Z = -15wo_1 - 10wo_2 - 10wo_3 + 85wo_4$

Third, we need to state the efficiency constraints for each airline company:

$$-15wo_1 - 10wo_2 - 10wo_3 + 85wo_4 - 8{,}000{,}000wi_1 - 2{,}500{,}000wi_2 - 300wi_3 \leq 0$$
$$-20wo_1 - 15wo_2 - 20wo_3 + 80wo_4 - 10{,}000{,}000wi_1 - 3{,}000{,}000wi_2 - 400wi_3 \leq 0$$
$$-7wo_1 - 5wo_2 - 5wo_3 + 95wo_4 - 6{,}000{,}000wi_1 - 2{,}000{,}000wi_2 - 200wi_3 \leq 0$$

Fourth, we need to state the input constraint that the sum of the input weights equals 1.0.

$$8{,}000{,}000wi_1 + 2{,}500{,}000wi_2 + 300wi_3 = 1$$

Finally we need to state the nonnegativity constraint for each variable:

$wo_1, wo_2, wo_3, wo_4, wi_1, wi_2, wi_3 \geq 0$

Solving this using a linear programming software package results in the following: Z = relative efficiency of Beta = 67.11 percent with wo_4 = .0084 and the values of the rest of the decision variables equal to zero. Using the same formulation approach but changing the objective function (for instance, the objective function for Unified Airlines is: Maximize $Z = -20wo_1 - 15wo_2 - 20wo_3 + 80wo_4$) and the input constraints to reflect the values of Unified and Southeast, the relative efficiencies of Unified and Southeast are found to be 56.14 percent and 1.0, respectively.

Note that the relative efficiency of 100 percent does not mean that the department or the organization does not have any inefficiencies. It simply means that no linear combination of the other departments' values results in a composite score of 1.0 using the same or less input. More than one department or organization can achieve a relative efficiency of 1.0. The goal of the DEA is to identify departments or organizations that are relatively inefficient. In other words, there exists a linear combination of efficient departments that results in a composite score that yields as much output using the same or less input. However, the results of the DEA is not capable of identifying departments or organizations that are more efficient than others. Once the inefficient departments are identified, we can study the reasons for possible inefficiencies and try to improve the relative efficiency score for a department.

In our example problem, Unified's relative efficiency measure was the lowest at 56.14 percent. Looking at the values of the output measures, on the average, its planes were 20 minutes late, the company lost 15 pieces of luggage per 10,000 customers, the waiting time for check-in was 20 minutes, and the air service quality rating was 80. In all of these output measures, the performance of the company was not as good as its competitors. In addition, the achievement of the current levels of the output measures was possible with higher labor and overhead cost and by scheduling more flights (higher investment in input measures). The company should try to decrease cost or schedule fewer flights while improving its service record in waiting time for check-in, late arrivals, number of luggage lost, and the quality of air service. This may seem like a difficult task to achieve; however, once we begin to study each output measure, we can find ways of improving it without increasing the associated cost.

In summary, the goal of data envelopment analysis (DEA) is to identify the inefficient operating units. However, the goal of DEA is not to identify the relatively efficient operating units. In various DEA studies, it has been found that multiple operating units are classified as inefficient. The challenge of DEA is to understand how each relatively inefficient unit can be improved. One way to analyze the relatively inefficient operating units is to compare the various scores of that inefficient operating unit against the average score or the composite score of given criteria.

◾ Comment about the Use of Excel

Throughout the chapter, Excel solutions are provided for only certain problems. The reason for not providing the Excel solution to all of the problems is that the principal ideas for setting up and using Excel to solve various problems are essentially the same for each problem. Therefore, if we had solved each problem using Excel, we would have wasted valuable space in the book that could be utilized to cover other important topics or concepts. However, the Excel solutions to all of the problems are included on the CD-ROM that comes with this book.

◾ Other Applications

The preceding examples illustrate some of the frequently encountered applications of LP models to real-world problems. There are, however, many other applications of linear programming models, including the following:

- **Transportation problems.** A typical problem might involve a set of factories that produce the same product and a set of warehouses to which the product is to be shipped. The objective is to determine a distribution plan that will minimize total distribution cost given the capacities of the various factories and the needs of the warehouses.
- **Assignment problems.** A typical problem might include a set of jobs to be performed, a set of machines that can perform the job, and a cost per job for each job/machine combination. The objective is to assign the jobs to machine in such a way that the total cost of performing the jobs is minimized. Variations of this problem include minimizing total time for a set of assignments and maximizing profits from a set of assignments.
- **Project management problems.** A typical problem might involve finding the minimum time for project competition given times for the tasks required and specified specified precedence relationships among tasks. A variation may involve shortening project duration given costs to shorten various project tasks. The objective would be to minimize total cost: project costs and shortening costs.

A Modern Management Science Application: *Deere and Company*

Deere and Company was founded in 1837 and is headquartered in Moline, Illinois. Deere is a worldwide leading producer of equipment for agriculture and forestry. The company's worth is estimated at $15.5 billion and it employs approximately 43,000 people. Deere products are sold through international networks of independently owned dealership and retailer outlets.

Deere's Commercial and Consumer Equipment Division (C&CE) declared a goal of improving its on-time delivery from plants to dealers, while at the same time reducing inventory and maintaining customer service. Most of Deere's C&CE products must be available at the dealerships; otherwise its customers would just purchase from competitors. C&CE serves 2,500 dealers, has 100 product families, and utilizes a 26-week planning horizon.

C&CE hired SmartOp to assist with accomplishing this goal. SmartOp used state-of-the-art inventory optimization techniques, which included the use of linear programming. SmartOp developed a multistage inventory planning and optimization (MIPO) system for products that enabled C&CE to set acceptable inventory targets. By implementing MIPO, C&CE changed from a "push" system to a "pull" system, integrating the inventory targets it has set with appropriate dealer incentives to assist in this transformation.

Optimization of inventory in such a complex supply chain is not easy. Many manufacturers and distributors set a reasonable goal of reducing inventory while investing in enterprise resource planning (ERP). However, these companies continue to have problems managing their inventories. The problem is complicated by the following facts: changing demand and supply (caused by seasonality, product life cycles, and promotions), changing capacities (caused by expanding plants, applying new processes and technologies, and scheduled shutdowns), and uncertainty about the expected time of delivery of the supply quantity from the supplier. All of these combine to make it very difficult to set reasonable inventory target levels. This problem translates into attempting to solve a probabilistic, capacitated, multi-echelon, multiproduct production and inventory problem. This is not only a difficult problem to solve mathematically, but it is also very difficult to optimize levels of inventory in the real world. MIPO is effectively able to find resolutions to these complications by using an algorithm that includes stochastic or probabilistic analysis. MIPO determines recommended stocking levels (RSLs) by looking at the supply chain as a discrete time, stochastic, capacitated, multistage model.

C&CE reduced inventory by $890 million while maintaining service levels and improved its factories' on-time shipment from 63 to 92 percent. The MIPO algorithm that uses linear programming enabled C&CE to offer the dealerships an interest-free financial agreement up to the new RSL value. Reliable inventory targets were a key factor in reducing inventory levels of not only C&CE but also the dealership partners.

Source: L. Troyer, J. Smith, S. Marshall, E. Yaniv, S. Tayur, M. Barkman, A. Kaya, and Y. Liu, "Improving Asset Management and Order Fulfillment at Deere & Company's C&CE Division," *Interfaces* 35, no. 1 (January–February 2005), pp. 76–87.

Summary

There are many successful real-world applications of linear programming. Some of these applications are listed in Table 3-1.

In this chapter, we have shown the formulation of 13 example applications of linear programming. These applications include product mix, diet, blending, marketing applications in media selection and marketing research, financial applications in financial planning for banks and portfolio selection, production applications in multiperiod production scheduling, make-or-buy decisions, workforce scheduling, agricultural applications, and data envelopment analysis (DEA). The purpose of demonstrating so many different applications of linear programming is twofold. First, this shows the reader a wide variety of areas in which one can utilize linear programming. The second purpose involves the illustration of formulation of problems with different types of decision variables definitions, different types of constraints, and different types of objective functions. In addition, we have shown how to utilize Excel to solve linear programming problems and interpret the output provided by Excel. Although no examples are provided, discussions of other linear programming applications in transportation, assignment, and project management also have been briefly discussed.

Glossary

Agricultural Problems Problems that determine the best set of crops to plant on given farmland given demand constraints, land and cultivation, and fertilizer considerations.

Assignment Problems Problems that determine the best set of assignment of jobs to be performed by the best set of machines or workers to minimize total cost of the one-to-one assignments or to maximize the total profit associated with those assignments.

Blending Problems Problems that determine the optimal mixing of raw materials or other ingredients to obtain end products that have a specific consistency.

Data Envelopment Analysis (DEA) A linear programming application to measure the relative efficiency of departments or organizations with the same objectives.

Diet Problems Problems that determine the optimal mixing of raw materials or other ingredients to obtain end products that have certain characteristics.

Financial Planning Problems Problems that determine how a bank wants to allocate its funds among the various types of loans and investment securities. Decision is based on maximizing annual rate of return subject to state and federal regulations, and bank policies and restrictions.

Make or Buy Decision Problems Problems that determine when to produce and when to purchase a series of products given certain capacity, cost, and company-imposed restrictions.

Marketing Research Problems Problems that determine the best number of interviews, mailings, or phone calls given a number of client-specified constraints and cost considerations.

Media Selection Problems Problems that determine how to allocate an advertising budget among several different media.

Portfolio Selection Problems Problems that determine the allocation of a fixed dollar amount (budget) among a variety of investments such as bonds, stocks, and real estate such that income or total return is maximized.

Product-Mix Problems Problems that determine the mix of outputs of similar products that utilize similar resources to maximize the profit given the availability of scarce resources.

Production Scheduling Problems Problems that determine a production schedule of a product over several consecutive production periods, when the demand for the product varies across different time periods to maximize profit.

Project Management Problems Problems that determine the minimum time for project completion given times for the tasks required and specified precedence relationship among tasks. The objective is to minimize total cost or total completion time.

Transportation Problems Problems that determine the best transportation schedule from a set of factories or warehouses that produce or store the same product to a set of warehouses or retail outlets. The objective is to determine a distribution plan that will minimize total distribution cost given capacities of the various factories and the needs of the warehouses.

Workforce Scheduling Problems Problems that determine the best set of assignments of workers subject to demand and company-imposed restrictions to minimize the cost of making those assignments.

Solved Problems

Problem 1

A soup company wants to determine the optimal ingredients for its vegetable soup. The main ingredients are

> Vegetables:
> Potatoes
> Carrots
> Onions
> Meat
> Water
> Flavorings

The soup must meet these specifications:

a.   No more than half of the soup can be vegetables.
b.   The ratio of water to meat should be 8:1.
c.   The amount of meat should be between 5 and 6 percent of the soup.
d.   The flavorings should weigh no more than 1/2 ounce.

The cost per ounce of the ingredients is $.02 for the vegetables, $.05 for the meat, $.001 for the water, and $.05 for the flavorings.

Formulate an LP model that will determine the optimal amounts of the various ingredients to achieve 15-ounce cans of soup at minimum cost.

Solution

Identify the decision variables:

> x_1 = quantity of potatoes in ounces
> x_2 = quantity of carrots in ounces
> x_3 = quantity of onions in ounces
> x_4 = quantity of meat in ounces
> x_5 = quantity of water in ounces
> x_6 = quantity of flavorings in ounces

Write the objective function:

> minimize $.02x_1 + .02x_2 + .02x_3 + .05x_4 + .001x_5 + .05x_6$

Write constraints for each specification:

a. $x_1 + x_2 + x_3 \leq .50(15 \text{ oz.})$. Thus:

> $x_1 + x_2 + x_3 \leq 7.5$ ounces

b. $x_5/x_4 = 8/1$. Cross-multiplying yields $x_5 = 8x_4$. Then, subtracting $8x_4$ from both sides in order to have all variables on the left-hand side yields

> $-8x_4 + x_5 = 0$

c.   This requires *two* constraints:

> $x_4 \geq .05(15)$, which is $x_4 \geq .75$ ounce
> $x_4 \leq .06(15)$, which is $x_4 \leq .90$ ounce

d. $x_6 \leq .5$ ounce.

There is one additional constraint: The ingredients must add up to 15 ounces, the weight of a can of soup. Thus:

$$x_1 + x_2 + x_3 + x_4 + x_5 + x_6 = 15 \text{ ounces}$$

Finally, there are the nonnegativity constraints:

All variables ≥ 0

Discussion and Review Questions

1. List six areas of application of linear programming and discuss the usefulness of LP in three of these areas.
2. In using Excel, explain target cells, output cells, and data cells.
3. In using Excel to solve a linear programming problem, briefly explain the following:
   a. Input screen.
   b. Solver dialog box.
   c. Add constraint dialogue box.
   d. Solver options dialogue box.
   e. Solver results dialogue box.
   f. Output screen.
   g. Excel answer report.
4. Explain the SUMPRODUCT command. How is it used in solving linear programming problems? Why is it useful?
5. Explain the difference in solving diet and blending problems when using linear programming.
6. In formulating many LP problems, we have a budget constraint. Explain the different consequences of using an = sign versus ≤ sign in formulating this constraint.
7. Explain the usefulness of double subscript notation in formulating linear programming problems.
8. What is the purpose of data envelopment analysis? How do we apply linear programming in solving data envelopment analysis problems?
9. What does *proportionality constraint* mean? Give an example of setting up a proportionality constraint.
10. When is it useful to formulate a multiperiod production scheduling problem? In multiperiod production scheduling problems described in this chapter, what are the three types of variables?
11. In a multiperiod production scheduling problem, transition constraints are set up. State an example transition constraint involving regular production, overtime production, demand, and inventory.

Problems

1. Sharon Smith is the marketing manager of a large savings and loan association that has branches throughout the state. She would like to mail a promotional piece to prospective borrowers. Sharon has selected three regions in which to do a mailing. A marketing agency can supply lists of prospective borrowers in each region, as shown in Table 4-10.

Table 4-10 Data for Problem 1

Region	List Size	Cost per Name
I	10,000	$.11
II	20,000	.12
III	30,000	.13

Sharon would like to have a pool of 15,000 names and would like the mail to contain at least 10 percent of the people on each list. Also, she doesn't want more than 40 percent of the list to be drawn from any region. Formulate an LP model that will accomplish these requirements for the least cost. Assume that there is no overlap among lists and that any quantity can be ordered from each list.

2. Aviation Electronics produces three types of switching devices. Each type involves a two-step assembly operation. The assembly times are shown in Table 4-11.

Maximize $Z = 8.25x_1 + 7.50x_2 + 7.80x_3$
$2.5x_1 + 1.8x_2 + 2.0x_3 \leq 2,250$
$3.0x_1 + 1.6x_2 + 2.2x_3 \leq 2,250$
$x_1 \geq 20$
$x_2 \geq 20$
$x_3 \geq 20$
$x_1, x_2, x_3 \geq 0$

Table 4-11 Data for Problem 2

	Assembly Time per Unit (minutes)	
	Station 1	Station 2
Model A	2.5	3.0
Model B	1.8	1.6
Model C	2.0	2.2

Each workstation has a daily working time of 7.5 hours. Manager Bob Parkes wants to obtain the greatest possible profit during the next five working days. Model A yields a profit of $8.25 per unit, Model B a profit of $7.50 per unit, and Model C a profit of $7.80 per unit. Assume that the firm can sell all it produces during this time, but it must fill outstanding orders for 20 units of each model type.

Formulate the linear programming model of this problem.

3. A manager of an automobile dealership must decide how many cars to order for the end of the model year. Midsize cars yield an average profit of $500 each, and compact cars yield an average profit of $400 each. Either type of car will cost the dealership $8,000 each, and no more than $720,000 can be invested. The manager wants at least 10 of each type, but no more than 50 of the midsize cars and no more than 60 of the compact cars. Formulate the linear programming model of this problem.

Maximize $Z = .20x_1 + .18x_2 + .25x_3$
$1/3x_1 + 1/2x_2 \leq 1,500$
$1/3x_1 + 1/4x_2 + 1/10x_3 \leq 1,000$
$1/3x_1 + 1/4x_2 + 9/10x_3 \leq 1,000$
$x_1, x_2, x_3 \geq 0$

4. Petfoods makes dog food using a blend of three ingredients: K9, K8, and K1. The company has a regular blend, an extra blend, and puppy delite. The regular blend consists of one-third of each ingredient; the extra blend is 50 percent K9 and 25 percent each of K8 and K1. The puppy delite is 10 percent K8 and the rest K1. The dog food is produced in one-pound cans. There are 1,500 pounds of K9 and 1,000 pounds of each of the other ingredients available. The regular blend yields a profit of $.20 per can, the extra blend yields $.18 per can, and the puppy delite a profit of $.25 per can. Formulate an LP model that can be used to determine the maximum profit combination of the different types of dog food.

5. A manufacturer of lawn and garden equipment makes two basic types of lawn mowers: a push-type and a self-propelled model. The push-type requires 9 minutes to assemble and 2 minutes to package; the self-propelled mower requires 12 minutes to assemble and 6 minutes to package. Each type has an engine. The company has 12 hours of assembly time available, 75 engines, and 5 hours of packing time. Profits are $70 for the self-propelled model and $45 for the push-type mower, per unit. Formulate a linear

programming model that will enable the manager to determine how many mowers of each type to make in order to maximize total profit.

6. A farm consists of 600 acres of land, of which 500 acres will be planted with corn, soybeans, and wheat, according to these conditions:
   1. At least half of the planted acreage should be in corn.
   2. No more than 200 acres should be soybeans.
   3. The ratio of corn to wheat planted should be 2:1.

   It costs $20 an acre to plant corn, $15 an acre to plant soybeans, and $12 an acre to plant wheat.
   a. Formulate this problem as an LP model that will minimize planting cost while achieving the specified conditions.
   b. How would the model change if the acreage to be planted was *at least* 500?

7. A client has approached a stockbroker with the following request: Invest $100,000 for maximum annual income under these conditions:
   1. Spread the investment over no more than three different stocks.
   2. Put no more than 40 percent of the money into any one stock.
   3. Put a minimum of $10,000 into oil stock.

   The broker has identified three stocks for investing the funds. Their estimated annual returns and price per share are shown in Table 4-12.

Table 4-12 Data for Problem 7

Stock	Price per Share	Estimated Annual Return per Share
Oil	$120	$11
Auto	52	4
Health	18	2

Formulate an LP model of the problem.

8. A high school dietician is planning menus for the upcoming month. A new item will be spaghetti with sauce. The dietician wants each serving to contain at least 10 grams of protein and at least 40 grams of carbohydrates. Spaghetti contains 5 grams of protein and 32 grams of carbohydrates per cup, and the sauce contains 4 grams of protein and 5 grams of carbohydrates per cup. For aesthetic reasons, the dietician wants the ratio of spaghetti to sauce to be 4:1.

   Spaghetti costs $.30 per cup to buy and prepare, and sauce costs $.40 per cup to buy and prepare. The dietician wants to minimize the cost per serving and keep the calories per serving to 330 or less. The sauce contains 100 calories per cup, and the spaghetti contains 160 calories per cup.

   Formulate a linear programming model for this problem.

9. A fuel oil company intends to distribute a new gasoline that has an octane rating of 94 percent. The company has three fuels that can be blended to achieve a range of octanes. The cost per gallon and the octane ratings of these fuels are shown in Table 4-13.

Table 4-13 Cost per Gallon and Octane Rating of Fuels

Fuel	Cost per Gallon	Octane
A10	$.45	.87
B11	.55	.90
C12	.60	.98

Margin answers:

a. Minimize $Z = 20x_1 + 15x_2 + 12x_3$
$x_1 + x_2 + x_3 = 500$
$x_1 \geq 250$
$x_2 \leq 200$
$x_1 - 2x_3 = 0$
$x_1, x_2, x_3 \geq 0$
b. Land: $x_1 + x_2 + x_3 \geq 500$

Minimize $Z = .30x_1 + .40x_2$
$5x_1 + 4x_2 \geq 10$
$32x_1 + 5x_2 \geq 40$
$x_1 - 4x_3 = 0$
$160x_1 + 100x_2 \leq 330$
$x_1, x_2 \geq 0$

Due to technical reasons, the ratio of C12 to A10 cannot be more than 3:1.

Prepare an LP model that will achieve the desired octane rating at minimum cost. Assume the octanes mix linearly. *Hint:* See Example 4-4.

10. The trust department of a commercial bank must make frequent decisions on customer portfolios. A typical case might involve a portfolio of $120,000. The bank's policy is to use conservative investments such as treasury notes, municipal bonds, and blue-chip stocks. Treasury notes have an annual return of 9 percent, municipal bonds a return of 8 percent, and blue-chip stocks a return of 10 percent. The bank also has a policy of not placing more of a portfolio into stocks than into treasury notes and bonds combined.

Formulate an LP model that will yield the largest annual return for the $120,000 portfolio, given the bank's policies. Ignore transaction costs, fees, tax consequences, and so on.

11. A meat packing company makes pork sausage in 2,000-pound batches. The sausage is made from pork, beef, and filler. The cost of pork is $2.50 per pounds, the cost of beef is $1.80 per pound, and the cost of filler is $1.00 per pound. Each batch must contain the following:

1. At least 800 pounds of pork.
2. No more than 30 percent filler.
3. At least 300 pounds of beef.

The manager wants to know the mix of ingredients that will minimize cost. Formulate an LP model for this problem.

12. A pharmaceutical company is investigating the possibility of marketing a new dietary supplement that would contain iron, calcium, and phosphorous. The supplement would be made by mixing together three inputs, which the company refers to as T5, N1, and T4. The amounts of the three minerals (mg per ounce) contained in each input, the minimum and maximum levels of each mineral per 12-ounce bottle, and the cost per ounce of the inputs are shown in Table 4-14.

Table 4-14   Data for Problem 12

Cost per Ounce: Input:	$.75 T5	$.60 N1	$.55 T4	Minimum per Bottle	Maximum per Bottle
Mineral					
Iron	10	16	12	100 mg	150 mg
Calcium	400	600	800	6,000 mg	8,000 mg
Phosphorous	800	550	500	6,600 mg	8,000 mg

The manager would like to know what the lowest cost combination of inputs is that would achieve the desired dietary ranges for the three minerals on a per-bottle basis. Formulate this problem as an LP model.

13. A small specialty shop. Nuts-to-You, sells a variety of candy and nuts. The owner is concerned with the problem of how to package nuts. The shop carries four types of nuts, which are sold in one-pound bags. It also sells one-pound bags of its own special mix, which consists of 40 percent peanuts and equal parts of the other three types of nuts. The shop has a limited supply of nuts on hand, and the owner believes that before the next shipment of nuts arrives, the current supply can be sold. However, the owner recognizes that different combinations of nuts (individual bags versus bags of the special mix) will yield different profits. The owner would like to know how much of the current supply to allocate to the mix and how much to each individual type in order to maximize profits.

Maximize $Z = .09x_1 + .08x_2 + .10x_3$
$x_1 + x_2 + x_3 = 120{,}000$
$x_1 + x_2 - x_3 \geq 0$
$x_1, x_2, x_3 \geq 0$

Minimize $Z = .75x_1 + .60x_2 + 55x_3$
$x_1 + x_2 + x_3 = 12$
$10x_1 + 16x_2 + 12x_3 \geq 100$
$10x_1 + 16x_2 + 12x_3 \leq 150$
$400x_1 + 600x_2 + 800x_3 \geq 6{,}000$
$400x_1 + 600x_2 + 800x_3 \leq 8{,}000$
$800x_1 + 550x_2 + 500x_3 \geq 6{,}600$
$800x_1 + 550x_2 + 500x_3 \leq 8{,}000$
$x_1, x_2, x_3 \geq 0$

The current supply and cost per pound of each nut type are

Nut	Cost per Pound	Pounds Available
Peanuts (x_2)	$1.00	600
Cashews (x_3)	3.00	360
Walnuts (x_4)	2.50	500
Pecans (x_5)	3.50	400

The selling prices of the packaged nuts are

Package	Price
Mix (x_1)	$4.00
Peanuts (x_2)	1.50
Cashews (x_3)	4.80
Walnuts (x_4)	4.60
Pecans (x_5)	5.00

Assume that mixing costs are negligible.

Formulate this linear programming problem.

Maximize $Z = .64x_1 + 1.28x_2 + 1.28x_3 + 2.816x_4 + 3.584x_5 + 1.792x_6 + 4.672x_7$

$2x_1 + 1.4x_4 + 1.2x_5 + 1.2x_6 + x_7 \le 800$

$2x_2 + .6x_4 + .4x_7 \le 400$

$2x_3 + .8x_5 + .8x_6 + .6x_7 \le 600$

$x_1 \ge 10$

$x6 \ge 12$

All variables ≥ 0

14. The AGC Company supplies fruit juice and juice blends to wholesale grocers in the northeast. A list of the firm's products and their revenue per ounce are shown in Table 4-15.

Table 4-15   Revenue per ounce for Different Juices

Product	Revenue per Ounce
Apple juice (x_1)	$.03
Grape juice (x_2)	.06
Cranberry juice (x_3)	.05
Apple-grape juice (x_4)	.07
Apple-cranberry juice (x_5)	.08
Apple-cranberry juice-1 qt. (x_6)	.08
All-in-one juice (x_7)	.10

The apple-grape juice is 70 percent apple juice and 30 percent grape juice. The apple cranberry juice is 60 percent apple juice and 40 percent cranberry juice, and the all-in-one is 50 percent apple juice, 20 percent grape juice, and the rest cranberry juice.

The company has 200 gallons of apple juice, 100 gallons of grape juice, and 150 gallons of cranberry juice on hand, and the owner wants to know how many containers of each product to prepare in order to maximize profit. Cost per ounce for apple juice is $.02; for grape juice, $.04; and for cranberry juice, $.03.

All products are sold in 64-ounce (two-quart) containers. The apple-cranberry juice is also sold in a one-quart size. *Hint:* Use quarts rather than ounces.

The company has an order for 10 containers of apple juice and 12 containers of the apple-cranberry one-quart size that must be filled from current supplies.

Formulate the linear programming model of this problem.

15. A small shop located on the edge of a large city sells a variety of dried fruits and nuts. The shop caters to travelers of all types; it sells one-pound boxes of individual items, such as dried bananas, as well as one-pound boxes of mixed fruits and nuts, although its popular trail mix is sold only in the two-pound size.

Because of complaints from customers about long lines at the counters, the manager has decided to prepare boxes ahead of time and place them on shelves for self-service. The manager has specified that 50 percent of current supplies should be prepackaged, and the rest should be unpackaged. The amounts of current supplies are listed in Table 4-16.

Table 4-16   Amount of Supply for Problem 15

Item	Supply (pounds)
Dried bananas	800
Dried apricots	600
Coconut pieces	500
Raisins	700
Walnuts	900

The selling prices of the various types of boxes offered are shown in Table 4-17.

Table 4-17   Prices for Problem 15

Type	Price per Box
Trail mix (x_1)	$7.00
Subway mix (x_2)	3.00
Dried bananas (x_3)	2.80
Dried apricots (x_4)	3.25
Coconut pieces (x_5)	3.60
Raisins (x_6)	3.50
Walnuts (x_7)	5.50

The manager would like to obtain as much revenue as possible from prepackaged sales. The manager has stipulated that no more than 30 percent of the prepackaged stock should be allocated to the mixes. The trail mix consists of equal parts of all individual items, whereas the subway mix consists of two parts walnuts and one part each of dried bananas, raisins, and coconut pieces.

Formulate the linear programming model for this problem.

16. A financial adviser recently received a call from a client who wanted to invest a portion of a $150,000 inheritance. The client wanted to realize an annual income, but also wanted to spend some of the money. After discussing the matter, the client and the adviser agreed that a mutual fund, corporate bonds, and a money market account would make suitable investments. The client was willing to leave allocation of the funds among these investment vehicles to the financial adviser, but with these provisions:

1. At least 20 percent of the amount invested should be in the money market account.
2. The investment must produce at least $12,000 annually.
3. The uninvested portion should be as large as possible.

The annual returns would be 11 percent for the mutual fund, 8 percent for the bonds, and 7 percent for the money market. Formulate an LP model that will achieve the client's requests. Ignore transaction costs, the adviser's fee, and so on. (*Hint:* All terms in the objective function must include a variable.)

17. Wineco produces wine coolers and sells them to retail distributors. One popular blend consists of wine, apple juice, and grape juice. Operators must adhere to certain guidelines when preparing the wine cooler:

1. At least 10 percent of the mix must be grape juice.
2. The ratio of apple juice to grape juice must be 2 1/2:1.
3. The mix must contain between 20 percent and 25 percent wine.

Minimize $Z = x_1 + x_2 + x_3$
$x_1 + x_2 + x_3 \leq \$150,000$
$.20x_1 + .20x_2 - .80x_3 \leq 0$
$.11x_1 + .08x_2 + .07x_3 \geq \$12,000$
$x_1, x_2, x_3 \geq 0$
$x_4 =$ uninvested amount
and Max $Z = x_4$
$x_1 + x_2 + x_3 + x_4 = 150,000$
$.2x_1 + .2x_2 - .8x_3 \leq 0$
$.11x_1 + .08x_2 + .07x_3 \geq 12,000$
$x_1, x_2, x_3, x_4 \geq 0$

The company pays $1.20 per gallon for wine, $1.40 per gallon for grape juice, and $.60 per gallon for apple juice.

Formulate an LP model that will help the owner to determine how much wine cooler to mix each day if the capacity of the mixing equipment is 200 gallons per day and the wine cooler is sold for $4 a gallon. The owner wants to maximize profits. Ignore mixing and bottling costs.

18. The planning committee of a bank makes monthly decisions on the amount of funds to allocate to loans and to government securities. Some of the loans are secured (backed by collateral such as a home or an automobile), and some are unsecured. A list of the various types of loans and their annual rates of return are shown in Table 4-18.

Table 4-18 Annual Rate of Return for Investments

Type of Investment	Annual Rate of Return
Secured loans	
Residential mortgage (x_1)	11
Commercial mortgage (x_2)	12
Automobile (x_3)	15
Home improvement (x_4)	13
Unsecured loans	
Vacation (x_5)	17
Student (x_6)	10
Government securities (x_7)	9

In making its decision, the planning committee must satisfy certain legal requirements and bank policies. These can be summarized by the following set of conditions:

1. The amount allocated to secured loans must be at least four times the amount allocated to unsecured loans.
2. Auto and home loans should be no more than 20 percent of all secured loans.
3. Student loans should be no more than 30 percent of unsecured loans.
4. The amount allocated to government securities should be at least 10 percent, but no more than 20 percent, of available funds.
5. The amount allocated to vacation loans must not exceed 10 percent of all loans.

The bank has $5 million available for loans and investments in the next month. Formulate a linear programming model that will enable the planning committee to determine the optimal allocation of funds if the objective is to maximize the annual return, given the preceding list of conditions.

Maximize $Z = .11x_1 + .12x_2 + .15x_3 + .13x_4 + .17x_5 + .10x_6 + .09x_7$

$x_1 + x_2 + x_3 + x_4 - 4x_5 - 4x_6 \geq 0$

$.2x_1 - .2x_2 + .8x_3 + .8x_4 \leq 0$

$-.3x_5 + .7x_6 \leq 0$

$x_7 \geq \$500,000$

$x_7 \leq \$1,000,000$

$-x_1 - .1x_2 - .1x_3 - .1x_4 + .9x_5 - .1x_6 \leq 0$

$x_1 + x_2 + x_3 + x_4 + x_5 + x_6 + x_7 = \$5,000,000$

All variables ≥ 0

19. A classic linear programming problem involves minimizing trim loss. Here is one version of the problem:

A mill cuts 20-foot pieces of wood into several different lengths: 8-foot, 10-foot, and 12-foot. The mill has a certain amount of 20-foot stock on hand and orders for the various sizes. The objective is to fill the orders with as little waste as possible. For example, if two 8-foot lengths are cut from a 20-foot piece, there will be a loss of 4 feet, the leftover amount.

Currently, the mill has 350 20-foot pieces of wood on hand and the following orders, which must be filled from stock on hand:

Size in feet	Number Ordered
8	276
10	100
12	250

a. Formulate an LP model that will enable the mill operator to satisfy the orders with minimum trim loss. (*Hint:* List the different ways the 20-foot pieces could be cut into the desired sizes.)

b. Using your notation from *a*, write an equation for
    (1) The amount of waste that would result given a solution.
    (2) The number of pieces of each size (8-foot, 10-foot, and 12-foot).

20. This is a multiperiod production scheduling problem. Plastic Molding Manufacturer is planning the production storage and marketing of a product whose demand and selling price vary seasonally. The company is in the process of developing a manufacturing strategy. According to the formulated strategy, the company wants to manufacture the product in the seasons during which production costs are low, and then store and sell the product when the selling price is high. The manufacturer has obtained the following estimates of the demand, cost, capacity, and expected selling price of the product for each period.

Period	Production Costs ($)	Production Capacity (tons)	Demand (tons)	Price ($)
1	20	1,500	1,100	180
2	25	2,000	1,500	180
3	30	2,200	1,800	250
4	40	3,000	1,600	270
5	50	2,700	2,300	300
6	60	2,500	2,500	320

Let:

See the IM

P_j = Product made (in tons) during period j
I_j = Product left in storage at the end of period j
D_j = Product demanded during period j
Beginning inventory = 500 tons
Desired ending inventory = 300 tons
(Inventory) storage costs = $2 per ton from one period to the next

Formulate the linear programming problem that provides the optimal production schedule and maximizes the total profit.

21. Use the data envelopment analysis to measure the relative efficiency of the three fast food restaurant franchises located in three different cities in Northwest Indiana operated by the same owner. The owner wants to identify the relatively inefficient operations and try to improve their relative efficiency scores. The relevant information is given in Table 4-19.

Table 4-19   Data for Problem 21

	Restaurants		
	Portage, IN	Hammond, IN	Michigan City, IN
Input Measures			
Weekly hours of operation	84	70	88
Daily number of employees	6	8	7
Daily cost of ingredients	$2,000	$4,000	$3,000
Output Measures			
Weekly profit	4,000	$3,000	$2,500
Number of customers served/week	1,500	1,000	1,200
City fast food market share	30%	20%	15%

Use DEA and identify the most efficient and inefficient fast food restaurants.

Maximize $Z = 1.25x_1 +$
$1.75x_2 + 1.45x_3$
s.t. $x_1 \le 3,000$
$x_2 \le 2,500$
$x_3 \le 2,000$
$x_1 + 2x_2 + 1.5x_3 \le 9,000$
$.7x_1 + .9x_2 + .8x_3 \le 5,000$
$x_1, x_2, x_3 \ge 0$
$x_1 = 3,000$
$x_2 = 1,800$
$x_3 = 1,600$
$Z = \$9,220$

22. A publisher produces three monthly magazines: *Living Right, Living Today*, and *Living Room*. Printing one copy of a magazine requires the amounts of time and paper shown in Table 4-20, which also includes information on selling prices and demands:

Table 4-20   Information about Magazine Selling Prices and Demands

Title	Time (min.)	Paper (lb.)	Selling Price ($)	Maximum Demand/Month
Living Right	1.0	.70	2.25	3,000
Living Today	2.0	.90	2.75	2,500
Living Room	1.5	.80	2.45	2,000

The printer has 150 hours available each month for printing and 5,000 pounds of paper. Production cost is a dollar an issue, regardless of which magazines are printed. The manager wants to know how many of each magazine to run each month in order to maximize profits, given these conditions. Solve using Excel.

◼◼ Chapter 4 Case   Direct Marketing

A direct marketing agency has been asked by a client to do a lead-generation mailing. The purpose of the mailing will be to offer prospective investors longterm notes at preferred rates. Names and addresses for the mailing will be obtained from three lists: CPAs, real estate developers, and personal investors. The cost and response rates for these are shown in Table 4-21:

Table 4-21   Cost and Response Rates

List	Cost per 1,000	Expected Response Rate
CPAs	$ 85	2%
Real estate developers	110	3
Personal investors	95	6

The conversion of leads into sales is expected to be 1 in 20. Moreover, the client has stipulated several additional conditions:

1. Between 10 and 20 percent of the mailing should be to CPAs.
2. No fewer than 10,000 pieces should go to real estate developers.

For purposes of analysis, assume that the lists are large enough to support the mailing sizes that will be called for and assume that the amount of duplication in the lists is negligible. However, assume that 5 percent of the names on a list will be unusable because of deaths, changes in address, and so on. Lists can be ordered in any amount.

The account executive in charge of the mailing wants to answer these questions before deciding whether to approve the mailing:

1. What size mailing will be needed?
2. How many names from each list will be needed?
3. What will the list cost be?

4. What is the expected number of responses?
5. What will the cost per lead be?

Required

Prepare a report that addresses the following points:

1. Formulate this as an LP model that will minimize cost assuming the client wants to achieve at least 250 responses.
2. Formulate this as an LP model that will maximize expected responses given a budget of $20,000.
3. For each of the questions posed in the problem, write an equation that can be used to answer the question.

Linear Programming: Sensitivity Analysis and Duality

Chapter 5

Learning Objectives

After completing this chapter, you should be able to:

1. Explain how sensitivity analysis can be used by a decision maker.
2. Explain why it can be useful for a decision maker to extend the analysis of a linear programming problem beyond determination of the optimal solution.
3. Explain how to analyze graphically and interpret the impact of a change in the value of the objective function coefficient.
4. Explain how to graphically analyze and interpret the impact of a change in the right-hand-side value of a constraint.
5. Explain what a dual is.
6. Formulate the dual of a problem.
7. Read and interpret the solution to a dual problem and relate the dual solution to the primal solution.
8. Explain in economic terms the interpretation of dual variables and the dual solution.
9. Determine if adding another variable to a problem will change the optimal solution mix of the original problem.

Chapter Outline

Introduction to Sensitivity Analysis, 208
A Change in the Value of an Objective Function Coefficient, 209
A Change in the RHS Value of a Constraint, 213
Minimization Problems, 219
Sensitivity Analysis with Excel, 219
Multiple Changes, 224
Summary of Sensitivity Analysis, 226

Duality, 226
Formulating the Dual, 227
Formulating the Dual When the Primal Has Mixed Constraints, 229

Comparison of the Primal and Dual Solutions, 231
Economic Interpretation of the Dual, 231
Adding Another Variable, 232
Computational Considerations, 232

Summary, 236

Glossary, 237

Solved Problems, 238

Discussion and Review Questions, 246

Problems, 246

Chapter 5 Case: Red Brand Canners, 270

◼️◼️ Introduction to Sensitivity Analysis

This chapter describes **sensitivity (postoptimality) analysis** of LP models, analysis that *begins* with the optimal solution in order to gain additional insights into how potential changes to the model would impact the optimal solution.

The material in the chapter is presented in two sections. The first section deals with sensitivity analysis and the last section deals with duality.

The purpose of sensitivity analysis is to explore the effects of potential changes in parameters of LP models on the optimal solution. It is designed to give a decision maker the ability to answer "what if . . .?" questions about an LP model that involve changing the value of a model parameter, such as changing the right-hand-side (RHS) value of a constraint, or changing the value of an objective function coefficient. For example, the decision maker may be considering a price change that will cause a change in a profit coefficient. Two obvious questions come to mind: Will the optimal values of the decision variables change? Will the optimal value of the objective function change? Sensitivity analysis enables the decision maker to easily answer these and similar questions concerning potential changes in values of parameters without having to re-solve an entire problem.

There are three categories of model parameters that might be subject to potential changes:

1. A change in the value of an objective function coefficient.
2. A change in the right-hand-side (RHS) value of a constraint.
3. A change in a coefficient of a constraint.

The discussion here will be limited to the first two of these; it will not cover changes to coefficients of constraints. And unless otherwise noted; the discussion will assume that only *one* parameter is being changed, while all other parameters remain unchanged.

Sensitivity analysis involves identification of ranges of change for various parameters. A central concept in sensitivity analysis is that changes to parameters that fall within prescribed ranges either have no effect or have an easily determinable effect on the optimal solution. There are three aspects of these ranges that are important for understanding sensitivity analysis:

1. Which range pertains to a given situation? For example, which range relates to a change in the RHS value of a constraint?
2. How can the range be determined?
3. What impact on the optimal solution does a change that is within the range have?

This chapter begins by describing how graphical methods can be used for sensitivity analysis, determining the impact that a change in one of the parameters (numerical values) of an LP model will have on the optimal solution and on the optimal value of the objective function.

Sensitivity analysis is useful because it enables a decision maker to quickly assess the impact of a change. Graphical analysis is useful because it provides a visual portrayal of the process and the results.

A decision maker's interest in analyzing the impact of a change in the value of a parameter can come from a variety of sources. For example, changes in either costs or revenues can cause a change in the value of an objective function coefficient. Or a decision maker might wonder what the impact would be if a change in cost or revenue *could* be made (i.e., would it be worth the time, cost, etc.?). Another example would be an opportunity to obtain additional amounts of a scarce resource (e.g., raw material). It could be very useful to

Figure 5-1   A Graph of the Server Problem

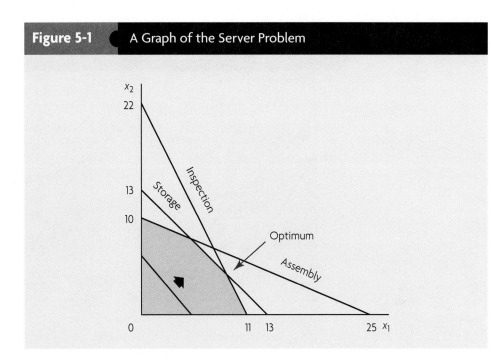

know if acquiring additional amounts would be profitable, and how much more could be profitably used, given other constraints of the problem.

Sensitivity analysis pertains to a change in the value of one parameter *while all other parameters are held constant.* Thus, the procedure and interpretations described here do not apply to situations that involve changes to more than one parameter.

For purposes of illustration, the Web server problem from Chapter 3 will be used. That problem is repeated here for easy reference:

x_1 = quantity of server model 1 to produce
x_2 = quantity of server model 2 to produce

maximize $Z = 60x_1 + 50x_2$ (profit)

subject to

Assembly	$4x_1 + 10x_2 \leq 100$ hours
Inspection	$2x_1 + 1x_2 \leq 22$ hours
Storage	$3x_1 + 3x_2 \leq 39$ cubic feet
	$x_1, x_2 \geq 0$

The graph of this problem and optimal solution are repeated in Figure 5-1.

Let us begin with an analysis of changes in an objective function coefficient.

A Change in the Value of an Objective Function Coefficient

If there is a change in the value of one of the objective function coefficients (while the other one remains fixed), this will cause the slope of the objective function line to change. However, if the change in slope is relatively small, the optimal corner point of the feasible solution space will not change. Of particular interest is the amount by which a coefficient can be changed without changing the optimal solution point. This is known as the **range of optimality.**

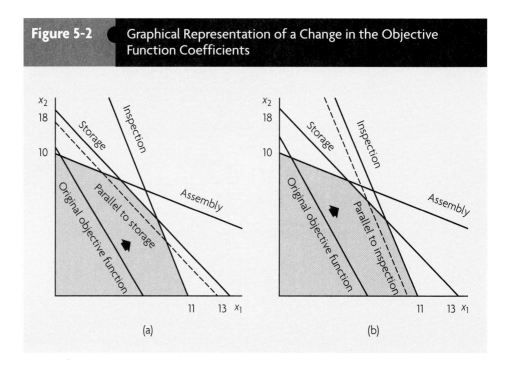

Figure 5-2   Graphical Representation of a Change in the Objective Function Coefficients

We can see graphically in Figure 5-2 how much the slope of the objective function line can change and not change the optimal solution point. If the direction of change causes the slope to become less steep (see Figure 5-2a), the same solution point (intersection of inspection and storage constraints) will be optimal as long as the revised objective function line does not go beyond being parallel to the storage constraint. If it is just parallel to the storage constraint line, multiple solutions are optimal, *including* the original solution point. But beyond that, the next intersection (storage and assembly constraints) will become optimal.

Similarly, if changing the coefficient results in a *steeper* slope (see Figure 5-2b), the same solution will hold as long as the objective function line does not go beyond being parallel to the inspection constraint. If it does, the optimal solution will move to the intersection of the inspection constraint and the x_1 axis.

Thus, as long as a change in the coefficient does not cause the slope of the objective function line to exceed either of those parallel conditions, the same solution will be optimal.

A change in either of the objective function coefficients can cause its slope to change in either direction. In either case, a coefficient change in one direction will cause the slope to increase, while a change in the opposite direction will cause the slope to decrease. Let's take one of the coefficients at a time and see how we can determine its range of optimality.

Suppose we begin with the objective function coefficient of x_1, which is 60. Let's determine what its value would have to be in order for the objective function line to be parallel to the storage constraint line. Note that the two lines will be parallel if the ratio of the x_1 coefficient to the x_2 coefficient is the same for both lines. As they currently exist, the two sets of coefficients are

Storage	$3x_1 + 3x_2$
Objective function	$60x_1 + 50x_2$

As you can see, the storage constraint coefficient ratio (x_1 to x_2) is 3 to 3. Consequently, for the objective function line to be parallel to storage constraint line, its coefficients would have to be equal. If we are changing the x_1 coefficient while holding the x_2 coefficient constant at 50, this would mean the x_1 coefficient would also have to be equal to 50. Hence, the objective function would be $50x_1 + 50x_2$.

Similarly, to be parallel to the inspection line, the coefficients of the objective function would have to be such that the x_1 coefficient was double the x_2 coefficient, as you can see by comparing the two sets of coefficients as they are in the original problem:

Inspection	$2x_1 + 1x_2$
Objective function	$60x_1 + 50x_2$

In order to achieve the 2 to 1 ratio of the inspection constraint line, the x_1 coefficient must be 100. Hence, the objective function would be $100x_1 + 50x_2$.

Thus, our analysis shows:

Parallel to storage	$50x_1 + 50x_2$
Parallel to inspection	$100x_1 + 50x_2$

Therefore, we can say that the range of optimality for the x_1 coefficient of the objective function is 50 to 100. (Note that the x_2 coefficient remained at 50.) This means that for *any* value of the x_1 coefficient in this range, including the end-points, the same values of x_1 and x_2 will be optimal, which is $x_1 = 9$ and $x_2 = 4$.

We can determine the range of optimality for the x_2 coefficient of the objective function in the same manner. First, determine what x_2 coefficient is needed to achieve parallelism with the storage constraint line, with the x_1 objective function coefficient held at 60.

Storage	$3x_1 + 3x_2$
Objective function	$60x_1 + 50x_2$

We can see that an x_2 coefficient of 60 would make the lines parallel:

Storage	$3x_1 + 3x_2$
Objective function	$60x_1 + 60x_2$

Similarly, in order for the objective function to be parallel to the inspection line, the ratio would have to be 2 to 1:

Inspection	$2x_1 + 1x_2$
Objective function	$60x_1 + 50x_2$

This can be achieved by making the x_2 coefficient 30:

Inspection	$2x_1 + 1x_2$
Objective function	$60x_1 + 30x_2$

Comparing these two objective functions will indicate the range of optimality for the x_2 coefficient of the objective function:

Parallel to storage	$60x_1 + 60x_2$
Parallel to inspection	$60x_1 + 30x_2$

Hence, the range of optimality for the x_2 coefficient is 30 to 60. Again, for any value of the x_2 coefficient in this range, the optimal solution will remain the same.

We have just seen that the optimal values of decision variables do not change if a change in the value of an objective function coefficient is within that coefficient's range of optimality. But what about the optimal value of the objective function? Does it change? The answer is yes, it does. The reason is that its value is determined by *both* the values of the decision variables and the values of the objective function coefficients. Hence, if one of the coefficients changes, while everything remains the same, its value must change.

Example 5-1

In Chapter 3, the optimal values for the decision variables and the objective function for the server problem were determined. They were

$x_1 = 9$
$x_2 = 4$
$Z = 740$

In this chapter, we just found the range of optimality for each coefficient of the objective function for the server problem. They were

For the x_1 coefficient, 50 to 100
For the x_2 coefficient, 30 to 60

Given this information, analyze the impact of a change in the x_1 coefficient of the objective function from 60 to 82.50. Specifically, what impact will there be on the optimal values of the decision variables and the objective function?

Solution

First, check to see if the new value of the x_1 coefficient is within the range of optimality. We can see that 82.50 is within the range of 50 to 100. Consequently, there will be no change in the optimal values of x_1 and x_2.

However, the optimal value of Z will change. To find its new value, we must substitute the new coefficient into the objective function with the optimal values of the decision variables and solve. Thus:

$Z = 82.50(9) + 50(4) = 942.50$

An interesting situation occurs when a decision variable has a value of zero in the optimal solution. For example, suppose in the server problem that the x_2 coefficient in the objective function had been 20 instead of 50, so the objective would have been

maximize $Z = 60x_1 + 20x_2$

If we assume an arbitrary profit of \$360, we get the following coordinate points for the objective function: (0, 18) and (6, 0).

The optimal solution would have been $x_1 = 11$, $x_2 = 0$ (20 is outside the range of optimality for x_2). This is illustrated in Figure 5-3. The slope of the objective function in this case is such that the lower right-hand corner of the feasible solution space is now optimal.

The reason that x_2 is zero is that it is not profitable enough relative to x_1. The question of interest then becomes, "What would the profit per unit (objective function coefficient) of x_2 have to be in order for it to have a nonzero optimal value?" The answer depends on the value of the x_2 coefficient of the objective function that would make the objective function just parallel to the inspection constraint, because then the solution would include a nonzero value of x_2.

The objective function would be parallel to the inspection constraint if its coefficients were in the ratio of 2 to 1. With the x_1 objective function coefficient held at 60, this would mean an x_2 objective function coefficient of 30. Hence, we can say that the value of the x_2 coefficient must be at least 30 in order for x_2 to "come into" the solution. This is a special case of the range of optimality; it is sometimes referred to as the **range of insignificance**, meaning the

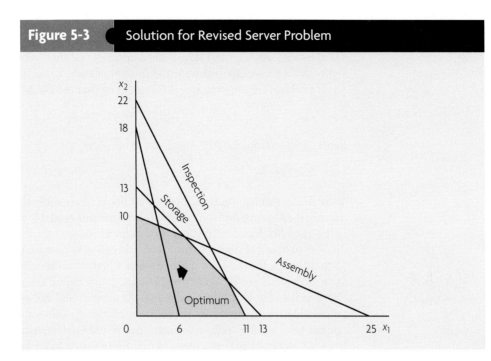

Figure 5-3   Solution for Revised Server Problem

range of values for which a decision variable will be zero. In this example, the range of insignificance for the x_2 coefficient of the objective function is less than 30: any value less than 30 will be too small to cause x_2 to have a nonzero value in the optimal solution.

In summary, in performing sensitivity analysis on objective function coefficients, we can determine the range of optimality for variables that are nonzero in the optimal solution, and we can determine the range of insignificance for variables that are zero in the optimal solution. For a change in the value of an objective function that is within its range of optimality, the optimal values of the decision variables will not change although the value of the objective function will change. For a variable that has a value of zero in the optimal solution, if a change in its objective function coefficient occurs that is within the range of insignificance, no change will occur in either optimal values of decision variables or the optimal value of the objective function.

A Change in the RHS Value of a Constraint

In analyzing the impact of a change in the **right-hand-side (RHS) value** of a constraint, it is first necessary to observe if the constraint in question is a *binding constraint* (i.e., forms the intersection of the optimal corner point of the feasible solution space). There are two types of constraints, binding (left-hand side of the constraint equals the right-hand side of the constraint) and nonbinding and the procedure differs depending on which type of constraint we are dealing with.

Let's take the case of a nonbinding constraint first. The assembly constraint in the server problem is nonbinding on the optimal solution because it does not pass through the optimal corner point (the left-hand side of the constraint is less than the right-hand side of the constraint) (see Figure 5-1). The constraint is

$4x_1 + 10x_2 \leq 100$ hours

Because it is nonbinding, and a less-than-or-equal-to constraint, it will have a certain amount of slack in the optimal solution. By substituting the optimal values of the decision variables into the left-hand side of the constraint and then subtracting the result from the right-hand side, we can determine the amount of slack. Recall that the optimal values in the server problem were $x_1 = 9$, $x_2 = 4$. Substituting into the assembly constraint gives us

$$4(9) + 10(4) = 76$$

Subtracting 76 from the RHS value of 100 hours, we get

$$100 - 76 = 24 \text{ hours}$$

Thus, in the optimal solution, there are 24 hours of assembly time that are unused. Consequently, if additional hours of assembly time became available (say, by scheduling overtime in the assembly department), that would simply increase the amount of slack. So if an additional 10 hours of assembly time were scheduled, the amount of slack would increase by 10 to 34 hours. It would not make sense to schedule additional hours because the department already has excess capacity of 24 hours. Conversely, if there were fewer hours available (say, because of absenteeism), as long as the decrease did not exceed the 24 hours of slack, this would have no impact on the solution. Hence, no amount of increase would affect the optimal values of the decision variables, nor would a decrease that left at least 76 hours (i.e., $100 - 24 = 76$). This range, from 76 to infinity (or 76 to no upper limit) is known as the **range of feasibility** for the assembly constraint. Because the assembly constraint is a nonbinding constraint, any change within this range will have no effect on the solution quantities or on the optimal value of the objective function.

Let us now consider how to determine the range of feasibility for a binding constraint. For the optimal solution in the server problem, both the storage and the inspection constraints were binding; the optimal corner point occurred at their intersection (see Figure 5-1). Because each is a binding constraint, even a slight change in the RHS value of either constraint will cause the optimal corner point to shift, and consequently, cause the optimal values of the decision variables and the optimal value of the objective function to change. However, an interesting phenomenon occurs as long as the change in the RHS value of a binding constraint is within its range of feasibility: The change in the optimal value of the objective function is linearly related to the amount of change. For example, we will be able to determine that the value of the objective function will change by $10 for each one-unit change in the RHS value of the inspection constraint, increasing $10 for each additional hour of inspection time and decreasing $10 for each hour the inspection constraint is decreased from its original amount of 22 hours, as long as the increase or decrease is within the range of feasibility. A $10 change per additional inspection hour in the objective function will be explained in the next few paragraphs. At the end of this section, the issue of changes that go beyond the range of feasibility will be addressed.

For binding constraints, there are two pieces of information that are of interest. One relates to the procedure for determining the range of feasibility for the RHS value of the constraint, and the other relates to determining the amount by which the optimal value of the objective function will change for each one-unit change in the RHS value of the constraint within the range of feasibility. This amount is referred to as the **shadow price** of a constraint. We begin with the change in the optimal value of the objective function for a one-unit change in the RHS of a constraint.

We can determine the impact of a one-unit change in the RHS value of a constraint on the optimal value of the objective function by increasing (or decreasing) the RHS value of the constraint in question by one unit and solving this revised problem. For instance, for the inspection constraint, this would yield the following:

$2x_1 + 1x_2 = 22 + 1$ (i.e., $2x_1 + 1x_2 = 23$)

Although we could graph the problem again using this revised inspection constraint, we would find that the new graph would appear almost identical to the former graph; the solution point would move only slightly. It would still be at the intersection of the storage and inspection constraints. Therefore, we can simply avoid replotting the graph and instead proceed to using a simultaneous solution of the two constraints to determine the new optimal values of x_1 and x_2:

Inspection $2x_1 + 1x_2 = 23$
Storage $3x_1 + 3x_2 = 39$

One way to solve this is to multiply the entire inspection constraint by 3 and then subtract the storage constraint from it. Thus:

Inspection $\times$ 3 $6x_1 + 3x_2 = 69$
Storage $\underline{-(3x_1 + 3x_2 = 39)}$
        $3x_1 \quad\quad = 30$

Solving, we find that $x_1 = 10$. Then, substituting this value into either the storage or the inspection constraint and solving, we can determine the new optimal value of x_2. For instance, using the inspection constraint, we find

$2(10) + 1x_2 = 23$

Solving, $x_2 = 3$.
   Now, if we substitute these new optimal values into the objective function, we obtain

$60(10) + 50(3) = 750$

previously, with $x_1 = 9$ and $x_2 = 4$, we found

$60(9) + 50(4) = 740$

Thus, we see that the one-unit increase in inspection time produced an increase in the objective function of 10. Hence, the shadow price of the inspection constraint is 10, and for *each* one-unit increase or decrease that is within the range of feasibility for the RHS of the inspection constraint, the optimal value of the objective function will increase or decrease by 10. For example, an increase of 2 in the RHS of the inspection constraint will cause an increase of 20 in the optimal value of the objective function. This relationship holds as long as the amount of change in the RHS is within the range of feasibility for that particular constraint.
   We can determine the shadow price of the storage constraint in the same manner. Adding one unit to its RHS changes it to 40. Solving using simultaneous equations yields:

Inspection $\times$ 3 $6x_1 + 3x_2 = 66$
Storage + 1 $\underline{-(3x_1 + 3x_2 = 40)}$
        $3x_1 \quad\quad = 26$

Solving, $x_1 = 8.67$. Substituting into the inspection constraint and solving for x_2, we find $x_2 = 4.67$. Using these new values in the objective function, we obtain the following (note that rounding will give a slightly larger value):

$60(8.67) + 50(4.67) = 753.33$

Compared to the original value of 740 for the objective function, we can see that an increase in one unit in the RHS of the storage constraint caused an increase of 13.33. Hence, the shadow price for the storage constraint is 13.33. This tells us that for a change in the amount of storage space that is within the range of feasibility, the value of the objective function will change by 13.33 times the amount of change in storage space. This shows the importance of knowing what the range of feasibility is: "Over what range of values is the shadow price valid?" That is our next topic.

The shadow price that is in effect at the optimal solution will remain in effect (i.e., it will not change) as long as the same constraints that are binding continue to be binding. Thus, as long as the optimal solution is at the point where the same constraints intersect, the shadow price will be the same.

A key factor in understanding analysis of the range of feasibility is recognizing that when the RHS value of a constraint is changed, the resulting graph of the revised constraint line will be *parallel* to the original line. The new line will be closer to the origin if the RHS has been decreased or farther from the origin if the RHS value has been increased. Moreover, the larger the change, the farther apart the revised line and the original line will be.

In order to determine the range of feasibility for binding constraints using the graphical approach, we follow this procedure:

1. Place a straight edge along the constraint.
2. Slide it away from the origin, making sure to keep it parallel to the constraint. Continue until you come to the last point where your straight edge intersects the other binding constraint. Note that point on the graph.
3. Return the straight edge to the original line. Now move it parallel to the constraint but in the direction of the origin until you get to the last point where the two binding constraints intersect. Note this point.
4. Determine the coordinates of the two points you identified. Substitute each set of values into the left-hand side of the constraint and solve. The resulting two values are the endpoints of the range of feasibility.

Example 5-2

Determine the range of feasibility for each of these binding constraints in the server problem:

1. The inspection constraint.
2. The storage constraint.

Solution

1. Following the above procedure, we determine the last point where the storage constraint intersects with the line that is parallel to the inspection constraint line, moving away from the origin. See Figure 5-4.

   Next, we repeat the procedure moving toward the origin. See Figure 5-5.

   The coordinates of the upper limit, the point where the storage constraint intersects with the line parallel to the inspection constraint line, are easy to obtain directly from the graph: $x_1 = 13$, $x_2 = 0$. For the lower limit, note that at that last point, the storage and assembly lines intersect. Hence, we can determine

Figure 5-4   The Upper Limit on Using Additional Inspection Time

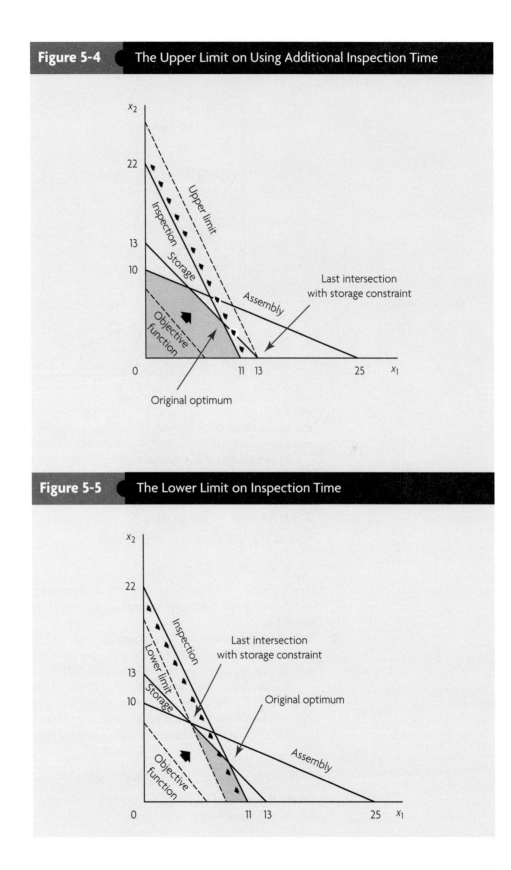

Figure 5-5   The Lower Limit on Inspection Time

Figure 5-6 Range of Feasibility for Changes in Inspection Time

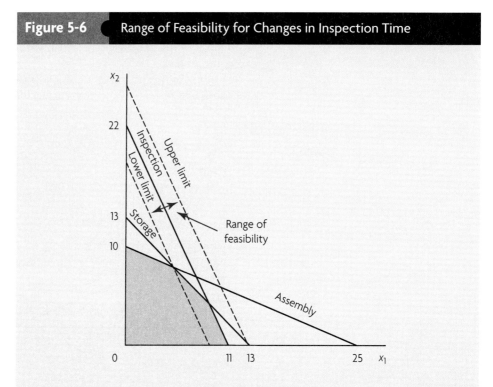

the coordinates of that point by solving the equations of the storage and assembly lines simultaneously. This will yield $x_1 = 5$ and $x_2 = 8$.

By substituting these two sets of coordinates into the left-hand side of the inspection constraint, we obtain the upper and lower ends of the range of feasibility for the inspection constraint. For $x_1 = 13$, $x_2 = 0$, we get

$$2(13) + 1(0) = 26 \quad \text{(upper limit)}$$

For $x_1 = 5$, $x_2 = 8$, we get

$$2(5) + 1(8) = 18 \quad \text{(lower limit)}$$

Hence, the range of feasibility for the RHS of the inspection constraint is 18 to 26.

The range of feasibility is bordered by these two limits, as illustrated in Figure 5-6.

2. Repeating the process for the storage constraint, we determine the last points (upper limit and lower limit) for which the line parallel to *storage* constraint intersects the *inspection* constraint (see Figure 5-7).

We can see on the graph in Figure 5-7 that the lower limit intersects at $x_1 = 11$, $x_2 = 0$, and at the upper limit the inspection and assembly lines cross. Solving those two equations simultaneously yields $x_1 = 7.5$ and $x_2 = 7$.

Substituting these two sets of values into the storage constraint gives us

$$3(7.5) + 3(7) = 43.5 \quad \text{(upper limit)}$$
$$3(11) + 3(0) = 33 \quad \text{(lower limit)}$$

Hence, the range of feasibility for the RHS of the storage constraint is 33 cubic feet to 43.5 cubic feet.

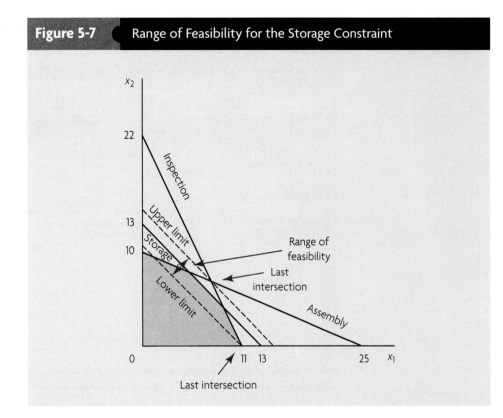

Figure 5-7   Range of Feasibility for the Storage Constraint

As a final note, let us consider what happens if a change in the RHS value of a constraint takes it beyond its range of feasibility. There are two cases. One is a decrease that results in a RHS that is below the lower limit of the range of feasibility. Should this occur, it would be necessary to solve the modified problem in order to find the new optimal solution and find the new shadow prices. The other case occurs when the upper limit of the range of feasibility is exceeded. In such instances, the excess beyond the upper limit becomes slack and the shadow price for that constraint becomes zero. For example, suppose analysis indicates that the upper limit of the range of feasibility of a constraint is 200. If the RHS of this constraint is changed to, say, 210, the excess of 10 will become slack.

Minimization Problems

Minimization problems are handled in exactly the same way that maximization problems are, except that in finding the range of feasibility, *subtract* 1 from the RHS instead of adding 1 to the RHS. Note, too, that for the range of insignificance, the value will be *lower* than the current value, instead of higher.

Sensitivity Analysis with Excel

Excel has the capability of performing sensitivity analysis of the objective function coefficients and the right-hand-side values. The Excel input screen along with the necessary formulas for the server problem is given in Exhibit 5-1. Once the necessary formulas and the

Exhibit 5-1 Excel Input Screen for the Server Problem

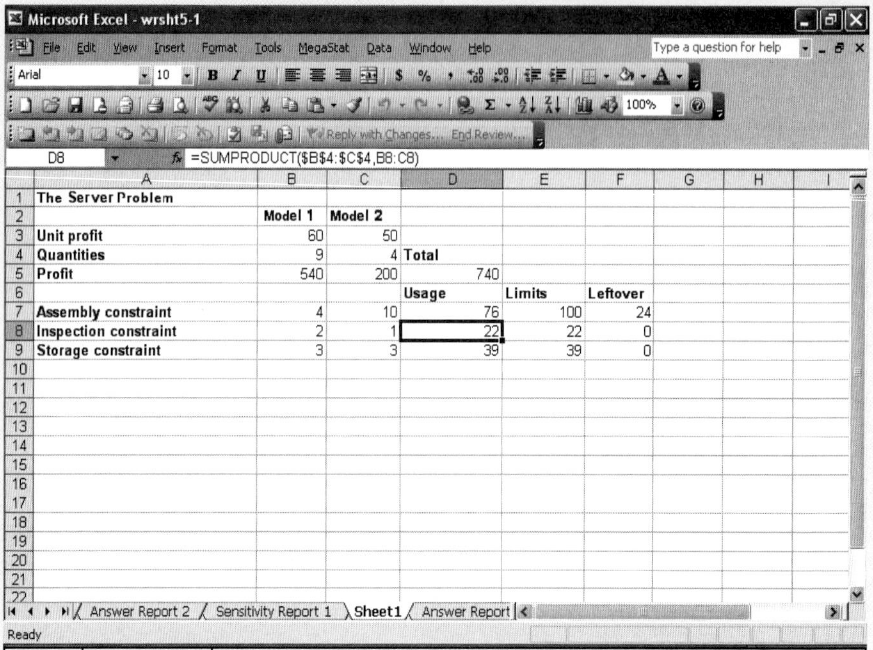
Microsoft Excel - wrsht5-1

D8 =SUMPRODUCT($B$4:$C$4,B8:C8)

	A	B	C	D	E	F
1	The Server Problem					
2		Model 1	Model 2			
3	Unit profit	60	50			
4	Quantities	9	4	Total		
5	Profit	540	200	740		
6				Usage	Limits	Leftover
7	Assembly constraint	4	10	76	100	24
8	Inspection constraint	2	1	22	22	0
9	Storage constraint	3	3	39	39	0

Answer Report 2 / Sensitivity Report 1 / Sheet1 / Answer Report

Cell	Copied to	Formula
D7	D8, D9	= SUMPRODUCT ($B$4 : $C$4, B7 : C7)
F7	F8, F9	= E7 − D7
D5		= SUM (B5 : C5)
B5	C5	= B3 * B4

data have been entered as shown in Exhibit 5-1, we choose **Tools | Solver** and specify the input parameters the same way as we specified the input parameters in solving Example 5-1. The completed Solver input specification screen is shown in Exhibit 5-2. Once the Solver input specification screen is completed as shown in Exhibit 5-2, we click on Solve, and the Solver will show the optimization output screen given in Exhibit 5-3. The optimization output screen states that the Solver has found an optimal solution. On the right-hand side of this screen is the specification of output reports made available by Solver. Clicking on these will generate the following reports. The first report is the Answer Report, as shown in Exhibit 5-4. This report begins with the Target Cell, which is cell D5 in the server data input screen. The target cell specifies the total profit as $740. The next portion of the Answer Report states the optimal values of the decision variables. These optimal values are given in cells B4 and C4 as specified in the Answer Report under the heading of Adjustable Cells. As it can be observed in Exhibit 5-4, the optimal value of server model 1 is 9 and of server model 2 is 4.

Exhibit 5-2   Solver Input Specification (parameter) Screen

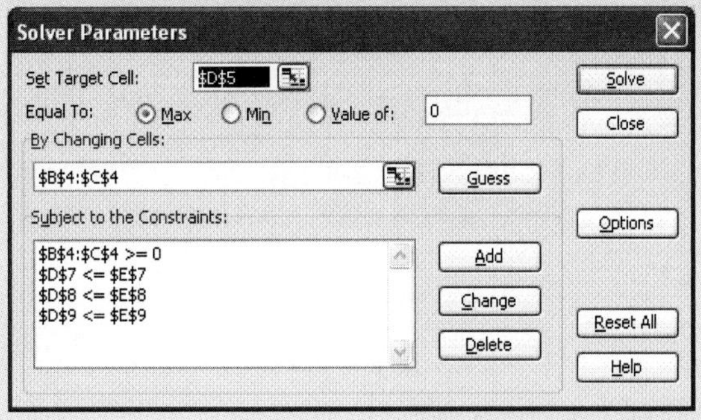

The third section of the Answer Report deals with the constraints. Cells D7, D8, and D9 specify the amount of resources used in each constraint. For example, cell D7 specifies the amount of hours used in the assembly department, which is equal to 76. Since there were 100 hours available in the assembly department as specified in cell E7, the difference between cell E7 and cell D7 indicates the amount of slack available in the assembly department, which is 24 hours. The 24 hours is also the value of the slack variable $1(s_1)$. The values of the slack variables are not only specified in the constraint section of the Answer Report, but also specified in the Leftover column of the input screen shown in Exhibit 5-1. The values of the other two slack variables (s_2 and s_3) are zeros since we use all of the inspection hours (22 hours) and all of the storage space (39 square feet). The cell values of D8 and D9 are 22 and 39 respectively, which also confirms the usage of all of the inspection hours and the storage space in terms of square footage. Note that in the third section of the Answer Report, slack values are given in the last column. The last two rows of the third section of the Answer Report repeats the values of the decision variables.

The second report generated by Solver is entitled Sensitivity Report and is shown in Exhibit 5-5. The first part of this report is the statement of the optimal values of the decision variables. The first row of this report indicates the cell in which the optimal values

Exhibit 5-3   Optimization Output Screen

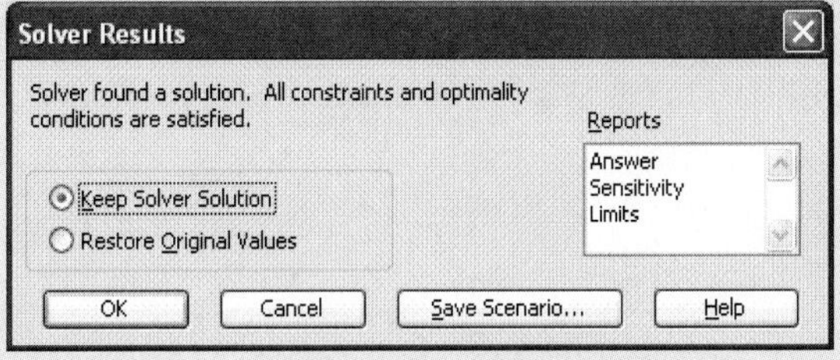

Exhibit 5-4   Excel Basic Output (Answer) Report for the Server Problem

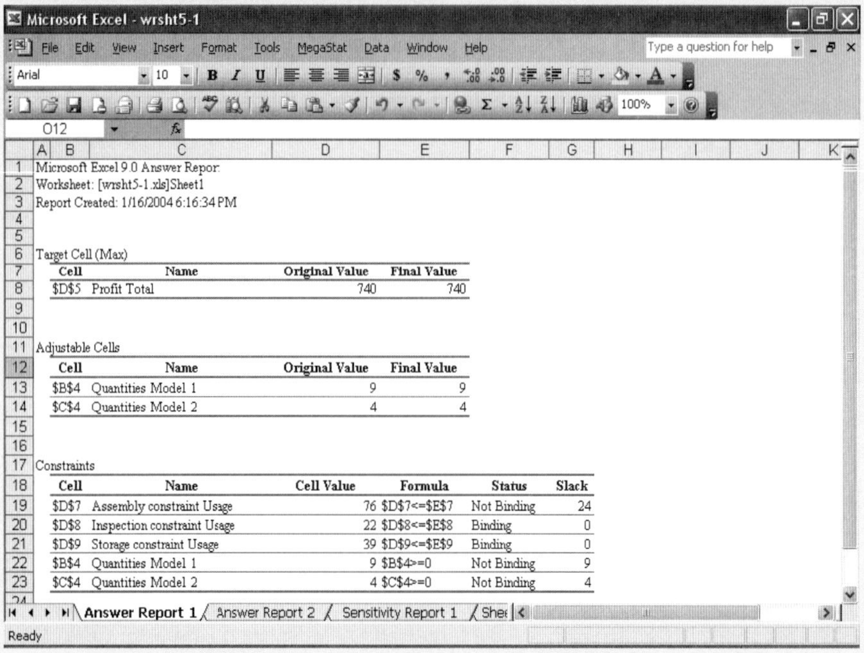

Microsoft Excel - wrsht5-1

File   Edit   View   Insert   Format   Tools   MegaStat   Data   Window   Help   Type a question for help

Arial   10   **B** *I* U $ %   O12

	A B	C	D	E	F	G	H	I	J	K
1	Microsoft Excel 9.0 Answer Report									
2	Worksheet: [wrsht5-1.xls]Sheet1									
3	Report Created: 1/16/2004 6:16:34 PM									
4										
5										
6	Target Cell (Max)									
7	Cell	Name	Original Value	Final Value						
8	$D$5	Profit Total	740	740						
9										
10										
11	Adjustable Cells									
12	Cell	Name	Original Value	Final Value						
13	$B$4	Quantities Model 1	9	9						
14	$C$4	Quantities Model 2	4	4						
15										
16										
17	Constraints									
18	Cell	Name	Cell Value	Formula	Status	Slack				
19	$D$7	Assembly constraint Usage	76	$D$7<=$E$7	Not Binding	24				
20	$D$8	Inspection constraint Usage	22	$D$8<=$E$8	Binding	0				
21	$D$9	Storage constraint Usage	39	$D$9<=$E$9	Binding	0				
22	$B$4	Quantities Model 1	9	$B$4>=0	Not Binding	9				
23	$C$4	Quantities Model 2	4	$C$4>=0	Not Binding	4				

Answer Report 1 / Answer Report 2 / Sensitivity Report 1 / Shee

Ready

Exhibit 5-5   Excel Sensitivity Analysis Report for the Server Problem

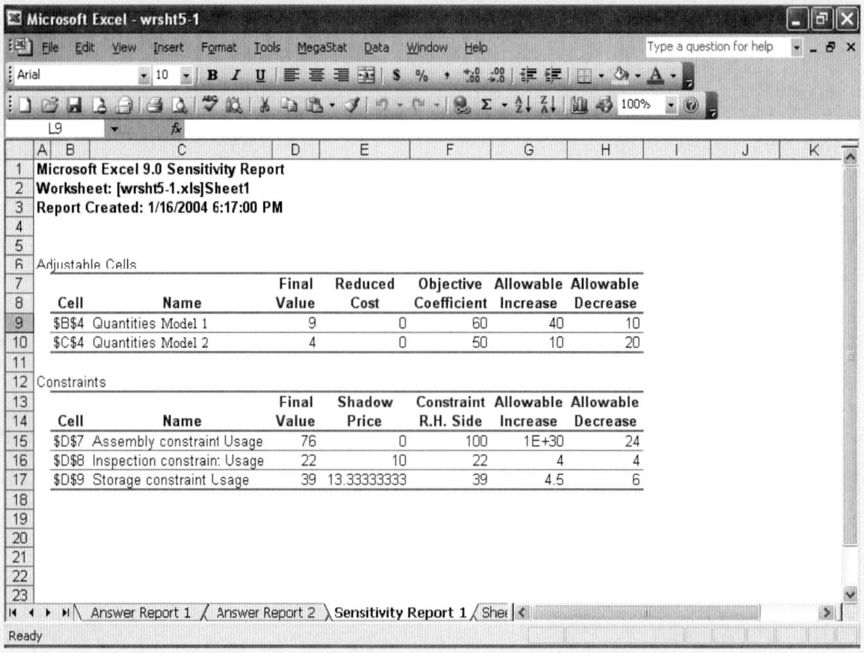

Microsoft Excel - wrsht5-1

File   Edit   View   Insert   Format   Tools   MegaStat   Data   Window   Help   Type a question for help

Arial   10   **B** *I* U $ %   L9

	A B	C	D	E	F	G	H	I	J	K
1	**Microsoft Excel 9.0 Sensitivity Report**									
2	**Worksheet: [wrsht5-1.xls]Sheet1**									
3	**Report Created: 1/16/2004 6:17:00 PM**									
4										
5										
6	Adjustable Cells									
7			Final	Reduced	Objective	Allowable	Allowable			
8	Cell	Name	Value	Cost	Coefficient	Increase	Decrease			
9	$B$4	Quantities Model 1	9	0	60	40	10			
10	$C$4	Quantities Model 2	4	0	50	10	20			
11										
12	Constraints									
13			Final	Shadow	Constraint	Allowable	Allowable			
14	Cell	Name	Value	Price	R.H. Side	Increase	Decrease			
15	$D$7	Assembly constraint Usage	76	0	100	1E+30	24			
16	$D$8	Inspection constraint Usage	22	10	22	4	4			
17	$D$9	Storage constraint Usage	39	13.33333333	39	4.5	6			

Answer Report 1 / Answer Report 2 \ Sensitivity Report 1 / Shee

Ready

of the decision variables appear in the input sheet of the server problem. In the input sheet, cell B4 provides the optimal value of the model 1 server (9 units) and cell C4 specifies the optimal value of the model 2 server (4 units). Just to the right of the optimal values of the decision variables are reduced costs. A nonzero reduced cost would appear if a decision variable was not in the solution. A nonzero reduced cost would indicate the amount that the variable's objective function coefficient could be increased without that variable coming into the solution. Thus, if a reduced cost was 3.0, that variable's objective function would have to be increased by more than 3.0 in order for it to be in the solution if the problem was to be reworked with that one change. In other words, a reduced cost of 3.0 shows that variable would not be coming into the solution as long as that variable's objective function would be increased by less than 3.0. In the server problem example, since both of the decision variables are in the optimal solution (both decision variables have nonzero values in the optimal solution), the reduced costs associated with both variables are equal to zero. The column immediately to the right of the reduced costs provides the initial value of the objective function coefficients and the final two columns all the way to the right of the first table in the Sensitivity Report (Exhibit 5–5) display the objective function ranges (range of optimality). The column heading labeled as Allowable Increase shows the amount of increase allowed without changing the optimal mix of the products. In this example, the profit margin of server model 1 could be increased by $40 up to $100 (60 + 40) without changing the optimal product mix. The final column, labeled Allowable Decrease, shows the amount of decrease allowed without changing the optimal mix of the products. In this example, the profit margin of server model 1 could be decreased by $10 down to $50 (60 − 10) without changing the optimal product mix. Likewise the Allowable Increase column indicates that the profit margin of server model 2 could be increased by $10 up to $60 (50 + 10) without changing the optimal product mix. On the other hand, Allowable Decrease shows that the profit margin of server model 2 could be decreased by $20 down to $30 (50 − 20) without changing the optimal product mix.

The second (bottom) portion of the Sensitivity Report given in Exhibit 5-5 begins the constraint analysis. Each row of this portion of the report deals with a separate constraint. The column headings Cell, Name, and Final Value indicate the amount of resource used for each particular constraint. For example, for the assembly constraint, we used 76 of the 100 available hours. Thus, under the column heading Cell, we specify cell D7 ($D-$7) from Exhibit 5–1; under the column heading Name, we specify the name of the constraint, and under the column heading Final Value, we specify the value of the resource used, which is 76 hours as specified in cell D7 of the input sheet in Exhibit 5-1. The column next to the final value is the shadow price associated with that constraint's slack and/or surplus variables (slack variables for the server problem). In the server problem, the shadow prices are 0,10 and 13.333 for the three constraints respectively. Since we have slack assembly hours left in the assembly constraint, we would not be willing to pay any additional funds to obtain labor hours in the assembly department because we have some labor hours left over in this department. Therefore, the shadow price associated with the labor hours in the assembly department is equal to zero. However, since we have used up all of the inspection hours and all of the storage space, constraint 2 and constraint 3 would have a nonzero shadow price. The shadow price of $10 indicates the amount we are willing to pay to obtain one additional labor hour in the inspection department. The shadow price of $13.33 indicates the amount we are willing to pay to obtain one additional square foot of space for the third constraint. If we decide to use another computer software package, we may see another name in lieu of a shadow price: dual price. The next column to the right of the shadow price specifies the original RHS value of each constraint. In other words, we had 100 labor hours in the assembly department, 22 labor hours in the inspection department, and 39 square feet of storage space. The final two columns of the second (bottom) portion of the Sensitivity Report show the range of feasibility for the RHS ranges. Therefore, the next column to the right of the original RHS value indicates the amount of possible increase and the final column indicates the amount of possible decrease in the original RHS value that will result in the same product mix or the same combination of the variables that are in the solution. In other words the Allowable Increase and the Allowable Decrease show the amounts by which the right-hand side of a constraint can be changed and still be within the range of feasibility. For example, for the storage constraint, the allowable increase is 4.5 and the allowable decrease is 6; therefore, the range of feasibility of the RHS value of the storage constraint is from $39 - 6 = 33$ to $39 + 4.5 = 43.5$. In other words, the current variables in the optimal solution (x_1 = model 1 and x_2 = model 2) will stay in the optimal solution with the current shadow prices as long as square footage available for storage remains between 33 and 43.5.

Multiple Changes

Up until this point, the discussion of sensitivity analysis has been restricted to cases that involve *one* change of either a coefficient of an objective function or the RHS value of a constraint. Ranges of optimality for objective function coefficients and ranges of feasibility for RHS values of constraints were said to be applicable to a change in one parameter only; multiple changes (e.g., values of two or more objective function coefficients are changed or values of two or more of the RHS amounts of constraints are changed) were not discussed. Let us now address that issue.

In certain instances, the impact of multiple changes can be readily evaluated. It begins with a determination of the ranges of optimality (if objective function changes are involved) or a determination of the ranges of feasibility (if RHS values are involved). That reveals the amount that each parameter is allowed to change (the allowable increase or the allowable decrease) and still be within the range of optimality or the range of feasibility. Next, a set of specific changes is analyzed by computing the percentage of the allowable increase or allowable decrease that each change represents. For instance, suppose we want to evaluate multiple changes that involve two objective function coefficients, and we determine that the first coefficient's change would be 20 percent of its allowable increase and the second coefficient's change would be 40 percent of its allowable increase. As long as the total of these percentages does not exceed 100 percent, the impact of the combined changes will be very similar to the result of a single change that falls within its range of optimality. That is, the original optimal values of all variables with a positive value will remain the same,[1] but the optimal value of the objective function would change, taking into account the new coefficients of the objective function.

Similarly, if, say, three RHS values were to be changed and we determined that the first change would constitute an increase that was 30 percent of the allowable increase for that constraint's RHS, the second was an increases of 30 percent of *its* allowable increase, and the third was 30 percent of *its* allowable *decrease,* the sum of these would be 90 percent (note that the percentage are *added* even though two are for increases and one for a decrease). Because the sum of the percentages does not exceed 100 percent, the changes satisfy the 100 percent requirement. However, the **100 percent rule** does not imply that the optimal solution will change if the sum of the percentage change exceeds 100 percent. When the 100 percent rule is not satisfied, we must resolve the problem to determine if the optimal solution changes, and if it does, we can easily determine the new optimal values of the

---

[1]If the total percentage *equals* 100 percent, an alternate optimal solution may cause the optimal Quantity values to change.

decision variables. In the case of RHS changes, this means that the shadow prices remain the same. Consequently, the impact on the optimal value of the objective function can be determined by taking into account the combined effects of RHS changes and the corresponding shadow prices. Similarly, revised Quantity values can be computed using values from the original final solution. The 100 percent rule cannot be applied to changes in both objective function coefficients and right-hand sides simultaneously. In order to consider simultaneous changes for both RHS and objective function coefficients, the problem must be resolved.

Example 5-3

Let us consider how the solution to the server problem would be affected by multiple changes to *either* its objective function coefficients *or* the RHS values of its constraints. Let's consider these changes:

a. A change in the objective function from maximize $60x_1 + 50x_2$ to maximize $70x_1 + 56x_2$.
b. A change in the RHS of the inspection constraint from 22 to 23 hours and a change in the storage constraint from 39 to 36 cubic feet.

Solution
(Values for allowable increases and decreases are taken from Exhibit 5-5.)

a. The change in the x_1 coefficient is +10 (i.e., 60 to 70), and the change in the x_2 coefficient is +6 (i.e., 50 to 56). From Exhibit 5-5, the allowable increase for the x_1 coefficient is 40, and the allowable increase for the x_2 coefficient is 10. Thus, we have

Variable	x_1	x_2
Change	+10	+6
Allow. inc. or dec.	+40	+10
percent change	25% + 60% = 85%	

As you can see, the sum of the percentage change does not exceed 100 percent, so it is within the acceptance range for multiple changes. Therefore, we can say that the optimal values of x_1 and x_2 remain the same as in the original problem. However, the optimal value of Z will increase by the sum of the increase in the x_1 coefficient multiplied by the optimal value of x_1 and the increase in the x_2 coefficient multiplied by the optimal value of x_2. Thus, the increase will be 10(9) + 5(4) = 110; the new value will be 740 + 110 = 850.

b. For the RHS changes, we have

Constraint	Inspection	Storage
Change	1	−3
Allow. inc. or dec.	4	−6
percent change	25%	+ 50% = 75%

The total change would be 75 percent. Because this does not exceed 100 percent, it is within the range of sensitivity. Consequently, the shadow prices (10.00 and 13.33) do not change. The optimal value of Z will change. The amount of change will be

$+1(10.00) - 3(13.33) = -30$

Hence, the optimal value of Z will be $740 - 30 = 710$.

Table 5-1	Summary of Results of Changes That Are within Ranges of Optimality and Feasibility

Objective Function Coefficient Change within the Range of Optimality

Factor	Result
Variables in solution	Same variables still in solution
Optimal values of solution variables	Don't change
Optimal value of Z	Will change

RHS Change within the Range of Feasibility

Factor	Result
Shadow price	Remains the same
List of variables with positive values	Remains the same
Values of variables with positive values	Changes
Optimal value of Z	Changes

Summary of Sensitivity Analysis

Sensitivity analysis is an extension of linear programming that goes beyond finding the optimal solution to a problem. It enables managers to answer "what if . . .?" questions related to potential changes to parameters of a model.

The discussion pertained to two types of changes: changes to objective function coefficients and changes to the RHS values of constraints. Sensitivity analysis is always appropriate for situations in which *one* such change is being contemplated; multiple changes require changes to satisfy the 100 percent rule.

Sensitivity analysis can be performed using a computer package such as Excel or by performing simple computations using the information contained in the optimal solution to the linear programming problem.

Table 5-1 provides a summary of the impact of a change that falls within the range of optimality or within the range of feasibility.

Duality

Every linear programming problem can have two forms. The optimal formulation of a problem is referred to as its **primal** form. The other form is referred to as its **dual** form. As you will see, the dual is kind of a "mirror image" of the primal because in both its formulation and its solution, the values of the dual are flip-flop versions of the primal values.

The solution to the primal problem contains the solution to the dual problem, and vice versa. Consequently, once either the primal or the dual problem has been solved, the solution to the other is also apparent. You might wonder, then, why we even bother to discuss duality. The answer is mainly in the economic interpretation of the results of the dual solution. Analysis of the dual can enable a manager to evaluate the potential impact of a new product, and it can be used to determine the marginal values of resources (i.e., constraints). Relative to a new product, a manager would want to know what impact adding a new product would have on the solution quantities and the profit; relative to resources, a manager can refer to a dual solution to determine how much profit one unit of each resource is equivalent to. This can help the manager to decide which of several alternative uses of resources is most profitable.

Formulating the Dual

All of the problems formulated in the preceding chapters can be classified as primal problems because they were formulated directly from descriptions of the problem. The dual, on the other hand, is an alternate formulation of the problem that requires the existence of the primal. In general terms, a primal formulation such as

minimize $\Sigma c_j x_j$

subject to

$a_{ij} \geq b_i$

becomes the following dual formulation:

maximize $\Sigma b_j y_j$

subject to

$a_{ji} \leq c_j$

Let's now consider how the dual can be formulated from the primal problem.

Example 5-4

Write the dual of the following:

minimize $40x_1 + 44x_2 + 48x_3$

subject to

$1x_1 + 2x_2 + 3x_3 \geq 20$
$4x_1 + 4x_2 + 4x_3 \geq 30$
$x_1, x_2, x_3 \geq 0$

Solution
The dual of this problem is

maximize $20y_1 + 30y_2$

subject to

$1y + 4y_2 \leq 40$
$2y_1 + 4y_2 \leq 44$
$3y_1 + 4y_2 \leq 48$
$y_1, y_2 \geq 0$

A comparison of these two versions of the problem will reveal why the dual might be termed the "mirror image" of the primal. Table 5-2 shows how the primal problem is transformed into its dual.

We can see in Table 5-2 that the original objective was to minimize, whereas the objective of the dual is to maximize. In addition, the coefficients of the primal's objective function become the right-hand-side values for the dual's constraints, whereas the primal's right-hand-side values become the coefficients of the dual's objective function.

Table 5-2   Transforming the Primal into Its Dual

		Primal			Dual	
Objective function and right-hand-side values	minimize subject to	$40x_1 - 44x_2 - 48x_3$		maximize subject to	$20y_1 + 30y_2$	
	1		≥ 20	1		≤ 40
	2		≥ 30	2		≤ 44
				3		≤ 48

		Primal		Dual
Constraint	1	$1x_1 + 2x_2 + 3x_3 \geq$	1	$1y_1 + 4y_2 \leq$
Coefficients	2	$4x + 4x_2 + 4x_3 \geq$	2	$2y_1 + 4y_2 \leq$
			3	$3y_1 + 4y_2 \leq$

Note that the primal has three decision variables and two constraints, whereas the dual has two decision variables and three constraints.

The constraint coefficients of the primal are constraint coefficients of the dual, except that the coefficients of the first "row" of the primal become the coefficients of the first "column" of the dual, and the coefficients of the second "row" of the primal become the coefficients of the second "column" of the dual.

Finally, note that the $\geq$ constraints of the primal become $\leq$ constraints in the dual.

When the primal problem is a *maximization* problem with all $\leq$ constraints, the dual is a *minimization* problem with all $\geq$ constraints, as the next example illustrates.

Example 5-5

Formulate the dual of the server problem.

Solution

The original (primal) problem was

maximize $Z = 60x_1 + 50x_2$

subject to

$4x_1 + 10x_2 \leq 100$
$2x_1 + 1x_2 \leq 22$
$3x_1 + 3x_2 \leq 39$

To formulate the dual, we can follow this sequence:

1   For the objective function:
    a.   Because the primal is a maximization, the dual will be a minimization.
    b.   The right-hand-side values for the constraints of the primal become the co-efficients of the objective function of the dual.

Thus, the objective function of the dual is:

minimize $Z = 100y_1 + 22y_2 + 39y_3$

The variable names are ys for the dual, simply to differentiate them from the primal variables. There will be one dual variable for each constraint.

2. For the constraints:
   a. There will be one dual constraint for each primal decision variable. Hence, because the primal has two such variables, the dual will have two constraints.
   b. The right-hand-side values of the dual constraints will equal the primal's objective function coefficients taken in order. That is, the right-hand-side value of the first dual constraint will equal the first coefficient of the primal's objective function coefficient, and the right-hand-side value of the second dual constraint will equal the second objective function coefficient of the primal.
   c. The coefficients of the first primal constraint will become the first coefficients in each of the dual constraints: The x_1 coefficient in the first primal constraint becomes the y_1 coefficient in the first dual constraint and the x_2 coefficient in the first primal constraint becomes the y_1 coefficient in the second dual constraint, and so on.

   Thus, the constraints of the dual are

   1     $4y_1 + 2y_2 + 3y_3 \geq 60$
   2     $10y_1 + 1y_2 + 3y_3 \geq 50$

Putting these two parts together, the dual for the server problem is

minimize $Z = 100y_1 + 22y_2 + 39y_3$

subject to

1     $4y_1 + 2y_2 + 3y_3 \geq 60$
2     $10y_1 + 1y_2 + 3y_3 \geq 50$
      $y_1, y_2, y_3 \geq 0$

Formulating the Dual When the Primal Has Mixed Constraints

In order to transform a primal problem into its dual, it is easier if all constraints in a maximization problem are of the $\leq$ variety, and in a minimization problem, every constraint is of the $\geq$ variety.

To change the direction of a constraint, multiply both sides of the constraint by -1. For example:

$-1(2x_1 + 3x_2 \geq 18)$ is $-2x_1 - 3x_2 \leq -18$

If a constraint is an equality, it must be replaced with *two* constraints; one with a $\leq$ sign and the other with a $\geq$ sign. For instance:

$4x_1 + 5x_2 = 20$

will be replaced by

$4x_1 + 5x_2 \leq 20$
$4x_1 + 5x_2 \geq 20$

Then one of these must be multiplied by -1, depending on whether the primal is a maximization or a minimization problem.

Example 5-6

Formulate the dual of this problem:

maximize $Z = 50x_1 + 80x_2$

subject to

$3x_1 + 5x_2 \leq 45$
$4x_1 + 2x_2 \geq 16$
$6x_1 + 6x_2 = 30$
$\quad x_1, x_2 \geq 0$

Solution

Since this is a maximization problem, put constraints into the $\leq$ form.

The first constraint is already in that form. The second constraint can be converted to that form by multiplying both sides by -1. Thus:

$-1(4x_1 + 2x_2 \geq 16)$ becomes $-4x_1 - 2x_2 \leq -16$

The third constraint is an equality and must be restated as two separate constraints. Thus, it becomes

$6x_1 + 6x_2 \leq 30$ and $6x_1 + 6x_2 \geq 30$

The second of these two must now be multiplied by -1, which yields

$-6x_1 - 6x_2 \leq -30$

Hence, the form of the primal is

maximize $Z = 50x_1 + 80x_2$

subject to

$\quad 3x_1 + 5x_2 \leq 45$
$-4x_1 - 2x_2 \leq -16$
$\quad 6x_1 + 6x_2 \leq 30$
$-6x_1 - 6x_2 \leq -30$
$\qquad x_1, x_2 \geq 0$

The dual is

minimize $Z = 45y_1 - 16y_2 + 30y_3 - 30y_4$

subject to

$3y_1 - 4y_2 + 6y_3 - 6y_4 \geq 50$
$5y_1 - 2y_2 + 6y_3 - 6y_4 \geq 80$
$\qquad y_1, y_2, y_3, y_4 \geq 0$

Comparison of the Primal and Dual Solutions

The flip-flopping of values between the primal and the dual carries over to the solution of both problems. We have three questions that need to be answered:

1. Which variables are in solution?
2. How much of each variable is in the optimal solution?
3. What are the shadow prices for the constraints?

Let's consider how we can obtain the answers to these questions from the dual solution. The *solution quantities* of the dual are equal to the *shadow prices* of the primal (i.e., $^{40}/_3$ and 10). Slack variable in the primal solution becomes a real variable (i.e., a decision variable) in the dual. The reverse is also true: A real variable in the primal solution becomes a slack variable in the dual. Therefore, in the primal solution, we have $x_1 = 9$ and $x_2 = 4$: in the dual, 9 and 4 are the shadow prices for constraints 1 and 2 respectively. In essence, then, the *variables* of the primal problem become the *constraints* of the dual problem, and vice versa.

Economic Interpretation of the Dual

In order to fully appreciate the correspondence between the primal and dual formulations of a problem, we shall now focus on the economic interpretation of the dual, using the server problem for purposes of illustration.

Suppose the server firm has been approached by a representative of a department store chain that wants the firm to make servers that will be sold under the store's brand name. The server company has only a limited capacity for producing servers and, therefore, must decide whether to produce its own servers or produce servers for the department store.

For convenience, the original problem is repeated here:

x_1 = number of server model 1s
x_2 = number of server model 2s

maximize $Z = 60x_1 + 50x_2$

subject to

Assembly time	$4x_1 + 10x_2 \le 100$
Inspection time	$2x_1 + 1x_2 \le 22$
Storage space	$3x_1 + 3x_2 \le 39$

The manager of the firm would reason in the following way: For each unit of Model 1 that the firm sacrifices to produce servers for the department store, it will gain 4 hours of assembly time, 2 hours of inspection time, and 3 cubic feet of storage space, which can be applied to the store servers. However, it will also give up a unit profit of $60. Therefore, in order for the firm to realistically consider the store's offer, the amounts of scarce resources that will be given up must produce a return to the firm that is at least equal to the forgone profit. Hence, the value of 4 assembly hours +2 inspection hours +3 cubic feet of storage space should be $\ge \$60$. By similar reasoning, giving up one unit of Model 2 will require that the value received by giving up 10 assembly hours +1 inspection hour +3 cubic feet of storage must equal or exceed the Model 2 profit of $50 per unit. These, then, become the constraints of the dual problem. Thus:

Value Received per Unit of	Resources Freed Up	Minimum Profit Required
Server model 1	$4y_1 + 2y_2 + 3y_3$	$60
Server model 2	$10y_1 + 1y_2 + 3y_3$	$50

Hence, the constraints of the dual refer to the *value* of capacity (i.e., the scarce resources). The formulation indicates that in order to switch from making units of models 1 and 2 to making servers for the department store, the value received from that switch must be at least equal to the profit forgone on the server models. The variables y_1, y_2, and y_3 are the *marginal values* of scarce resources 1 (assembly time), 2 (inspection time), and 3 (storage space). Solving the dual will tell us the *imputed* values of the resources given our optimal solution.

Naturally, the department store would want to *minimize* the use of the scarce resources, because the server firm almost certainly would base its charges on the amount of resources required. Consequently, the objective function for the dual problem focuses on minimizing the use of the scarce resources. Thus:

minimize $Z = 100y_1 + 22y_2 + 39y_3$

Solving the dual formula above, we reach the following optimal solution: $y_1 = 0$, $y_2 = 10$, and $y_3 = {}^{40}/_3$. Note that 10 and ${}^{40}/_3$ are the values of the shadow prices for constraint 2 and constraint 3. However, the shadow price for constraint 1 is zero because the optimal solution to the primal did not completely use up all of the assembly capacity. Consequently, no amount of either x_1 or x_2 would need to be given up to obtain one free hour of assembly time. Thus, the marginal value or shadow price of one hour of assembly time is $0.

Finally, the optimal dual solution always yields the same value of the objective function as the primal optimal. In this case, it is 740. The interpretation is that the inputed value of the resources that are required for the optimal solution equals the amount of profit that the optimal solution would produce.

Adding Another Variable

The concepts introduced in the preceding section also can be applied to evaluating the feasibility of adding another decision variable to the problem. For example, suppose the server firm is considering a third model of server that will yield a profit of $70 per unit, and this will require resource requirements of 8 hours of assembly time, 4 hours of inspection time, and 5 cubic feet of storage space per unit. The dual constraint for this model would be

$8y_1 + 4y_2 + 5y_1 \geq 70$

In order to determine if this new variable would come into the optimal (primal) solution, we can substitute the dual solution of $y = 0$, and $y_2 = 10$, and $y_3 = 40/3$ (i.e., the *shadow prices*, or marginal values of the resources) into this constraint to see if it would be satisfied. Thus, we find, $8(0) + 4(10) + 5({}^{40}/_3) = 106.67$. Because this amount is greater than the new dual constraint, *the original solution remains optimal*. Hence, the new variable (x_3) would not come into solution. Conversely, if the dual constraint has not been satisfied, the new variable would have come into solution. In this instance, the marginal value of scarce resources that would be required for the new model exceeds the marginal contribution to profit that the new model would provide. That is, $106.67 > $70.

The value of this approach is that it is not necessary to rework the entire problem in order to test the potential impact that adding a new decision variable would have on the optimal solution.

Computational Considerations

In addition to facilitating the economic interpretation of the problem, the dual can be formulated for computational purposes. Let's consider a linear programming problem with 8 decision variables and 80 constraints. Since the number of constraints usually determines the maximum number of iterations required to solve a linear programming problem, it is wiser to formulate and solve the dual, which would consist of 8 constraints and 80 decision variables (assuming there are no equality constraints). In this instance, the computational time required for solution can be substantially reduced by solving the dual because it has fewer constraints.

Example 5-7

Susan Frank is the operations manager of Arc Manufacturing Inc. She has developed a linear programming model to help her determine the product mix on one of the three production lines for Arc Manufacturing Inc.:

maximize $Z = 15x_1 + 20x_2 + 14x_3$

subject to

$$5x_1 + 6x_2 + 4x_3 \leq 210 \text{ pounds per day} \quad \text{(Material A constraint)}$$
$$10x_1 + 8x_2 + 5x_3 \leq 200 \text{ pounds per day} \quad \text{(Material B constraint)}$$
$$4x_1 + 2x_2 + 5x_3 \leq 170 \text{ pounds per day} \quad \text{(Material C constraint)}$$
$$x_1, x_2, x_3 \geq 0 \quad \text{(nonnegativity constraint)}$$

where x_1, x_2, and x_3 represent production line (product) 1, 2, and 3 respectively.

a.   Use Excel to solve the problem for Arc Manufacturing Inc.
b.   What is the maximum profit?
c.   How much of each product should be produced each day in order to achieve the maximum profit?
d.   Are any materials left unused in the solution? If so, how much of each material is unused?
e.   Explain the amount by which each variable's unit profit would have to increase in order for that variable to be profitable enough to produce it.
f.   Explain what the shadow prices represent. How are they useful?
g.   Determine the range of feasibility for each constraint.
h.   What is the meaning of range of optimality for the objective function coefficients? What is the range of optimality for the objective function coefficients of product 1, product 2, and product 3?
i.   What rule is employed to see if multiple changes in the objective function or the right-hand side of the constraints can be contemplated? Under what conditions does this rule work?

Solution

a.   The Excel worksheet and the associated answer sheets are displayed in Exhibits 5-6, 5-7, and 5-8.
b.   As displayed in the worksheet of Exhibit 5-6 and also in Exhibit 5-7, the optimal profit is $Z = \$548$.
c.   As displayed in the Excel output, in the worksheet of Exhibit 5-6 and also in Exhibit 5-7, $x_1 = 0$, $x_2 = 5$, and $x_3 = 32$
d.   We can tell this by looking at the slack column of Exhibit 5-7 of the first row. In this column, in cell G19, there is a value of 52. This indicates that 52 pounds per day of material A will be unused by this solution.

Exhibit 5-6 Excel Worksheet for Arc Manufacturing Inc.

	A	B	C	D	E	F	G	H	I
1	Production Problem								
2		Product I	Product II	Product III					
3	Unit profit	15	20	14					
4	Quantities	0	5	32	Total				
5	Profit	0	100	448	548				
6					Usage	Limits	Leftover		
7	Material A constraint	5	6	4	158	210	52		
8	Material B constraint	10	8	5	200	200	0		
9	Material C constraint	4	2	5	170	170	0		

E7 = SUMPRODUCT($B$4:$D$4,B7:D7)

Sheet tabs: Answer Report 6 / Sensitivity Report 5 / Sheet2 / Sheet3

Cell	Copied to	Formula
E7	E8, E9	= SUMPRODUCT ($B$4 : $D$4, B7 : D7)
G7	G8, G9	= F7 − E7
E5		= SUM (B5 : D5)
B5	C5, D5	= B3 ∗ B4

e. This information is given by the reduced cost column in Exhibit 5-8. According to the reduced cost values, the profit on x_1 would have to increase by at least $10.60 in order to make it profitable enough to produce it. The other two variables (x_2 and x_3) have reduced costs of 0 because they are already included in the optimal solution.

f. Another name for shadow price is dual price. There is a shadow price for each constraint. For instance, the shadow price for material A is zero, and material B has a shadow price $2.40. The shadow price tells us how much the optimal value of the objective function would increase if one additional unit of that resource (e.g., one pound of material B per day) was available. The shadow price for material A is zero because the optimal solution leaves some of this resource unused. The shadow price for material B is nonzero ($2.40) because it is a binding constraint. In interpreting this value, the objective function would increase by $2.40 if one additional pound of material B became available. If the cost per

Exhibit 5-7	Excel Basic Output (Answer) Report for Arc Manufacturing Inc.

Microsoft Excel - wrsht5-1

Microsoft Excel 9.0 Answer Report
Worksheet: [wrsht5-1.xls]Sheet2
Report Created: 1/19/2004 10:20:03 AM

Target Cell (Max)

Cell	Name	Original Value	Final Value
$E$5	Profit Total	548	548

Adjustable Cells

Cell	Name	Original Value	Final Value
$B$4	Quantities Product I	0	0
$C$4	Quantities Product II	5	5
$D$4	Quantities Product III	32	32

Constraints

Cell	Name	Cell Value	Formula	Status	Slack
$E$7	Material A constrain: Usage	158	$E$7<=$F$7	Not Binding	52
$E$8	Material B constrain: Usage	200	$E$8<=$F$8	Binding	0
$E$9	Material C constrain: Usage	170	$E$9<=$F$9	Binding	0
$B$4	Quantities Product I	0	$B$4>=0	Binding	0
$C$4	Quantities Product II	5	$C$4>=0	Not Binding	5
$D$4	Quantities Product III	32	$D$4>=0	Not Binding	32

Answer Report 6 / Sensitivity Report 5 / Sheet2 / Sheet3 /

Exhibit 5-8	Excel Sensitivity Analysis for Arc Manufacturing Inc.

Microsoft Excel - wrsht5-1

Microsoft Excel 9.0 Sensitivity Report
Worksheet: [wrsht5-1.xls]Sheet2
Report Created: 1/19/2004 10:20:03 AM

Adjustable Cells

Cell	Name	Final Value	Reduced Cost	Objective Coefficient	Allowable Increase	Allowable Decrease
$B$4	Quantities Product I	0	-10.6	15	10.6	1E+30
$C$4	Quantities Product II	5	0	20	2.4	10.6
$D$4	Quantities Product III	32	0	14	36	1.5

Constraints

Cell	Name	Final Value	Shadow Price	Constraint R.H. Side	Allowable Increase	Allowable Decrease
$E$7	Material A constrain: Usage	158	0	210	1E+30	52
$E$8	Material B constrain: Usage	200	2.4	200	70.90909091	30
$E$9	Material C constrain: Usage	170	0.4	170	30	120

Sensitivity Report 4 / Answer Report 6 \ **Sensitivity Report 5** / S /

pound of material B is less than $2.40, then it is worthwhile to obtain additional pounds of this resource.

g.   The range of feasibility for each constraint can be determined from the bottom portion of Exhibit 5-8. The column labeled Constraint R.H. Side indicates the current RHS values that were used to obtain the current solution. The next two columns indicate the amount each of these values can be increased or decreased without exceeding the range of feasibility of the shadow prices. For instance, the right-hand side of material A has no upper limit (Allowable Increase = 1E + 30). Since the allowable decrease is 52, the right-hand side of material A can be decreased to 158 (210 − 52) pounds per day. Similarly, the allowable increase, and allowable decrease for material B are 70.91 and 30 pounds respectively. Therefore, material B has a range of feasibility of 200 − 30 = 170 pounds to 200 + 70.91 = 270.91 pounds per day. For material C, the range of feasibility is 170 − 120 = 50 pounds to 170 + 30 = 200 pounds per day.

h.   The range of optimality enables us to determine the amount by which one of the objective function coefficients can change without changing the optimal values of x_1, x_2, or x_3. For instance, the coefficient of x_3 can change from its current coefficient value of 14 by as much as the allowable increase of 36 to (14 + 36) = $50 or decrease by as much as the allowable decrease of 1.5 from 14 to (14 − 1.5) = $12.5 without causing the current optimal solution to change. The coefficient of x_2 can change from its current coefficient value of 32 by as much as the allowable increase of 2.4 to (2.4 + 32) = $34.40 or decrease by as much as the allowable decrease of 10.6 from 32 to 21.4 (32 − 1.60) without causing the current optimal solution to change. However, x_1 has a value of zero in the optimal solution. For variables with zero values in the optimal solution, the alternate term is "range of insignificance." The range of x_1 is found by adding the allowable increase to the current objective function coefficient: 15 + 10.6 = $25.60. since the allowable decrease is ∞ (1E + 30), as long as the profit per unit on x_1 is less than $25.60, x_1 will have a value of zero in the optimal solution, assuming all other variables remain unchanged.

i.   If multiple changes in the objective function or the right-hand side of the constraints are considered, we can use the 100 percent rule provided that certain requirements are met. Basically, there are two requirements. The first requirement is that all changes be of the same type (e.g., all changes involve the right-hand-side values). The second requirement is that each change is measured as a percentage of allowable increase or allowable decrease. The percentages for all changes are added. If their sum does not exceed 100 percent, sensitivity analysis of multiple changes is permissible.

Summary

Sensitivity analysis enables the decision maker to determine how a change in one of the numerical values of a model will impact the optimal solution and the optimal value of the objective function. The primary purpose of such analysis is to provide the decision maker with greater insight about the sensitivity of the optimal solution to changes in various parameters of a problem. Interest in changes may arise due to improved information relating to a problem or because of the desire to know the potential impact of changes that are contemplated. This chapter begins by describing graphical sensitivity analysis of an optimal solution of a linear programming model, which provides the reader with good intuitive feel toward sensitivity analysis. The chapter continues with a discussion of how sensitivity analysis can be done using Excel and the interpretation of the Excel output.

Sensitivity analysis included in this chapter consists of two main parts. First, analysis of a change in the value of an objective function coefficient involves finding the range of objective function values for which the optimal values of the decision variables would not change. This is referred to as the range of optimality for that objective function coefficient. A value of the objective function that falls within the range of optimality will not change the optimal solution, although the optimal value of the objective function will change. Second, analysis of right-hand-side (RHS) changes begins with determination of a constraint's shadow price in the optimal solution. The range of values over which the RHS value can change without causing the shadow price to change is called its range of feasibility. Within this range of feasibility, the same decision variables will remain optimal, although their values and the optimal value of the objective function will change.

This chapter also discusses the concept of the dual, which is an alternate formulation of the linear programming problem. Either the original problem or its mirror image, the dual, can be solved to obtain the optimal solution. Awareness of the dual provides increased insight into linear programming problems. In particular, the dual variables have a different economic interpretation than the original formulation of the linear programming problem, which is called the primal. Further, the dual formulation can be easily used to determine if the addition of another variable to a problem will change the optimal. In addition, the number of decision variables in the primal is equal to the number of constraints in the dual and the number of decision variables in the dual is equal to the number of constraints in the primal. Since it is computationally easier to solve problems with fewer constraints in comparison to solving problems with fewer variables, the dual gives us the flexibility to choose which problem to solve.

◗ Glossary

Dual An alternate form of a linear programming problem that is the mirror image of the primal problem.

100 percent Rule A rule used to determine whether simultaneous changes for two or more objective function values, or two or more RHS values, are valid.

Primal The original formulation of a linear programming problem.

Range of Feasibility The range in value over which the RHS of a constraint can change without changing its shadow price.

Range of Insignificance The range in value over which an objective function coefficient can change without causing the corresponding decision variable to take on a nonzero value. Applicable only to variables that have a value of zero in the optimal solution.

Range of Optimality The range in value over which an objective function coefficient can change without changing the optimal values of solution variables.

Right-Hand-Side (RHS) Value The amount of resource available for a ≤ constraint or the minimum requirement for some criterion for a ≥ constraint.

Sensitivity (Postoptimality) Analysis Analysis of the impact of a change in one of the numerical values of a linear programming model on the optimal solution and the optimal value of the objective function.

Shadow Price For a change in the RHS value of a constraint that is within its range of feasibility, the amount of change in the optimal value of the objective function per unit change of the RHS value (e.g., $2 per pound, $.53 per minute).

Solved Problems

Problem 1

Given this LP model:

$$\text{maximize} \quad Z = 3x_1 + 3x_2$$

subject to

$$
\begin{array}{llll}
A & 6x_1 + & 4x_2 \le 24 \\
B & 10x_1 + & 20x_2 \le 80 \\
 & & x_1, x_2 \ge 0
\end{array}
$$

a. Find the range of optimality, or the range of insignificance, whichever is appropriate, for each objective function coefficient.

b. Find the shadow price and the range of feasibility for the RHS of each constraint.

Solution

Begin by plotting the graph and solving for the optimal solution:

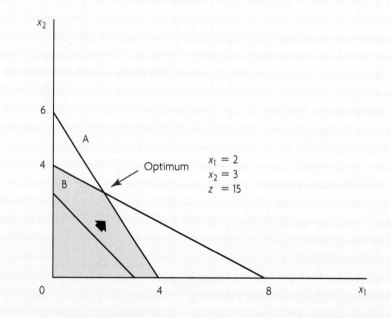

a. We can see that neither decision variable has a value of zero in the optimal solution. Therefore, the range of optimality is appropriate for both of their objective function coefficients. The range of optimality is the amount that an objective function coefficient can change (thereby changing the slope of the objective function line) and still not cause the solution to move to another corner point.

We can determine the range of optimality for each coefficient by determining the value it would need to cause the objective function line to be just parallel to each of the binding constraints. Thus, for the x_1 coefficient, for the objective function line to be parallel to the first constraint, its value would have to be $^6/_4 = 1.5$ times that of the x_2 coefficient, which would make it 4.5. Then, to be parallel to the second constraint, the x_1 coefficient would have to be $^1/_2$ (i.e., $^{10}/_{20} = ^1/_2$) of the x_2 coefficient, which would make the objective function coefficient of x_1 1.5. Hence, the range of optimality for the x_1 coefficient is 1.5 to 4.5.

Similarly, for the x_2 coefficient, we must find the value that will make the objective function line parallel to the first constraint and then the second constraint. For the first constraint, we know that the ratio of the two coefficients must be $^6/_4 = 1.5$. Given that the x_1 coefficient is 3, the x_2 coefficient would then be $2(^4/_6 * 3)$. And, to be parallel to the second constraint, the ratio must be $^{10}/_{20} = ^1/_2$. So with the x_1 coefficient equal to 3, the x_2 coefficient must be $6 = (2 * 3)$. Hence, the range of optimality for the x_2 coefficient is 2 to 6.

b. To find the shadow price of a constraint that is a binding constraint (both constraints here are binding constraints), increase its RHS by 1 and determine the new optimal values of the decision variables. Then substitute those new values into the objective function to find its new optimal value. Subtract the original Z from the new Z to obtain the shadow price. Note: If a constraint is not binding, its shadow price is 0.

Thus, adding 1 to the RHS of the first constraint and solving for the new intersection with the second constraint, we find $x_1 = 2.25$ and $x_2 = 2.875$. This yields $Z' = 15.375$. The original Z was 15. Therefore, the shadow price is $15.375 - 15 = .375$ for the first constraint.

Similarly, by adding 1 to the RHS of the second constraint (making it 81), and using the original first constraint, we obtain an intersection of $x_1 = 1.95$, $x_2 = 3.075$. Then $Z' = 15.075$, so the shadow price is $15.075 - 15 = .075$ for the second constraint.

Now, to find the range of feasibility for the RHS of a constraint, place a straight edge along the line on the graph. First, hold it parallel to the line while moving away from the origin. Stop when it reaches the last intersection with the other binding constraint in this quadrant. You can see from the graph that the upper limit is at 8, 0. Similarly, moving parallel to the first constraint but toward the origin, the lower limit is at 0, 4.

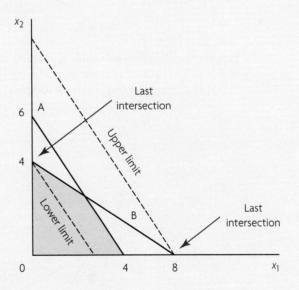

Substituting each of these sets of values into the first constraint will give us our range of feasibility:

8, 0: $6(8) + 4(0) = 48$
0, 4: $6(0) + 4(4) = 16$

Hence, the range of feasibility for the first constraint is 16 to 48.

Similarly, to find the range of feasibility for the second constraint, we hold a straight edge along its graph and move it parallel to the line away from the origin until we reach the last intersection $(0, 6)$ and toward the origin until we reach the last intersection with the other binding constraint $(4, 0)$. Substituting these sets of values into the second constraint, we find

$0, 6:$ $10(0) + 20(6) = 120$
$4, 0:$ $10(4) + 20(0) = 40$

Hence, the range of feasibility for the second constraint is 40 to 120.

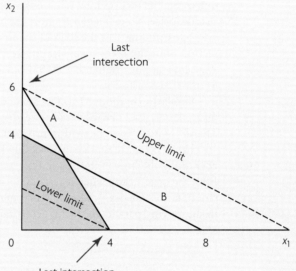

Problem 2

Suppose the objective function in a previous problem had been maximize $Z = 9x_1 + 2.25x_2$. The optimal solution would then have been $x_1 = 4$, $x_2 = 0$.

Find the range of insignificance for the x_2 coefficient in the objective function.

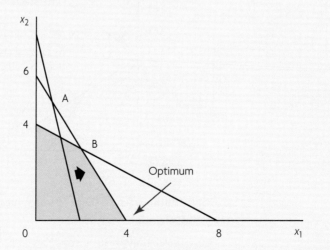

Solution

x_2 will have an optimal value of zero (i.e., it will be insignificant) unless its objective function coefficient becomes large enough for it to make a positive contribution to the objective. This would occur if its value increased to where it caused the objective function line to be at least parallel to the first constraint (constraint A). Thus, the ratio of the x_1 and x_2 coefficients would have to be $^6/_4 = 1.5$. With the x_1 coefficient equal to 9, this would require an x_2 coefficient of at least 6. Hence, the range of insignificance for the x_2 coefficient is a value of less than 6 in the objective function.

Problem 3

Given this LP model

$$\text{maximize} \qquad Z = 10x_1 + 6x_2 + 5x_3$$

subject to

$$2x_1 + 3x_2 + 4x_3 \leq 25$$
$$x_1 + 3x_2 + 2x_3 \leq 22$$
$$6x_1 + 3x_2 + 4x_3 \leq 32$$
$$x_1, x_2, x_3 \geq 0$$

where x_1, x_2, and x_3 represent products 1, 2, and 3 and constraints 1, 2, and 3 represent the availability of materials A, B, and C.

a. Use Excel and determine the range of feasibility for each RHS (i.e., original right-hand-side value).

b. Use Excel and determine the range of optimality for the coefficients of the decision variables that are in solution.

c. By how much would the objective function coefficient of x_3 have to increase before it would come into solution? What is the range of insignificance for the coefficient of x_3?

Solution

a. The *range of feasibility* refers to the range over which the RHS value of a constraint can be changed without changing the shadow price for that particular constraint.

The shadow price for the first constraint is 0 because s_1 is in solution. Therefore, the first constraint has slack ($s_1 = 1$ in the Allowable Decrease (slack) column of Exhibit 5-9). A constraint that has slack can be increased forever because any increase means that it will have even more slack. It can be decreased by 1 (the amount of slack) before it becomes a binding constraint. Hence, its range of feasibility is from 24 (i.e., $25 - 1$) to $+ \infty$.

For variables that are not in solution, such as s_2 and s_3, the range of feasibility can be obtained from the Excel Sensitivity Report given in Exhibit 5-9.

For the second constraint, since the Allowable Increase is 1.25 and Allowable Decrease is 16.67, we find

Upper end $= 22 + 1.25 = 23.25$ Range: 5.33 to 23.25
Lower end $= 22 - 16.67 = 5.33$

For the third constraint, since the Allowable Increase is 5 and Allowable Decrease is 10, we find

Upper end $= 32 + 5 = 37$ Range: 22 to 37
Lower end $= 32 - 10 = 22$

Thus, the range of feasibility for each constraint is

Constraint	Current Value	Range of Feasibility
1	25	24 to $+ \infty$
2	22	5.33 to 23.25
3	32	22 to 37

Exhibit 5-9	Excel Sensitivity Report for Solved Problem 3

Microsoft Excel - wrsht5-1

File Edit View Insert Format Tools MegaStat Data Window Help   Type a question for help

Arial   10   B I U $ %   100%

M5

	A	B	C	D	E	F	G	H	I	J
1			Microsoft Excel 11.0 Sensitivity Report							
2			Worksheet: [wrsht5-1.xls]Sheet3							
3			Report Created: 3/18/2005 5:13:23 PM							
4										
5										
6			Adjustable Cells							
7					Final	Reduced	Objective	Allowable	Allowable	
8			Cell	Name	Value	Cost	Coefficient	Increase	Decrease	
9			$B$4	Quantities Product I	2	0	10	2	5.5	
10			$C$4	Quantities Product II	6.666666667	0	6	24	1	
11			$D$4	Quantities Product III	0	-2.2	5	2.2	1E+30	
12										
13			Constraints							
14					Final	Shadow	Constraint	Allowable	Allowable	
15			Cell	Name	Value	Price	R.H. Side	Increase	Decrease	
16			$E$7	Material A constrain: Usage	24	0	25	1E+30	1	
17			$E$8	Material B constrain: Usage	22	0.4	22	1.25	16.66666667	
18			$E$9	Material C constrain: Usage	32	1.6	32	4.999999999	10	
19										
20										
21										
22										
23										

Sensitivity Report 5 / Sheet2 \ Sensitivity Report 6 / Sheet3 /

Ready   NUM

b. The ranges of optimality can be obtained from the Excel Sensitivity Report given in Exhibit 5-9. The Allowable Increase and Allowable Decrease columns on the top half of the report in Exhibit 5-9 can be used to obtain the range of optimality for the variables in the solution as follows.

For x_1, the allowable decrease is -5.5 and allowable increase is $+2$. Therefore, the range of optimality for x_1 is

$$(10 - 5.5 = 4.5)   \text{to}   (10 + 2 = 12)$$

For x_2, the allowable decrease is -1 and the allowable increase is $+24$. Thus, the x_2 coefficient of 6 in the objective function can be decreased by as much as 1 or increased by as much as 24. The range of optimality for the x_2 coefficient in the objective function, therefore, is

$$(6 - 1 = 5)   \text{to}   (6 + 24 = 30)$$

Thus, the range of optimality for each variable that is in solution is

Variable	Range of Optimality
x_1	4.5 to 12
x_2	5 to 30

c. For variables that are not in solution, such as x_3 in this example, their contribution per unit is too small (in a maximization problem) to cause them to have an optimal value that is nonzero. However, if the objective function coefficient is increased by a sufficient amount, that variable, variable x_3, would come into the solution. Since the allowable increase for variable x_3 is 2.2 in Exhibit 5-9, the objective function coefficient of x_3 must be 2.2 more than the original objective function coefficient for x_3, which is $5 + 2.2$, or 7.2, for it to come into solution. Therefore, the range of insignificance for variable x_3 is $-\infty$ to 7.2. In other words, the objective function coefficient for x_3 could be decreased by an unlimited amount and x_3 would not come into the solution. However, if the objective function coefficient of x_3 is increased to 7.2 or more, x_3 would come into the solution as a nonzero value.

Problem 4

(Refer to Solved Problem 3.) Manager Tom Oakley is considering making multiple changes to the original model. For each set of changes, decide if the impact of the changes can be determined without resolving the entire problem.

a. Increase every RHS value by 1.
b. Increase the objective function coefficient of x_1 by 1 and decrease the objective function coefficient of x_2 by 1.
c. Increase the objective function coefficient of x_1 by .80 and decrease the objective function coefficient of x_2 by .50.
d. Determine the optimal value of the objective function value after the changes in part c are incorporated.

Solution

a. Using the feasibility ranges for RHS changes from Solved Problem 3:

Constraint	RHS	Range of Feasibility
1	25	24 to $+\infty$
2	22	5.33 to 23.25
3	32	22 to 37

There is no limit on the first constraint as an upper limit, so we can ignore that increase. (Generally, there would be no benefit in increasing the RHS of a constraint that currently has slack.) The second constraint's increase as a percentage of the allowable increase would be $^1/_{1.25} = 80$ percent; the third constraint's percentage increase would be $^1/_5 = 20$ percent. (Note: The 5 in the last computation is the difference between the 37 upper limit of the range of feasibility and the current RHS value of 32.) The sum of these two percentages is 100 percent. It just satisfies the requirement that the sum of the percentage changes must not exceed 100 percent. Therefore, the proposed changes are *within* the acceptable range.

b. The ranges of optimality were determined in Solved Problem 3:

Variable	Current Value	Range of Optimality
x_1	10	4.5 to 12
x_2	6	5 to 30

Increasing the x_1 coefficient from 10 to 11 would be an increase of 50 percent of the allowable increase: $^1/_2 = 50$ percent. Decreasing the x_2 coefficient by 1 would be 100 percent of the allowable decrease: $^1/_1 = 100$ percent. The total percentage would be 50 percent $+$ 100 percent $=$ 150 percent; this would exceed the 100 percent limitation. Consequently, these two changes would cause a change in the optimal solution quantities and the optimal solution mix of the variables.

c. Increasing the objective function coefficient of x_1 by .80 would constitute 40 percent of its allowable increase $(^{.8}/_2)$, as determined in part b. Decreasing the objective function coefficient of x_2 by .50 would constitute 50 percent of its allowable decrease. The total percentage would be 90 percent. Because this total is less than the 100 percent limitation, the optimal values of variables in solution will not change.

d. To find out what the revised profit-based on the changes mode in part C would be, we can multiply the optimal quantities by their respective objective function changes and then adjust the optimal value of the objective function accordingly. Thus, with $x_1 = 2$ and $x_2 = 6^2/_3$, and ($\Delta c_1 = .80$ and ($\Delta c_2 = -.50$, we have

$$\Delta Z = .80(2) - .50(6\ 2/3) = -1.733$$

The revised value of Z is then

$$Z' = 60 - 1.733 = 58.267$$

Problem 5

(Refer to Solved Problem 3.) The manager of the department for which the LP model was formulated would like to know the answers to certain questions:

a. If one additional unit of the third constraint could be obtained at the same cost as the previous units (so that the profits per unit in the objective function did not change), what impact would this have on profit?
b. If one additional unit of the third resource (constraint) could be obtained at a *premium* of $.50, what impact would this have on profit?
c. If 4 units of the third resource were obtained at the original cost per unit, what impact would this have on the optimal value of profit?
d. What would happen if the RHS of the third constraint was increased from 32 to 39?

Solution

a. The shadow price for the third constraint is $^8/_5$. Therefore, for one additional unit, profit would increase by $^8/_5$, or $1.60.
b. The premium must be deducted from the shadow price. Hence, the net impact would be $1.60 - $.50 = $1.10 increase in total profit.
c. First, we must check to see if the specified change is within the range of feasibility. An additional 4 units would make the RHS of the third constraint $32 + 4 = 36$; the upper end of the range of feasibility for the third constraint is 37 (see Solved Problem 3). Hence, the change is within the range of feasibility.

    Since the change is within the range of feasibility and the optimal profit is $60, adding 4 units of the third resource will increase the total profit by $4 \times 1.60 = $6.40, where $1.60 is the shadow price associated with the third resource. Therefore, the total profit would be $60 + 6.4 = $66.40.
d. The upper end of the range of feasibility is 37. Any resource beyond that would be slack. Consequently, an increase from 32 to 39 units means that only 5 units could be used; 2 units would be left over. Consequently, s_3 would appear in the solution, and it would have a value of 2. Profit would increase to $60 + 5(1.60) = 68$, rather than $60 + 7(1.6) = 71.2$, because only 5 units could be used.

Problem 6

Write the dual associated with the following primal problem:

maximize $Z = 5x_1 + 3x_2$

subject to

$$x_1 + x_2 \le 10$$
$$x_1 \qquad \le 4$$
$$x_1, x_2 \ge 0$$

Solution

Since the primal is a maximization problem, the dual must be a minimization problem and can be stated as follows:

$$\text{minimize} \quad Z = 10y_1 + 4y_2$$

subject to

$$y_1 + y_2 \geq 5$$
$$y_1 \qquad \geq 3$$
$$y_1, y_2 \geq 0$$

Note that the objective function coefficients of the primal become the RHS values of the dual, and the RHS values of the primal become the objective function coefficients of the dual. The primal consists of two less-than-or-equal-to constraints, while the dual consists of two greater-than-or-equal-to constraints. Since the primal is a maximization problem, it consists of less-than-or-equal-to constraints. Since the dual is a minimization problem, its constraints have greater-than-or-equal-to signs.

Problem 7

Write the dual associated with the following primal problem:

$$\text{maximize} \quad Z = -2x_1 + 3x_2$$

subject to

$$x_1 + 2x_2 \leq 12$$
$$4x_1 - 2x_2 \geq 3$$
$$6x_1 - x_2 = 10$$
$$x_1, x_2 \geq 0$$

Solution

First, we need to convert all of the constraints in the primal to less-than-or-equal-to constraints. Since the first constraint is already a less-than-or-equal-to constraint, we do not need to manipulate it. The second constraint is multiplied by -1 and rewritten as

$$-4x_1 + 2x_2 \leq -3$$

Since the third constraint is an equality, it must be restated as two separate constraints. Thus, it becomes

$$6x_1 - x_2 \leq 10 \quad \text{and} \quad 6x_1 - x_2 \geq 10$$

The second of these two constraints must now be multiplied by -1, which yields the following:

$$-6x_1 + x_2 \leq -10$$

Hence, the final form of the primal becomes

$$\text{maximize} \quad Z = -2x_1 + 3x_2$$

subject to

$$x_1 + 2x_2 \leq 12$$
$$-4x_1 + 2x_2 \leq -3$$
$$6x_1 - x_2 \leq 10$$
$$-6x_1 + x_2 \leq -10$$
$$x_1, x_2 \geq 0$$

Since the primal is a maximization problem consisting of all less-than-or-equal-to constraints, the dual is a minimization problem consisting of all greater-than-or-equal-to constraints. The objective function coefficients of the dual consist of the RHS values of the primal. Since the primal has 2 variables and 4 constraints (after converting the equality constraint into two inequality constraints) and since the primal and dual are mirror images of each other, the corresponding dual will have 2 constraints and 4 variables. The RHS values of the dual will consist of the objective function coefficients of the primal. Thus, the dual is

$$\text{minimize} \qquad Z = 12y_1 - 3y_2 + 10y_3 - 10y_4$$

subject to

$$y_1 - 4y_2 + 6y_3 - 6y_4 \geq -2$$
$$2y_1 + 2y_2 - y_3 + y_4 \geq 3$$
$$y_1, y_2, y_3, y_4 \geq 0$$

Discussion and Review Questions

1. Explain how a change in resource availability can affect the optimal solution of a linear programming problem.
2. Explain how we can ensure that the optimal solution to a linear programming problem does not change when we simultaneously change the objective function values of the decision variables.
3. Explain how a change in objective function value of a decision variable can affect the optimal solution of a linear programming problem.
4. Discuss the importance of sensitivity analysis in solving linear programming problems. Compare using sensitivity analysis and solving a problem by changing one of the objective function values from scratch.
5. What is a binding constraint? What is a nonbinding constraint? Discuss the difference between them.
6. What is a shadow price? Explain carefully.
7. Describe how a firm would use the shadow price associated with a given constraint.
8. If the objective function value of a decision variable changes within its allowable change, explain if it will affect the current variable value and the objective function value.
9. Explain the meaning of slack and surplus in a linear programming constraint.
10. Explain the effect of increasing the RHS value of a constraint beyond the allowable increase value shown in the sensitivity report.

Problems

1. Sensitivity analysis can provide a decision maker with additional insights about an optimal solution to an LP model.
   a. Explain in general terms what sensitivity analysis accomplishes.
   b. Why might sensitivity analysis be useful to a decision maker?
   c. List the two types of parameters the discussion of sensitivity analysis the chapter focused on.

a. Amount of change that will occur in the value of the objective function based on a 1 unit change in the RHS value of a constraint.

b. Range of values of RHS of a constraint for which the shadow price is valid

c. Range of values for which the optimal values of all variables will not change

d. Range of values for which the variable will remain out of solution

e. Left-hand side equals right-hand side

2. Briefly define or explain each of these terms.
   a. Shadow price.
   b. Range of feasibility.
   c. Range of optimality.
   d. Range of insignificance.
   e. Binding constraint.

3. Given this LP model and its graph:

$$\text{maximize} \quad Z = 5x_1 + 9x_2$$

subject to

$$
\begin{array}{lll}
A & 2x_1 + 1x_2 \le 10 \\
B & 1x_1 + 3x_2 \le 12 \\
& x_1, x_2 \ge 0
\end{array}
$$

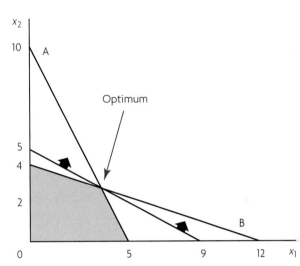

a. Find the range of optimality for the x_2 coefficient in the objective function.
b. Find the range of optimality for the x_1 coefficient of the objective function.
c. Find the shadow price for each constraint's RHS.
d. Determine the range of feasibility for each constraint's shadow price.
e. What impact would a change in the objective function coefficient of x_1 from 5 to 4 have on the optimal values of the decision variables? What effect would it have on the optimal value of the objective function.
f. What effect would a decrease of 1 in the value of the x_2 coefficient of the objective function have on the optimal values of the decision variables? What effect would it have on the optimal value of the objective function? Explain.

4. Given this LP model:

$$\text{maximize} \quad Z = 8x_1 + 3x_2$$

subject to

$$
\begin{array}{lll}
\text{Labor} & 5x_1 + 2x_2 \le 30 \text{ hours} \\
\text{Equipment} & 1x_1 + 2x_2 \le 16 \text{ hours} \\
\text{Material} & 10x_1 + 7x_2 \le 70 \text{ pounds} \\
& x_1, x_2 \ge 0
\end{array}
$$

a. See the IM
b. $7.5 \leq c_1 \leq \infty$, and
   $x_1 = 6, x_2 = 0, Z = 48$
   $-\infty \leq c_2 \leq 3.2$
c. Constraint = 1.6;
   Constraint 2, 3 = 0
d. $0 \leq b_1 \leq 35$
   $6 \leq b_2 \leq \infty$
   $60 \leq b_3 \leq \infty$

a. Plot the graph and determine the optimal solution.
b. Find the range of optimality or insignificance for each objective function coefficient.
c. Determine the shadow price of each constraint for the optimal solution.
d. Determine the range of feasibility for the RHS of each constraint.

5. Given this LP model:

   minimize $Z = 4x_1 + 8x_2$

   subject to

Fiber	$5x_1 + 8x_2 \geq 40$
Protein	$6x_1 + 4x_2 \geq 24$
	$x_1, x_2 \geq 0$

   a. Find the range of optimality or insignificance for each objective function coefficient.
   b. How would a decrease of $1 in the x_1 coefficient of the objective function affect the optimal values of the decision variables? How would it affect the optimal value of the objective function?
   c. What is the shadow price for the fiber constraint's RHS? Over what range of values is it valid?
   d. What is the shadow price for the RHS of the protein constraint? Over what range of values is it valid?
   e. What impact on cost would a decrease of 2 units in the RHS of the protein constraint have?

6. The manager of FYZ Incorporated has been presented with the following LP model:

   minimize $Z = 30A + 45B$ (cost)

   subject to

   $$5A + 2B \geq 100$$
   $$4A + 8B \geq 240$$
   $$B \geq 20$$
   $$A \text{ and } B \geq 0$$

   The manager would like your assistance in answering her questions:

a. $A = 10, B = 25,$
   $Z = \$1425$
b. $B = 25, Z = \$1,350$

c. Shadow price = 1.875
   $60 \leq b_1, \leq 140$

d. The cost would
   increase by $18.75,
   new Z = $1443.75

   a. What are the optimal values of A and B? What is the minimum cost?
   b. If the cost of B could be reduced to $42 per unit, how many units of B would be optimal? What would the minimum cost be?
   c. What is the shadow price for the RHS of the first constraint? Over what range is it valid?
   d. By what amount would the cost change, and in what direction, if the first constraint was changed to 110?

7. The manager of the assembly department of 1KW, Inc., has developed this LP model:

   maximize $Z = 12P + 10Q$ (profit)

   subject to

Line 1	$11P + 11Q \leq 121$ hours
Line 2	$8P + 15Q \leq 120$ hours
Inspection	$3P + 15Q \leq 60$ minutes
	$P, Q \geq 0$

   a. What are the optimal values of P, Q, and Z?
   b. By how much can the profit per unit of P change without changing the optimal values of P and Q?

c. If the amount of time on line 1 could be increased without changing the optimal mix of variables, how much more could be used? What would be the new profit? What would happen if more time than this was added to Line 1?

d. If Line 2 time was reduced by one hour, what impact would this have on profit?

e. If one additional hour for Line 1 could be obtained, how much would profit increase?

8. Sensitivity analysis can provide a decision maker with additional insights about a linear programming solution.

a. List the three types of parameters that sensitivity analysis might focus on. Which two are covered in this chapter?

b. What is an advantage of sensitivity analysis as opposed to solving an LP problem from scratch?

c. Discuss the role of sensitivity analysis in solving LP problem. Under what circumstances is it very useful?

9. For the following LP model

maximize $Z = 20x_1 + 12x_2$

subject to

1	$3x_1 + 2x_2 \leq 180$	(Raw material 1)
2	$x_1 \leq 50$	(Raw material 2)
3	$x_2 \leq 51$	(Raw material 3)
	$x_1, x_2 \geq 0$	

Use Excel in answering the following questions.

a. Identify the shadow prices and indicate the constraint with which each shadow price is associated. Interpret each shadow price.

b. Determine the range of feasibility for raw material 1 and interpret your answer.

c. Determine the range of feasibility for raw material 2 and interpret your answer.

d. Determine the range of feasibility for raw material 3 and interpret your answer.

e. Which of these two possible changes would have the greater impact on the value of the objective function in the final solution?

(1) Increase the RHS of second constraint by 10 units.

(2) Increase the RHS of third constraint by 40 units.

f. Determine the range of optimality (or the range of insignificance, if appropriate) for the coefficient of each decision variable.

10. For the following linear programming problem, use Excel and

maximize $Z = 9x_1 + 6x_2$

subject to

1	$12x_1 + 5x_2 \leq 600$ hours
2	$x_2 \leq 72$ hours
	$x_1, x_2 \geq 0$

a. What are the optimal values of x_1, x_2 and Z?

b. Identify the shadow prices and indicate the constraint with which each shadow price is associated. Interpret each shadow price.

c. Determine the range of feasibility for the first constraint and interpret your answer.

d. Determine the range of feasibility for the second constraint and interpret your answer.

e. If the first constraint was revised to 450 hours, what impact would that have on the solution quantities and the value of Z?

a. 1. Objective function coefficients 2. right-hand side 3. constraint coefficients

b. See the IM

c. See the IM

a. $x_1 = 20$
$x_2 = 72$
$Z = 612$
Shadow price,
b. constraint 1 = .75
Shadow price,
constraint 2 = 2.25
c. $360 \leq b_1 \leq \infty$
d. $0 \leq b_2 \leq 120$
e. New $x_1 = 7.5$, New $Z = 499.5$

f.   Determine the range of optimality for each coefficient of the objective function for the original problem.

11. Given the following LP problem, use Excel to complete the sensitivity analysis.

maximize $Z = 11x_1 + 10x_2 + 14x_3$

subject to

A $\quad\quad 4x_2 - 1x_3 \le 0$
B $\quad 5x_1 + 2x_2 + 5x_3 \le 72$
$\quad\quad x_1 \quad\quad\quad\quad\quad \le 13$
$\quad\quad x_1, x_2, x_3 \ge 0$

a.   Determine the range of insignificance, or the range of optimality (whichever is appropriate), for each of the variables in the objective function.
b.   Determine the range of feasibility for each of the constraints and interpret each range.
c.   Suppose that the right-hand side of constraint A will be changed to 10. Determine the impact that this change would have on the following:
   (1)   The quantities.
   (2)   The value of the objective function.

12. (Refer to the preceding problem.) Answer these questions concerning changes in the objective function coefficients:

a.   By how much would the contribution of variable x_1 have to change, and in which direction, before x_1 would come into the solution?
b.   If the objective function coefficient of variable x_2 were to increase by 5, what impact would this have on the value of the variables and the objective function?
c.   If the coefficients of variables x_2 and x_3 were each decreased by 2, would that be within the range of optimality for multiple changes? If so, what would the values of the decision variables be in the optimal solution?
d.   Suppose the RHS value of constraint A was 10 and the RHS value of constraint B was 80. Would this be within the range of feasibility for multiple changes? If so, what would the values be in the optimal solution?

13. The manager of FGH, a small manufacturer of horseback riding accessories, has received a staff report that contains an LP model.

F = quality of Product F
G = quantity of Product G
H = quantity of Product H

maximize $Z = 15F + 20G + 14H$

subject to

A $\quad 5F + 6G + 4H \le 210$ pounds
B $\quad 10F + 8G + 5H \le 200$ minutes
C $\quad 4F + 2G + 5H \le 170$ square feet
$\quad\quad F, G, H \ge 0$

Use Excel and determine the following:
a.   What are the optimal Values of F, G, and H? What is the optimal profit?
b.   What is the range of optimality for the 20 in the objective function? Interpret your result (i.e., what values of decision variables do not change within this range?)

c. How would the value of the total profit (Z) change if the 20 in the objective function were decreased by 10? Increased by 2?

d. What is the range of feasibility for RHS of constraint A? Interpret your answer.

e. What is the range of feasibility for the RHS of the last constraint?

f. What would the values of decision variables be in the optimal solution if the last constraint were increased by 20 units?

g. What is the value of the total profit (Z) if the RHS of the last constraint was 210?

14. The manager of a knitting department has developed the following LP model and the following Excel output in Table 5-3 summarizes the results.

x_1 = units of Product 1
x_2 = units of Product 2
x_3 = units of Product 3

maximize $Z = 7x_1 + 3x_2 + 9x_3$ (profit)

subject to

Labor $4x_1 + 5x_2 + 6x_3 \leq 360$ hours
Machine $2x_1 + 4x_2 + 6x_3 \leq 300$ hours
Material $9x_1 + 5x_2 + 6x_3 \leq 600$ pounds
            $x_1, x_2,$ and $x_3 \geq 0$

a. $x_1 = 48, x_2 = 0, x_3 = 28,$ $Z = 588$

b. Profit is too small, $c_2 \geq 7.5$

c. $6 \leq c_1 \leq 13.5$

d. Variabe values remain the same, new $Z = 732$

e. $266.67 \leq b_1 \leq 385.7143$

f. $x_1 = 50, x_2 = 0, x_3 = 25,$ $Z = 575$

g. 210 pounds; solution would change

a. What are the values of x_1, x_2, x_3, and Z in the optimal solution.

b. Why isn't any product 2 called for in the optimal solution? How much would the pre-unit profit of Product 2 have to be in order for it to enter into the optimal solution mix?

c. What is the range of optimality for the profit per unit of Product 1?

d. What would the values in the optimal solution be if the objective coefficient of x_1 were to increase by 3?

e. What is the range of feasibility of the labor constraint?

f. What would the values in the optimal solution be if the amount of labor available decreased by 10 hours?

g. If the manager could obtain additional material, how much more could be used effectively? What would happen if the manager obtained more than this amount?

15. (Refer to the preceding problem.) The manager has some additional questions relative to the optimal solution:

a. If it is possible to obtain an additional amount of *one* of the resources, which one should be obtained, and how much can be effectively used? Explain.

b. If the manager is able to obtain an additional 100 pounds of material at the usual price, what impact would that have on the optimal value of the objective function?

c. If the manager is able to obtain an additional 100 pounds of material but has to pay a premium of 5 cents a pound, what will the net profit be?

d. If knitting machines operate for 10 hours a day, and one of the machines will be out of service for two and a half days, what impact will this have on the optimal value of Z?

16. The A-B-C department of a large company makes three products (A, B, and C). The department is preparing for its final run next week, which is just before the annual two-week vacation during which the entire department shuts down. The manager wants to use up existing stocks of the three raw materials used to fabricate products A, B, and C.

Table 5-3	Excel Reports for Problem 14

A. Answer Report

Target Cell (Max)

Cell	Name	Original Value	Final Value
$E$5	Profit Total	588	588

Adjustable Cells

Cell	Name	Original Value	Final Value
$B$4	Quantities Product I	48	48
$C$4	Quantities Product II	0	0
$D$4	Quantities Product III	28	28

Constraints

Cell	Name	Cell Value	Formula	Status	Slack
$E$7	Labor Usage	360	$E$7<=$F$7	Binding	0
$E$8	Machine Usage	264	$E$8<=$F$8	Not Binding	36
$E$9	Material Usage	600	$E$9<=$F$9	Binding	0

B. Sensitivity Report

Adjustable Cells

Cell	Name	Final Value	Reduced Cost	Objective Coefficient	Allowable Increase	Allowable Decrease
$B$4	Quantities Product I	48	0	7	6.5	1
$C$4	Quantities Product II	0	−4.500000001	2.999999999	4.500000001	1E+30
$D$4	Quantities Product III	28	0	9	1.5	4.333333333

Constraints

Cell	Name	Final Value	Shadow Price	Constraint R. H. Side	Allowable Increase	Allowable Decrease
$E$7	Labor Usage	360	1.3	360	25.71428571	93.33333333
$E$8	Machine Usage	264	0	300	1E+30	36
$E$9	Material Usage	600	0.2	600	210	90

She has formulated the LP model and obtained an optimal solution using Excel, which is displayed in Table 5-4.

A = quantity of Product A
B = quantity of Product B
C = quantity of Product C

maximize $\quad Z = 12A + 15B + 14C$

subject to

Material 1	$3A + 5B + 8C \le 720$ pounds
Material 2	$2A \quad + 3C \le 600$ pounds
Material 3	$4A + 6B + 4C \le 640$ pounds
	$A, B,$ and $C \ge 0$

As a staff person, the manager has asked you to answer each of the following questions concerning the final solution:

a. B uses more of the constrained resources
b. B would not be produced, $c_B \ge 18.2$
c. $360 \le b_3 \le 960$
d. Z would increase by \$270;
   Z would increase by $(2.7)(320) = 864$

e. No, there is a slack of 232 lbs.
   $C = 52, Z = 228, A = 108, Z = 2,024$
g. $\dfrac{1}{2.286} + 0 + \dfrac{1}{2} < 1$,
   therefore within range

h. Within range

a. Although Product B is the most profitable, and Product A the least profitable, the solution calls for making none of B but 112 of A. Why?
b. If B's profit per unit could be increased to \$18, how much B would be produced? Explain how you obtained your answer.
c. What is the range of feasibility for the Material 3 RHS?
d. By how much would profit increase if an additional 100 pounds of material 3 could be obtained as its usual cost? What if the amount were an additional 400 pounds?
e. Do you see any difficulty in allowing the X-Y-Z department to take 200 pounds of material 2? Explain.
f. What would the values in the optimal solution be if 20 additional pounds of Material 1 could be obtained without paying a premium for it? (In order to obtain 1 lb of material 1, the company uses .2 lbs more of material 1 in product C, .2 lbs less of material 1 in product A, and .2 lbs less of material 1 in slack of material 2)
g. Suppose the manager wants to evaluate the effect of cost changes that would reduce each of the objective function coefficients by 1. Would these changes be within the range of optimality for multiple changes?
h. If the manager can obtain an additional 20 pounds of Material 1 and 3, is that within the range of feasibility?

17. The manager in the server problem is considering scheduling overtime in either the assembly or the inspection department.
    a. Which department would be the best choice for overtime? Why? (See Exhibits 5-4 and 5-5)
    b. Suppose overtime will cost \$7 per hour over the current rate. Does it make sense to schedule overtime? If so, how much overtime, and what effect would there be on total profit by scheduling this overtime?

18. Given this problem and its solution from Excel summarized in Table 5-5:

minimize $\quad Z = 10x_1 + 3x_2$

subject to

1	$2x_1 + 1x_2 \ge 80$	(A)
2	$2x_1 + 4x_2 \ge 200$	(B)

$6 \le c_1 \le \infty$
$0 \le c_2 \le 5$
$50 \le b_1 \le \infty$
$-\infty \le b_2 \le 320$

a. Determine the range of optimality or the range of insignificance (whichever is appropriate) for each decision variable.
b. Determine the range of feasibility for each of the constraints.

Table 5-4   Excel Reports for Problem 16

A. Answer Report

Target Cell (Max)

Cell	Name	Original Value	Final Value
$E$5	Profit Total	0	2016

Adjustable Cells

Cell	Name	Original Value	Final Value
$B$4	Quantities Product A	0	112
$C$4	Quantities Product B	0	0
$D$4	Quantities Product C	0	48

Constraints

Cell	Name	Cell Value	Formula	Status	Slack
$E$7	Material 1 constraint Usage	720	$E$7<=$F$7	Binding	0
$E$8	Material 2 constraint Usage	368	$E$8<=$F$8	Not Binding	232
$E$9	Material 3 constraint Usage	640	$E$9<=$F$9	Binding	0
$B$4	Quantities Product A	112	$B$4>=0	Not Binding	112
$C$4	Quantities Product B	0	$C$4>=0	Binding	0
$D$4	Quantities Product C	48	$D$4>=0	Not binding	48

B. Sensitivity Report

Adjustable Cells

Cell	Name	Final Value	Reduced Cost	Objective Coefficient	Allowable Increase	Allowable Decrease
$B$4	Quantities Product A	112	0	12	2	2.285714286
$C$4	Quantities Product B	0	−3.2	15	3.2	1E+30
$D$4	Quantities Product C	48	0	14	18	2

Constraints

Cell	Name	Final Value	Shadow Price	Constraint R. H. Side	Allowable Increase	Allowable Decrease
$E$7	Material 1 constraint Usage	720	0.4	720	560	240
$E$8	Material 2 constraint Usage	368	0	600	1E+30	232
$E$9	Material 3 constraint Usage	640	2.7	640	320	280

Table 5-5	Excel Reports for Problem 18

A. Answer Report

Target Cell (Min)

Cell	Name	Original Value	Final Value
$D$5	Cost Total	240	240

Adjustable Cells

Cell	Name	Original Value	Final Value
$B$4	Quantities Product I	0	0
$C$4	Quantities Product II	80	80

Constraints

Cell	Name	Cell Value	Formula	Status	Slack
$D$7	Material A constraint Usage	80	$D$7>=$E$7	Binding	0
$D$8	Material B constraint Usage	320	$D$8>=$E$8	Not Binding	120
$B$4	Quantities Product I	0	$B$4>=0	Binding	0
$C$4	Quantities Product II	80	$C$4>=0	Not Binding	80

B. Sensitivity Report

Adjustable Cells

Cell	Name	Final Value	Reduced Cost	Objective Coefficient	Allowable Increase	Allowable Decrease
$B$4	Quantities Product I	0	4	10	1E+30	4
$C$4	Quantities Product II	80	0	3	2	3

Constraints

Cell	Name	Final Value	Shadow Price	Constraint R. H. Side	Allowable Increase	Allowable Decrease
$D$7	Material A constraint Usage	80	3	80	1E+30	30
$D$8	Material B constraint Usage	320	0	200	120	1E+30

19. Given this problem and the Excel output given in Table 5-6:

$$\text{minimize} \quad Z = 20x_1 + 12x_2 + 18x_3$$

subject to

$$
\begin{array}{lrl}
1 & x_1 + x_2 + x_3 \geq 25 & \text{(A)} \\
2 & 2x_1 + x_2 \leq 52 & \text{(B)} \\
3 & x_3 \geq 5 & \text{(C)} \\
& x_1, x_2, x_3 \geq 0
\end{array}
$$

Table 5-6   Excel Reports for Problem 19

A. Answer Report

Target Cell (Min)

Cell	Name	Original Value	Final Value
$E$5	Cost Total	450	330

Adjustable Cells

Cell	Name	Original Value	Final Value
$B$4	Quantities Product x_1	0	0
$C$4	Quantities Product x_2	0	20
$D$4	Quantities Product x_3	25	5

Constraints

Cell	Name	Cell Value	Formula	Status	Slack
$E$7	Material A constraint Usage	25	$E$7>=$F$7	Binding	0
$E$8	Material B constraint Usage	0	$E$8<=$F$8	Not Binding	52
$E$9	Material C constraint Usage	5	$E$9>=$F$9	Binding	0
$B$4	Quantities Product x_1	0	$B$4>=0	Binding	0
$C$4	Quantities Product x_2	20	$C$4>=0	Not Binding	20
$D$4	Quantities Product x_3	5	$D$4>=0	Not Binding	5

B. Sensitivity Report

Cell	Name	Final Value	Reduced Cost	Objective Coefficient	Allowable Increase	Allowable Decrease
$B$4	Quantities Product x_1	0	8.000000001	20	1E+30	8.000000001
$C$4	Quantities Product x_2	20	0	12	6	12
$D$4	Quantities Product x_3	5	0	18	1E+30	6

Cell	Name	Final Value	Shadow Price	Constraint R. H. Side	Allowable Increase	Allowable Decrease
$E$7	Material A constraint Usage	25	12	25	1E+30	20
$E$8	Material B constraint Usage	0	0	52	1E+30	52
$E$9	Material C constraint Usage	5	6	5	20	5

a. What are the optimal values of x_1, x_2, x_3, and Z.
b. What impact on the solution would a decrease of 10 units in the RHS of the first constraint have?
c. If the first constraint could be decreased 10 units at a cost per unit of $15, would it be worthwhile to do so? Explain.
d. What change in the coefficient of x_1 in the objective function would cause it to come into solution?
e. If the cost coefficient of x_3 decreased by $5, what impact would that have on the quantities and on the value of the objective function in the final solution?

20. (Refer to Problem 9.) It has been proposed that a new product be added. The manager has two possibilities, x_3 and x_4. Their resource requirements and unit contributions to profits would be

Material		Raw Material Requirements		
Product	1	2	3	Unit Profit
x_3	2	—	1	15
x_4	—	4	1	10

Yes, choose x_4

If the manager decides to add a product, she must select only one of these due to marketing considerations. Should one of these be added, or would it be better to produce only x_1 or x_2. Explain.

21. The manager of the department depicted in Problem 11 would like to know if a fourth variable would have a positive impact on profits. The new variable would have resource requirements of 3 units for product B in the second constraint and a profit per unit of $12. Determine if the new variable would come into solution and, if so, what impact there would be on profits.

Solving the dual may be simpler than solving the original dual (primal) problem due to having fewer constraints.

22. What is a dual problem? How is the dual useful?
23. Formulate the dual of this problem:

minimize $Z = 5x_1 + 7x_2 + 9x_3$

subject to

1    $20x_1 + 10x_2 + 30x_3 \geq 300$
2    $40x_1 + 5x_2 + 10x_3 \geq 200$
$x_1, x_2, x_3 \geq 0$

Which problem would you prefer to solve, the primal or the dual? Why?

24. Formulate the dual of this problem but do not solve it:

Dual:
Minimize $Z = 1,000y_1 + 1,200y_2$
subject to
$5y_1 + 4y_2 \geq 30$
$7y_1 + 6y_2 \geq 50$
$3y_1 + 8y_2 \geq 40$
$y_1, y_2 \geq 0$

maximize $Z = 30x_1 + 50x_2 + 40x_3$

subject to

1    $5x_1 + 7x_2 + 3x_3 \leq 1,000$
2    $4x_1 + 6x_2 + 8x_3 \leq 1,200$
$x_1, x_2, x_3 \geq 0$

25. Formulate the dual of the model given in problem 9.
26. The manager of the Happy Dog Company, Sam Smart, has developed this LP model:

x_1 = quantity of regular blend
x_2 = quantity of extra blend
x_3 = quantity of puppy delite

maximize $Z = .20x_1 + .18x_2 + .25x_3$

subject to

K9	$\frac{1}{3}x_1 + \frac{1}{2}x_2$	$\leq 1{,}500$ pounds
K8	$\frac{1}{3}x_1 + \frac{1}{4}x_2 + \frac{1}{10}x_3$	$\leq 1{,}000$ pounds
K1	$\frac{1}{3}x_1 + \frac{1}{4}x_2 + \frac{9}{10}x_3$	$\leq 1{,}000$ pounds
	$x_1, x_2, x_3 \geq 0$	

The final solution is given in the Excel output in Table 5-7.

a. .12, $1{,}000 \leq b_1 \leq 2{,}000$

b. $.48

c. No, $c_3 \geq .432 = .25 +$
   .182

d. No, because $.16 > .15$;
   new $Z = 620$

e. Yes, the sum of
   percent change does
   not exceed 1.0

a. What is the marginal value of a pound of K9? Over what range is that value valid?

b. By how much would profit decrease if there was one less pound of K1 available?

c. The manager believes it is possible to increase the profit per pound of puppy delite to $.40. Would that alter the optimal solution? Explain.

d. If the profit per unit of the extra blend dropped to $.16 a pound, would the optimal quantities of the variables in solution change? Would the optimal value of the objective function change? If so, would its new value be?

e. If the unit profits were changed to .22 for regular blend, .20 for extra blend, and .26 for puppy delite, would these changes be within the range of optimality for multiple changes?

27. A firm makes four products. Each product requires material, labor, and machine time. A linear programming model has been developed to describe the situation:

maximize $Z = 12x_1 + 10x_2 + 15x_3 + 11x_4$ (profit)

subject to

Material	$5x_1 + 3x_2 + 4x_3 + 2x_4 \leq 240$ pounds
Machine	$6x_1 + 8x_2 + 2x_3 + 3x_4 \leq 240$ hours
Labor	$2x_1 + 3x_2 + 3x_3 + 2x_4 \leq 180$ hours
	$x_1, x_2, x_3 \leq 0$

where

$x_1 =$ quantity of Product 1
$x_2 =$ quantity of Product 2
$x_3 =$ quantity of Product 3
$x_4 =$ quantity of Product 4

The optimal solution is given in the Excel output in Table 5-8.

a. The manager is concerned because none of Product 1 is called for in the optimal solution. At what profit per unit would Product 1 come into solution?

b. What is the marginal value of an hour of machine time? Over what range of machine time is this amount valid?

c. The manager can secure additional labor hours by the use of overtime. This involves paying a premium of $2 per hour. How much overtime can be effectively used, and what will the *net* total profit be if that amount of overtime is scheduled?

28. A garden store prepares various grades of pine bark for mulch: nuggets (x_1), mininuggets (x_2), and chips (x_3). The process requires pine bark, machine time, labor time, and storage space. The following linear programming model has been developed:

maximize $Z = 9x_1 + 9x_2 + 6x_3$ (profit)

Table 5-7   Excel Reports for Problem 26

A. Answer Report

Target Cell (Max)

Cell	Name	Original Value	Final Value
$E$5	Profit Total	660.00003	660.00003

Adjustable Cells

Cell	Name	Original Value	Final Value
$B$4	Quantities Regular	1500.00015	1500.00015
$C$4	Quantities Extra	2000	2000
$D$4	Quantities Puppy delite	0	0

Constraints

Cell	Name	Cell Value	Formula	Status	Slack
$E$7	K9 Usage	1500	$E$7<=$F$7	Binding	0
$E$8	K8 Usage	1000	$E$8<=$F$8	Binding	0
$E$9	K1 Usage	1000	$E$9<=$F$9	Binding	0
$B$4	Quantities Regular	1500.00015	$B$4>=0	Not Binding	1500.00015
$C$4	Quantities Extra	2000	$C$4>=0	Not Binding	2000
$D$4	Quantities Puppy delite	0	$D$4>=0	Binding	0

B. Sensitivity Report

Adjustable Cells

Cell	Name	Final Value	Reduced Cost	Objective Coefficient	Allowable Increase	Allowable Decrease
$B$4	Quantities Regular	1500.00015	0	0.2	0.039999976	0.03370372
$C$4	Quantities Extra	2000	0	0.18	0.050555586	0.029999985
$D$4	Quantities Puppy delite	0	−0.182000108	0.25	0.182000108	1E+30

Constraints

Cell	Name	Final Value	Shadow Price	Constraint R. H. Side	Allowable Increase	Allowable Decrease
$E$7	K9 Usage	1500	0.11999994	1500	500	500
$E$8	K8 Usage	1000	0	1000	1E+30	1.42109E−13
$E$9	K1 Usage	1000	0.48000012	1000	1.42109E−13	250

Table 5-8   Excel Reports for Problem 27

A. Answer Report

Target Cell (Max)

Cell	Name	Original Value	Final Value
$F$5	Profit Total	972	972

Adjustable Cells

Cell	Name	Original Value	Final Value
$B$4	Quantities Product I	1.33227E−14	0
$C$4	Quantities Product II	0	0
$D$4	Quantities Product III	12	12
$E$4	Quantities Product IV	72	72

Constraints

Cell	Name	Cell Value	Formula	Status	Slack
$F$7	Material Usage	192	$F$7<=$G$7	Not Binding	48
$F$8	Machine Usage	240	$F$8<=$G$8	Binding	0
$F$9	Labor Usage	180	$F$9<=$G$9	Binding	0
$B$4	Quantities Product I	0	$B$4>=0	Binding	0
$C$4	Quantities Product II	0	$C$4>=0	Binding	0
$D$4	Quantities Product III	12	$D$4>=0	Not Binding	12
$E$4	Quantities Product IV	72	$E$4>=0	Not Binding	72

B. Sensitivity Report

Adjustable Cells

Cell	Name	Final Value	Reduced Cost	Objective Coefficient	Allowable Increase	Allowable Decrease
$B$4	Quantities Product I	0	−0.8	12	0.8	1E+30
$C$4	Quantities Product II	0	−8.6	10	8.6	1E+30
$D$4	Quantities Product III	12	0	15	0.666666667	7.666666667
$E$4	Quantities Product IV	72	0	11	11.5	0.285714286

Constraints

Cell	Name	Final Value	Shadow Price	Constraint R. H. Side	Allowable Increase	Allowable Decrease
$F$7	Material Usage	192	0	240	1E+30	48
$F$8	Machine Usage	240	0.6	240	30	120
$F$9	Labor Usage	180	4.6	180	30	20

subject to

Bark	$5x_1 + 6x_2 + 3x_3 \leq 600$ pounds
Machine	$2x_1 + 4x_2 + 5x_3 \leq 660$ minutes
Labor	$2x_1 + 4x_2 + 3x_3 \leq 480$ hours
Storage	$1x_1 + 1x_2 + 1x_3 \leq 150$ bags

$$x_1, x_2, x_3 \geq 0$$

In addition, the optimal solution is summarized in the Excel output in Table 5-9.

a. 1.50, $510 \leq b_1 \leq 750$

b. $1.50/bag

c. $0, $375 \leq b_3 \leq \infty$
d. None, machine time has slack

e. 150 lbs. of pine bark

f. No, $5.4 \leq c_3 \leq 9.0$; Z would increase by $75, new Z = $1200

a. What is the marginal value of a pound of pine bark? Over what range is this value valid?
b. What is the maximum price the store would be justified in paying for additional storage space?
c. What is the marginal value of labor? Over what range is this value in effect?
d. The manager obtained additional machine time through better scheduling. How much additional machine time can be effectively used for this operation? Why?
e. If the manager can obtain *either* additional pine bark *or* additional storage space, which one should be chosen and how much should be obtained (assuming additional quantities cost the same as usual)?
f. If a change in the chip operation would increase the profit on chips from $6 per bag to $7 per bag, would the optimal quantities change? Would the value of the objective function change? If so, what would the new value(s) be?

29. A firm produces jars of chilled fruit that are sold to restaurants. Three varieties of fruit are sold: California mix (x_1), Florida mix (x_2), and Hawaiian mix (x_3). A linear programming model for the process is

maximize $Z = 4x_1 + 3x_2 + 6x_3$ (profit)

subject to

Oranges	$3x_1 + 2x_2 + 1x_3 \leq 920$ pounds
Grapefruit	$2x_1 + 2x_2 + 2x_3 \leq 900$ pounds
Pineapple	$1x_1 + 2x_2 + 3x_3 \leq 930$ pounds
Peeling/cutting	$1.2x_1 + 1.4x_2 + 1.5x_3 \leq 1,260$ minutes
Mixing/packaging	$1x_1 + 2x_2 + 1x_3 \leq 600$ minutes

$$x_1, x_2, x_3 \geq 0$$

The optimal solution is summarized in the Excel output in Table 5-10.

a. The equipment used for peeling and cutting must be replaced. The new equipment will have a capacity of only 1,200 minutes. What impact will this change have on the optimal values of the decision variables and on profit?
b. What would the unit profit on the Florida mix have to be before it would become profitable to produce?
c. If management had a choice of obtaining more oranges or more pineapples, which one should be chosen? Why?
d. Management has just learned that an additional 50 pounds of pineapples are on hand. What will the optimal values of the decision variables change to?
e. Management is considering making changes that will cause the profit on the Hawaiian mix to be $8 per unit. Would this affect the solution? Will it affect the optimal value of the objective function?
f. Management is considering a change in equipment that would result in increasing the profit on the Hawaiian mix to $8 per unit but result in decreasing the profit on the California mix by $1. Would these changes be within the range of optimality? If so, how much would the optimal profit change?

Table 5-9	Excel Reports for Problem 28

A. Answer Report

Target Cell (Max)

Cell	Name	Original Value	Final Value
$E$5	Profit Total	0	1125

Adjustable Cells

Cell	Name	Original Value	Final Value
$B$4	Quantities Nuggets	0	75
$C$4	Quantities Mini-nuggets	0	0
$D$4	Quantities Chips	0	75

Constraints

Cell	Name	Cell Value	Formula	Status	Slack
$E$7	Bark Usage	600	$E$7<=$F$7	Binding	0
$E$8	Machine Usage	525	$E$8<=$F$8	Not Binding	135
$E$9	Labor Usage	375	$E$9<=$F$9	Not Binding	105
$E$10	Storage Usage	150	$E$10<=$F$10	Binding	0
$B$4	Quantities Nuggets	75	$B$4>=0	Not Binding	75
$C$4	Quantities Mini-nuggets	0	$C$4>=0	Binding	0
$D$4	Quantities Chips	75	$D$4>=0	Not Binding	75

B. Sensitivity Report

Adjustable Cells

Cell	Name	Final Value	Reduced Cost	Objective Coefficient	Allowable Increase	Allowable Decrease
$B$4	Quantities Nuggets	75	0	9	1	1
$C$4	Quantities Mini-nuggets	0	−1.5	9	1.5	1E+30
$D$4	Quantities Chips	75	0	6	3	0.6

Constraints

Cell	Name	Final Value	Shadow Price	Constraint R. H. Side	Allowable Increase	Allowable Decrease
$E$7	Bark Usage	600	1.5	600	150	90
$E$8	Machine Usage	525	0	660	1E+30	135
$E$9	Labor Usage	375	0	480	1E+30	105
$E$10	Storage Usage	150	1.5	150	14.21052632	30

Table 5-10   Excel Reports for Problem 29

A. Answer Report

Target Cell (Max)

Cell	Name	Original Value	Final Value
$E$5	Profit Total	0	2280

Adjustable Cells

Cell	Name	Original Value	Final Value
$B$4	Quantities California mix	0	210
$C$4	Quantities Florida mix	0	0
$D$4	Quantities Hawaiian mix	0	240

Constraints

Cell	Name	Cell Value	Formula	Status	Slack
$E$7	Oranges Usage	870	$E$7<=$F$7	Not Binding	50
$E$8	Grapefruit Usage	900	$E$8<=$F$8	Binding	0
$E$9	Pineapple Usage	930	$E$9<=$F$9	Binding	0
$E$10	Peeling/cutting Usage	612	$E$10<=$F$10	Not Binding	648
$E$11	Mixing/packaging Usage	450	$E$11<=$F$11	Not Binding	150
$B$4	Quantities California mix	210	$B$4>=0	Not Binding	210
$C$4	Quantities Florida mix	0	$C$4>=0	Binding	0
$D$4	Quantities Hawaiian mix	240	$D$4>=0	Not Binding	240

B. Sensitivity Report

Adjustable Cells

Cell	Name	Final Value	Reduced Cost	Objective Coefficient	Allowable Increase	Allowable Decrease
$B$4	Quantities California mix	210	0	4	2	2
$C$4	Quantities Florida mix	0	−2	3	2	1E+30
$D$4	Quantities Hawaiian mix	240	0	6	6	2

Constraints

Cell	Name	Final Value	Shadow Price	Constraint R. H. Side	Allowable Increase	Allowable Decrease
$E$7	Oranges Usage	870	0	920	1E+30	50
$E$8	Grapefruit Usage	900	1.5	900	25	280
$E$9	Pineapple Usage	930	1	930	420	50
$E$10	Peeling/cutting Usage	612	0	1260	1E+30	648
$E$11	Mixing/packaging Usage	450	0	600	1E+30	150

30. Special D, Inc., is a new firm that is engaged in recycling. Its main facility uses a three-step system to process beverage containers. A consultant has developed the following LP model of the process:

maximize $\quad Z = 14Q + 11R + 15T \quad$ (revenue)

subject to

Sorting	$2.4Q + 3.0R + 4.0T \le 960$ minutes
Crushing	$2.5Q + 1.8R + 2.4T \le 607$ minutes
Packing	$12Q + 18R + 24T \le 3{,}600$ minutes
	$Q, R,$ and $T \ge 0$

The consultant has also included an Excel output of sensitivity analysis, shown in Table 5-11.

Answer these questions using the information in Table 5–11:

a. Which decision variables are in the final solution? What are their optimal values?
b. Find the range of optimality for the variables that are in the final solution.
c. Find the range of insignificance for R.
d. Identify the shadow price for each constraint.
e. Determine the range over which each shadow price is valid.
f. By how much would revenue decrease if sorting time was reduced to 900 minutes? How much would revenue increase if sorting time was increased to 1,269 minutes?
g. What effect would an increase of $2 in the revenue per unit of T have on the optimal value of T? On the total revenue?
h. Would an increase of $1 in the revenue per unit of R have any impact on the optimal solution? Explain.
i. If you could obtain additional quantities of one resource (either sorting, crushing, or packing) at no additional cost, and your goal was to achieve the greatest increase in revenue, which resource would you add, and how much of it would you add? Explain.

a. $Q = 190, T = 55$
b. $7.5 \le C_Q \le 15.625$
c. $14.667 \le C_T \le 28$
   $-\infty \le C_R \le 11.25$
d. Constraint 1 = 0
   Constraint 2 = 5
   Constraint 3 = .125
e. $676 \le b_Q \le \infty$
   $360 \le b_R \le 750$
   $2{,}913.6 \le b_T \le 5{,}689.81$
f. No impact, there is enough slack
g. No change in variable values, Z increases by $(2)(55) = 110$
h. Yes, because $1 > .25$
i. Choose crushing; Crushing $= 5(143) = 715$ $>$ Packing $= (.125)(2{,}089) = 261.125$

31. Fashion Designs produces four clothing products in one of its factories. The following LP model has been developed and solved using Excel.

$x_1 =$ weekly quantity of slacks
$x_2 =$ weekly quantity of dresses
$x_3 =$ weekly quantity of skirts
$x_4 =$ weekly quantity of blouses

maximize $\quad Z = 15x_1 + 15x_2 + 12x_3 + 16x_4 \quad$ (profit)

subject to

Cutting	$x_1 + 2x_2 + 4x_3 + x_4 \le 800$ hours per week
Sewing	$4x_1 + 2x_2 \qquad\quad + 3x_4 \le 700$ hours per week
Inspecting	$2x_1 + 2x_2 + x_3 + x_4 \le 600$ minutes per week
Packing	$3x_1 + 2x_2 + 2x_3 \qquad \le 660$ minutes per week
	$x_1, x_2, x_3, x_4 \ge 0$

The results are summarized in Table 5-12.

a. Which departments have capacities that limit output? Explain
b. The plant manager is considering scheduling overtime. Is there any department or departments that should be excluded from consideration? Why?
c. What is the marginal value of overtime scheduled in the cutting department? How much overtime could be effectively used?
d. Overtime costs the company a premium of $3 per hour over regular costs. If one department is scheduled for overtime, which one should be scheduled, and how

Table 5-11	Excel Reports for Problem 30

A. Answer Report

Target Cell (Max)

Cell	Name	Original Value	Final Value
$E$5	Profit Total	0	3485

Adjustable Cells

Cell	Name	Original Value	Final Value
$B$4	Quantities Q	0	190
$C$4	Quantities R	0	0
$D$4	Quantities T	0	55

Constraints

Cell	Name	Cell Value	Formula	Status	Slack
$E$7	Sorting constraint Usage	676	$E$7<=$F$7	Not Binding	284
$E$8	Crushing constraint Usage	607	$E$8<=$F$8	Binding	0
$E$9	Packing constraint Usage	3600	$E$9<=$F$9	Binding	0
$B$4	Quantities Q	190	$B$4>=0	Not Binding	190
$C$4	Quantities R	0	$C$4>=0	Binding	0
$D$4	Quantities T	55	$D$4>=0	Not Binding	55

B. Sensitivity Report

Adjustable Cells

Cell	Name	Final Value	Reduced Cost	Objective Coefficient	Allowable Increase	Allowable Decrease
$B$4	Quantities Q	190	0	14	1.625	6.5
$C$4	Quantities R	0	−0.25	11	0.25	1E+30
$D$4	Quantities T	55	0	15	13	0.333333333

Constraints

Cell	Name	Final Value	Shadow Price	Constraint R. H. Side	Allowable Increase	Allowable Decrease
$E$7	Sorting constraint Usage	676	0	960	1E+30	284
$E$8	Crushing constraint Usage	607	5	607	143	247
$E$9	Packing constraint Usage	3600	0.125	3600	2089.811321	686.4

Table 5-12   Excel Reports for Problem 31

A. Answer Report

Target Cell (Max)

Cell	Name	Original Value	Final Value
$F$5	Profit Total	0	5508.333333

Adjustable Cells

Cell	Name	Original Value	Final Value
$B$4	Quantities Slacks	0	0
$C$4	Quantities Dresses	0	225
$D$4	Quantities Skirts	0	66.66666667
$E$4	Quantities Blouses	0	83.33333333

Constraints

Cell	Name	Cell Value	Formula	Status	Slack
$F$7	Cutting constraint Usage	800	$F$7<=$G$7	Binding	0
$F$8	Sewing constraint Usage	700	$F$8<=$G$8	Binding	0
$F$9	Inspecting constraint Usage	600	$F$9<=$G$9	Binding	0
$F$10	Packing constraint Usage	583.3333333	$F$10<=$G$10	Not Binding	76.66666667
$B$4	Quantities Slacks	0	$B$4>=0	Binding	0
$C$4	Quantities Dresses	225	$C$4>=0	Not Binding	225
$D$4	Quantities Skirts	66.66666667	$D$4>=0	Not Binding	66.66666667
$E$4	Quantities Blouses	83.33333333	$E$4>=0	Not Binding	83.33333333

B. Sensitivity Report

Adjustable Cells

Cell	Name	Final Value	Reduced Cost	Objective Coefficient	Allowable Increase	Allowable Decrease
$B$4	Quantities Slacks	0	−5.583333333	15	5.583333333	1E+30
$C$4	Quantities Dresses	225	0	15	11.66666667	0.333333333
$D$4	Quantities Skirts	66.66666667	0	12	1	8.75
$E$4	Quantities Blouses	83.33333333	0	16	0.5	6.7

Constraints

Cell	Name	Final Value	Shadow Price	Constraint R. H. Side	Allowable Increase	Allowable Decrease
$F$7	Cutting constraint Usage	800	2.916666667	800	460	200
$F$8	Sewing constraint Usage	700	4.25	700	900	153.3333333
$F$9	Inspecting constraint Usage	600	0.333333333	600	57.5	225
$F$10	Packing constraint Usage	583.3333333	0	660	1E+30	76.66666667

much overtime can be effectively used? What would the revised optimal value of the objective function be, after an allowance for the premium?

e. If the unit profit on x_3 dropped by 50 percent, how would that affect the optimal values of the decision variables and the optimal value of the objective function?

32. Serious Toys, Unlimited, produces three types of building blocks preschoolers. Recently, the company underwent a major reorganization of its manufacturing facility and a restructuring of its prices. As a result, a new linear programming model has been formulated to describe the situation:

A = number of advanced sets
B = number of beginner sets
C = number of intermediate sets

maximize $Z = 1.2A + 1.6B + 1.4C$ (profit)

subject to

Plastic	$6A + 5B + 3C \leq 300$ pounds
Labor	$9A + 4B + 5C \leq 280$ minutes
Machine	$2A + 8B + 4C \leq 320$ minutes
B	$B \geq 18$ sets
	$A, B, C \geq 0$

The model has been processed through Excel. The results are summarized in Table 5-13.

a. How would you interpret the shadow price of 0.2 for labor constraint?

b. What is the range of feasibility for the RHS of the labor constraint?

c. If the amount of labor available were to increase by 60 minutes per hour, would the optimal quantities of the decision variables change? Would the optimal profit change?

d. If machine time increased by 50 minutes per hour, by how much would profit increase?

e. If machine time increased by 100 minutes per hour, by how much would profit increase?

f. How much would another 10 pounds of plastic per hour be worth in terms of increased profit? Explain?

g. If the profit per unit on advanced sets increased by 70 percent, would that affect the optimal solution? Explain.

Margin answers:
a. Marginal value of an additional hour of labor
b. $160 \leq b_2 \leq 400$
c. Yes, optimal values of variables and Z would change
d. $(.1)(50) = \$5$
e. $(.1)(100) = \$10$
f. None, plastic has slack
g. Yes $(.84 > .8)$

33. Dog Daze Manufacturing produces a variety of dog food products. These are made in batches and then kept in inventory that is used to fill orders from kennels and pet stores. The manager has helped to develop a linear programming model of the process for the company's three raw material inputs:

x_1, x_2, x_3:

x_1 = bags of raw material 1
x_2 = bags of raw material 2
x_3 = bags of raw material 3

minimize $Z = 38x_1 + 19x_2 + 60x_3$ (cost)

subject to

Protein	$2.5x_1 + 4x_2 + 3x_3 \geq 794$ pounds
Fiber	$3x_1 + 2x_2 + 4x_3 \geq$ pounds
Fat	$2x_1 + x_2 + 2x_3 \geq 600$ pounds
	$x_1, x_2, x_3 \geq 0$

The manager has obtained the Excel output of sensitivity analysis for the model. The results are summarized in the answers and sensitivity reports given in Table 5-14.

Table 5-13   Excel Reports for Problem 32

A. Answer Report

Target Cell (Max)

Cell	Name	Original Value	Final Value
$E$5	Profit Total	0	88

Adjustable Cells

Cell	Name	Original Value	Final Value
$B$4	Quantities Advanced Sets	0	0
$C$4	Quantities Beginner sets	0	20
$D$4	Quantities Intermediate sets	0	40

Constraints

Cell	Name	Cell Value	Formula	Status	Slack
$E$7	Plastic Usage	200	$E$7<=$F$7	Not Binding	80
$E$8	Labor Usage	280	$E$8<=$F$8	Binding	0
$E$9	Machine Usage	320	$E$9<=$F$9	Binding	0
$B$4	Quantities Advanced Sets	0	$B$4>=0	Binding	0
$C$4	Quantities Beginner Sets	20	$C$4>=0	Not Binding	20
$D$4	Quantities Intermediate sets	40	$D$4>=0	Not Binding	40

B. Sensitivity Report

Adjustable Cells

Cell	Name	Final Value	Reduced Cost	Objective Coefficient	Allowable Increase	Allowable Decrease
$B$4	Quantities Advanced Sets	0	−0.8	1.2	0.8	1E+30
$C$4	Quantities Beginner sets	20	0	1.6	0.738461538	0.48
$D$4	Quantities Intermediate sets	40	0	1.4	0.6	0.3

Constraints

Cell	Name	Final Value	Shadow Price	Constraint R. H. Side	Allowable Increase	Allowable Decrease
$E$7	Plastic Usage	220	0	300	1E+30	80
$E$8	Labor Usage	280	0.2	280	120	120
$E$9	Machine Usage	320	0.1	320	147.6923077	96

Table 5-14   Excel Reports for Problem 33

A. Answer Report

Target Cell (Min)

Cell	Name	Original Value	Final Value
$E$5	Cost Total	0	11400

Adjustable Cells

Cell	Name	Original Value	Final Value
$B$4	Quantities Raw Material 1	0	292
$C$4	Quantities Raw Material 2	0	16
$D$4	Quantities Raw Material 3	0	0

Constraints

Cell	Name	Cell Value	Formula	Status	Slack
$E$7	Protein constraint Usage	794	$E$7>=$F$7	Binding	0
$E$8	Fiber constraint Usage	908	$E$8>=$F$8	Not Binding	608
$E$9	Fat constraint Usage	600	$E$9>=$F$9	Binding	0
$B$4	Quantities Raw Material 1	292	$B$4>=0	Not Binding	292
$C$4	Quantities Raw Material 2	16	$C$4>=0	Not Binding	16
$D$4	Quantities Raw Material 3	0	$D$4>=0	Binding	0

B. Sensitivity Report

Adjustable Cells

Cell	Name	Final Value	Reduced Cost	Objective Coefficient	Allowable Increase	Allowable Decrease
$B$4	Quantities Raw Material 1	292	0	38	0	26.125
$C$4	Quantities Raw Material 2	16	0	19	41.8	0
$D$4	Quantities Raw Material 3	0	22	60	1E+30	22

Constraints

Cell	Name	Final Value	Shadow Price	Constraint R. H. Side	Allowable Increase	Allowable Decrease
$E$7	Protein constraint Usage	794	0	794	1606	44
$E$8	Fiber constraint Usage	908	0	300	608	1E+30
$E$9	Fat constraint Usage	600	19	600	35.2	401.5

Use Table 5-14 to answer the following questions about the model:

a. Which constraints are binding on the solution? How do you know?

b. What does the reduced cost of 22 indicate?

c. How do you interpret the 608 in the Allowable Increase section of the fiber constraint?

d. Determine the range of optimality for the objective function coefficients of x_1 and x_2.

e. What does the shadow price of 19 reveal?

f. What is the range of feasibility for the fat constraint's RHS?

g. Would a decrease to 575 for the RHS of the fat constraint affect the optimal value of the objective function? If so, by how much?

h. The manager is considering reducing each RHS by 9 percent and may ask you to provide information on how that would impact the total cost. If you are asked, what would you need to do? Why?

No, it would not

34. The manager of the server problem analyzed in this chapter wants to reconsider adding a third server model to the product line. After reevaluating the third server model, the manager now estimates that it will yield a profit of $80 per unit, with resource requirements of 7 hours of assembly time, 3 hours of inspection time, and 5 cubic feet of storage space. Determine if the third model would come into the solution.

35. Formulate the dual of the following linear programming problem:

$$\text{maximize} \quad Z = 4x_1 + 3x_2$$

subject to

$$6x_1 + 2x_2 \leq 24$$
$$3x_1 \qquad \leq 18$$
$$2x_1 + 8x_2 \leq 32$$
$$\qquad 4x_2 \leq 28$$
$$x_1, x_2 \geq 0$$

Would it be computationally easier to solve the primal or the dual?

Dual:
minimize $Z =$
$12y_1 + 20y_2 - 20y'_2 - 8y_3$
subject to
$y_1 + 2y_2 - 2y'_2 - y_3 \geq 1$
$y_1 + y_2 - y'_2 - y_3 \geq 2$
$2y_1 + 5y_2 - 5y'_2 + y_3 \geq 2$
$y_1, y_2, y'_2, y_3 \geq 0$

36. Given the following linear programming problem, formulate the dual.

$$\text{maximize} \quad Z = x_1 + 2x_2 + 2x_3$$

subject to

$$x_1 + x_2 + 2x_3 \leq 12$$
$$2x_1 + x_2 + 5x_3 = 20$$
$$x_1 + x_2 - x_3 \geq 8$$
$$x_1, x_2, x_3 \geq 0$$

◼ Chapter 5 Case Red Brand Canners

On Monday, September 13, Mr. Mitchell Gordon, Vice President of Operations, asked the Controller, the Sales Manager, and the Production Manager to meet with him to discuss the amount of tomato products to pack that season. The tomato crop, which had been purchased at planting, was beginning to arrive at the cannery, and packing operations would have to be started by the following Monday. Red Brand Canners was a medium-sized company that canned and distributed a variety of fruit and vegetable products under private brands in the western states.

Source: Reprinted from *Stanford Business Cases 1965, 1977* with permission of the Publishers. Stanford University Graduate School of Business, © 1965 and 1977 by the Board of Trustees of the Leland Stanford Junior University.

Figure 6-1	Schematic Diagram of a Transportation Problem

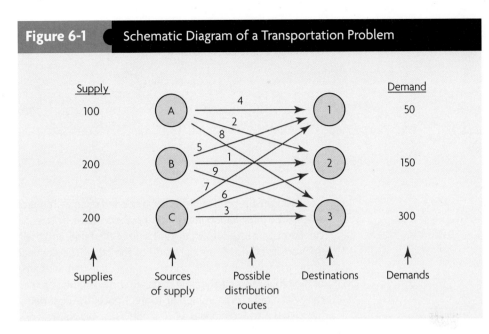

In the example given in Figure 6-1, there are 100 units of supply available at source A. There are 50 units demanded at destination 1. The cost of shipping one unit from source A to destination 1 is equal to $4, and the cost of shipping one unit from source B to destination 3 is $9. The remaining supply, demand, and per-unit cost values can be interpreted in a similar way.

The transportation problem requires the assumption that all goods be homogeneous, so that any origin is capable of supplying any destination, and the assumption that transportation costs are a direct linear function of the quantity shipped over any route. We shall add one additional requirement that will simplify the problem: The total quantity available for shipment is equal to the total quantity demanded. Later in the chapter we shall see how the problem can be modified to handle cases where this assumption is not met.

Example 6-1

Harley's Sand and Gravel Pit has contracted to provide topsoil for three residential housing developments. Topsoil can be supplied from three different "farms" as follows:

Farm	Weekly Capacity (cubic yards)
A	100
B	200
C	200

Demand for the topsoil generated by the construction projects is

Project	Weekly Demand (cubic yards)
1	50
2	150
3	300

The manager of the sand and gravel pit has estimated the cost per cubic yard to ship over each of the possible routes:

Cost per Cubic Yard
To

From	Project #1	Project #2	Project #3
Farm A	$4	$2	$8
Farm B	5	1	9
Farm C	7	6	3

This constitutes the information needed to solve the problem. The next step is to arrange the information into a transportation table. This is shown in Table 6-1. The origins (farms) are listed down the left side of the table, and their respective supply quantities are listed down the right side of the table. The destinations (projects) are listed across the top of the table, and their respective demands are listed across the bottom of the table. The unit shipping costs are shown in the upper-right-hand corner of each cell, which represents a shipping route. Hence, the cost per cubic yard to ship topsoil from Farm A to Project #1 is $4. (For convenience, dollar signs are not shown).

Table 6-1   Transportation Table (Tableau) for Harley's Sand and Gravel

To: / From:	Project #1	Project #2	Project #3	Supply
Farm A	4	2	8	100
Farm B	5	1	9	200
Farm C	7	6	3	200
Demand	50	150	300	

We can write this in the general format of a linear programming model and use Excel or other LP packages to solve it on a computer. With that in mind, we can replace the numerical values in the preceding transportation table with more general symbols, and then use the symbols to illustrate how the problem can be expressed in the general format of a linear programming model. Thus, the model in Table 6–2 can be observed.

Table 6-2   Transportation Table—General Expression of the LP Model

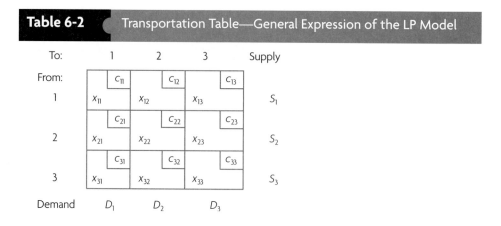

To: / From:	1	2	3	Supply
1	c_{11} / x_{11}	c_{12} / x_{12}	c_{13} / x_{13}	S_1
2	c_{21} / x_{21}	c_{22} / x_{22}	c_{23} / x_{23}	S_2
3	c_{31} / x_{31}	c_{32} / x_{32}	c_{33} / x_{33}	S_3
Demand	D_1	D_2	D_3	

where c_{ij} = cost per unit to transport units from origin i to destination j
    x_{ij} = quantity shipped from origin i to destination j
    S_i = Supply for origin i
    D_j = Demand for destination j

The numerical information given in Table 6-1 can be translated into a general expression given in Table 6-2 such that $c_{11} = 4$ (cost of shipping 1 cubic yard from farm A to project 1 is $4), $S_1 = 100$ (total supply available in farm A is 100 cubic yards), and $D_1 = 50$ (total demand at destination project 1 is 50 cubic yards).

In transportation problems, the objective is to minimize the cost of distributing the supplies to the destinations. Moreover, the supplies of the origins and demands of the destinations can be thought of as constraints. For purposes of illustration, let us assume that total supply is equal to total demand. Later in the chapter, there is a section that shows how to deal with problems in which total supply and total demand are not equal.

Here is the model in the general LP format (assuming total supply and total demand are equal):

minimize $Z = c_{11}x_{11} + c_{12}x_{12} + c_{13}x_{13} + c_{21}x_{21} + c_{22}x_{22} + c_{23}x_{23} + c_{31}x_{31} + c_{32}x_{32} + c_{33}x_{33}$

subject to

$$
\begin{array}{llll}
\text{row 1:} & x_{11} + x_{12} + x_{13} & = S_1 & \left.\right\} \\
\text{row 2:} & x_{21} + x_{22} + x_{23} & = S_2 & \left.\right\} \quad \text{Supply} \\
\text{row 3:} & x_{31} + x_{32} + x_{33} & = S_3 & \left.\right\}
\end{array}
$$

$$
\begin{array}{llll}
\text{col. 1:} & x_{11} + x_{21} + x_{31} & = D_1 & \left.\right\} \\
\text{col. 2:} & x_{12} + x_{22} + x_{32} & = D_2 & \left.\right\} \quad \text{Demand} \\
\text{col. 3:} & x_{13} + x_{23} + x_{33} & = D_3 & \left.\right\}
\end{array}
$$

All variables ≥ 0

Using this format, the Harley problem would be written as follows:

minimize $Z = 4x_{11} + 2x_{12} + 8x_{13} + 5x_{21} + 1x_{22} + 9x_{23} + 7x_{31} + 6x_{32} + 3x_{33}$

subject to

$$
\begin{array}{lllll}
\text{Farm A:} & x_{11} + x_{12} + x_{13} & = & 100 & \left.\right\} \\
\text{Farm B:} & x_{21} + x_{22} + x_{23} & = & 200 & \left.\right\} \quad \text{Supply} \\
\text{Farm C:} & x_{31} + x_{23} + x_{33} & = & 200 & \left.\right\}
\end{array}
$$

$$
\begin{array}{lllll}
\text{Project \#1:} & x_{11} + x_{21} + x_{31} & = & 50 & \left.\right\} \\
\text{Project \#2:} & x_{12} + x_{22} + x_{32} & = & 150 & \left.\right\} \quad \text{Demand} \\
\text{Project \#3:} & x_{13} + x_{23} + x_{33} & = & 300 & \left.\right\}
\end{array}
$$

All variables ≥ 0

Notice that the unit costs appear only in the objective function, and not in the constraints. Also, because total supply equals total demand, all of the constraints can be written as equalities.

Once we have the problem in this format, we can use Excel to obtain the optimal solution (i.e., the quantities to be shipped from each origin to each destination, some of which will be equal to zero, and the minimal total cost to ship all units.)

Various transportation problems present special cases. Some of these special cases are discussed in the following section.

Special Cases of Transportation Problems

Maximization Problems   Some transportation-type problems concern profits or revenues rather than costs. In such cases, the objective is to *maximize* rather than to minimize. Such problems are automatically handled by Excel or other software packages. When the optimal distribution plan has been identified, use the *original cell* (profit per unit) *values* to compute the total profit for that plan.

Unacceptable Routes In some cases, certain origin-destination combinations may be unacceptable. This may be due to weather factors, equipment breakdowns, labor problems, or skill requirements that either prohibit, or make undesirable, certain combinations (routes).

Suppose that in the Harley problem route A–3 was suddenly unavailable because of recent flooding. In order to prevent that route from appearing in the final solution (as it originally did), the manager could assign a unit cost to that cell that was large enough to make that route uneconomical and, hence, prohibit its occurrence. One rule of thumb would be to assign a unit cost of $9999 instead of the original cost of $8 per unit. Then this revised problem could be solved using Excel.

Unequal Supply and Demand Up to this point, examples have involved cases in which supply and demand were equal. As you might guess, there are situations in which the two are not equal. When such a situation is encountered, it is necessary to modify the original problem so that supply and demand are equal. This is accomplished by adding either a dummy column or a dummy row; a dummy row is added if supply is less than demand and a dummy column is added if demand is less than supply. The dummy is assigned unit costs of zero for each cell, and it is given a supply (if a row) or a demand (if a column) equal to the difference between supply and demand. Quantities in dummy routes in the optimal solution are not shipped. Rather, they serve to indicate which supplier will hold the excess supply, and how much, or which destination will not receive its total demand, and how much it will be short.

In the next section, we will learn how to solve transportation problems using Excel.

Solving Transportation Problems Using Excel

Since we formulated the transportation problem as a linear programming model, we can solve it using Excel. In this section, we will demonstrate how to solve our topsoil example using Excel spreadsheets. If we use standard Excel, the transportation problem must be formulated and solved as a linear programming problem as we demonstrated in Chapters 4 and 5. Exhibit 6-1 shows how we can set up a spreadsheet formulation of the topsoil problem that was stated earlier in this chapter. We set up a table similar to the transportation tableau presented in Table 6-1. In the spreadsheet shown in Exhibit 6-1, the supply locations (farms) are the rows and destinations (projects) are the columns in the upper portion of the worksheet. The right side of the table consists of the supply quantities and the demand quantities are listed at the bottom of the table. A column is inserted on the far right of the spreadsheet with column heading "Topsoil shipped." This column consists of the formulas for each row (or supply location) such that the values of supply stated in the supply column equal the amount shipped from each of the supply locations in each row. For example, supply in farm A must equal 100 cubic inches. Thus, the amount shipped from Farm A to Project 1, Farm A to Project 2, and Farm A to Project 3 must equal a total of 100. In order to ensure that the above-mentioned constraint is satisfied, the values in cells B5, C5, and D5 add up to 100. The formula for this row is shown in Exhibit 6-1. The topsoil shipped for cell F5 consists of the sum of the values in cells B5, C5, and D5. Likewise we insert a row at the bottom of the table with the row heading "Topsoil shipped." This row includes the formulas for each column (or destination location)

Exhibit 6-1   Input and Output Worksheet for the Transportation (topsoil) Problem

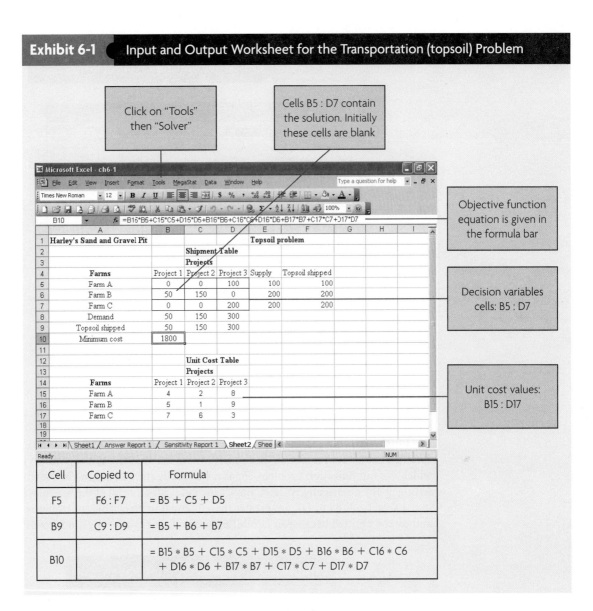

Cell	Copied to	Formula
F5	F6 : F7	= B5 + C5 + D5
B9	C9 : D9	= B5 + B6 + B7
B10		= B15 * B5 + C15 * C5 + D15 * D5 + B16 * B6 + C16 * C6 + D16 * D6 + B17 * B7 + C17 * C7 + D17 * D7

such that the values of demand stated in the destination column equal the amount shipped to each of the destination locations. For example, demand for Project 2 must equal 150 cubic inches. Thus, the amount shipped from Farm A to Project 2, Farm B to Project 2, and Farm C to Project 2 must equal 150. In order to ensure that the above-mentioned constraint is satisfied, the values in cells C5, C6, and C7 add up to 150. The topsoil shipped for cell B9 consists of the sum of the values in cells B5, B6, and B7. The formula for this column is also shown in Exhibit 6-1. In Exhibit 6-1, we see the formula for the objective function that is stated in cell B10. This formula utilizes the cell references from the bottom portion of the worksheet labeled "unit cost table." The formula for this cell consists of the cross products of cells associated with the shipping routes (decision variables) as well as the cost of shipping one unit on each of these routes. The formula for cell B10

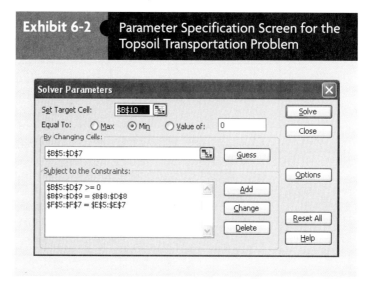

Exhibit 6-2 Parameter Specification Screen for the Topsoil Transportation Problem

(the objective function formula for total cost) is as follows:

=B15*B5+C15*C5+D15*D5+B16*B6+C16*C6+D16*D6+B17*B7+C17*C7+D17*D7

and is shown on the formula bar of Exhibit 6-1.

Initially, the values of the decision variables in cells B5: D7 are zero and the objective function value in cell B10 also has a value of zero. To solve this problem, we click on **Tools | Solver;** the Solver Parameters screen is displayed (see Exhibit 6-2).

On this screen, we define the parameters. First, the location of the objective function is specified in the "Set Target Cell" box as B10. Then, the objective of the problem is specified, which is a minimization problem. Finally, we specify the constraints. We start initially by setting up the nonnegativity constraints, which indicates that all of the variables highlighted in the area, from B5 to D7, are greater than or equal to zero. This constraint is redundant and can be omitted because in Exhibit 6-3 we will specify that the model consists of only

Exhibit 6-3 Solver Options Screen

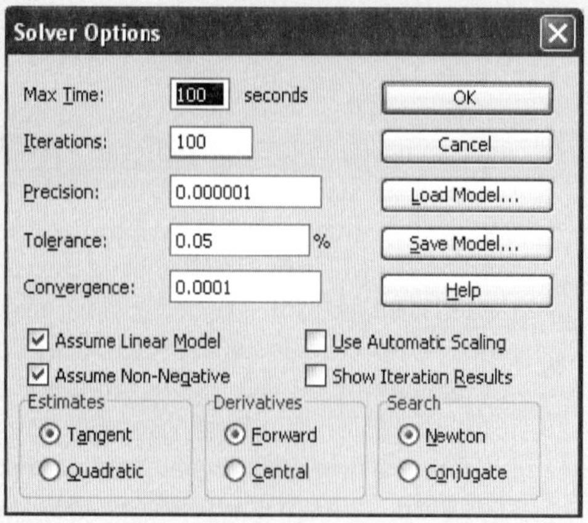

Exhibit 6-4   Solver Results

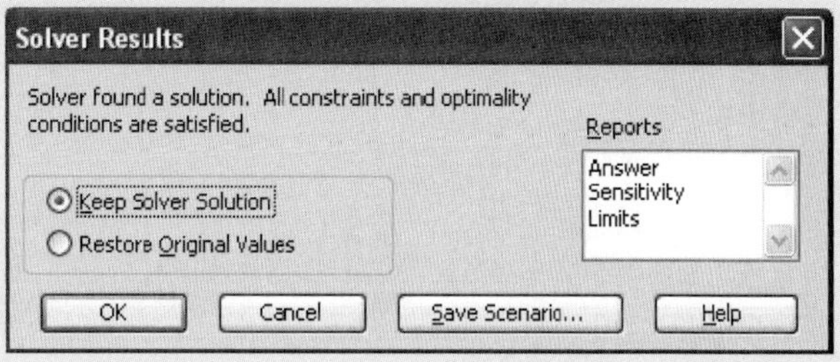

Solver Results   ☒

Solver found a solution. All constraints and optimality conditions are satisfied.

Reports

Answer
Sensitivity
Limits

◉ Keep Solver Solution

○ Restore Original Values

OK   Cancel   Save Scenario...   Help

nonnegative variables. Second, we specify the three demand constraints, which state that the amount of shipment to projects 1, 2, and 3 cannot exceed the amount specified in the demand row. Third, we specify the three supply constraints, which states that the amount of shipment from farms A, B, and C cannot exceed the amount specified in the supply row. For instance, the first demand constraint is \$B\$9 = \$B\$8, which ensures that project 1's demand is not exceeded by the amounts scheduled to be transported to project 1. Likewise, the first supply constraint is \$F\$9 = \$F\$8, which ensures that farm A's supply is not exceeded by the amounts scheduled to be transported from farm A. Note that we could have stated each of the demand and supply constraints separately. For example, the three demand constraints would be separately stated as

\$B\$9 = \$B\$8
\$C\$9 = \$C\$8
\$D\$9 = \$D\$8

However, in order to save some time, we specify the three demand constraints in aggregate as follows: \$B\$9:\$D\$9 = \$B\$8:\$D\$8. After specifying the constraints, we click on Options, which displays the Solver Options dialog shown in Exhibit 6-3.

Clicking on or checking off the "Assume Linear Model" box ensures that the linear programming method is utilized as opposed to a nonlinear programming method. In addition, checking off "Assume Non-Negative" ensures that all of the decision variables will assume nonnegative values. After clicking OK and "Solve," Solver displays the Solver Results screen displayed in Exhibit 6-4.

On this screen, we choose the answer report and the sensitivity report. The answer to the transportation problem is displayed in the sheet where the data were entered, as shown in Exhibit 6-1. In other words, in order to minimize total transportation cost, we ship 100 units from farm A to project 3, 50 units from farm B to project 1, 150 units from farm B to project 2, and 200 units from farm C to project 3.

The optimal solution to the transportation problem also can be stated in terms of the variables specified in the linear programming formulation of the transportation problem specified earlier. The optimal solution corresponds to the following variable values: $x_{13} = 100$, $x_{21} = 50$, $x_{22} = 150$, and $x_{33} = 200$. If we want a more detailed report, we click on the "Answer Report" tab at the bottom of the worksheet. Exhibit 6-5 displays the answer report, which is a more detailed display of the answer than given in the original sheet.

The report displayed in Exhibit 6-5 shows the total cost of the transportation schedule as well as the amounts shipped between various destinations. In addition, the last part of the answer report shows whether the constraints are binding and the amount of slack or

Exhibit 6-5 Answer Report for the Topsoil Transportation Problem

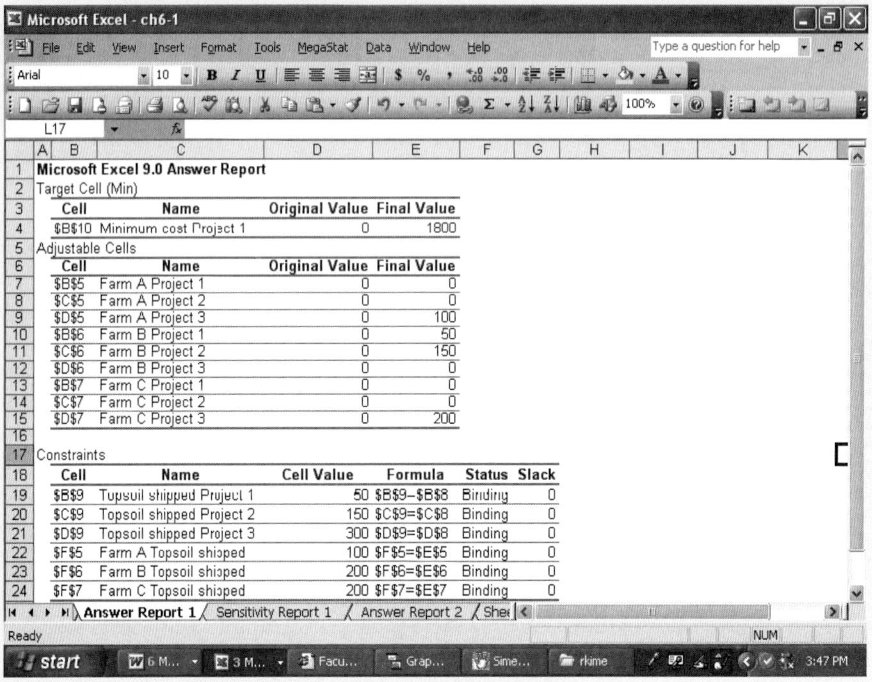

Microsoft Excel 9.0 Answer Report

Target Cell (Min)

Cell	Name	Original Value	Final Value
$B$10	Minimum cost Project 1	0	1800

Adjustable Cells

Cell	Name	Original Value	Final Value
$B$5	Farm A Project 1	0	0
$C$5	Farm A Project 2	0	0
$D$5	Farm A Project 3	0	100
$B$6	Farm B Project 1	0	50
$C$6	Farm B Project 2	0	150
$D$6	Farm B Project 3	0	0
$B$7	Farm C Project 1	0	0
$C$7	Farm C Project 2	0	0
$D$7	Farm C Project 3	0	200

Constraints

Cell	Name	Cell Value	Formula	Status	Slack
$B$9	Topsoil shipped Project 1	50	$B$9=$B$8	Binding	0
$C$9	Topsoil shipped Project 2	150	$C$9=$C$8	Binding	0
$D$9	Topsoil shipped Project 3	300	$D$9=$D$8	Binding	0
$F$5	Farm A Topsoil shipped	100	$F$5=$E$5	Binding	0
$F$6	Farm B Topsoil shipped	200	$F$6=$E$6	Binding	0
$F$7	Farm C Topsoil shipped	200	$F$7=$E$7	Binding	0

surplus associated with each constraint. Of course, in solving this problem the answer report indicates that there is no slack and all of the constraints are binding because all of the constraints have been set up as equalities.

If we click on the tab "Sensitivity Report" at the bottom of the worksheet displayed in Exhibit 6-1, we will get the Sensitivity Report displayed in Exhibit 6-6.

The solution displayed in Exhibit 6-1 is a "degenerate" solution. The number of supply sources (m) is three and the number of demand destinations (n) is three. If the number of variables with nonnegative solutions is less than $n + m - 1$ (# of destinations + # of sources $-$ 1) then it is said that we have a degenerate solution. Since there are only four decision variables or four shipping routes being utilized, this solution is degenerate. We show the reader how to deal with degeneracy when we manually solve transportation problems in CD-ROM Chapter 6 supplement. However, since Excel Solver automatically handles degeneracy, no further explanation will be provided in this chapter.

As we discussed in Chapter 5, the sensitivity report provides information about how much the objective function coefficients and the right-hand-side values would have to change before we change the shipping routes. In the first portion of the sensitivity report displayed in Exhibit 6-6, "Adjustable Cells," each row represents a decision variable and the first column, labeled "Cell," represents the cell in which each decision variable is located. The second column, labeled "Name," displays the name of the shipping route. The next (third) column, labeled "Final Value," shows the optimal values of the decision variables or the optimal amounts shipped on various shipping routes. The next (fourth) column, labeled "Reduced Cost," shows how much the objective function coefficient of each decision

Exhibit 6-6   Sensitivity Report for the Topsoil Transportation Problem

```
Microsoft Excel - ch6-1

File  Edit  View  Insert  Format  Tools  MegaStat  Data  Window  Help    Type a question for help

Arial       10     B  I  U                $  %            100%

A1            fx   Microsoft Excel 9.0 Sensitivity Report
```

	A B	C	D	E	F	G	H	I	J	K
1	Microsoft Excel 9.0 Sensitivity Report									
2	Worksheet: [Book1]Sheet2									
3	Adjustable Cells									
4			Final	Reduced	Objective	Allowable	Allowable			
5	Cell	Name	Value	Cost	Coefficient	Increase	Decrease			
6	$B$5	Farm A Project 1	0	0	4	2	0			
7	$C$5	Farm A Project 2	0	2	2	1E+30	2			
8	$D$5	Farm A Project 3	100	0	8	0	8			
9	$B$6	Farm B Project 1	50	0	5	0	2			
10	$C$6	Farm B Project 2	150	0	1	2	1E+30			
11	$D$6	Farm B Project 3	0	0	9	1E+30	0			
12	$B$7	Farm C Project 1	0	8	7	1E+30	8			
13	$C$7	Farm C Project 2	0	11	6	1E+30	11			
14	$D$7	Farm C Project 3	200	0	3	8	1E+30			
15										
16	Constraints									
17			Final	Shadow	Constraint	Allowable	Allowable			
18	Cell	Name	Value	Price	R.H. Side	Increase	Decrease			
19	$B$9	Topsoil shipped Project 1	50	5	50	0	50			
20	$C$9	Topsoil shipped Project 2	150	1	150	0	150			
21	$D$9	Topsoil shipped Project 3	300	9	300	0	50			
22	$F$5	Farm A Topsoil shipped	100	-1	100	50	0			
23	$F$6	Farm B Topsoil shipped	200	0	200	0	1E+30			
24	$F$7	Farm C Topsoil shipped	200	-6	200	50	0			

```
    Answer Report 1 \ Sensitivity Report 1 / Answer Report 2 / She
Ready                                                              NUM
```

variable would have to improve before that variable would assume a nonnegative value and come into the solution. In the topsoil problem, the reduced cost is zero for the decision variables that already have a nonnegative solution (variables in cells D5, C6, D6, and D7). For example, since the reduced cost is equal to 2 for the decision variable located in cell C5, the shipping route from farm A to project 2, the shipping cost on this route would have to decrease by $2 before we utilize this route.

Note that cell B5 (the shipping route from farm A to project 1) and cell D6 (the shipping route from farm B to project 3) are not being utilized since their value in the "Final Value" column is 0. However, since their reduced cost is also equal to zero, they provide alternative optimal solutions. In other words, we can utilize cell B5 (shipping route from farm A to project 1) or cell D6 (shipping route from farm B to project 3) in the final solution and our total cost would not increase from its minimum level of $1,800. For instance, let's suppose that due to road construction or bad weather conditions, the route from farm B to project 1 becomes (from 5) unusable. We could solve this revised problem by substituting the cost of cell B6 as "9999" in cell B16, or a very large undesirable cost, so we can ensure that the variable in cell B6 will no longer be utilized. When we solve the revised problem, we get the optimal solution shown in Exhibit 6-7.

By observing Exhibit 6-7, we find that instead of shipping 50 units from farm B to project 1, we ship 50 units from farm A to project 1 utilizing cell B5. Instead of shipping 100 units from farm A to project 3, we ship 50 units from farm A to project 3, and we ship 50 units from farm B to project 3 utilizing cell D6. We continue to ship 150 units from farm B to project 2 and 200 units from farm C to project 3. Note that the solution is no longer degenerate as we have five ($n + m - 1 = 3 + 3 - 1$) shipping routes being utilized. More importantly, since the reduced costs in cells B5 and D6 are equal to zero in Exhibit 6-6,

Exhibit 6-7	Input and Output Sheet for the Revised Transportation (topsoil) Problem When the Shipping Route between Farm B and Project 1 Is Prohibited

Very high unit shipping cost of 9999 for prohibited cell

we are able to utilize those cells without increasing the total transportation cost of $1,800. Thus, even when the transportation route from farm B to project 2 is prohibited, we are able to achieve the same minimum cost solution as we obtained originally in Exhibit 6-1.

Column five of the top portion of the Sensitivity Report, labeled "Objective Coefficient," lists the original objective function coefficient for each decision variable. For example, the cost of shipping one cubic inch from farm A to project 1 is $4. The last two columns in the top portion of the Sensitivity Report record the allowable increase "and" allowable decrease for the objective function coefficients of each decision variable. We can analyze and rationalize some of these entries. Let us start with the variable in cell C5: farm A to project 2. Since the reduced cost associated with this variable is equal to 2, this variable's objective function coefficient can be increased to positive infinity (∞). The "allowable increase" for this variable is 1E + 30, which in essence is equal to ∞. This particular variable will not come into the solution or the route from farm A to project 2 will not be utilized no matter how much we increase its per-unit cost coefficient. However, since the "allowable decrease" for this objective function coefficient is 2 (this is the same value as we observed in the "Reduced Cost" column), a decrease in the objective function coefficient by more than $2 will result in the variable coming into the solution, or the route from farm A to project 2 will be utilized. In other words, if the cost of shipping one cubic inch from farm A to project 2 is decreased from its current level of 2 to zero, the route from farm A to project 2 becomes desirable.

Cell C6, which represents the shipping route between farm B and project 2, has an "allowable increase" value of 2 and "allowable decrease" value of ∞ (1E + 30). This means that we can increase the per-unit cost coefficient by $2 from $1 to a maximum value of $3 and decrease it to negative infinity, and we would continue to ship from farm B to project 2. In other words, reducing the per-unit shipping cost from its current level will result in maintaining the shipping route in the solution as a positive value. However, increasing the per-unit shipping cost above $3 will result in nonutilization of the shipping route. Cell D7 involves the shipping route from farm 3 to project 3. This route has an "allowable increase" value of 8 and "allowable decrease" value of ∞ (1E + 30). Like cell C6, since this is a utilized route, it means that we can increase the per-unit cost coefficient by $8 from its current level of $3 to a maximum value of $11 and decrease it to negative infinity, and we would continue to ship from farm C to project 3. Again, since we are utilizing this route at the optimal solution, we can decrease its cost indefinitely. However, if we increase the per-unit shipping cost beyond $11, it becomes too expensive to utilize this route.

Other Applications

There are a number of other kinds of situations in which the transportation method has proved useful. They include the transshipment problem, which is a variation of a transportation problem.

Transshipment Problems

Certain transportation problems may involve the use of *intermediate* destinations where goods are temporarily stored before being shipped on to their final destinations. Thus, these intermediate points are both destinations and origins. These are called **transshipment problems.** The goal generally is the same as with other transportation problems: to minimize total transportation cost.

Figure 6-2 depicts a transshipment problem. In the figure, the nodes (circles) represent locations where goods are stored or received, and the branches (lines) represent shipping routes. In order to completely specify a problem, it would be necessary to indicate the quantity available at each source and the demand of each destination as well as the per-unit shipping cost for each route. Also, in some situations, the transshipment points and the routes may have capacity limitations, although we will assume there are no such capacity limitations.

We can easily formulate a linear programming model for this problem. Suppose we define x_{ij} as the quantity shipped from node i to node j. For example, x_{14} would represent the quantity shipped from node 1 to node 4. The supply of each supply node is a constraint on the quantity that can be shipped from that node. Hence, the model must include a constraint for each supply node. For node 1, this would be

$$x_{14} + x_{15} \leq S_1$$

Similarly, for nodes 2 and 3, the constraints would be

Node 2: $x_{24} + x_{25} \leq S_2$
Node 3: $x_{34} + x_{35} \leq S_3$

S_i represents the supply available at source i

Figure 6-2   A Network Diagram of a Transshipment Problem

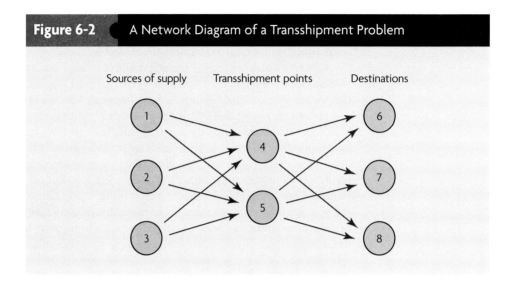

For the transshipment nodes, if we assume that the incoming and outgoing quantities must be equal, we would have

$$\qquad\qquad\text{(incoming)}\qquad\text{(outgoing)}$$
Node 4: $x_{14} + x_{24} + x_{34} = x_{46} + x_{47} + x_{48}$

This can be rewritten as

$$x_{14} + x_{24} + x_{34} - x_{46} - x_{47} - x_{48} = 0$$

$$\qquad\qquad\text{(incoming)}\qquad\text{(outgoing)}$$
Node 5: $x_{15} + x_{25} + x_{35} = x_{56} + x_{57} + x_{58}$

This can be rewritten as

$$x_{15} + x_{25} + x_{35} - x_{56} - x_{57} - x_{58} = 0$$

For the destination nodes, the demands must be satisfied by the shipments from the transshipment points. Thus,

Node 6: $x_{46} + x_{56} = D_6$
Node 7: $x_{47} + x_{57} = D_7$
Node 8: $x_{48} + x_{58} = D_8$

D_j represents the demand at destination j

The objective is to minimize the total cost of shipping. Using c_{ij} to represent the cost per unit to ship from node i to node j, we have

$$Z = \text{(from sources to transshipment points)}$$
minimize $c_{14}x_{14} + c_{24}x_{24} + c_{34}x_{34} + c_{15}x_{15} + c_{25}x_{25} + c_{35}x_{35} +$

$$\text{(from transshipment points to destinations)}$$
$$c_{46}x_{46} + c_{47}x_{47} + c_{48}x_{48} + c_{56}x_{56} + c_{57}x_{57} + c_{58}x_{58}$$

Hence, the model consists of source node constraints, transshipment node constraints, and destination constraints. In its entirety, the model is

minimize $Z = c_{14}x_{14} + c_{24}x_{24} + c_{34}x_{34} + c_{15}x_{15} + c_{25}x_{25} + c_{35}x_{35} + c_{46}x_{46} +$
$c_{47}x_{47} + c_{48}x_{48} + c_{56}x_{56} + c_{57}x_{57} + c_{58}x_{58}$

subject to

$$
\begin{array}{ll}
\text{Node 1:} \quad x_{14} + x_{15} \quad & \leq S_1 \\
\text{Node 2:} \quad x_{24} + x_{25} \quad & \leq S_2 \\
\text{Node 3:} \quad x_{34} + x_{35} \quad & \leq S_3
\end{array}
\left.\right\} \text{ Source constraints}
$$

$$
\begin{array}{ll}
\text{Node 4:} \quad x_{14} + x_{24} + x_{34} - x_{46} - x_{47} - x_{48} = 0 \\
\text{Node 5:} \quad x_{15} + x_{25} + x_{35} - x_{56} - x_{57} - x_{58} = 0
\end{array}
\left.\right\} \text{ Transshipment constraints}
$$

$$
\begin{array}{ll}
\text{Node 6:} \quad x_{46} + x_{56} \quad & = D_6 \\
\text{Node 7:} \quad x_{47} + x_{57} \quad & = D_7 \\
\text{Node 8:} \quad x_{48} + x_{58} \quad & = D_8
\end{array}
\left.\right\} \text{ Destination constraints}
$$

All variables ≥ 0

Example 6-2

Transshipment Problem

Suppose the manager of Harley's Sand and Gravel Pit has decided to utilize two intermediate nodes as transshipment points for temporary storage of topsoil. The revised network diagram of the transshipment problem is given in Figure 6-3.

Figure 6-3   A Network Diagram of Harley's Sand and Gravel Pit Transshipment Example

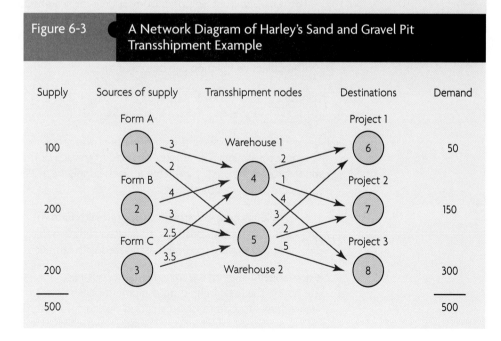

The cost of shipping one unit from the farms to warehouses is given in Table 6-3. The cost of shipping one unit from the warehouses to projects is given in Table 6-4. The unit shipping costs shown in these two tables are also included on the respective arcs in Figure 6-3. For example, we display the number "3" on the arc that connects farm A to warehouse 1.

Table 6-3   Cost of Shipping One Unit from the Farms to Warehouses

From/To	Warehouse 1 (4)	Warehouse 2 (5)
Farm A (1)	3	2
Farm B (2)	4	3
Farm C (3)	2.5	3.5

Table 6-4   Cost of Shipping One Unit from the Warehouses to Projects

From/To	Project 1 (6)	Project 2 (7)	Project 3 (8)
Warehouse 1 (4)	2	1	4
Warehouse 2 (5)	3	2	5

Each source, or farm, is numbered as 1, 2, and 3. The two intermediate nodes (warehouses) are numbered as follows: warehouse 1 = 4, and warehouse 2 = 5. The three destinations (projects 1, 2, and 3) are numbered as 6, 7, and 8 respectively.

Given the information presented above, we can formulate Harley's topsoil transshipment problem as follows:

Let x_{ij} = amount shipped from source or warehouse i to destination or warehouse j.

c_{ij} = cost of shipping one unit from source or warehouse i to destination or warehouse j.

The objective function can be stated as

$$\text{minimize } Z = 3x_{14} + 2x_{15} + 4x_{24} + 3x_{25} + 2.5x_{34} + 3.5x_{35} + 2x_{46} + x_{47} + 4x_{48} + 3x_{56} + 2x_{57} + 5x_{58}$$

Now we are ready to state the constraints of the problem. We can start by stating the supply constraints. The amount shipped from each of the sources (supply nodes) cannot exceed the supply available at each supply node. Therefore, the following supply constraints can be stated:

$x_{14} + x_{15} \leq 100$ (supply constraint associated with farm A)
$x_{24} + x_{25} \leq 200$ (supply constraint associated with farm B)
$x_{34} + x_{35} \leq 200$ (supply constraint associated with farm C)

Next, we need to set up the transshipment constraints for each warehouse (intermediate node). The logic behind transshipment constraints is that what is shipped into a transshipment node must be shipped out. In other words, no units may be left over in a transshipment node. Therefore we can formulate the transshipment constraints for warehouse 1 and warehouse 2 as follows:

$$x_{14} + x_{24} + x_{34} \quad = \quad x_{46} + x_{47} + x_{48}$$

(units shipped into warehouse 1)   (units shipped out of warehouse 1)

$$x_{15} + x_{25} + x_{35} \quad = \quad x_{56} + x_{57} + x_{58}$$

(units shipped into warehouse 2)   (units shipped out of warehouse 2)

The amount shipped from the transshipment (warehouse) nodes to destination nodes must satisfy the demand at each destination node. The demand constraints are set as "equal to" constraints. The three demand constraints are stated as follows:

$$x_{46} + x_{56} = 50 \text{ (demand at project 1)}$$
$$x_{47} + x_{57} = 150 \text{ (demand at project 2)}$$
$$x_{48} + x_{58} = 300 \text{ (demand at project 3)}$$

In summary, the final formulation of Harley's topsoil transshipment problem can be stated as follows:

$$\text{minimize } Z = 3x_{14} + 2x_{15} + 4x_{24} + 3x_{25} + 2.5x_{34} + 3.5x_{35} + 2x_{46} + x_{47} + 4x_{48} + 3x_{56} + 2x_{57} + 5x_{58}$$

subject to

$$x_{14} + x_{15} \leq 100 \text{ (supply constraint associated with farm A)}$$
$$x_{24} + x_{25} \leq 200 \text{ (supply constraint associated with farm B)}$$
$$x_{34} + x_{35} \leq 200 \text{ (supply constraint associated with farm C)}$$
$$x_{14} + x_{24} + x_{34} - x_{46} - x_{47} - x_{48} = 0 \text{ (transshipment/warehouse constraint 1)}$$
$$x_{15} + x_{25} + x_{35} - x_{56} - x_{57} - x_{58} = 0 \text{ (transshipment/warehouse constraint 2)}$$
$$x_{46} + x_{56} = 50 \text{ (demand at project 1)}$$
$$x_{47} + x_{57} = 150 \text{ (demand at project 2)}$$
$$x_{48} + x_{58} = 300 \text{ (demand at project 3)}$$
$$x_{ij} \geq 0 \text{ for all } i, j \text{ combinations}$$

Solving the Transshipment Problem using Excel We prepare the spreadsheet shown in Exhibit 6-8 to solve a transshipment problem using Excel. In preparing the spreadsheet, we divide the sheet into five parts. In part 1, in the upper-left-hand corner, we include the amounts shipped between the farms and warehouses. The Qty Shipped column on the right-hand side of this portion of the sheet is obtained by adding the values shipped from a farm to each warehouse. For example, the quantity shipped from farm A is displayed in cell E5 and can be obtained by using the formula = SUM(B5:C5). This indicates the amount shipped from farm A to warehouse 1 (cell B5) plus the amount shipped from farm A to warehouse 2 (cell C5). Similarly, the total quantity shipped to warehouse 1 is displayed in cell B8 in Exhibit 6-8. The formula for cell B8 is given by = SUM(B5:B7). In this formula, we sum the amount shipped from farm A to warehouse 1 (cell B5), the amount shipped from farm B to warehouse 1 (cell B6), and the amount shipped from farm C to warehouse 1 (cell B7). The quantity-shipped values from farm A, farm B, and farm C to quantity shipped to warehouse 2 are calculated in a similar fashion.

The second part of the table on the lower-left-hand side includes the amounts shipped from warehouses to projects. The Qty Shipped column on the right-hand side of this portion of the sheet shows the total quantity shipped from each warehouse. This value is

Exhibit 6-8 Excel Input and Output Screen for the Transshipment Problem

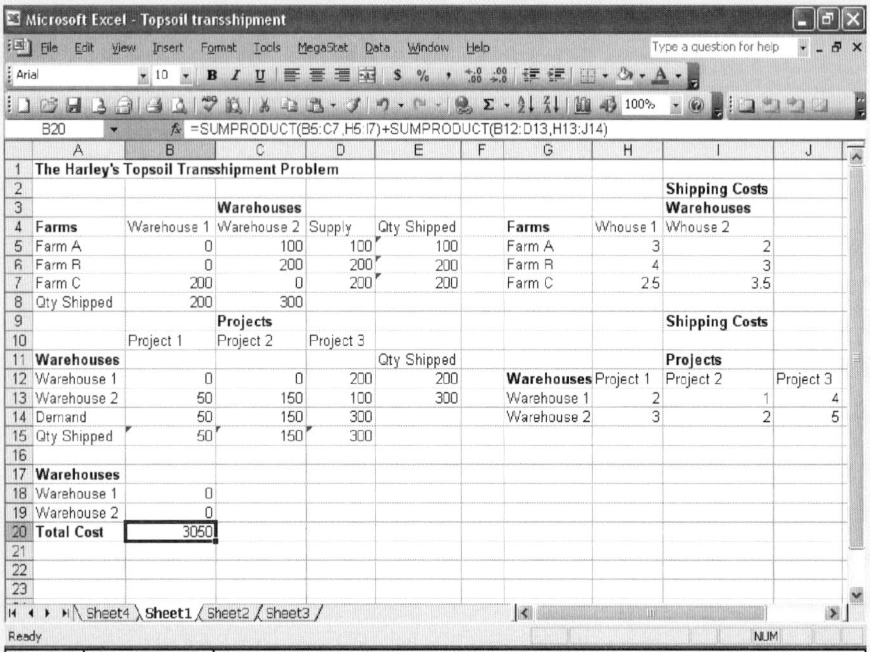

Microsoft Excel - Topsoil transshipment

File Edit View Insert Format Tools MegaStat Data Window Help

B20 = SUMPRODUCT(B5:C7,H5:I7)+SUMPRODUCT(B12:D13,H13:J14)

	A	B	C	D	E	F	G	H	I	J
1	The Harley's Topsoil Transshipment Problem									
2									Shipping Costs	
3			Warehouses						Warehouses	
4	Farms	Warehouse 1	Warehouse 2	Supply	Qty Shipped		Farms	Whouse 1	Whouse 2	
5	Farm A	0	100	100	100		Farm A	3	2	
6	Farm B	0	200	200	200		Farm B	4	3	
7	Farm C	200	0	200	200		Farm C	2.5	3.5	
8	Qty Shipped	200	300							
9			Projects						Shipping Costs	
10		Project 1	Project 2	Project 3						
11	Warehouses				Qty Shipped				Projects	
12	Warehouse 1	0	0	200	200		Warehouses	Project 1	Project 2	Project 3
13	Warehouse 2	50	150	100	300		Warehouse 1	2	1	4
14	Demand	50	150	300			Warehouse 2	3	2	5
15	Qty Shipped	50	150	300						
16										
17	Warehouses									
18	Warehouse 1	0								
19	Warehouse 2	0								
20	Total Cost	3050								
21										
22										
23										

Sheet4 \ Sheet1 / Sheet2 / Sheet3 /

Ready | NUM

Cell	Copied to	Formula
E5	E6 : E7	= SUM (B5 : C5)
B8	B9	= SUM (B5 : B7)
E12	E13	= SUM (B12 : D12)
B15	C15 : D15	= SUM (B12 : B13)
B18		= B8 − E12
B19		= C8 − E13
B20		= SUMPRODUCT (B5 : C7, H5 : I7) + SUMPRODUCT (B12 : D13, H13 : J14)

obtained by adding the values shipped from a warehouse to each project. For example, the quantity shipped from warehouse 1 is displayed in cell E12 and can be obtained by using the formula = SUM(B12:D12) as shown in Exhibit 6-8. This indicates the amount shipped from warehouse 1 to project 1 (cell B12) plus the amount shipped from warehouse 1 to project 2 (cell C12) plus the amount shipped from warehouse 1 to project 3 (cell D12). Similarly, the total quantity shipped to project 1 is displayed in cell B15 in Exhibit 6-8. The formula for cell B15 is given by = SUM(B12:B13). In this formula, we sum the amount shipped from warehouse 1 to project 1 (cell B12) and the amount shipped from warehouse 2 to project 1 (cell B13). The quantity-shipped values from warehouse1 and 2 and to project 2 and project 3 are calculated in a similar fashion.

The third portion of the table in Exhibit 6-8, on the upper-right-hand side, indicates the unit shipping costs from each of the farms to each of the warehouses. The fourth portion of the table indicates the unit shipping costs from each of the warehouses to each project.

In part 5, which appears at the very bottom of the worksheet, we state the transshipment constraints as well as the objective function. As we discussed earlier, what is shipped in to a warehouse must be shipped out. For warehouse 1, the quantity shipped in is given in cell B8 and the quantity shipped out of warehouse 1 is given in cell E12. Therefore, the formula for cell B18 is = B8 − E12. The formula for warehouse 2 is determined in a similar fashion in cell B19. In setting up the constraints for the transshipment nodes, we will show that we force the values in cell B18 and cell B19 to be equal to zero. The formula for the objective function (total cost) is given in cell B20. This objective function is constructed somewhat differently than the objective function in Exhibit 6-1 and Exhibit 6-7 for the transportation problems. Instead of entering a single objective function, two cost arrays with SUMPRODUCT functions are developed and added together. For example, the first cost array represented in the first SUMPRODUCT function includes the sum of the cross product of the unit shipping costs from farms to warehouses given in cells H5 through I7 with their respective quantity-shipped values given in cells B5 through C7. The second SUMPRODUCT function includes the sum of the cross products of the unit shipping costs from warehouses to projects given in cells H13 through J14 with their respective quantity-shipped values given in cells B12 through D13. The calculation described above results in the following formula:

= SUMPRODUCT(B5:C7, H5:I7) + SUMPRODUCT(B12:D13, H13:J14)

given in the formula bar at the top of Exhibit 6-8. Stating the objective function with cost arrays as described above is simpler and easier than stating it as a single objective function by entering all the variables and their respective costs.

After the spreadsheet is prepared, we can proceed to solve the problem by choosing **Tool | Solver**, which will bring up the Solver Parameters screen displayed in Exhibit 6-9. In this screen, first, we specify the objective function in the "Set Target Cell" box. After specifying the objective function, we state the decision variables in the "By Changing Cells" box.

Exhibit 6-9 Parameter Specifications Screen for the Transshipment Problem

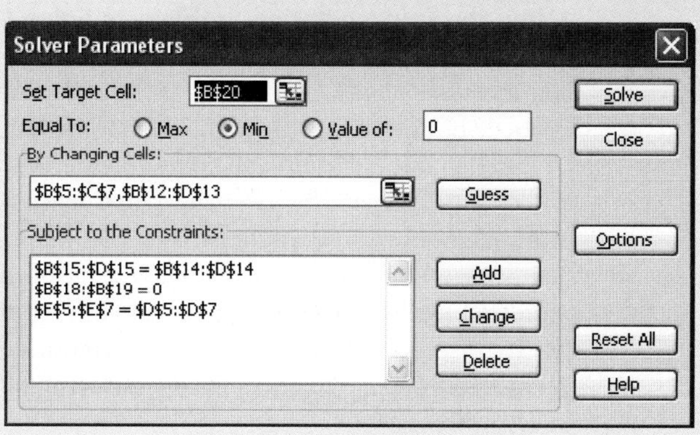

The decision variables consist of the variables between supply sources and warehouses (cells B5 to C7) and between warehouses and destinations (cells B12 to D13). The last portion of the parameter screen consists of specification of the constraints.

The first set of constraints are specified as $B$15:$D$15 = $B$14:$D$14. These constraints are equivalent to demand constraints.

The second set constraints are specified as $B$18:$B$19 = 0. These constraints refer to the transshipment constraints. In other words, what is shipped into the transshipment nodes must be shipped out. Note that cell B18 = [B8 (amount shipped into warehouse 1) minus E12 (amount shipped out of warehouse 1)].

The third set of constraints are specified as $E$5:$E$7 = $D$5:$D$7. These constraints are equivalent to supply constraints. After specifying the constraints, we click on "Options" and then clicking on or checking off the "Assume Linear Model" box ensures that the linear programming method is utilized as opposed to a nonlinear programming method. In addition, checking off the box "Assume Non-Negative" ensures that all of the decision variables will assume nonnegative values. After clicking OK and "Solve," Solver displays the Solver Results screen displayed in Exhibit 6-8.

Before solving the problem, there are no shipment values included on the spreadsheet. The results given in Exhibit 6-8 are summarized below:

- Cells B5 to C7 provide the shipment values from supply sources to warehouses. We show the values of the corresponding linear programming variables for each shipment quantity in parentheses.

  Ship 100 units from farm A to warehouse 2 ($x_{15} = 100$)
  Ship 200 units from farm B to warehouse 2 ($x_{25} = 100$)
  Ship 200 units from farm C to warehouse 1 ($x_{34} = 100$)

- Cell B12 to D13 provide the shipment values from warehouses to destinations.

  Ship 200 units from warehouse 1 to project 3 ($x_{48} = 100$)
  Ship 50 units from warehouse 2 to project 1 ($x_{56}\ = 100$)
  Ship 100 units from warehouse 2 to project 3 ($x_{58} = 100$)
  Ship 150 units from warehouse 2 to project 2 ($x_{57} = 100$)

- The total cost associated with the transshipment problem is $3,050 and is given in cell B20.

Aggregate Planning

Using the Transportation Problem to Solve Aggregate Planning Problems Aggregate planning involves the long-term production plan of a manufacturing firm. Aggregate planners usually avoid thinking in terms of individual products. The planners are concerned about the quantity and timing of production to meet the expected demand. If the demand is uneven within the planning period, the planners attempt to achieve equality of demand and capacity over the entire planning horizon. Aggregate planners attempt to minimize the production cost over the planning horizon. The transportation method happens to be a good way of tackling some of these issues. In order to use the transportation problem to solve the aggregate planning problem, the planners first identify the capacity of regular time, overtime subcontracting, and inventory on a period-by-period basis. Table 6-5 shows the notation and setup of a transportation table for aggregate planning purposes.

| Table 6-5 | | Transportation Table for Aggregate Planning Purposes | | | | | | |

		Period 1	Period 2	Period 3	...	Ending inventory period n	Unused capacity	Capacity
Period	Beginning inventory	0	h	$2h$	...	nh	0	I_0
1	Regular time	r	$r+h$	$r+2h$	...	$r+nh$	0	R_1
	Overtime	l	$l+h$	$l+2h$	...	$l+nh$	0	O_1
	Subcontract	s	$s+h$	$s+2h$	...	$s+nh$	0	S_1
2	Regular time	$r+b$	r	$r+h$	...	$r+(n-1)h$	0	R_2
	Overtime	$l+b$	l	$l+h$	...	$l+(n-1)h$	0	O_2
	Subcontract	$s+b$	s	$s+h$	...	$s+(n-1)h$	0	S_2
3	Regular time	$r+2b$	$r+b$	r	...	$r+(n-2)h$	0	R_3
	Overtime	$l+2b$	$l+b$	l	...	$l+(n-2)h$	0	O_3
	Subcontract	$s+2b$	$s+b$	s	...	$s+(n-2)h$	0	S_3
	Demand				...			Total

r = Regular production cost per unit

l = Overtime cost per unit

s = Subcontracting cost per unit

h = Holding cost per unit period

b = Backorder cost per unit per period

n = Number of periods in planning horizon

Note the systematic way that costs change as you move across a row from left to right. Regular cost, overtime cost, and subcontracting cost are at their lowest when the output is consumed (i.e., delivered, etc.) in the same period it is produced (at the intersection of period 1 row and column for regular cost, at the intersection of period 2 row and column for regular cost, and so on). If goods are made available in one period but carried over to later periods (i.e., moving across a row), holding costs are incurred at the rate of h per period. Thus, holding goods for two periods results in a unit cost of $2h$, whether or not the goods came from regular production, overtime, or subcontracting. Conversely, with back orders, the unit cost increases as you move across a row from right to left, beginning at the intersection of a row and column for the same period (e.g., period 3). For instance, if some goods are produced in period 3 to satisfy backorders from period 2, a unit backorder cost of b is incurred. And if goods in period 3 are used to satisfy back orders two periods earlier (e.g., from period 1), a unit cost of $2b$ is incurred. Unused capacity is generally given a unit cost of 0, although it is certainly possible to insert an actual cost if that is relevant. Finally, beginning inventory is given a unit cost of 0 if it is used to satisfy demand in period I. However, if it is held over for use in later periods, a holding cost of h per unit is added for each period. If the inventory is to be held for the entire planning horizon, a total unit cost of h times the number of periods, n, will be incurred.

Example 6-3 illustrates the setup and final solution of an aggregate planning problem using the transportation model.

Example 6-3

Given the following information, set up the problem in a transportation table and solve for the minimum-cost plan:

	Period		
	1	2	3
Demand	550	700	750
Capacity			
Regular	500	500	500
Overtime	50	50	50
Subcontract	120	120	100
Beginning inventory	100		
Costs			
Regular time	$60 per unit		
Overtime	$80 per unit		
Subcontract	$90 per unit		
Inventory carrying cost	$1 per unit per month		
Backorder cost	$3 per unit per month		

Table 6-6 Transportation Table for the Aggregate Planning Problem of Example 6-3

	Supply from	Demand for Period 1	Demand for Period 2	Demand for Period 3	Unused capacity (dummy)	Total capacity available (supply)
Period	Beginning inventory	0 100	1	2	0	100
1	Regular	60 450	61 50	62	0	500
	Overtime	80	81 50	82	0	50
	Subcontract	90	91 30	92	0 90	120
2	Regular time	63	60 500	61	0	500
	Overtime	83	80 50	81	0	50
	Subcontract	93	90 20	91 100	0	120
3	Regular time	66	63	60 500	0	500
	Overtime	86	83	80 50	0	50
	Subcontract	96	93	90 100	0	100
	Demand	550	700	750	90	2,090

> **Solution**
>
> The transportation table and solution are shown in Table 6-6. Some of the entries require additional explanation:
>
> a. In this example, inventory carrying costs are $1 per unit per period (costs are shown in the upper-right-hand corner of each cell in the table). Hence, units produced in one period and carried over to a later period will incur a holding cost that is a linear function of the length of time held.
> b. Linear programming models of this type require that supply (capacity) and demand be equal. A dummy column has been added (unused capacity) to satisfy that requirement. Since it does not "cost" anything extra to not use capacity in this case, cell costs of $0 have been assigned.
> c. No backlogs were needed in this example.
> d. The quantities (e.g., 100 and 450 in column 1) are the amounts of output or inventory that will be used to meet demand requirements. Thus, the demand of 550 units in period I will be met using 100 units from inventory and 450 obtained from regular-time output.

When backlogs are not permitted, the cell costs for the backlog positions can be made prohibitively high so that no backlogs will appear in the solution. The main limitations of LP (transportation) models are the assumptions of linear relationships among variables, the inability to continuously monitor and adjust output rates, and the need to specify a single objective (e.g., minimize costs) instead of using multiple objectives (e.g., minimize cost while stabilizing the workforce).

Location Analysis

Another use of the transportation method is to compare transportation costs for alternative locations. For instance, a company may be preparing to build a new warehouse, and there may be a number of potential locations under consideration. One aspect of the decision may be differences in transportation costs that would result from each alternative.

Suppose that currently the firm has three factories that supply four warehouses, and another warehouse will be added. Suppose that two separate locations for the new warehouse, Chicago and Detroit, are being studied. The impact of each of the two potential locations can be determined by solving *two* transportation problems, one for each location. In other words, one extra column would be added to the transportation table, representing one of the warehouses, and the problem would be solved for the minimum total cost. That column, then, would be replaced in the table by a column representing the other warehouse, and again the problem would be solved for the minimum cost. This would give decision makers an opportunity to assess the impact of each warehouse location on the total distribution costs for the system (see Tables 6-7 and 6-8).

It should be noted that transportation cost typically would be one of a number of variables that would be taken into account in making such a decision. Moreover, some other factor, such as nearness of the warehouse to a target market, might take precedence over transportation cost.

Table 6-7	System with Chicago Warehouse				
	Warehouse #1	Warehouse #2	Warehouse #3	Warehouse #4	Warehouse Chicago
Factory A	☐	☐	☐	☐	9
Factory B	☐	☐	☐	☐	6
Factory C	☐	☐	☐	☐	5

Table 6-8	System with Detroit Warehouse				
	Warehouse #1	Warehouse #2	Warehouse #3	Warehouse #4	Warehouse Detroit
Factory A	☐	☐	☐	☐	4
Factory B	☐	☐	☐	☐	10
Factory C	☐	☐	☐	☐	7

Assignment Problems

Assignment problems are a special case of linear programming problem. Assignment problems are characterized by a need to pair items in one group with items in another group in a one-for-one matching. For example, a manager may be faced with the task of assigning four jobs to four machines, one job to a machine. Another manager may be faced with the task of assigning five projects to five staff members, with each staff member responsible for a single project. A marketing manager may be required to assign four salespeople to four territories.

Typically, the time or cost required to complete a job or a project will differ, depending on the machine used for the job or the staff member doing the project. The manager's goal in such cases is to develop a set of assignments that will *minimize* the total time or cost of doing the work. In other cases, the goal may be to minimize distance traveled, scrap, or some other measure of effectiveness. Moreover, some problems involve profit or revenue, and in those cases, the obvious goal would be to develop a set of assignments that would lead to the *maximum* total profit or revenue. Because minimization problems are more common, we begin with a minimization problem.

Example 6-4

A manager has prepared a table that shows the cost of performing each of five jobs by each of five employees (see Table 6-9). According to this table, job I will cost $15 if done by Al. $20 if it is done by Bill, and so on. The manager has stated that his goal is to develop a set of job assignments that will minimize the total cost of getting all

Table 6-9	Numerical Example for the Assignment Problem				
	Employee				
Job	Al	Bill	Cindy	David	Earl
1	15	20	18	24	19
2	12	17	16	15	14
3	14	15	19	17	18
4	11	14	12	13	15
5	13	16	17	18	16

five jobs done. It is further required that the jobs be performed simultaneously, thus requiring one job be assigned to each employee.

In the past, to find the minimum-cost set of assignments, the manager has resorted to listing all of the different possible assignments (i.e., complete enumeration) for small problems such as this one. But for larger problems, the manager simply guesses because there are too many possibilities to try to list them. For example, with a 5×5 table, there are $5! = 120$ different possibilities; but with, say, a 7×7 table, there are $7! = 5,040$ possibilities.

Linear Programming Formulation of the Assignment Problem

Similar to the formulation of the transportation and transshipment problems, we can easily formulate an assignment problem as a linear programming problem. Let us consider an assignment problem with four assignors or jobs ($i = 1, 2, 3, 4$) and four assignees or employees ($j = 1, 2, 3, 4$). First we define the decision variable as $x_{ij} = 1$ if job i is assigned to employee j and $x_{ij} = 0$ if job i is not assigned to employee j. $c_{ij} =$ cost of assigning job i to employee j.

minimize $Z = c_{11}x_{11} + c_{12}x_{12} + c_{13}x_{13} + c_{14}x_{14} + c_{21}x_{21} + c_{22}x_{22} + c_{23}x_{23} + c_{24}x_{24} + c_{31}x_{31} +$
$c_{32}x_{32} + c_{33}x_{33} + c_{34}x_{34} + c_{41}x_{41} + c_{42}x_{42} + c_{43}x_{43} + c_{44}x_{44}$

subject to

$\left. \begin{array}{l} x_{11} + x_{12} + x_{13} + x_{14} = 1 \\ x_{21} + x_{22} + x_{23} + x_{24} = 1 \\ x_{31} + x_{32} + x_{33} + x_{34} = 1 \\ x_{41} + x_{42} + x_{43} + x_{44} = 1 \end{array} \right\}$ (These are the row constraints. Each job can be assigned to only one employee.)

$\left. \begin{array}{l} x_{11} + x_{21} + x_{31} + x_{41} = 1 \\ x_{12} + x_{22} + x_{32} + x_{42} = 1 \\ x_{13} + x_{23} + x_{33} + x_{43} = 1 \\ x_{14} + x_{24} + x_{34} + x_{44} = 1 \end{array} \right\}$ (These are the column constraints. Each employee can only be assigned to one job.)

All $x_{ij} \geq 0$

First we will provide a linear programming formulation of this numerical example, then we will provide the Excel solution.

Linear Programming Formulation of the Numerical Example given in Table 6–9 for the Assignment Problem

minimize $Z = 15x_{11} + 20x_{12} + 18x_{13} + 24x_{14} + 19x_{15} + 12x_{21} + 17x_{22} + 16x_{23} + 15x_{24} + 14x_{25} + 14x_{31} +$
$15x_{32} + 19x_{33} + 17x_{34} + 18x_{35} + 11x_{41} + 14x_{42} + 12x_{43} + 13x_{44} + 15x_{45} + 13x_{51} + 16x_{52} +$
$17x_{53} + 18x_{54} + 16x_{55}$

subject to

$$
\left.
\begin{aligned}
x_{11} + x_{12} + x_{13} + x_{14} + x_{15} &= 1 \\
x_{21} + x_{22} + x_{23} + x_{24} + x_{25} &= 1 \\
x_{31} + x_{32} + x_{33} + x_{34} + x_{35} &= 1 \\
x_{41} + x_{42} + x_{43} + x_{44} + x_{45} &= 1 \\
x_{51} + x_{52} + x_{53} + x_{54} + x_{55} &= 1
\end{aligned}
\right\}
$$

(These are the row constraints. Each job can be assigned to only one employee.)

$$
\left.
\begin{aligned}
x_{11} + x_{21} + x_{31} + x_{41} + x_{51} &= 1 \\
x_{12} + x_{22} + x_{32} + x_{42} + x_{52} &= 1 \\
x_{13} + x_{23} + x_{33} + x_{43} + x_{53} &= 1 \\
x_{14} + x_{24} + x_{34} + x_{44} + x_{54} &= 1 \\
x_{15} + x_{25} + x_{35} + x_{45} + x_{55} &= 1
\end{aligned}
\right\}
$$

(These are the column constraints. Each employee can only be assigned to one job.)

All xij $\geq$ 0

Solving the Assignment Problem Using Excel

In the next few paragraphs, we will demonstrate how to solve the assignment problem using Excel. In order to do this, we use the numerical example given in Table 6-9. We begin developing the worksheet given in Exhibit 6-10.

The worksheet provided in Exhibit 6-10 consists of two parts. The first part (top portion), labeled "Cost of Each Assignment," is the data input portion where the cost/time/distance of assigning row i to column j is specified. The second part (bottom portion) specifies the optimal values of the decision variables (assignments). Before we run Solver, the values of the decision variables specified at the bottom portion of the worksheet are equal to zero. At the very bottom of the worksheet (in cell C23) is the value of the optimal minimum cost, which is the objective function value for the assignment problem. Again, before we execute Solver, the value of the objective function, or the minimum total cost, is equal to zero. In Exhibit 6-10, the formula bar shows the following formula of the objective function in cell C23: = SUMPRODUCT(C6:G10,C15:G19). This formula is a cross product of the unit cost information provided in the first part of the worksheet (cells C6 through G10) with the decision variables (assignments) provided in the second part of the worksheet (cells C15 through G19). We provide the Jobs Available row and column at the bottom and at the right side of the second part of the worksheet. The Jobs Available section provides the right-hand-side values of all the constraints specified in the linear programming formulation of the assignment problem. Since we have one-to-one assignments, the values of the Jobs Available row and column are equal to one. The far-right-hand-side column and the last row of the second part of the worksheet contain the column and row that are both labeled as "Jobs Assigned." These indicate the number of jobs assigned for that row (job) and column (employee) respectively. The formula for cell I15 is given at the bottom of Exhibit 6-10. This formula, = SUM(C15:G15), represents the total number of assignments for job 1 for all employees. In addition, the formula for cell C21 is given in Exhibit 6-10. This formula, = SUM(C15:C19), shows the number of jobs assigned to Bill.

After completing the worksheet given in Exhibit 6-10, we can proceed to solve the problem by choosing **Tools | Solver,** which will bring up the Solver Parameters screen displayed in Exhibit 6-11. In this screen, first, we specify the objective function in the "Set Target Cell" box: $C$23. After specifying the location of the objective function, we state the decision variables in the "By Changing Cells" box. The decision variables consist of the variables of assigning all possible jobs to all potential employees (cells C15 to G19). The last portion of the parameter screen consists of specification of the constraints. There are two sets of constraints to be specified. First, we specify the constraints for the columns, or

Exhibit 6-10 Excel Input and Output Worksheet for the Assignment Problem

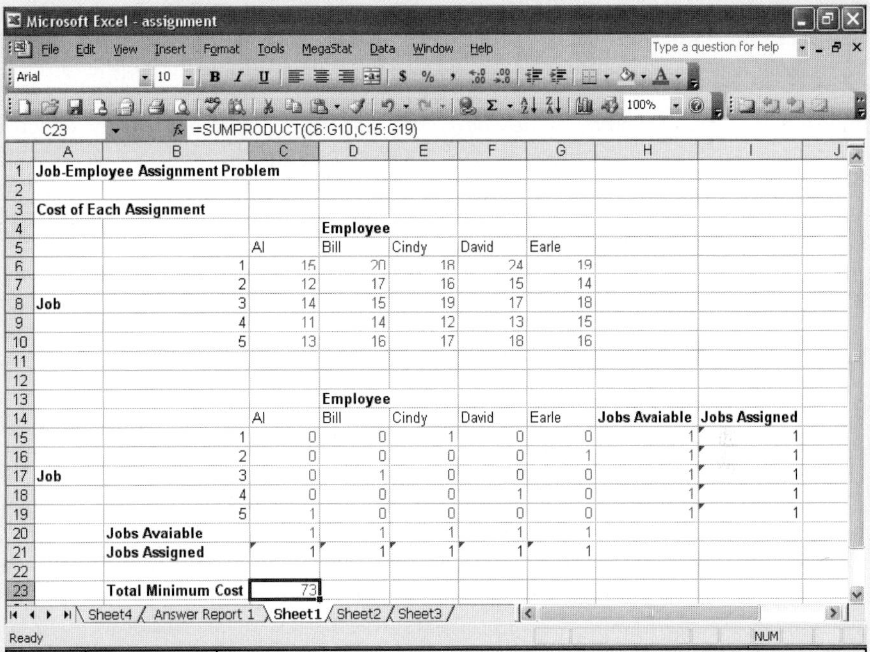

	A	B	C	D	E	F	G	H	I
1	Job-Employee Assignment Problem								
2									
3	Cost of Each Assignment								
4				Employee					
5			Al	Bill	Cindy	David	Earle		
6		1	15	20	18	24	19		
7		2	12	17	16	15	14		
8	Job	3	14	15	19	17	18		
9		4	11	14	12	13	15		
10		5	13	16	17	18	16		
11									
12									
13				Employee					
14			Al	Bill	Cindy	David	Earle	Jobs Avaiable	Jobs Assigned
15		1	0	0	1	0	0	1	1
16		2	0	0	0	0	1	1	1
17	Job	3	0	1	0	0	0	1	1
18		4	0	0	0	1	0	1	1
19		5	1	0	0	0	0	1	1
20		Jobs Avaiable	1	1	1	1	1		
21		Jobs Assigned	1	1	1	1	1		
22									
23		Total Minimum Cost	73						

Cell	Copied to	Formula
I15	I16 : I19	= SUM (C15 : G15)
C21	D21 : G21	= SUM (C15 : C19)
C23		= SUMPRODUCT (C6 : G10, C15 : G19)

Exhibit 6-11 Parameter Specifications Screen for the Assignment Problem

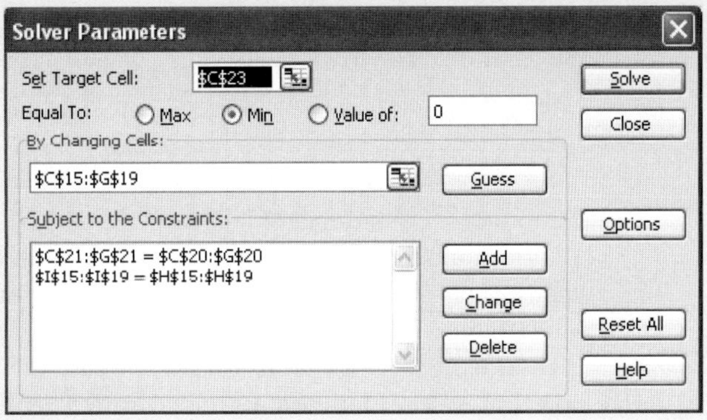

A Modern Management Science Application: *Medpin Drug Allocations*

As a result of a court settlement, 19 pharmaceutical firms were required to distribute $150 million worth of drugs free of charge to approximately 200 California clinics. Medpin (Medicine for People in Need), an independent, nonprofit organization, was given the responsibility to distribute these drugs using a fair and equitable system. As a result of another court settlement, six more pharmaceutical companies were forced to join the initial 19 companies. This increased the budget to $171 million. This project, called DDP (Drug Distribution Project), went into effect in the fall of 1999. DDP was successful in distributing 99 percent of the $171 million of drugs in a timely fashion.

As a part of the settlement, each drug company was able to negotiate the amount of drugs that it could supply in a given period. On the other hand, clinics had restrictions on the minimum amount of drugs needed per period. Based on this information, Medpin allocated a maximum dollar amount to each clinic for the drugs the clinic is to receive. Medpin determined the budget for each clinic based on various clinic characteristics including size, location, and population served. Since the clinics were receiving the drugs free of charge, they were told to order the most critical drugs to the maximum value allocated to the clinic.

Medpin was to the point of developing an ordering and distribution system. However, the organization realized that this particular task was beyond the capabilities of the organization. Medpin contracted a company called Choice Systems to develop a custom-designed, Web-based system to track the DDP orders. The system developed by Choice Systems not only enabled the clinics to enter and change orders but also to ensure that the clinics did not exceed their budget. However, there were significant differences between the orders received and orders delivered, which resulted in a demand-supply mismatch. For instance, the clinics requested drugs valued at $128 million and Medpin was able to distribute only $72 million. The discrepancy occurred as a result of pharmaceutical companies going over the ordering restrictions on budgeted amounts for certain drugs. Although Choice Systems had the capability to develop the ordering system, it did not have the expertise to allocate drugs in a fair manner to the clinics.

In developing a decision support system, Medpin considered that ordered values of drugs exceeded the available

quantities. Medpin's goal was to ensure that as many clinics on the approved list as possible participated and that drugs were distributed to the clinics in a fair, timely manner. In order to accomplish its goals of distributing these drugs, Medpin considered efficiency, effectiveness, and equity. Efficiency was measured as a percent of available resources distributed. Effectiveness was measured using a priority-weight matrix that considered the importance of drug k for clinic i. Equity was measured as a percentage of the requested amount. However, in measuring equity, the weights (percentages) for drugs were multiplied by the priority weight of the drug in short supply. Therefore, as the shortage increased, higher weights were assigned to the drugs.

The drug allocation problem had two objectives: (1) maximize the dollar value of the drug allocation and (2) minimize the difference between the ratio of the allocations and weighted orders from the clinics. Since the allocation problem had multiple objectives, the size of the problem (250 clinics, 25 pharmaceuticals firms, 125 drugs) made it very difficult to achieve an optimal solution in an acceptable time frame. A fast heuristic solution was developed to allocate the maximum amount of each drug to each clinic. Then, if the drug was scarce, it was allocated in proportion to the requested amount weighted by the clinic's priority.

Medpin encountered special challenges in administering this drug allocation program. For example, the pharmaceutical companies differed in their information system in the way they maintained data on product shipping information. Back-order information was entered in various ways by different clinics, which resulted in confusion of Medpin personnel.

Medpin's program benefited many uninsured patients who would otherwise have little or no access to prescription drugs. In addition, many pharmaceutical companies are exploring the possibility of using Medpin's decision support system in implementing other charity-based drug distribution programs in a fair and equitable manner.

Source: J. Swaminathan, M. Ashe, K. Duke, L. Maslin, and L. Wilde, "Distributing Scarce Drugs for the Medpin Program," *Interfaces* 34, no. 5 (September–October 2004), pp. 353–58.

employees. The number of jobs assigned to each employee (cells C21 to G21) must be equal to the number of jobs available for each employee (cells C20 to G20). Second, we specify the constraints for the rows, or jobs. The number of employees assigned to each job (cells I15 to I19) must be equal to the number of employees available for each job (cells H15 to H19).

After specifying the constraints, we click on "Options" and then clicking on or checking off the "Assume Linear Model" box ensures that the linear programming method is utilized as opposed to a nonlinear programming method. In addition, checking off the box "Assume

Non-Negative" ensures that all of the decision variables will assume nonnegative values. After clicking OK and "Solve", Solver displays the Solver Results screen displayed in Exhibit 6-10.

Summary

This chapter describes two types of problems that lend themselves to solution using linear programming techniques: transportation problems and assignment problems. These problems are part of a larger class of problems known as network flow problems. We will study other network flow problems in Chapter 8. Transportation-type problems, which include standard transportation problems with multiple sources and multiple destinations, and transshipment problems, which include intermediate nodes in addition to multiple sources and multiple destinations, involve the distribution of goods. The assignment-type problems involve the matching or pairing of two sets of items such as jobs and machines, secretaries and reports, lawyers and cases, and so forth. Transportation problems have different costs for different distribution alternatives, while the assignment problems have different cost or time requirements for different pairings. The objective for both types of problems is to identify the transportation or assignment schedule that minimizes total cost or alternatively maximized profits. The manual solution procedures for the transportation and the assignment problems are described in the Chapter 6 Supplement on the CD-ROM. The transshipment problem is also covered in this chapter. It is a variation of the transportation problem. In addition to multiple souces and multiple destinations, the transshipment problem includes multiple intermediate nodes. We show how the model is formulated as an LP model and setup and solved using Excel. The transshipment problem can easily be converted into a transportation problem and solved with the manual approach described in the Chapter 6 Supplement.

For each type of problem, we describe how to formulate it as a linear programming problem. In addition, we provide detailed explanation as to how to solve these problems using Excel and how to interpret the solution provided by Excel.

Glossary

Assignment Problem   A problem that requires pairing two sets of items given a set of paired costs or profits in such a way that the total cost (profit) of the pairings is minimized (maximized).

Transportation Problem   A distribution-type problem in which supplies of goods that are held at various locations are to be distributed to other receiving locations at minimum cost or maximum profit.

Transshipment Problem   A transportation problem in which some locations are used as intermediate shipping points, thereby serving both as origins and as destinations.

Solved Problems

Problem 1

A company ships its products from its two plants to three warehouses. This company wants to minimize total transportation cost of shipment. The cost of shipping one unit from each source (plant) to each destination (warehouse) is given in the following table:

Source	Supply	Destination	Demand
Milwaukee (1)	61	Chicago (1)	50
Cleveland (2)	61	South Bend (2)	55
		Pittsburgh (3)	17

	Unit Cost of Shipping		
From\To	**Chicago (1)**	**South Bend (2)**	**Pittsburgh (3)**
Milwaukee (1)	2	3	9
Cleveland (2)	7	6	4

Formulate the transportation problem as a linear programming problem given the above and solve it using Excel.

Solution

Let x_{ij} = number of units shipped from source i to destination j.

$$\text{minimize} \quad Z = 2x_{11} + 3x_{12} + 9x_{13} + 7x_{21} + 6x_{22} + 4x_{23}$$

subject to

$$\begin{aligned} x_{11} + x_{12} + x_{13} &\le 61 \\ x_{21} + x_{22} + x_{23} &\le 61 \\ x_{11} + x_{21} &= 50 \\ x_{12} + x_{22} &= 55 \\ x_{13} + x_{23} &= 17 \\ \text{All } x_{ij} &\ge 0 \end{aligned}$$

The Excel solution to this transportation problem is displayed in Exhibit 6-12. The parameter specification screen is displayed in Exhibit 6-13. The shipment schedule is shown on page 305.

Exhibit 6-12 Excel Worksheet for the Transportation Problem in Solved Problem 1

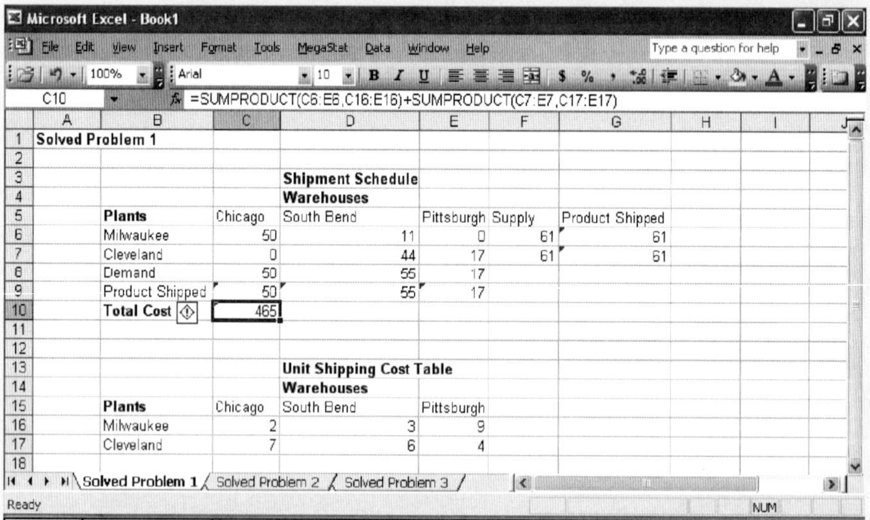

	A	B	C	D	E	F	G
1	Solved Problem 1						
3				Shipment Schedule			
4				Warehouses			
5		Plants	Chicago	South Bend	Pittsburgh	Supply	Product Shipped
6		Milwaukee	50	11	0	61	61
7		Cleveland	0	44	17	61	61
8		Demand	50	55	17		
9		Product Shipped	50	55	17		
10		Total Cost	465				
13				Unit Shipping Cost Table			
14				Warehouses			
15		Plants	Chicago	South Bend	Pittsburgh		
16		Milwaukee	2	3	9		
17		Cleveland	7	6	4		

Cell	Copied to	Formula
G6	G7	= SUM (C6 : E6)
C9	D9 : E9	= SUM (C6 : C7)
C10		= SUMPRODUCT (C6 : E6, C16 : E16) + SUMPRODUCT (C7 : E7, C17 : E17)

Exhibit 6-13	Parameter Specification Screen for Solved Problem 1

	Units
Milwaukee to Chicago	50
Milwaukee to South Bend	11
Cleveland to South Bend	44
Cleveland to Pittsburgh	17

The total cost for this problem is $465.

Problem 2

Consider the following assignment problem where there are three jobs and three employees and each job has to be performed by one employee and the table values represent the cost of making the particular assignment.

		Employee	
Job	**Al(1)**	**Bob(2)**	**Cheryl(3)**
Job D (1)	6	4	7
Job E (2)	9	5	2
Job F (3)	5	7	1

Formulate the above problem as a linear programming problem and solve it using Excel. What are the job/employee assignments? What is the total cost of the optimal assignment schedule?

$$\text{minimize} \quad Z = 6x_{11} + 4x_{12} + 7x_{13} + 9x_{21} + 5x_{22} + 2x_{23} + 5x_{31} + 7x_{32} + x_{33}$$

Solution

subject to

$$\left.\begin{array}{l} x_{11} + x_{12} + x_{13} = 1 \\ x_{21} + x_{22} + x_{23} = 1 \\ x_{31} + x_{32} + x_{33} = 1 \end{array}\right\} \begin{array}{l} \text{Each job can only be assigned to one employee.} \\ \text{(employee constraints)} \end{array}$$

$$\left.\begin{array}{l} x_{11} + x_{21} + x_{31} = 1 \\ x_{12} + x_{22} + x_{32} = 1 \\ x_{13} + x_{23} + x_{33} = 1 \end{array}\right\} \begin{array}{l} \text{Each employee can only be assigned to one job. (job constraints)} \end{array}$$

All $x_{ij} \geq 0$

Note that there is one constraint for each employee and one constraint for each job. Since the number of employees is equal to the number of jobs, the first three constraints for employees are written as equalities. However, if there were more employees than jobs, the first three constraints for employees must be written as less-than-or-equal-to constraints. On the other hand, if there were more jobs than employees, the last three constraints for jobs would have to be written as inequalities.

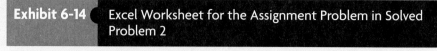

Exhibit 6-14 Excel Worksheet for the Assignment Problem in Solved Problem 2

Cell	Copied to	Formula
G13	G14 : G15	= SUM (C13 : E13)
C17	D17 : E17	= SUM (C13 : C15)
C19		= SUMPRODUCT (C4 : E8, C13 : E17)
G16	G17	= SUM (C16 : E16)

The Excel solution to this assignment problem is displayed in Exhibit 6-14. The parameter specification screen is displayed in Exhibit 6-15. The assignment schedule is as follows:

Job D	to	Bob
Job E	to	Cheryl
Job F	to	Al

The total cost for this problem is $11.

Problem 3

Consider the following transshipment problem for a grain manufacturing company.

Farms				Mills	
Source Location	Supply	Warehouse Locations	Destination Locations		Demand
Dubuque (IA)	2,000	Iowa City (IA)	St. Louis (MO)		2,500
Springfield (IL)	3,500	South Bend (IN)	Chicago (IL)		2,500
Omaha (NE)	2,000		Toledo (OH)		2,500

The supply and demand values are given in tons per week.

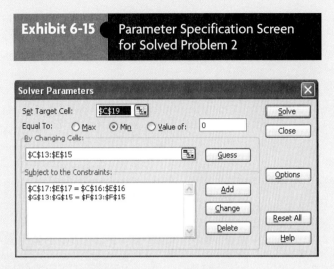

Exhibit 6-15   Parameter Specification Screen for Solved Problem 2

The unit shipping cost from each source to each warehouse and from each warehouse to each destination is given in the following tables.

Unit Shipping Cost from the Farms to the Warehouses

From/To	Iowa City (IA) (4)	South Bend (IN) (5)
Dubuque (IA) (1)	1.00	2.40
Springfield (IL) (2)	1.50	2.20
Omaha (NE) (3)	1.20	2.80

Unit Shipping Cost from the Warehouses to the Mills

From\To	St. Louis (MO) (6)	Chicago (IL) (7)	Toledo (OH) (8)
Iowa City (IA) (4)	1.00	1.10	2.40
South Bend (IN) (5)	2.00	0.90	1.20

Formulate this problem as a linear programming problem to minimize the total transportation cost and solve it using Excel.

Solution

Let x_{ij} = number of units shipped from farm or warehouse i to mill or warehouse j.

$$\text{minimize} \quad Z = x_{14} + 1.5x_{24} + 1.2x_{34} + 2.4x_{15} + 2.2x_{25} + 2.8x_{35} + x_{46} + 1.1x_{47} + 2.4x_{48} + 2x_{56} + .9x_{57} + 1.2x_{58}$$

subject to

$$\left.\begin{array}{l} x_{14} + x_{15} \le 2{,}000 \\ x_{24} + x_{25} \le 3{,}500 \\ x_{34} + x_{35} \le 2{,}000 \end{array}\right\} \quad \text{(supply constraints)}$$

$$x_{14} + x_{24} + x_{34} = x_{46} + x_{47} + x_{48}$$
$$x_{15} + x_{25} + x_{35} = x_{56} + x_{57} + x_{58}$$

Moving the variables on the right-hand side of the constraint to the left, we get

$$\left.\begin{array}{l} x_{14} + x_{24} + x_{34} - x_{46} - x_{47} - x_{48} \\ x_{15} + x_{25} + x_{35} - x_{56} - x_{57} - x_{58} \end{array}\right\} \quad \text{(intermediate node constraints)}$$

$$\left.\begin{array}{l} x_{46} + x_{56} = 2{,}500 \\ x_{47} + x_{57} = 2{,}500 \\ x_{48} + x_{58} = 2{,}500 \end{array}\right\} \quad \text{(demand constraints)}$$

$$x_{ij} \geq \text{ for all i and j combinations}$$

Exhibit 6-16 Excel Worksheet for the Transshipment Problem in Solved Problem 3

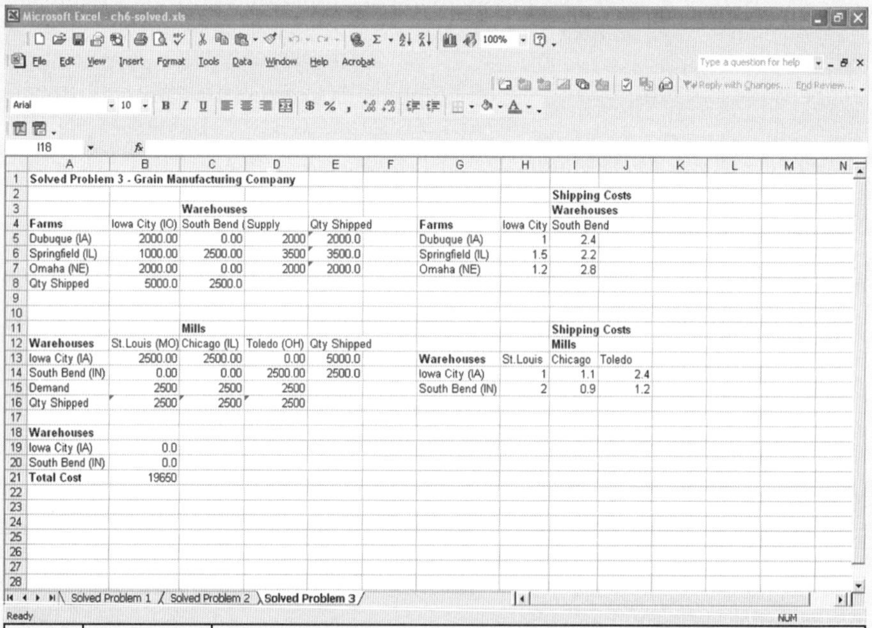

	A	B	C	D	E	F	G	H	I	J
1	**Solved Problem 3 - Grain Manufacturing Company**									
2									**Shipping Costs**	
3			**Warehouses**						**Warehouses**	
4	**Farms**	Iowa City (IO)	South Bend (	Supply	Qty Shipped		**Farms**	Iowa City	South Bend	
5	Dubuque (IA)	2000.00	0.00	2000	2000.0		Dubuque (IA)	1	2.4	
6	Springfield (IL)	1000.00	2500.00	3500	3500.0		Springfield (IL)	1.5	2.2	
7	Omaha (NE)	2000.00	0.00	2000	2000.0		Omaha (NE)	1.2	2.8	
8	Qty Shipped	5000.0	2500.0							
9										
10										
11			**Mills**						**Shipping Costs**	
12	**Warehouses**	St.Louis (MO)	Chicago (IL)	Toledo (OH)	Qty Shipped				**Mills**	
13	Iowa City (IA)	2500.00	2500.00	0.00	5000.0		**Warehouses**	St.Louis	Chicago	Toledo
14	South Bend (IN)	0.00	0.00	2500.00	2500.0		Iowa City (IA)	1	1.1	2.4
15	Demand	2500	2500	2500			South Bend (IN)	2	0.9	1.2
16	Qty Shipped	2500	2500	2500						
17										
18	**Warehouses**									
19	Iowa City (IA)	0.0								
20	South Bend (IN)	0.0								
21	**Total Cost**	19650								

Cell	Copied to	Formula
E5	E6 : E7	= SUM (B5 : C5)
B8	C8	= SUM (B5 : B7)
E13	E14	= SUM (B13 : D13)
B16	C16 : D16	= SUM (B13 : B14)
B19		= B8 − E13
B20		= C8 − E14
B21		= SUMPRODUCT (B5 : C7, H5 : I7) + SUMPRODUCT (B13 : D14, H14 : J15)

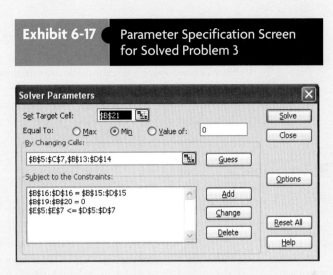

Exhibit 6-17 Parameter Specification Screen for Solved Problem 3

The Excel solution is displayed in Exhibit 6-16. The parameter specification screen is displayed in Exhibit 6-17. Based on Exhibit 6-16, the shipment schedule is as follows:

From	To	Shipment
Pubuaue (IA)	Iowa City (IA)	2000
Springfield (IL)	Iowa City (IA)	1000
Springfield (IL)	South Bend (IN)	2500
Omaha (NE)	Iowa City (IA)	2000
Iowa City (IA)	St. Louis (Mo)	2500
Iowa City (IA)	Chicago (IL)	2500
South Bend (IN)	Toledo (Off)	2500

The total cost for this problem is $19,650.

Discussion and Review Questions

1. What is the difference between solving a balanced transportation problem and an unbalanced transportation problem?
2. Describe possible applications of an assignment problem.
3. How can a transportation problem be used in making facility location decisions? Describe this application with an example.
4. Describe how a transshipment problem differs form a transportation problem. Formulate two constraints for intermediate nodes, where there are 2 sources, 2 intermediate nodes (warehouses), and 3 destinations.
5. How can we convert a transshipment problem into a transportation problem?
6. Briefly describe how to balance transportation problems that have more supply than demand.
7. Describe how you would go about setting the constraints for intermediate nodes in the linear programming formulation of the transshipment problem. Formulate two constraints for intermediate nodes, where there are 2 sources, 2 intermediate nodes (warehouses), and 3 destinations.

8. In an assignment problem, the number of sources (assignments) exceeds the number of destinations (assignees). Describe what adjustment you would make to the linear programming formulation of the assignment problem.

9. How can we solve a maximization transshipment problem or maximization transportation problem using Excel?

10. In formulating the transportation problem as a linear programming problem, why are the signs for supply constraints ≤ and the signs for demand constraints = ?

Problems

1. Consider the following transportation table where the values in the upper-right-hand corner of each cell represent unit shipping cost:

To: From:	Warehouse #1	Warehouse #2	Warehouse #3	Supply
Plant A	50	32	40	700
Plant B	16	30	20	200
Plant C	35	28	42	200
Demand	300	400	400	

a. Formulate it as a linear programming problem.
b. Use Excel and develop a distribution plan that minimizes total shipping cost.
c. If route 3–A is a unacceptable for some reason, what distribution plan would be optimal? What would its total cost be?

A–1 = 300, A–2 = 400,
B–3 = 200, C–3 = 200,
Z = 40,200

2. Suppose the cell values in the previous problem represent unit profits and that all routes are acceptable. Use Excel and determine the distribution plan that would be best in terms of maximizing profits? What would be the total profit for that plan?

3. The owner of Go-Ride, Tom Rider, projects that within three years, demand for riding mowers will exceed supply by approximately 550 units a month. Projected demand and current capacities and unit costs are:

To: From:	Warehouse #1	Warehouse #2	Warehouse #3	Warehouse #4	Supply (mowers per month)
Plant A	10	27	7	14	250
Plant B	12	20	8	30	270
Demand (mowers per month)	340	140	140	450	

a. Formulate it as a linear programming problem.
b. Use Excel and solve this problem to obtain the lowest-cost shipping schedule. What is the minimum shipping cost?

4. A soft drink manufacturer, Sara Soda, Ltd., has recently begun negotiations with brokers in the areas where it intends to distribute its products. Before finalizing the agreements, however, Manager Dave Pepper wants to determine shipping routes and costs. The firm has three plants with capacities as shown below:

Plant	Capacity (cases per week)
Metro (M)	40,000
Ridge (R)	30,000
Colby (C)	25,000

Estimated demands in each of the warehouse localities are

Warehouse	Demand (cases per week)
RS1	24,000
RS2	22,000
RS3	23,000
RS4	16,000
RS5	10,000

The estimated per unit shipping costs per case for the various routes are

From:	RS1	RS2	RS3	RS4	RS5
Metro	.80	.75	.60	.70	.90
Ridge	.75	.80	.85	.70	.85
Colby	.70	.75	.70	.80	.80

To:

a. M–RS2 = 1, M–RS3 = 23, M–RS4 = 16, R–RS2 = 20, R–RS5 = 10, C–RS1 = 24, C–RS2 = 1, Z = $67.8

b. M–RS2 = 17, M–RS3 = 23, R–RS2 = 4, R–RS4 = 16, R–RS5 = 10, C–RS1 = 24, C–RS2 = 1, Z = $67

c. 67.8 − 67 = .8 or $800

Use Excel and determine the optimal shipping plan that will minimize total shipping cost under these conditions:

a. Route Ridge–RS4 is unacceptable.
b. All routes are acceptable.
c. What is the additional cost of the Ridge–RS4 route not being acceptable?

5. Solve the following transportation problem formulation using Excel. Find the optimal transportation plan and the minimum cost. Also, decide if there is an alternate solution. If there is one, identify it.

minimize $Z = 8x_{11} + 2x_{12} + 5x_{13} + 2x_{21} + x_{22} + 3x_{23} + 7x_{31} + 2x_{32} + 6x_{33}$

subject to

$x_{11} + x_{12} + x_{13} = 90$
$x_{21} + x_{22} + x_{23} = 105$
$x_{31} + x_{32} + x_{33} = 105$
$x_{11} + x_{21} + x_{31} = 150$
$x_{12} + x_{22} + x_{32} = 75$
$x_{13} + x_{23} + x_{33} = 75$
All variables ≥ 0

6. Guess Tech is a small plastics company whose products may or may not be biodegradable. Three of its products can be manufactured on either of two machines. Neither machine has the capacity to handle all of the load: therefore, some of the work must be

handled by one and the remainder by the other. The manager of the shop wants to minimize total cost. Cost information is given in the following table:

Production Cost per Unit

	Machine 1 (M1)	Machine 2(M2)
Product A	$1.20	$1.40
Product B	1.50	1.30
Product C	1.60	1.50

A–M1 = 400, B–M2 = 400, C–M1 = 50, C–M2 = 350, Dummy–M1 = 150, Z = 1605

Daily capacity of machine 1 is 600 units and daily capacity of machine 2 is 750 units. Production quotas are 400 units of each product per day.

Formulate this problem as a linear programming model, then use Excel and solve for the optimal solution.

7. Use Excel and solve the Harley problem from the first section of this chapter, treating the cell values as unit profits instead of unit costs. Determine the optimal distribution plan and the total profit for that plan.

8. The Future Furniture company recently began construction of a new warehouse. During the construction period, several changes have occurred that require development of a new distribution plan. The current figures for supply are

Plant	Capacity (pieces per week)
East L.A. (ELA)	600
West L.A. (WLA)	800
El Toro (ET)	400

Current figures for demand are

Warehouse	Demand (pieces per week)
Orange County # 1 (OC1)	300
Orange County # 2 (OC2)	400
Long Beach (LB)	200
Los Angeles (LA)	900

Average shipping costs per unit are

a. See the IM

b. ELA–LA = 600, WLA–OC2 = 300, WLA–LB = 200, WLA–LA = 300, ET–OC1 = 300, ET–OC2 = 100, Z = $8,000

c. ELA–OC1 = 300, ELA–LA = 300, WLA–LB = 200, WLA–LA = 600, ET–OC2 = 400, Z = $8,600

From: \ To:	Orange County #1	Orange County #2	Long Beach	Los Angeles
East L.A.	$8	$9	$6	$4
West L.A.	10	7	2	3
El Toro	5	7	9	12

a. Formulate the problem given above as a linear programming problem.
b. Use Excel and solve to determine the shipping schedule that minimizes the total cost.
c. Use Excel and solve to determine the shipping schedule that minimizes the total cost if EL Toro to Orange County #1 is unavailable.

9. Consider the transportation problem of Doors Plus, a producer of steel doors for public schools:

To: From:	Charlotte (Ch)	Columbus (Co)	Chicago (Ci)	Supply
Rochester (R)	26	15	22	160
Dallas (D)	18	12	17	125
Buffalo (B)	28	24	20	30
Demand	75	90	150	

a.   Formulate this problem as a linear programming problem.

b.   Use Excel and determine a distribution plan that will minimize the total cost of shipping.

c.   Now suppose that the Rochester–Chicago route is temporarily unavailable. Beginning with the solution from (a), determine a distribution plan that will avoid this route. How much extra does this plan cost compared to the plan when all routes are possible?

10.   Rod Steele, superintendent of Rochester Forging, has developed the following transportation model.

To: From:	Detroit (De)	Denver (Dn)	Kansas City (Kc)	Supply
Chicago (Ch)	2	17	12	64
St. Louis (Sl)	9	12	6	44
Omaha (Om)	7	5	10	36
Demand	48	48	48	

Pi–Cl = 40, To–Bu = 60,
Ph–Al = 30, Ph–Cl = 30,
Dummy–Al = 40,
Z = $860

Use Excel and determine the minimum-cost shipping schedule. What is the total shipping cost?

11.   Consider the following transportation problem.

To: From:	Albany (Al)	Buffalo (Bu)	Cleveland (Cl)	Supply (tons per day)
Pittsburgh (Pi)	14	8	3	40
Toronto (To)	9	5	7	80
Philadelphia (Ph)	6	12	4	60
Demand (tons per day)	70	60	50	

a.   Formulate it as a linear programming problem.

b.   Use Excel and determine the minimum-cost shipping schedule. What is the total shipping cost?

12. The manager of Home Office Supplies, Gigi Staples, has just received demand forecasts and capacity (supply) figures for next month. These are summarized along with unit shipping costs in the following transportation table.

O_1–D_1 = 40
O_1–D_2 = 180
O_2–D_4 = 140
O_2–D_5 = 120
O_3–D_3 = 150
O_3–D_5 = 50
Du–D_1 = 100
Du–D_5 = 25
Z = \$4,260

From: \ To:	D_1	D_2	D_3	D_4	D_5	Supply
O_1	8	4	12	11	9	220
O_2	7	6	10	5	6	260
O_3	12	13	9	16	9	200
Demand	140	180	150	140	195	

Use Excel and determine the minimum-cost shipping schedule. What is the total shipping cost?

13. Given this LP model of a transportation problem with three sources and three destinations

$$\text{minimize} \quad Z = 5x_{11} + 8x_{12} + 4x_{13} + 5x_{21} + 3x_{22} + 5x_{23} + 9x_{31} + 8x_{32} + 6x_{33}$$

subject to

A: $x_{11} + x_{12} + x_{13} = 35$
B: $x_{21} + x_{22} + x_{23} = 45$
C: $x_{31} + x_{32} + x_{33} = 60$
D: $x_{11} + x_{21} + x_{31} = 50$
E: $x_{12} + x_{22} + x_{32} = 50$
F: $x_{13} + x_{23} + x_{33} = 40$
All variables ≥ 0

a. Solve for the minimum-cost solution using Excel.
b. What does x_{12} represent in the model?

14. A manager has formulated this LP model for assigning tasks to employees. Solve for the optimal solution using Excel.

$$\text{minimize} \quad Z = 2x_{11} + 5x_{12} + 9x_{13} + 7x_{21} + 4x_{22} + 6x_{23} + 1x_{31} + 7x_{32} + 5x_{33}$$

subject to

T_1–E_1, T_2–E_2, T_3–E_3, Z = 11

Task 1: $x_{11} + x_{12} + x_{13}$ = 1
Task 2: $x_{21} + x_{22} + x_{23}$ = 1
Task 3: $x_{31} + x_{32} + x_{33}$ = 1

Employee 1: $x_{11} + x_{21} + x_{31}$ = 1
Employee 2: $x_{12} + x_{22} + x_{32}$ = 1
Employee 3: $x_{13} + x_{23} + x_{33}$ = 1

All variables ≥ 0

15. A manager has prepared the following information on a transshipment problem. Locations 1 and 2 are sources, locations 3 and 4 are transshipment points (warehouses), and locations 5 and 6 are destinations.

Unit Shipping Costs to Transshipment Points

From \ To	3	4
1	9	11
2	10	12

Unit Shipping Costs from Transshipment Points

From \ To	5	6
3	8	4
4	6	7

The source supplies and destination demands are shown in the following tables. Assume that there are no restrictions on route quantities or quantities at the transshipment points.

Source	Supply	Destination	Demand
1	200	5	250
2	300	6	250

a.   Formulate a linear programming model of this problem.
b.   Using Excel, solve for the optimal solution and indicate the quantities to be shipped on each route.

16.   The manager of Home Office Supplies has prepared the following information on a transshipment problem. Locations labeled as 1,2, and 3 are supply points; locations 4 and 5 are intermediate transshipment nodes; and locations 6, 7, and 8 are destinations.

Unit Shipping Costs to Transshipment Points

From \ To	4	5
1	20	15
2	12	14
3	11	12

Unit Shipping Costs from Transshipment Points

From \ To	6	7	8
4	9	7	4
5	8	6	5

The source supplies and destination demands are shown in the following tables. There are no restrictions on quantities at the transshipment points.

Source	Supply	Destination	Demand
1	200	6	150
2	300	7	400
3	100	8	50

a. See the IM
b. See the IM
c. $x_{15} = 200$, $x_{24} = 300$,
   $x_{34} = 100$, $x_{47} = 350$,
   $x_{48} = 50$, $x_{56} = 150$,
   $x_{57} = 50$,
   $Z = \$11,850$

a.   Draw the network diagram for this problem.
b.   Formulate a linear programming model of this problem.
c.   Using Excel, solve for the optimal solution and indicate the quantities to be shipped on each route.

17.   A firm operates a plant that has a capacity of 650 units per month. The company currently ships to four warehouses with the following demand values: warehouse 1 = 350, warehouse 2 = 200, warehouse 3 = 400, and warehouse 4 = 150 units. The cost of shipping one unit of product from the existing plant to each of the four warehouses is given below

Unit cost in dollars

	Warehouse 1	Warehouse 2	Warehouse 3	Warehouse 4
Plant	20	15	25	18

The firm intends to build a plant with a capacity of 550 units per month, and has narrowed the choices of location to two sites, C1 and C2. Transportation costs for each potential origin (plant) are

C1 to	Unit Cost (in $)		C2 to	Unit Cost (in $)
# 1	13		#1	24
# 2	27		#2	17
# 3	17		#3	15
# 4	25		#4	21

Use Excel and determine the optimal shipping plan and the minimum total cost for each possible location. Which has the lower total cost? What would the annual savings be if the location with the lower cost is selected?

18. A large manufacturing company based in Dayton, Ohio, is trying to optimize its shipping schedule. Currently the monthly manufacturing capacity at three of its plants as is follows:

Plant	Capacity
Cleveland, Ohio (CL)	16,000 units
Toledo, Ohio (TO)	10,000 units
Cincinnati, Ohio (CI)	26,000 units

The company owns three warehouses—in Columbus, Ohio; Detroit, Michigan; and Ft. Wayne, Indiana. Demand at these destinations is as follows:

Warehouse	Demand
Columbus, Ohio (CO)	15,000
Detroit, Michigan (DE)	12,000
Ft. Wayne, Indiana (FW)	18,000

a. See the IM
b. See the IM

c. CL–CO = 7,000,
CL–DE = 2,000,
TO–DE = 10,000,
CL–CO = 8,000,
CL–FW = 18,000,
Z = $109,500

d. CL–CO = 9,000,
TO–DE = 10,000,
CL–CO = 6,000,
CL–DE = 2,000,
CL–FW = 18,000,
Z = $109,900
109,900 − 109,500
= $400 more

The unit shipping cost from each plant to each warehouse is given in the following table:

From\ To	Columbus	Detroit	Ft. Wayne
Cleveland	2.5	3.5	4
Toledo	4.5	1.5	2
Cincinnati	2.0	3.2	3

a. Draw the transportation diagram.
b. Formulate this problem as a linear programming problem.
c. Use Excel and determine the optimal transportation schedule for this company.
d. If the route from Cleveland to Detroit is blocked or not feasible, what is the best schedule and how much more does it cost the company to utilize this route?

19. A shop foreman has prepared the following table, which shows the costs for various combinations of job-machine assignments.

		Machine		
		A	B	C
	1	20	35	22
Job	2	42	18	25
	3	8	23	15

a. Use Excel and determine the optimal (minimum-cost) assignment for this problem.
b. What is the total cost for the optimum assignment?

20. The foreman of a machine shop wants to determine a minimum-cost matching for operators and machines. The foreman has determined the hourly cost for each of four operators for the four machines, as shown in the following cost table.

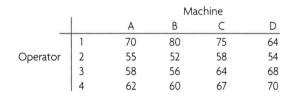

		Machine			
		A	B	C	D
	1	70	80	75	64
Operator	2	55	52	58	54
	3	58	56	64	68
	4	62	60	67	70

a. See the IM

b. 1–D, 2–C, 3–B, 4–A

c. Z = 240

d. 1–D, 2–C, 3–A, 4–B, Z = 240

    a. Formulate the problem stated above as a linear programming problem.
    b. Use Excel to determine the minimum-cost assignment for this problem.
    c. What is the total cost for the optimal assignment?
    d. Is there an alternate optimal assignment? What is it? Calculate the total cost for the alternate optimal assignment.

21. The approximate travel times for officiating crews for college basketball for four games scheduled for a weekend are shown in the following table:

		Game site			
		Syracuse	Buffalo	Rochester	Ithaca
	A	1.2*	1.4	0.2	1.5
Crew	B	1.0	2.0	0.5	1.0
	C	1.2	3.4	2.4	0.5
	D	2.1	3.1	1.1	0.8

*Time in hours.

Use Excel to answer the following questions:

    a. What set of crew assignments will minimize travel time?
    b. What is the total travel time required for the optimal assignment?

22. On Monday morning, the manager of a small print shop, Carri Fonts, finds that four jobs must be handled on a "rush" basis. Fortunately, there are four employees available to work on these jobs, and each will handle one of the jobs. Each employee has a slightly different estimated completion time for each job, as shown in the table below:

		Completion time (hours)			
		Job			
		A	B	C	D
	Tom	4.2	4.1	5.4	5.0
Employee	Dick	4.4	4.0	5.2	4.8
	Harry	4.3	4.2	5.0	4.9
	Jane	4.0	4.1	5.4	5.0

Carri wants to determine how to assign the employees to jobs so that the total completion time is as low as possible.

a. See the IM

b. Tom–B, Dick–D, Harry–C, Jane–A, Z = 17.9

    a. Formulate this as a linear programming model
    b. Solve this problem using Excel.

23. The accompanying table shows projected profits for all possible combinations of four workers and jobs awaiting processing.

    a. Formulate an LP model of this problem.
    b. Use Excel and find the solution that will yield optimal pairings in terms of total profits.

		Job		
		1	2	3
	A	$500	400	450
Worker	B	800	300	200
	C	700	400	500
	D	900	500	799

A–Buf, B–Syr, C–Ith, D–Roc, Z = 4.0; travel time increases by .1

24. (Refer to Problem 21.) Because of a previous conflict between crew D and one of the teams playing at Ithaca, crew D cannot be assigned to that location. With this in mind, determine an optimal set of assignments. What effect, if any, does this restriction have on the total travel time for all crews?

25. (Refer to Problem 21.) Suppose that another crew (Crew E) is added to select from. Crew E's travel times to Syracuse, Buffalo, Rochester, and Ithaca are 1.8, .5, .6, and 2.0 hours, respectively. Assume, too, that the D–Ithaca assignment is undesirable.

    a. Use Excel and determine the set of assignments that will minimize total travel time.
    b. Which crew will not be assigned?
    c. Is there an alternate optimal solution? Explain.

26. An industrial engineer has prepared a table that shows the costs for each possible combination of job and machine for four jobs and four machines, as shown:

		Machine			
		A	B	C	D
	1	45	75	80	35
Job	2	55	60	60	65
	3	70	65	50	45
	4	60	75	70	65

a. See the IM

b. 1–D, 2–B, 3–C, 4–A

c. Z = $205

d. No alternate optimal solution

    a. Formulate the problem, given the above, as a linear programming problem.
    b. Use Excel and determine the set of assignments that will minimize total processing cost.
    c. What is total processing cost?
    d. Is there an alternate optimal solution? What is it?

27. If the numbers in the previous problem reflected profits rather than costs, what set of assignments would have been optimal?

28. (Refer to Problem 26.) Suppose that job I could not be assigned to machine D because of a technical problem.

a. 1–A, 2–B, 3–C, 4–D, Z = $220; Additional cost = $15

b. 1–A, 2–B, 3–D, 4–C, Z = $220

    a. What set of assignments would minimize total cost of the assignments? What additional cost is incurred because of the technical problem?
    b. What is the alternate optimal solution?

29. An analyst has kept track of the number of defectives produced by five workers on five different machines. The results are shown below for a run of 400 units per machine:

Machine

		A	B	C	D	E
	1	9	7	4	6	2
	2	7	4	5	2	1
Worker	3	3	4	3	2	3
	4	9	7	8	6	5
	5	0	3	2	4	3

a. Formulate this problem as a linear programming problem.
b. Use Excel and determine a set of assignments that will minimize the total number of errors for a given run size.
c. Is there an alternate optimal solution? If so, what is it?
d. What is the total number of defectives expected for the optimal assignment?

30. In the previous problem, if another machine was available and the number of defectives produced by the five workers for a run of 400 units was 4, 4, 2, 3, and 1. respectively, use Excel and determine the following:

a. 1–B, 2–D, 3–C, 4–F,
   5–A, Z = 10
b. Machine B or
   machine E

c. 1–C, 2–E, 3–D, 4–F,
   Z = 10

a. A set of assignments that will minimize the total number of expected defectives.
b. Which machine will not be used?
c. Is there an alternate optimal solution? If so, what is it?

31. A manager has four jobs that must be assigned. Estimated processing times for each of four employees are shown in the accompanying table.

Employee

		Smith (S)	Jones (J)	Green (G)	Mehl (m)
	1	6.2*	8.0	5.4	4.8
Job	2	6.0	7.2	5.8	4.4
	3	5.5	6.0	6.6	6.8
	4	6.3	6.6	7.0	7.3

*Time in hours.

a. Formulate this as an LP problem.
b. Use Excel and determine a set of assignments that will minimize total processing time.
c. What is the total processing time for the optimal assignments?

32. A company has four manufacturing plants and four warehouses. Each of the plants will supply one of the warehouses. Each warehouse has a demand that is equal to a factory's output for a given period. Assume that all capacities and all demands are 300 units per period. The shipping costs for all routes are shown in the table below. The costs are in thousands.

Warehouse

		1	2	3	4
	A	2.4	1.8	2.6	1.8
	B	2.0	1.9	2.2	2.2
Plant	C	1.4	1.7	2.0	1.4
	D	1.6	2.1	2.1	1.6

a. A–2, B–3, C–1, D–4

b. 7.0

c. Yes, A–2, B–3, C–4, D–1

d. No, still a minimization problem

a. Use Excel and determine a set of assignments that will minimize total shipping cost for a period.
b. What is the total shipping cost for your plan?
c. Is there an alternate optimal solution? If so, what is it?
d. Would the optimal solution change if the values represented shipping *time* instead of shipping *cost*? Explain.

33. Consider the transportation problem of Sunbelt Heat Pumps:

To: From:	Cincinnati (C)	Miami (Mi)	Memphis (Me)	Tampa (T)	Supply
Houston (H)	12	5	7	2	98
Atlanta (A)	11	3	6	1	80
Demand	35	50	25	68	

a. Formulate it as a linear programming problem.
b. Use Excel and determine the minimum-cost shipping schedule. What is the total shipping cost?

34. Consider the transportation problem of the California Dishwasher Company:

To: From:	Store 1	Store 2	Store 3	Supply
Warehouse A	12	20	15	50
Warehouse B	9	11	4	15
Warehouse C	20	14	8	55
Demand	25	50	45	120

a. See the IM

b. A–1, A–2, B–3, C–2,C–3, Z = 1,450

a. Formulate it as a linear programming problem.
b. Use Excel and determine the minimum-cost shipping schedule. What is the total shipping cost?

35. Consider the previous problem. Treat the values in each cell as revenue per unit instead of cost per unit.
a. Use Excel and determine the total optimal profit.
b. What is the optimal shipment schedule?

TC = Z = $124,960

36. Refer to Example 6-3. Suppose that an increase in warehousing costs and other costs brings inventory carrying costs to $2 per unit per month. All other costs and quantities remain the same. Determine a revised solution to this transportation problem.

37. Refer to Example 6-3. Suppose that regular-time capacity will be reduced to 440 units in period 3 to accommodate a companywide safety inspection of equipment. What will the additional cost of the optimal plan be as compared to the one shown in Example 6-3? Assume all costs and quantities are the same as given in Example 6-3 except for the regular-time output in period 3.

Chapter 6 Case   Sunshine Tomato Inc.

The Sunshine Tomato Soup Shippers produce tomato soup at three West Coast canneries in Bakersfield, Phoenix, and Eugene. The soup is shipped to four regional warehouses. Due to high demand, the company is considering opening a fourth cannery. The company is considering opening up the fourth cannery either at San Diego, San Jose, Los Angeles, or Stockton. The following table shows the cost of shipping a case from each cannery (existing and proposed) to each regional warehouse. The company wishes to ship all of its cannery capacity to the regional warehouses so that monthly transportation cost is minimized.

Source	Seattle, Washington	Los Angeles, California	Denver, Colorado	Dallas, Texas	Maximum Monthly Cannery Capacity
Phoenix, Arizona	$2.80	$0.60	$1.20	$1.50	70,000
Eugene, Oregon	$0.50	$1.20	$2.20	$2.90	80,000
Bakersfield, California	$1.80	$0.40	$1.80	$2.20	90,000
Los Angeles, California	$1.70	$0.75	$1.75	$2.50	110,000
San Diego, California	$1.80	$0.60	$1.60	$2.60	110,000
San Jose, California	$1.40	$0.70	$2.00	$2.40	110,000
Stockton, California	$1.60	$0.80	$1.80	$2.50	110,000
Monthly warehouse demand	80,000	90,000	70,000	100,000	

Discussion questions

1. What is the total transportation cost if each of the four sites should be selected?
2. Which site should be selected to locate the next cannery? Why?
3. State the shipment schedule associated with the selected site.

Integer Programming

Chapter 7

After completing this chapter, you should be able to:

1. Tell how integer programming problems differ from general linear programming problems.

2. Explain the difference among pure, mixed, and 0–1 integer programming problems.

3. Formulate and use Excel to solve integer programming problems.

4. Formulate and use Excel to solve 0–1 integer programming problems.

5. Formulate specialized integer programming problems including knapsack, set covering, fixed charge, and facility location problems.

Chapter Outline

Introduction to Integer Programming, 324

Types of Integer Programming Problems, 324
Pure-Integer Problems, 324
Mixed-Integer Problems, 324
0–1 Integer Problems, 324

Graphical Representation of Integer Programming Problems, 325

Solving Integer Programming Problems Using Excel, 326

A Comment about Sensitivity, 329

Formulating Integer Programming Problems with 0–1 Constraints, 329
Either-Or Alternatives, 330
k-Out-of-*n* Alternatives, 330
If-Then Alternatives, 330
Either-Or Constraints, 331

Variables That Have Minimum Level Requirements, 331

Specialized Integer Programming Problems, 332
Fixed-Charge Problem, 333
Set Covering Problem, 336
Knapsack Problem, 340
Facility Location Problem, 341
Traveling Salesperson Problem, 344

Difficulties in Solving Integer Programming Problems, 349

Summary, 351

Glossary, 351

Solved Problems, 352

Discussion and Review Questions, 356

Problems, 357

Chapter 7 Case: Suburban Suntime, 365

◼️ Introduction to Integer Programming

In the preceding chapters, which dealt with linear programming solutions, the issue of noninteger solutions was largely ignored. This was done for a number of reasons. One was that to require integer solutions would have added considerably to the complexity of the models. Another was that numerous applications exist in which integer solutions are not necessary. This is especially true for problems that involve variables that are measured on a *continuous* scale (e.g., volume, weight, length, and time). In other cases, a rounded solution may be acceptable. For example, if a problem involved determining the numbers of various types of nails to produce, an answer of 9,200.7 could easily be rounded up to 9,201 with little or no consequence. Even if the solution turned out to be infeasible, reality would force a feasible solution (e.g., after making 9,200 nails, there might not be enough raw material to make one more nail).

On the other hand, there are important cases in which integer solutions are required. For instance, if a problem concerned the optimal number of cargo ships, apartment houses, or office buildings to build, a noninteger answer would not be acceptable. Similarly, simply rounding to the nearest integer will not necessarily produce an answer that is optimal or near optimal, especially if millions of dollars are involved. Obviously, in cases such as these, it is desirable to identify the optimal, *integer* values of decision variables. This chapter describes methods for doing that.

When we solve a continuously divisible linear programming problem, where the variables take on fractional values, the solution will travel from corner point to corner point until an optimal solution is reached. However, solving an integer linear programming problem is more difficult because even though we begin by considering all of the corner points, since many of these will not satisfy the integer constraint, we need to consider other integer feasible points. In essence, when we use an integer linear programming problem, the number of feasible points considered is significantly higher compared to a linear programming problem without any integer constraints that considers only the corner points.

◼️ Types of Integer Programming Problems

Basically, there are three types of linear programming problems that involve integer solutions: pure-integer problems, mixed-integer problems, and 0–1 problems.

Pure-Integer Problems

Problems requiring that *all* decision variables have integer solutions are referred to as **pure-integer problems.** Examples include the number of each type of plane to produce, the number of each type of large machine to produce, the number of each type of house to construct, and so on.

Mixed-Integer Problems

In **mixed-integer problems,** some, but not all, of the decision variables are required to have integer values in the final solution, whereas others need not have integer values. For example, a landscape design may have a project that requires a decision on what percentage of an area to plant grass (a continuous variable) and how many trees to plant (some integer number).

0–1 Integer Problems

A third kind of problem is where the integer variables require a value of 0 or 1. This type of problem, the **0–1 integer problem,** relates to situations in which decision variables are of the yes-no type. For example, a bank may be considering possible locations for new branch offices. Sites that are chosen would receive a 1, whereas those not chosen would receive a 0. Similarly, in a problem requiring matching, say, of jobs and machines or workers and jobs, the optimal matches would receive a 1 and all others would receive a 0.

This is an important category of integer programming problems that relates to *binary* decisions. Other examples include a manager who may have to decide whether to fund a project (yes) or not (no), whether to hire a person or not, whether to replace an existing machine or not, and so on. Generally, these problems involve multiple variables, such as the need to choose three locations for new convenience stores from a list of 20 potential sites. Even so, a yes-no decision must be made for each potential site (i.e., there are 20 decision variables).

Graphical Representation of Integer Programming Problems

Integer programming problems can be solved graphically, but only for two-variable problems. With that in mind, let's consider a graphical solution to a very simple problem in order to better understand the nature of integer programming problems and solutions.

Figure 7-1 shows a simple integer programming problem and a graph of the constraints and the objective function. Note that the feasible solution space consists entirely of positive integers (represented by the dark points) that satisfy the constraints. In an LP problem that did not require an integer solution, the objective function would be plotted, then moved manually away from the origin in order to determine the optimal intersection. We can see this in Figure 7-1, but we also can see that this is not one of the integer solutions. In order to obtain a feasible integer solution using the objective function, we must move it (parallel

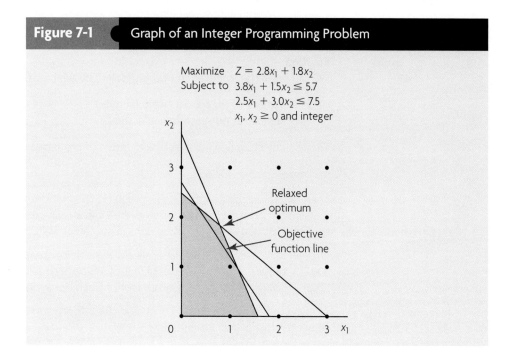

Figure 7-1   Graph of an Integer Programming Problem

Maximize $Z = 2.8x_1 + 1.8x_2$
Subject to $3.8x_1 + 1.5x_2 \leq 5.7$
$2.5x_1 + 3.0x_2 \leq 7.5$
$x_1, x_2 \geq 0$ and integer

Relaxed optimum

Objective function line

to itself) back toward the origin. Hence, in order to achieve a feasible integer solution, we must settle for a lower value of the objective function (because moving the objective function toward the origin decreases its value). In moving the line toward the origin, the *first* point we come to will be the optimal integer solution. As you can see in Figure 7-1, that point is 1, 1. Thus, the optimal integer solution is $x_1 = 1, x_2 = 1$.

Solving Integer Programming Problems Using Excel

We can solve integer programming problems with Excel as well as other computer software packages. In this section, we will demonstrate how to solve a pure-integer programming problem using Excel. Later in the chapter, we will demonstrate how to solve 0–1 integer programming problems using Excel.

Consider the following example.

Example 7-1

A producer of pleasure boats wants to maximize profits during the next season. Two types of boats are sold. The first type of boat is a speedboat (x_1), and the second type of boat is a pontoon (x_2). The speedboat sells for $40,000 and the pontoon sells for $30,000. The speedboat takes 10 weeks to manufacture, while the pontoon takes 3 weeks to manufacture. One speedboat uses 600 board feet of lumber, while one pontoon uses 1,000 board feet of lumber. Each speedboat requires 500 square feet of fiberglass, while each pontoon requires 200 square feet of fiberglass. There are 30 weeks of labor, 3,000 board feet of lumber, and 1,800 square feet of fiberglass available during the season. Because of the desire to avoid ending up with semicomplete boats, the manager has specified that only integer solutions will be acceptable. Use Excel and determine how many speedboats and how many pontoons the company should manufacture for the next season. What is the optimal profit?

Solution
We can begin the formulation of this problem by defining the variables:

Let x_1 = number of speedboats manufactured
    x_2 = number of pontoons manufactured

The objective function involves maximization of profit and can be stated as follows:

maximize $Z = 40{,}000x_1 + 30{,}000x_2$

There are three constraints for this problem: The first one involves the labor time requirements, the second one involves the lumber usage, and the third one involves the fiberglass consumption. These constraints can be stated as follows:

$$\begin{array}{lll} 10x_1 + 3x_2 & \le 30 & \text{(labor weeks available constraint)} \\ 600x_1 + 1{,}000x_2 & \le 3{,}000 & \text{(board feet of lumber available for production)} \\ 500x_1 + 200x_2 & \le 1{,}800 & \text{(square feet of fiberglass available during season)} \end{array}$$

Along with the nonnegativity constraint, this information can be entered into the computer as shown in Exhibit 7-1.

Microsoft Excel - ch7-1

F8   =SUMPRODUCT($C$8:$D$8,C5:D5)

	A	B	C	D	E	F	G	H	I	J
1	Boat Manufacturing Example									
2										
3			Speed	Pontoon						
4	Profit per unit		40,000	30,000						
5	# of boats		2	2	Total Profit					
6	Profit per unit		80,000	60,000	140,000					
7	Resource requirements				Available	Used	Leftover			
8	Labor time		10	3	30	26	4			
9	Lumber		600	1000	3600	3200	400			
10	Fiberglass		500	200	1800	1400	400			
11										
12	Production									
13	Speedboat	2								
14	Pontoon boat	2								
15	Total profit	140,000								
16										
17										
18										
19										

Sheet2 \ Sheet1

Cell	Copied to	Formula
C6	D6	= C4 ∗ C5
E6		= SUM (C6 : D6)
F8	F9 : F10	= SUMPRODUCT ($C$8 : $D$8, C5 : D5)
G8	G9 : G10	= E8 − F8

After clicking on **Tools I Solver,** the screen shown in Exhibit 7-2 is displayed. In Exhibits 7-2 and 7-3, we illustrate parameter specification associated with this pure integer programming problem. In Exhibit 7-1, the objective function is specified in cell E6, and we specify this in "Set Target Cell" box in Exhibit 7-2. The decision variables are located in cells C5 and D5 and are specified in the "By Changing Cells" box in Exhibit 7-2. The three constraints are all less-than-or-equal-to types and they are specified in Exhibit 7-2 in aggregate as follows: $F$8:$F$10<=$E$8:$E$10. The left-hand side of the inequality ($F$8:$F$10) is stated in column labeled "Used" and the right-hand side of the inequality ($E$8:$E$10) is stated under the column labeled "Available" in Exhibit 7-1.

Up to this point, the specification of the problem using Excel was identical to the specification of typical linear programming problems covered in Chapter 4. The integer requirement distinguishes this problem from other noninteger linear programming problems. In order to solve this problem as a pure integer programming problem using Excel, we need to specify that decision variables may only assume integer values.

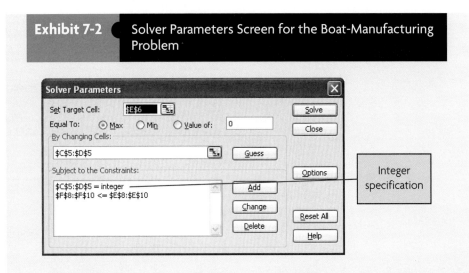

Exhibit 7-2   Solver Parameters Screen for the Boat-Manufacturing Problem

To do that, we click on "Add" and "Add Constraint," the screen shown in Exhibit 7-3 is displayed. In Exhibit 7-3, on the left side of the screen labeled as "Cell Reference," we simply specify the location of the decision variables in Exhibit 7-1 ($C$5:$D$5). The middle of Exhibit 7-3 shows the sign or the variable type requirements of the constraint. When we click on the down arrow and choose "int," the word "integer" shows up on the left side of the screen in the Constraint box; after we click OK, we see $C$5:$D$5 = integer in the Subject to the Constraints box in Exhibit 7-2. This concludes parameter specification of the boat-manufacturing problem.

After clicking on the "Solve" button, the solution in Exhibit 7-1 is displayed. Before clicking on the "Solve" button in Exhibit 7-2, the values of the decision variables in Exhibit 7-1 were simply equal to zero. After clicking the "Solve" button, the Solver Results screen shown in Exhibit 7-4 will appear. A more detailed answer report could be obtained by simply clicking on "Answer" in the Reports box on the right side of the "Solver Results" screen.

Based on the results given in Exhibit 7-1, the solution to this problem can be summarized as follows:

$x_1 = 2$ (number of speedboats manufactured)
$x_2 = 2$ (number of pontoon boats manufactured)
$Z = \$140,000$ (optimal profit associated with the boat production schedule)

Exhibit 7-3   Integer Requirement Specification

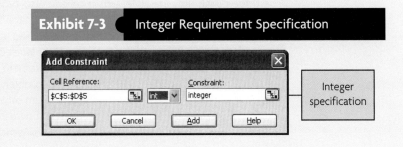

Exhibit 7-4   Solver Results Screen

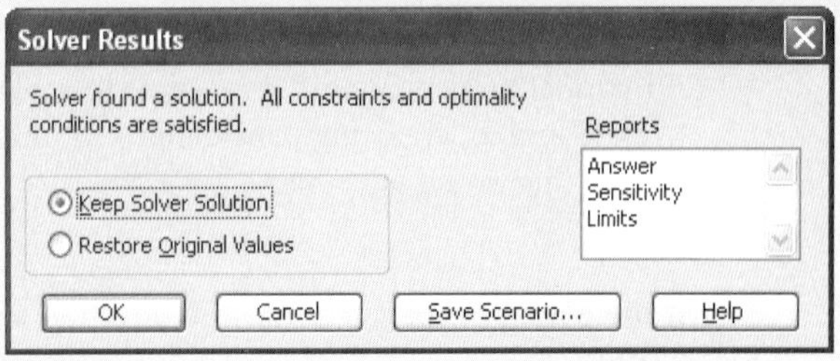

Had we solved this problem as a linear programming problem, we would have obtained the following answer:

$x_1 = 2.561$ (number of speedboats manufactured)
$x_2 = 1.4634$ (number of pontoon boats manufactured)
$Z = \$146,341.46$ (optimal profit associated with the boat production schedule)

As can be observed, rounding down the linear programming solution ($x_1 = 2$, $x_2 = 1$) is not the same as the optimal integer solution.

A Comment about Sensitivity

Integer programming problems do not readily lend themselves to the sort of sensitivity analysis that was described in Chapter 5. This stems from the fact that only a relatively few of the infinite solution possibilities in a feasible solution space will meet integer requirements. Unfortunately, there is no easy way to determine the extent to which changes in a right-hand-side quantity will alter the choice of integer alternatives. The only way to accomplish that is to rework the problem with the changes and observe the effect. This is, indeed, unfortunate, because it often happens that relatively small changes in constraints can have large changes on the value of the objective function. If these amounts were known to management, it is highly likely that management would elect to take the necessary action to change the constraints. For this reason, it may make sense to explore a range of constraint quantities in order to ascertain if the value of the objective function would change materially. In cases in which it would change materially, say, for a slight increase in the right-hand-side value of a constraint, this potential could then be presented to management for consideration.

Similarly, there is no simple way to determine the impact of changes to the objective function coefficients on the solution to a problem. Again, trial-and-error examination of a range of reasonable alternatives involving completely solving each revised problem is required.

Formulating Integer Programming Problems with 0–1 Constraints

Formulating a problem correctly is often the most important phase of decision analysis. In the case of integer programming, problem formulation sometimes requires a fair degree of ingenuity in order to correctly portray a situation. In this section, a variety of formulations

are demonstrated that have proved very useful in setting up commonly encountered integer programming requirements.

Either-Or Alternatives

A manufacturer may need a machine to replace one that recently has failed. Two alternatives, x_1 and x_2, are being considered, but only one will be needed. The constraint that expresses this would be

$$x_1 + x_2 = 1$$

If there is a possibility that neither machine will be acquired, then the constraint would be written as

$$x_1 + x_2 \leq 1$$

In either of these cases, the variables are 0–1 variables.

k-Out-of-n Alternatives

In many problems, a decision maker must choose a specified number of alternatives; say, choose two machines from a list of five alternative machines. Or the requirement may be to choose *at least two*, or, perhaps, *no more than two* machines from the list.

The formulation for exactly two machines out of five would be

$$x_1 + x_2 + x_3 + x_4 + x_5 = 2$$

For at least two machines out of five, the formulation would be

$$x_1 + x_2 + x_3 + x_4 + x_5 \geq 2$$

For no more than two out of five machines; the formulation would be

$$x_1 + x_2 + x_3 + x_4 + x_5 \leq 2$$

Sometimes a problem will permit a range of choices. For example, a situation may call for the purchase of anywhere from two to four machines. The problem would then require two constraints, one for the upper bound and the other for the lower bound. Thus, for two to four machines, the constraints would be

$$x_1 + x_2 + x_3 + x_4 + x_5 \geq 2$$
$$x_1 + x_2 + x_3 + x_4 + x_5 \leq 4$$

If-Then Alternatives

It sometimes happens that a decision to take some action necessitates another action that supports the initial decision. For example, the purchase of machine x_2 may necessitate the purchase of another machine, x_1. The formulation would be

$$x_1 \geq x_2$$

Note that this formulation implies that the reverse case is not required: The purchase of x_1 does not require the purchase of x_2. In order to satisfy the requirement that the right-hand side consist solely of a numerical quantity, this can be rewritten as

$$x_1 - x_2 \geq 0$$

If the purchase of either machine requires the purchase of the other, the appropriate formulation would be

$$x_1 - x_2 = 0$$

Either-Or Constraints

Situations may arise in which a constraint will apply *only if* a particular alternative is chosen. For instance, the choice of a certain machine may necessitate special power requirements. Consequently, it can be useful to be able to "turn on" or "turn off" a constraint as appropriate. This can be accomplished by tying the constraint to the decision variable that will govern its applicability. Suppose the machine in question is choice x_8, which will require the constraint $5x_4 + 3x_5 \geq 100$ if x_8 is chosen. This can be incorporated into the problem by writing the constraint as $5x_4 + 3x_5 \geq 100x_8$

where x_8 is a 0–1 decision variable. Then, if x_8 is selected, $x_8 = 1$, and the constraint will stand. If x_8 is not selected, then $x_8 = 0$, and the constraint will, in effect, drop out. Rearranging terms so that all variables are on the left-hand side and a constant on the right-hand side results in

$$5x_4 + 3x_5 - 100x_8 \geq 0$$

If there are two potential constraints, one of which will apply if a certain choice (say, x_8) is made and the other if that choice is not made, the formulation would be slightly different. For example, suppose the constraints are $5x_4 + 3x_5 \geq 100$ if x_8 is chosen and $5x_4 + 3x_5 \geq 50$ for any other choice (i.e., x_8 is not chosen). This could be expressed as

$5x_4 + 3x_5 \geq 100x_8$ (applies if $x_8 = 1$)
$5x_4 + 3x_5 \geq 50(1 - x_8)$ (applies if $x_8 = 0$)

These can be written as

$5x_4 + 3x_5 - 100x_8 \geq 0$ and
$5x_4 + 3x_5 + 50x_8 \geq 50$

If the constraints relate to *upper limits* (i.e., the constraints are $\leq$), then a slightly different approach should be used. Suppose the constraints are either $4x_1 + 8x_2 \leq 40$, or $2x_1 + x_2 \leq 16$, depending on whether project y_1 is commissioned. Say the first constraint applies if y_1 is not commissioned and the second if it is. This can be handled by writing the constraints in this form:

1   $4x_1 + 8x_2 \leq 40 + My_1$ where M is a very large number
2   $2x_1 + x_2 \leq 16 + M(1 - y_1)$ where

$y_1 = 1$ indicates the project is commissioned
$y_1 = 0$ indicates that the projects is not commissioned

If y_1 is commissioned, then $y_1 = 1$ and the right-hand side of the first constraint becomes so large that it is not binding. Conversely, if $y_1 = 0$, the reverse is true: The first constraint becomes binding, whereas the right-hand side of the second becomes very large and, therefore, not binding.

Variables That Have Minimum Level Requirements

In some cases, a variable either will have to be zero or an amount that exceeds a specified value. For instance, a minimum order size for a purchased part might be required by a vendor. Say the minimum quantity for x_1 is 200 units. This can be expressed using another variable, y_1, that is a 0–1 variable:

$$x_1 - 200y_1 \geq 0$$

where x_1 is integer
            $y_1 = 0$ or 1

Then, if $x_1 = 0$, the first constraint would cause y_1 to be zero as well.

Modern Management Science Application: *Waste Management*

We all have to put out garbage approximately once a week to be collected by a garbage collection company. Waste Manage-ment (WM) is a private firm that provides comprehensive waste management services in North America. The company manages a network of 293 active landfill disposal sites, 16 waste energy plants, 72 landfill gas-to-energy facilities, 146 recycling plants, 346 transfer stations, and 435 collection depots. WM provides garbage collection and disposal to nearly 20 million residential and 2 million commercial customers throughout the United States and Canada. The company has a large fleet of vehicles that has to be maintained, routed, and dispatched; initially that was done using a decentralized system. WM recog-nized an opportunity to save a considerable amount of money by improving the routing of its vehicles. WM contracted with the Institute of Information Technology (IIT) to develop a comprehensive route-management system.

The company's garbage collection business consisted of three major areas: (1) residential, (2) commercial; and (3) industrial. Residential customers include people living in individual homes. Commercial customers include strip malls, restaurants, and small office buildings, while industrial customers include rather large businesses. Typically, a commercial container consisted of eight "loose yards", while an industrial container may range from 20 to 40 loose yards.

WM wanted to design a routing system where each route became as profitable as possible. In order to accomplish this goal, the company invested in a geographical information system (GIS). This system tightly integrates spatial information based on customer addresses. GIS can show the location of the customer on a map along with the surrounding street network. To accomplish the goal, WM and IIT centralized its routing system of 19,600 daily routes and implemented a new scheduling system. The new scheduling system incorporated new variables such as frequency of service based on climate, geography, competition, and the price of service. On one route, a garbage collection truck may serve a small number of customers, while on another route a truck may serve many more customers. However, the first driver may drive a longer distance to serve the smaller number of customers while the second driver has short hops between customers.

The residential and commercial collection problems can be classified as vehicle routing problems (VRP), which is a special case of a traveling salesperson problem. VRPs may have different characteristics (homogeneous versus heterogeneous vehicles, single versus multiple depots). WM's goal was to minimize the number of vehicles and travel time while meeting the following constraints: vehicle capacity, route capacity, routing time limit, disposal trips, and time windows at stops. If the routing capacity exceeds vehicle capacity, the driver will be forced to make multiple disposal stops. On the other hand, if the routing capacity is less than the vehicle capacity, then the driver will make only one disposal stop. WM contracted with IIT to develop a user-friendly, Web-based system to schedule the entire routing for the company. The new routing system resulted in fewer vehicles and, thus, 10 percent fewer drivers were required. WM reduced the number of drivers through regular attrition and did not lay off drivers. The company identified the new routing system (WasteRoute) as one of the key components of its operational excellence.

In less than four years, the company had 984 fewer routes, which translated into savings of $18 million, with future estimated annual savings expected to reach $44 million. The improved routing not only resulted in the company cutting costs, but also enabled the company to focus on revenue enhancement. Because of the better efficiency provided by WasteRoute, WM also has a new higher total capacity, and therefore could focus on adding new customers, new routes, and new revenue.

Source: S. Sahoo, S. Kim, B. Kim, B. Kraas, and A. Popov Jr., "Routing Optimization for Waste Management," *Interfaces* 35, no. 1 (January–February 2005), pp. 24–36.

◼◼ Specialized Integer Programming Problems

There are special types of business applications that require the decision variables to take on a value of 1 or 0. These include capital budgeting and assignment problems where partial acceptance or rejection of a project, investment alternative, or a job is not acceptable. In such cases, the project, investment, or job is either accepted or rejected.

There are a number of specialized integer programming problems with 0–1 decision variables that deserve discussion in this chapter. These problems are as follows:

1. Fixed-charge problem.
2. Set covering problem.
3. Knapsack problem.
4. Facility location problem.
5. Traveling salesperson problem.

Fixed-Charge Problem

In the business world, companies face situations that involve fixed costs if a certain activity is undertaken as well as a variable cost, which generally involves the per-unit production cost. In such cases, the objective is to minimize the total cost, which is the sum of the fixed cost plus the variable cost.

It very often happens that the contribution that a variable makes to profit is linear *after* a fixed charge has been deducted. For instance, the profit per unit produced on a machine may be $20 per unit after a setup cost of $80 has been allowed for. Suppose the product is x_1. Then without the setup charge, the portion of the objective function with x_1 would be $20x_1$. It might seem that we could simply subtract the fixed charge from the objective function. However, this approach overlooks the possibility that the optimum value of x_1 might be zero, in which case there would be *no* setup charge and, hence, no subtraction from the objective function value. To allow for this, we can introduce another variable, y_1, which can assume values of 0 or 1: 0 if x_1 is 0 and 1 if x_1 is greater than 0.

The portion of the objective function for these two variables is

$$20x_1 - 80y_1$$

In addition, the following constraint will be needed:

$$x_1 \leq My_1 \qquad \text{where } M \text{ is a very large number}$$

This constraint will force x_1 to be zero if y_1 is zero. If $y_1 = 1$, there will be no limit on x_1, assuming a very large value has been selected for M. To conform with having a constant on the right-hand side, this constraint can be written as

$$x_1 - My_1 \leq 0$$

Note that this constraint and the portion of the objective function shown would be in addition to any other constraints and other portions of the objective function that may be required by a problem.

Consider the following two examples of **fixed-charge problems.**

Example 7-2

A company makes two products, x_1 and x_2. Product x_1 generates a profit of $20 per unit before a fixed charge of $80 per batch for setup is allowed for; product x_2 generates a profit of $30 per unit before a setup charge of $90 is allowed for. Each product requires two hours of machine time, and 400 hours of machine time are available. Integer values of each product are required for technical reasons. The manager wants to maximize profits. Set up this all-integer linear programming problem.

Solution

x_1 = quantity of Product 1
x_2 = quantity of Product 2
y_1 = 1 if $x_1 > 0$, y_1 = 0 if $x_1 = 0$
y_2 = 1 if $x_2 > 0$, y_2 = 0 if $x_2 = 0$
M = a very large number

maximize $z = 020x_1 + 30x_2 - 80y_1 - 90y_2$

subject to

Machine time	$2x_1 + 2x_2 \leq 400$ hours
x_1 fixed charge	$x_1 - My_1 \leq 0$
x_2 fixed charge	$x_2 - My_2 \leq 0$
	x_1 and x_2 integer and ≥ 0
	y_1 and y_2 are 0 or 1

Solving,

$x_2 = 200$	(quantity of product 2)
$y_2 = 1$	(set up for product 2)
$Z = \$5,910$	(profit)

Example 7-3

A company manufactures three different products: A, B, and C. The per-unit profit margins for the three products are $6, $10, and $5. The products could be manufactured using one of two processes. The per-unit production requirements for each product for each process is given in Table7-1.

Table 7-1   Per-Unit Production Requirements

Process	Product A	Product B	Product C	Total Hours Available
Process 1	4 hours	6 hours	3 hours	2,000 hours per week
Process 2	5 hours	7 hours	4 hours	2,400 hours per week

The demand for product A is predicted to be between 50 and 100 units per week, demand for product B is predicted to be between 150 and 200 units per week, and demand for product C is predicted to be between 100 and 150 units per week.

If the company decides to use process 1, it will incur a setup cost of $100 and the setup will take 24 hours. If the company decides to use process 2, it will incur a setup cost of $80 and the setup will take 18 hours. Determine the production schedule that will maximize the profits for the company and also determine which of the two processes should be utilized.

Solution
We start formulating this problem by defining the decision variables. There are two types of decision variables in this problem. The first type of decision variable is x_j = the number of units of product j manufactured. This is an integer variable, as fractional quantities are not acceptable. The second type of decision variable is y_i = 0 or 1. If process i is not used in manufacturing the products, then $y_i = 0$, in which case the setup cost associated with process i will not be incurred. If process

i is used in manufacturing the products, then $y_i = 1$, in which case the setup cost associated with process i will be incurred. After defining the decision variables, the next step is to prepare the objective function. Since the objective is to maximize profit, the objective function is maximization. In the objective function, the fixed costs can be represented as negative profits.

maximize $Z = 6x_1 + 10x_2 + 5x_3 - 100y_1 - 80y_2$

In setting up the constraints, we not only have to consider and sum the per-unit production hours for each product, but we also need to add the setup time for each product. If the product is not manufactured, the value of the associated y variable is 0 and no setup cost will be incurred. The constraints for each department can be stated as follows:

$4x_1 + 6x_2 + 3x_3 + 24y_1 \leq 2{,}000y_1$ hours   (constraint for process 1—milling and lathe departments)

$5x_1 + 7x_2 + 4x_3 + 18y_2 \leq 2{,}400y_2$ hours   (constraint for process 2—assembly department)

Note that the right-hand side of each constraint for each process contains the y_i variable. If we utilize process 1, y_1 takes on a value of 1; if we do not utilize process 1, $y_1 = 0$. If $y_1 = 0$, the right-hand side of constraint 1 goes to zero, which means that process 1 is not utilized.

Demand constraints are stated below:

$x_1 \geq 50$
$x_1 \leq 100$
$x_2 \geq 150$
$x_2 \leq 200$ (minimum and maximum demand constraints)
$x_3 \geq 100$
$x_3 \leq 150$

Note that there are two demand constraints for each product. One of the two constraints, the greater-than-or-equal-to constraint, is the lower bound (minimum demand); the other, the less-than-or-equal-to constraint, is the upper bound (maximum demand).

The formulation of the above problem can be summarized as follows:

maximize $Z = 6x_1 + 10x_2 + 5x_3 - 100y_1 - 80y_2$

subject to

$4x_1 + 6x_2 + 3x_3 + 24y_1 \leq 2{,}000y_1$ hours   (constraint for the milling and lathe departments)

$5x_1 + 7x_2 + 4x_3 + 18y_2 \leq 2{,}400y_2$ hours   (constraint for the assembly department)

$x_1 \geq 50$
$x_1 \leq 100$
$x_2 \geq 150$
$x_2 \leq 200$
$x_3 \geq 100$
$x_3 \leq 150$
$x_1, x_2, x_3 \geq 0$ and integer
$y_1, y_2 = 0$ or 1

Excel solution and worksheet to this problem are not given to reduce redundancy of Excel worksheets within the chapter, but rather they are included on the CD-ROM.

$x_1 = 99$ (# of units of product A scheduled to be manufactured)
$x_2 = 185$ (# of units of product B scheduled to be manufactured)
$x_3 = 148$ (# of units of product C scheduled to be manufactured)
$y_1 = 1$ (process 1 is being utilized)
$y_2 = 1$ (process 2 is being utilized)
$Z = \$2,634$ (total maximum profit)

Set Covering Problem

In many business situations, coverage needs to be provided to all areas with minimum cost or time requirements. The **set covering problem** involves deciding on which nodes provide coverage so that all areas are served. In other words, this problem involves deciding which nodes should be used to provide coverage to all areas with minimum cost or time requirements. As the number of locations increases, this can be a difficult problem to solve intuitively.

Consider the following problem from the telecommunication industry.

Example 7-4

A telecommunication company is considering expanding its cable and Internet service operations into a new area. The area is divided into 10 neighborhoods. The company is considering 7 location nodes to reach all 10 neighborhoods. Of course, it costs a significant amount of money to open a node or make a node operational. The company would like to minimize total cost but at the same time reach all of the neighborhoods. The cost of opening a node differs based on the characteristics of the land and the technical aspects of setting up a node.

The costs of opening seven nodes are as follows:

Node 1	Node 2	Node 3	Node 4	Node 5	Node 6	Node 7
125	85	70	60	90	100	110

The seven nodes can reach or provide Internet/cable coverage to the following areas:

Node 1   Neighborhoods 1, 3, 4, 6, 9, 10
Node 2   Neighborhoods 2, 4, 6, 8
Node 3   Neighborhoods 1, 2, 5
Node 4   Neighborhoods 3, 6, 7, 10
Node 5   Neighborhoods 2, 3, 7, 9
Node 6   Neighborhoods 4, 5, 8, 10
Node 7   Neighborhoods 1, 5, 7, 8, 9

Determine which nodes should be opened to provide coverage to all neighborhoods at a minimum cost.

Solution
This set covering problem can be formulated as 0–1 integer programming problem. We first start by defining the decision variables:

Let $x_j = 1$ if node j provides service

$x_j = 0$ if node j does not provide service

c_j = cost of opening or setting up node j.

The objective function involves minimization of total cost and can be stated as follows:

minimize $Z = 125x_1 + 85x_2 + 70x_3 + 60x_4 + 90x_5 + 100x_6 + 110x_7$

This objective function is subject to constraints that ensure that Internet and cable service are provided to all areas. Therefore, we need a constraint for each area.

For example, neighborhood 1 is covered by nodes 1, 3, and 7; therefore, in order for neighborhood 1 to be covered, at least one of these three nodes must be operational. Therefore, we can set up the constraint for neighborhood 1 as a greater-than-or-equal-to 1 constraint: $x_1 + x_3 + x_7 \geq 1$. In other words, at least one of nodes 1, 3, or 7 must be open in order for neighborhood 1 to receive coverage. Setting up the constraints using similar logic for the other neighborhoods results in the following formulation:

minimize $Z = 125x_1 + 85x_2 + 70x_3 + 60x_4 + 90x_5 + 100x_6 + 110x_7$

subject to

$x_1 + x_3 + x_7 \geq 1$	(coverage of neighborhood 1)
$x_2 + x_3 + x_5 \geq 1$	(coverage of neighborhood 2)
$x_1 + x_4 + x_5 \geq 1$	(coverage of neighborhood 3)
$x_1 + x_2 + x_6 \geq 1$	(coverage of neighborhood 4)
$x_3 + x_6 + x_7 \geq 1$	(coverage of neighborhood 5)
$x_1 + x_2 + x_6 \geq 1$	(coverage of neighborhood 6)
$x_4 + x_5 + x_7 \geq 1$	(coverage of neighborhood 7)
$x_2 + x_6 + x_7 \geq 1$	(coverage of neighborhood 8)
$x_1 + x_5 + x_7 \geq 1$	(coverage of neighborhood 9)
$x_1 + x_4 + x_6 \geq 1$	(coverage of neighborhood 10)

$x_1, x_2, x_3, x_4, x_5, x_6, x_7 = 0 \text{ or } 1$

Excel Solution of the 0–1 (Set Covering) Problem

The formulation given above can be entered into a worksheet as shown in Exhibit 7-5. In Exhibit 7-5, all of the costs if node i is open are entered into cells C4 thorough I4 Coverage requirements for areas 1 through 10 are listed in rows 7 through 16. In each of these rows, column J, labeled as "Required," provides the right-hand side of the coverage requirement constraints. The Required column for all of these constraints is equal to 1. Column K, labeled as "Used," shows the left-hand side of the coverage requirements constraints. The formula for the left-hand side, shown in Exhibit 7-5, is "= SUMPRODUCT ($C$5:$I$5,C7:I7)," which is the sum of the products of the decision variables and the constraint coefficients on the left-hand side of each constraint. Cell B18 provides the objective function value, which is the minimum total cost for the problem. The formula for the total cost, "= SUMPRODUCT(C4:I4,C5:I5)" in cell B18, is shown in the formula bar in Exhibit 7-5; it is simply the cross-product of the respective decision variable values and the cost of opening the respective nodes. After all the data and the formulas are entered into the computer, choose **Tools | Solver**; the screen displayed in Exhibit 7-6 appears. In Exhibit 7-6, we illustrate parameter specification associated with this 0–1 integer programming problem. In Exhibit 7-5, the objective function is specified

Exhibit 7-5 Worksheet for the 0–1 Integer Programming Set Covering Problem

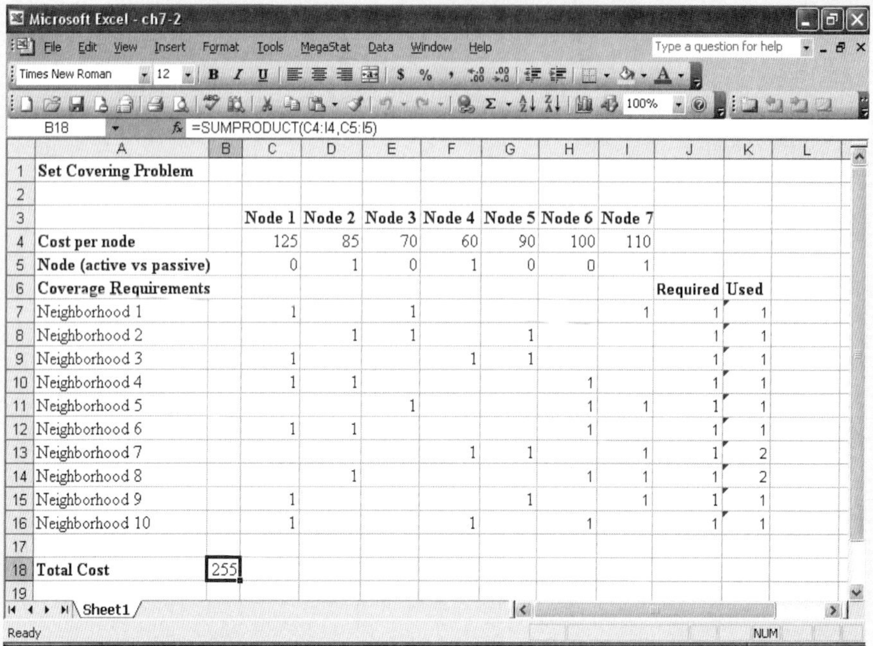

	A	B	C	D	E	F	G	H	I	J	K	L
1	Set Covering Problem											
2												
3			Node 1	Node 2	Node 3	Node 4	Node 5	Node 6	Node 7			
4	Cost per node		125	85	70	60	90	100	110			
5	Node (active vs passive)		0	1	0	1	0	0	1			
6	Coverage Requirements									Required	Used	
7	Neighborhood 1		1		1					1	1	
8	Neighborhood 2			1	1		1			1	1	
9	Neighborhood 3		1			1	1			1	1	
10	Neighborhood 4		1	1				1		1	1	
11	Neighborhood 5				1			1	1	1	1	
12	Neighborhood 6		1	1				1		1	1	
13	Neighborhood 7					1	1		1	1	2	
14	Neighborhood 8			1				1	1	1	2	
15	Neighborhood 9		1				1		1	1	1	
16	Neighborhood 10		1			1		1		1	1	
17												
18	Total Cost	255										
19												

B18 ▾ fx =SUMPRODUCT(C4:I4,C5:I5)

Cell	Copied to	Formula
B18		= SUMPRODUCT (C4 : I4, C5 : I5)
K7	K8 : K16	= SUMPRODUCT ($C$5 : $I$5, C7 : I7)

Exhibit 7-6 Solver Parameters Screen for the Set Covering Problem

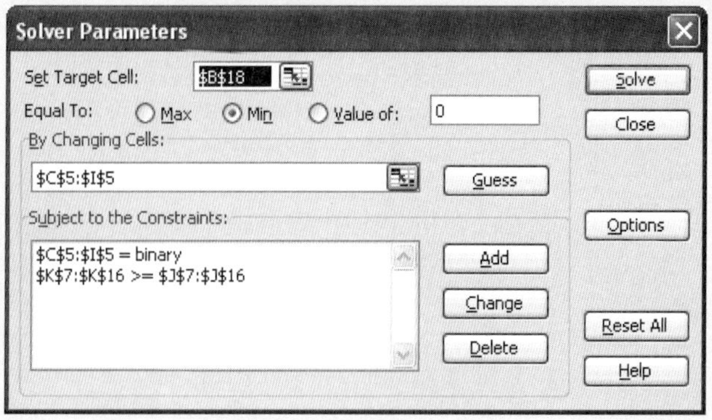

Solver Parameters

Set Target Cell: $B$18

Equal To: ○ Max ● Min ○ Value of: 0

By Changing Cells:

$C$5:$I$5

Subject to the Constraints:

$C$5:$I$5 = binary
$K$7:$K$16 >= $J$7:$J$16

Solve
Close
Guess
Options
Add
Change
Delete
Reset All
Help

Exhibit 7-7   Binary Requirement Specification

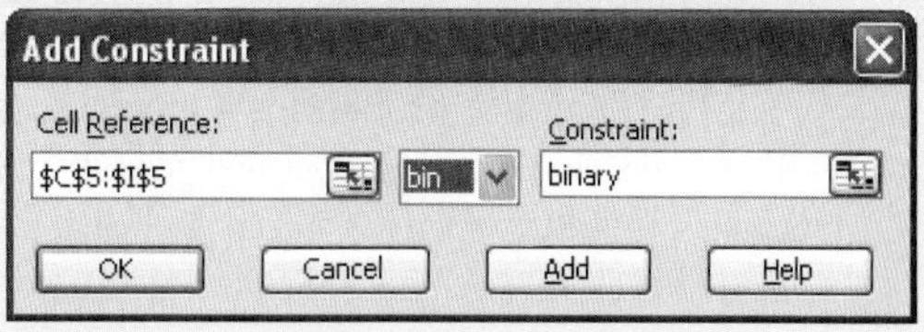

in cell B18; we specify this in the Set Target Cell box in Exhibit 7-6. The decision variables are located in cells C5 through I5 and are specified in the By Changing Cells box in Exhibit 7-6. The 10 coverage constraints are all greater-than-or equal-to types and are specified in aggregate in Exhibit 7-6 as \$K\$7:\$K\$16>=\$J\$7:\$J\$16. The left-hand side of the inequality (\$K\$7:\$K\$16) is stated in the column labeled "Used" and the right-hand side of the inequality (\$J\$7:\$J\$16) is stated under the column labeled "Required" in Exhibit 7-5.

The 0–1 integer requirement distinguishes this problem from other noninteger or pure-integer linear programming problems. In order to solve this problem as a 0–1 integer programming problem using Excel, we need to specify that decision variables may only assume 0–1 or binary integer values. To do that, we click on Add in Exhibit 7-6; this displays the screen shown in Exhibit 7-7. On the left side of the screen in the Cell Reference box, we simply specify the location of the decision variables in Exhibit 7-5 (\$C\$5:\$I\$5). The middle of screen displayed in Exhibit 7-7 shows the sign or the variable type requirements of the constraint. When we click on the down arrow and choose "bin," the word "binary" shows up on the right-hand side of the screen in the Constraint box; after we click OK, we see \$C\$5:\$I\$5 = binary in the Subject to the Constraints box in Exhibit 7-6. The above specification ensures that all the variables are 0–1, or binary, variables. This concludes parameter specification of the set covering problem. After clicking on the Solve button, the solution given in Exhibit 7-5 is displayed. Before clicking on the Solve button in Exhibit 7-6, the values of the decision variables in Exhibit 7-5 were equal to zero. After clicking the Solve button in Exhibit 7-6, the Solver Results screen of Exhibit 7-4 will appear. A more detailed answer report could be obtained by clicking on answer in the Reports box on the right-hand side of the Solver Results screen.

The solution to this set covering problem can be summarized as follows:

$x_2 = 1$ (open Node 2)
$x_4 = 1$ (open Node 4)
$x_7 = 1$ (open Node 7)
$z = \$255$ (minimum cost to serve the 10 neighborhoods)

The set covering problem can be expanded to accommodate situations where certain neighborhoods need additional coverage or coverage by more than one node due to the high volume of business in that neighborhood. For instance, there might be a need for at least two nodes to provide coverage for neighborhood 1; therefore, constraint 1 may read as

$x_1 + x_3 + x_7 \geq 2$ (coverage of neighborhood 1)

Knapsack Problem

The **knapsack problem** is defined as how many units of each different kind of item or product to put in a knapsack with a given capacity in order to maximize profit. This general basic framework of the knapsack problem is the foundation for many different types of resource allocation problems.

The knapsack problem is a special case of integer linear programming problems where the objective function is a linear maximization function with all positive profit coefficients and a single less-than-or-equal-to linear constraint with all positive constraint coefficients.

Therefore, the general form of the knapsack problem can be stated as

maximize: $Z = c_1x_1 + c_2x_2 + \cdots + c_nx_n$

subject to

$a_1x_1 + a_2x_2 + \cdots + a_nx_n \leq B$
$x_i \geq 0$ and integer, for all $i = 1, 2, 3, \ldots, n$

where

x_i = number of units of product i
c_i = profit (objective function coefficient) per unit of product i
a_i = weight of one unit of product i
B = total capacity
n = number of different products (product types)

Example 7-5

Tri-State Food Corporation is a food wholesale company that sells various food items to restaurants, hospitals, and the military. One of the superfreezers for this food wholesaler has five tons of capacity remaining. Tri-State has three possible major food items that it wants to store in the superfreezer: beef, poultry, and ice cream. In order to realize the desired quantity discounts, Tri-State must purchase the food items in batches. One batch (purchase quantity) of poultry weighs two tons, one batch of beef weighs three tons, and one batch of ice cream weighs one ton. The batch weights and the average profit value per batch for each food item are summarized in Table 7-2:

Table 7-2 Batch Weights and Profit Per Batch

Food Type	Batch Weight (tons)	Profit per Batch ($1,000s)
Poultry	2	$90
Beef	3	$150
Ice cream	1	$30

a. Formulate this problem as a knapsack problem.
b. Determine the optimal number of batches of each type of food item that Tri-State should purchase and store in its superfreezer in order to maximize total profit using the dynamic programming solution approach.

Solution

a. maximize $Z = 90x_1 + 150x_2 + 30x_3$

subject to

$2x_1 + 3x_2 + x_3 \leq 5$
$x_1, x_2, x_3 \geq 0$ and integer

b. Solving this problem using Excel, we reach the following optimal solution (the Excel solution and worksheet to this problem are not given to reduce redundancy of Excel worksheets within the chapter, but rather they are included on the CD-ROM):

$x_1 = 1$ (number of batches of poultry stored)
$x_2 = 1$ (number of batches of beef stored)
$Z = \$240$ (optimal profit)

The knapsack problem has many applications in the real world. The cargo-loading problem faced by transportation companies is a typical application of the knapsack problem. Even though it may seem easy to solve, the knapsack problem can be computationally burdensome if there are a large number of products involved. The number of possible solutions with n items (products) is 2^n. For instance, a problem with 3 items ($n = 3$) has $2 \times 2 \times 2 = 8$ possible solutions. A problem with 4 items has $2 \times 2 \times 2 \times 2 = 16$ possible solutions. A problem with 8 items has 256 possible solutions. However, a problem with 16 items has 65,536 solutions.

Facility Location Problem

In Chapter 6, we discussed the transportation problem and we learned about how to solve the facility location problem using the transportation method when there were two choices and capacity was not an issue. However, the location problem can be more complicated. Instead of considering just two competing locations, we may have to consider numerous new locations at a given point in time. In addition, we may have to take capacity into consideration. In situations like this, we cannot utilize the transportation method because it does not result in a feasible solution. However, utilizing 0–1 mixed-integer programming problem formulation can assist in finding a feasible and an optimal solution to the multiple **facility location problem.** There are many applications of the 0–1 mixed-integer programming formulation of the multiple facility location problem. They include location of plants, hospitals, health care facilities, fast food restaurants, schools, police, and fire stations.

In order to better understand this type of problem, let's examine the following example.

Example 7-6

Monson and Robinson Manufacturing Company is going through a major expansion. It is in need of adding a few manufacturing plants. At the present time, it has two plants, one in Dearborn, Michigan, and the other in Minneapolis, Minnesota. The capacities of these plants are roughly 26,000 units per year in Dearborn and 30,000 units per year in Minneapolis. The company sells exclusively through its retail outlet stores located in Milwaukee, Wisconsin; Chicago, Illinois; Cleveland, Ohio; and Cincinnati, Ohio. The demand for the product at these retail outlet facilities is as follows:

- Milwaukee, Wisconsin: 27,000 units per year
- Chicago, Illinois: 32,000 units per year
- Cleveland, Ohio: 23,000 units per year
- Cincinnati, Ohio: 30,000 units per year.

The company is in the process of considering four new manufacturing plant locations. The locations, their capacities, and the cost of purchasing or building the facility are stated in Table 7-3:

Table 7-3   Capacities and Purchase Cost of Proposed Facilities

Manufacturing Facility	Capacity (units per year)	Building/Purchasing Cost
Akron, Ohio	30,000	$220,000
Indianapolis, Indiana	33,000	$260,000
Toledo, Ohio	26,000	$200,000
Ft. Wayne, Indiana	37,000	$280,000

Even though the unit manufacturing cost in each of these plants is comparable, the unit shipping costs from the existing and the proposed plants to the retail outlets are given in Table 7-4.

Table 7-4   Per Unit Shipping Costs

Plant\Outlet	Milwaukee (1)	Chicago (2)	Cleveland (3)	Cincinnati (4)
Dearborn (1)	7	5	4.5	5.5
Minneapolis (2)	5	7	12	11
Akron (3)	9	6.5	2	3.5
Indianapolis (4)	6	3.5	5	3
Toledo (5)	8	6	2.5	4
Ft. Wayne (6)	6.5	4.5	5	3

The objective of the Monson and Robinson Manufacturing Company is to minimize the total cost, which consists of shipping cost and the building/purchasing cost, such that demand at all retail outlets is satisfied. Determine the optimal shipping schedule that minimizes the total cost. Which locations should be used to build the new plants?

Solution

We will begin formulating this problem by defining the decision variables. There are two types of decision variables. The first type is the type we have utilized in formulating the transportation and transshipment problems in Chapter 6. The definitions associated with that type of variable and the transportation problem presented in Chapter 6 are given below:

Let x_{ij} = number of units shipped from source i to destination j
$\quad c_{ij}$ = cost of shipping one unit from source i to destination j
$\quad m$ = number of sources of supply
$\quad k$ = number of proposed sources of supply
$\quad n$ = number of destinations
$\quad S_i$ = supply available at source i
$\quad D_j$ = demand at destination j

The second type of decision variable is a 0–1 integer variable that will indicate whether a plant is constructed in location i. In other words

Let $y_i = 1$ if a plant is constructed in proposed plant location i
$\quad y_i = 0$ if a plant is not constructed in proposed plant location i

In addition,

Let p_i = cost of constructing or purchasing plant i

The following is the general formulation of the facility location mixed-integer linear programming problem:

$$\text{minimize } Z = \sum_{i=1}^{n} \sum_{j=1}^{n} C_{ij} x_{ij} + \sum_{i=1}^{n} p_i y_i$$

subject to

$$\sum_{j=1}^{n} x_{ij} \leq S_i \quad i = 1, 2, \ldots, m$$

$$\sum_{j=1}^{n} x_{ij} \leq S_i y_i \quad i = 1, 2, \ldots, k$$

$$\sum_{i=1}^{n} x_{ij} = D_j \quad j = 1, 2, \ldots, n$$

$x_{ij} \geq$ for all i and j
$y_i = 0$ or 1

Based on the above notation, the formulation for the Monson and Robinson Manufacturing Company problem is as follows:

Minimize $Z = 7x_{11} + 5x_{12} + 4.5x_{13} + 5.5x_{14} + 5x_{21} + 7x_{22} + 12x_{23} + 11x_{24} + 9x_{31} +$
$6.5x_{32} + 2x_{33} + 3.5x_{34} + 6x_{41} + 3.5x_{42} + 5x_{43} + 3x_{44} + 8x_{51} + 6x_{52} +$
$2.5x_{53} + 4x_{54} + 6.5x_{61} + 4.5x_{62} + 5x_{63} + 3x_{64} + 220{,}000y_1 +$
$260{,}000y_2 + 200{,}000y_3 + 280{,}000y_4$

Subject to

$x_{11} + x_{12} + x_{13} + x_{14}$	$\leq 26{,}000$	(1)
$x_{21} + x_{22} + x_{23} + x_{24}$	$\leq 30{,}000$	(2)
$x_{31} + x_{32} + x_{33} + x_{34}$	$\leq 30{,}000y_1$	(3)
$x_{41} + x_{42} + x_{43} + x_{44}$	$\leq 33{,}000y_2$	(4)
$x_{51} + x_{52} + x_{53} + x_{44}$	$\leq 26{,}000y_3$	(5)
$x_{61} + x_{62} + x_{63} + x_{64}$	$\leq 37{,}000y_4$	(6)
$x_{11} + x_{21} + x_{31} + x_{41} + x_{51} + x_{61}$	$= 27{,}000$	(7)
$x_{12} + x_{22} + x_{32} + x_{42} + x_{52} + x_{62}$	$= 32{,}000$	(8)
$x_{13} + x_{23} + x_{33} + x_{43} + x_{53} + x_{63}$	$= 23{,}000$	(9)
$x_{14} + x_{24} + x_{34} + x_{44} + x_{54} + x_{64}$	$= 30{,}000$	(10)

$x_{ij} \geq$ for all i and j
$y_i = 0$ or 1

In the above formulation, the value of $4.5x_{13}$ in the objective function shows that cost of shipping one unit from source 1 (Dearborn, Michigan) to destination 3 (Cleveland, Ohio) is $4.50. Note that 0–1 variables (y_i, s_i) are included in the objective function. For instance, $220{,}000y_1$ indicates that if $y_1 = 1$, we will build or purchase a plant in Akron, Ohio, and the cost of building/purchasing that plant will be $220{,}000 C_{si}. However, if the value of y_1 is zero, which means that we will not build/purchase a facility in Akron, Ohio, we will not incur the cost of $220{,}000 because $220{,}000 will be multiplied by zero. Constraints 3, 4, 5, and 6 will only become operational if we decide to build a plant in the proposed location. For example, if we decide to build/purchase a plant in Akron, Ohio, the value of $y_1 = 1$ and the right-hand side of the inequality will be multiplied by 1, making Akron's production facility operational. However, if we choose not to build/purchase a facility in Akron, Ohio, the value of $y_1 = 0$ and the right-hand side of the third constraint inequality will be multiplied by 0, making Akron's production facility nonoperational.

The Excel solution and worksheet to this problem are not given to reduce redundancy of Excel worksheets within the chapter, but rather they are included on the CD-ROM.

$x_{12} = 26,000$	(number of units shipped from Dearborn to Chicago)
$x_{21} = 27,000$	(number of units shipped from Minneapolis to Milwaukee)
$x_{22} = 3,000$	(number of units shipped from Minneapolis to Chicago)
$x_{34} = 30,000$	(number of units shipped from Akron to Cincinnati)
$x_{52} = 3,000$	(number of units shipped from Toledo to Chicago)
$x_{53} = 23,000$	(number of units shipped from Toledo to Cleveland)
$y_1 = 1$	(build a production facility in Akron, Ohio)
$y_3 = 1$	(build a production facility in Toledo, Ohio)
$Z = \$886,500$	(total minimum cost of shipping and building the new facilities)

Traveling Salesperson Problem

In solving the **traveling salesperson problem,** we try to minimize total cost, distance, or time of departing location i and returning to the same location i in a tour, visiting all locations once. The decision variable is a 0–1 variable and the value of the variable is equal to 1 if we travel from location i to location j. Otherwise the value of the decision variable is equal to zero. The integer programming formulation of the traveling salesperson problem is similar to the formulation of the transportation problem. However, complete formulation of the traveling salesperson problem is relatively complicated, but we can begin to provide a simplified formulation of this problem in its simplest form.

$$\text{minimize } Z = \sum_{i=1}^{n} \sum_{j=1}^{n} C_{ij} X_{ij}$$

subject to

$$\sum_{j=1}^{n} x_{ij} = 1 \quad i = 1, 2, \ldots, n, i \neq j \tag{7-1}$$

A tour (visiting each city once) must be formed and a tour must start in all cities.

$$\sum_{j=1}^{n} x_{ij} = 1 \quad j = 1, 2, \ldots, n, i \neq j \tag{7-2}$$

A tour (visiting each city once) must be formed and a tour must arrive at all cities.

$x_{ij} = 0 \text{ or } 1$

Let's add another subscript k, which represents the leg of the tour. The subscript k is added to assist in the formulation of the traveling salesperson problem. If there are four locations, then there are four legs of the trip. If node 1 is the home location, one possible routing scheme would involve going from node 1 to node 2 during the first leg, node 2 to node 3 during the second leg, node 3 to node 4 during the third leg, and node 4 to node 1 during the fourth and final leg. In other words, x_{ijk} stands for a trip from location i to location j in leg k. We also can specify the beginning and ending nodes. For example, the beginning node is node 1 on a four-node network, $i = 1$. The following set of constraints will guarantee that not only each node is visited only once, but the tour must start and end at node 1.

$$\sum_{j=2}^{n} x_{1j1} = 1 \qquad i \neq j \tag{7-3}$$

The constraint given above ensures that the tour starts in node 1. This results in the following constraint for our four-node example:

$x_{121} + x_{131} + x_{141} = 1$ (leg 1 visits are limited to 1)

The constraint given below stipulates that the trip must end in node 1 in leg n.

$$\sum_{i=2}^{n} x_{i1n} = 1 \qquad i \neq j \tag{7-4}$$

The constraint given above ensures that the tour ends at node 1 at leg n (the last leg of the tour). This results in the following constraint for our four-node example:

$x_{214} + x_{314} + x_{414} = 1$ (leg 4 visits are limited to 1)

The constraint given in Equations 7-1 and 7-2 can be revised as follows:

$$\sum_{i=2}^{n} \sum_{j=2}^{n} x_{ijk} = 1 \qquad \text{for } k = 2, \ldots, n - 1; i \neq j \tag{7-5}$$

The constraints given above in Equation 7-5 ensure that we visit each node once in the tour after the first leg. Note that summations start at node 2 in leg 2 and end in node $n - 1$ because traveling from node 1 is already specified in leg 1 in Equation 7-3 and traveling to node 1 in leg n is specified in Equation 7-4. For our four-node example, the constraint given in Equation 7-5 can be stated as follows:

$x_{232} + x_{242} + x_{322} + x_{342} + x_{422} + x_{432} = 1$ (leg 2 visits are limited to 1)
$x_{233} + x_{243} + x_{323} + x_{343} + x_{423} + x_{433} = 1$ (leg 3 visits are limited to 1)

$$\sum_{j=1}^{n} \sum_{k=2}^{n} x_{ijk} = 1 \qquad \text{for } i = 2, \ldots, n; i \neq j \tag{7-6}$$

if $j = 1, k = n$ or if $k = n, j = 1$

The constraints specified in Equation 7-6 guarantee that there is exactly one departure from each of the nodes. For our four-node example, let's assume that $i = 2$. The constraint in Equation 7-6 would be written as follows:

$x_{214} + x_{232} + x_{242} + x_{233} + x_{243} = 1$ (visits from node 2 are limited to 1)

$$\sum_{i=1}^{n} \sum_{k=1}^{n-1} x_{ijk} = 1 \qquad \text{for } j = 2, \ldots, n; i \neq j \tag{7-7}$$

if $i = 1, k = 1$ or if $k = 1, i = 1$

The constraints specified in Equation 7-7 guarantee that there is exactly one arrival at each of the nodes. For our four-node example, let's assume that $j = 2$. The constraint in Equation 7-7 would be written as follows:

$x_{121} + x_{322} + x_{422} + x_{323} + x_{423} = 1$ (visits to node 2 are limited to 1)

$$x_{1j1} = \sum_{k=2}^{n} x_{jk2} \quad \text{for } j = 2, \ldots, n; j \neq k \tag{7-8}$$

Equation 7-8 ensures that if leg 1 of the trip ends at location j, then leg 2 of the trip starts at location j. For our four-node example, if we assume that $j = 2$, the formula in Equation 7-8 can be written as follows: $x_{121} = x_{232} + x_{242}$.

$$\sum_{i=2}^{n} x_{ijk} = \sum_{l=2}^{n} x_{jm(k+1)} \quad \text{for } j = 2, \ldots, n; k = 2, i \neq j, j \neq m \tag{7-9}$$

Equation 7-9 ensures that if leg k of the trip ends at location j, then leg $k + 1$ of the trip starts at location j. For our four-node example, if we assume that $j = 2$ and $k = 2$, then the formula in Equation 7-9 can be written as follows: $x_{322} + x_{422} = x_{233} + x_{243}$

$$\sum_{k=2}^{n} x_{kj(n-1)} = x_{j1n} \quad \text{for } j = 2, \ldots, n; j \neq k \tag{7-10}$$

Equation 7-10 ensures that if leg $n - 1$ of the trip ends at location j, then the last leg of the trip starts at location j and ends at location 1 to complete the tour. For our four-node example, if we assume that $j = 2$, the formula in Equation 7-10 can be written as follows: $x_{323} + x_{423} = x_{214}$

The constraints 7-8, 7-9, and 7-10 are prepared to prevent subtours from occurring. A subtour is a premature return to the initial city in the tour. For example, in an eight-city problem, if we do not include the constraints 7-8, 7-9, and 7-10, it is possible that two subtours may form. The first subtour may consist of the following sequence of cities: 1–4–3–5–1. The second subtour may consist of the remaining cities in the following sequence: 2–7–6–8–2. The constraints 7-8, 7-9, and 7-10 will prevent these subtours from occurring and force the solution to include only one tour, starting at the home city and ending at the home city while visiting each city once. The traveling salesperson problem has numerous applications in the business world ranging from scheduling vehicles and truck routing to production scheduling.

We have two versions of the traveling salesperson problem. The first version assumes that the travel time from location A to location B is the same as the travel time from location B to location A. This version is referred to as a symmetric traveling salesperson problem. In the second version, travel time from location A to location B is not the same as the travel time from location B to location A. This version is referred to as an asymmetric traveling salesperson problem. Solving the traveling salesperson problem can be extremely computationally burdensome. In the symmetric version, there are $(n - 1)!$ possible routes to consider, where $n =$ number of decision variables. For example if we solve an 11-location traveling salesperson problem, $n = 11$ and there are 10! possible routes (10! $= 3,628,800$). Of course, if we add one more location, 11! $= 39,916,800$. In other words, just by adding one more location, the number of possible solutions increases by 36,288,000. Because of the extreme computational burden, using integer linear programming to solve a traveling salesperson problem is not a viable option. There are a number of heuristics developed to deal with the computational burden of the Traveling Salesperson Problem. A simple heuristic is the **nearest-neighbor rule,** where a tour is started at a particular location and we simply go to the nearest location from that location. From there, we go to the nearest location that has not been visited. We continue in this fashion until all the locations are visited. However, even though we can reach a solution relatively fast, solution quality of the nearest-neighbor method leaves a lot to be desired.

Let's consider the following example to demonstrate the formulation of a traveling salesperson problem.

Example 7-7

The City of Elmhurst garbage collection team wants to determine the best route for their garbage trucks. There are four sections of the city under consideration. The time of travel (in minutes) between the various sections of the city is given in Table 7-5.

Table 7-5   Travel Time (in minutes) Between Locations

From\To	1	2	3	4
1	0	8	6	5
2	8	0	3	7
3	6	3	0	9
4	5	7	9	0

a.   If location 1 is the garage from which garbage trucks leave and to which they return, formulate this problem as a traveling salesperson problem.

b.   Solve this problem using Excel.

Solution

The objective function can be stated as follows:

$$\text{minimize } Z = 8x_{121} + 6x_{131} + 5x_{141} + 8x_{214} + 6x_{314} + 5x_{414} + 3x_{232} + 3x_{233} + 7x_{242} + 7x_{243} + 9x_{342} + 9x_{343} + 7x_{422} + 7x_{423} + 9x_{432} + 9x_{433} + 3x_{322} + 3x_{323}$$

subject to

$$x_{121} + x_{131} + x_{141} = 1 \qquad \text{(starting node is node 1)}$$
$$x_{214} + x_{314} + x_{414} = 1 \qquad \text{(ending node is node 1)}$$

$$x_{232} + x_{242} + x_{342} + x_{422} + x_{322} + x_{432} = 1 \qquad \text{(leg 2 visits limited to 1)}$$
$$x_{233} + x_{243} + x_{343} + x_{423} + x_{323} + x_{433} = 1 \qquad \text{(leg 3 visits limited to 1)}$$

$$\left.\begin{array}{l} x_{214} + x_{232} + x_{242} + x_{233} + x_{243} = 1 \\ x_{314} + x_{322} + x_{323} + x_{342} + x_{343} = 1 \\ x_{414} + x_{422} + x_{432} + x_{423} + x_{433} = 1 \end{array}\right\}$$ (visits from nodes 2, 3, and 4 are limited to 1)

$$\left.\begin{array}{l} x_{121} + x_{322} + x_{422} + x_{323} + x_{423} = 1 \\ x_{131} + x_{232} + x_{233} + x_{432} + x_{433} = 1 \\ x_{141} + x_{242} + x_{243} + x_{342} + x_{343} = 1 \end{array}\right\}$$ (visits to nodes 2, 3, and 4 are limited to 1)

$$\left.\begin{array}{l} x_{121} = x_{232} + x_{242} \\ x_{131} = x_{322} + x_{342} \\ x_{141} = x_{422} + x_{432} \end{array}\right\}$$ (leg 1 of the tour ends and leg 2 of the tour starts where leg 1 of the tour ends)

$$\left.\begin{array}{l} x_{322} + x_{422} = x_{233} + x_{243} \\ x_{232} + x_{432} = x_{323} + x_{343} \\ x_{242} + x_{342} = x_{423} + x_{433} \end{array}\right\}$$ (if leg 2 of the trip ends at location 2, 3, or 4, leg 3 of the trip must start at node 2, 3, or 4, respectively; the first equation is for node 2, the second equation is for node 3, and the third equation is for node 4)

$$\left.\begin{array}{l} x_{323} + x_{423} = x_{214} \\ x_{233} + x_{433} = x_{314} \\ x_{243} + x_{343} = x_{414} \end{array}\right\}$$ (last leg of the trip must end at location 1)

All $x_{ijk} = 0$ or 1

There are two optimal solutions.

1. $x_{141} = 1$, $x_{422} = 1$, $x_{233} = 1$, $x_{314} = 1$, $z = 21$ minutes
   An optimal sequence is 1–4–2–3–1 or
2. $x_{131} = 1$, $x_{322} = 1$, $x_{243} = 1$, $x_{414} = 1$, $z = 21$ minutes
   An optimal sequence is 1–3–2–4–1

Solving Traveling Salesperson Problem Using Excel

Although it is cumbersome, the traveling salesperson problem can be solved using Excel. Exhibit 7-8 shows the worksheet for the traveling salesperson problem of Example 7-7. In row 2 of the worksheet, all of the decision variables are defined. In row 3 the appropriate distances are specified. Row 4 displays the values associated with all of the decision variables. Row 5 is simply the multiplication of row 3 (distances) and row 4 (value of the decision variable, either zero or one). We are trying to minimize the value of cell T5 subject to all of the constraints listed in rows 7

Exhibit 7-8 Excel Worksheet for Example 7-7 (Traveling Salesperson Problem)

	A	B	C	D	E	F	G	H	I	J	K	L	M	N	O	P	Q	R	S	T	U
1	Elmhurst Garbage Collection				Traveling Salesman Problem																
2		x121	x131	x141	x214	x314	x414	x232	x233	x242	x243	x342	x343	x422	x423	x432	x433	x322	x323		
3	Travel Time	8	6	5	8	6	5	3	3	7	7	9	9	7	7	9	9	3	3		
4	Route Traveled	0	0	1	0	1	0	0	1	0	0	0	0	1	0	0	0	0	0	Total	
5	Travel Time	0	0	5	0	6	0	0	3	0	0	0	0	7	0	0	0	0	0	21	
6		x121	x131	x141	x214	x314	x414	x232	x233	x242	x243	x342	x343	x422	x423	x432	x433	x322	x323	Usage	Limits
7	Starting Node 1	1	1	1																1	1
8	Ending Node 1				1	1	1													1	1
9	Leg 2 visits limit = 1							1		1		1		1		1		1		1	1
10	Leg 3 visits limit = 1								1		1		1		1		1		1	1	1
11	Visits from Node 2 limit = 1				1			1	1	1	1									1	1
12	Visits from Node 3 limit = 1					1						1	1			1	1			1	1
13	Visits from Node 4 limit = 1						1							1	1	1	1			1	1
14	Visits to Node 2 limited to 1	1												1	1			1	1	1	1
15	Visits to Node 3 limited to 1		1					1	1					1	1					1	1
16	Visits to Node 4 limited to 1			1						1	1	1	1							1	1
17	End of Leg 1 = Start of Leg 2	1				-1		-1												0	0
18	End of Leg 1 = Start of Leg 2		1									-1					-1			0	0
19	End of Leg 1 = Start of Leg 2			1										-1	-1					0	0
20	End of Leg 2 = Start of Leg 3							-1		-1				1				1		0	0
21	End of Leg 2 = Start of Leg 3								1			-1			1				-1	0	0
22	End of Leg 2 = Start of Leg 3									1	1		-1		-1					0	0
23	Last Leg ends at Location 1			-1											1			1		0	0
24	Last Leg ends at Location 1				-1		1									1				0	0
25	Last Leg ends at Location 1					-1						1	1							0	0

Cell	Copied to	Formula
B5	C5 : S5	= B3 * B4
T5		= SUM (B5 : S5)
T7	T8 : T25	= SUMPRODUCT ($B$4 : $S$4, B7 : S7)

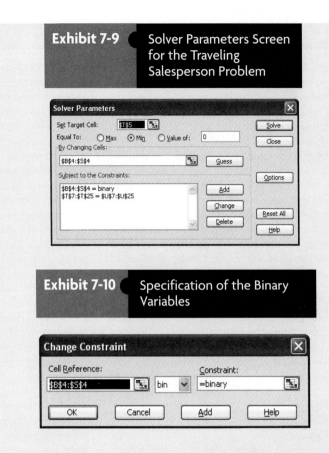

Exhibit 7-9 Solver Parameters Screen for the Traveling Salesperson Problem

Exhibit 7-10 Specification of the Binary Variables

through 25. Column T represents the left-hand side of the constraints, and column U represents the right-hand side of the constraints.

Once the worksheet in Exhibit 7-8 is prepared, we choose **Tools I Solver;** the screen displayed in Exhibit 7-9 appears. In Exhibit 7-9, we illustrate parameter specification associated with this traveling salesperson problem. In Exhibit 7-8, the objective function is specified in cell T5, and we specify this in the "Set Target Cell" box in Exhibit 7-9. The decision variables are located in cells B4 through $4 and are specified in the "By Changing Cells" box in Exhibit 7-9. The 19 constraints are all equal-to types and are specified in aggregate in Exhibit 7-9 as follows: $T$7:$T$25 = $U$7:$U$25. In Exhibit 7-10, we also specify each variable as binary; the binary variables are shown in Exhibit 7-9 as $B$4:$S$4 = binary. After clicking the Solve button, the results in Exhibit 7-8 will appear.

◼◼ Difficulties in Solving Integer Programming Problems

From our previous discussion of integer programming problems and linear programming problems, the integer programming problems may seem easy to solve. As was discussed in earlier chapters, the simplex method is very efficient in solving linear programming problems because we have relatively few extreme points to consider. In solving integer programming problems, we consider a finite number of integer solutions. We consider more feasible points in solving an integer linear programming problem compared to solving linear programming

---

General Motors (GM) designs and develops vehicles that meet corporate engineering standards and government regulations. In order to achieve attractive designs that meet the standards and regulations, GM tests samples of its completed vehicles under a wide range of conditions. One of the tests involving cold weather is done at the GM Cold Weather Development Center in Kapuskasing, Ontario. Vehicles that perform well in Kapuskasing will perform well anywhere since Kapuskasing is the coldest available environment available for testing. Testing takes place from November though April in the coldest temperatures Kapuskasing has to offer. During the testing season, the facility performs full vehicle road (durability) tests. Vehicles are evaluated over different distances as well as different road conditions, and data are collected about oil pressure, coolant temperatures, and battery condition. Engineers use this information to identify and resolve design issues. Since the testing season is limited and the severity of winter weather varies, it is important to maximize and even improve "throughput" (the number of vehicles tested) in this system.

The GM management at the facility schedules and executes all vehicle tests. Since the daily temperature determines what tests are possible, the staff develop a master testing schedule each day. In preparing the master schedule, variables the schedulers consider include vehicle test limits, soaking requirements, grouping policies, and driver break policies. Vehicle test limits are such that the facility can perform a maximum of three tests on any single vehicle per day. "Soaking requirements" is the time that a vehicle must be inactive for cooling off between tests. Vehicle grouping policy involves testing a group of vehicles together. Driver break policies means that the drivers must be provided with two short breaks and a lunch break per shift. The objective in scheduling is to take all these variables and constraints into account and then maximize the overall efficiency. This turns out to be a special case of the resource constrained project scheduling problem (RCPSP). GM developed a multipass heuristic and a decision support tool to implement the heuristic. The decision support tool consisted of a front-end-user interface and the scheduling module.

As a result of implementing this new scheduling approach, which involves an integer programming model, GM realized reduction in operation risk, improvement in throughput, a reduction in warranty costs, and improvement in employee relationships GM significantly reduced the time required to generate the master schedule. The company was able improve information accuracy by 192 percent and reduced waste test mileage by 96 percent. The improved scheduling resulted in 129 percent improvement in the total vehicle completion rate (percentage of vehicles that complete the required testing during the winter season). GM also realized 25 percent improvement in total test completion rate. It is estimated that the company saved millions of dollars in warranty costs as a result of timely correction of design issues revealed through the testing. The successful implementation of this system also helped worker–management relations as employee enthusiasm improved by 23 percent (as measured by employee surveys). In implementing this system, it is important to point out that there was significant support from GM top management, which helped to successfully execute the system.

Source: C. Hsu, Y. de Blois, and M. Pyle, "General Motors Optimizes Its Scheduling of Cold-Weather Tests," Interfaces 34, no. 5 (September–October 2004), pp. 334–41.

---

problems using the simplex method. However, while we consider a finite number of feasible solutions to an integer programming problem, as the number of variables increases, the numbers of possible solutions increase at an exponential rate. For instance, in solving 0–1 integer programming problems, if the number of decision variables is equal to n, we need to consider 2^n solutions. For a small-size problem with $n = 10$, there are $2^{10} = 1,024$ possible solutions. However, if $n = 20$, there are $2^{20} = 1,048,576$ solutions. Even with the advances in computer technology and the increasing speed of computer processing, the complete enumeration of all possible solutions is problematic for large 0–1 integer programming problems. Of course, the difficulty is compounded when we solve pure-integer programming problems that can take on any integer value as opposed to being restricted to the values of 0 and 1.

The second problem stems from the fact that integer linear programming problems do not have one set of extreme points to visit. For instance, if we use the branch and bound method (see Chapter 7 supplement on the CD-ROM), we need to visit a set of extreme points at each node. The set of extreme points visited at node 1 is different than the set of extreme points visited at node 2. Because of this characteristic, the computational requirements and solution of a linear programming problem are much easier than solving integer linear programming problems.

◤ Summary

Problems that lend themselves to a linear programming formulation are frequently encountered in practice. In many instances, some or all of the decision variables may also be required to be integer. In such cases, the goal is to identify the best solution that will meet the integer requirements. In general, the simplex method cannot be used to directly obtain integer solutions. Instead, an intelligent search procedure usually must be employed to identify an optimal solution. This involves the use of the branch and bound method. The branch and bound method creates subproblems to be solved. The subproblems are solved by successive application of the simplex method until an optimal solution is found.

An important class of integer programming problems involves situations in which decision variables can take on values of only 0 to 1, often synonymous with yes-no decisions. Large 0–1 integer programming problems are solved using the branch and bound method and small 0–1 integer programming problems can be solved using enumeration. The manual solution of the branch and bound and the enumeration methods are illustrated in the CD-ROM supplement to Chapter 7. The formulations of the 0-1 problems that involve either-or alternatives, k-Out-of-n alternatives, if-then alternatives are discussed and the formulation of the constraints for each situation is provided.

Using 0-1 integer programming, we can solve many specialized problems. These include: fixed charge problems, set covering problems, knapsack problems, facility location problems, traveling salesperson problems, as well as others. We utilize examples to illustrate the formulation of the aforementioned problems. However, the difficulty is not in the formulation of the model, but in finding an efficient solution to the model. Even with fast computers available today, many large size integer programming problems are difficult to solve by integer programming methods such as branch and bound. We hope that continued research would provide faster solution methods to solve integer programming problems.

◤ Glossary

Facility Location Problem   This mixed-integer programming problem involves providing service to multiple market areas by deciding on multiple facility locations. Demand is known at various markets and transportation costs are known from potential facilities to destinations. The location variable is a 0–1 variable. The value of the location variable is 1 if a certain location is selected, 0 if the location is not utilized.

Fixed-Charge Problem   A 0–1 mixed-integer programming problem that involves fixed costs (0–1 variable) if a certain activity is undertaken as well as a variable cost.

Knapsack Problem   This problem is defined as how many units of each different kind of item or product to put in a knapsack with a given capacity in order to maximize profit.

Mixed-Integer Problem   A problem that requires that some, but not all, decision variables will have integer or binary values.

Nearest-Neighbor Rule   A method of the traveling salesperson problem where a tour is started at a particular location and then goes to the nearest location. It then goes to the nearest location not yet visited, continuing until all locations have been visited.

Pure-Integer Problem   An integer programming problem requiring that all decision variables have integer values.

Set Covering Problem   It involves a number of nodes and a number of areas, where nodes provide coverage to the areas. This problem involves deciding which nodes should be used to provide coverage to all areas with minimum cost or time requirements.

Traveling Salesperson Problem   In solving this problem, we try to minimize total cost, distance, or time of departing location i and returning to the same location i in a tour, visiting all locations once. The decision variable is a 0–1 variable and the value of the variable is equal to 1 if we travel from location i to location j, and zero otherwise.

Zero–One (0–1) Integer Programming Problem An integer programming problem requiring that all decision variables have a value of either zero (0) or one (1).

Solved Problems

Problem 1

PPRS Construction Company has an opportunity to build five shopping malls during the next year. The expected net profit and expected cost for each of the shopping malls are shown in Table 7-6.

Table 7-6 The Expected Net Profit and Expected Net Cost

Shopping Mall	Expected Net Profit ($000)	Expected Cost ($000)
1	200	150
2	150	90
3	140	50
4	125	80
5	180	100

The company has budgeted $300,000 for the construction of shopping malls during the next year. Also, due to various legal restrictions and marketing considerations, the following relationships among the projects must be met.

1. Exactly one of three shopping malls 1, 2, and 5 must be constructed.
2. At most only one of the two shopping malls 1 and 4 may be constructed.
3. If shopping mall 4 is constructed, then shopping mall 5 also must be constructed.

a. Formulate this problem as an integer programming model and use Excel to determine the best set of shopping malls that PPRS Construction Company should build in order to maximize total net profit.

b. Assume that the top management for PPRS Construction Company has cut the budget for the shopping mall construction project to $225,000. Show the change in the formulation and use Excel to determine the best set of shopping malls that PPRS Construction Company should build in order to maximize total net profit.

Solution

a.

Let $x_i = 1$ if shopping mall i is selected
$x_i = 0$ if shopping mall i is not selected

maximize $Z = 200x_1 + 150x_2 + 140x_3 + 125x_4 + 180x_5$

subject to

$150x_1 + 90x_2 + 50x_3 + 80x_4 + 100x_5 \leq 300$	(1) (budget constraint)
$x_1 + x_2 + x_5 = 1$	(2)
$x_1 + x_4 \leq 1$	(3)
$x_4 \geq x_5$ or $x_4 - x_5 \geq 0$	(4)
$x_i = 0$ or 1	(5)

The Excel solution to this problem is depicted in Exhibit 7-11 and with the specifications given in Exhibits 7-12 and 7-13. The company should invest in malls 3, 4, and 5 for a total net profit of $445,000.

Exhibit 7-11   Excel Worksheet for Solved Problem 1, Part a (Shopping Mall Problem)

	A	B	C	D	E	F	G	H	I	J	K
1	**Variables**	X_1	X_2	X_3	X_4	X_5	**Shopping Mall Problem**				
2		0	0	1	1	1					
3		X_1	X_2	X_3	X_4	X_5					
4	Objective Function	200	150	140	125	180	445				
5	Constraints						Used	Available	Leftover		
6	Budget	150	90	50	80	100	230	300	70		
7	One Mall of 1, 2, 5	1	1			1	1	1	0		
8	At Most One of 1 & 4	1			1		1	1	0		
9	If 4 then 5				1	-1	0	0	0		

Cell G4: `=SUMPRODUCT(B4:F4,B2:F2)`

Worksheets: Solved Problem1 / Solved Problem 2

Cell	Copied to	Formula
G4		= SUMPRODUCT (B4 : F4, B2 : F2)
G6	G7 : G9	= SUMPRODUCT ($B$2 : $F$2, B6 : F6)
I6	I7 : I9	= H6 − G6

b.

Let $x_i = 1$ if shopping mall i is selected

$\quad\quad x_i = 0$ if shopping mall i is not selected

maximize $Z = 200x_1 + 150x_2 + 140x_3 + 125x_4 + 180x_5$

subject to

$$150x_1 + 90x_2 + 50x_3 + 80x_4 + 100x_5 \leq 225 \quad \text{(1) (budget constraint)}$$
$$x_1 + x_2 + x_5 = 1 \quad\quad\quad\quad\quad\quad\quad\quad\quad (2)$$
$$x_1 + x_4 \leq 1 \quad\quad\quad\quad\quad\quad\quad\quad\quad\quad\quad (3)$$
$$x_4 \geq x_5 \quad \text{or} \quad x_4 - x_5 \geq 0 \quad\quad\quad\quad\quad (4)$$
$$x_i = 0 \text{ or } 1 \quad\quad\quad\quad\quad\quad\quad\quad\quad\quad\quad (5)$$

After updating the problem by changing the right-hand side of the budget constraint, we obtain the following result, displayed in Exhibit 7-14. The company should invest in malls 2, 3, and 4 for a total net profit of $415,000

Problem 2

A cargo plane is contracted to transport heavy machinery from Cleveland to Los Angeles. The plane has a cargo capacity of eight tons. The company that contracted this cargo plane wants to transport four types of machinery. The weights and values of the four types of machinery are given in Table 7-7.

Exhibit 7-12 Solver Parameters Screen for Solved Problem 1 (Shopping Mall Problem)

Exhibit 7-13 Specification of the Binary Variables

Exhibit 7-14 Excel Worksheet for Solved Problem 1, Part b (Shopping Mall Problem)

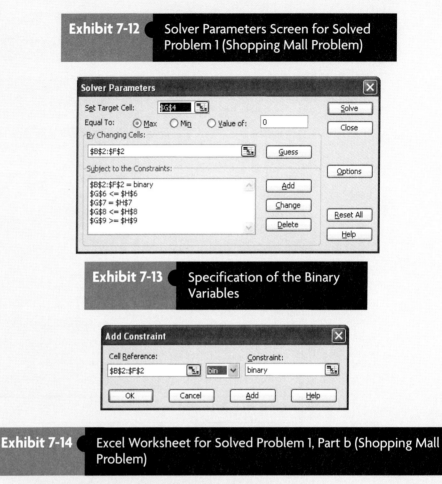

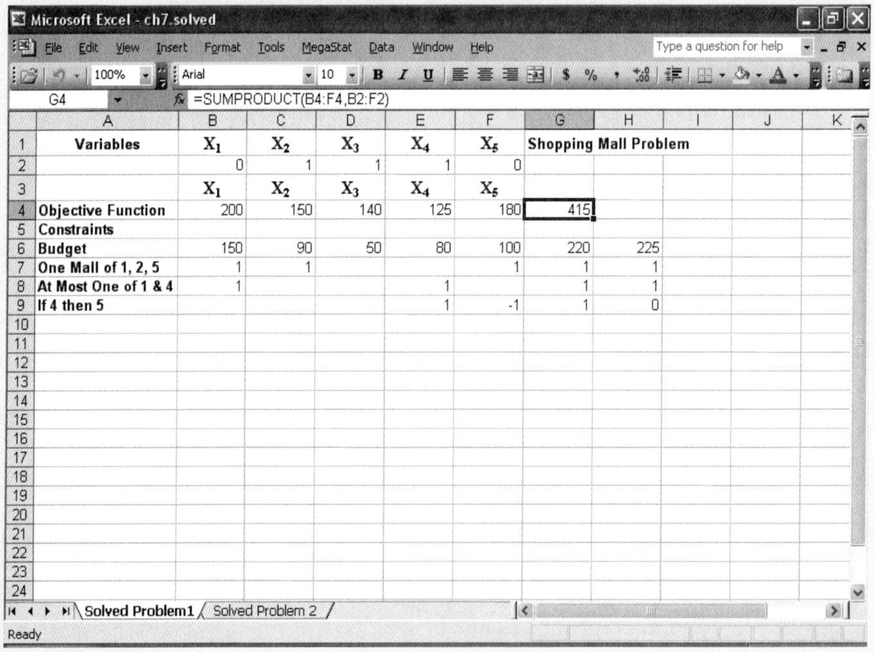

Table 7-7   Weights and Profit Values of Machines

Machine Type	Weight	Value ($1,000s)
A	2	65
B	3	90
C	1.5	40
D	1	28

a. Formulate the above problem as an integer programming problem. The cargo company wants to determine how many of each machine to ship on the cargo plane to maximize the total value of the products shipped.

b. Use Excel and solve the above problem to determine how many of each machine to ship on the cargo plane from Cleveland to Los Angeles.

Solution

a. Let x_i = number of machine i shipped

maximize $Z = 65x_1 + 90x_2 + 40x_3 + 28x_4$

subject to

$$2x_1 + 3x_2 + 1.5x_3 + 1x_4 \leq 8.5 \quad (1)$$
$$x_i = \text{integer} \quad (2)$$

b. The Excel solution to this problem is shown in Exhibit 7-15, with the specifications given in Exhibits 7-16 and 7-17. The most profitable option for the company is to ship three units of machine 1, one unit of machine 2, and one unit of machine 3, for a total profit of $263,000.

Exhibit 7-15   Excel Worksheet for Solved Problem 2 (Cargo Plane Problem)

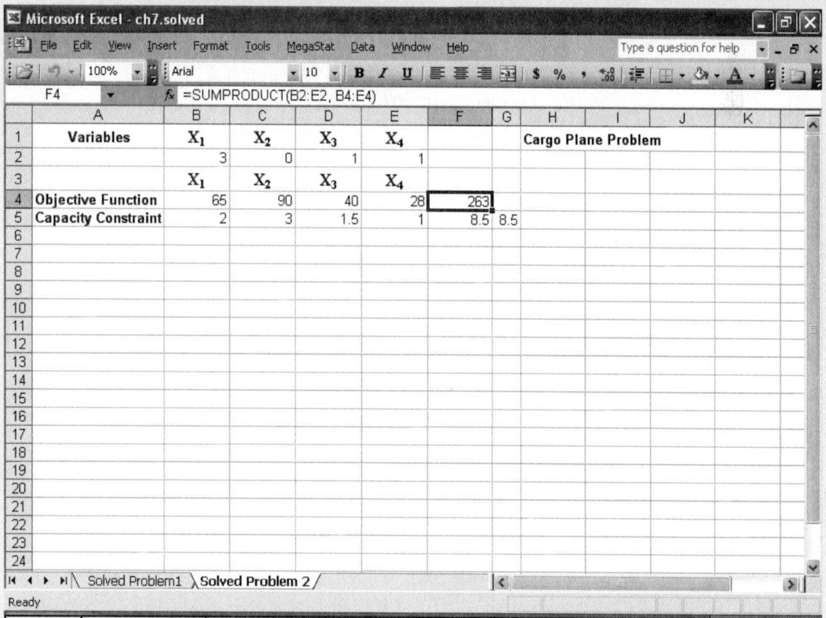

Cell	Copied to	Formula
F4		= SUMPRODUCT (B2 : E2, B4 : E4)
F5		= SUMPRODUCT (B2 : E2, B5 : E5)

Exhibit 7-16	Solver Parameters Screen for Solved Problem 2 (Cargo Plane Problem)

Solver Parameters

Set Target Cell: `$F$4`

Equal To: ● Ma_x ○ Mi_n ○ _V_alue of: `0`

By Changing Cells:

`$B$2:$E$2`   Guess

Subject to the Constraints:

```
$B$2:$E$2 = integer
$F$5 <= $G$5
```

Add
Change
Delete

Solve
Close
Options
Reset All
Help

Exhibit 7-17	Specification of the Integer Variables

Add Constraint

Cell Reference: `$B$2:$E$2`   int   Constraint: `integer`

OK   Cancel   Add   Help

Discussion and Review Questions

1. Discuss the computational difficulties associated with solving integer linear programming problems.
2. Explain why it is computationally easier to solve linear programming problems as compared to integer linear programming problems.
3. Explain the difference between pure-integer programming, mixed-integer programming, and 0–1 integer programming problems.
4. Describe why a facility location problem is formulated as a mixed-integer programming problem. What are the continuous variables and what are the 0–1 integer variables?
5. What assumption of linear programming has to be violated for being prompted to solve a problem using integer programming? Explain.

6. If a problem requires an integer solution, under what circumstances is it appropriate to use a linear programming problem instead of integer programming? Under what circumstances is it required that we use integer programming.
7. Explain the difficulties involved in solving large traveling salesperson problems.
8. Why is it difficult to perform sensitivity analysis when we use integer programming?
9. Describe an example of a set covering problem.
10. Define a knapsack problem and describe an example of a knapsack problem.
11. Explain the difficulties involved in solving large integer programming problems.

▶ Problems

1. A manufacturer of executive jet aircraft is concerned with its profit picture over the short run. It produces two different models of planes, x_1 and x_2. Its profits are $30,000 for each x_1 and $20,000 for each x_2. There are two major constraints on production:

Labor $4x_1 + 2x_2 \leq 17$ weeks
Materials $5x_1 + 4x_2 \leq 21$ tons
$x_1, x_2 \geq 0$ and integer

Also, assume that no more than 4 x_2's can be produced due to a prior union agreement. Solve this problem using Excel.

$x_1 = 3, x_2 = 0, Z = 120$

2. A producer of pleasure boats wants to maximize revenue during the next month. Two types of boats are sold, x_1 and x_2. Type x_1 sells for $40,000 and type x_2 sells for $30,000. The x_1 boats require 10 weeks of labor and 600 board feet of lumber each. The x_2 boats need 3 weeks of labor and 1,000 board feet of lumber. There are 30 weeks of labor and 3,000 board feet of lumber available this season. Because of the desire to avoid ending up with uncompleted boats, the manager has specified that only integer solutions will be accepted. Use Excel to obtain the optimal solution.
3. A janitorial service, Mother's Helpers, provides workers to clean office buildings during late evening hours using workers with two skill levels, 1 and 2. Each level 1 person is paid $12 per hour and each level 2 person is paid $8 per hour. The workers wash floors and vacuum offices. Each level 1 person can vacuum 9 offices per hour, whereas each level 2 person can vacuum only 2 offices per hour. Each level 1 person can wash 2 floors per hour and each level 2 person can wash 3 floors per hour. In order to complete a new job in the allotted time, 18 offices must be vacuumed per hour and 12 floors must be washed per hour. Use Excel and determine the number of each type of person that will be needed to complete the job within the allotted time and at minimum cost.

$x_1 = 3, x_2 = 2, Z = 29$

4. Answer the previous problem with this modification: The objective is to minimize $5x_1 + 7x_2$.
5. Answer Problem 4 with this modification: x_1 need not be integer, but x_2 must be. This is due to the potential for using level 1 people on a nearby job. For example, one level 1 person might be used for one-third time on this job.

$x_1 = 2, x_2 = 2.67,$
$Z = 22.6$

6. Answer Problem 3 (janitorial service) for the case where only x_1 is required to be integer. Use the objective function $6x_1 + 4x_2$. Explain how x_2 could be noninteger.

7. Solve the following 0–1 problem for the optimal integer solution using Excel.

maximize $Z = 70x_1 + 40x_2 + 60x_3 + 80x_4$

subject to

$$5x_1 + 6x_2 + 8x_3 + 10x_4 \leq 20$$
$$4x_1 + 2x_2 + 2x_3 + 5x_4 \leq 6$$

All variables 0 or 1

$x_1 = 0, x_2 = 0, x_3 = 12,$
$Z = 300$

8. All Electronics Manufacturer produces a toy robot that suddenly is in great demand. The firm can produce three versions of the robot. One version yields a contribution to profit of $22 per unit; the second, a contribution to profit of $18 per unit; and the third, a contribution to profit of $25 per unit. The firm can produce and sell any of the versions, subject to these limitations for each hour: 40 pounds of raw material are available, four assembly workers are available, and there are two inspectors who work exclusively on this plus another who works 40 percent of the time on this. Each version 1 robot requires 4 pounds of raw material, 12 minutes for assembly, and 12 minutes for inspection; whereas each version 2 requires 8 pounds of raw material, 24 minutes for assembly, and 6 minutes of inspection; and each version 3 requires 3 pounds of raw material, 18 minutes for assembly, and 12 minutes for inspection. Assuming that only integer values will be acceptable because the robots are packaged and shipped hourly, use Excel and determine the quantity of each type that will maximize total hourly contribution to profits.

9. A direct marketing manager wants to select prototypes of letters to send out to the company's customers. There are four prototypes to choose from. In previous trials, type 1 had a response rate of 30 percent, type 2 a response rate of 25 percent, type 3 a response rate of 35 percent, and type 4 a response rate of 40 percent. No more than three types will be chosen, however, due to other considerations. Type 1 will mean a cost of $6,000, type 2 a cost of $4,000, type 3 a cost of $5,000, and type 4 a cost of $7,000. The manager has $18,000 to spend. If the goal is to maximize total responses, which letter or letters should be sent out? Use Excel to determine the optimal solution.

$x_1 = 0, x_2 = 1, x_3 = 1,$
$Z = 250$

10. A franchise operation that sells frozen custard intends to open one or more new stores in a medium-sized metropolitan area. Three sites are under consideration. Each site has a somewhat different projected profit contribution and different supervision requirements. The first site has an estimated daily profit of $200 and a weekly supervision requirement of 48 hours; the second site has a projected profit of $100 per day a weekly supervision requirement of 30 hours; and the third site has a projected profit of $150 per day and a weekly supervision requirement of 20 hours. The firm will have 65 hours available per week for supervision. Use Excel to determine which site or sites should be selected in order to obtain the highest projected daily profit? What projected daily profit will your solution produce?

11. A vice president of finance of a bank holding company recently faced this problem. Proposals for four projects were submitted to her. Project A had an estimated total return to the company of $210,000, project B had an estimated return of $180,000, project C a return of $160,000, and project D a return of $175,000. In weighing these proposals, the vice president had to take into account the cash requirements of the projects and the available cash for the time periods involved. This information is summarized below.

| | Cash Needs | | | |
Project	Period 1	Period 2	Period 3	Period 4
A	$8,000	$8,000	$10,000	$10,000
B	7,000	9,000	9,000	11,000
C	5,000	7,000	9,000	11,000
D	9,000	8,000	7,000	6,000

Cash availability is $22,000 for period 1, $25,000 for period 2, $38,000 for period 3, and $30,000 for period 4. Using Excel, determine which projects to fund and the amount of cash that will be needed per period in order to maximize the total estimated return.

$x_1 = 1, x_2 = 6, x_3 = 8,$
$Z = 880$

12. The operations manager of a power company must design a set of crew assignments for cleanup duties after a severe windstorm, which knocked out power in various spots throughout the county. At least 40 workers and 20 supervisors must be assigned. The operations manager is particularly determined to minimize the cost of operating the trucks assigned for cleanup. Three types of trucks are suitable: type 1, with an hourly operating cost of $60; type 2, with an hourly operating cost of $30; and type 3, with an hourly operating cost of $80. The type 1 trucks have a crew of two workers and one supervisor; the type 2 trucks have one worker and two supervisors; and the type 3 trucks have four workers and one supervisor. Use Excel and determine the number of each truck type that should be used in order to both minimize the total hourly operating cost and satisfy the worker and supervisor requirements. Assume only integer solutions are acceptable. Also, determine the total cost of your solution.

13. Deregulation Airlines is planning to expand its fleet of aircraft. Four different models are under consideration: A, B, C, and D. The estimated annual contribution to profits of these models is $4.5 million, $6 million, $6.5 million, and $5 million respectively. Two important factors that must be taken into account are the fuel requirements and the maintenance requirements for each model. The weekly fuel requirements (in thousands of gallons) are 18, 25, 28, and 20, respectively, and the monthly maintenance requirements (in hours) are 20, 18, 28, and 30, respectively. Fuel availability will be 710,000 gallons per month and maintenance capacity is 900 worker-hours per month. Use Excel and determine the number of aircraft of each model that the company should purchase if its goal is to achieve the greatest contribution to annual profits. Assume that only integer solutions are acceptable.

$x_1 = 1, x_2 = 0, x_3 = 1,$
$x_4 = 2, Z = 230$

14. An investor must decide how to invest $70,000. After considerable research, the investor has narrowed the investment alternatives to four possibilities: Invest $25,000 in a real estate plan, invest $20,000 in a new product, invest $30,000 in a certificate of deposit, and invest $35,000 in a certain stock. The first three investments must be in the exact amounts listed, although the last can be in any amount up to $35,000. The expected returns for each dollar invested are $3 for the real estate, $2 for the new product, $4 for the CD, and $2.50 for the stock. Assume that stock amounts must be in multiples of $7,000. Solve for the optimum solution using Excel.

15. Solve the following problem using Excel:

maximize $Z = 5x_1 + 8x_2 + 4x_3$

subject to

1	$1.5x_1 + 2x_2 + 1.6x_3 \leq 10$
2	$25x_1 + 50x_2 + 20x_3 \leq 160$
	$x_1, x_2,$ and $x_3 \geq 0$ and integer

16. The Rubber Blanket Company has recently undergone a reorganization. It must now decide on quantity levels for these products: x_1, x_2, and x_3. Their respective contributions to profits are estimated to be $10, $15, and $18 per unit, in thousands. The products are subject to the following constraints:

$$4x_1 + 6x_2 + 3x_3 \leq 70$$
$$90x_1 + 80x_2 + 100x_3 \leq 1,200$$

The variables (quantities of x_1, x_2, and x_3) do not need to be integer. In addition, there is a one-time cost associated with the production of each product. For x_1 the cost would be $3,000, for x_2 the cost would be $4,000, and for x_3 the cost would be $6,000.

a. See the IM
b. $x_1 = 0$, $x_2 = 9.44$, $x_3 =$
  4.44, $y_1 = 0$, $y_2 = 1$, $y_3 = 1$
  $Z = 221,520$

a. Formulate the problem.
b. Use Excel and determine the optimal values for the decision variables and the maximum profit.

17. Manager Cheryl Carver is faced with this problem: A product can be made on either one of two machines: x_1 or x_2. However, the machines have different processing requirements and different profit and cost structures. These differences are summarized in the following table:

Machine	Profit per Unit	Setup Cost	Raw Material #1 per unit	Raw Material #2 per unit
x_1	$50	$250	2 pounds	4 quarts
x_2	40	210	3 pounds	2 quarts

Cheryl wants to determine whether all of the output should be produced on one of the machines (if so, which machine) or whether the output should be split between these two machines. The goal is to maximize the contribution to profit. Thirty pounds of raw material #1 and thirty-six quarts of raw material #2 will be available for this production run.
a. Set up (formulate) her problem in a format suitable for integer programming.
b. Assuming that an integer solution is required, determine the optimal solution to Cheryl's problem.

18. (Refer to Problem 17.) Treat the unit profits in the previous problem as unit costs. In addition, suppose that the firm has an order for 10 units of the product.

a. See the IM
b. $x_1 = 0$, $x_2 = 1$, $y_1 = 0$,
  $y_2 = 1$, $Z = 610$

a. Formulate this problem in an integer programming format.
b. Use Excel and solve for the optimal integer solution. Interpret your answer.

19. The product manager at a savings and loan must have a large mailing printed and sent out to customers. A previous mailing was delayed due to a problem at the printer's shop, and the product manager wants to reduce that risk by giving no more than 3/4 of the job to one printer. The total job will consist of 400 pieces. The product manager has obtained cost quotations from the four local shops that she feels can handle the job and meet quality specifications. This information is summarized in the following table:

Printer	Cost per Piece	Base Fee
A	$.50	$300
B	.40	350
C	.45	380
D	.47	320

Assume that the goal is to minimize the total cost of printing the mailing pieces. Use Excel and determine the integer solution that will yield the lowest possible total cost.

$x_1 = 0$, $x_2 = 0$, $x_3 = 41$,
$Z = $9,840$

20. The new manager of a plastics division must make a decision on shipping containers that will be used to ship products by truck. The main issue is to decide how many of each type container to use. Three types are available: A, B, and C. Type A has a loaded weight of 60 pounds and a volume of 16 cubic feet, type B has a weight of 64 pounds and a volume of 20 cubic feet, and type C has a weight of 48 pounds and a volume of 14 cubic feet. Each truck has a volume of 1,200 cubic feet and a weight limit of 2,000 pounds. The containers have profit contributions of $200 for each A, $220 for each B, and $240 for each C. Use Excel and determine how many of each container should be allocated per truck in order to maximize the total contribution to profit.

21. The owner of a new cab company wants to determine locations for cab waiting points. He has gathered the following information:

Location	Can Serve Areas	Cost per Day
1	A, E	$400
2	A, C, D	500
3	B, C, E	450
4	B, D	440
5	D, E	430

The owner wants to be sure that all areas can be served, yet he wants this done for as little cost as possible. Use Excel and determine the choice of locations that will accomplish this goal.

22. A group of investors is contemplating opening a number of restaurants in a large metropolitan area. Some of these will offer full service and some take-out service only. The group has identified five potential locations for take-out restaurants, of which it will select at least three, and it has identified six potential locations for full-service restaurants, of which it will select at least two. Operating costs will be $15,000 per month for take-out service only and $25,000 per month for full-service restaurants. The group has a monthly budget of $195,000 for operating costs. Estimated profits are $5,000 per month for take-out service and $7,000 a month for full-service restaurants. The group needs to know how many of each type restaurant to select and the profit that will be generated.

    a. Formulate a model for this problem.
    b. Solve for the optimal solution using Excel.
    c. How much of the operating budget will be unused?

a. See the IM
b. x_1 = # of take-outs,
   x_2 = # of full-serve;
   $x_1 = 3, x_2 = 6, Z = 57,000$
c. None

23. Solve this all-integer problem for the optimal solution using Excel:

    maximize $Z = 13x_1 + 26x_2 + 14x_3$

    subject to

    $$16x_1 + 9x_2 + 4x_3 \le 44$$
    $$6x_2 + 10x_3 \le 20$$
    $$x_1, x_2, \text{ and } x_3 \ge 0 \text{ and integer}$$

$x_1 = 2, x_2 = 0, x_3 = 3,$
$Z = 33$

24. Find the optimal solution to this problem using Excel:

    maximize $Z = 9x_1 + 5x_2 + 5x_3$

    subject to

    $$20x_1 + 14x_2 + 19x_3 \le 100$$
    $$8x_1 + 4x_2 \le 18$$
    $$x_1, \quad x_2, \text{ and } x_3 \ge 0 \text{ and integer}$$

25. The manager of a stamping department is getting ready to begin a new operation. A single product is to be produced. It can be produced on any of three machines. Information concerning the machines is contained in the following table:

Machine	Setup Cost	Profit per Unit	Daily Capacity
A	$300	$10	500
B	250	12	450
C	325	13	450

Each machine requires an operator, and two operators are available. The profit per unit excludes setup cost, and setups must be done at the start of each new day.

a. Formulate this profit maximization problem.

b. Use Excel and solve for the optimal quantities to produce per day on each machine.

26. A department has three machines available, and the new department manager must select one of the machines to assign to a new product line. The product line will consist of three slightly different products, A, B, and C. Production requirements, machine capacities, and setup costs are given in the following table:

Machine	Setup Cost	Production Time per Piece			Capacity (hours)
		A	B	C	
1	$150	4	3	5	1,000
2	120	3	2	4	800
3	110	2	4	2	700

The profit per pound on the three products is listed in the following table:

Product	Profit
A	$13
B	10
C	12

a. Formulate this problem taking into account an additional factor: At least 40 pounds of each product must be made.

b. Solve for the optimal solution and profit using Excel.

27. Find the optimal solution to this problem using Excel.

$$\text{maximize } Z = 12x_1 + 18x_2 + 14x_3$$

subject to

$$6x_1 + 5x_2 + 5x_3 \leq 48$$
$$x_1, x_2, \text{ and } x_3 \geq 0 \text{ and integer}$$

28. Find the optimal solution to this problem using Excel. If there are multiple optimal solutions, identify each one.

$$\text{maximize } Z = 5x_1 + 6x_2 + 5x_3 + 4x_4$$

subject to

$$10x_1 + 11x_2 + 9x_3 + 7x_4 \leq 39$$
$$2x_1 + 3x_2 + 3x_3 + 2x_4 \leq 13$$
$$\text{All variables} \geq 0 \text{ and integer}$$

29. Find the optimal solution to this problem using Excel.

$$\text{minimize } Z = x_1 + x_2 + 2x_3 + x_4$$

subject to

$$3x_1 + 2x_2 + 4x_3 + x_4 \geq 41$$
$$\text{All variables} \geq 0 \text{ and integer}$$

a. See the IM
b. $A = 230$,
   $B = 40$,
   $C = 40$,
   $Y_1 = 0$,
   $Y_2 = 1$,
   $Y_3 = 0$,
   $Z = 3{,}760$

$x_1 = 0$
$x_2 = 0$
$x_3 = 2$
$x_4 = 3$, $Z = 22$
Alternate optimal
$x_1 = 0$
$x_2 = 1$
$x_3 = 0$
$x_4 = 4$, $Z = 22$

$x_1 = 3, x_2 = 1, x_3 = 0,$
$Z = 41$

30. Determine the optimal solution to this all-integer problem using Excel.

$$\text{minimize } Z = 10x_1 + 11x_2 + 12x_3$$

subject to

$$8x_1 + 9x_2 + 10x_3 \geq 20$$
$$3x_1 + 4x_2 + 3x_3 \geq 13$$
$$\text{All variables} \geq 0 \text{ and integer}$$

31. A cargo plane is flying from Chicago to San Diego. The plane has a remaining capacity of five tons. Joe's machinery company wants to ship two types of large machinery on the plane. The weights and dollar profit values of each type of machinery are given in the following table:

Machinery	Weight (tons)	Profit ($1,000s)
Lathe	1	$13
Punch press	2	$27

a. State the integer programming formulation of this problem.
b. Using Excel determine the optimal number of each type of machinery to ship on the cargo plane in order to maximize total profit.

32. A company is interested in minimizing total travel time of its trucks for garbage collection. There are five neighborhoods that trucks serve. Location 1 serves as the home location from which trucks leave and to which they must return. The company is interested in minimizing total travel time starting at the home location, visiting each of the neighborhoods once, and then returning to the home location.

Let $x_{ijk} = 1$ if a truck travels from node i to node j during leg k of the trip
   $x_{ijk} = 0$ if a truck does not travel from node i to node j during leg k of the trip

Prepare the following constraints for this problem:

a. The constraint that ensures that if leg 3 of the trip ends at location 2, then leg 4 of the trip starts at location 2.
b. The constraint that ensures that if leg 3 of the trip ends at location 2, then the fourth leg of the trip starts at location 3.
c. The constraint that ensures that the tour starts in node 1.
d. The constraint that stipulates that the trip must end in node 1 in leg 5.
e. The constraint that specifies that there is exactly one arrival at node 3.
f. The constraint that specifies that there is exactly one departure from node 2.
g. The constraint that ensures that we visit any node once in the second leg of the trip.

a. $x_{323} + x_{423} + x_{523} = x_{234} + x_{244} + x_{254}$
b. $x_{233} + x_{433} + x_{533} = x_{324} + x_{344} + x_{354}$
c. $x_{121} + x_{131} + x_{141} + x_{151} = 1$
d. $x_{215} + x_{315} + x_{415} + x_{515} = 1$
e. $x_{131} + x_{232} + x_{432} + x_{532} + x_{233} + x_{433} + x_{533} + x_{234} + x_{434} + x_{534} = 1$
f. $x_{215} + x_{232} + x_{242} + x_{252} + x_{233} + x_{243} + x_{253} + x_{234} + x_{244} + x_{254} = 1$
g. $x_{232} + x_{242} + x_{252} + x_{322} + x_{342} + x_{352} + x_{422} + x_{432} + x_{532} = 1$

33. The Meadow Cutting and Tooling Manufacturing Company is experiencing a large increase in demand. The production at the current manufacturing facilities is not able to satisfy demand. The company is in need of adding new manufacturing plants. At the present time it has two plants, one in Omaha, Nebraska, and the other in Kansas City, Missouri. The capacities of these plants are roughly 23,000 units per year in Omaha and 27,000 units per year in Kansas City. The company sells through its retail outlet stores located in St. Louis, Missouri; Des Moines, Iowa; Topeka, Kansas, and Tulsa, Oklahoma. The demand for the product at these retail outlet facilities is as follows:
 • St. Louis, Missouri: 28,000 units per year
 • Des Moines, Iowa: 30,000 units per year
 • Topeka, Kansas: 24,000 units per year
 • Tulsa, Oklahoma: 32,000 units per year

The company is in the process of considering five new manufacturing plant locations. The locations, their capacities, and the cost of purchasing or building the facility are stated in the following table:

Manufacturing Facility	Capacity (units per year)	Building/ Purchasing Cost
Iowa City, Iowa (y_1)	28,000	$210,000
Lincoln, Nebraska (y_2)	30,000	$240,000
Springfield, Illinois (y_3)	25,000	$200,000
Wichita, Kansas (y_4)	27,000	$205,000
Oklahoma City, Oklahoma (y_5)	24,000	$185,000

Even though the unit manufacturing cost in each of these plants is comparable, the unit shipping cost from the existing and the proposed plants to the retail outlets is given in the following table.

	Per-Unit Shipping Costs			
Plant\Outlet	St. Louis (1)	Des Moines (2)	Topeka (3)	Tulsa (4)
Omaha (1)	7	3	3.5	7.5
Kansas City (2)	2	4	2.5	4
Iowa City (3)	3.5	3	4.5	8
Lincoln (4)	7.5	4.5	5	6.5
Springfield (5)	2.5	5	5.5	6
Wichita (6)	4	5	3	5
Oklahoma City (7)	5.5	8	4	2

The objective of the Meadow Cutting and Tooling Manufacturing Company is to minimize the total cost, which consists of the shipping cost and the building/purchasing cost, such that demand at all retail outlets is satisfied.

a. Use the numbers given next to each city in the per-unit shipping cost table given above and formulate this problem as a 0–1 mixed-integer linear programming problem.

b. Use Excel and determine the optimal shipping schedule that minimizes the total cost. Which locations should be used to build the new plants?

34. The following matrix represents the changeover times (in minutes) of 10 products for a cable manufacturer.

a. Use the nearest-neighbor method and determine the sequence of jobs.

b. How long will it take to do the changeovers among the 10 products? You can begin production with any of the 10 products.

a. The product sequence is 4–2–5–6–1–9–3–7–2–8–10;

b. Total setup time = .5 + 4 + 11 + 37 + 16 + 20 + 2 + 4 + 11 = 105.5 minutes

Changeover Matrix (times in minutes)
To Product

From Product	1	2	3	4	5	6	7	8	9	10
1	0	58	48	44	67	2	34	28	16	51
2	17	0	31	24	4	44	74	4	68	99
3	44	38	0	5.1	8	32	20	81	74	88
4	10	.5	53	0	24	1	4	46	36	8
5	41	15	77	12	0	11	4	41	70	38
6	37	71	95	15	34	0	44	75	82	72
7	98	47	3	39	12	28	0	50	51	20
8	36	61	100	62	95	79	57	0	40	43
9	52	25	60	48	32	6	84	26	0	11
10	74	72	19	21	31	63	11	13	41	0

35. Determine the number of possible solutions for a 0–1 integer programming problem with the following number of decision variables:
    a.   5 decision variables
    b.   10 decision variables
    c.   15 decision variables
    d.   18 decision variables

a. 6! = 720
b. 8! = 40,320
c. 10! = 3,628,800
d. ! = 6,227,020,800
e. As the number of locations increases, the number of possible routes increases unmanageably fast.

36. Consider a symmetric traveling salesperson problem. Determine the number of possible routes, if there are
    a.   7 locations
    b.   9 locations
    c.   11 locations
    d.   14 locations
    e.   Based on the answers you have obtained in parts *a* through *d*, comment on the potential problems in solving traveling salesperson problems.

37. Florida Power and Gas Company needs an efficient schedule for their meter readers. The are five neighborhoods to be served. The headquarters is located in neighborhood 1. The time estimates (in minutes) of traveling between the neighborhoods in given in the following table.

From\To	1	2	3	4	5
1	0	3	7.5	6.6	2.5
2	3	0	2	8	7.7
3	7.5	2	0	3	8.5
4	6.6	8	3	0	3.5
5	2.5	7.7	8.5	3.5	0

    a.   Formulate this problem as a traveling salesperson problem.
    b.   Use the formulation from part *a* and Excel and determine the schedule that minimizes the total transportation time of a meter reader starting in neighborhood 1 and ending in neighborhood 1.

◼▶ Chapter 7 Case   Suburban Suntime

The Suburban Suntime Corporation manufactures a line of high-priced outdoor furniture consisting of a picnic table, a bench, an armchair, and a chaise lounge. The picnic table is sold in a set with two of the benches; the benches also may be sold separately. Here is information on pieces and resource availability for next month.

	Picnic Table (set)	Bench (separate)	Armchair	Chaise Lounge	Available
Price	$725	$225	$275	$300	
Redwood (board ft.)	22	6	7	8	4,500
Cedar (board ft.)	12	4	4	0	3,600
12-inch fittings (number)	18	4	0	2	2,250
8-inch fittings (number)	12	4	6	6	2,075
Bolts (number)	48	12	12	20	5,925
Labor (hours)	20	5	8	12	4,800

Redwood costs $8 per board foot; cedar costs $6 per board foot; 12-inch fittings cost $2.50; 8-inch fittings cost $1.50; bolts cost $.50. The hourly wage rate and fringe benefits of the workers average $9.00 per hour.

Because of prior orders, at least 50 (separate) benches and at least 40 chaise lounges must be produced.

Discussion Question

Determine the quantity of each product to be produced next month. Assume partial units are unacceptable.

Source: Written by Professor Paul Van Ness, College of Business, Rochester Institute of Technology. Reprinted by permission.

Network Optimization Models

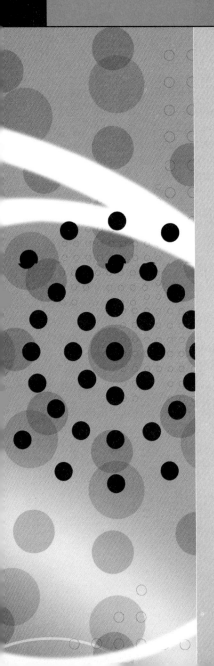

Learning Objectives

After completing this chapter, you should be able to:

1. State why network models are important tools for problem solving.
2. Describe the kinds of problems that can be solved using the shortest-route algorithm and use the algorithm to solve typical shortest-route problems.
3. Formulate the shortest-route problem as a linear programming problem.
4. Solve the shortest-route problem using Excel.
5. Describe the kinds of problems that can be solved using the minimal-spanning-tree algorithm and use the algorithm to solve typical minimal-spanning-tree problems.
6. Describe the kinds of problems that can be solved using the maximal-flow algorithm and use the algorithm to solve typical maximal-flow problems.
7. Formulate the maximal-flow problem as a linear programming problem.
8. Solve the maximal-flow problem using Excel.

Chapter Outline

Introduction, 370

The Shortest-Route Problem, 371

The Shortest-Route (Labeling) Algorithm (Concept Development), 371

Summary of Procedure, 375

Linear Programming Formulation of the Shortest-Route Problem, 376

Solving the Shortest-Route Problem Using Excel, 378

The Minimum Spanning Tree Problem, 384

Algorithm for the Minimum Spanning Tree Problem (Concept Development), 384

The Maximal Flow Problem, 387

Maximal Flow Algorithm (Concept Development), 388

Demonstration of Reverse Flow, 391

Linear Programming Formulation of the Maximal Flow Problem, 393

Comment, 400

Summary, 401

Glossary, 401

Solved Problems, 401

Discussion and Review Questions, 411

Problems, 412

Chapter 8 Case: Furnace County Emergency Response Routes, 420

▟ Introduction

Network models consist of a set of circles, or **nodes**, and lines, which are referred to as either **arcs** or *branches*, that connect some nodes to other nodes. Figure 8-1 illustrates a simple network diagram. This network has four nodes and five branches. Notice that the branches meet only at nodes; the nodes are *intersections* of the branches. For purposes of reference, the nodes are numbered. Moreover, a branch can be referred to by specifying the nodes on each of its ends (e.g., branch 1–2).

Networks are important tools of management science. Not only can networks be used to model a wide variety of problems, they often can be solved more easily than other models of the same problem and they present models in a visual format.

The three network models described in this chapter are

1. Shortest route.
2. Minimum spanning tree.
3. Maximal flow.

In the first of these, shortest route, networks are used to represent the distance, time, or cost of getting from one location (node) to various other locations, with the branches representing those distances, costs, or times. The objective is to determine the shortest route (distance, time, or cost) from one location to each of the other locations.

Spanning trees are concerned with interconnecting the nodes of a network using as little of the branch "material" as possible. Typical examples include linking towns and villages to a cable TV network, connecting electrical motors or appliances to a network, and so on.

Flow networks that are used to solve maximal flow problems represent flow through a system, and the objective is to achieve as much flow as possible. Examples include flow through a system of pipelines, a flow of traffic through a system of highways, a flow of products through a production system, phone calls through a system, and messages through the Web.

As you can see, many different kinds of problems seem to lend themselves to network models. Moreover, the solutions to many of the problems described in this chapter are quite simple. In fact, many small problems presented in this chapter could be solved by inspection. Nonetheless, it is important to be able to use the algorithms described in the chapter to solve large problems. This relates to the fact that more complex problems are less amenable to solution by inspection; the simple problems are designed to facilitate learning

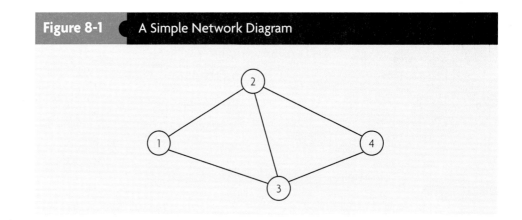

Figure 8-1 ◖ A Simple Network Diagram

solution techniques. Furthermore, the algorithms are the basis for computer solution of the problems. Fortunately, the algorithms involve very few steps, and they are intuitively appealing. In this chapter, we show the specialized algorithms to solve the network-flow problems, and then also illustrate, where possible, linear programming formulation and Excel solution of these models.

The purposes of illustrating the specialized algorithms are:

1. They are very handy to solve relatively small problems manually without the benefit of the computer.
2. They help demonstrate the concepts associated with solving the various network-flow problems.
3. The reader does not get a very good feel about the problems without demonstration of these algorithms.

The first model we shall explore involves solving the shortest-route problem.

The Shortest-Route Problem

In the **shortest-route problem,** the objective is to find the shortest distance from one location (origin) to another location (destination) through a network. Very often, the total distance traveled is the measure of effectiveness. Delivery systems and transportation systems are typical examples of where such problems occur. Other measures of effectiveness could be cost or time.

The Shortest-Route (Labeling) Algorithm (Concept Development)

The algorithm used to solve for the shortest routes assumes that all node distances are nonnegative. The algorithm finds the shortest route from a specified node (usually Node 1) to every node in a network. The algorithm requires $n - 1$ steps, where n equals the number of nodes in a network.

The analysis uses a *labeling procedure,* wherein a label is developed for each node. The labels consist of two numbers separated by a comma: The first number refers to the distance from Node 1 to the labeled node along a certain path, while the second number refers to the node that immediately precedes this node along that path. Thus, if Node 5, say, has the label 18,3, this tells us that there is a path from Node 1 to Node 5 that has a distance of 18 from Node 1 and that the preceding node on that path is Node 3. In order to find out which node precedes Node 3, we would have to refer to the label at Node 3. Hence, once the analysis has been completed, the shortest route to any given node from Node 1 can be found by tracing the node labels backwards through the network.

The labeling procedure begins with the originating node (e.g., home base, central office, starting point). Usually this is Node 1. Its label is 0,S. The 0 indicates the distance from Node 1 to this node; because this is Node 1, the distance is 0. The S indicates that this is the starting node. This node is considered to be *permanently labeled*, a term used to indicate that no shorter route to a node exists. Obviously, since Node 1 is the starting point, we can be sure that there is no "shorter route" to this node. In general, once we have determined the shortest distance to a node, we give that node a permanent label. We signify this by shading in the node or using brackets.

Initially, none of the nodes are labeled. Then, as the analysis progresses, certain nodes are assigned *temporary* labels, which may be revised as part of the analysis. The label remains temporary until it can be ascertained that no shorter route to a node exists. At that point, the label becomes permanent, and the node is shaded in or brackets replace the node parentheses to reflect this. When all nodes have received permanent labels, the shortest routes can be determined by inspection of the permanent labels on the nodes. Permanent nodes are represented in brackets while temporary nodes are stated using parentheses.

The essence of the analysis is to determine permanent labels for the nodes, one at a time. Once a node receives its permanent label, the analysis focuses on that section of the network for assigning temporary labels. The following example will illustrate this simple procedure.

Example 8-1

Given this network that shows the distance in miles between delivery destinations, find the shortest route to each destination from Node 1. Travel between nodes can be in either direction.

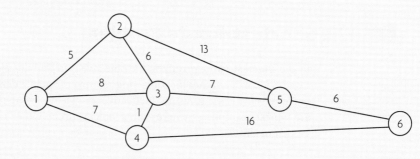

Note: Distances are not drawn to scale.

Begin by permanently labeling Node 1 with [0,S]. Indicate that the label is permanent by shading in Node 1. Then, obtain temporary labels for every node that can be reached *directly* from Node 1 (i.e., Nodes 2, 3, and 4). The label should show the distance from Node 1 and indicate that Node 1 is the predecessor node. Thus, the temporary label for Node 2 is (5, 1) because it is 5 miles from Node 1, and Node 1 precedes it. Similarly, the temporary label for Node 3 is (8, 1) and the temporary label for Node 4 is (7, 1).

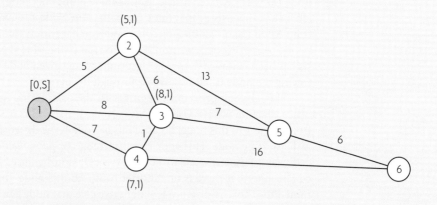

First iteration   Determine which temporary label has the *smallest* distance from Node 1. It is the label for Node 2, with a distance of 5. Make this label permanent, and shade in Node 2 or replace the node parentheses with brackets. Now determine temporary labels for each node that can be reached directly from this latest permanent node *unless* a node already has a permanent label (e.g., Node 1), or unless a current temporary label already exists that cannot be improved on. For example, the current temporary label for Node 3 is (8, 1), the distance from Node 1 along path 1–2–3 would be 5 + 6 = 11. Hence, the current label is shorter, so we should keep that label. Node 5, however, does not have a label. Its cumulative distance from Node 1 through Node 2 is 18; hence, its temporary label is (18, 2) because Node 2 is its predecessor.

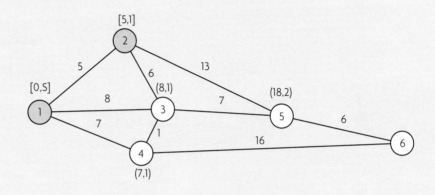

Second iteration Identity the node that has the smallest temporary label. (The choices are Node 3, with a label of (8, 1), Node 4 with a label of (7, 1), and Node 5 with a label of (18, 2) Because 7 is the smallest distance, Node 4 has the smallest temporary label. Make this label permanent (shade in or replace the node parentheses with brackets). Next, find each nonpermanent node that can be reached directly from this newest permanent node. These are Nodes 3 and 6. Node 6 has no temporary label; its temporary label will now be (23, 4), indicating that its distance from Node 1 is 23 miles (the Node 4 label of 7 plus 16 miles from Node 4 to Node 6). Node 3 already has a temporary label of (8, 1), indicating that it can be reached directly from Node 1 with a distance of 8 miles. We can see that it also can be reached in 8 miles by Route 1–4–3. Hence, there is a tie, so *either* label can be used. For simplicity then, suppose we retain the current label.

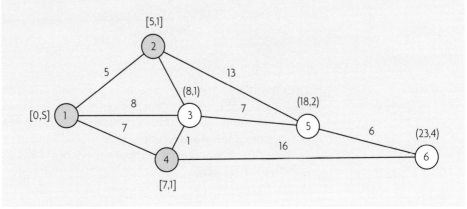

Third iteration   The node with the smallest temporary label is Node 3. Therefore, its label now becomes a permanent label, and Node 3 is shaded in or temporary node parentheses are replaced with brackets. It also can be helpful to indicate that a tie exists at this point, meaning that an alternate route exists to this node. Next, find each nonpermanent node that can be reached directly from Node 3. We see that Node 5 is the only such node. It has a temporary label of (18, 2). However, we can see that by following a route from Node 3 to Node 5 directly, the cumulative distance from Node 1 will be only 15 (i.e., 8 + 7 = 15). Because the route through Node 3 is shorter, we *update* the temporary label of Node 5 to reflect this shorter route.

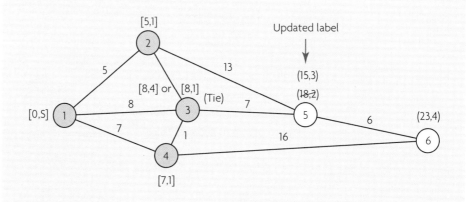

Fourth iteration   Identify the node with the smallest temporary label. Node 5 has a label of (15, 3) and Node 6 has the label (23, 4). Because 15 is smaller than 23, Node 5 is selected and converted to a permanent label.

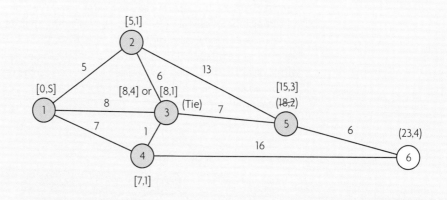

Fifth iteration   The only node with a nonpermanent label, and the only such node that can be reached directly from the newest permanent node, is Node 6. Using this route, its cumulative distance from Node 1 would be 15 + 6 = 21. Because this is less than its current label shows, we update the label to [21, 5]. And because this is the only node without a permanent label, we can now permanently label it, using [21, 5].

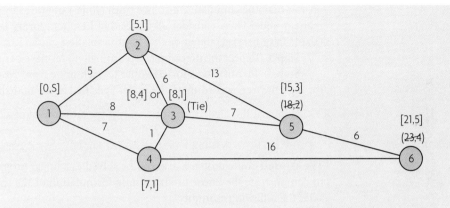

This completes the analysis of the routes. Using the final network, we can read the distances from Node 1 to each node from each node's permanent label. For example, the shortest distance from Node 1 to Node 5 is 15 miles, and the shortest distance from Node 1 to Node 6 is 21 miles.

In order to identify the route that yields the shortest distance to a particular node, it is necessary to work backwards through the network. This is sometimes referred to as *backtracking*. Here is how it is done. Begin with the node in question (say, Node 6). The second part of the label indicates the previous node in the shortest path. Hence, the previous node for Node 6 is Node 5. Turning our attention to Node 5, we see that its predecessor node is Node 3. Hence, so far we have 3–5–6. At Node 3, we note that there was a tie, meaning that either of two routes (1–3 or 1–4–3) will yield the same distance. Thus, we can choose either of these as our route and identify the other as an alternate route. Thus, we can say 1–3–5–6 is the route, but that 1–4–3–5–6 is an alternate route.

All of the routes can be obtained in this manner. They are summarized in the following table.

Node	Distance	Shortest Route	Alternate Shortest Route
2	5	1–2	
3	8	1–3	1–4–3
4	7	1–4	
5	15	1–3–5	1–4–3–5
6	21	1–3–5–6	1–4–3–5–6

Summary of Procedure

The procedure for determining the shortest routes and their lengths can be summarized by these steps:

Step 1. Begin at Node 1. Find the distance from Node 1 to each node that can be reached *directly* from Node 1. Temporarily label each of these nodes with their distance from Node 1 followed by a comma and number 1. Then select the node that has the smallest distance from Node 1 and make its label permanent. Do this by shading in the node and, or bracketing the distance and incoming node numbers.

Step 2. Find the distance from the new permanent node to each nonpermanent node that can be reached directly from this node. Temporarily label each of these nodes with the cumulative distance from Node 1 if a node has no label, or if its current temporary label is greater than the cumulative distance from Node 1 obtained by going through the new permanent node. Then, consider all nodes that have temporary labels and permanently label (shade in or bracket) the node that has the smallest cumulative distance from Node 1.

Step 3. Repeat the preceding step until all nodes have permanent labels.

Step 4. Identify the shortest route to each node from Node 1 by working backwards through the tree, according to the nodes specified in the node labels.

Note that this algorithm works only if the arcs consist of all nonnegative values (costs).

Linear Programming Formulation of the Shortest-Route Problem

The shortest-route problem also can be solved as a linear programming problem. In order to demonstrate the linear programming formulation of the shortest-route problem, consider the following example.

Example 8-2

The Tri-State Shipping Company transports paint from Chicago, Illinois (node 1), to six cities in the Midwest. The cities that the company ships to include

Node 2: Indianapolis, Indiana
Node 3: Green Bay, Wisconsin
Node 4: South Bend, Indiana
Node 5: Detroit, Michigan
Node 6: Cincinnati, Ohio
Node 7: Cleveland, Ohio

Figure 8-2 shows the road network and distances in miles between the cities. Formulate this problem as a linear program.

Solution
To formulate this problem, we can begin by defining the decision variables as follows:

$x_{ij} = 0$ if the flow from node i to node j is not selected
$x_{ij} = 1$ if the flow from node i to node j is selected

The objective is to minimize the distance between node 1 and each of the remaining 6 nodes. We can express the objective function as follows:

$$\text{minimize } Z = 180x_{12} + 180x_{21} + 200x_{13} + 200x_{31} + 100x_{14} + 100x_{41} + 145x_{24} + 145x_{42} +$$
$$300x_{34} + 300x_{43} + 120x_{26} + 120x_{62} + 450x_{35} + 450x_{53} + 215x_{45} +$$
$$215x_{54} + 240x_{46} + 240x_{64} + 250x_{47} + 250x_{74} + 225x_{67} + 225x_{76} +$$
$$160x_{57} + 160x_{75}$$

The best value for each variable will be either 0 or 1 depending on whether a truck uses the particular route.

There is one constraint for each node. In setting up the constraint for node 1, the right-hand side of the constraint is equal to 1, indicating supply of one at node 1. We assume that one truck leaves node 1 (the origin) and arrives at node 7 (the destination). This is why the right-hand side associated with the node-1 constraint and node-7 constraint will be equal to 1. The left-hand side shows the three possible routes from branch 1: branch 1 to branch 2, branch 1 to branch 3, and branch 1 to branch 4.

$x_{12} + x_{13} + x_{14} = 1$ (supply of one unit at node 1)

| Figure 8-2 | Network for Tri-State Shipping Company Shortest-Route Problem |

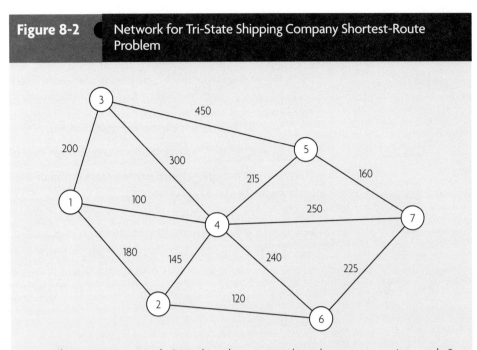

The constraint at node 2 involves the concept that whatever comes into node 2 must leave node 2. This type of constraint is similar to the transshipment constraints we developed in Chapter 6 for the transshipment problem. At node 2, a truck would come from node 1, from node 4, or from node 6. Also, a truck would leave by going to node 1, node 4, or node 6. In other words, what comes into node 2 ($x_{12} + x_{42} + x_{62}$) must leave node 2 ($x_{21} + x_{24} + x_{26}$).

$$x_{12} + x_{42} + x_{62} = x_{21} + x_{24} + x_{26}$$

Transferring the outgoing decision variables from the right-hand side to the left-hand side of the equation, we get the following:

$$x_{12} + x_{42} + x_{62} - x_{21} - x_{24} - x_{26} = 0 \qquad \text{(transshipment constraint for node 2)}$$

Based on the information given in Figure 8-2, we repeat this process for nodes 3, 4, 5, and 6.

For node 3 we have

$$x_{13} + x_{43} + x_{53} = x_{31} + x_{34} + x_{35}$$

After moving all of the decision variables to the left side of the inequality, we get

$$x_{13} + x_{43} + x_{53} - x_{31} - x_{34} - x_{35} = 0 \qquad \text{(transshipment constraint for node 3)}$$

Repeating this process for nodes 4, 5, and 6, we get the following equations:

$$x_{14} + x_{34} + x_{24} + x_{64} + x_{74} + x_{54} - x_{41} - x_{43} - x_{42} - x_{46} - x_{47} - x_{45} = 0$$
$$\text{(transshipment constraint for node 4)}$$
$$x_{35} + x_{45} + x_{75} - x_{54} - x_{53} - x_{57} = 0 \qquad \text{(transshipment constraint for node 5)}$$
$$x_{26} + x_{46} + x_{76} - x_{62} - x_{64} - x_{67} = 0 \qquad \text{(transshipment constraint for node 6)}$$

We will use Cleveland (node 7) as the ending node since it is geographically located at the opposite end of the network from Chicago. Therefore, we will have the route terminated at node 7 (Cleveland). In order to ensure that the route is terminated in Cleveland, we only consider the routes or branches going in to node 7 and we will not consider the branches coming out of node 7 (7 to 4, 7 to 5, and 7 to 6). Since this is the ending node, the supply of one that was started at node 1 will end up in node 7. In other words, the right-hand side of the equality constraint for node 7 is equal to 1.

The node 7 constraint can be written as follows:

$$x_{47} + x_{57} + x_{67} = 1 \qquad \text{(demand of one unit at node 7)}.$$

The complete 0–1 integer programming formulation of the Tri-State shortest-route problem can be stated as follows:

$$x_{ij} = 0 \qquad \text{if the route from node } i \text{ to node } j \text{ is not selected}$$
$$x_{ij} = 1 \qquad \text{if the route from node } i \text{ to node } j \text{ is selected}$$

$$
\begin{aligned}
\text{minimize } Z = {} & 180x_{12} + 180x_{21} + 200x_{13} + 200x_{31} + 100x_{14} + 100x_{41} + 145x_{24} + 145x_{42} + \\
& 300x_{34} + 300x_{43} + 120x_{26} + 120x_{62} + 450x_{35} + 450x_{53} + 215x_{45} + \\
& 215x_{54} + 240x_{46} + 240x_{64} + 250x_{47} + 250x_{74} + 225x_{67} + 225x_{76} + \\
& 160x_{57} + 160x_{75}
\end{aligned}
$$

subject to

$$x_{12} + x_{13} + x_{14} = 1 \qquad \text{(supply of one unit at node 1)}$$
$$x_{12} + x_{42} + x_{62} - x_{21} - x_{24} - x_{26} = 0 \qquad \text{(transshipment constraint for node 2)}$$
$$x_{13} + x_{43} + x_{53} - x_{31} - x_{34} - x_{35} = 0 \qquad \text{(transshipment constraint for node 3)}$$
$$x_{14} + x_{34} + x_{24} + x_{64} + x_{74} + x_{54} - x_{41} - x_{43} - x_{42} - x_{46} - x_{47} - x_{45} = 0$$
$$\qquad \text{(transshipment constraint for node 4)}$$
$$x_{35} + x_{45} + x_{75} - x_{54} - x_{53} - x_{57} = 0 \qquad \text{(transshipment constraint for node 5)}$$
$$x_{26} + x_{46} + x_{76} - x_{62} - x_{64} - x_{67} = 0 \qquad \text{(transshipment constraint for node 6)}$$
$$x_{47} + x_{57} + x_{67} = 1 \qquad \text{(demand of one unit at node 7)}$$
$$x_{ij} = 0 \text{ or } 1 \text{ for all } i, j \text{ combinations}$$

After formulating the above linear programming problem, we can solve it in a very similar fashion to all of the other linear programming problems we have solved in the previous chapters using Excel.

Solving the Shortest-Route Problem Using Excel

Exhibit 8-1 shows the Excel input worksheet for the Tri-State Shipping Company shortest-route problem. The worksheet consists of three distinct parts. The top portion, labeled "Variable Matrix," includes the 0–1 decision variables. The bottom portion, labeled "Distance Matrix," includes the distances between the existing routes. If a route is used between location i and location j, then the value of the decision variable in the top portion of the matrix will be equal to one; otherwise the value of the decision variable will be equal to zero. In the variable matrix, many of the decision variables do not exist because there is not a direct route between various nodes. In order to prevent a nonexistent variable from occurring in the solution, we will input "9999" or a very large value so that the corresponding nonexistent decision variable will never come in the solution because the distance is prohibitively large. For instance, there is no direct route between Chicago and Detroit; therefore, we will enter "9999" in cell F14. Since this value is unusually large, the corresponding decision variable in the variable matrix will assume a value of zero. Displaying a series

Exhibit 8-1 Input Worksheet for the Tri-State Shipping Company Shortest-Route Problem (Beginning Node 1, Ending Node 7)

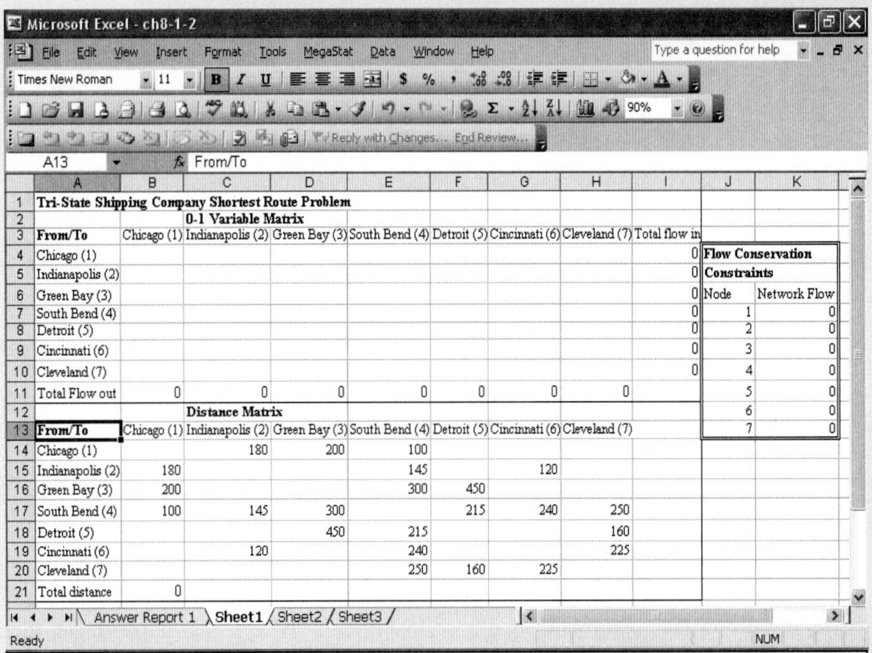

	A	B	C	D	E	F	G	H	I	J	K
1	Tri-State Shipping Company Shortest Route Problem										
2			0-1 Variable Matrix								
3	From/To	Chicago (1)	Indianapolis (2)	Green Bay (3)	South Bend (4)	Detroit (5)	Cincinnati (6)	Cleveland (7)	Total flow in		
4	Chicago (1)								0	Flow Conservation	
5	Indianapolis (2)								0	Constraints	
6	Green Bay (3)								0	Node	Network Flow
7	South Bend (4)								0	1	0
8	Detroit (5)								0	2	0
9	Cincinnati (6)								0	3	0
10	Cleveland (7)								0	4	0
11	Total Flow out	0	0	0	0	0	0	0		5	0
12			Distance Matrix							6	0
13	From/To	Chicago (1)	Indianapolis (2)	Green Bay (3)	South Bend (4)	Detroit (5)	Cincinnati (6)	Cleveland (7)		7	0
14	Chicago (1)		180	200	100						
15	Indianapolis (2)	180			145		120				
16	Green Bay (3)	200			300	450					
17	South Bend (4)	100	145	300		215	240	250			
18	Detroit (5)			450	215			160			
19	Cincinnati (6)		120		240			225			
20	Cleveland (7)				250	160	225				
21	Total distance	0									

Cell	Copied to	Formula
I4	I5 : I10	= SUM(B4 : H4)
B11	C11 : H11	= SUM(B4 : B10)
B21		= SUMPRODUCT(B4 : H10, B14 : H20)
K7		= C4 + D4 + E4
K8		= C4 + C7 + C9 − B5 − E5 − G5
K9		= D4 + D7 + D8 − B6 − E6 − F6
K10		= SUM(E4 : E10) − SUM(B7 : H7)
K11		= F6 + F7 + F10 − E8 − D8 − H8
K12		= G5 + G7 + G10 − C9 − E9 − H9
K13		= H7 + H8 + H9

of "9999" values in the distance matrix will unnecessarily crowd the distance matrix. Therefore, in order to prevent the "9999" occurring numerous times in the distance matrix, we will hide these values so that the cell they are in will appear blank even though the number "9999" is actually registered in the cell. To hide these cells, choose **Format | Cells | Number | Custom** and enter or choose **;;;**.

Exhibit 8-2   Parameter Specification Screen for the Tri-State Shipping Company Shortest-Route Problem (Beginning Node 1, Ending Node 7)

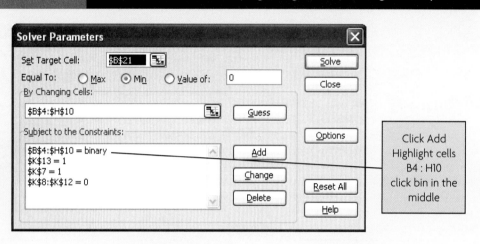

The third part of the input worksheet is located on the right-hand side of Exhibit 8-1 and is entitled "Flow Conservation Constraints." We enter the transshipment, supply, and demand formulas as shown in the linear programming formulation of the shortest route problem. The cell formulas for these cells (cells K7 through K13) are shown at the bottom of Exhibit 8-1 for the seven nodes. For example, the formula in K7, =C4 + D4 + E4, is equivalent to the left side of the equation for node 1. Cell C4 is x_{12}, cell D4 is x_{13}, and so on. The formula in cell K11 is equivalent to the left side of the equation in node 5: =F6 + F7 + F10 − E8 − D8 − H8. From the variable matrix we can easily ascertain that cell F6 is the variable x_{35}, cell F7 is variable x_{45}, and so forth. Since flow is possible from node 4 to each of the other nodes, and since flow is also possible from each of the other nodes to node 4, we use the SUM command in formulating the equation for node 4 in cell K10. The sum of the values going into node 4, =SUM(E4 : E10), minus the sum of all the values coming out of node 4, =SUM(B7 : H7), must be equal to zero.

The objective function for the problem is stated in cell B21, which is given by the sum of the cross products of the values in the variable matrix and the respective values in the distance matrix. The formula for this cell can be written using the following SUMPRODUCT term: =SUMPRODUCT(B4 : H10, B14 : H20). In this formula, B4 : H10 represents the decision variables in the decision matrix, and B14 : H20 represents the corresponding distance values in the distance matrix. After entering the information given above in the worksheet shown in Exhibit 8-1, we choose **Tools | Solver,** which brings up the parameter specification screen illustrated in Exhibit 8-2.

On this screen, we choose cell B21, which displays the objective function, for the "Set Target Cell" box. We choose "Min" as our objective since we are trying to find the shortest route. In the "By Changing Cells" box, we enter the range for the 0–1 decision variables based on the 0–1 variable matrix ($B$4 : $H$10). In the constraints portion of Exhibit 8-2, first we specify the decision variables as 0–1 decision variables by clicking "on Add." This brings up the "Add Constraints" screen. On this screen, we specify in the "Cell Reference" box the range for the decision variables, $B$4 : $H$10, and choose bin, for binary variables, from the signs given in the middle box. After specifying the decision variables as binary (0–1), we proceed to specify the supply constraint for node 1 and demand constraint for node 7.

Exhibit 8-3	Output Worksheet for the Tri-State Shipping Company Shortest-Route Problem (Beginning Node 1, Ending Node 7)

In specifying the constraints for node 1 and node 7, we click on "Add" and from the Add Constraints screen we specify the locations of the formula for node 1 and node 7, which are specified in cell K7 and cell K13 respectively. We choose equality for the sign of the constraint and 1 for the right-hand side, labeled as "Constraint." This indicates that node 1 (Chicago) is the beginning node and node 7 (Cleveland) is the ending node. Therefore, the constraint for node 1 is specified as K7$=1$ and the constraint for node 7 is specified as K13$=1$. We proceed in the same fashion to add all of the transshipment constraints. The final statement of the transshipment constraints is as follows: $K$8 : K12$=0$. In other words, the values of cell K8 (node 2) through cell K12 (node 6) must be equal to zero. After specifying all of the constraints, in cells K6 through K13 we choose "Options" and check the "Assume linear model" and "Assume nonnegative" boxes in cells K6 through K13 to ensure that linear programming is utilized and to ensure that all of the variables assume nonnegative values. We click on "Solve" and obtain the output worksheet given in Exhibit 8-3.

In Exhibit 8-3, the values of 1 in cells E4 and H7 indicate the shortest route from Chicago (node 1) to Cleveland (node 7). Since cell E4 is variable x_{14} and cell H7 is variable x_{47}, the minimum distance solution involves traveling from Chicago (node 1) to South Bend (node 4, variable x_{14}), and then traveling from South Bend (node 4) to Cleveland (node 7, variable x_{47}). Since the distance from Chicago to South Bend is 100 miles and the distance from South Bend to Cleveland is 250 miles, the total minimum distance is specified in cell B22, which is $100 + 250 = 350$. Note that the flow conservation portion of the worksheet now shows that cells K7 and K13 have values equal to 1 based on the way we specified the supply and demand constraints (K7=Chicago, K13=Cleveland).

If we need to determine the shortest route from node 1 to node 6 instead of from node 1 to node 7, we need to modify the constraints associated with node 6 and node 7. Node 7's constraint was written as $x_{47} + x_{57} + x_{67} = 1$. However, since we want to determine the shortest route to node 6, we need to change the constraint at node 7 to a transshipment constraint, where whatever comes into node 7 must leave node 7. Therefore, $x_{47} + x_{57} + x_{67} = x_{74} + x_{75} + x_{76}$. Converting this equation so that the problem can be solved using Excel, we move the variables from the right-hand side to the left-hand side of the equation. After this manipulation, we have the following equation: $x_{47} + x_{57} + x_{67} - x_{74} - x_{75} - x_{76} = 0$.

The constraint associated with node 6 was written as a typical transshipment constraint, as stated below, because the ending node was node 7 and not node 6:

$x_{26} + x_{46} + x_{76} - x_{62} - x_{64} - x_{67} = 0$ (transshipment constraint for node 6)

Since we are now trying to determine the shortest route to node 6, there will not be a need to include the $-x_{62} - x_{64} - x_{67}$ portion of the equation because we will not be leaving node 6 to visit any other node since node 6 is now the ending node. Because node 6 is the ending node, the flow or supply of one unit from the constraint associated with node 1 must end up in node 6. Therefore, the right-hand side of the equation for node 6 will be equal to 1. This results in the following equation for node 6 as the ending node: $x_{26} + x_{46} + x_{76} = 1$.

The resulting worksheet that shows the shortest route from node 1 to node 6 is displayed in Exhibit 8-4. Here, the flow conservation constraints are modified to show that the

Exhibit 8-4	Output Worksheet for the Tri-State Shipping Company Shortest-Route Problem (Beginning Node 1, Ending Node 6)

	Key Cell Fomulas	
Cell	Formula	
K12	= G5 + G7 + G10	
K13	= H7 + H8 + H9 − E10 − F10 − H10	

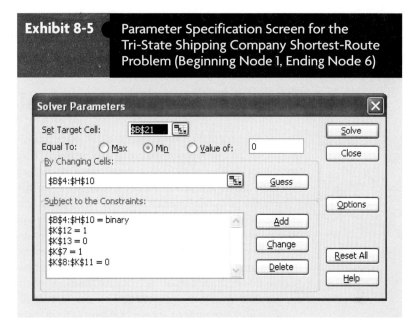

Exhibit 8-5   Parameter Specification Screen for the Tri-State Shipping Company Shortest-Route Problem (Beginning Node 1, Ending Node 6)

ending node is node 6 (Cincinnati) rather than node 7 (Cleveland). This change requires changing the specification of the formulas in cells K12 (node 6) and K13 (node 7). The revised formulas for cells K12 and K13 are shown at the bottom of Exhibit 8-4 in the Key Cell Formulas section. Exhibit 8-5 shows the parameter specification screen when the ending node is node 6 rather than node 7. This change requires specifying node 7 as a transshipment node, $K$13 = 0, and node 6 as a demand node, $K$12 = 1.

After clicking on "Solve" in Exhibit 8-5, we achieve the solution given in Exhibit 8-4. Since there are values of 1 in cells C4 (x_{12}) and G5 (x_{26}), the solution indicates that the shortest route from Chicago (node 1) to Cincinnati (node 6) is

1.   Chicago–Indianapolis (x_{12}).
2.   Indianapolis–Cincinnati (x_{26}).

Since the distance from Chicago to Indianapolis is 180 miles and the distance from Indianapolis to Cincinnati is 120 miles, the total distance from Chicago to Cincinnati is 180 + 120 = 300, displayed in cell B22. Note that in the flow conservation constraints, the values of 1 now appear in nodes K7 and K12 instead of K7 and K13.

We can make other similar changes to modify the beginning node or the ending node. For example, if we want to determine the shortest route from node 3 to node 7, using the original formulation, node 1's constraint is changed as follows because it no longer is the originating node:

$$x_{12} + x_{13} + x_{14} - x_{21} - x_{31} - x_{41} = 0 \quad \text{(transshipment constraint for node 1)}$$

Since node 3 is the new origin, it can be written without the variables going into node 3, and the supply at the origin is equal to 1, which makes the right-hand side of the equation equal to 1. This can be written as

$$x_{31} + x_{34} + x_{35} = 1 \quad \text{(supply of one unit at node 3)}$$

Companies are faced with many real-world business applications of the shortest-route problems. The Internet business organization www.mapquest.com provides a typical example of the application of the shortest-route problem.

The Minimum Spanning Tree Problem

One of the simplest of all management science techniques is the *minimum spanning tree* technique. The **minimum spanning tree problem** is to connect all of the nodes of a network using as little of the connecting "material" as possible. For instance, the nodes might represent oil storage tanks, and the arcs or branches might represent pipelines that are used to carry the oil between tanks. The cost of the pipeline would be proportional to the length of pipeline used. Hence, the objective would be to connect all of the tanks using as little pipeline as possible. Similar applications include connecting outlying communities for cable television service using minimal cable wiring, designing communications systems using minimal amounts of electrical wiring, designing highway networks using minimal amounts of road materials, and so on. Alternative measures of effectiveness that lead to even broader applications involve minimizing cost or time instead of distance or quantity of material.

Consider the network shown in Figure 8-3, where the nodes represent fuel storage tanks and the connecting arcs represent possible pipeline connections. The numbers on the arcs indicate the distance in meters for a particular pipeline connection. The purpose of the analysis is to obtain the shortest system of pipeline that will interconnect all of the storage tanks.

Algorithm for the Minimum Spanning Tree Problem (Concept Development)

The algorithm is quite straightforward:

1. Start at any node. (Generally, Node 1 is used as the starting point.) Identify the shortest connecting arc to another node. Shade in the starting node and the other node, and make the connecting arc a jagged line.

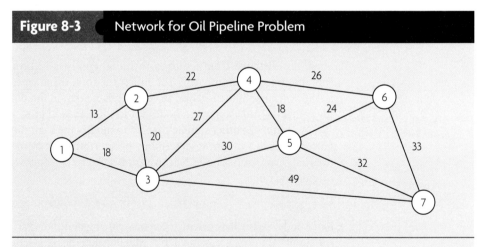

Figure 8-3   Network for Oil Pipeline Problem

Note: Arc lengths are not precisely proportional to the distances shown on the arcs.

2. Find the shortest arc from the connected nodes (i.e., the shaded nodes) to a node that is not yet connected. Shade in that node. If a tie occurs, break it arbitrarily. Make the connecting arc jagged.
3. Continue until all nodes have-been connected to the tree.
4. To find the total (minimal) length of the connecting arcs, sum their values.

Example 8-3

Suppose the manager for the fuel depot wants to determine the minimum spanning tree for the network of storage tanks given in Figure 8-3 and the amount of pipe that will be needed to make the connections.

Let's begin at Node 1. Two arcs are potential connectors with other nodes; one is 13 meters in length and the other is 18 meters. Choose 13 because it is the smaller of the two. Darken that arc and shade in Nodes 1 and 2.

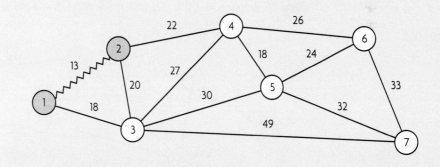

Now compare all possible arcs that could connect the connected nodes of the tree (i.e., Nodes 1 and 2) to another node. The arcs are 18 (Node 1 to Node 3), 20 (Node 2 to Node 3), and 22 (Node 2 to Node 4). Select 18 because it is the smallest, and add Arc 1–3 and Node 3 to the tree or to the set of connected nodes.

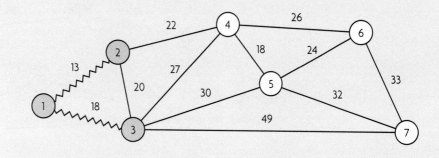

Again, find the arcs that lead from the connected nodes to nodes that are not currently connected. The arcs are 22 (Node 2 to Node 4), 27 (Node 3 to Node 4), 30 (Node 3 to Node 5), and 49 (Node 3 to Node 7). Because 22 is the smallest, it becomes the next link, and Node 4 becomes part of the tree or set of connected nodes.

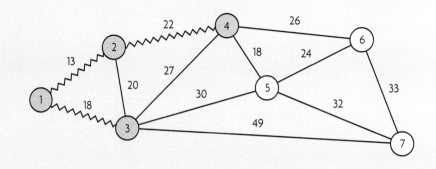

The possible arcs from the connected nodes to unconnected nodes are 49, 30, 18, and 26. Because 18 is the shortest, make Arc 4–5 and Node 5 part of the tree.

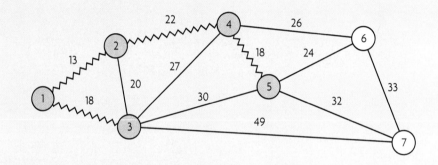

The possible arcs now are 26, 24, 32, and 49. Because 24 is the smallest, make Arc 5–6 and Node 6 part of the tree.

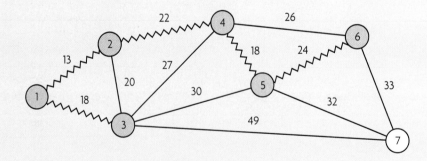

One node remains unconnected. Taking a slightly different perspective, we can see that the shortest link for this node and the completed portion of the tree is Arc 5–7. Hence, the minimum spanning tree is now complete. The last diagram shows the completed tree with the unused arcs omitted.

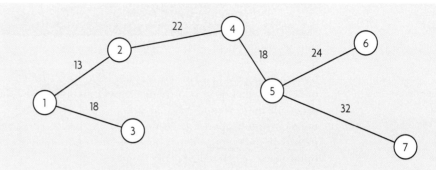

The length of pipe that will be needed for this system can be found by summing the arc lengths: 18 + 13 + 22 + 18 + 24 + 32 = 127 meters.

The algorithm used to solve the minimal spanning tree problems is referred to as a greedy algorithm. The greedy algorithm works well in some situations but can have arbitrarily bad performance in others.

◼◖ The Maximal Flow Problem

In a **maximal flow problem,** the objective is to maximize flow through a network. For example, a network might represent a system of roads and highways, and the objective might be to maximize the rate of flow of vehicles through the system. Other examples of maximal flow networks can be systems of pipelines that carry natural gas, oil, or water; paperwork systems; airlines routes; production system; and distribution systems.

In order to determine the maximal flow of a system, it is necessary to take into account the *flow capacities* of the various branches of a network. Branch capacities limit the rate of flow through a branch (arc) of the network. Hence, the objective is to determine the amount of flow through each branch that will achieve the maximum possible flow for the system as a whole.

It is assumed that there is a single input node (called a **source**) and a single output node (called a **sink**). It is also assumed that there is *flow conservation*, which means that the flow of any node is equal to the flow into that node.

As an example of a maximal flow network, consider the network shown in Figure 8-4. As you can see, Node 1 is the input node: therefore, all flow entering the system must come through that node. Node 4 is the output node; therefore, all flow leaving the system must go through that node. The numbers of the branches indicate the flow capacity of a branch *in a given direction.* For example, the 10 on Branch 1–2 indicates a maximum possible flow rate of 10 coming out of Node 1 along that branch. Now some branches permit flow in either direction. However, that is not the case for Branch 1–2; the 0 on Branch 1–2 indicates that no flow is possible *from* Node 2 to Node 1. Now consider Branch 2–3. We can see that the maximum flow rate along this branch is 2, and that flow can be in *either* direction. However, it is important to recognize that in such a branch flows cannot occur simultaneously in both directions. Consequently, for any branch, flow can occur in one direction only (i.e., it must be *unidirectional*), even though it may be allowable in both directions. The determination of which direction, or if there should be any flow at all, is a matter for analysis to resolve.

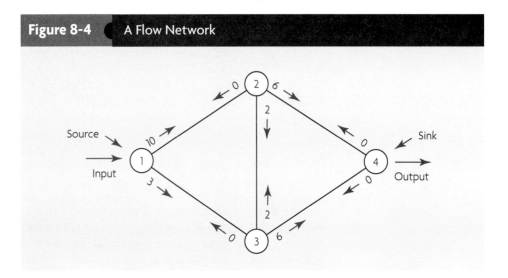

Figure 8-4 A Flow Network

Maximal Flow Algorithm (Concept Development)

The algorithm for the maximal flow problem is quite simple, and it consists of relatively few steps. These are

1. Find any **path** from the source node to the sink node that has a positive flow capacity. (Flow capacity of a path is determined by the smallest branch capacity along the path chosen in the direction of flow.) If no such path can be found, the current solution is optimal. If no such path can be found at the start, no flow is possible (i.e., there is no feasible solution). If a path with positive flow is found, continue the analysis.
2. Adjust the flow capacities of branches on the chosen path in the following manner. For each branch, at the end where the flow enters the branch, reduce the capacity by the amount of flow; at the end of the branch where flow leaves, increase the capacity by the amount of flow. For instance, consider Branch 1–3:

Suppose we decide to assign a flow of 3 to this branch, flowing from Node 1 to Node 3. According to the preceding rule, we must reduce the left capacity of the branch to 0 and the right side to 3. Hence, the revised branch would look like this:

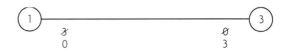

For clarity, we could also show the amount and direction of flow through this branch:

The interpretation of the information on the left end of the revised branch is that originally a maximal flow of 3 was possible; now, no additional flow is possible because the maximal flow is being used. If the revised value was positive (say, 2), this would indicate that additional flow from left to right in this branch is possible. On the right-hand side of Branch 1–3, we see that, originally, *no* flow was possible from Node 3 to Node 1 through this branch. That is still true, even though the revised value is a 3. The 3 indicates how much of the current flow *can be reversed*. For example, at some point in the analysis of this network, we may assign a flow of 3 from Node 1 to Node 3 through this branch, and end up with the numbers shown. However, that assignment might not be optimal; at a later point in the analysis, we might want to undo some, or all, of this flow assignment. The revised value on the right end of the branch (i.e., 3) indicates the extent to which the current flow can be reduced. Had the original value on the right end been nonzero, we might well wish to consider flow in the other direction. Hence, as a matter of course, we always revise the values on both ends of a branch at the same time. Note, too, that the sum of the revised values will *always* equal the sum of the original values.

3. Return to step 1.

Example 8-4

In order to demonstrate the algorithm, let's analyze the network shown in Figure 8-4. We can begin by choosing *any* path that will allow a positive flow from the source (Node 1) to the sink (Node 4). Obviously, there are a number of paths, such as 1–2–4, 1–2–3–4, 1–3–2–4, and 1–3–4. Suppose we arbitrarily select 1–2–4.

The maximum flow from Node 1 to Node 2 is 10, whereas the maximum flow from Node 2 to Node 4 is 6. Thus, the limiting capacity along this path is the 6 for Branch 2–4, so we can assign a flow of 6 for each branch on this path. This requires that the capacities at the end of each branch on the path be adjusted accordingly. Thus, we have

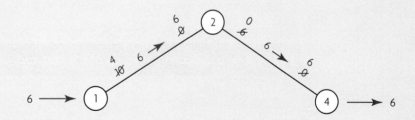

Branch 2–4 is fully loaded; no additional flow can be sent in the 2–4 direction. However, Branch 1–2 can still accept an additional flow of 4. In selecting our next path, either we might want to explore additional flow through Branch 1–2 or we might investigate some other path. Suppose we elect to further explore flow through 1–2, say by examining Path 1–2–3–4.

The revised network, as it now stands, is shown in Figure 8–5. By scanning Path 1–2–3–4, we can see that Branch 2–3 is the most restrictive: its flow capacity from Node 2 to Node 3 is 2. Hence, we can only assign a flow of 2 along this path. For Branch 1–2, this will add 2 to the current flow, making a total flow of 8 for that

Figure 8-5   Updated Flow Network

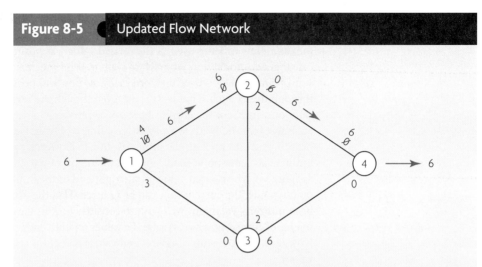

branch. For Branch 2–3, the flow will be 2, and for Branch 3–4, which now has no flow, the assigned flow also will be 2. The revised network is shown in Figure 8-6.

If no further positive flow from the source to the sink is possible, an optimal solution has been found. That is not the case, here, though. Path 1–3–4 can still accept some flow: Branch 1–3 can accept a flow of 3, whereas Branch 3–4 can accept a flow of 4. Hence, the limiting branch is 1–3; therefore, a flow of 3 can be assigned to this path. The resulting network is shown in Figure 8-7.

At this point, no additional flow is possible because no path has a positive flow capacity. Hence, this solution is optimal; the maximal flow rate is 11, which is shown as both the sum of the inputs and the sum of the outputs. Moreover, the flow through the various branches of the network is also shown. These values are summarized in Figure 8-8.

For a network as small as this, it often is possible to determine the maximal rate of flow by inspection. However, for larger, more complicated networks, the more formal approach outlined here is prudent. In that regard, when trying to determine

Figure 8-6   Second Revision of the Network

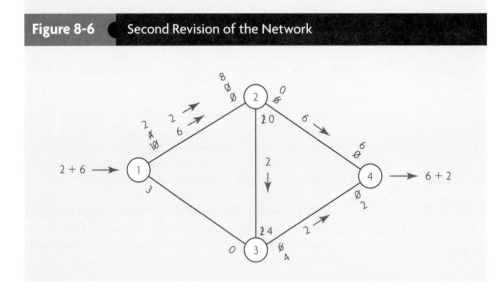

Figure 8-7 ● **Third Revision of Flow Network**

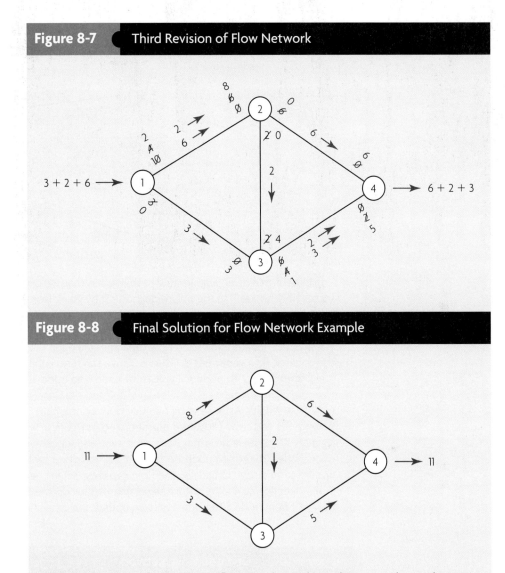

Figure 8-8 ● **Final Solution for Flow Network Example**

if a path exists that has a positive flow rate during the analysis, note the total capacity of branches leaving the source as well as the total capacity of the branches entering the sink. The flow capacity of the network cannot exceed either of these.

Demonstration of Reverse Flow

We mentioned earlier that the flow on a branch can be reversed. To demonstrate the reverse flow, consider the following example.

Example 8-5

Consider the network shown in Figure 8-9. Determine the maximal flow from node 1 (source node) to node 5 (sink node) for this network. Indicate the paths and the associated flows that resulted in the maximal flow.

Figure 8-9	Flow Network for Demonstration of Reverse Flow

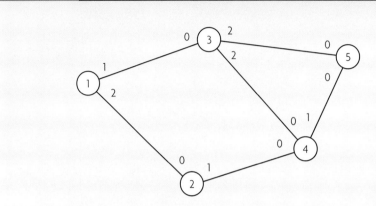

In determining an augmenting path, we see that we can form a path form the source node (node 1) to the sink node (node 5) by going from node 1 to node 3, from node 3 to node 4, and from node 4 to node 5. The augmenting path 1–3–4–5 can accommodate a flow of 1. After sending 1 unit of flow on the augmenting path 1–3–4–5, the updated flows and flow capacities are depicted in Figure 8-10. Based on the updated flow capacities in Figure 8-10, we can send 1 unit from node 1 to node 2, 1 unit from node 2 to node 4, 1 unit from node 4 to node 3, and 1 unit from node 3 to node 5. The augmenting path is 1–2–4–3–5 and the flow is 1 unit, which makes the total flow 2 units. After sending 1 unit of flow on the path 1–2–4–3–5, the updated flow values and flow capacities are depicted in Figure 8-11. As can be observed in Figure 8-11, there are no other paths that can send a positive flow from the source node (node 1) to the sink node (node 5). Let's take a closer look at the branch between node 3 and node 4. Originally, the flow capacity is 2 in the direction of 3–4 and 0 in the direction of 4–3. When we sent 1 unit of flow on the path 1–3–4–5, we have a flow of 1 from node 3 to node 4 and we update the capacities by reducing the flow

Figure 8-10	Updated Flow Network

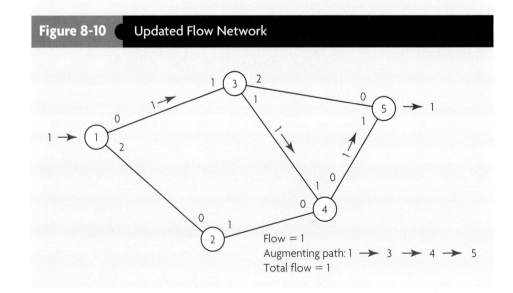

Flow = 1
Augmenting path: 1 → 3 → 4 → 5
Total flow = 1

Figure 8-11   **Revised Flow Network**

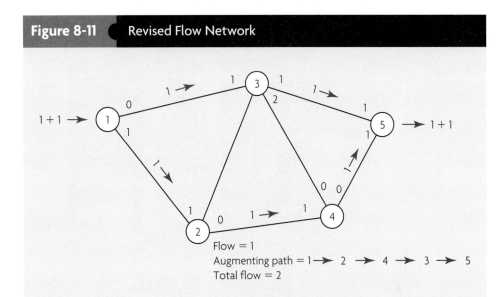

Flow = 1
Augmenting path = 1 ➤ 2 ➤ 4 ➤ 3 ➤ 5
Total flow = 2

capacity in the direction of 3–4 and increasing the flow capacity in the direction of 4–3. In the second iteration, when we utilize the path 1–2–4–3–5, we are sending flow in the reverse direction on the branch between node 3 and node 4. Note that it would not be feasible to select the path 1–2–4–3–5 and send any flow on the 4–3 direction during the first iteration because the flow capacity from node 4 to node 3 was equal to zero. After we sent 1 unit of flow in the direction of 3–4, we updated the flow capacities so that there is a flow capacity of 1 from node 4 to node 3, which makes it possible to utilize the path 1–2–4–3–5. In essence this means that we are reversing the flow that was initially allocated on the 3–4 direction to the 4–3 direction and we end up with 0 flow on the branch between node 3 and node 4. Since no additional flow is possible from the source node (node 1) to the sink node (node 5), the solution is optimal and the maximal flow rate is 2.

Linear Programming Formulation of the Maximal Flow Problem

The maximal flow problem also can be solved as a linear programming problem. In order to demonstrate the linear programming formulation of the maximal flow problem, consider the following example.

Example 8-6

Turkmen Oil Ltd. is an oil conglomerate that has a network of pipelines and intermediate oil storage facilities connecting oil fields in Baku, Azerbaijan, and to the newly built oil refinery in Adana, Turkey. Crude oil can be pumped from the oil field to any of the three intermediate storage facilities A, B, and C in Azerbaijan. The maximum flow capacity from the oil field to intermediate storage facilities A, B, and C is 20, 15, and 22 thousand barrels of oil per day respectively. Oil is pumped from these three major intermediate storage facilities to other intermediate processing facilities in

Table 8-1 Branches of the Network and Flow Capacities of the Branches for the Turkmen Oil Ltd. Maximal Flow Problem

Network Branches	Maximum Flow Capacity
A→D	18
A→B	20
B→A	10
B→D	20
B→E	13
C→B	5
C→F	18
D→G	14
D→E	10
E→G	25
E→F	5
E→H	5
F→H	20
G→Refinery	30
G→H	10
H→Refinery	25

Turkey labeled D, E, F, G, and H. The oil is finally pumped from these facilities (D, E, F, G, and H) to the oil refinery in Adana for final processing. The pipeline branches comprising this network and their maximum respective flow capacities are given in Table 8-1.

a. Draw the network diagram.
b. Formulate this problem as a linear programming problem.
c. Use Excel and determine the maximal flow of oil in thousands of barrels per day from the oil field to the oil refinery.
d. State the amount of flow in thousands of barrels on each branch.

Solution

a. The network diagram for this problem is drawn in Figure 8-12.
b. In formulating this problem as a linear programming problem, we will first define the decision variables. There will be one variable for each unidirectional branch in the problem. There are 17 branches in the network and 16 of the 17 branches flow is in one direction since the capacity of the flow in the opposite direction is equal to zero. However, the branch between node A (2) and node B (3) has a flow capacity in both directions. Therefore, we need two variables for this branch; one of the variables will account for the possible flow from node 2 to node 3 and one variable will account for the flow from node 3 to node 2. Therefore, there will be a total of 18 decision variables.

Let x_{ij} = thousands of barrels of oil that flow from node i to node j
i = 1, 2, 3, 4, 5, 6, 7, 8, 9, 10   and j = 1, 2, 3, 4, 5, 6, 7, 8, 9, 10
x_{ij} only exists for nodes that are connected in the network.

Since we need to determine the maximum flow in thousands of barrels of oil that originate in the Baku oil field (node 1) and terminate in the oil refinery in

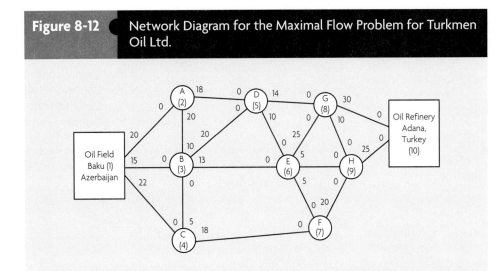

Adana (node 10), we need to modify the network by adding a fictitious dummy branch between node 10 and node 1. We need to set the flow capacity to a very high number such as 9999 from node 10 to node 1, and a capacity of zero from node 1 to node 10. This dummy node is necessary to specify the objective function. After defining the decision variables and establishing the dummy branch (variable), we are ready to determine the objective function. The objective is to maximize the total number of barrels of oil flowing from node 1 (oil field) to node 10 (oil refinery). The flow on the dummy branch from node 10 to node 1 represents the total amount of flow into node 10 from node 1. Thus, the objective is to maximize the flow of the dummy branch. This can be written as

maximize $Z = x_{10,1}$

In formulating the shortest-route problem, we have seen that the intermediate nodes are treated as transshipment nodes. All of the nodes of the maximum flow network also can be shown as transshipment nodes. A unit of flow coming into a node must exit that node. Using this logic, the node 1 transshipment constraint can be written as follows:

$x_{12} + x_{13} + x_{14} = x_{10,1}$

After rearranging the constraint for node 1 so that the right-hand side only consists of numerical values, the net flow constraint for node 1 is as follows:

$x_{12} + x_{13} + x_{14} - x_{10,1} = 0$ (net flow transshipment constraint at node 1)

Using similar logic, the rest of the net flow or transshipment constraints would be written as follows:

$x_{23} + x_{25} - x_{12} - x_{32} = 0$ (net flow transshipment constraint at node 2)
$x_{32} + x_{35} + x_{36} - x_{13} - x_{23} - x_{43} = 0$ (net flow transshipment constraint at node 3)
$x_{43} + x_{47} - x_{14} = 0$ (net flow transshipment constraint at node 4)

$x_{56} + x_{58} - x_{25} - x_{35} = 0$ (net flow transshipment constraint at node 5)

$x_{67} + x_{68} + x_{69} - x_{36} - x_{56} = 0$ (net flow transshipment constraint at node 6)

$x_{79} - x_{47} - x_{67} = 0$ (net flow transshipment constraint at node 7)

$x_{89} + x_{8,10} - x_{58} - x_{68} = 0$ (net flow transshipment constraint at node 8)

$x_{9,10} - x_{69} - x_{79} - x_{89} = 0$ (net flow transshipment constraint at node 9)

$x_{10,1} - x_{8,10} - x_{9,10} = 0$ (net flow transshipment constraint at node 10)

The second type of constraints are the branch capacity constraints and they simply represent the flow capacity of each branch. These constraints can be written as follows:

$x_{12} \leq 20$

$x_{13} \leq 15$

$x_{14} \leq 22$

$x_{23} \leq 20$

$x_{25} \leq 18$

$x_{32} \leq 10$

$x_{35} \leq 20$

$x_{36} \leq 13$

$x_{43} \leq 5$

$x_{47} \leq 18$

$x_{56} \leq 10$

$x_{58} \leq 14$

$x_{67} \leq 5$

$x_{68} \leq 25$

$x_{69} \leq 5$

$x_{79} \leq 20$

$x_{89} \leq 10$

$x_{8,10} \leq 30$

$x_{9,10} \leq 25$

$x_{10,1} \leq 9999$

Note that all of these constraints, including the dummy branch, are less-than-or-equal-to constraints.

The addition of the nonnegativity constraint ($x_{ij} \geq 0$, for all available i, j combinations) completes the linear programming formulation of this maximal flow problem.

c.   After formulating the maximal flow problem as a linear programming problem, we can easily solve it using Excel. Exhibit 8-6 shows the input worksheet for the Turkmen Oil Ltd. maximal flow problem. The worksheet illustrated in Exhibit 8-6 is divided into three parts. The first part, represented in the top portion of Exhibit 8-6, is the matrix that shows the actual flow values of each of the branches. These values, ranging from cell B4 to cell H7, represent the values of the decision variables. The values in column L represent the values of the flow going into each of the nodes and the values in row 14 represent the values of the flow going out of each of the nodes. The bottom (second) part of the worksheet represents the flow capacities of each node. For example, the value in cell C17 is 20. This value represents the flow capacity of the branch going from

Exhibit 8-6	Input Worksheet for the Turkmen Oil Ltd. Maximal Flow Problem

Cell	Copied to	
L4	L5 : L13	= SUM(B4 : K4)
B14	C14 : K14	= SUM(B4 : B13)
M17		= C4 + D4 + E4 − B13
M18		= D5 + F5 − C4 − C6
M19		= C6 + F6 + G6 − D4 − D5 − D7
M20		= D7 + H7 − E4
M21		= G8 + I8 − F5 − F6
M22		= H9 + I9 + J9 − G6 − G8
M23		= J10 − H7 − H9
M24		= J11 + K11 − I8 − I9
M25		= K12 − J9 − J10 − J11
M26		= B13 − K11 − K12
B27		= B13

Exhibit 8-7   Parameter Specification Screen for the Turkmen Oil Ltd. Maximal Flow Problem

the oil fields in Baku (node 1) to node A or 2. Note that the third and final portion of the input worksheet is the Node flow equations, represented next to the flow capacity matrix. For example, for node 1, the flow equation is stated as $x_{12} + x_{13} + x_{14} - x_{10,1} = 0$. Since x_{12}, x_{13}, x_{14}, and $x_{10,1}$ are cells C4, D4, E4, and B13 respectively, the left-hand side of the equation for node 1 in cell M17 can be written as C4 + D4 + E4 - B13. Likewise, the equation for node 3 was written as $x_{32} + x_{35} + x_{36} - x_{13} - x_{23} - x_{43} = 0$. Based on this formula, the left-hand side of this formula in cell M19 is =C6 + F6 + G6 - D4 - D5 - D7. The spreadsheet formulas for all 10 nodes are listed at the bottom of Exhibit 8-6. After Exhibit 8-6 is completely prepared, we choose **Tools | Solver** and obtain the Solver Parameters screen displayed in Exhibit 8-7.

On this screen, we choose cell B13, which displays the objective function for the "Set Target Cell" box. We choose "Max" as our objective since we are trying to find the maximal flow. In the "By Changing Cells" box we enter the range for the decision variables based on the matrix of actual flow ($B$4 : $K$13). In the constraints portion of Exhibit 8-7, we have two types of constraints to specify. First, we specify that the decision variables ($B$4 : $K$13) stated in the matrix of actual flow may not exceed the flow capacities ($B$17 : $K$26) specified in the matrix of flow capacities. Second, we specify the node flow equations as transshipment constraints for each of the nodes so that the flow that comes into a node must leave that node. The left-hand sides of the constraints for the 10 nodes are listed in nodes M17 through M26. The right-hand side of all of these constraints are specified as zero in cells N17 through N26. After completely specifying the "Solver" Parameters screen, we click on "Solve" and obtain the output worksheet illustrated in Exhibit 8-8.

The maximal flow of oil in thousands of barrels per day from the oil field to the oil refinery is 55 thousand barrels of oil, as shown in cells B13 and B27.

d. The amount of flow in thousands of barrels on each branch is given in Exhibit 8-8. The optimal values of the decision variables, which indicate the flow in thousands of barrels, is summarized in Table 8-2.

Exhibit 8-8   Output Worksheet for the Turkmen Oil Ltd. Maximal Flow Problem

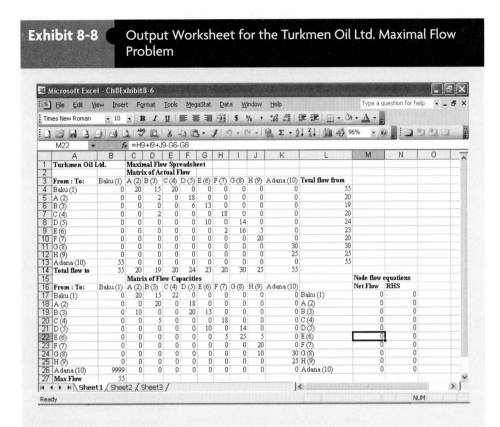

Table 8-2   Summary of the Optimal Flow Quantities for Turkmen Old Ltd.

Branch	Decision Variable	Cell	Flow in 1,000s of Barrels
Baku to A	x_{12}	C4	20
Baku to B	x_{13}	D4	15
Baku to C	x_{14}	E4	20
A to B	x_{23}	D5	2
A to D	x_{25}	F5	18
B to D	x_{35}	F6	6
B to E	x_{36}	G6	13
C to B	x_{43}	D7	2
C to F	x_{47}	H7	18
D to E	x_{56}	G8	10
D to G	x_{58}	I8	14
E to F	x_{67}	H9	2
E to G	x_{68}	I9	16
E to H	x_{69}	J9	5
F to H	x_{79}	J10	20
G to Adana	$x_{8,10}$	K11	30
H to Adana	$x_{9,10}$	K12	25

A Modern Management Science Application: *Philips Electronics*

The 'bullwhip effect' is a phenomenon where the demand variability increases as one moves up a supply chain. In other words, there is less variability in inventory for finished goods than for the individual components that go into those goods.

Philips Electronics Company is the 10th largest electronics company in the world with annual sales over $30 billion and 164,000 employees worldwide. Two subsidiaries of Philips Electronics—Philips Semiconductors (PS) and Philips Optical Storage (POS)—were experiencing problems with the bullwhip effect in managing their supply chain. PS, one of the world's major semiconductor suppliers, has over $5 billion in annual sales and over 33,000 employees. POS develops and builds optical storage products and has only about 9,000 employees. Both companies made a commitment to manage relationships on their supply chains to compensate for the bullwhip effect.

However, this problem could not be solved using existing software. Since POS purchases parts from PS, the companies worked together to reduce the bullwhip effect by developing a collaborative-planning (CP) project to address issues related to the bullwhip effect and the supporting computerized decision support system. The CP project team identified four key requirements to consider:

1. Intensive collaboration on the supply chain improves success.
2. Supply-chain information must be shared with customers and suppliers.
3. Decisions related to capacities and material flows must be synchronized.
4. We must make quick decisions regarding questions that relate to the supply chain.

Because this was a major project, it needed acceptance from users and employees in order to succeed. This was accomplished using two methods:

1. Workshops with all the primary users and their managers.
2. Face-to-face discussions conducted with all the primary users.

CP used many operations research (management science) techniques to solve the problem faced by the companies, including mathematical programming techniques such as integer programming, and network models to manage multi-echelon inventories. Since PS is a supplier to POS, Philips must manage one level of inventory at PS and a second level of inventory at POS, making it a two-echelon inventory system.

The production planning process involved integration of medium-level planning with short-term planning to avoid miscommunication among the departments. The short-term planning problem is to decide quantities of each "end-item" to release to the shop floor, while medium-term planning involves demand forecasting and overall aggregate production planning. Integrating the short- and medium-term plans is a matter of synchronizing weekly and daily production planning. There are three production "numbers," or factors, that are driven by these plans:

1. The number of wafers to fabricate.
2. The number of integrated circuits to assemble.
3. The number of integrated circuits to ship to various destinations.

The CP process consists of four "stages":

1. Gather data.
2. Make a decision about supply chain components.
3. Escalate to top management.
4. Deploy and execute decisions.

A major advantage of the computerized collaborative-planning support tool is that it is able to compute the complete schedule very fast. This speed allows the users to develop a feasible plan within seconds, and it then also allows users to perform what-if analysis, and, therefore, to also develop multiple contingency plans.

Collaborative planning provides both PS and POS with an opportunity to use tactical decision making rather than fire-fighting. The software signals potential problems in filling orders and identifies the effective measures to alleviate problems. The key to the success of this program is great communication between the operations research consultants and operations managers at Philips.

This CP project has resulted in savings, of up to $5 million annually, for PS, but, more importantly, both companies (PS and POS) improved customer and supplier delivery times.

Source: T. de Kok, F. Jansses, J. van Doremlen, E. van Wachem, M. Clerkx, and W. Peeters, "Philips Electronics Synchronizes Its Supply Chain to End the Bullwhip Effect," *Interfaces* 35, no. 1 (January–February 2005), pp. 37–48.

Comment

Sometimes it can be difficult to decide on the most appropriate representation of a problem; this is often the most difficult part of the process. Once the *type* of network problem has been identified, Excel or other software packages are available to solve network problems.

Summary

Network models are an important approach for problem solving. Not only can they be used to model a wide range of problems, they also are relatively simple to work with and provide a visual portrayal of a problem.

This chapter describes three frequently used algorithms: the shortest-route algorithm, which is useful for determining the shortest distance (cost, etc.) from an origin to a destination through a network; the minimum spanning tree algorithm, which is useful in determining the minimum distance (cost, time) needed to connect a set of locations into a single system; and the maximal flow algorithm, which is useful for determining the greatest amount of flow that can be transmitted through a system in which various branches, or connections, have specified flow capacity limitations.

Glossary

Arc A branch, or line, in a network.

Maximal Flow Problem Determining the maximum amount of flow that can be obtained for a system of pipes, roads, and so on.

Minimum Spanning Tree Problem Finding the shortest set of arcs that will connect all of the nodes of a network.

Network A set of nodes and connecting arcs or branches. Can be useful in representing various systems, such as distribution systems, production systems, and transportation systems.

Node A circle in a network. It may represent location or a switching point.

Path A connected sequence of nodes and branches from one node (usually the source or origin) to another node (usually the sink or destination). Also called a route.

Shortest-Route Problem Determining the shortest path from an origin to a destination through a network.

Sink The one node in a flow network to which all flow is directed; the exit point of a system.

Source The one node in a flow network through which all flow enters the system.

Spanning Tree A set of branches, or arcs, that connects all of the nodes in a network.

Solved Problems

Problem 1

Shortest route

a. Given this network, which shows the distance in miles between each of five delivery locations, manually find the shortest route from the home office (node 1) to each delivery location.

b. Formulate this problem as a linear programming problem where the delivery location is nodes.

c. Use Excel and find the shortest route from the home office (node 1) to delivery location 5 (node 5).

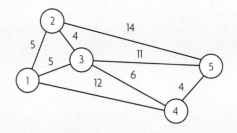

Solution   a. Using a single diagram for the entire analysis, begin by assigning the permanent label of [0, S] to node 1, then shade in the node to indicate that its label is permanent. Then, assign a temporary label to each node that can be reached directly from node 1. The label should consist of two numbers: the first number will indicate the distance from node 1 and the second number will indicate that node 1 is the predecessor node:

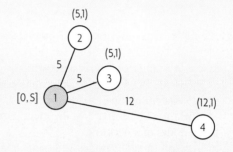

Determine which node shows the shortest temporary label distance. In this instance, there is a tie between nodes 2 and 3. Both show a distance of 5, whereas node 4 shows a distance of 12. Choose either node 2 or node 3 arbitrarily. Suppose we choose node 2. Its label now becomes permanent, which we indicate by shading in node 2 and changing its label from parentheses to brackets. Now identify each nonpermanently labeled node that can be reached directly from this newest permanently labeled node. These are nodes 3 and 5. The cumulative distance from node 1 through node 2 to node 3 is 9. Because this distance exceeds the current temporary label of node 3, no change should be made to the label at node 3. Because node 5 has no label, it will now get a temporary label of (19,2). The 19 is the cumulative distance for path 1–2–5, and the 2 indicates that node 2 is the next node before 5 on that path.

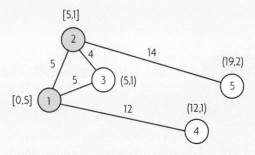

The smallest temporary label is now at node 3, which has a distance from node 1 of 5 (node 4 has a distance of 12 and node 5 has a distance of 19). Convert the label at node 3 to a permanent label and shade in the node. Now find the cumulative distance from node 1 through node 3 to each nonpermanent node. The distance to node 4 is

$5 + 6 = 11$. Because this distance is *less than* the current temporary label at node 4, update the label with this smaller value. The cumulative distance to node 5 through node 3 is $5 + 11 = 16$. Again, this amount is less than the temporary label, so the label at node 5 must be updated to (16,3) showing a distance of 16 miles achieved with node 3 as the previous node on the route.

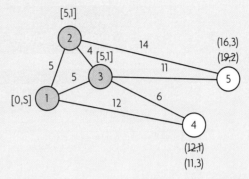

At this point, node 4 has the smaller temporary label of the two remaining nodes. Hence, its label becomes permanent. Next, we see that the cumulative distance to node 5 through node 4 is equal to the 11 miles at node 4 plus 4 miles from node 4 to node 5, which is 15 miles. Because this amount is less than the temporary label at node 5, the label at node 5 is updated to show this. And since that is the last node, the analysis is complete.

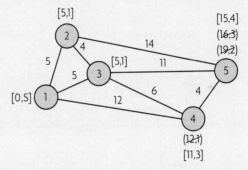

Backtracking through the network, using the sequence indicated by the node labels, and obtaining the distances from the node labels, we get

Node	Distance	Route
2	5	1–2
3	5	1–3
4	11	1–3–4
5	15	1–3–4–5

b. Here is the linear programming formulation of the shortest-route problem:

$$\text{minimize } Z = 5x_{12} + 5x_{13} + 14x_{25} + 11x_{35} + 6x_{34} + 12x_{14} + 4x_{23} + 4x_{45} + 5x_{21} + 5x_{31} + 14x_{52} + 11x_{53} + 6x_{43} + 12x_{41} + 4x_{32} + 4x_{54}$$

subject to

$$x_{12} + x_{13} + x_{14} = 1 \quad \text{(supply of one unit at node 1)}$$

$$x_{32} + x_{52} + x_{12} = x_{25} + x_{23} + x_{21}$$
$$x_{32} + x_{52} + x_{12} - x_{25} - x_{23} - x_{21} = 0 \quad \text{(transshipment constraint for node 2)}$$

$$x_{23} + x_{13} + x_{53} + x_{43} = x_{31} + x_{32} + x_{35} + x_{34}$$
$$x_{23} + x_{13} + x_{53} + x_{43} - x_{31} - x_{32} - x_{35} - x_{34} = 0 \quad \text{(transshipment constraint for node 3)}$$

$$x_{14} + x_{34} + x_{54} = x_{41} + x_{43} + x_{45}$$

$$x_{14} + x_{34} + x_{54} - x_{41} - x_{43} - x_{45} = 0 \quad \text{(transshipment constraint for node 4)}$$

$$x_{25} + x_{35} + x_{45} = 1 \quad \text{(demand of one unit at node 5)}$$

$$x_{ij} = 0 \text{ or } 1 \text{ for all } i, j \text{ combinations}$$

Exhibit 8-9   Worksheet for Solved Problem 1, the Shortest-Route Problem (Beginning Node 1, Ending Node 5)

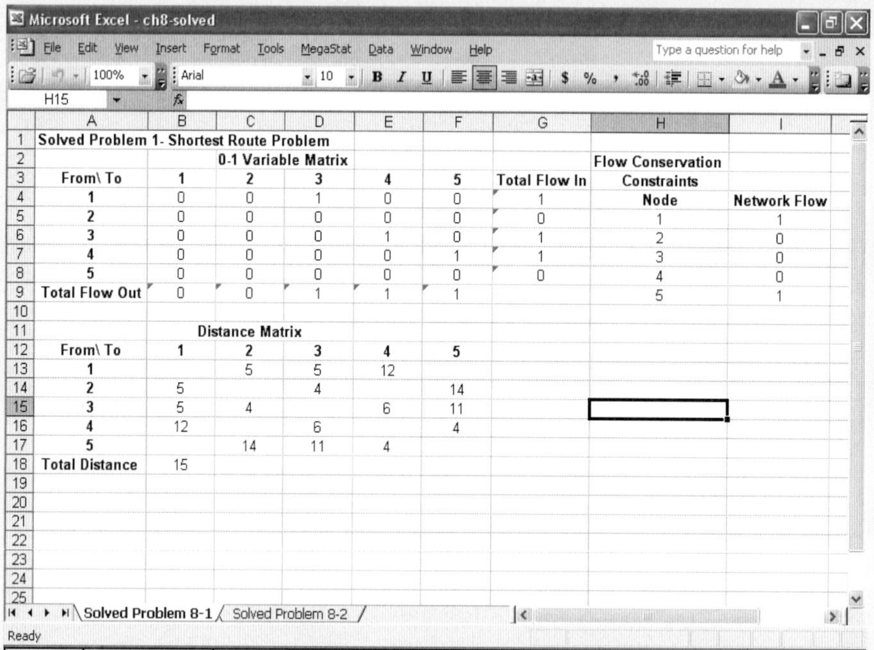

Microsoft Excel - ch8-solved

File Edit View Insert Format Tools MegaStat Data Window Help

H15

	A	B	C	D	E	F	G	H	I
1	Solved Problem 1- Shortest Route Problem								
2			0-1 Variable Matrix					Flow Conservation	
3	From\ To	1	2	3	4	5	Total Flow In	Constraints	
4	1	0	0	1	0	0	1	Node	Network Flow
5	2	0	0	0	0	0	0	1	1
6	3	0	0	0	1	0	1	2	0
7	4	0	0	0	0	1	1	3	0
8	5	0	0	0	0	0	0	4	0
9	Total Flow Out	0	0	1	1	1		5	1
10									
11			Distance Matrix						
12	From\ To	1	2	3	4	5			
13	1		5	5	12				
14	2	5		4		14			
15	3	5	4		6	11			
16	4	12		6		4			
17	5		14	11	4				
18	Total Distance	15							
19									

Solved Problem 8-1 / Solved Problem 8-2

Ready

Cell	Copied to	Formula
B9	C9 : F9	= SUM(B4 : B8)
G4	C5 : G8	= SUM(B4 : F4)
B18		= SUMPRODUCT(B4 : F8, B13 : F17)
C14	E14, B13, F13 D15, C16 E16, B17, F17	Click **FORMAT I CELLS I NUMBER I CUSTOM**, then Type: ;;; to hide the value of 9999
I5		= C4 + D4 + E4
I6		= C6 + C8 + C4 − F5 − B5 − D5
I7		= D5 + D4 + D8 + D7 − B6 − C6 − F6 − E6
I8		= E4 + E6 + E8 − B7 − D7 − F7
I9		= F5 + F6 + F7

c. The Excel solution is displayed in Exhibit 8-9. After selecting **Tools I Solver,** the parameter specification screen shown in Exhibit 8-10 is prepared. Note that in Exhibit 8-10

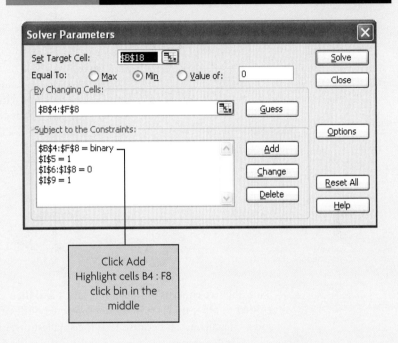

Exhibit 8-10 Parameter Specification Screen for Solved Problem 1, the Shortest-Route Problem (Beginning Node 1, Ending Node 5)

all of the variables are defined as binary. The worksheet shown in Exhibit 8-9 is developed very similarly to the worksheet shown in Exhibit 8-1; the formulas for Exhibit 8-9 are given at the bottom of the worksheet. The shortest distance from node 1 to node 5 is 15, and, as indicated by 1's in the 0–1 matrix, the shortest route is 1–3–4–5.

Problem 2

Minimum spanning tree   Given this network that shows distances in miles for potential node connections, find the minimum spanning tree and the minimum total of the connections.

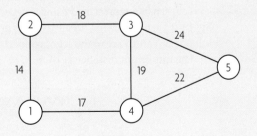

Solution

Start at node 1 and choose the shortest arc to another node. There are two arcs to choose from: 1–2, which is 14, and 1–4, which is 17. Hence, choose 1–2. Indicate this by making arc 1–2 a jagged line and shade in nodes 1 and 2.

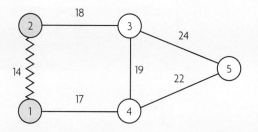

At this point, the (partial) tree consists of nodes 1 and 2 and the arc between them. Find the smallest arc that will connect the partial tree with another node. There are two arcs to choose from: 1–4, which is 17, and 2–3, which is 18. Because 17 is the smaller of the two, arc 1–4 is chosen. Indicate this by making arc 1–4 a jagged line and shade in node 4.

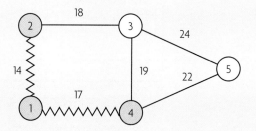

Now the tree consists of nodes 1, 2, and 4 and their connecting links. The possible direct links to other nodes from these connected nodes are 2–3, which is 18; 4–3, which is 19; and 4–5, which is 22. Because 18 is the smallest distance, arc 2–3 is selected and a jagged line is drawn between nodes 2 and 3. Also, node 3 is shade in.

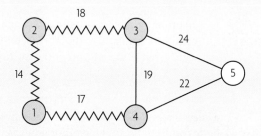

Only one node remains to be linked to the spanning tree, node 5. It can be linked at node 4 for a distance of 22, or at node 3 for a distance of 24. Because 22 is the smaller distance, arc 4–5 is chosen and represented using a jagged line. (Note that although arc 3–4 has a value of only 19, it isn't considered because it does not offer a link with a node not already in the tree; both nodes 3 and 4 are in the set of connected nodes.) This completes the tree.

The minimum distance is $14 + 17 + 18 + 22 = 71$ miles.

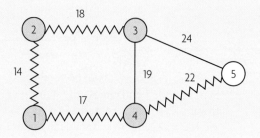

Problem 3   *Maximal flow*

      a.   Manually determine the maximal flow through this system of pipelines from node 1 to node 5.

      b.   Formulate this problem as a linear programming problem.

      c.   Use Excel and determine the maximal flow through this system of pipelines from node 1 to node 5.

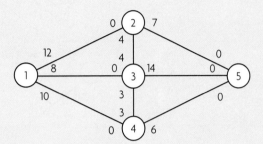

Solution   a.   Begin by selecting *any* path through the network that has a positive flow capacity. One such path is 1–2–5, where branch 1–2 has a capacity of 12 and branch 2–5 has a capacity of 7. The limiting capacity is the smallest capacity along the path, which is 7.

          Assign 7 to each branch on this path and revise the flow capacities accordingly.

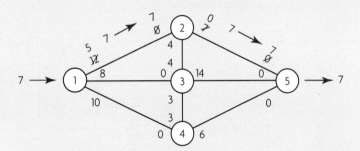

          Find another path that has a positive flow capacity from node 1 to node 5. For simplicity, suppose we continue with branch 1–2, using path 1–2–3–5. The flow capacities of the branches on this path are 5 on 1–2, 4 on 2–3, and 14 on 3–5. Hence, 4 is the limiting capacity. Assigning 4 to each branch on the path and adjusting the branch capacities yields this updated network:

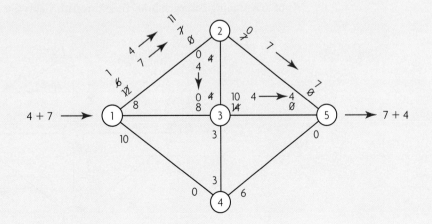

At this point, no further flow can pass through node 2 because both branches that exit from it are loaded to capacity. However, path 1–3–5 has a positive flow capacity of 8 (1–2 has 8 and 3–5 has 10). Assigning a flow of 8 to each branch on 1–3–5 yields this updated network:

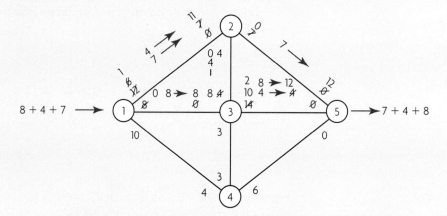

A remaining branch from node 1 that has a path with positive flow capacity is 1–4. Path 1–4–5 has a capacity of 6. Assigning 6 to the branches on this path yields this updated network.

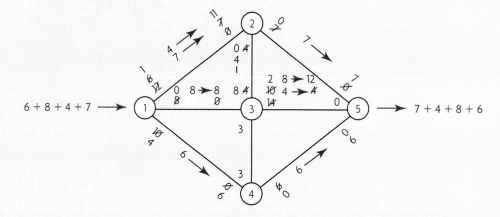

Only one path that has a positive flow capacity remains: 1–4–3–5, with a capacity of 2. Assigning 2 to each branch on this path yields this updated network:

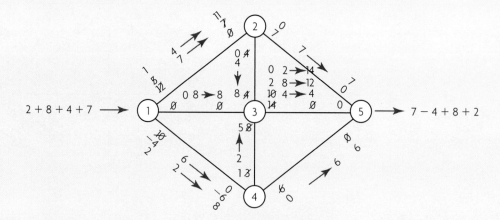

Since no paths from node 1 to node 5 have positive flow capacity, the analysis is complete. The maximal flow rate equals the sum of the entering flows at node 1: $2 + 6 + 8 + 4 + 7 = 27$. This, of course, equals the flow leaving the system at node 5. The final results are summarized in the following network:

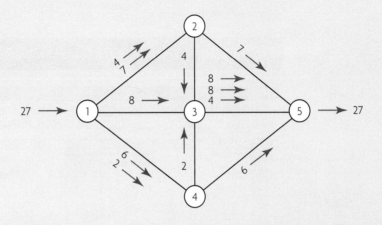

The flows through each branch are shown according to the way they were derived, simply for purposes of illustration and clarity. Thus, the total flow through branch 1–2 is 11, and the total flow through branch 3–5 is 14.

Finally, it should be noted that in many instances, slightly different branch assignments are possible that will produce the same maximal flow. Often, many alternative solutions are possible. However, as long as no path with a positive flow capacity can be found, the maximal flow solution has been found.

b. Here is the linear programming formulation of the maximal flow problem (Solved Problem 3):

maximize $Z = x_{51}$

subject to

$x_{12} + x_{13} + x_{14} = x_{51}$ or,
$x_{12} + x_{13} + x_{14} - x_{51} = 0$ (net flow transshipment constraint at node 1)

$x_{12} + x_{32} = x_{23} - x_{25}$ or,
$x_{12} + x_{32} - x_{23} - x_{25} = 0$ (net flow transshipment constraint at node 2)

$x_{13} + x_{23} + x_{43} = x_{32} + x_{34} + x_{35}$ or,
$x_{13} + x_{23} + x_{43} - x_{32} - x_{34} - x_{35} = 0$ (net flow transshipment constraint at node 3)

$x_{14} + x_{34} = x_{43} + x_{45}$ or,
$x_{14} + x_{34} - x_{43} - x_{45} = 0$ (net flow transshipment constraint at node 4)

$x_{25} + x_{35} + x_{45} = x_{51}$ or,
$x_{25} + x_{35} + x_{45} - x_{51} = 0$ (net flow transshipment constraint at node 5)

The second type of constraints are the branch capacity constraints, which simply represent the flow capacity of each branch. These constraints can be written as follows:

$x_{12} \leq 12$
$x_{13} \leq 8$
$x_{14} \leq 10$
$x_{23} \leq 4$
$x_{32} \leq 4$
$x_{25} \leq 7$

$x_{35} \leq 14$
$x_{34} \leq 3$
$x_{43} \leq 3$
$x_{45} \leq 6$
$x_{51} \leq 9999$
All $x_{ij} \geq 0$

Exhibit 8-11 Worksheet for Solved Problem 3, the Maximal Flow Problem

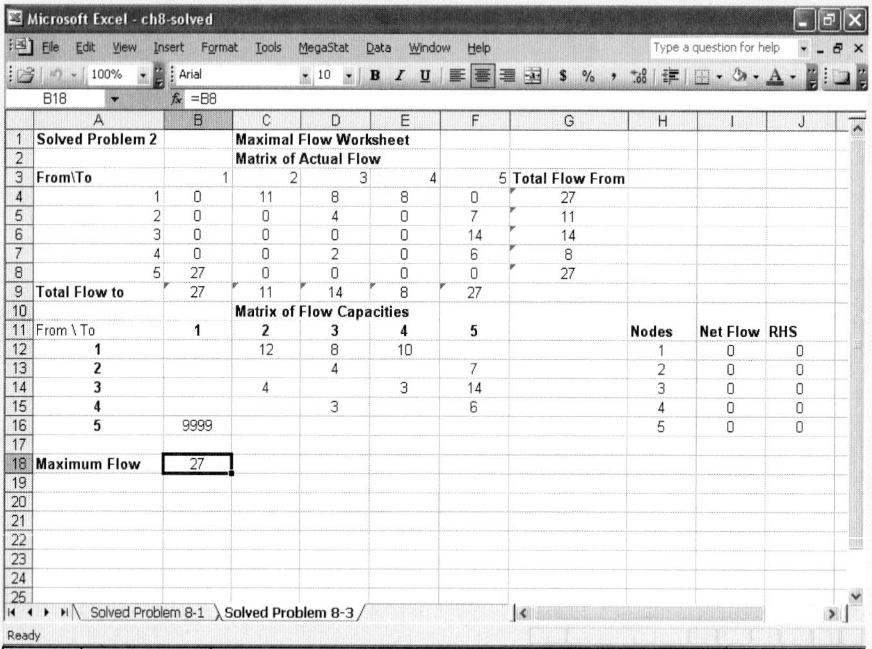

	A	B	C	D	E	F	G	H	I	J
1	Solved Problem 2		Maximal Flow Worksheet							
2			Matrix of Actual Flow							
3	From\To	1	2	3	4	5	Total Flow From			
4	1	0	11	8	8	0	27			
5	2	0	0	4	0	7	11			
6	3	0	0	0	0	14	14			
7	4	0	0	2	0	6	8			
8	5	27	0	0	0	0	27			
9	Total Flow to	27	11	14	8	27				
10			Matrix of Flow Capacities							
11	From \ To	1	2	3	4	5		Nodes	Net Flow	RHS
12	1		12	8	10			1	0	0
13	2			4		7		2	0	0
14	3		4		3	14		3	0	0
15	4			3		6		4	0	0
16	5	9999						5	0	0
17										
18	Maximum Flow	27								

Cell	Copied to	Formula
B9	C9 : F9	= SUM(B4 : B8)
G4	G5 : G8	= SUM(B4 : F4)
B18		= B8
I12		= C4 + D4 + E4 − B8
I13		= C4 + C6 + D5 − F5
I14		= D4 + D5 + D7 − C6 − E6 − F6
I15		= E4 + E6 − D7 − F7
I16		= F5 + F6 + F7 − B8

c. The Excel solution is displayed in Exhibit 8-11. After selecting **Tools | Solver,** the parameter specification screen shown in Exhibit 8-12 is prepared. The worksheet shown in Exhibit 8-11 is developed very similarly to the worksheet shown in Exhibit 8-6, the formulas for Exhibit 8-11 are given at the bottom of the worksheet. The maximum flow

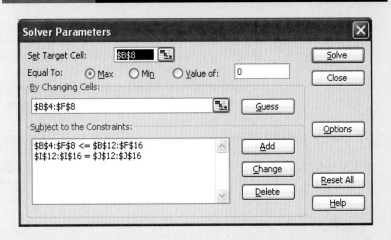

Exhibit 8-12 Parameter Specification Screen for Solved Problem 3, the Maximal Flow Problem

from node 1 to node 5 is 27 and is shown in cell B18, and the matrix of actual flows indicates the flow between various nodes.

Discussion and Review Questions

1. In solving the shortest-route problem, the labeling algorithm is utilized and the nodes are labeled as either "permanently labeled" or "temporarily labeled." Carefully explain the difference between these two types of labels.

2. In formulating the shortest-route problem as a linear programming problem, describe the definition of the decision variable x_{ij}.

3. In a shortest-route problem, there are 6 nodes and 9 arcs, how many decision variables should there be?

4. In a shortest-route problem, if there are 6 nodes and 9 arcs, how many constraints should there be in the linear programming formulation. If node 1 is the source (starting) node and node 6 is the sink (terminal) node, how many of these constraints will be transshipment constraints. Which of these constraints should be formulated as supply constraints, demand constraints, and transshipment constraints and why? Indicate the signs on the supply, demand, and transshipment constraints.

5. Give two examples of potential business applications for the minimal spanning tree problem.

6. Give two examples of potential applications for the maximal flow problem.

7. a. The linear programming formulation of the maximal flow problem involves which of the following: a maximization? Or minimization objective function?
   b. If the starting node of the maximal flow problem is node 1 and the ending node is node 9, set up the objective function for this hypothetical problem.

8. If a maximal flow problem consists of 9 nodes and 16 arcs with one direction flow, how many constraints and how many decision variables will be involved in the linear

programming formulation of this hypothetical problem? How many of these constraints will be transshipment constraints, and how many of them will be capacity constraints?

9. In a maximal flow problem, if the objective is to maximize the number of cars per hour from the source (node 1) to the sink (node 10), then what would be the definition of x_{ij}? State the objective function for this-hypothetical problem.

10. In a minimal spanning tree problem with 7 nodes and 15 arcs, the optimal solution consists of the connection of nodes that involve how many arcs? If the minimal spanning problem has 12 nodes and 22 arcs, the optimal solution consists of the connection of nodes that involve how many arcs? Based on your answer to the above two questions, what is the general number of connected arcs in the optimal solution of a minimal spanning tree problem?

11. In the Excel formulation of the shortest-route problem, what is the purpose of flow conservation constraints? Explain carefully.

12. In the Excel formulation of the maximal flow problem, what is the purpose of Node flow equations? Explain carefully. How would we go about formulating the node flow equations?

■ Problems

1. The following network shows road distances in miles between a firm's warehouse locations.

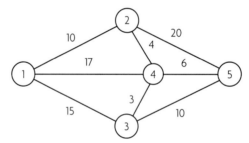

a. Using the shortest-route algorithm, find the shortest route to each location from the central warehouse, which is located at node 1.

b. List the shortest distance to each of the warehouse locations and the route that will result in the shortest distance traveled.

2. The following network represents construction sites (nodes) and access roads (arcs) to those sites. The numbers on the arcs show distances in miles between various locations. Company trucks deliver supplies to the sites from the main office (node 1). Using the shortest-route algorithm, find the length of the shortest route, and identify the route to each construction site.

Node	Distance	Shortest Route
2	6	1–2
3	8	1–2–3
4	15	1–2–3–4
5	20	1–2–3–4–5

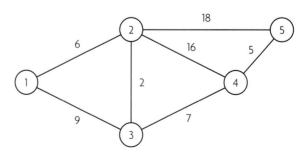

3. A taxi company dispatches cabs from a satellite office to any of five pickup points (airport, shopping mall, medical arts building, etc.). A system of roads and highways connects some of the locations, as shown in the following network diagram. Node 1 represents the satellite office. Use the shortest-route algorithm to find the shortest route and distance to each of the pickup points.

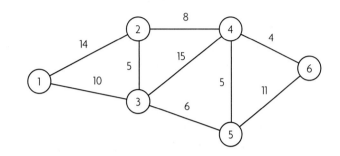

4. The network shown represents points of interest at a popular historic village and the approximate walking time (in minutes) along certain pathways. Assuming that node 1 represents the main lodge and the other nodes the points of interest, use Excel and find the shortest walking time to each point of interest from the main lodge, and indicate which points of interest will be encountered along that path.

	Shortest	
Node	Distance	Route
2	23	1–3–4–2
3	12	1–3
4	18	1–3–4
5	22	1–3–4–5
6	19	1–3–6
7	32	1–3–4–5–6

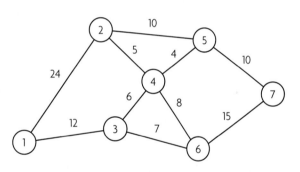

5. The values on the arcs connecting in various nodes represent the distance between nodes in miles for the following network.
   a. Find the shortest route to each node from node 1 using the shortest route algorithm.
   b. Find the *round-trip* distance to each node from node 1, assuming the shortest route is used in both directions.
   c. Would another route for the return trip yield a shorter total round trip? Explain.

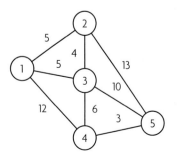

6. Distances shown on the arcs of the following network are in meters. Use Excel and find the shortest route from node 1 to each of the other nodes. If any alternate routes exist, identify them.

Node	Distance	Shortest Route
2	15	1–2
3	17	1–3
4	16	1–4
5	26	1–3–5
6	27	1–4–6
7	37	1–3–5–7
8	42	1–3–5–8
9	37	1–4–6–9
10	57	1–4–6–9–10

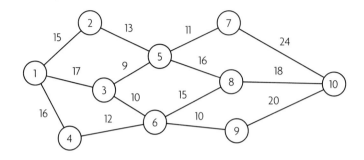

7. Approximate travel times between various customer locations are shown on the accompanying network. Assuming all delivery trucks leave from node 1, use Excel and find the shortest travel time to each customer location. If trucks could make multiple stops and, thereby, reduce the number of trucks required for this system, and assuming truck capacity is not a factor, how many trucks would be needed if the shortest travel times are used?

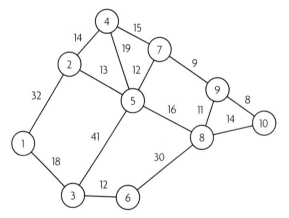

8. The following network shows distances in miles between villages and hamlets in a certain area of New York State. A dealer must decide on the route to use to send weekly shipments to a new customer located at node 12. The dealer is located at node 1. Using Excel, find the shortest route and the distance for a round trip.

Node	Distance	Shortest Route
2	35	1–3–2
3	20	1–3
4	28	1–4
5	43	1–3–6–9–5
6	30	1–3–6
7	30	1–3–7
8	34	1–4–8
9	38	1–3–6–9
10	41	1–3–6–10
11	37	1-3–7–11
12	60	1–3–6–9–12

Round trip from node 1 to node 12 is 120 miles (2*60)

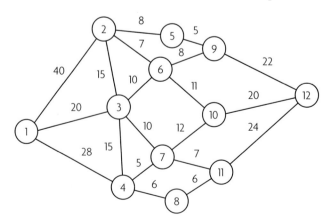

9. Find the minimum spanning tree for this network:

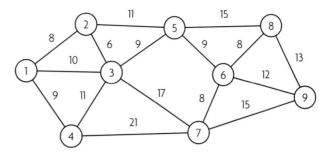

10. Find the set of arcs that will interconnect all of the nodes in this network using as little of the arc material as possible.

Iteration	Connected Nodes
1	1–2
2	1–3
3	3–4
4	3–6
5	6–7
6	7–9
7	6–5
8	6–8
Minimum = 54	

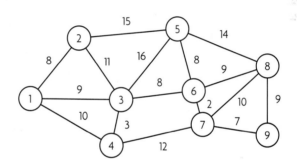

11. A cable television firm wants to connect a number of towns and villages to its cable system. The firm has identified various alternatives for connections and the cost of each potential connecting link, as shown in the accompanying network. Determine the set of connections that will minimize the total cost of linking these towns and villages to the system.

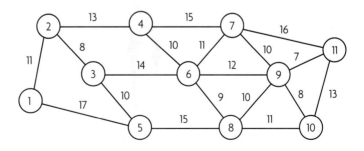

12. A company is in the process of designing a security system that will monitor key locations of its facilities. The locations are represented by the nodes in the accompanying network. The firm wants to minimize the cost of connecting these points to one another to form a system. Determine the set of connections that will accomplish this. Cost figures for the connections are shown on the arcs.

Minimum = $805

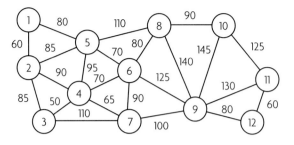

13. A designer involved in a project to construct access roads to a new park wants to minimize roadways, while still connecting key areas (e.g., lodges, picnic sites, boat launch). The key areas are designated by nodes on the accompanying diagram, and the figures on the arcs reflect distance between certain locations in miles. Determine the system of roadways that will accomplish these objectives.

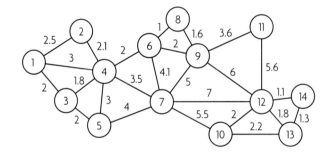

14. A system that will interconnect a set of storage tanks is in the design stages. The issue at present is to determine which connectors to use in order to minimize the amount of pipeline used. The different possibilities can be seen in the accompanying diagram, which shows distances in meters. Find the least amount of pipeline and a set of connections that will accomplish this. Also, identify any alternate connections.

Minimum = 595 meters
(See the IM for details)

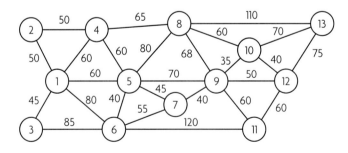

15. A manufacturer wants to install air conditioning in an existing plant. Various alternatives are being considered for laying the ducts that will connect desired locations of outlets. Locations of outlets are represented by nodes in the accompanying diagram. The arcs connecting various nodes represent the ducts, and the figures on the arcs show the cost of particular connections. Find the system of connections that will minimize the total cost of the system.

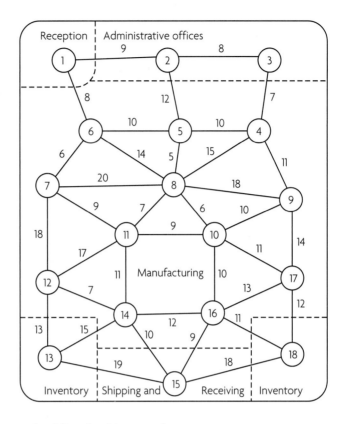

16. Find the maximal flow for this network:

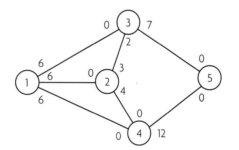

17. Determine the maximal flow for this network:

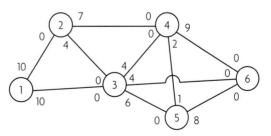

18. The network shows traffic capacity for a system of roads, all of which are one way. What is the peak load the system can handle, assuming flow is from node 1 to node 5? Figures on arcs represent hundreds of cars per hour.

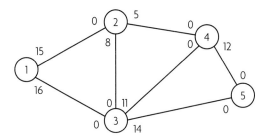

Total flow = 26

19. Given this flow network with arc capacities in units per minute, do the following:
    a. Determine the maximal flow rate of the system.
    b. If capacity of *one* of the arcs could be increased, which arc would you select and by how much would you increase its capacity? Explain.

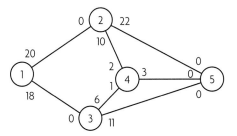

20. During the summer months, major construction projects are planned for a metropolitan area. This will result in closing certain bridges and reducing lanes open to traffic on some streets. Planners have developed the following network that shows major intersections (nodes), streets and bridges (arcs), and flow capacities in cars per minute.
    a. Find the maximal flow rate of the system, assuming cars enter at node 1 and leave at node 7.
    b. Are there alternate flows that would accomplish the same result? If so, identify one of these.
    c. If the capacity of one arc could be increased, which arc would you choose, and how much increase would be usable? Explain.

a. Total flow = 120 cars
   per minute
b. 10 more on 1–3–4–5
c. Increase arc 6–7 30 cars
   per minute

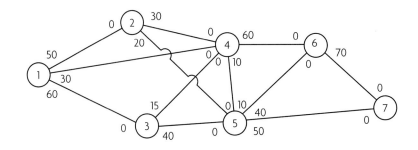

21. The accompanying network represents a possible design for a system of pipelines and storage tanks.
    a. Determine the maximal flow rate for the network assuming node 1 is the source and node 7 the sink.

b. Suppose now there is an additional requirement: Flows in the pipelines leaving the source node should be approximately equal. What is the flow pattern and its maximal rate given this additional requirement?

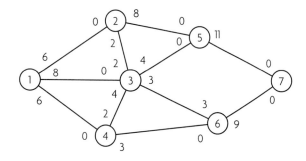

22. Using Excel, determine the maximal flow rate for this system of bicycle paths, given the flow rates shown on the diagram. Assume node 1 is the source node and node 13 the sink node.

Total flow = 125

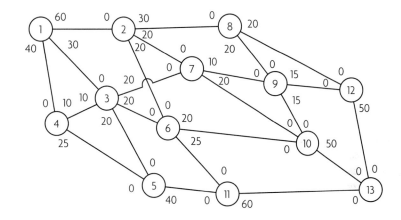

23. The accompanying network represents a possible design for a system of pipelines for an oil field.
    a. Using Excel, determine the maximal flow of oil based on flow capacities given in the network from the oil field on node 1 to the oil refinery at node 14.

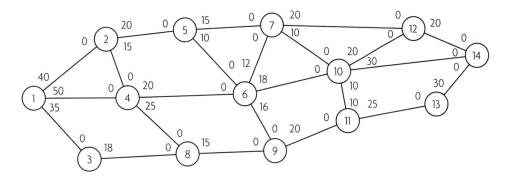

b. If the capacity of the arc from node 4 to node 6 is increased to 30, what is the maximal flow from node 1 to node 14?

Chapter 8 Case   Furnace County Emergency Response Routes

After several complaints about slow response times to police, fire, and ambulance calls, and hoping to receive federal funds, Furnace County Supervisor Grant Wise has decided to seek a plan that will identify travel routes that minimize travel time between the county's police, fire, and ambulance station in Furnace City and every town or village in the county.

Assume you are the consultant Mr. Wise has hired to develop the plan. The accompanying map shows travel distances in miles between various Furnace County towns and villages. And because emergency equipment has the right-of-way, travel distances correlate closely with travel times in minutes when multiplied by 1.50, except for travel between Mountain View and Hidden Valley, and Apresville and Hidden Valley, where travel time in minutes is twice the distance shown due to rough and winding roads. *Note:* The close proximity of the station to Furnace City obviates the need to include the city in the plan.

Furnace County

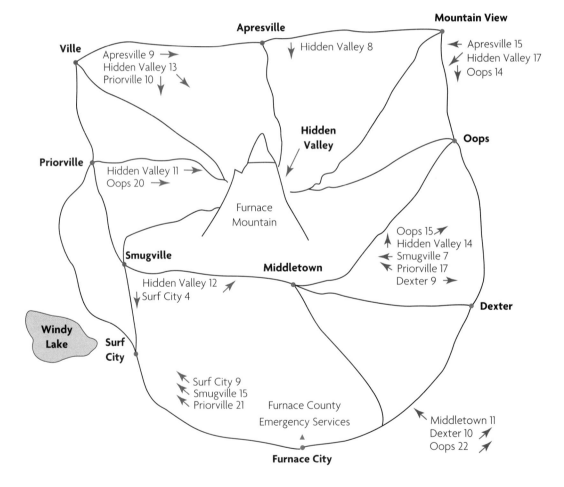

Nonlinear Programming

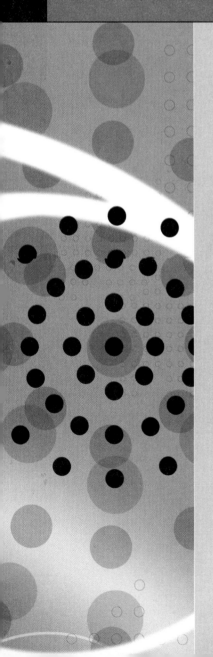

Learning Objectives

After completing this chapter, you should be able to:

1. Explain the difference between optimization problems that can be solved using linear programming methods and those that require nonlinear programming or calculus-based methods.
2. Find the optimal values of the decision variable and the objective function in problems that involve one decision variable (unconstrained and constrained).
3. Solve one-decision variable problems with a nonlinear objective function using Excel (unconstrained or constrained).
4. Find the optimal values of the decision variables and the objective function in unconstrained problems that involve two decision variables.

5. Solve one-decision-variable unconstrained problems with a nonlinear objective function using Excel.
6. Use the Lagrange multiplier to find the optimal values of two decision variables and the objective function in problems that involve equality constraints.
7. Solve two-decision-variable problems with a nonlinear objective function and an equality constraint using Excel.
8. Find the optimal values of the decision variables and the objective function in problems that involve two decision variables and one inequality constraint.
9. Solve two-decision-variable problems with a nonlinear objective function and multiple constraints using Excel.

Chapter Outline

Introduction, 424

Models with One Decision Variable, 425

Unconstrained Problem with One Decision Variable, 425

Solution of One-Decision-Variable, Unconstrained Problem with Excel, 429

Constrained Problem with One Decision Variable, 433

Solution of One-Decision-Variable, Constrained Problem with Excel, 435

Models with Two Decision Variables, Unconstrained Problem, 439

Solution of Unconstrained Problems with Two Decision Variables Using Excel, 442

Models with Two Decision Variables and an Equality Constraint (Lagrange Multipliers), 444

Interpreting λ, 446

Solution of Problems with Two Decision Variables and a Single Equality Constraint Using Excel, 446

Models with Two Decision Variables and a Single Inequality Constraint, 449

Solution of Problems with Two Decision Variables and Multiple Constraints Using Excel, 451

Summary, 454

Glossary, 456

Solved Problems, 457

Discussion and Review Questions, 466

Problems, 466

Chapter 9 Case: Koch International Incorporated, 469

Many of the chapters in this book describe models that involve only linear relationships. The widespread use of linear models in practice necessitates devoting substantial coverage to linear models. However, an important class of problems involves nonlinear relationships. This chapter illustrates methods that can be used to find optimal solutions for simple models that involve nonlinear relationships.

◼️ Introduction

The models described in this chapter are in some ways similar to the *linear programming* models described in Chapters 3 through 8. For example, all of the models have an objective function that is to be maximized or minimized. Some also have one or more constraints, but others involve only an objective function. However, all of the models in this chapter involve one or more *nonlinear relationships*.

There are many real-life examples of problems that involve nonlinear relationships. For instance, the inventory EOQ model's objective is to minimize the cost function:

$$TC = \frac{Q}{2}H + \frac{D}{Q}S$$

where

TC = total annual cost
Q = order quantity
H = annual holding cost per unit
D = annual demand
S = ordering cost

A graph of this U-shaped cost function is illustrated in Figure 9-1. Similar U-shaped cost curves can be used to describe other inventory cost functions as well as costs in forecasting

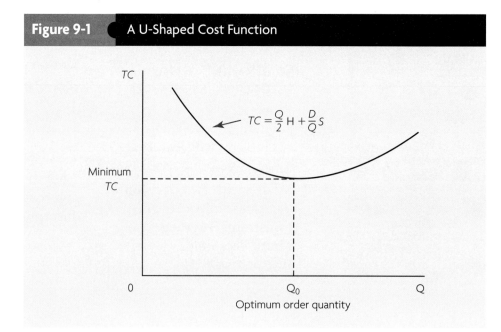

Figure 9-1   A U-Shaped Cost Function

models, waiting-line models, and quality control. Moreover, cost-profit-volume models may also involve nonlinear relationships.

Nonlinear relationships occur because one or more of the causes of linearity are absent. For example, there may be a nonproportional relationship between two variables (such as price and quantity demanded; the relationship may only be linear over a limited range of price), or the relationship may be nonadditive (if you add one cup of sugar to one cup of water, the resulting volume will be less than two cups).

The difficulty with nonlinear models in general is that they can be significantly harder to solve than linear models. Moreover, linear models often provide reasonably good approximations to nonlinear models. Thus, the efficiency of solution techniques for linear models and the fact that they perform well as approximations in many cases that involve nonlinear relationships explain the popularity of linear models. Nonetheless, there are many instances for which linear approximations are not acceptable. Judgment and experience on the part of the decision maker are necessary to determine when linear approximations are suitable and when they are not. For those cases that are deemed unsuitable for linear models, the methods described in this chapter may be of use if the model is fairly simple.

The chapter begins with a discussion of models that have one decision variable, including both unconstrained models (i.e., models that have only an objective function) and constrained models. It then moves on to a discussion of unconstrained models with two decision variables. For the special case of equality-constrained models, the use of *Lagrange multipliers* is demonstrated.

Models with One Decision Variable

In this section, the use of first and second derivatives for identifying maximum and minimum values of a mathematical function is illustrated. The section is presented in two parts. The first part illustrates the procedure for an *unconstrained function*, while the second part illustrates the procedure for a *constrained function*.

Unconstrained Problem with One Decision Variable

Example 9-1

Consider the case of Larry Brown, manager of a small manufacturing company. Larry has ordered a new machine that will increase the productivity of an existing machine. Larry must now select a location for the new machine. He knows that the closer the new machine is to the existing machine, the lower the cost of transporting work in process between the two machines. On the other hand, the closer the two machines are, the greater the cost to remodel the area to accommodate the new machine.

With the help of the accounting department, Larry developed a model that expressed the combined cost of remodeling and transporting work on a per-unit basis:

Cost per piece = 1.5(Distance)^2 − 42(Distance) + 300

In mathematical terms, this can be expressed as

$Z = 1.5x^2 - 42x + 300$

where

Z = cost per unit

x = distance between the two machines in feet

Larry's problem is to determine the value of x that will minimize this cost function. He can do this by using differential calculus.[1] By taking the first derivative of the cost function and setting that equal to zero, he can solve for the value(s) of x for which the function reaches a local maximum or a local minimum. Then, by finding the second derivative of the function, he will be able to determine that at that value of x the function is a minimum. Let's see how this is accomplished.

There are two conditions that must be satisfied:

Condition 1 (necessary): The first derivative of a function must equal zero at every point that is a local maximum or a local minimum.

Condition 2 (sufficient): If the first condition is satisfied at a point, then it can be concluded that

1. The point will be a local minimum *if* the sign of the second derivative is positive.
2. The point will be a local maximum *if* the sign of the second derivative is negative.

The term **local minimum** means that the function reaches a minimum value *relative* to nearby values. Similarly, a **local maximum** occurs when a function reaches a value that is higher than its value at nearby points. If that local maximum (or minimum) is the highest (lowest) value reached by the function for any value of x, then that value is also a **global maximum** (or **minimum**).

Consider the functions shown in Figure 9-2. In 9-2a, we see a function that is convex; it has a single minimum, so the local minimum is also the global minimum. Similarly, in 9-2b, we see a function that is strictly concave, with a single maximum that is a global maximum. Figure 9-2c shows a more complex function; it has a number of turns. The function has two minimum points and one maximum. The lower of the two minimum points is both a local minimum and a global minimum (assuming that these three turning points are the only ones the function has). Similarly, if the maximum is the only maximum point for the function, then it is also the global maximum. In the case of a function with more turning points, there would be an even greater number of local maxima and local minima.

It is generally not practical to plot the graph of a function in order to determine the point(s) at which it achieves a local maximum or local minimum. Instead, the procedure involves finding the first derivative of the function and setting it equal to zero. Condition 1—necessary condition—requires that the first derivative equal zero at a local maximum or a local minimum. The solution (or solutions, if there are more than one) that makes the first derivative equal to zero is the point that must be evaluated to determine if it is a local maximum or a local minimum. That is accomplished by taking the second derivative of the function and noting its sign (Condition 2— sufficient condition); a plus sign indicates a local minimum and a minus sign indicates a local maximum. Note that if there are multiple solutions for the second derivative (e.g., $x = 2$, $x = -2$), each of these would be substituted into the second derivative in order to obtain the sign of the second derivative.

---

[1] The CD-ROM supplement to this chapter illustrates rules that can be used to differentiate frequently encountered simple mathematical expressions.

Figure 9-2   Illustrations of Local Maximum and Local Minimum Points

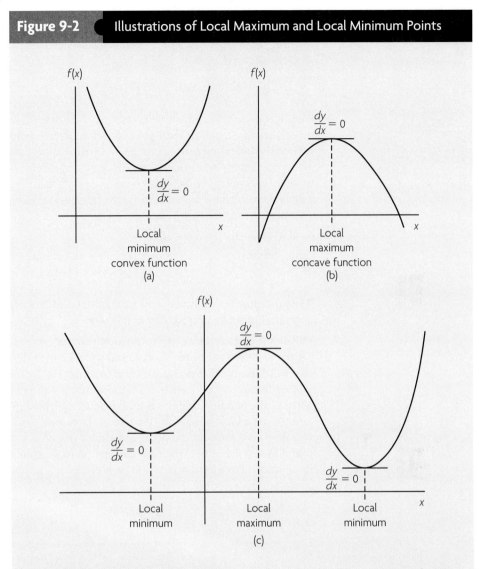

Local minimum convex function
(a)

Local maximum concave function
(b)

Local minimum   Local maximum   Local minimum
(c)

Now let's see how we can use calculus and the two conditions mentioned previously to determine the solution to Larry's problem. Recall that the cost function was

$Z = 1.5x^2 - 42x + 300$

The first derivative of this function is

$$\frac{dz}{dx} = 3x - 42$$

Setting this equal to zero (Condition 1) and solving for x, we find

$3x - 42 = 0$
$x = 14$

This indicates that the slope of the function (i.e., the first derivative) is zero at only one point, where $x = 14$. We must now determine whether this one point is a maximum or a minimum. To do this, we must obtain the second derivative of the function, which we do by applying to the first derivative the same procedure used to obtain the first derivative (i.e., take the derivative of the first derivative to obtain the second derivative).

The second derivative is

$$\frac{d^2z}{dx^2} = +3$$

The positive sign tells us that the function has a local minimum at the point where $x = 14$. Because there is only one value of x for which the first derivative equals zero, we can say that the local minimum is also the *global* minimum. Hence, to minimize cost. Larry should position the new machine at a distance of 14 feet from the existing machine.

By substituting $x = 14$ into the original (cost) function, we can determine the cost per piece that will result from locating the new machine at a distance of 14 feet from the existing machine. Thus:

$$Z = 1.5(14)^2 - 42(14) + 300 = 6$$

Hence, the cost will be $6 per piece to move pieces between the two machines.

The procedure for finding the optimal solution of an unconstrained model with one decision variable can be summarized as follows:

1. Obtain the first derivative of the function.
2. Set the first derivative equal to zero and solve for the value(s) of the decision variable that will make the first derivative equal to zero.
3. Obtain the second derivative. If it is a constant (e.g., $+5$, -2), its sign will indicate whether the function achieves a local maximum (the sign of the second derivative is negative) or a local minimum (the sign of the second derivative is positive). If the second derivative includes the decision variable (e.g., $4x$, $x + 6$), substitute the value(s) found in step 2 and note the resulting sign(s) to determine if the function achieves a local max ($-$) or a local min ($+$) at each value.

Example 9-2

Given this function:

$$Z = \frac{1}{3}x^3 - 5x^2 + 21x + 100$$

a. Determine the value of x for which the function is a maximum.
b. Compute the value of the function at its maximum.
c. Determine the value of x for which the function is a minimum.
d. Compute the value of the function at its minimum.

Solution

a. 1. Obtain the first derivative of the function:

$$\frac{dz}{dx} = x^2 - 10x + 21$$

2. Set the first derivative equal to zero and solve for x:

$$x^2 - 10x + 21 = 0$$

This can be factored into

$$(x - 3)(x - 7) = 0$$

Solving, $x = +3$ or $x = +7$, in order for this to equal zero.

3. The second derivative is

$$\frac{d^2z}{dx^2} = 2x - 10$$

At $x = +3$, this is $2(3) - 10 = -4$
At $x = +7$, this is $2(7) - 10 = +4$

The *negative* result (-4) indicates a local maximum; the positive result $(+4)$ indicates a local minimum. Hence, the function reaches a local maximum at $x = +3$.

b. To find the value of the function at its maximum, substitute the value of x for which it is a maximum into the original function and solve. Thus:

$$Z = \frac{1}{3}(3)^3 - 5(3)^2 + 21(3) + 100 = 127$$

c. The function reaches a local minimum at $x = +7$ because at that point, the second derivative of the original function is positive $(+4)$.

d. To find the value of the function at its minimum, substitute the value of x for which it is a minimum into the original function and solve. Therefore:

$$Z = \left(\frac{1}{3}\right)(7)^3 - 5(7)^2 + 100$$

$$Z = 114.33 - 245 + 100 = -30.6$$

Solution of One-Decision-Variable, Unconstrained Problem with Excel

In order to demonstrate the solution of an unconstrained nonlinear programming problem with a single decision variable, consider the following example.

Example 9-3

X-Tech Inc. produces specialized bolts for the aerospace industry. The operating cost of producing a single bolt is $2.00. The company sells the bolts for $6.00 per unit. Each time the company arranges to sell a batch, it incurs a fixed cost of $20. This fixed cost mainly includes administrative expenses. The volume of sales is primarily dependent on the price of the product. The manager has come up with the following relationship between volume and price:

Volume = 500 − 25(Price)

a. Draw the volume–price relationship diagram.
b. Draw the profit function as it relates to the price.
c. Determine the optimal price and the optimal volume that will result in the maximum profit.

Solution

a. Figure 9-3 represents a schematic diagram of the relationship between volume and price. On one extreme, if the company decides not to charge anything for

Figure 9-3   Volume–Price Relationship for the X-Tech Inc. Problem

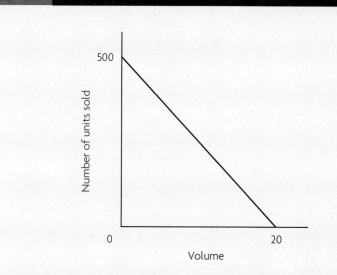

the specialty bolt, it could sell or give away 500 units. However, a rational businessperson would not choose this option. On the other extreme, if the company charges $20 (500/25) or more, X-Tech would not be able to sell any units. Even though this relationship is good to know, the company is interested in estimating the profit. The profit function is given by the following basic equation:

Profit = Revenue − Cost
Profit = Revenue − (Variable cost + Fixed cost)

Revenue = Price × Volume
Variable cost = Volume × Operating cost
Volume = 500 − 25(Price)

Therefore,

Profit = Price[Volume] − (Volume × Operating cost) − Fixed cost
Profit = Price[500 − 25(Price)] − (Volume × 2) − 20
Profit = Price[500 − 25(Price)] − [500 − 25(Price)] × 2) − 20

Simplifying the above equation results in the following:

Profit = 500(Price) − 25(Price)² − 1,000 + 50(Price) − 20
Profit = −25 (Price)² + 550(Price) − 1,020   (9−1)

b.   The graph of this relationship can be seen in Figure 9-4.
c.   The first derivative of this function is

$$\frac{d(\text{profit})}{d(\text{Price})} = -50(\text{Price}) + 550$$

Setting this equal to zero and solving for price results in the following:

−50(Price) + 550 = 0

$$\text{Price} = \frac{550}{50} = 11$$

Figure 9-4   The Graph of the Profit Function for the X-Tech Inc. Problem

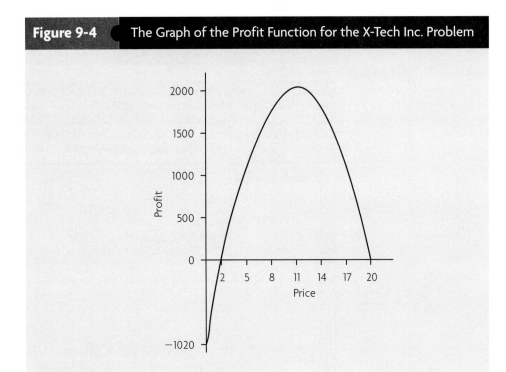

This indicates that the slope of a tangent line at this point on this function is equal to zero only where Price equals $11. Next, we have to determine if this one point is a minimum or a maximum. In order to do this, we take the second derivative of the profit function with respect to price. The second derivative is

$$\frac{d^2(\text{Profit})}{d(\text{Price})^2} = -50$$

Because the second derivative is a negative number, the profit function has a local maximum at this point. In addition, because there is only one value of price for which the first derivative is equal to zero, we can conclude that the local maximum is also the global maximum. By substituting 11 into the profit function formula, we can calculate the value of the profit at the optimal price. Therefore:

Profit $= -25(11)^2 + 550(11) - 1{,}020 = \$2{,}005$

Substituting 11 into the volume formula can determine the volume, or the number of specialty bolts to be sold:

Volume $= 500 - 25(\text{Price})$
Volume $= 500 - 25(11)$
Volume $= 225$

From Figure 9-4, the profit increases as price increases up to $11. However, any further increase in price beyond $11 results in the decline of profits. At the maximum price of $20, the expected profit is −$20.

Exhibit 9-1	Worksheet for the One-Decision-Variable, Unconstrained Problem (X-Tech Inc., Example 9-3)

Microsoft Excel - ch9-1

File Edit View Insert Format Tools MegaStat Data Window Help

Type a question for help

Times New Roman ▾ 12 ▾ **B** *I* U | ≡ ≡ ≡ | $ % , | 田 ▾ ▦ ▾ A ▾

Reply with Changes... End Review...

C7 ▾ fx =C4*C3-C3*C6-C5

	A	B	C	D	E	F	G	H	I	J
1	X-Tech Incorporated									
2										
3		Volume	225							
4		Price	11							
5		Fixed Cost	20							
6		Variable Cost	2							
7		Profit	2005							
8										
9										
10										
11										
12										
13										
14										
15										
16										
17										
18										
19										
20										

Sheet1 / Sheet2 / Sheet4 / Sheet5 / Sheet3 /

Ready NUM

start 3 Microsoft O... ▾ 5 Microsoft O... ▾ 2 NTVDM.EXE ▾ Simeon - [VU M... 11:01 AM

Cell	Copied to	Formula
C7		= C4 ∗ C3 − C3 ∗ C6 − C5
C3		= 500 − 25 ∗ C4

Exhibit 9-1 shows the Excel worksheet for this problem. The formula for the profit function is contained in cell C7 and is shown in the formula bar of Exhibit 9-1. This formula looks a little different than Equation 9-1, because there is a separate equation for the volume in cell C3, $=500 − 25 \times C4$. Thus, if we substitute $500 − 25 \times C4$ into the equation given in the formula bar of Exhibit 9-1, and simplify, then we will obtain the equivalent of Equation 9-1. After choosing **Tools | Solver,** we will get the Solver Parameters screen shown in Exhibit 9-2. On this screen, for the "Set Target Cell" box, we choose the profit function specified in cell C7. In the "Equal To" portion, we click on "Max." In the "By Changing Cells" box, we include the input variable Price, which is given in C4. In the constraints section, we simply specify that the value of the input variable (Price) has to be a nonnegative value (i.e., $\$C\$4 \geq 0$). Since this is a nonlinear model, in order to ensure that a linear model is not utilized, we click on "Options" and make sure that the "Assume linear model" box is *not* checked. After clicking on "Solve" we obtain the solution given in Exhibit 9-1. We could determine the effect of changing the price on volume and on profits. For example, if we decide to price the specialty bolt at $15, we can expect to sell 125 units for a total profit of $1,605.

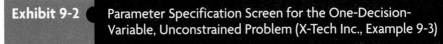

Exhibit 9-2   Parameter Specification Screen for the One-Decision-Variable, Unconstrained Problem (X-Tech Inc., Example 9-3)

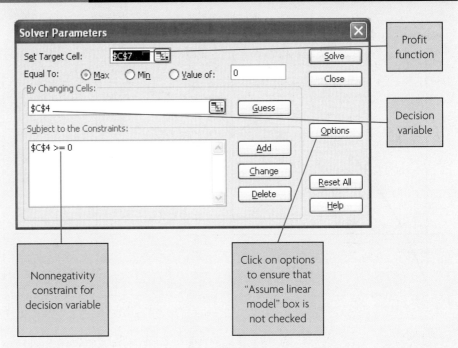

Constrained Problem with One Decision Variable

The procedure for finding the optimal value of a constrained decision variable is very similar to the procedure for an unconstrained decision variable. The key difference between the two is that the existence of a constraint means that there is a *feasible solution space* that must be taken into account. The feasible solution space may or may not include the optimum that would be indicated if the function were not constrained. In order to understand the consequences of this, consider the two cases depicted in Figure 9-5.

Figure 9-5a illustrates a case where the function attains its optimum *within* the feasible solution space. In Figure 9-5b, the function attains its optimum *outside* of the feasible solution space. In the first case, the optimum is unaffected by the constraint; in the second case, the optimum is determined by the constraint. It occurs at the point where the decision variable equals the constraint. Note, too, an important difference between nonlinear models and linear models: The optimal solution is not always on the boundary of the feasible solution space, although it may be.

The procedure for constrained optimization is to proceed as in the case of unconstrained optimization to identify local maximum and local minimum points. Then, check to see if the solution satisfies the constraint. For instance, suppose you find $x = 5$, and the constraint is that $x \leq 7$. Obviously, the solution satisfies the constraint, so $x = 5$ *may be* the optimal solution. The other possibility is that the value of x equal to the constraint (e.g., $x = 7$) may yield a better solution. In order to complete the analysis, substitute that value

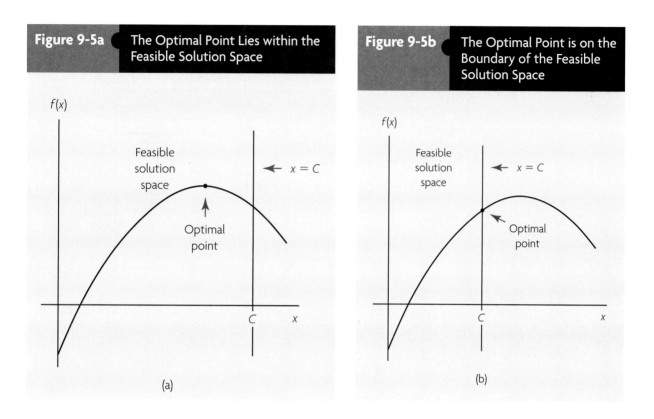

Figure 9-5a   The Optimal Point Lies within the Feasible Solution Space

(a)

Figure 9-5b   The Optimal Point is on the Boundary of the Feasible Solution Space

(b)

($x = 7$) into the objective function and compare the result to the value of the objective function with the apparent optimum (e.g., $x = 5$) to see which actually gives the better solution. Figure 9-6 illustrates a case for which the constraint provides a better solution than the apparent (local) optimum.

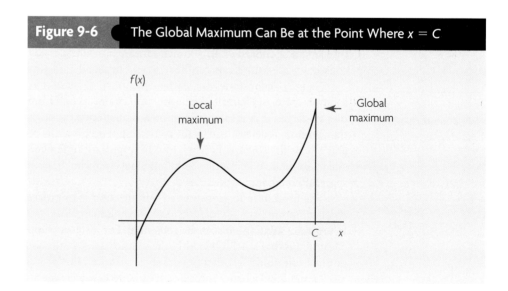

Figure 9-6   The Global Maximum Can Be at the Point Where $x = C$

Example 9-4

Determine the minimum cost for this model:

minimize $\quad Z = 2x^2 - 20x + 60$

subject to

$x \le 8$

Solution

1. Obtain the first derivative and set it equal to zero:

$$\frac{dy}{dx} = 4x - 20 = 0$$

Solving, $x = 5$. Note that this value *satisfies* the constraint $x \le 8$.

2. Obtain the second derivative and note its sign:

$$\frac{d^2y}{dx^2} = +4$$

The plus sign indicates that at $x = 5$, the function $2x_2 - 20x + 60$ reaches a local minimum.

3. Compute the value of the function at $x = 8$ (the constraint):

$$2(8)^2 - 20(8) + 60 = 28$$

4. Compute the value of the function at its local minimum, $x = 5$:

$$2(5)^2 - 20(5) + 60 = 10$$

5. Comparing the results at step 3 and 4, we can see that the function is lower at $x = 5$ than at $x = 8$. Hence, we can say that the function is minimized at $x = 5$, and the minimum cost (see step 4) is 10.

Solution of One-Decision-Variable, Constrained Problem with Excel

In order to demonstrate how to solve a constrained single-decision-variable problem, we will slightly modify Example 9-3. Consider the following example that involves a slight modification of Example 9-3.

Example 9-5

X-Tech Inc. produces specialized bolts for the aerospace industry. The operating cost of producing a single bolt is $2.00. The company sells the bolts for $6.00 per unit. Each time the company arranges to sell a batch, it incurs a fixed cost of $20. This fixed cost mainly includes administrative expenses. The volume of sales is mainly dependent on the price of the product. The manager has come up with the following relationship between volume and price:

Volume = 500 − 25(Price)

However, due to marketing and competitive considerations, X-Tech decided to limit its price to $8.

a. State the nonlinear programming formulation of this problem.
b. Draw the profit function and the feasible solution space.
c. Determine the optimal price and optimal volume that will result in the maximum profit.
d. Repeat parts *a*, *b*, and *c*, by changing the restriction on price from a maximum of $8 to a maximum of $14.

Solution

a. maximize Profit = $Z = -25(\text{Price})^2 + 550(\text{Price}) - 1{,}020$

subject to

Price ≤ 8
Price ≥ 0

b. The drawing of the profit function and the feasible solution space is given in Figure 9-7.
c. In observing Figure 9-7, we see that the feasible region does not include the optimal price of $11. Furthermore, the price that results in the highest profit is $8. To verify this answer, we utilize Excel. The preparation of the worksheet is

Figure 9-7   The Graph of the Profit Function and the Feasible Space for the X-Tech Inc. Problem

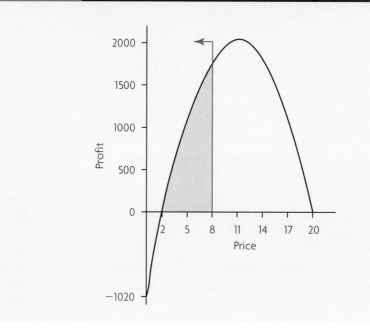

identical to the preparation of the worksheet in Exhibit 9-1. The only difference in the preparation of this version of the problem is the specification of the Price ≤ 8 constraint in the Solver Parameters screen. The solution to this problem is given in Exhibit 9-3. As expected, the optimal solution has a price of $8 per unit, with a volume of 300 units, resulting in a total profit of $1,780.

Exhibit 9-4 shows the parameter specification screen. The only difference between the contents of this screen in Exhibit 9-4 and the contents of Exhibit 9-2 is the specification of the new constraint (Price ≤ 8, specified as $C$4 ≤ 8).

d.   maximize Profit = $Z = -25(\text{Price})^2 + 550(\text{Price}) - 1{,}020$

subject to

Price ≤ 14

Price ≥ 0

The drawing of the profit function and the feasible solution space is given in Figure 9-8. As we mentioned earlier, the optimal solution to a constrained nonlinear programming problem may or may not occur at a corner point. As we

---

Exhibit 9-3   Worksheet for the One-Decision-Variable, Constrained Problem (X-Tech Inc., Example 9-5)

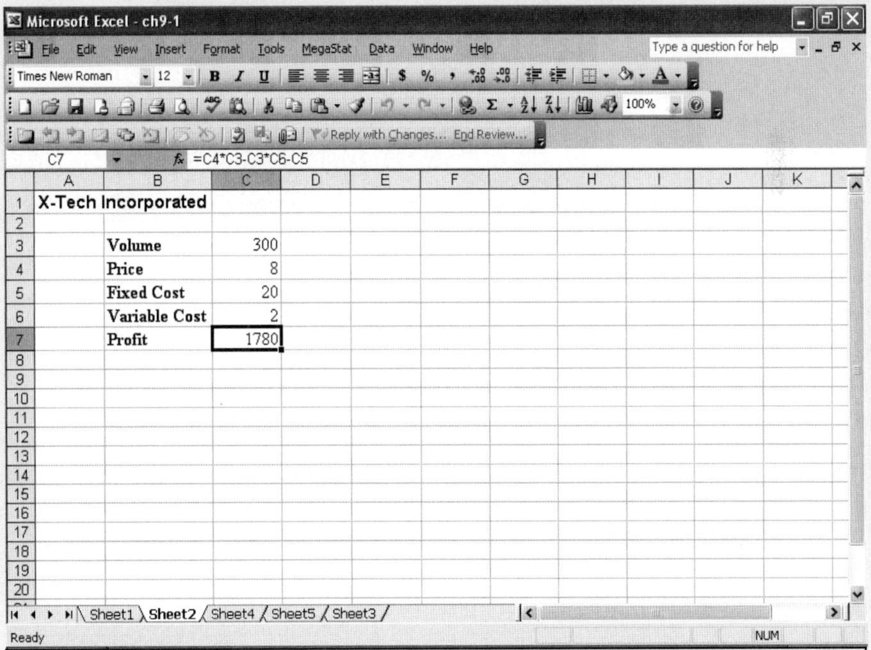

Microsoft Excel - ch9-1

	A	B	C	D
C7			f_x =C4*C3-C3*C6-C5	
1	X-Tech Incorporated			
2				
3		Volume	300	
4		Price	8	
5		Fixed Cost	20	
6		Variable Cost	2	
7		Profit	1780	

Cell	Copied to	Formula
C7		= C4 * C3 − C3 * 6 − C5
C3		= 500 − 25 * C4

can see from Figure 9-8, since the maximum point of the function is feasible, the corner point A provides a lower profit than the peak of the function (point B). Therefore, the optimal solution occurs at a price of $11 (point B), which results in a volume of 225 units and an optimal profit of $2,005.

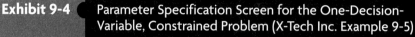

Exhibit 9-4   Parameter Specification Screen for the One-Decision-Variable, Constrained Problem (X-Tech Inc. Example 9-5)

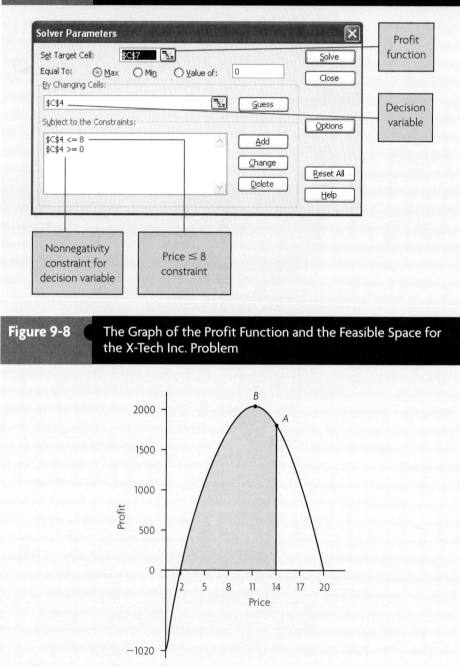

Figure 9-8   The Graph of the Profit Function and the Feasible Space for the X-Tech Inc. Problem

---

The fractional aircraft market is the fastest-developing sector of the business aircraft industry. The fractional aircraft ownership program allows individuals or companies to buy a share of a business airplane at a fraction of the full cost of ownership. The cost to the buyer depends on the number of hours of flight time per year.

The scheduling of flights and the associated crews in a fractional aircraft market is different than scheduling commercial flights. Major airlines decide the flight schedule of their aircraft months in advance, while fractional aircraft scheduling takes place only several hours before the flight. Therefore, fractional aircraft scheduling can be very complicated as firms guarantee the buyers 24-hour access within a four-hour decision-making window. The airplanes in the fractional aircraft market fly 10 times more frequently than the commercial flights. These airplanes can fly anywhere in the world with as little as 48 hours' notice.

The fractional aircraft owners have to pay monthly management and usage fees. Operators of these aircraft must manage maintenance, crews, fuel, and insurance on behalf of the fractional owners. Operators also must meet owners' demand for flight schedules at the requested times, schedule crew members, perform maintenance, schedule flights taking into account bad weather, and provide flight services (such as ground transportation).

Bombardier Flexjet is a company that competes in the fractional aircraft industry. The scheduling system utilized by the company has been ineffective. Flexjet hired AD-OPT Technologies, a leading management consulting company. AD-OPT along with the personnel from Flexjet were responsible for maximizing Flexjet's aircraft, crew, and facilities planning and scheduling.

AD-OPT considered the following when scheduling fractional aircrafts for Flexjet:

1. Build a flight schedule subject to constraints imposed by fractional owners.
2. Match the aircraft types and flights.
3. Route the aircraft and schedule the required maintenance.
4. Schedule crews for the scheduled flights.

In the past, this type of problem has been approached as a multicommodity network flow problem where they schedule the aircrafts first and impose the crew schedule based on the scheduled aircrafts. AD-OPT Technologies modified this approach by developing three integrated modules instead of the sequential processing. These modules consist of the following:

1. Prepare monthly crew schedules based on demand forecasts and preferences of the crew members.
2. Simultaneously schedule aircraft and crews, which involves matching aircraft and flights and aircraft routing.
3. Assign crew members to working periods on specific aircrafts.

AD-OPT uses TOSCA (The Optimizer for Scheduling Corporate Aircraft) to schedule the flights and crews for Flexjet. TOSCA decides the type of aircraft to schedule for each flight request and when and where to perform maintenance and swap crews. The scheduling is determined for a one- to three-day period by considering Federal Aviation Administration (FAA) regulations, company-enforced constraints, aircraft performance limits, and required maintenance schedule. AD-OPT Technologies developed the three modules described above using the GENCOL optimizer. This software package decomposes a large-scale, mixed-integer, nonlinear programming problem to assist the implementation of TOSCA.

This project enabled Flexjet to consider constraints and variables that it previously could not. The new system is able to assign multiple crews to one aircraft, when the aircraft is able to travel longer than one crew duty day. The new system also uses crews more efficiently by performing effective crew swaps, reducing crew members by 20 percent. The new integrated system improved operational efficiency considerably at Flexjet, saving the company $27 million annually, and reducing the aircraft fleet by 40 percent.

Source: R. Hicks, R. Madrid, C. Milligan, R. Pruneau, M. Kanaley, Y. Dumas, B. Lacroix, J. Desrosiers, and F. Soumis, "Bombardier Flexjet Significantly Improves Its Fractional Aircraft Ownership Operations," *Interfaces* 35, no. 1 (January–February 2005), pp. 59–60.

◗ Models with Two Decision Variables, Unconstrained Problem

Solution of models that involve two decision variables parallels the procedure used for models with one decision variable, except that the analysis is a bit more complicated, owing to the presence of a second decision variable. It becomes necessary to obtain the

partial derivative of a function (i.e., the derivative of the function with respect to one variable, treating the other variable as a *constant*), as well as the second partial derivative of a function with respect to each of the variables. As before, the first derivatives are set equal to zero and solved, and second derivative conditions are checked to determine the nature of the function at the values obtained from the first derivative results.

Example 9-6

Consider the case of a company that makes imaging equipment that it sells primarily to hospitals. The company makes two different models. Suppose we let x_1 = the quantity of Model 1 and x_2 = the quantity of Model 2. Model 1 sells for $64,000 and Model 2 sells for $72,000. The fixed cost of producing Model 1 equipment is $500,000 and the fixed cost of producing Model 2 is $600,000. The variable cost to produce each model (c_1, c_2) is complex and dependent on the quantity of each model that is produced and can be expressed as follows:

$c_1 = .4x_1 + .2x_2$ (in thousands of dollars)
$c_2 = .3x_2 + .2x_1$ (in thousands of dollars)

The manager of the company wants to determine the values of x_1 and x_2 that will maximize profit.

Solution
Variable costs can be calculated as follows:

$x_1c_1 = .4x_1^2 + .2x_1x_2$
$x_2c_2 = .3x_2^2 + .2x_1x_2$

The formula for the total profit is

$$Z = \text{Total revenue} - (\text{Variable cost} - \text{Fixed cost})$$
$$= 64x_1 + 72x_2 - [x_1c_1 + x_2c_2 - (500 + 600)]$$
$$= 64x_1 + 72x_2 - .4x_1^2 - .2x_1x_2 - .3x_2^2 - .2x_1x_2 - 1{,}100$$

Combining the two x_1x_2 terms, we have

$$Z = 64x_1 + 72x_2 - .4x_1^2 - .4x_1x_2 - .3x_2^2 - 1{,}100$$

In order to solve problems of this type, it is necessary to obtain the partial derivative of the function (i.e., P) with respect to each of the decision variables, and then set these equal to zero.

Condition 3 (*necessary*): The partial derivatives of an unconstrained function of two variables must both equal zero at a local maximum or a local minimum of the function.

Finding the partial derivatives and setting them equal to zero, we obtain

$$\frac{\partial Z}{\partial x_1} = 64 - .8x_1 - .4x_2 = 0$$

$$\frac{\partial Z}{\partial x_2} = 72 - .4x_1 - .6x_2 = 0$$

Rearranging terms, we can write

$$\frac{\partial Z}{\partial x_1}: \quad .8x_1 + .4x_2 = 64$$

$$\frac{\partial Z}{\partial x_1}: \quad .4x_1 + .6x_2 = 72$$

We can solve this by multiplying the second equation by 2 and then subtracting the first equation from the revised second equation. Thus:

$$-.8x_1 + 1.2x_2 = 144$$
$$\underline{.8x_1 + .4x_2 = 64}$$
$$.8x_2 = 80, \quad x_2 = 100$$

Substituting this value into either equation and solving for x_1, we obtain $x_1 = 30$. Hence, the optimal values *appear* to be $x_1 = 30$ and $x_2 = 100$.

Once these values have been obtained, we can check the second-order conditions to determine what sort of point they represent.

First, compute D, where

$$D = \left(\frac{\partial^2 Z}{\partial x_1^2}\right)\left(\frac{\partial^2 Z}{\partial x_2^2}\right) - \left(\frac{\partial^2 Z}{\partial x_1 \partial x_2}\right)^2$$

Then check the second-order conditions:

Condition 4 (*sufficient*). If Condition 3 is satisfied, and:

  a. $D > 0$

      1. The point is a local minimum if $\dfrac{\partial^2 Z}{\partial x_1^2} > 0$

      2. The point is a local maximum if $\dfrac{\partial^2 Z}{\partial x_1^2} < 0$

  b. $D < 0$

      The point is neither a local minimum nor a local maximum. Instead, it is a **saddle point,** which means one of the variables reaches a local maximum at the same point that the other variable reaches a local minimum.

In this example, the second partials and the mixed partial are

$$\frac{\partial^2 Z}{\partial x_1^2} = -.8, \qquad \frac{\partial^2 Z}{\partial x_2^2} = -.6, \qquad \text{and} \qquad \frac{\partial^2 Z}{\partial x_1 \partial x_2} = -.4,$$

Hence, $D = (-.8)(-.6) - (.4)^2 = +.32$. Because $D > 0$ and $\dfrac{\partial^2 Z}{\partial x_1^2} < 0$ this point $(x_1 = 30, x_2 = 100)$ is a local maximum (see Condition 4).

By substituting the optimal values into the original profit function, we also can determine the maximum profit:

$$Z = 64(30) + 72(100) - .4(30^2) - .4(30)(100) - .3(100^2) - 1{,}100$$
$$Z = 3{,}460, \text{ or } \$3{,}460{,}000$$

Solution of Unconstrained Problems with Two Decision Variables Using Excel

In order to see how an unconstrained nonlinear programming model with two decision variables may be solved using Excel, we will consider Example 9-6. In Example 9-6, the goal was to maximize the following profit equation:

$$Z = 60x_1 + 72x_2 - .4x_1^2 - .4x_1x_2 - .3x_2^2 - 1{,}100$$

In maximizing this profit equation, we prepare the worksheet shown in Exhibit 9-5. In preparing this worksheet, we begin by defining the variables in cells B5 and C5. Row 7 shows the headings used for the revenue and variable cost terms. Row 8 actually defines

Exhibit 9-5 Worksheet for the Two-Decision-Variable, Unconstrained Problem (Example, 9-6, Imaging Equipment)

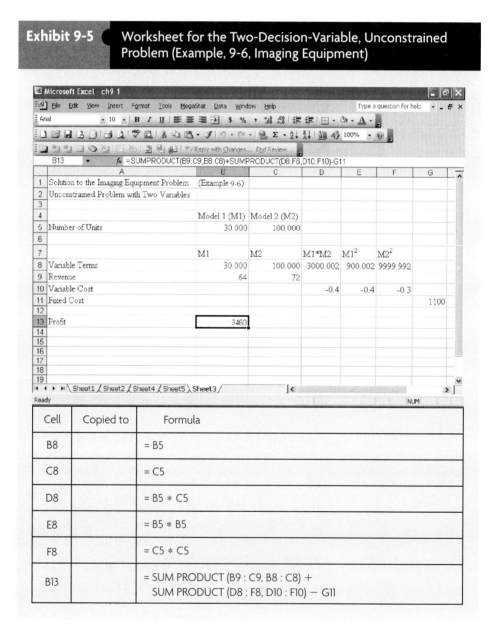

Cell	Copied to	Formula
B8		= B5
C8		= C5
D8		= B5 ∗ C5
E8		= B5 ∗ B5
F8		= C5 ∗ C5
B13		= SUM PRODUCT (B9 : C9, B8 : C8) + SUM PRODUCT (D8 : F8, D10 : F10) − G11

these in terms of Excel variables. For example, we set the values in cell B8 and C8 equal to the value of the decision variables in cells B5 and C5. The formula for cell D8 is the product of the two decision variables; x_1x_2, represented as B5 × C5. The formulas for the squared decision variable terms x_1^2 and x_2^2 in cells E8 and F8 are given in Exhibit 9-5. In the revenue, variable cost, and the fixed cost rows (rows 9, 10, and 11), we simply enter the appropriate revenue or cost coefficient from the profit equation given above. The profit is calculated by the profit equation given in cell B13 of Exhibit 9-5. This equation is shown in the formula bar at the bottom of Exhibit 9-5 and repeated here: =SUMPRODUCT (B9 : C9, B8 : C8) + SUMPRODUCT (D8 : F8, D10 : F10) − G11. In this equation, the first SUMPRODUCT term includes the calculation of the revenue. Cells B9 : C9 represent the revenue coefficient of the decision variables and cells B8 : C8 represent the decision variables. The second SUMPRODUCT term consists of the calculation of the variable cost. Cells D8 : F8 are the nonlinear terms involving the variable cost and cells D10 : F10 are the appropriate coefficients for the variable cost. Finally, the value in cell G11 represents the fixed cost. After preparing the worksheet in Exhibit 9-5, we click **Tools | Solver** and obtain the Solver Parameters specification screen given in Exhibit 9-6.

On this screen, for the "Set Target Cell" box location, we choose the profit function specified in cell B13. In the "Equal To" portion, we click on "Max." In the "By Changing Cells" box, we specify the decision variables Model 1 in cell B5 and Model 2 in cell C5. In addition, we also format these two cells to prevent reporting a rounding error. In formatting these cells, we choose **Format | Cells | Number** and specify the decimal places as 2. In the constraints section, we simply specify that the value of both of the decision variables has to be a nonnegative value, that is, $\$B\$5 : \$C\$5 \geq 0$. Because this is a nonlinear model, in order to ensure that a linear model is not utilized, we click on "Options" and make sure that the "Assume Linear Model" box is *not* checked. After clicking on "Solve," we obtain the solution given in Exhibit 9-5. Based on the results given in Exhibit 9-5, we should produce 30 units of Model 1 and 100 units of Model 2 for a total profit of $3,460.

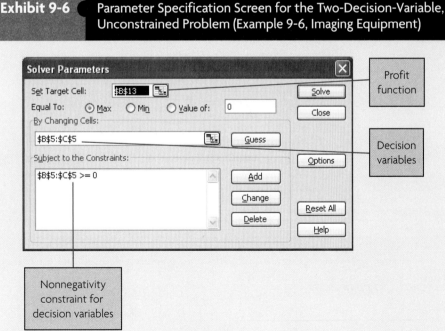

Exhibit 9-6   Parameter Specification Screen for the Two-Decision-Variable, Unconstrained Problem (Example 9-6, Imaging Equipment)

Models with Two Decision Variables and an Equality Constraint (Lagrange Multipliers)

The solution to a problem that involves two variables and one or more equality constraints when either the function or the constraints (or both) are nonlinear can be handled using the *Lagrangian method*. For example, consider the following example.

Example 9-7

maximize $Z = -2.5x_1^2 - x_2^2 + 3x_1x_2 + 18x_1 + 6x_2 + 100$

subject to

$x_1 + x_2 = 40$

Solution
The procedure involves setting the constraint equal to zero:

$x_1 + x_2 - 40 = 0$

and multiplying this by λ, the **Lagrange multiplier**:

$\lambda(x_1 + x_2 - 40)$

Then this new expression is added to the objective function to obtain a **Lagrangian function** that consists of the original decision variables and the Lagrangian multiplier, λ:

$L(x_1, x_2, \lambda) = -2.5x_1^2 - x_2^2 + 3x_1x_2 + 18x_1 + 6x_2 + 100 + \lambda(x_1 + x_2 - 40)$

Note that adding this new term does not really change the objective function because the new term is equal to zero.

Once we have obtained the Lagrangian function, we can analyze the problem in a way that is very similar to the procedure described in the preceding section for two-variable, unconstrained models. The only difference is that we now have a third variable to deal with.

As before, we obtain the partial derivative of the objective function with respect to each of the variables (x_1, x_2, and λ):

$\dfrac{\partial L}{\partial x_1} = -5x_1 + 3x_2 + 18 + \lambda = 0$

$\dfrac{\partial L}{\partial x_2} = -2x_2 + 3x_1 + 6 + \lambda = 0$

$\dfrac{\partial L}{\partial \lambda} = x_1 + x_2 - 40 = 0$

We can solve this system of equations for the values of x_1, x_2, and λ by first eliminating λ from the first two equations (e.g., subtract the first equation from the second). The result is

$(-2x_2 + 3x_1 + 6 + \lambda) - (-5x_1 + 3x_2 + 18 + \lambda) = 0$
$(5x_1 + 3x_1) + (-3x_2 - 2x_2) + (-18 + 6) + (-\lambda + \lambda) = 0$
$8x_1 \qquad\quad - 5x_2 \qquad\quad - 12 \qquad\qquad\qquad = 0$

Then, using this new equation and the third partial derivative, we have

(new) $\qquad 8x_1 - 5x_2 - 12 = 0$
(third) $\qquad x_1 + x_2 - 40 = 0$

Solving these equations simultaneously, we get

$$x_1 = 16.307$$

and substituting this into the (third) equation, we find that $x_2 = 23.693$.

We can now determine the value of λ, using $x_1 = 16.307$ and $x_2 = 23.693$, and either of the first two partial derivative equations. For example, using the first partial derivative equation, we find

$$-5(16.307) + 3(23.693) + 18 + \lambda = 0$$

Solving, $\lambda = -7.544$.

At this point, we have found what appear to be optimal values of x_1 and x_2. However, instead of *maximizing* the original function, it may be that they actually *minimize* the function. Or they may constitute a *saddle point*. The same conditions that applied in the previous section apply here. In order to check them, we must first substitute the value of $\lambda = -7.544$ into the first partial derivatives of L with respect to x_1 and x_2. Thus:

$$\frac{\partial L}{\partial x_1} = -5x_1 + 3x_2 + 18 - 7.544$$

$$\frac{\partial L}{\partial x_2} = -2x_2 + 3x_1 + 6 - 7.544$$

The second partials and the mixed partial are

$$\frac{\partial^2 L}{\partial x_1^2} = -5, \qquad \frac{\partial^2 L}{\partial x_2^2} = -2, \qquad \text{and} \qquad \frac{\partial^2 L}{\partial x_1 \partial x_2} = +3$$

As before, we compute the value of D:

$$D = \left(\frac{\partial^2 L}{\partial x_1^2}\right)\left(\frac{\partial^2 L}{\partial x_2^2}\right) - \left(\frac{\partial^2 L}{\partial x_1 \partial x_2}\right)^2 = (-5)(-2) - (3)^2 = 10 - 9 = 1$$

Because $D > 0$ and $\dfrac{\partial^2 L}{\partial x_1^2} < 0$, we do, in fact, have a local maximum. We can determine the value of the function at its local maximum by substituting the values we found for x_1 and x_2 into the original function, Thus:

$$Z = -2.5(16.307)^2 - (23.693)^2 + 3(16.307)(23.693) + 18(16.307) + 6(23.693) + 100 = 468.61$$

Let's take a moment to recap the Lagrange procedure:

1. Form the Lagrange function. Do this by making the constraint equal to zero, multiplying it by λ, and adding the result to the original objective function.
2. Obtain the partial derivative of the Lagrange function with respect to each of the decision variables and to λ. Set these equal to zero.
3. Find the solution(s) for the decision variables. Do this by eliminating λ from the partials of x_1 and x_2, and then using the partial of the Lagrange multiplier. Then find the value of λ.

4. Treating the value of λ as fixed, find the second partials of x_1 and x_2, and the mixed partial.
5. Determine if the solution(s) is (are) a local maximum, local minimum, or a saddle point, according to Condition 4 that was described in the previous section.

Interpreting λ

The Lagrange multiplier, λ, has an important economic interpretation, analogous to dual variables in linear programming. Its value indicates the (sometimes approximate) amount that the objective function will change for a one-unit change in the right-hand-side value of the constraint. For instance, in the preceding example, we found $\lambda = 7.544$. This means that if the right-hand-side value of the constraint were to be increased by one unit (from 40 to 41) the resulting optimal value of the objective function would increase by 7.544. Conversely, if the right-hand-side value of the constraint were to be decreased by one unit, the optimal value of the objective function would decrease by 7.544. Moreover, if the sign of λ had been positive (say, $+22$), the opposite would have been true: A one-unit decrease in the right-hand-side value of the constraint would have caused an *increase* of 22 in the optimal value of the objective function, and a one-unit increase in the right-hand-side value of the constraint would have caused a *decrease* of 22 in the end optimal value of the objective function.

Solution of Problems with Two Decision Variables and a Single Equality Constraint Using Excel

In order to see how a nonlinear programming model with two decision variables may be solved using Excel, we will consider the following example.

Example 9-8

The Daisy-Fresh Company produces two types of deodorants. Let x_1 be equal to the quantity of Roll-On deodorant and let x_2 be equal to the quantity of Stick deodorant. The profit per unit for the Roll-On deodorant is estimated as $3.2x_1 - .02x_1^2$. In interpreting this equation, the expected revenue is \$3.20 for each Roll-On deodorant. However, the variable cost of production is a nonlinear function of the number of units produced. In other words, each unit of Roll-On deodorant (x_1) being produced by Daisy-Fresh Company costs Daisy-Fresh \$0.02x_1^2 in production costs. Likewise, per-unit profit for the Stick deodorant is estimated as $4x_2 - .03x_2^2$. The estimated profit per unit of stick deodorant is \$4 ($4x_2$), and the variable cost per unit is .03x_2^2. The hourly fixed cost of producing both products together is estimated as \$150. Each unit of Roll-On deodorant takes 20 seconds to manufacture on a machine, while each unit of Stick deodorant takes 30 seconds to manufacture on a machine. A machine has 60 minutes of productive capacity in an hour before minor maintenance has to be performed.

a. Formulate this problem as a single constrained nonlinear programming problem.
b. Use Excel and determine the hourly number of units of each deodorant type to produce.
c. What is the optimal profit?

Solution

a. Formulation:

$x_1 = $ quantity of Roll-On deodorant
$x_2 = $ quantity of Stick deodorant

maximize $Z = 3.2x_1 - .02x_1^2 + 4x_2 - .03x_2^2 - 150$

subject to

$$20x_1 + 30x_2 = 3,600 \text{ seconds}$$
$$x_1, x_2 \geq 0$$

b.   As a starting point, we prepare the worksheet shown in Exhibit 9-7. In preparing this worksheet, first we begin by defining the variables in cells B5 and C5. Row 7 shows the headings used for the revenue and variable cost terms. Row 8 actually defines these items in terms of Excel variables. For example, we set the values in cell B8 and C8 equal to the value of the decision variables in cells B5 and C5. The formulas for the squared decision variable terms x_1^2 and x_2^2 in cells D8 and E8 are given in Exhibit 9-7. Cell D8 contains B5 $*$ B5, and cell E8 contains C5 $*$ C5. In the revenue, variable cost, and fixed-cost rows (rows 9, 10, and 11), we simply

Exhibit 9-7	Worksheet for the Problem with Two Decision Variables and a Single Equality Constraint (Example 9-8, Daisy-Fresh Company Deodorant Problem)

Cell	Formula
G12	= SUMPRODUCT (B12 : C12, B5 : C5)
B8	= B5
C8	= C5
D8	= B5 $*$ B5
E8	= C5 $*$ C5
B13	= SUMPRODUCT (B9 : C9, B8 : C8) + SUMPRODUCT (D8 : F8, D10 : F10) − F11 $*$ This formula is also in the formula bar

enter the appropriate revenue or cost coefficient from the profit equation given in the objective function of this problem. The profit is calculated by the profit equation given in cell B13 of Exhibit 9-7. This equation is shown in the formula bar of Exhibit 9-7 and is repeated here: $=SUMPRODUCT(B9:C9, B8:C8) + SUMPRODUCT(D8:E8, D10:E10) - F11$. In this equation, the first SUMPRODUCT term includes the calculation of the revenue. Cells $B9:C9$ represent the revenue coefficient of the decision variables, and cells $B8:C8$ represent the decision variables. The second SUMPRODUCT term consists of the calculation of the variable cost. The cells $D8:E8$ are the nonlinear terms involving the variable cost and the cells $D10:E10$ are the appropriate coefficients for the variable cost. Finally, the value in cell F11 represents the fixed cost. The machine time constraint is specified in row 12. In this row, we first specify the amount of time it takes to produce each unit in cells B12 (20 seconds to produce one unit of Roll-On deodorant) and C12 (30 seconds to produce one unit of Stick deodorant). The right-hand side of the constraint is entered in the Time Available column in cell H12. The sum of the left-hand side of the constraint is calculated by cross-multiplying the decision variable values with the amount of time it takes to produce one unit. This is accomplished by the following formula: $=SUMPRODUCT(B12:C12, B5:C5)$. In this formula, cells $B12:C12$ represent the production time per unit, and cells $B5:C5$ are the values of decision variables x_1 and x_2.

After preparing the worksheet in Exhibit 9-7, we click **Tools I Solver** and obtain the Solver parameter specification screen given in Exhibit 9-8. Exhibit 9-8 is very similar to Exhibit 9-6. On this screen, for the "Set Target Cell" box, we choose the profit function specified in cell B13. In the "Equal To" portion, we click on "Max."

Exhibit 9-8 Parameter Specification Screen for Two Decision Variables and a Single Equality Constraint Problem (Example 9-8, Daisy-Fresh Co. Deodorant Problem)

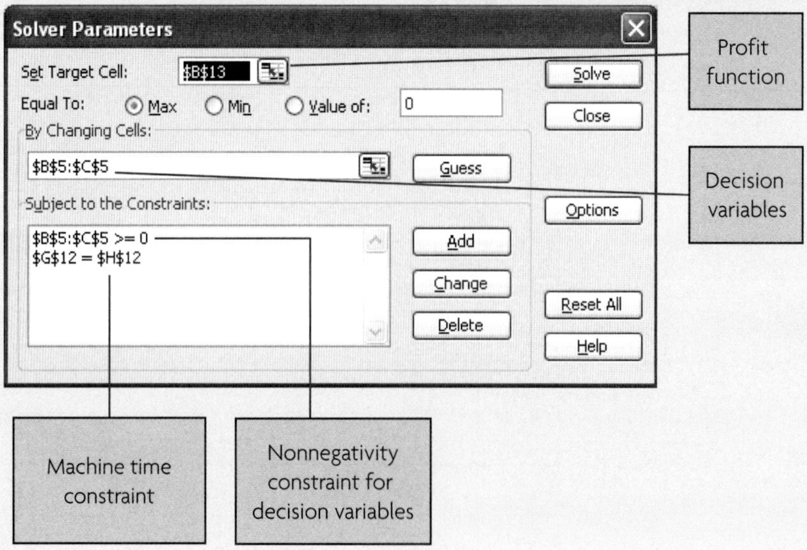

In the "By Changing Cells" box, we specify the decision variables Roll-On deodorant in cell B5 and Stick deodorant in cell C5. In addition, we also format these two cells to prevent reporting a rounding error. In formatting these cells, we choose **Format I Cells I Number** and specify the decimal places as 2. In the constraints section, first we simply specify that the value of both of the decision variables has to be a nonnegative value, that is, $B$5 : $C$5 \geq 0$. Second, we specify the machine hour constraint. In specifying this constraint the left-hand side of the constraint (time used) is given by cell G12 and the right-hand side of this constraint is given by cell H12 (time available). Since this is a nonlinear model, in order to ensure that a linear model is not utilized, we click on "Options" and make sure that the "Assume Linear Model" box is *not* checked. After clicking on "Solve", we obtain the solution given in Exhibit 9-7. Based on the results given in Exhibit 9-7, the Daisy-Fresh Company should produce 80 units of Roll-On deodorant and 66.67 units of Stick deodorant.

c. Total optimal profit associated with this production schedule is specified in cell B13 and it is $111.33 per hour, per machine.

Models with Two Decision Variables and a Single Inequality Constraint

The procedure described in the previous section can be modified a little if we have a problem that involves two variables and a single inequality constraint. In demonstrating how to solve this type of problem, let's consider Example 9-7 from the last section. We will switch the constraint from $=$ to $\leq$.

Example 9-9

Let

x_1 = number of units of product 1 manufactured
x_2 = number of units of product 2 manufactured

maximize $Z = -2.5x_1^2 - x_2^2 + 3x_1x_2 + 18x_1 + 6x_2 + 100$

subject to

$x_1 + x_2 \leq 40$ (labor hours constraint)

There are two possibilities with respect to the constraint. The first one involves the possibility that the constraint is binding. If it is a binding constraint, then the left-hand side of the constraint must equal the right-hand side of the constraint. Since it becomes an "equal to" constraint, it can be solved by the method described in answering Example 9-7. However, if $x_1 + x_2 < 40$, then the constraint is not binding. In this case, we will ignore the constraint and solve it as an unconstrained problem. This solution procedure can be summarized as follows:

1. Assume the constraint is not binding and solve it as an unconstrained problem. In solving it this way, we are attempting to determine if a global maximum exists.

We can determine if a given point is a global maximum by applying the necessary and sufficient conditions test from the previous section. If we establish that the point is indeed the global maximum, then we need to test it to see if it satisfies the constraint. If the global maximum satisfies the constraint, we stop and the global maximum found is the optimal solution to this problem. Based on the necessary and sufficient conditions test, if the point is not a global maximum, then we will simply maintain any local maximum that satisfies the constraints in our records and go to step 2.

2. We assume that the constraint is binding and apply the solution procedure utilized with a single equality constraint utilized in solving Example 9-7. If a local maximum is found in step 1, we compare the results from step 2 with the local maximum results from step 1. The global maximum is given by the solution that gives the largest profit among these values.

In other words, if the constraint is not satisfied in step 1, we go to step 2. If the constraint is satisfied but necessary and sufficient conditions for global optimality are not satisfied, the values of the decision variables at the local maximum are recorded and step 2 is executed.

Solution

1. *(Necessary conditions)*   Take the partial derivative with respect to each variable and set the resulting equations equal to zero.

$$\frac{\partial Z}{\partial x_1} = -5x_1 + 3x_2 + 18 = 0$$

Rearranging the terms:

$$5x_1 - 3x_2 = 18$$

$$\frac{\partial Z}{\partial x_2} = 3x_1 - 2x_2 + 6 = 0$$

Rearranging the terms:

$$-3x_1 + 2x_2 = 6$$

We can solve the two rearranged equations simultaneously.

$$(2)(5x_1 - 3x_2) = (2)18 \quad \text{or}$$
$$10x - 6x_2 = 36$$
$$(3)(-3x_1 + 2x_2) = (3)6 \quad \text{or}$$
$$-9x_1 + 6x_2 = 18$$

$$10x_1 - 6x_2 = 36$$
$$+ -9x_1 + 6x_2 = 18$$
$$\overline{\rule{3cm}{0.4pt}}$$
$$x_1 = 54$$

$$5(54) - 3x_2 = 18$$
$$-3x_2 = -252$$
$$x_2 = 84$$

Once these values have been obtained, we can check the second-order conditions.

Sufficient Conditions   In this example, second partial derivatives and mixed partial derivatives are as follows:

$$\frac{\partial^2 Z}{\partial x_1^2} = -5$$

$$\frac{\partial^2 Z}{\partial x_2^2} = -2$$

$$\frac{\partial^2 Z}{\partial x_1 \partial x_2} = -3$$

$$D = \left(\frac{\partial^2 Z}{\partial x_1^2}\right)\left(\frac{\partial^2 Z}{\partial x_2^2}\right) - \left(\frac{\partial^2 Z}{\partial x_1 \partial x_2}\right)^2 = (-5)(-2) - (-3)^2$$

$$D = 10 - 9 = 1$$

Since D > 0 and $\frac{\partial^2 Z}{\partial x_1^2} < 0$, this point ($x_1 = 54$, $x_2 = 84$) is an optimal solution to the unconstrained problem. However, since $x_1 + x_2 = 54 + 84 = 138 > 40$, the constraint is not satisfied. Therefore, we go to step 2.

2. Since we have already utilized the solution procedure for step 2 in solving Example 9-7, the optimal solution to this problem is

$$x_1 = 16.307 \qquad x_2 = 23.693 \qquad \text{and} \qquad Z = 468.61$$

Had the constraint been satisfied as the end of step 1, then the solution found in step 1 would have been the optimal solution to Example 9-9. The constraint represents the availability of weekly labor hours. There are 40 labor hours available each week and each unit of product 1 and product 2 takes 1 hour to manufacture respectively. Solving the unconstrained problem resulted in production of 54 units of product 1 and 84 units of product 2. However, producing these values will exceed the labor hours available and violate the constraint. That is why we utilize the method involving the Lagrange multiplier because the Lagrange multiplier method assumes that the constraint is binding and solves for the optimal values of x_1 and x_2. Had we found a local optimal point that satisfies the constraint but does not satisfy the necessary and sufficient conditions for global optimality, we would have recorded that solution and compared it to the solution found in step 2 and then chosen the solution with the larger profit.

The solution procedure we have described in this section cannot be applied to problems that involve multiple constraints. In many real-world problems, there are multiple constraints. In solving these problems, we utilize Excel or other software packages. The solution procedures that solve these problems are iterative and complex; therefore, we do not provide the steps or detailed description of these algorithms. However, in the next section, we will provide an example with multiple constraints and solve it using Excel.

Solution of Problems with Two Decision Variables and Multiple Constraints Using Excel

We can use Excel to solve nonlinear programming problems with two decision variables and multiple constraints. Let's consider the following example for demonstration purposes.

Example 9-10

East-West Computer Storage produces CDs, DVDs, and diskettes. The company earns a profit of $5 for each CD and $2.80 for each diskette. However, in producing the DVDs, we take advantage of fixed overhead costs. The more DVDs produced, the higher the profit. Let's define the variables as CD = CD, Diskette = DI, and DVD = DV. The profits on the DVDs can be expressed as $1DV + .02DV^2$. East-West Computer Storage Company's nonlinear objective function can be stated as follows:

maximize $Z = 5CD + 2.8DI + 1DV + .02DV^2$

This objective function is subject to the following labor and machine constraints. East-West Computer Storage Company has 40 hours of labor available per week and 36.66 machine hours available per week. Each unit of CD, Diskette, and DVD requires the following number of labor and machine hours:

	CD	Diskette	DVD
Labor hours per unit (minutes)	4	2	8
Machine hours per unit (minutes)	3	2.5	6.5

Based on marketing considerations, the minimum production requirement of DVDs is 100 units.

Formulate the nonlinear program for this problem and use Excel to determine the optimal production schedule of these three products. What is the maximum profit?

Solution

The nonlinear programming formulation of this problem is as follows:

maximize $Z = 5CD + 2.8DI + 1DV + .02DV^2$

subject to

$$4CD + 2DI + 8DV \leq 2,400 \text{ minutes} \quad \text{(labor time available)}$$
$$3CD + 2.5DI + 6.5DV \leq 2,200 \text{ minutes} \quad \text{(machine time available)}$$
$$DV \geq 100 \quad \text{(minimum DVD production requirement)}$$
$$CD, DI, DV \geq 0$$

The Excel worksheet shown in Exhibit 9-9 includes the input as well as the output from this model. In preparing this worksheet, we begin by defining the location of the three decision variables CD, Diskette (DI), and DVD (DV) in cells B5, C5, and D5 respectively. Variable terms are defined in cells B8, C8, D8, and E8. Cells B8, C8, and D8 are simply the values of the decision variables in cells B5, C5, and D5. However, we define the formula in cell E8 (D5 × D5) as the square of the DVD variable in cell D5. Row 9 shows the revenue values from the objective function, while rows 10 and 11 indicate the labor and machine constraints. Cell F10, labor minutes used, represents the left-hand side of the labor constraint. Cell F11, machine minutes used, represents the left-hand side of the machine constraint. Cells G10 and G11 represent the right-hand side of the labor and machine constraints respectively. In developing the formula for cell F10, we use the following: =SUMPRODUCT (B10 : D10, B5 : D5). In this equation, B10 : D10 are the coefficients of the labor constraints (amount of labor time required to produce one unit of each product). B5 : D5 represent the values of the decision

Exhibit 9-9   Worksheet for a Two-Decision-Variable, Multiple-Constraint Problem (Example 9-10, East-West Company Computer Storage Problem)

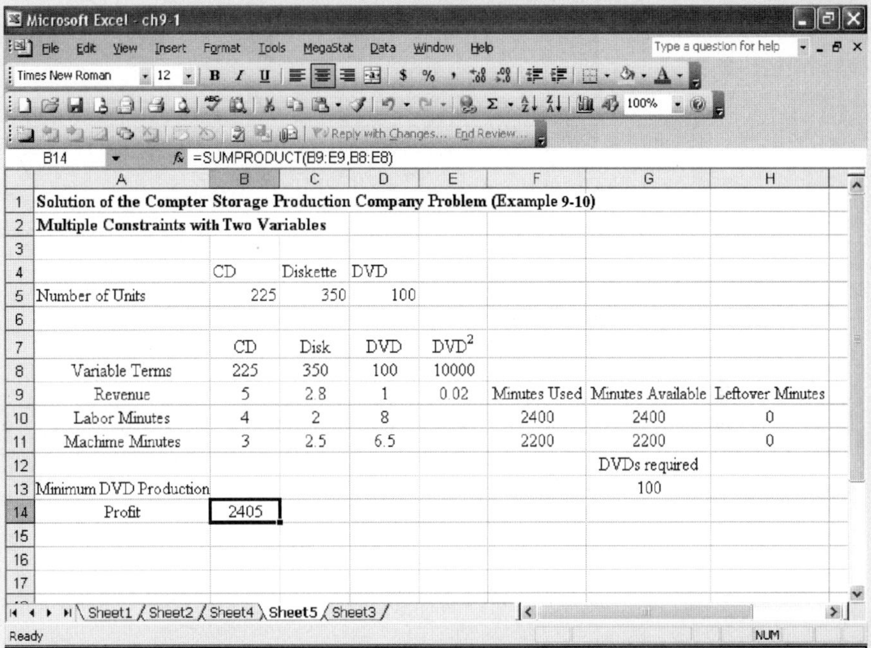

	Microsoft Excel - ch9-1							
	File Edit View Insert Format Tools MegaStat Data Window Help							
B14			=SUMPRODUCT(B9:E9,B8:E8)					
	A	B	C	D	E	F	G	H
1	Solution of the Compter Storage Production Company Problem (Example 9-10)							
2	Multiple Constraints with Two Variables							
3								
4		CD	Diskette	DVD				
5	Number of Units	225	350	100				
6								
7		CD	Disk	DVD	DVD^2			
8	Variable Terms	225	350	100	10000			
9	Revenue	5	2.8	1	0.02	Minutes Used	Minutes Available	Leftover Minutes
10	Labor Minutes	4	2	8		2400	2400	0
11	Machine Minutes	3	2.5	6.5		2200	2200	0
12							DVDs required	
13	Minimum DVD Production						100	
14	Profit	2405						
15								
16								
17								

Sheet1 / Sheet2 / Sheet4 \ Sheet5 / Sheet3 /

Cell	Formula
B8	= B5
C8	= C5
D8	= D5
E8	= D5 * D5
B14	= SUMPRODUCT (B9 : E9, B8 : E8)
F10	= SUMPRODUCT (B10 : D10, B5 : D5)
F11	= SUMPRODUCT (B11 : D11, B5 : D5)

variables. The formula for cell F11 is developed in a similar fashion for the machine time constraint. Column H provides the values of slack associated with labor and machine time constraints. The formula for profit, =SUMPRODUCT (B9 : E9, B8 : E8), is shown in the formula bar of Exhibit 9-9. This formula is the cross-product of the decision variables with the profit margin for each variable. B9 : E9 represent the profit margin for each product as well as the squared DVD term. B8 : D8 includes the values of the decision variables. Finally, in cell E8 the number of DVDs is squared to

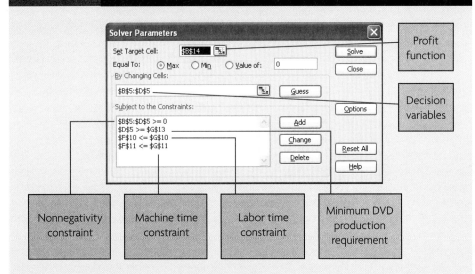

| Exhibit 9-10 | Parameter Specification Screen for the Two-Decision-Variable, Multiple-Constraints Problem (Example 9-10, East-West Company Computer Storage Problem) |

reflect the DV^2 term in the objective function. The formulas used to prepare the worksheet shown in Exhibit 9-9 are stated at the bottom of the worksheet.

After entering the values and the formulas shown at the bottom of Exhibit 9-9, we proceed to choose **Tool I Solver**. This action brings up the Solver Parameters specification screen shown in Exhibit 9-10. On this screen, for the "Set Target Cell" box, we choose the profit function specified in cell B14. In the "Equal To" portion, we click on "Max" since we are maximizing profit. In the "By Changing Cells" box, we specify the decision variables CD in cell B5, Diskette in cell C5, and DVD in cell D5. In the constraints section, first we simply specify that the value of both of the decision variables have to be a nonnegative value, that is, $B$5 : $D$5 $\geq$ 0. Second, we specify the machine time constraint. In specifying this constraint, the left-hand side of the constraint (time used) is given by cell F11. and the right-hand side of this constraint (time available) is given by cell G11. Since this is a nonlinear model, in order to ensure that a linear model is not utilized, we click on "Options" and make sure that the "Assume Linear Model" box is *not* checked. After clicking on "Solve," we obtain the solution given in Exhibit 9-9. Based on these results, East-West Computer Storage Company should produce 225 CDs, 350 Diskettes, and 100 DVDs. Total optimal profit associated with this production schedule is specified in cell B14 as $2,405.

Summary

The models presented in this chapter are similar to the linear programming models presented in earlier chapters. The essential difference is that the models presented in this chapter have one or more *nonlinear* components. These models generally cannot be handled using conventional linear programming techniques. Instead, nonlinear programming procedures must be used.

A Modern Management Science Application: *General Electric*

General Electric (GE) produces jet engines, power generators, plastics, and medical imaging equipment, to name a few products. It also provides financial services, news, and information technology, employing over 300,000 people worldwide and providing services and products in more than 100 countries. In 2004, GE's total revenue was $152.4 billion with earnings of $16.66 billion.

The GE Plastics (GEP) unit is a subsidiary of GE. GEP supplies plastic materials to automotive, appliance, computer, medical equipment, and other industries and contributes $5 billion in annual revenues to GE. GEP consists of seven major divisions, one of which, High Performance Polymers (HPP), produces heat-tolerant material that can be used to make products such as microwaves, fire helmets, and utensils. HPP is the fastest-growing division, and was chosen as the unit to implement a prototype production plan because of its need for increasing capacity as a high-growth organization.

One of HPP's primary goals is to achieve the highest customer satisfaction at the lowest cost. In order to accomplish this goal, HPP developed a decision support system (DSS) to optimize its two-echelon global manufacturing supply chain. The two-echelon supply chain consists of the following components: level 1—the resin plants (converts feedstock into resins) and level 2—finishing plants (combines resins with additives to produce different end products). There are 8 resin plants and 21 finishing plants that produce 24 end products. After a product goes through both echelons, it is shipped to GE Polymerland, which is a subsidiary of GE and is the only direct customer of GEP. GE Polymerland then delivers the products to the customers.

This HPP DSS uses a mathematical programming model to maximize contribution margin, determine how to integrate the newly acquired capacity into the existing supply chain, and decide whether a new plant is needed, and if so, the location of choice. In order to optimize the HPP supply chain, the DSS considers, as variables, product demand, prices, the capacities of existing plants, production distribution volume, and raw material costs. As the supply chain gets more complicated, GEP has to make decisions concerning the allocation of the capacity of each of its plants such that the demands at various facility sites can be met.

In the past, GEP tried to manufacture the product where it was needed. However, it soon discovered that there was a capacity-demand mismatch. There was overcapacity in the

America region, which includes the United States and Canada, and there was undercapacity in the Pacific region. The main objective of GEP was to have a better balance between capacity and demand. However the company also had secondary objectives, including

1. Reduction of operational and raw material costs.
2. Reduction of its tax burden by taking advantage of the tax structure in certain countries.
3. Minimization of the cost of transporting the resins from the resin plants to finishing plants, and from finishing plants to GE warehouses.

The best way to reach the company's goals would be to determine a schedule that meets all demand and maximizes the contribution margin.

The DSS was developed using Excel and LINGO (a commercial solver of management science problems). An advantage of using Excel in conjunction with LINGO is the ease with which data are transferred between the two software packages. While LINGO was used to solve the mathematical programming model, Excel provided a user friendly, data entry/user interface feature, developed by using Visual Basic for Application (VBA) a computer programming language that offers not only the visual basic programming language, but also is extended with Excel functions. The flexibility and accessibility of Excel made it a very attractive addition to the DSS.

GEP's DSS allowed them to address the following company objectives:

1. Better match between market demand and plant capacities.
2. Reduction in manufacturing operating and raw materials costs.

When demand exceeds capacity, DSS determines which products should be produced based on the highest contribution margin. As demand increases, the DSS has the flexibility to perform what-if analysis. The helps the company to determine which products to produce less of in order to maximize its contribution margin. For GEP, the expected increase in its total annual contribution margin is over $70 million.

Source: R. Tyagi, P. Kalish, K. Akbay, and G. Munshaw, "GE Plastics Optimizes the Two-Echelon Global Fulfillment Network at Its High Performance Polymers Division," *Interfaces* 34, no. 5 (September–October 2004), pp. 359–66.

The nonlinear programming procedures typically involve obtaining the first derivative of the objective function, finding all solutions for which the first derivative is equal to zero, and then checking second derivative conditions to ascertain the nature of the zero points (e.g., a local maximum or a local minimum). If two or more decision variables are involved, partial derivatives are used. If equality or inequality constraints and two or more decision variables are involved, a method that involves a *Lagrange multiplier* is used. If the model includes an inequality constraint and two or more decision variables, first we solve the model as unconstrained and see if the solution satisfies the necessary and sufficient conditions and also satisfies the constraint. If the necessary and sufficient conditions for optimality and the constraint are satisfied, then the solution to the unconstrained model is the optimal solution. However, if the constraint is violated, we go to the next step (step 2). In the next step, we assume that the constraint is binding and use the *Lagrange multiplier* method that we employed when we solved the problem with a single equality constraint.

Throughout the chapter, we show the Excel solution to various nonlinear programming problems. In the last section of the chapter, we demonstrate how a problem with multiple decision variables and multiple constraints can be solved using Excel.

The models presented in this chapter are relatively simple. More complex models are more challenging to deal with. Some lend themselves to computer solution. Unfortunately most management science computer packages including Excel are not equipped to handle these sort of more complicated problems. These problems require the use of more specialized software. Formulating and solving nonlinear programming problems may require considerable expertise and some such problems do not truly lend themselves to solution, even with a specialized computer software.

◼◣ Glossary

Global Maximum The highest value attained by a function over its entire range.

Global Minimum The lowest value attained by a function over its entire range.

Lagrange Multiplier, λ An additional variable used to incorporate the constraint(s) into the objective function in a model that has equality constraints.

Lagrangian Function In models that have equality constraints, a modified objective function that incorporates the constraint(s) as part of the objective function.

Local Maximum The highest point of a function relative to nearby values. It may or may not be the highest point overall.

Local Minimum The lowest point of a function relative to nearby values. It may or may not be the lowest point overall.

Necessary Conditions In order for the solution to be a candidate for the optimal solution, these conditions require first derivatives to be set equal to zero. However, satisfying these conditions do not guarantee optimality.

Partial Derivative When a function has more than one decision variable, a derivative of the function with respect to one of the decision variables with all other variables treated as constants.

Saddle Point A point that is neither a maximum nor a minimum; with two variables, the function attains a maximum with respect to one variable while attaining a minimum with respect to the other variable.

Sufficient Conditions Assist in determining whether a solution is associated with a maximum, minimum, or no solution. They involve taking the second partial derivative of the objective function and observing the signs of the second partial derivatives and the sign of D

where $D = \left(\dfrac{\partial^2 Z}{\partial x_1^2} \right) \left(\dfrac{\partial^2 Z}{\partial x_2^2} \right) - \left(\dfrac{\partial^2 Z}{\partial x_1 \partial x_2} \right)^2.$

Solved Problems

Problem 1

One variable, unconstrained. Given the following function:

$$y = \frac{1}{3}x^3 - 6x^2 + 27x$$

a. Determine the value of x for which the function reaches (1) a local maximum and (2) a local minimum.
b. Determine the value of the function at the local maximum and local minimum.
c. Use Excel to solve the above problem. What is the maximum value of the function and the optimum value of x?

Solution

a. 1. Obtain the first derivative of the function:

$$\frac{dy}{dx} = x^2 - 12x + 27$$

2. Set the first derivative equal to zero and solve for x:

$$x^2 - 12x - 27 = 0$$

Factoring, we obtain

$$(x - 3)(x - 9) = 0$$

Hence, the roots are $x = +3$ and $x = +9$.

3. Obtain the second derivative:

$$\frac{d^2y}{dx^2} = 2x - 12$$

Substitute the roots obtained in step 2 into the second derivative:

At $x = +3$, the second derivative equals -6
At $x = +9$, the second derivative equals $+6$

We can conclude that the function reaches a local maximum at $x = 3$ because the sign of the second derivative is negative for $x = +3$: and we can conclude that the function reaches a local minimum at $x = 9$ because the sign of the second derivative is positive for that value of x.

b. Substituting $x = 3$ and $x = 9$ into the original function, we find

At $x = 3$, the value of the function y equals 36
At $x = 9$, the value of the function y equals 0

c. The Excel spreadsheet along with all of the necessary formulas and Solver Parameters screen for Solved Problem 1 are given in Exhibits 9-11 and 9-12. Once Exhibit 9-11 is completed, Exhibit 9-12 is obtained by choosing **Tools I Solver.**

Exhibit 9-11	Worksheet for Solved Problem 1: One-Decision-Variable, Unconstrained Problem

Microsoft Excel - ch9-solved1

B10 = SUMPRODUCT(B9:D9, B8:D8)

	A	B	C	D	E	F	G	H	I
1	Solution to Solved Problem 1								
2	Unconstrained Problem with One Variable								
3									
4		X							
5	Number of Units	3.000							
6									
7		X	X^3	X^2					
8	Variable Terms	3.000	26.996	8.999					
9	Cost/Profit Coefficients	27	0.3333	-6					
10	Profit	36.00							
11									
12									
13									
14									
15									
16									
17									

Solved Problem 5 / **Solved Prob. 1** / Solved Problem 4 / Solved P|

Ready

Cell	Formula
C8	= B5 * B5 * B5
D8	= B5 * B5
B10	= SUMPRODUCT (B9 : D9, B8 : D8)

Problem 2   *Constrained optimization with one variable.*

a. Manually find the optimal profit for the model, and the value of the decision variable that will produce the optimal profit for the following model.

maximize $Z = -10x^2 + 5x + 1,000$

subject to

$x \leq 12$

b. Use Excel and solve the problem given above.

Solution   a. 1. Obtain the first derivative of the function, set it equal to zero, and solve for x:

$$\frac{dy}{dx} = -20x + 5 = 0$$

Solving, $x = \frac{1}{4}$. Note that this value *satisfies* the constraint $x \leq 12$.

Exhibit 9-12   Parameter Specification Screen for Solved Problem 1: One-Decision-Variable, Unconstrained Problem

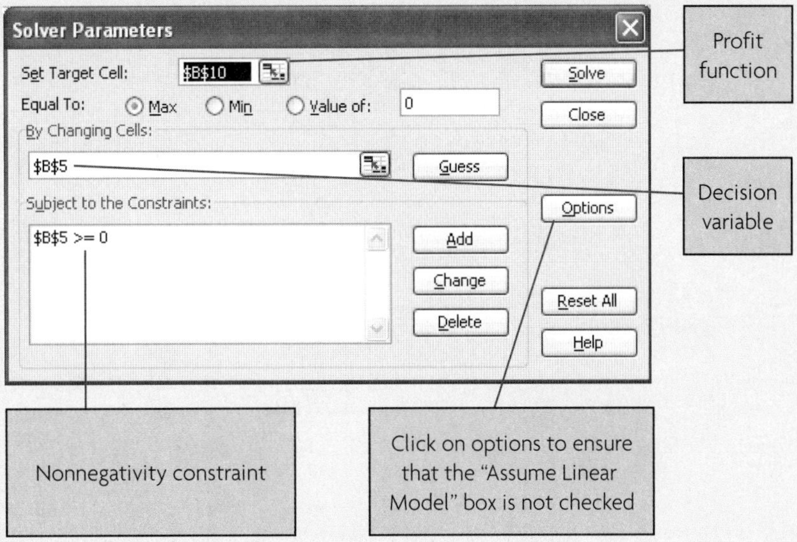

2. Obtain the second derivative and note its sign:

$$\frac{d^2y}{dx^2} = -20$$

The negative sign indicates that the function reaches a local maximum at $x = \frac{1}{4}$.

3. Compute the value of the function at the local maximization point and compare the result to the result to the result obtained when $x = 12$ (the constraint):

At $x = \frac{1}{4}$, $f(x) = -10(\frac{1}{4})^2 + 5(\frac{1}{4}) + 1,000 = 1,000.625$
At $x = 12$, $f(x) = -10(12)^2 + 5(12) + 1,000 = -380$

The value of the function at $x = \frac{1}{4}$ is greater than the value of the function at $x = 12$. Hence, the maximum value of the function (the optimal profit) is 1,000.625, where the optimal value of $x = \frac{1}{4}$.

b. The Excel spreadsheet along with all of the necessary formulas and the Solver Parameters screen for Solved Problem 2 are given in Exhibits 9-13 and 9-14. Once Exhibit 9-13 is completed, Exhibit 9-14 is obtained by choosing **Tools | Solver.**

Problem 3

Equality constraints: Lagrange multiplier.

a. Manually solve the problem given below for the optimal values of the decision variables and determine if the optimal values produce a point that is a local maximum, a local minimum, or a saddle point.

$$Z = -6x_1^2 - 4x_2^2 - 9x_1x_2 + 17x_1 + 10x_2$$

subject to

$$x_1 + x_2 = 3$$

b. Use Excel to find the maximum profit and the optimal values of x_1 and x_2.

Exhibit 9-13	Worksheet for Solved Problem 2: One-Decision-Variable, Constrained Problem

Cell	Formula
B8	= B5
B11	= B5
C8	= B5 * B5
B12	= SUMPRODUCT (B9 : C9, B8 : C8) + D10

Solution

a.   1.   Let $\lambda = x_1 + x_2 - 3$.

2.   Form a Lagrangian function incorporating λ:

$$L(x_1, x_2, \lambda) = -6x_1^2 - 4x_2^2 - 9x_1x_2 + 18.5x_1 + 12x_2 + \lambda(x_1 + x_2 - 3)$$

3.   Obtain partial derivatives for x_1, x_2, and λ and set each equal to zero:

$$\frac{\partial L}{\partial x_1} = -12x_1 - 9x_2 + 18.5 + \lambda = 0$$

$$\frac{\partial L}{\partial x_2} = -8x_2 - 9x_1 + 12 + \lambda = 0$$

$$\frac{\partial L}{\partial \lambda} = x_1 + x_2 - 3 = 0$$

4.   Subtract the first partial from the second partial to obtain an equation without λ:

$$(12x_1 - 9x_1) + (9x_2 - 8x_2) + (-18.5 + 12) + (-\lambda + \lambda) = 0$$
$$= \quad 3x_1 \quad + \quad x_2 \quad + \quad (-6.5) \quad\quad\quad = 0$$

Exhibit 9-14	Parameter Specification Screen for Solved Problem 2: One-Decision-Variable, Unconstrained Problem

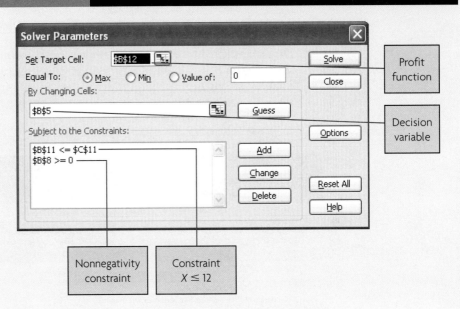

5. Use the third partial equation and this new equation to solve for x_1 and x_2. Subtract the third partial from the new equation:

    (new) $3x_1 + x_2 - 6.5 = 0$
    (third) $x_1 + x_2 - \;\;3 = 0$
    _____
             $2x_1 \quad\;\; - 3.5 = 0$

    Solving, $x_1 = 1.75$. By substituting this into the (third) equation, we obtain $x_2 = 1.25$.

6. Substituting $x_1 = 1.75$ and $x_2 = 1.25$ into either of the first two partial derivative equations, we can solve for λ. Using the first equation, we find

    $$-12(1.75) - 9(1.25) + 18.5 + \lambda = 0$$

    Solving, $\lambda = 13.75$.

7. With λ fixed at 13.75, the first partial derivatives of x_1 and x_2 become

    $$\frac{\partial L}{\partial x_1} = -12x_1 - 9x_2 + 18.5 + 13.75 \quad \text{or} \quad -12x_1 - 9x_2 + 32.25$$

    $$\frac{\partial L}{\partial x_2} = -8x_2 - 9x_1 + 12 + 13.75 \quad \text{or} \quad -8x_2 - 9x_1 + 25.75$$

8. The second partials and the mixed partial are

    $$\frac{\partial^2 L}{\partial x_1^2} = -12, \qquad \frac{\partial^2 L}{\partial x_2^2} = -8, \qquad \frac{\partial^2 L}{\partial x_1 \delta x_2} = -9$$

9. Computing D, we find

    $$D = \left(\frac{\partial^2 L}{\partial x_1^2}\right)\left(\frac{\partial^2 L}{\partial x_2^2}\right)\left(\frac{\partial^2 L}{\partial x_1 \delta x_2}\right)$$
    $$= (-12)(-8) - (-9^2) = +15$$

10. According to Condition 4, with the second partial derivative with respect to x_1 negative, and $D > 0$, this is a local maximum.

$$Z = -6(1.75)^2 - 4(1.25)^2 - 9(1.75)(1.25) + 18.5(1.75) + 12(1.25)$$
$$Z = 3.0625$$

b. The Excel spreadsheet along with all of the necessary formulas and the Solver Parameters screen for Solved Problem 3 are given in Exhibits 9-15 and 9-16. First we complete Exhibit 9-15, and then Exhibit 9-16 is obtained by choosing **Tools | Solver.**

Exhibit 9-15 Worksheet for Solved Problem 4: Two Decision Variables and a Single Equality Constraint

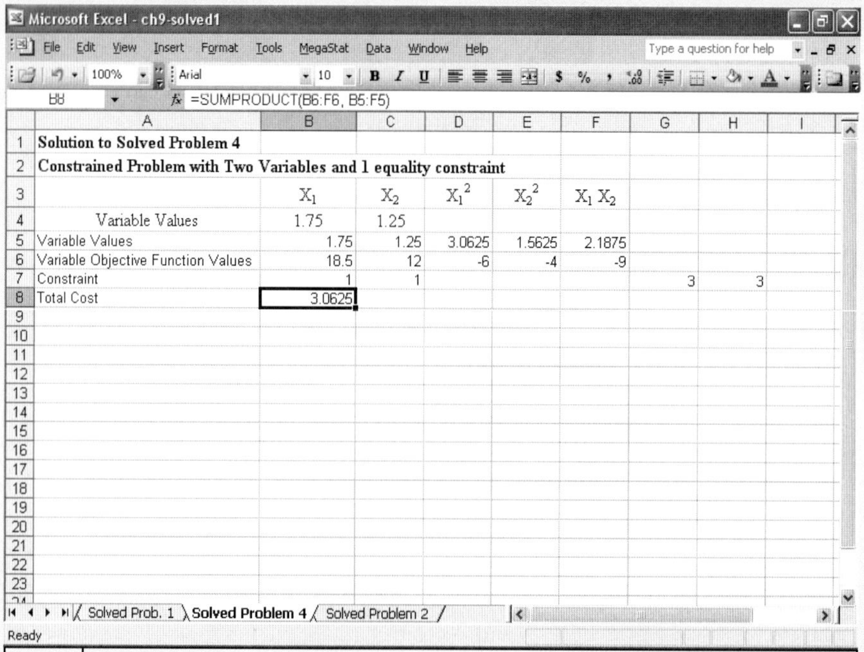

	A	B	C	D	E	F	G	H
1	**Solution to Solved Problem 4**							
2	**Constrained Problem with Two Variables and 1 equality constraint**							
3		X_1	X_2	X_1^2	X_2^2	$X_1 X_2$		
4	Variable Values	1.75	1.25					
5	Variable Values	1.75	1.25	3.0625	1.5625	2.1875		
6	Variable Objective Function Values	18.5	12	-6	-4	-9		
7	Constraint	1	1				3	3
8	Total Cost	3.0625						

Cell	Formula
B5	= B4
C5	= C4
D5	= B5 * B5
E5	= C5 * C5
F5	= B5 * C5
G7	= SUMPRODUCT (B5 : F5, B7 : F7)
B8	= SUMPRODUCT (B6 : F6, B5 : F5)

Exhibit 9-16	Parameter Specification Screen for Solved Problem 3: Two Decision Variables and a Single Equality Constraint Problem

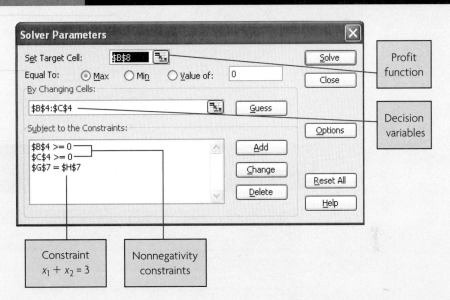

Solve a nonlinear programming problem with two decision variables and an inequality constraint:

Problem 4

a. Manually solve the following problem and determine the optimal values of the decision variables and the optimal profit (Z).

b. Solve the problem below using Excel and find the maximum profit and the optimal values of the decision variables.

> Let x_1 = number of units of product 1 manufactured
> x_2 = number of units of product 2 manufactured
>
> maximize $Z = -4x_1^2 - 3x_2^2 + 2x_1x_2 + 14x_1 + 24x_2$
>
> subject to
>
> $4x_1 + 3x_2 \leq 28$ (daily machine hours constraint)

Solution

a. First, we assume that the constraint is not binding and solve it as an unconstrained problem. In solving it as an unconstrained problem, we take the first derivative of the objective function with respect to x_1 and take the first derivative of the objective function with respect x_2.

1. *Necessary conditions.* Take the partial derivative with respect to each variable and set the resulting equations equal to zero.

$$\frac{\partial Z}{\partial x_1} = -8x_1 + 2x_2 + 14 = 0$$

Rearranging the terms:

$$8x_1 - 2x_2 = 14$$

$$\frac{\partial Z}{\partial x_2} = 2x_1 - 6x_2 + 24 = 0$$

Rearranging the terms:

$$-2x_1 + 6x_2 = 24$$

We can solve the two rearranged equations simultaneously.

$$(3)(8x_1 - 2x_2) = 3(14) \quad \text{or}$$

$$24x_1 - 6x_2 = 42 \quad \text{(rearranged equation 1)}$$

$$\underline{-2x_1 + 6x_2 = 24} \quad \text{(rearranged equation 2)}$$

$$22x_1 = 66$$

$$x_1 = 3$$

Exhibit 9-17 **Worksheet for Solved Problem 4: Two Decision Variables and a Single Inequality Constraint**

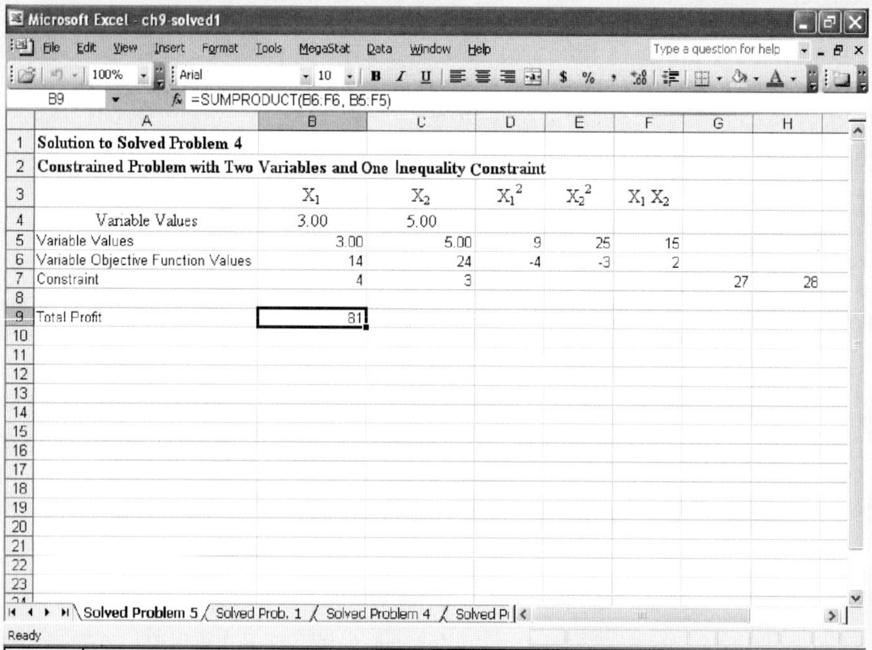

	A	B	C	D	E	F	G	H
1	**Solution to Solved Problem 4**							
2	**Constrained Problem with Two Variables and One Inequality Constraint**							
3		X_1	X_2	X_1^2	X_2^2	$X_1 X_2$		
4	Variable Values	3.00	5.00					
5	Variable Values	3.00	5.00	9	25	15		
6	Variable Objective Function Values	14	24	-4	-3	2		
7	Constraint	4	3				27	28
8								
9	Total Profit	81						

Cell	Formula
B5	= B4
C5	= C4
D5	= B5 * B5
E5	= C5 * C5
F5	= B5 * C5
G7	= SUMPRODUCT (B5 : F5, B7 : F7)
B9	= SUMPRODUCT (B6 : F6, B5 : F5)

Substituting $x_1 = 3$, into the first equation

$8x_1 - 2x_2 = 14$
$8(3) - 2x_2 = 14$
$-2x_2 = -10$
$x_2 = 5$

Once these values have been obtained, we can check the second-order conditions.

2. *Sufficient conditions.* In this example, second partial derivatives and mixed partial derivatives are as follows:

$$\frac{\partial^2 Z}{\partial x_1^2} = -8$$

$$\frac{\partial^2 Z}{\partial x_2^2} = -6$$

$$\frac{\partial^2 Z}{\delta x_1 \partial x_2} = -2$$

$$D = \left(\frac{\partial^2 Z}{\partial x_1^2}\right)\left(\frac{\partial^2 Z}{\partial x_2^2}\right) - \left(\frac{\partial^2 Z}{\partial x_1 \partial x_2}\right)^2 = (-8)(-6) - (-2)^2$$

$$D = 48 - 4 = 44$$

Since $D > 0$ and $\left(\dfrac{\partial^2 Z}{\partial x_1^2}\right) < 0$, this point ($x_1 = 3, x_2 = 5$) is an optimal solution to the unconstraint problem.

Next, we substitute these optimal values for x_1 and x_2 into the inequality constraint. Since $4x_1 + 3x_2 = 4(3) + 3(5) = 27 < 28$, the constraint is satisfied. Therefore, we do not need to go to step 2. $x_1 = 3, x_2 = 5$ is the optimal solution to our original problem.

Exhibit 9-18   Parameter Specification Screen for Solved Problem 4: Two Decision Variables and a Single Inequality Constraint Problem

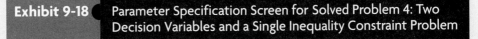

Substituting these values into the objective function, we get

$$Z = -4x_1^2 - 3x_2^2 + 2x_1x_2 + 14x_1 + 24x_2$$
$$Z = -4(3)^2 - 3(5)^2 + 2(3)(5) + 14(3) + 24(5)$$
$$Z = -36 - 75 + 30 + 42 + 120$$
$$Z = 81$$

Therefore, the optimal solution to this problem is $x_1 = 3$, $x_2 = 5$, and $Z = 81$.

b. The Excel spreadsheet along with all of the necessary formulas and the Solver Parameters screen for Solved Problem 4 are given in Exhibits 9-17 and 9-18. First we complete Exhibit 9-17, and then Exhibit 9-18 is obtained by choosing **Tools I Solver.**

Discussion and Review Questions

1. Describe the difference between satisfying the necessary and sufficient conditions for an unconstrained problem with one decision variable with satisfying the necessary and sufficient conditions for a problem two decision variables.
2. What is the difference between local maximum and global maximum? Explain briefly.
3. When is it appropriate to use the Lagrange multiplier approach? How can we use the Lagrange multiplier approach to solve nonlinear programming problems?
4. For a given problem with one decision variable with a single constraint, the value of $\lambda = 8.5$. What is the general economic interpretation of this value?
5. What do we have to do differently in running Excel to solve a nonlinear programming problem rather than a linear programming problem? Explain carefully.
6. What is the saddle point?
7. Does the optimal solution to a constrained nonlinear programming problem occur at a corner point? Why?
8. When there are multiple decision variables, briefly list and explain the steps of how to solve unconstrained nonlinear programming problems with two decision variables.
9. Briefly explain what *partial derivative* means?
10. List and discuss the steps briefly in solving a nonlinear programming problem with two decision variables with an equality constraint. How do we know whether we have reached a local maximum, a local minimum, or a saddle point?
11. Compare the methods to solve a nonlinear programming problem with two decision variables with an equality constraint and an unconstrained nonlinear programming problem with two decision variables.
12. Explain how partial derivatives are used to solve nonlinear programming problems.

Problems

1. Find the minimum of this function and then answer the following questions:
    $$Z = 4x^2 - 30x + 40$$
    a. At what value of x does the function have its minimum?
    b. How do you know that this is a minimum rather than a maximum?
2. For the function, given below, answer the following questions.
    $$Z = -5x^2 + 4x + 2$$
    a. Find the maximum value of Z.
    b. At what value of the decision variable does the function attain its maximum value?
    c. How can you be sure that the value you have found is a maximum?

a. $z = 2.8$
b. $x = .40$
   $\dfrac{d^2y}{dx^2} = -10$

c. negative sign of the second derivative indicates local maximum.

3. The manager of a small plastics company has developed the following cost function and determined its minimum value to be 68. Explain why you agree or disagree with this finding.

$$Z = \frac{1}{2}x^2 - 8x + 90$$

At $x = 6$,
$Z = 28$, local minimum;
at $x = 3$,
$Z = 32.5$, local maximum

4. For the following function, determine the value of x at which it attains a local maximum value, the value of x at which it attains a local minimum value, and the value of the function at each of those points.

$$Z = \frac{1}{3}x^3 - 4.5x^2 + 18x + 10$$

5. Determine the point at which the following function attains its local maximum, its local minimum, and the value of the function at each of those points.

$$Z = x^3 - 12x^2 + 36x + 3$$

$6,000

6. A manager has developed the following cost function:

$$Z = \frac{1}{3}x^3 - 3x^2 + 70$$

where

$x =$ amount spent on preventive maintenance of equipment (in thousands of dollars)

Find the optimal amount of preventive maintenance in thousands of dollars

7. Find the local maximum and local minimum points of this function:

$$Z = 2x^3 - 18x^2 + 48x$$

$x = 4, Z = 63$

8. Find the optimal solution to this problem:

maximize $\quad Z = -2x^2 + 20x + 15$

subject to

$x \leq 4$

9. Find the optimal solution to this problem:

minimize $\quad Z = 5x^2 - 20x + 18$

subject to

$x \geq 4$

$x = 3, Z = 29$

10. Find the optimal solution to this problem:

maximize $\quad Z = -10x^2 + 40x - 1$

subject to

$x \geq 3$

11. Given this model:

minimize $\quad Z = 2x_1^2 + 6x_2^2 - 10x_1 - 10x_2 + 3x_1x_2 + 8$

Find the optimal values of the decision variables and the value of the objective function.

Local minimum $x_1 = 7$, $x_2 = 8$, $f(x_1,x_2) = -46$

12. Given the following model, find the optimal values of x_1 and x_2 and determine if the result is a local maximum, local minimum, or saddle point:

$$f(x_1x_2) = 5x_1^2 + 4x_2^2 - 8x_1x_2 - 6x_1 - 8x_2 + 7$$

where

x_1 = setting on machine control 1
x_2 = setting on machine control 2

13. For the following model, find the optimal values of the decision variables and determine whether those values refer to a local maximum, a local minimum, or a saddle point.

$$f(x_1x_2) = -10x_1^2 - 6x_2^2 + 50x_1 + 40x_2 - x_1x_2 + 100$$

$x_1 = 1, x_2 = 2$
$Z = 24$

14. The cost to produce each of two products is dependent on the quantity of each product (x_1, x_2) that is produced:

$c_1 = x_1 + x_2$ (in thousands of dollars)
$c_2 = 2x_2 + x_1$ (in thousands of dollars)

The manager of the department wants to determine the quantity of each product to produce in order to maximize profits. Product 1 sells for $10,000 a unit, and product 2 sells for $12,000 a unit. Fixed cost is $2,000 for each product. Find the optimal quantity of each product and the maximum profit.

15. For the following model, find the optimal values of x_1 and x_2, and determine the solution that provides the maximum objective function value.

maximize $Z = -4x_1^2 - 2x_2^2 - 6x_1x_2 + 33x_1 + 22x_2 + 40$

subject to

$x_1 + 2x_2 = 8$

Minimum: $x_1 = x_2 = 2.5$, $Z = -150$

16. Find the values of the decision variables that will minimize the value of this function:

minimize $Z = 3x_1^2 + 3x_2^2 - 20x_1 - 20x_2 + 2x_1x_2 - 100$

subject to

$x_1 + x_2 = 5$

17. Given this model, find the minimum value of the function:

minimize $Z = -2x_1^2 - 2x_2^2 + 3x_1x_2 + 10x_1 + 10x_2$

subject to

$x_1 + x_2 = 7$

18. Given this model:

minimize $Z = x_1^2 + 3x_2^2 + 2x_1x_2 - 6x_1 - 14x_2 + 2$

subject to

$x_1 + x_2 = 12$

a. $x_1 = 10, x_2 = 2$, $Z = +66$
b. Increase by 18

a. Find the minimum value of the function and the optimal values of x_1 and x_2.
b. How much would you expect the optimal value to change if the constraint was changed from 12 to 13?

19. Consider problem 10. Use Excel and find the optimal solution (optimal value of decision variable x and the objective function).

$6,000

20. Consider problem 6. Set up the nonlinear programming model using Excel and find the optimal amount of preventive maintenance in thousands of dollars.

21. Consider problem 9. Set up the Excel worksheet. Based on the worksheet, find the optimal solution.

$x_1 = 1, x_2 = 2$, local maximum

22. Consider problem 14. Using Excel, determine the optimal quantity of each product to maximize the profits.

23. Use Excel and solve problem 15.

$x_1 = 5, x_2 = 2.5, Z = -150$

24. Use Excel and solve problem 16.

25. Use Excel and solve problem 17.

a. $x_1 = 10, x_2 = 2, Z = 66$;
b. Increase by 18

26. Use Excel and solve problem 18.

27. A computer manufacturing company manufactures and sells two types of computers (model 1 and model 2). Let m_1 denote the number of model 1's produced and let m_2 denote the number of model 2's produced respectively. The firm earns a profit of $30 for each unit of model 1 produced and $18 for each unit of model 2 produced. However, due to being able to spread fixed overhead cost, as more units of model 2 are produced, the company earns additional profit of $.1m_2^2$. Thus, the company's objective function is nonlinear. The firm's profit is subject to four constraints. The first two constraints are the minimum production constraints as specified by the marketing department. The company wishes to produce at least 50 units of computer model 1 and 40 units of computer model 2. In addition, the company has 40 machine hours and 50 labor hours available per week. The production time requirements for machines and labor are given in the following table.

	Model 1	Model 2
Machine hours required per unit	.30	.50
Labor hours required per unit	.40	.40

a. Formulate this problem as a quadratic programming problem.
b. Use Excel and solve this problem. How many units of each model should the company produce? What is the optimal profit?

$x_1 = 12.875, x_2 = 26.75,$
$x_3 = 5, Z = 446.531$

28. Set up and solve the following nonlinear programming problem with Excel:

$$\text{maximize } Z = 3x_1 + 2x_2 + x_1x_2 + x_3 + .2x_3^2$$

subject to

$$\begin{aligned}
3x_1 + 2x_2 + x_3 &\le 100 \\
2x_1 + x_2 + 1.5x_3 &\le 60 \\
2.5x_1 + 1.5x_2 + 3x_3 &\le 110 \\
x_3 &\ge 5 \\
x_1, x_2, x_3 &\ge 0
\end{aligned}$$

◼ Chapter 9 Case   Koch International Incorporated

Koch International Incorporated assembles two products: laptop computers and flat-screen televisions. The company believes that the price of the product is related to the demand for these products. The company would like to develop a model to plan production within the capacity constraints. Koch has three types of machines to produce these products:

(1) assembly, (2) drilling, and (3) cutting. Total number of hours per week and the number of hours it takes to process each unit of laptops and TVs for all of these three machines are given in the following table.

Products	Assembly	Departments Drilling	Cutting
Laptop computers	3*	2	1.5
Flat-screen TVs	4**	1	2
Department capacity	1600†	600‡	750

*Three hours are required to produce one unit of laptop computer.
**Four hours are required to produce one unit of flat-screen TVs.
†There are 1,600 hours available per week in the assembly department.
‡There are 600 hours available per week in the drilling department.

The board of directors of the company has met and made certain decisions. The management expressed concerns about one product dominating the sales of the company. The objective of the company is to maximize profit given the following constraints in addition to the capacity constraints:

1. The maximum number of laptop computers cannot exceed 60 percent of all units produced for both products.
2. The minimum number of laptop computers cannot be less than 30 percent of all units produced for both products.

If the company produces a total of 10 units for both products, then it cannot produce more than 6 computers or less than 3 computers.

Demand is a function of price for each product. The higher the price, the lower the demand where:

x_1 = demand for laptop computers
p_1 = price of a laptop computer
x_2 = demand for flat-screen TVs
p_2 = price of a flat-screen TV

The demand function for each product is defined as

Laptop computer: $x_1 = 5{,}000 - 7p_1$
Flat-Screen TV: $x_2 = 1{,}000 - 10p_2$

Discussion Question

Develop and solve a nonlinear programming model for Koch International Incorporated and determine the price and the demand for both products that will maximize the profit for the company.

Multicriteria Decision-Making Models

Chapter 10

After completing this chapter, you should be able to:

1. Describe the type of problems that goal programming is designed to handle.
2. Describe the similarities and differences between goal programming and linear programming models.
3. Formulate goal programming models.
4. Solve goal programming models that have two decision variables using a graphical approach.
5. Solve goal programming models using Excel and interpret solutions of goal programming models.
6. Describe the type of problems that the analytical hierarchy process is designed to handle.
7. Describe how to determine pairwise comparisons.
8. Describe what a consistency check is and calculate a consistency ratio, priority percentage, and priority score for each alternative using AHP.
9. Use Excel to solve analytical hierarchy process problems.
10. Describe and solve scoring model multicriteria decision-making problems.

Chapter Outline

Introduction, 474
Goal Programming versus
   Linear Programming, 474
Deviation Variables, 475

Model Formulation, 476
Graphical Solutions, 478

**Solving Goal Programming
Problems Using Excel, 482**
Weighted Goals, 490

**Analytical Hierarchy
Process, 493**
Pairwise Comparisons, 495
Normalized Pairwise
   Comparison Matrix, 496
Consistency Check for
   Criteria, 496

Analytical Hierarchy Process
   Using Excel, 501

Scoring Models, 504
The Steps for the Scoring
   Model, 504

Summary, 506

Glossary, 508

Solved Problems, 509

**Discussion and Review
Questions, 523**

Problems, 525

**Chapter 10 Case: Hi-Tech
Incorporated, 534**

◼◼ Introduction

Linear programming (LP) is a powerful analytical tool that can be applied to a wide range of problems. However, its use is limited to problems that can be expressed in terms of a single objective (e.g., maximize profits). There are many instances in which a single objective is appropriate. Nonetheless, there also are many instances in which multiple objectives are appropriate. For example, a manager may have quality, productivity, *and* profit objectives. But unless these can be reduced to a common unit of measure, such as dollars of profit, standard linear programming models cannot be used. One alternative is to use goal programming.

Goal programming is a variation of linear programming that can be used for problems that involve multiple objectives. Goal programming (GP) models are quite similar to LP models. Both are formulated under the same requirements and assumptions (e.g., linearity, nonnegativity, certainty). Moreover, graphical methods can be used to illustrate the basic concepts of goal programming, just as they were used to illustrate linear programming concepts, and computers (Excel) can be used to handle problems that do not lend themselves to graphical solution.

When it was first introduced in the 1960s, goal programming was designed to handle linear problems. Since then, it has been extended to integer and nonlinear problems. However, the discussion here will focus exclusively on linear problems.

The following section introduces the basic concepts of goal programming. It begins with a discussion of how GP differs from LP, then goes on to formulation and solution of GP models.

The second and third sections of the chapter cover two other multicriteria decision-making methods. In the second section of the chapter, we cover the analytical hierarchy process (AHP). While goal programming answers the question of "how much" for each decision variable, the AHP addresses the issue of "which" alternative to select based on multiple criteria. In the third section of the chapter, the scoring model is discussed; this simplistic, subjective method also answers the question of "which" alternative to select based on multiple criteria. The scoring model is easier to understand than AHP, but it is more subjective.

Goal Programming Versus Linear Programming

Goal programming models differ from the previously described linear programming models in two key ways. One relates to constraints and the other to model objectives.

In the context of goal programming, multiple objectives are referred to as **goals.** Each goal relates to a target level of performance. For instance, a problem may involve a goal for labor utilization: The performance target may be to use 100 hours of labor on a job. Another goal may relate to an advertising budget: The target may be an expenditure of $25,000 on advertising.

In goal programming models, goals are expressed as *constraints*. However, **goal constraints** are somewhat different than the ones encountered in previous chapters. Recall that in linear programming models, a solution would not be considered feasible if it violated any of the constraints. Because of the absolute requirement that constraints be satisfied, you might think of those constraints as **hard constraints.** In contrast, goal constraints specify desirable levels of performance. These are treated as approximate rather than absolute amounts that should be achieved to the extent possible. Therefore, you might think of a goal constraint as a **soft constraint.**

Goal programming models may consist entirely of soft (goal) constraints or they may consist of a combination of soft and hard (nongoal) constraints. The solution to a goal programming model must satisfy any hard constraints, although it may not necessarily achieve the target levels of the goal (soft) constraints. When one or more goals are not achieved by a solution, it is because there are conflicts either between goals or between goals and hard constraints. For example, one constraint might specify that x_1 should be 10 units, whereas another constraint might specify that x_1 should be at least 20 units. Because these two cannot both be satisfied by a single solution, we say that they conflict. In linear programming terms, we would say that such a problem has no feasible solution space. However, this is the sort of problem goal programming is designed to handle. *Deviations* from goals are permitted if they are needed to obtain a solution. Thus, in goal programming, the objective is to satisfy the hard constraints (if any) and achieve reasonably *acceptable levels* for the goal constraints. This is referred to as **satisficing.**

In order to obtain a solution that provides acceptable levels of satisfaction of goals when there are conflicts, it becomes necessary to make *trade-offs:* satisfying hard constraints and achieving higher levels of certain goals at the expense of other goals. When goal programming was originally introduced, the approach used was to treat goals as equally important in terms of searching for an acceptable solution. Thus, a deviation from one goal was just as acceptable as a deviation from another goal. Later versions permitted weighting of deviations so that differences in importance in goals could be taken into account. However, this required decision makers to come up with a set of weights that truly reflected differences in importance. Some decision makers found this process to be difficult and somewhat artificial. More recently, interest has centered on **prioritized goal programming models,** wherein decision makers are merely required to *rank* deviations from the various goals in their order of importance. That approach seems to hold considerable promise. It is the one we shall focus on. However, we also will present the goal programming approach involving weights called goal programming with weighted goals.

Deviation Variables

In order to account for possible deviation from a goal, **deviation variables** are incorporated into each goal to represent the differences between actual performance and target performance. There are two possible kinds of deviations from a target: being under the targeted amount (*underachievement*) and being over the targeted amount (*overachievement*). Deviation variables are included in each goal constraint: u_i for underachievement and v_i for overachievement, where i is the number of the constraint ($i = 1, 2, 3, \ldots$). Adding these two deviation variables to a goal constraint creates an equality because the deviation variables account for any discrepancy between actual and target. We can readily see this by considering a goal constraint.

Suppose a manager has formulated a goal for labor hours. The mathematical expression of the goal constraint might look like this:

$$4x_1 + 2x_2 + u_1 - v_1 = 100 \text{ hours}$$

Variables x_1 and x_2 represent decision variables, whereas u_1 stands for the amount of underutilization of labor and v_1 stands for overtime hours. The subscripts for u and v indicate that this is the first constraint (in a list of goal constraints).

The right-hand side of the equation indicates the target (goal) amount. In this case, it is 100 hours. The left-hand side of the equation contains both the decision variables and the deviation variables. The fact that both underachievement and overachievement variables are included in the goal indicates that a deviation in either direction is permissible (although not necessarily desirable). If a deviation is not permissible, it would not appear in the goal equation. For example, if overachievement were not permissible in the labor constraint, then v_1 would be omitted from the constraint.

Note the signs of the deviational variables and consider that the purpose of these variables is to indicate the amount of any discrepancy between the target level and the amount actually achieved by a particular solution. In effect, the deviation variables are equivalent to slack (amount of underachievement) and surplus (amount of overachievement). Hence, u is added and v is subtracted in a goal constraint. For instance, suppose that the quantity $4x_1 + 2x_2$ is equal to 80 hours, which is 20 hours less than the goal of 100 hours. Thus, utilization is *under* by 20 hours: $u_1 = 20$. Conversely, suppose the quantity $4x_1 + 2x_2$ is equal to 110. This is *over* the goal of 100 hours by 10 hours. Therefore, $v_1 = 10$. Now notice that in each of these cases, the other deviation variable would equal zero because it would be physically impossible to be over and under a goal simultaneously. Of course, if the quantity $4x_1 + 2x_2$ is exactly equal to 100, then both of the deviation variables would equal zero. Thus, at least one of the two deviation variables in each goal must equal zero in any solution.

Model Formulation

A goal programming model consists of an objective and a set of constraints. The constraints may be goal constraints or they may be a mix of goal and nongoal constraints. In addition, there is the nonnegativity requirement that all variables (decision variables and deviation variables) must be nonnegative.

In priority models, the **objective** indicates which deviation variables will be minimized and their order of importance. Thus, the objective is to minimize specified deviations from certain goals according to priority.

Consider this goal programming model:

minimize P_1u_1, P_2v_1, P_3u_2

subject to

A	$4x_1 + 2x_2 \leq 40$	Nongoal (hard)
B	$2x_1 + 6x_2 \leq 60$	
1	$3x_1 + 3x_2 + u_1 - v_1 = 75$	Goal (soft)
2	$x_1 + 2x_2 + u_2 - v_2 = 50$	

All variables ≥ 0

There are three deviation variables specified in the objective : u_1, v_1, and u_2. Their subscripts indicate the goal to which they pertain. The P's represent priorities, and their subscripts indicate order of importance, with 1 being the highest priority. Hence, we can see in the objective that the highest priority is to minimize being under on the first goal. (Note that u_1 appears only in that goal.) The next highest priority is to minimize being over on the first goal, and the last priority is to minimize being under on the second goal. Note that not every deviational variable is specified in the objective. The second deviation variable in the second constraint, v_2, is not included in the objective. Evidently, the decision maker does not want to minimize being over on the second goal. If, for example, that second goal relates to profit, we could understand why a decision maker would not want to minimize being over on that goal.

In order to differentiate goal and nongoal constraints, the nongoal constraints have been assigned capital letters, whereas the goal constraints have been assigned numbers. Note that only the goal constraints have deviation variables and all goal constraints are expressed as equalities.

Having now examined the goal model, let's turn our attention to formulating such a model. One approach would be as follows:

1. Identify the decision variables.
2. Identify the constraints and determine which ones are goal constraints.
3. Formulate the nongoal (hard) constraints (if any).
4. Formulate the goal (soft) constraints.
5. Formulate the objective function.
6. Add the nonnegativity requirement statement.

The next example illustrates this process.

Example 10-1

A company manufactures three products: x_1, x_2, and x_3. Material and labor requirements per unit are

Product	x_1	x_2	x_3	Availability
Material (lb./unit)	2	4	3	600 pounds
Assembly (min./unit)	9	8	7	900 minutes
Packing (min./unit)	1	2	3	300 minutes

The manager has listed the following objectives in order of priority:

1. Minimize overtime in the assembly department.
2. Minimize undertime in the assembly department.
3. Minimize both undertime and overtime in the packaging department.

Solution

Apparently, there are three constraints: material, assembly time, and packing time. Moreover, assembly and packing constraints should be expressed as goals because they are included in the priority list. Material is not included so it should be a nongoal constraint. The constraints are

Material	$2x_1 + 4x_2 + 3x_3$		≤ 600 pounds
Assembly	$9x_1 + 8x_2 + 7x_3 + u_1 - v_1$		$= 900$ minutes
Packing	$1x_1 + 2x_2 + 3x_3 + u_2 - v_2$		$= 300$ minutes

$$\text{All variables} \geq 0$$

The objective is based on the listing and the deviation variables as defined in the constraints. It is

minimize $P_1 v_1, P_2 u_1, P_3(u_2 + v_2)$

The third priority, P_1, expresses the fact that minimizing both under and over on the second goal are equally important. Thus, the complete model is

minimize $P_1 v_1, P_2 u_1, P_3(u_2 + v_2)$

subject to

A	$2x_1 + 4x_2 + 3x_3$	≤ 600 pounds
1	$9x_1 + 8x_2 + 7x_3 + u_1 - v_1$	$= 900$ minutes
2	$1x_1 + 2x_2 + 3x_3 + u_2 - v_2$	$= 300$ minutes

$$\text{All variables} \geq 0$$

Graphical Solutions

Graphical solutions are limited to goal problems that have two decision variables. As you might suspect, many real problems involve more than two decision variables. Nonetheless, the graphical approach provides a visual illustration of certain goal programming concepts. For that reason, it is invaluable in terms of the insight it can produce.

The graphical approach involves plotting all of the constraints, both hard and soft. In order to plot a goal constraint, ignore the deviation variables and simply plot it as you would a constraint that has no deviation variables. Thus, the goal constraint

$$x_1 + x_2 + u_1 - v_1 = 60$$

would be plotted as if it were

$$x_1 + x_2 = 60$$

The deviation variables do not appear on the graph; instead their values are determined algebraically at the end of the analysis along with the optimal values of the decision variables. However, over- and underdeviations correspond to the regions on either side of the line, as illustrated in Figure 10-1.

After plotting a goal constraint, indicate the direction that will satisfy the objective, as illustrated in Figure 10-2. Notice that the region that will satisfy the objective (minimize $P_1 u_1$) is the line itself plus the area *opposite* the deviation specified. In other words, we minimize being under by being *on or over* the goal.

Taken as a whole, the graphical approach to goal programming involves plotting all the nongoal constraints (if any), just as in LP, and identifying the feasible solution space. However, unlike LP, the objective is not plotted. Instead, the goals are plotted one at a time, according to the priorities given by the objective. After each is plotted, the best solution to that point is found. However, as successive goals are plotted, only solutions that do not require additional deviations from the higher-level goals already plotted are considered. In effect, minimizing the deviation with the highest priority is treated as infinitely more desirable

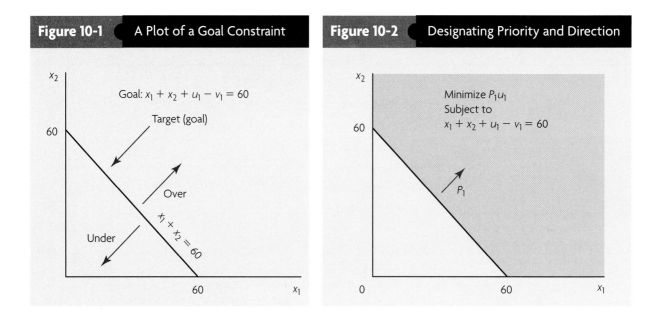

Figure 10-1   A Plot of a Goal Constraint

Goal: $x_1 + x_2 + u_1 - v_1 = 60$

Target (goal)

Over

Under

$x_1 + x_2 = 60$

Figure 10-2   Designating Priority and Direction

Minimize $P_1 u_1$
Subject to
$x_1 + x_2 + u_1 - v_1 = 60$

P_1

than minimizing the deviation with the next highest priority, and minimizing the next highest priority is treated infinitely more important than minimizing the deviation for the next highest priority, and so on, as each additional goal is added to the graph. This solution procedure will become more apparent as we work through a number of examples.

Consider this goal programming model:

minimize $\quad P_1u_1, P_2u_2, P_3u_3$

subject to

$$
\begin{array}{ll}
5x_1 + 3x_2 & \leq 150 \quad \text{(A)} \\
2x_1 + 5x_2 + u_1 - v_1 = 100 & \quad \text{(1)} \\
3x_1 + 3x_2 + u_2 - v_2 = 180 & \quad \text{(2)} \\
x_1 \quad\quad + u_3 - v_3 = 40 & \quad \text{(3)} \\
\end{array}
$$
$$\text{All variables} \geq 0$$

In order to solve this graphically, we first identify and plot any hard constraints: the constraints that do not have deviation variables. In this model, only the first is the hard type. It is plotted in Figure 10-3, and the feasible solution space is shaded in.

Next, we see in the objective that the highest priority is to minimize being under on the first goal constraint. So, we plot the first goal constraint (second constraint overall) and indicate that the desirable region is on the line and above it. (See Figure 10-4.) Now we can see that a portion of the feasible solution space also includes some of the desirable region. At this stage, any point in the overlap area would be acceptable.

Next, we see that the second highest priority relates to the second goal constraint (i.e., the subscript of u_2 tells us this). Hence, we plot the second goal constraint (third constraint overall) and indicate its area of desirability, which is on and above the line (see Figure 10-5). This region does not overlap the acceptable region as previously determined. However, we must not sacrifice a higher-level priority for a lower one. Therefore, there will be some underdeviation on the second goal. By inspecting Figure 10-5, we will find that the closest

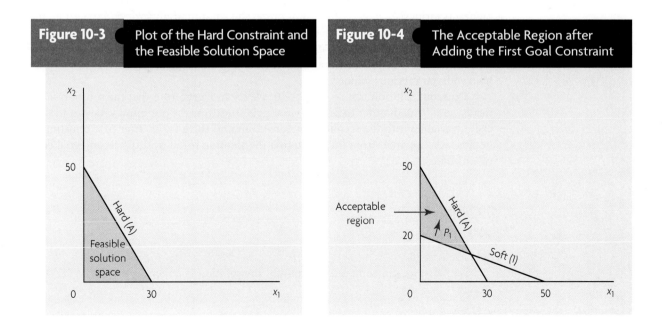

Figure 10-3   Plot of the Hard Constraint and the Feasible Solution Space

Figure 10-4   The Acceptable Region after Adding the First Goal Constraint

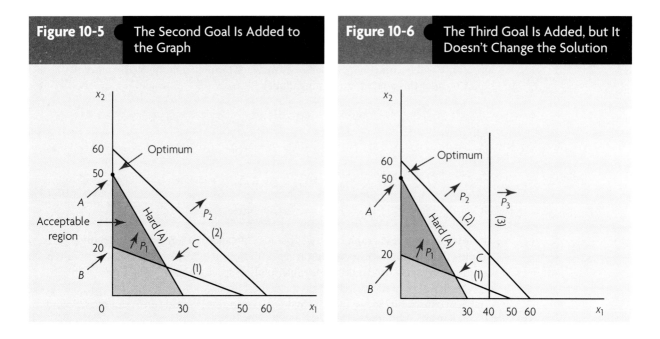

Figure 10-5 The Second Goal Is Added to the Graph

Figure 10-6 The Third Goal Is Added, but It Doesn't Change the Solution

portion of the acceptable region to the second goal is the point $x_1 = 0$, $x_2 = 50$. This is the best point because it satisfies the first two constraints while minimizing the amount of underdeviation from the third (i.e., second goal) constraint.

Finally, we see in the objective that the last priority is to minimize being under on the third goal. Hence, we add the third goal to the graph (see Figure 10-6). The third goal does not overlap the acceptable region either. As with the second goal, we must not sacrifice a higher-level priority (i.e., u_1) for a lower one (i.e., u_3). Therefore, adding the third goal does not change the previous solution because that solution satisfies the hard constraint and the highest priority (i.e., $u_1 = 0$) and it minimizes the amount of underdeviation (u_2) on the second goal. Even though another point in the acceptable region (point c) would yield a lower value for u_3, this would be at the expense of increasing u_2. Because higher-level priorities are treated as infinitely more valuable than lower-level priorities (i.e., P_2 and P_3), we hold with our previous solution.

Thus, our solution is $x_1 = 0$, $x_2 = 50$. We see in Figure 10-6 that the solution satisfies P_1, so $u_1 = 0$. In order to find u_2, we simply substitute the optimum values of the decision variables into the second goal constraint and solve for u_2 after first omitting v_2 because it is apparent from the graph that the solution is not over the second goal constraint. Thus:

$3x_1 + 3x_2 + u_2 - v_2 = 180$

becomes

$3(0) + 3(50) + u_2 = 180$

Solving, $u_2 = 30$.

Similarly, we can compute the amount the solution is under on the third goal constraint:

$x_1 + u_3 - v_3 = 40$

becomes

$0 + u_3 = 40$

Hence, $u_3 = 40$.

It is important to note that deviations generally cannot be read directly from the graph but, instead, must be computed using the appropriate goal constraints and the optimal values of the decision variables.

The next example illustrates a case in which there are no hard constraints, only goal constraints.

Example 10-2

Solve this goal programming model for the optimal values of the decision variables using the graphical approach, then determine the optimal values of each deviation variable specified in the objective function.

minimize P_1v_1, P_2u_2, P_3v_3

subject to

Material	$5x_1 + 4x_2 + u_1 - v_1 = 200$ pounds	(1)
Profit	$2x_1 + x_2 + u_2 - v_2 = 40$ (\$000)	(2)
Machine	$2x_1 + 2x_2 + u_3 - v_3 = 30$ minutes	(3)
	All variables ≥ 0	

Solution

Because there are no hard constraints, we begin by noting that the highest priority is to minimize being over on the first goal constraint. Hence, we plot the first constraint and indicate the acceptable region (see Figure 10-7a).

Figure 10-7

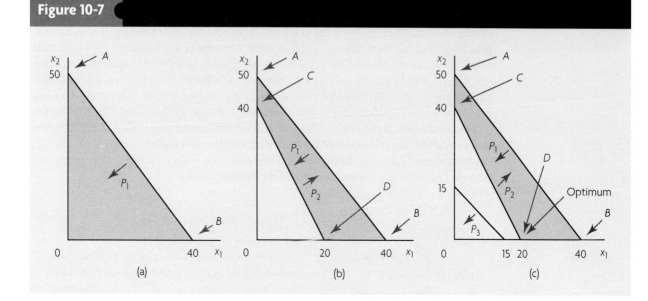

(a)   (b)   (c)

The second highest priority is to minimize being under the second goal constraint, so we plot the second goal and indicate the region that will satisfy both the first and second goals (see Figure 10-7b).

The third priority refers to the third goal, so we plot and see that it does not have any points in common with the acceptable region. Consequently, some amount of overdeviation on the third goal constraint will be unavoidable. We can see on the graph that this deviation can be minimized by the point $x_1 = 20$, $x_2 = 0$ (point D, see Figure 10-7c), since this point is closest to the third goal.

Now we can determine the values of the deviation variables specified in the objective. By inspection of the graph, we can see that the solution satisfies the first two priorities. Therefore, $v_1 = 0$ and $u_2 = 0$. We also can see that the solution is over on the third goal. We can determine this amount by substituting the optimal values of x_1 and x_2 into the third constraint and solving for v_3 (u_3 is omitted because we can see on the graph that the solution is not under on the third goal):

$$2(20) + 2(0) - v_3 = 30$$

Solving, $v_3 = 10$.

Solving Goal Programming Problems Using Excel

Goal programming problems can be solved using Excel. The approach is conceptually similar to the graphical solution, except that more than two decision variables can be handled when utilizing the computer and Excel. When we utilize Excel, goals are handled one at a time, starting with the highest priority goal. Once the first priority goal is satisfied, then try to solve in order to satisfy the second priority, while ensuring that the first priority goal is still satisfied. Using Excel to solve goal programming problems differs from the graphical approach in three important ways. The first difference is that the visual benefit of a graph is absent for problems that involve three or more decision variables. The second difference relates to the objective function. When using Excel, the objective function changes and the goals are added sequentially. As new priority goals are satisfied, lower priority goals are added, whereas, when utilizing the graphical approach, the objective function includes all priority goals. The third difference is that when using Excel, the results of each sequential solution may be used to modify a goal before proceeding to the next stage in the sequence.

The process begins by solving a model that includes any nongoal (hard) constraints and all goal constraints. We need to set up the Solver so that only the highest priority goal is considered. The goal constraint that contains the deviation variable has the highest priority from the objective function. The solution for that model fixes the value of that deviation variable for the remainder of the analysis. This process is repeated using the remaining deviation variable that has the highest priority, and so on, until all priorities have been considered. The following example illustrates the process.

Example 10-3

Robinson Chemical Manufacturing company produces two types of chemical compounds: Compound 100 ($x_1 = 1$ unit of Compound 100) and Compound 200 ($x_2 = 1$ unit of Compound 200). Each unit of Compound 100 uses 5 pounds of mixing material.

Each unit of Compound 200 uses 3 pounds mixing material. There are 150 pounds of mixing material available per day. It takes 2 hours of labor time to make one unit of Compound 100, while each unit of Compound 200 uses 5 hours of labor. There are 50 hours of labor available per shift and the company operates one shift per day and employs two employees per shift. The chemicals (materials used to mix the compounds) have to be mixed and cured using Mixer 5000. It takes 3 hours to mix and cure a unit of Compound 100 and 3.6 hours to mix and cure a unit of Compound 200. There are 180 machine hours per day available for Mixer 5000. Daily demand is estimated to be 40 units for Compound 100. Daily demand for Compound 200 is estimated at 50 units.

The company identified the following four priority goals for this problem:

1. Minimize being under the labor hours constraint.
2. Minimize being under the machine hours constraint.
3. Minimize being under the demand constraint for Compound 200.
4. Minimize being under the demand constraint for Compound 100.
5. Minimize labor overtime.

As you can see this problem involves five prioritized goals.
Formulate the problem described in Example 10-3 as a goal programming problem and solve it using Excel.

Solution
In formulating this problem, we begin to formulate the objective function as follows:

minimize $P_1u_1, P_2u_2, P_3u_4, P_4u_3, P_5v_1$

Note that the company has five different priority goals. These goals are subject to the following constraints:

$$5x_1 + 3x_2 \leq 150 \quad \text{(mixing material, nongoal constraint)}$$
$$2x_1 + 5x_2 + u_1 - v_1 = 100 \quad \text{(labor hours, goal constraint)}$$
$$3x_1 + 3.6x_2 + u_2 - v_2 = 180 \quad \text{(machine hours, goal constraint)}$$
$$x_1 + u_3 - v_3 = 40 \quad \text{(demand "goal" constraint for Compound 100)}$$
$$x_2 + u_4 - v_4 = 50 \quad \text{(demand "goal" constraint for Compound 200)}$$
$$\text{All variables} \geq 0$$

Solving a goal programming model with prioritized goals requires us to solve a series of linear programming problems. In solving the first model, we only consider the highest priority (P_1) goal and we do not consider any of the other goals (P_2 through P_5). Therefore, the objective is to minimize the deviation variable associated with priority 1. In other words, the objective function reduces to the following:

minimize P_1u_1

subject to the same constraints listed above.

In solving this goal programming problem, we prepare the Excel worksheet shown in Exhibit 10-1. After preparing the worksheet shown in Exhibit 10-1, from the Excel menu, we choose **Tools I Solver** and obtain the Solver Parameters screen shown in Exhibit 10-2. On this screen, we first specify the objective function in the "Set Target Cell" box by choosing cell B15 since our first priority goal is to minimize the labor underutilization goal (u_1). The formula for cell B15, simply minimizes the labor underutilization goal (u_1), which is = D5 * D14. We proceed by choosing minimization (Min) as our objective, and specify the variables in the "By Changing Cells" box.

Exhibit 10-1   Excel Worksheet for Robinson Chemical Company Goal Programming Problem, Considering Only Priority 1 (Minimizing Labor Underutilization) Goal

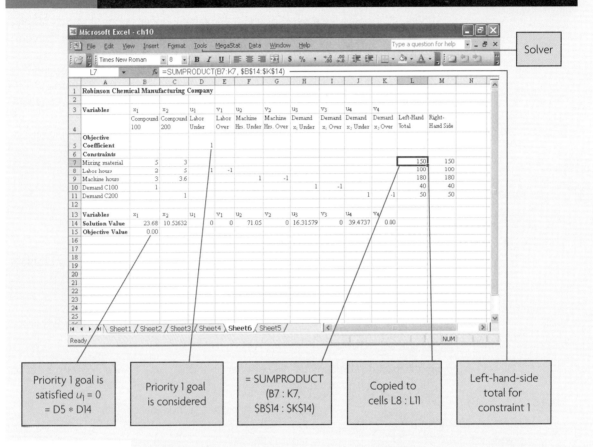

Priority 1 goal is satisfied $u_1 = 0$ = D5 * D14

Priority 1 goal is considered

= SUMPRODUCT (B7 : K7, $B$14 : $K$14)

Copied to cells L8 : L11

Left-hand-side total for constraint 1

Our variables include the two decision variables as well as all of the deviational variables. These variables are stated in cells B14 through K14. Next, we specify the constraints in the Subject to the Constraints area. In specifying the constraints, we first state the nongoal constraints. In our problem involving the Robinson Chemical Company, we have just one nongoal constraint (constraint 1, specified in row 7). Note that in Exhibit 10-1, the L column represents the total from the left-hand side of each constraint equation. In order to get the total of the left-hand side of the equation, the SUMPRODUCT function is utilized to calculate the total value obtained by multiplying the constraint coefficients on the left-hand side of the constraint with the values of the decision variables and then summing the cross-products. For example, to calculate the left-hand side of the mixing material constraint, we first multiply the constraint coefficients in cells B7 and C7 with the values of decision variables in cells B14 and C14 respectively. Summing the cross-products ($5 \times 0 + 3 \times 50$), results in the total left-hand-side value of 150. In Exhibit 10-1, the goal constraints are stated in rows 8 through 11. These goal constraints are specified in Exhibit 10-2 as follows: $L$8:$L$11 = $M$8:$M$11. The left-hand-side of the constraint equations is specified by stating $L$8:$L$11 and the right-hand side of the constraint equations is specified by stating $M$8:$M$11. Since all four of these equations are goal constraints, the sign

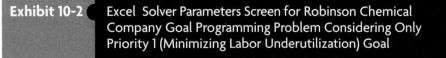

Exhibit 10-2   Excel Solver Parameters Screen for Robinson Chemical Company Goal Programming Problem Considering Only Priority 1 (Minimizing Labor Underutilization) Goal

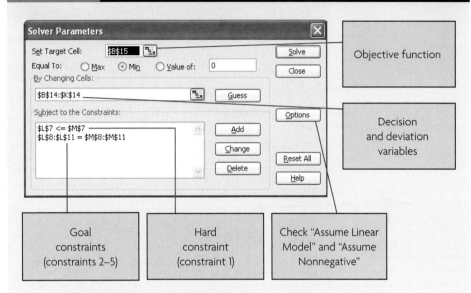

of all of these constraints is equality. After specifying the constraints, in Exhibit 10-2 we click "Options," and in the Options dialog screen, we check the boxes "Assume Linear Model" and "Assume Nonnegativity". We proceed by clicking on "OK" to close the Options dialog screen. Next, click on "Solve" in Exhibit 10-2 and obtain the solution given in Exhibit 10-1. In other words, we should produce 23.68 units of Compound 100 ($x_1 = 23.68$) and 10.526 units of Compound 200 ($x_2 = 10.53$) and we will be 71.05 ($u_2 = 71.05$) hours under the machine hours available. Since the demand for Compound 100 is 40 units, $u_3 = 16.32$, or $(40 - 23.68)$, meaning that the company is not supplying enough units of Compound 100 to satisfy the market demand of 40 units. Therefore, the company has a shortage of 16.32 units of Compound 100.

Likewise, the company also is not supplying enough units of Compound 200 to satisfy the market demand of 50 units. Since the demand for Compound 200 is 50 units, $u_4 = 39.47$, calculated as $(50 - 10.53)$. The shortage for Compound 200 is 39.47 units.

Since the first priority goal is satisfied, we solve the same goal programming problem with the objective of satisfying the second priority goal. In other words, the objective function reduces to the following:

minimize P_2u_2

subject to the same constraints listed above.

The new Excel worksheet shown in Exhibit 10-3 shows the problem being solved at the second stage. Note that the objective coefficient is no longer 1 for u_1 (labor underutilization). The objective coefficient is now equal to 1 for u_2 (machine hours underutilization). Also change the formula for the objective function located in cell B15 from minimizing u_1 to minimizing u_2. In other words, the formula in cell B15 is changed from $= D5 * D14$ to $= F5 * F14$.

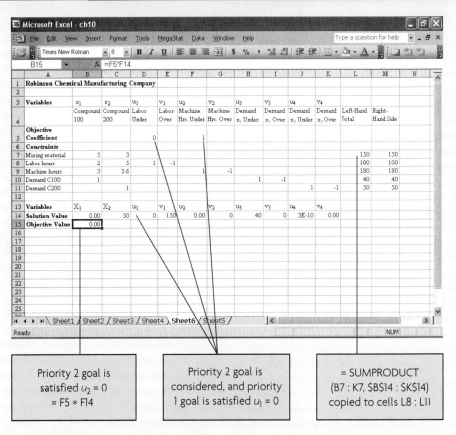

Exhibit 10-3   Excel Worksheet for Robinson Chemical Company Goal Programming Problem, Considering Priority 1 (Minimizing Labor Underutilization) and Priority 2 (Minimizing Machine Hour Underutilization) Goals

In addition, we now have to make sure that the first priority goal is not sacrificed at the expense of the second priority goal. In order to ensure that the first priority goal is still satisfied, we add a constraint equation that indicates that $u_1 = 0$. This new constraint is shown in the Solver Parameters screen shown in Exhibit 10-4. Exhibit 10-4 is identical to Exhibit 10-2 except that we have added the constraint that $D$14 = 0$ ($u_1 = 0$).

The solution values for this problem are given in row 14 of Exhibit 10-3; these solution values are summarized below:

$x_1 = 0,$ $x_2 = 50,$ $u_3 = 40,$ and all of the rest of the deviational variables are equal to zero

Since the priority 1 and priority 2 goals have been met, we proceed to solve the same goal programming problem with the objective of satisfying the priority 3 goal. In other words, the objective function reduces to the following:

minimize $P_3 u_4$

subject to all of the original constraints.

Exhibit 10-4   Excel Solver Parameters Screen for Robinson Chemical Company Goal Programming Problem, Considering Priority 2 (Minimizing Machine Hours Underutilization) Goal While Ensuring That Priority 1 Goal Is Satisfied

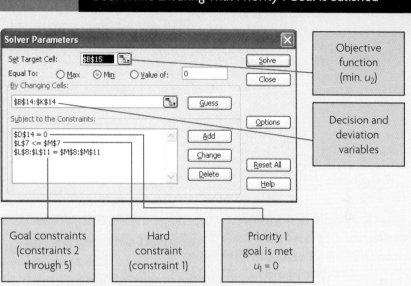

The objective coefficient is no longer 1 for u_2 (underutilization of machine hours). The objective coefficient is now equal to 1 for u_4 (unsatisfied demand for Compound 200). We also have changed the formula for the objective function located in cell B15 from minimizing u_2 to minimizing u_4. In other words, the formula in cell B15 is changed from $=F5 * F14$ to $=J5 * J14$. The result of this iteration is identical to the result of the previous iteration. Since the solution values do not change, we decided not to include the worksheet associated with this solution. However, Exhibit 10-5 shows the Solver Parameters screen, where we added two new constraints ($u_1 = u_2 = 0$) to ensure that the priority 1 goal ($D$14 = 0$) and priority 2 goal ($F$14 = 0$) are still satisfied.

Since the priority 1, priority 2, and priority 3 goals have been met, we proceed to solve the same goal programming problem with the objective of satisfying the priority 4 goal. In other words, the objective function reduces to the following:

minimize $P_4 u_3$

subject to all of the original constraints.

In solving this goal programming problem, the objective coefficient is no longer 1 for u_4 (unsatisfied demand for Compound 200). The objective coefficient is now equal to 1 for u_3 (unsatisfied demand for Compound 100). We also have changed the formula for the objective function located in cell B15 from minimizing u_4 to minimize u_3. In other words, the formula in cell B15 is now $=H5 * H14$.

The worksheet associated with solving this problem is given in Exhibit 10-6 and Exhibit 10-7 shows the Solver Parameters screen where three new constraints

Exhibit 10-5 Excel Solver Parameters Screen for Robinson Chemical Company Goal Programming Problem Considering Priority 3 (Minimizing the Unsatisfied Demand for Compound 200) Goal While Ensuring That the Priority 1 and Priority 2 Goals Are Still Satisfied

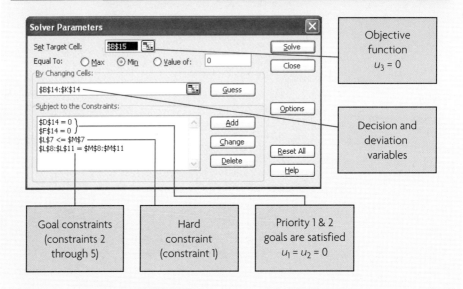

Objective function
$u_3 = 0$

Decision and deviation variables

Goal constraints (constraints 2 through 5)

Hard constraint (constraint 1)

Priority 1 & 2 goals are satisfied
$u_1 = u_2 = 0$

($u_1 = u_2 = u_4 = 0$) are added to ensure that the priority 1 goal ($\$D\$14 = 0$), priority 2 goal ($\$F\$14 = 0$), and priority 3 goal ($\$J\$14 = 0$) are still satisfied.

As can be observed from Exhibit 10-6, the fourth priority goal is not satisfied, because the objective function value in cell B15 is 40. In other words, since we are not producing any units of Compound 100, and since the demand for Compound 100 is 40, the company is underutilizing the demand for Compound 100 by 40 units. At this point, we can try to see how much of the fifth goal (minimizing overtime) we can meet without sacrificing any of the higher priority goals.

In other words, the objective function reduces to the following:

minimize $\qquad P_5 v_1$

subject to all of the original constraints.

In solving this goal programming problem, we have to make certain changes in the Excel worksheet given in Exhibit 10-6. The objective coefficient is not 1 for v_1 and the objective function located in B15 now involves the minimization of v_1. In other words, the formula in cell B15 is now $=E5 * E14$.

Since the first three goals are satisfied, in completing the Solver Parameters screen we need to continue setting the deviation variables associated with the first three priority goals equal to zero. In other words, $u_1 = u_2 = u_4 = 0$ are added to ensure that the priority 1 goal ($\$D\$14 = 0$), priority 2 goal ($\$F\$14 = 0$), and priority 3 goal ($\$J\$14 = 0$) are still satisfied. However, we need to also ensure that the priority 4 goal is not sacrificed from its current level. Even though the fourth

Exhibit 10-6 Excel Worksheet for Robinson Chemical Company Goal Programming Problem, Considering Priority 4 Goal (Minimizing Unsatisfied Demand for Compound 200) While Ensuring That Priority 1 (Minimizing Labor Underutilization), Priority 2 (Minimizing Machine Hour Underutilization), and Priority 3 (Unsatisfied Demand for Compound 200) Goals Are Satisfied

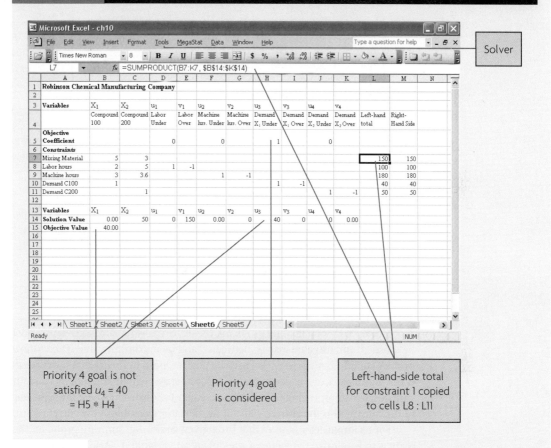

priority goal is not satisfied, we do not want to see an increase in its deviation variable at the expense of satisfying the fifth priority goal. Therefore, in the Solver Parameters screen we add another constraint, indicating that $u_3 \leq 40$, or \$H\$14 ≤ 40. In this example, since u_3 is at its maximum value of 40, it is impossible to increase it any further. Since the optimal solution to this problem is identical to the optimal solution to the problem involving priority goal 4, we did not show the results associated with solving the goal programming problem involving priority goal 5. In other words, the optimal values of the decision variables as well as the deviation variables remain the same, that is, $x_1 = 0$, $x_2 = 50$, $u_3 = 40$, and the rest of the deviation variables are equal to zero. Note that the solution to the priority 5 goal problem did not result in the improvement of the deviational variable v_1 (minimizing overtime ($v_1 = 150$)).

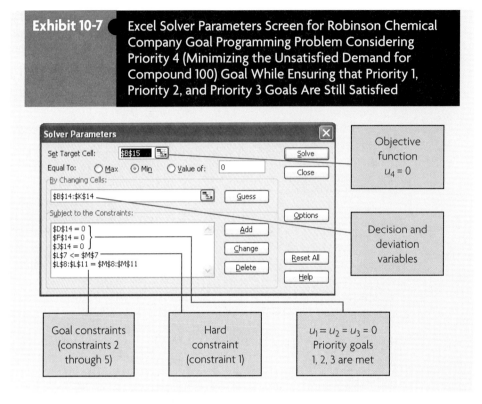

Exhibit 10-7 Excel Solver Parameters Screen for Robinson Chemical Company Goal Programming Problem Considering Priority 4 (Minimizing the Unsatisfied Demand for Compound 100) Goal While Ensuring that Priority 1, Priority 2, and Priority 3 Goals Are Still Satisfied

However, in solving other problems, the deviation variable at a given priority level may not be satisfied, and its value may be between 0 and its maximum value. Therefore, in solving the problem to improve a lower-level priority goal, we need to ensure that the current priority goal is not diminished, or the deviation variable associated with it does not increase. In order to ensure this, we simply include a less-than-or-equal to constraint where the right-hand-side value of the constraint is the current value of the deviation variable at the current solution.

For example, let's assume that for a given goal programming problem, the second priority is to minimize the value of the deviation variable u_2. Also assume the priority 1 goal (minimizing u_1) is completely satisfied and suppose that the maximum possible value of u_2 is 40. In solving the goal programming at the priority level 2, the goal is to minimize the deviation variable u_2. In solving this problem, we obtain a value of 20 for u_2. In other words, the second priority goal is not met. We can now proceed to solve the third priority goal, but we need to ensure that the second priority goal does not deteriorate. When solving the priority 3 goal programming problem, in order to ensure that u_1 and u_2 do not increase from their current levels, we include the following constraints: $u_1 = 0$ and $u_2 \leq 20$. These constraints will ensure that the priority 1 goal is still met and u_2 does not increase above 20, while trying to minimize the third priority goal.

Weighted Goals

Instead of prioritizing the goals, we can assign weights to the goals to distinguish the importance of various goals. The weights are utilized as the objective function coefficients for the goal programming problem.

Let's demonstrate an example with weighted goals by modifying Example 10-3. In Example 10-3, the company had five prioritized goals to satisfy. Now, we will ask the Robinson

Chemical Company manager, Michelle Robinson, to assign weights to the five goals. In order to make it easier for Michelle, we use the following allocation approach and we simply ask her to assign 100 points to the five goals. Michelle assigns the following weights to the five goals:

Goal	Weight
1. Minimize being under the labor hours constraint (u_1)	35
2. Minimize being under the machine hours constraint (u_2)	25
3. Minimize being under the demand constraint for Compound 200 (u_4)	20
4. Minimize being under the demand constraint for Compound 100 (u_3)	15
5. Minimize labor overtime (v_1)	5
Total	100

In order to provide some meaning to the goals, we can take the first goal (minimizing being under the labor hours constraint) and compare it against other goals based on the weights:

• Fully utilizing the desired labor hours is 1.4 times (35/25) as important as the goal of fully utilizing the desired machine hours.
• Fully utilizing the desired labor hours is 1.75 times (35/20) as important as the goal of meeting the demand for Compound 200.
• Fully utilizing the desired labor hours is 2.33 times (35/15) as important as the goal of meeting the demand for Compound 100.
• Fully utilizing the desired labor hours is 7 times (35/5) as important as the goal of minimizing overtime.

We also can compare other goals in terms of their weights against each other. For example, meeting the demand for Compound 200 is 4 times (20/5) as important as the goal of minimization of overtime.

However, assigning weights to the various goals introduces an element of subjectivity to the problem. Therefore, if the weights can be derived naturally from the process, the weighted goal programming problem becomes a more effective solution methodology. Since Example 10-3 doesn't lend itself to the natural derivation or statement of the weights, the procedure for assigning weights involves subjectivity. We can eliminate the subjectivity if the goals and the associated deviation variables involve the same unit of measurement. For example, if all of the deviation variables are measured in dollars, it becomes much easier to assign weights to the deviation variables. If each goal is measured in dollars, we can assign weights to the deviation variables based on per-unit cost of production, per-unit profit margin, and so forth. However, in solving Example 10-3, it is not possible to assign weights using the same units. Therefore, the weights are assigned by the allocation method described earlier. If the management of the company feels that the allocation method introduces too much subjectivity, then the company can use the priority goal programming problem described in the previous section.

Solution of the Weighted Goal Programming Problem The advantage of solving a weighted goal programming problem over solving the prioritized goal programming problem is that the weighted goal programming problem can be solved in one step because the **weighted goal programming model** is treated as a linear programming problem with a single objective function. The objective function minimizes the sum of the weighted deviation variables. As we demonstrated in the previous section, in utilizing the prioritized goal programming model, we needed to solve a sequence of goal programming problems. Therefore, preparing the Excel worksheet and solving the weighted goal programming problem is a relatively simple task compared to solving the prioritized goal programming problem

Exhibit 10-8 Excel Worksheet for Robinson Chemical Company Weighted Goal Programming Problem

Microsoft Excel - ch10

Solver

	A	B	C	D	E	F	G	H	I	J	K	L	M
1	**Robinson Chemical Manufacturing Company**												
2													
3	**Variables**	x_1	x_2	u_1	v_1	u_2	v_2	u_3	v_3	u_4	v_4		
4		Compound 100	Compound 200	Labor Under	Labor Over	Machine Hrs. Under	Machine Hrs. Over	Demand x_1 Under	Demand x_1 Over	Demand x_2 Under	Demand x_2 Over	Left-Hand Total	Right-Hand Side
5	**Objective Coefficient**			35	5	25		15		20			
6	**Constraints**												
7	Mixing material	5	3									150	150
8	Labor hours	2	5	1	-1							100	100
9	Machine hours	3	3.6			1	-1					180	180
10	Demand C100	1						1	-1			40	40
11	Demand C200		1							1	-1	50	50
12													
13	**Variables**	x_1	x_2	u_1	v_1	u_2	v_2	u_3	v_3	u_4	v_4		
14	**Solution Value**	0.00	50	0	150	0.00	0	40	0	0	0.00		
15	**Objective Value**	1350.00											

Sheet1 / Sheet2 / Sheet3 / Sheet4 / Sheet6 / Sheet5

Cell	Copied to	Formula
L7	L8 : L11	= SUMPRODUCT (B7 : K7, \$B\$14 : \$K\$14)
B15		= SUMPRODUCT (B14 : K14, B5 : K5)

since the prioritized goal programming problem involves multiple steps, where the same problem is solved using different objective function values in multiple iterations.

For the weighted goal programming problem example we stated earlier, the objective function and the constraints can be stated as follows:

minimize weighted deviation variables $35u_1 + 25u_2 + 20u_4 + 15u_3 + 5v_1$

subject to

$$
\begin{aligned}
5x_1 + 3x_2 &\le 150 && \text{(mixing material, nongoal constraint)}\\
2x_1 + 5x_2 + u_1 - v_1 &= 100 && \text{(labor hours, goal constraint)}\\
3x_1 + 3.6x_2 + u_2 - v_2 &= 180 && \text{(machine hours, goal constraint)}\\
x_1 + u_3 - v_3 &= 40 && \text{(demand "goal" constraint for Compound 100)}\\
x_2 + u_4 - v_4 &= 50 && \text{(demand "goal" constraint for Compound 200)}\\
\text{All variables} &\ge 0
\end{aligned}
$$

The Excel worksheet to solve this problem is shown in Exhibit 10-8. This worksheet is very similar to the worksheets used to solve the prioritized goal programming problem. The only difference is in the objective function, which is stated in cell B15. The formula for cell B15 is shown at the bottom of Exhibit 10-8. This formula =SUMPRODUCT(B14:K14,B5:K5) involves the sum of the multiplication of the weights and the resulting values of the deviation variables. The statement of the Solver Parameters screen is identical to the Solver Parameters screen displayed in Exhibit 10-2. Note that since the weights of the goals are consistent with the prioritized goals of the earlier section, the solution to the problem displayed in Exhibit 10-8 is identical to the solution to the goal programming problem with prioritized weights, that is, $x_1 = 0$, $x_2 = 50$, $u_3 = 40$, and the rest of the deviation variables are equal to zero. However, it is possible to obtain different results using prioritized goals versus weighted goals. The resulting objective function value of 1,350 is not a meaningful value because it is a function of the weights assigned to the different deviation variables, where the deviation variables are stated in different unit terms.

Analytical Hierarchy Process

In addition to goal programming, the **analytical hierarchy process (AHP)** is another multicriteria decision-making method. If we are deciding the quantity of each decision variable, then the goal programming model provides the right solution procedure since it generates the quantity of decision variables while taking priorities into account. On the other hand, if we want to decide the rank order of decision alternatives or select an alternative from a set of alternatives based on multiple criteria, then AHP can be utilized. AHP can be very useful when a decision maker is determining which type of car to buy, which major to choose, which university to attend, which job offer to choose, or at which site to locate the new plant based on several different criteria.

While the goal programming answers the question of "how much" for each decision variable, AHP addresses the issue of "which" alternative to select based on multiple criteria.

In developing an AHP model, first the decision maker provides weighted preferences for the criteria that are used to determine the preferences for the decision alternatives. Second, AHP rates each alternative using each criterion. Finally, AHP will develop a prioritized ranking of the decision alternatives based on the relative importance placed on each criterion as well as the ratings of each alternative on each criterion.

To demonstrate the utility of AHP, let us consider the following example.

Example 10-4

Julie is in the process of deciding which stereo system to purchase for the night club that is about to open for business. This expensive stereo system has to meet certain criteria before it's purchased by Julie, the owner of the night club. She has narrowed her choices to three products, brand named, (1) Sharp, (2) Lucidity, and (3) Clarity. She will utilize three criteria to evaluate these three products: (1) sound (clarity of sound) (2) price, and (3) options (the number of options available in playing the stereo system). The prices of the three stereo systems are as follows: Sharp, $15,000; Lucidity, $30,000; and Clarity, $22,500. With respect to sound, the products can be rank ordered as follows: Clarity, Lucidity, then Sharp. In terms of the options available, Sharp has by far the most options to choose from, followed by Clarity, then Lucidity.

Note that in this problem, some of the criteria, such as price and options available, are fairly objective, whereas sound is a subjective criterion. However, even for an objective criterion such as price, there could be a fair amount of subjectivity involved. For example, let us consider the price of Lucidity versus the price of Sharp. Clearly, Lucidity is the more expensive of the two products. However, different customers may have a completely different view of the price differential. If a customer is in a good financial situation, then the difference in price may not amount to much of a difference, while it might mean a significant difference for a person or a company that is in financial difficulty. The ability of the decision maker to include his or her subjective judgments makes AHP a very attractive multicriteria decision-making tool.

Solution

In order to clearly understand the hierarchical relationships between criteria and the decision alternatives, we first develop a graphical representation of the problem. The importance of the graph is that it clearly depicts the hierarchies in the specification of the criteria for the problem. Figure 10-8 shows the graphical representation of the stereo system problem.

In Figure 10-8, the first level of **hierarchy diagram** is the achievement of the overall objective, which is to buy a stereo system that fits the preferences of Julie. The second level of the graph includes the three criteria utilized by Julie. The third level includes the decision alternatives. In the next section, we will develop and explain the AHP procedure utilizing the stereo system example.

In this example, we first compare the three criteria in terms of importance to Julie; then we rate the three brands of stereo systems with respect to each criterion. In order to do these comparisons, we need to use pairwise comparisons.

Figure 10-8   Graphical Representation of the Hierarchies for the stereo system-selection problem

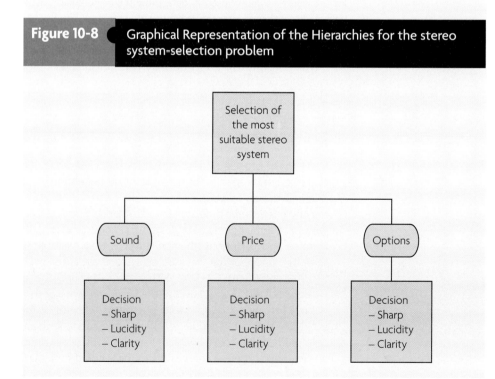

Table 10-1	Preference Scale for the Pairwise Comparisons

Verbal Statement of the Preference	Numerical Value
Equally preferred	1
Equally to moderately preferred	2
Moderately preferred	3
Moderately to strongly preferred	4
Strongly preferred	5
Strongly to very strongly preferred	6
Very strongly preferred	7
Very strongly to extremely preferred	8
Extremely preferred	9

Pairwise Comparisons

Pairwise comparisons are the foundation of AHP, and with the assistance of these pairwise comparisons we can effectively compare criteria and the decision alternative with respect to each criterion. We begin the pairwise comparison procedure by comparing the criteria in pairs. Since we have three criteria, we need three basic pairwise comparisons: price versus sound; price versus options; and sound versus options. In order to compare these criteria, the preference scale provided in Table 10-1 is used. This is a nine-point preference scale; numerical values and the associated verbal statement of the preference are stated in Table 10-1.

Julie felt that price was moderately preferred to sound, price was moderately to strongly preferred to options, and sound was moderately preferred to options.

Based on Julie's preferences, we formulate the pairwise comparison matrix shown in Table 10-2.

Table 10-2	Pairwise Comparison Table for the Stereo System Selection Problem		
Criterion	**Price**	**Sound**	**Options**
Price	1	3	4
Sound	1/3	1	3
Options	1/4	1/3	1
Totals	1.5833	4.333	8

Table 10-3	Normalized Pairwise Comparison Table for the Stereo System Selection Problem			
Criterion	**Price**	**Sound**	**Options**	**Average %**
Price	.6316	.6923	.500	.6079
Sound	.2105	.2308	.375	.2721
Options	.1579	.0769	.125	.1199
Totals	1.0	1.0	1.0	1.0

In Table 10-2, the diagonal values are 1, because we are comparing the criterion against itself. The price-sound preference rating is 3 because Julie indicated that price was moderately preferred to sound. From Table 10-1, a moderately preferred rating is 3. On the other hand, we observe that the sound-price preference rating is 1/3. Since the price-sound preference rating was 3, we utilize the reciprocal rating approach and indicate that the sound-price preference rating is 1/3. Similarly, the price-option preference rating is 4 because Julie indicated that price was moderately to strongly preferred to options. Likewise, we observe that the options-price preference rating is 1/4. Since the price-options preference rating was 4, the reciprocal rating approach is utilized to obtain the options-price preference rating of 1/4.

Normalized Pairwise Comparison Matrix

Dividing each value by its column total normalizes the values in the pairwise comparison matrix shown in Table 10-2. The **normalized pairwise comparison** matrix is given in Table 10-3. The row averages given in the far right column of Table 10-3 represent Julie's priority for each criterion. Thus, price with a priority of .6079 is the most important criterion while options, with .1199, is the least important criterion.

Consistency Check for Criteria

Since the analytical hierarchy process primarily depends on the pairwise comparisons provided by the decision maker, and since these comparisons are subjective, the preference indicated for a pairwise comparison has to be consistent with a different, but related, pairwise comparison. For example, if the preference score for the pairwise comparison A-B is 2 and B-C is 4, then the preference score A-C should be 8. If the decision maker scores the A-C preference rating as 6, then a certain amount of inconsistency exists in her preferences. This type of inconsistency increases as the number of pairwise comparisons increases. A certain level of inconsistency is expected; however, if the amount of inconsistency gets to be too high, then the results of AHP become questionable. In an AHP study, the inconsistencies are measured using a consistency index, or **consistency ratio**. If the consistency index is 0, then the decision maker has perfect consistency in his or her preferences. The consistency ratio (CR) is calculated as the ratio of the consistency index (CI) to the random index (RI). RI is the consistency index of a randomly generated pairwise comparison matrix. In other words, CR = CI/RI. If the consistency ratio exceeds .10, then

Table 10-4	Calculation of the Weighted Priorities for the Criteria		
Criterion (1)	Weighted Sum (2)	Priority (3)	Weighted Sum Priority (4) = (2)/(3)
Price	1.904	.608	3.13136
Sound	.8345	.2721	3.0669
Options	.3626	.1199	3.0242

there may be serious inconsistencies in the pairwise comparisons and the results provided by AHP may be questionable.

Multiplying the pairwise comparison matrix by the criteria percentages given in the last column of Table 10-3 results in the following matrix.

$$\begin{bmatrix} 1 & 3 & 4 \\ 1/3 & 1 & 3 \\ 1/4 & 1/3 & 1 \end{bmatrix} \begin{bmatrix} .608 \\ .2721 \\ .1199 \end{bmatrix} = \begin{bmatrix} 1.904 \\ .8345 \\ .3626 \end{bmatrix} \begin{pmatrix} \text{Price} \\ \text{Sound} \\ \text{Options} \end{pmatrix}$$

Dividing the weighted sums obtained above by the priority percentages results in the weighted sum priority values displayed in Table 10-4.

The weighted sum priority values displayed in Table 10-4 are averaged below to determine the average ratio, or λ_A.

$$\lambda_A = \text{average ratio} = \frac{3.13136 + 3.0669 + 3.0242}{3} = 3.0742$$

Using the value of λ_A calculated above, we calculate the consistency index formula using the following equation. In this equation, $n = 3$, which is the number of criteria being compared.

$$CI = \frac{\lambda_A - n}{n - 1} = \frac{3.0742 - 3}{2} = \frac{.0742}{2} = .0371$$

Using the consistency index value, we proceed to calculate the consistency ratio as follows. In calculating the consistency ratio, we divide the consistency index calculated above by the random index value, which is the value of the consistency index if each pairwise comparison is randomly generated. The random index values are given in Table 10-5. Since we have three criteria, $n = 3$, and the value of RI is .58.

$$CR = \frac{CI}{RI} = \frac{.0371}{.58*} = .064$$

*From Table 10-5.

Table 10-5	Random Index Values for the Comparison of *n* items								
n	2	3	4	5	6	7	8	9	10
RI	0	.58	.90	1.12	1.24	1.32	1.41	1.45	1.51

Table 10-6	Pairwise Comparison Matrix Price		
Product	**Sharp**	**Lucidity**	**Clarity**
Sharp	1	4	2
Lucidity	1/4	1	1/3
Clarity	1/2	3	1
Σ	1.75	8	3.333

As we discussed earlier, a consistency ratio greater than .10 will affect the results of AHP. However, in this study, since the consistency ratio is less than .10, the level of **consistency** is at an acceptable level; that is, .064 < .10.

Next we need to determine three pairwise comparison matrices, one for each criterion comparing the three products. The pairwise comparison matrix given in Table 10-6 includes the pairwise comparisons of the three products in relation to the price criterion. As before, diagonal values of this matrix are equal to 1 since we are comparing the same products. However, the pairwise comparison value of Sharp to Lucidity is equal to 4. This implies that the price of the Sharp product is moderately to strongly preferred to the price of the Lucidity product. In addition, the price of the Sharp product is equally to moderately preferred to the price of the clarity product which is equal to Z. Applying the reciprocal rule, we obtain the preference of Lucidity to Sharp as $1/4$ and the preference of clarity to Sharp as $1/2$. Addition of the column values results in the column totals. The smallest column total indicates that the product is the most preferred, while the largest column total indicates that the product is the least preferred. In our example, the column for the Sharp product has the smallest total, while the column Lucidity has the largest total. Therefore, the Sharp product is the most preferred in terms of the price criterion, while the Lucidity product is the least preferred in terms of price.

The information captured in the pairwise comparison matrix can be converted into percentages by simply dividing the cell value by the column total. For example, the pairwise comparison value of cell Sharp to Lucidity is 4 and the column total for Lucidity is 8; thus the proportion matrix value of Sharp to Lucidity is, $4/8 = .5$. The proportion matrix in Table 10-7 shows the percentage (proportion) value for each cell for the pairwise comparison matrix for price.

Table 10-7	Proportion Percentage Matrix for Price		
Product	**Sharp**	**Lucidity**	**Clarity**
Sharp	.5714	.5	.60
Lucidity	.1429	.125	.10
Clarity	.2857	.375	.30
Σ	1.0	1.0	1.0

Table 10-8	Priority Percentage for Price	
Product	**Percentage**	
Sharp	.5571*	
Lucidity	.1226	
Clarity	.3202	
Σ	1.0	

*(.5714 + .50 + .60)/3 = .5571

Averaging the proportions for each row, we determine the priority percentage for price exhibited in Table 10-8. In other words, the Sharp product captures 54.76 percent of the value and the Lucidity product captures only 13.69 percent of the value in terms of price.

The pairwise comparison matrix, the proportion matrix, and the priority percentages for sound and options are computed in the same way as the computations for the price criterion.

Pairwise Comparison Matrix for Sound

Product	Sharp	Lucidity	Clarity
Sharp	1	1/2	1/4
Lucidity	2	1	1/3
Clarity	4	3	1
Σ	7	4.5	1.5833

Proportion Matrix for Sound

Product	Sharp	Lucidity	Clarity	Priority Percentage
Sharp	.1429	.1111	.1579	.1373
Lucidity	.2857	.2222	.2105	.2395
Clarity	.5714	.6667	.6316	.6232
Σ	1.0	1.0	1.0	1.0

Pairwise Comparison Matrix for Options

Product	Sharp	Lucidity	Clarity
Sharp	1	4	2
Lucidity	1/4	1	1
Clarity	1/2	1	1
Σ	1.75	6	4

Proportion Matrix for Options

Product	Sharp	Lucidity	Clarity	Priority Percentage
Sharp	.5714	.6667	.50	.5794
Lucidity	.1429	.1667	.25	.1865
Clarity	.2857	.1667	.25	.2341
Σ	1.0	1.0	1.0	1.0

After the computation of the average priority percentages, we can develop the overall priority rankings for each product as follows. For instance, in calculating the weighted score for the Sharp product, we multiply the criteria weights for price, sound, and options with their respective priority percentage scores. The average priority percentage for the Sharp product is .5476 for price, .1373 for sound, and .5794 for options. In other words, according to Julie, the Sharp product is viewed favorably with respect to price and options and unfavorably with respect to sound. The weights used for the criteria by Julie indicate that price is by far the most important criterion (weight of .608), and options, with a weight of .1199, is the least important criterion. Summing the products of each criterion weight percentage and average priority

Table 10-9	Determination of the Overall Priority		

Sharp

Criterion	Weight % (1)	Priority % (2)	(1) * (2)
Price	.608	.5571	.3387
Sound	.2721	.1373	.0374
Options	.1199	.5794	.0695
Weighted score for Sharp			.4456

Lucidity

Criterion	Weight % (1)	Priority % (2)	(1) * (2)
Price	.608	.1226	.0745
Sound	.2721	.2395	.0652
Options	.1199	.1865	.0224
Weighted score for Lucidity			.1621

Clarity

Criterion	Weight % (1)	Priority % (2)	(1) * (2)
Price	.608	.3202	.1947
Sound	.2721	.6232	.1696
Options	.1199	.2341	.0281
Weighted score for Clarity			.3984

percentage results in the **weighted product scores** for each decision alternative. Table 10-9 shows the calculation of the weighted product score for each decision alternative. The sum of the weighted scores for the three products sum to one (.4456 + .1621 + .3924 = 1.0).

In our example, it appears that Julie favors Sharp to Clarity and also favors Clarity to Lucidity. In other words, since .4456 > .3924 > .1621, Julie should choose Sharp.

Analytical Hierarchy Process Using Excel

Excel can be a handy tool to utilize the analytical hierarchy process (AHP). We perform the AHP process in Exhibit 10-9. In this exhibit, we first state the pairwise comparison matrix comparing the criteria (B2:D4). In stating this matrix, we only specify the values in the upper diagonal (cells B2, C2, D2, C3, D3, and D4). The lower diagonal values (B3, B4, and C4 are obtained using the reciprocal rating formulas. For instance, the formula for cell B4 is the reciprocal value of cell B2; therefore, the formula for cell B4 is = 1/B2. We then normalize the pairwise comparisons by simply taking the ratio of each comparison value divided by the total for each column. For instance, the normalized value for cell B2 is specified in cell F2 and the formula for cell F2 is B2/B$5. In other words, 1/1.583 gives us the normalized value for this cell. We calculate the rest of the normalized matrix in a similar fashion. Next, we determine the average percentage for each row of the normalized matrix. The average weight for the first row of the normalized

Exhibit 10-9 Analytical Hierarchy Process for the Stereo System Selection Example

Microsoft Excel - ahp

F29 {=MMULT(B29:D31,E29:E31)}

	A	B	C	D	E	F	G	H	I	J	K	L	M	N	O
1		Price	Sound	Options		Normalized values			Avg. Weight	Sum	Weighted Sum			RI values for AHP	
2	Price	1.0000	3.0000	4.0000		0.6316	0.6923	0.5000	0.6080	1.9040	3.1318			*n*	*RI*
3	Sound	0.3333	1.0000	3.0000		0.2105	0.2308	0.3750	0.2721	0.8346	3.0672			2	0.00
4	Options	0.2500	0.3333	1.0000		0.1579	0.0769	0.1250	0.1199	0.3626	3.0234			3	0.58
5		1.5833	4.3333	8.0000						Lambda =	3.0741	0.037	=CI	4	0.90
6														5	1.12
7		Price Criterion										0.064	=CR	6	0.12
8		Sharp	Lucidity	Clarity		Normalized values								7	1.32
9	Sharp	1.0000	4.0000	2.0000		0.5714	0.5000	0.6000	0.5571	1.6881	3.0299			8	1.41
10	Lucidity	0.2500	1.0000	0.3333		0.1429	0.1250	0.1000	0.1226	0.3687	3.0065			9	1.45
11	Clarity	0.5000	3.0000	1.0000		0.2857	0.3750	0.3000	0.3202	0.9667	3.0186			10	1.51
12		1.7500	8.0000	3.3333						Lambda =	3.0183	0.009	=CI		
13															
14		Sound Criterion										0.016	=CR		
15		Sharp	Lucidity	Clarity		Normalized values									
16	Sharp	1.0000	0.5000	0.2500		0.1429	0.1111	0.1579	0.1373	0.4128	3.0071				
17	Lucidity	2.0000	1.0000	0.3333		0.2857	0.2222	0.2105	0.2395	0.7218	3.0140				
18	Clarity	4.0000	3.0000	1.0000		0.5714	0.6667	0.6316	0.6232	1.8908	3.0340				
19		7.0000	4.5000	1.5833						Lambda =	3.0183	0.009	=CI		
20															
21		Options Criterion										0.016	=CR		
22		Sharp	Lucidity	Clarity		Normalized values									
23	Sharp	1.0000	4.0000	2.0000		0.5714	0.6667	0.5000	0.5794	1.7937	3.0959				
24	Lucidity	0.2500	1.0000	1.0000		0.1429	0.1667	0.2500	0.1865	0.5655	3.0319				
25	Clarity	0.5000	1.0000	1.0000		0.2857	0.1667	0.2500	0.2341	0.7103	3.0339				
26		1.7500	6.0000	4.0000						Lambda =	3.0539	0.027	=CI		
27															
28		Price	Sound	Options								0.046	=CR		
29	Sharp	0.5571	0.1373	0.5794	0.6080	0.4456	1st choice								
30	Lucidity	0.1226	0.2395	0.1865	0.2721	0.1621	3rd choice								
31	Clarity	0.3202	0.6232	0.2341	0.1199	0.3924	2nd choice								
32															

Sheet1 / Sheet2 / Sheet3

Ready

Table 10-10	Excel Formulas for the AHP Worksheet in Exhibit 10-9	
Cell	**Copied to**	**Formula**
B5	C5:D5	=SUM(B2:B4)
B3		=1/C2
B4		=1/D2
C4		=1/D3
F2	F3:F4	=B2/B$5
G2	G3:G4	=C2/C$5
H2	H3:H4	=D2/D$5
I2	I3:I4	=AVERAGE(F2:H2)
J2	J3:J4	=MMULT(B2;D4,I2:I4)
K2	K3:K4	=J2/I2
K5		=AVERAGE(K2:K5)
L5		=(K5−COUNT(K2:K4))/((COUNT(K2:K4))−1)
L6		=L5/VLOOKUP(COUNT(K2:K4),$N$3:$O$11,2)
F29	F30:F31	=MMULT(B29:D31,E29:E31)
B23	B24	=I8
C23	C24	=I13
D23	D24	=I18
E23	E24:E25	=I2

matrix is calculated by averaging the normalized values. The average weight for the first row of the normalized matrix is given in cell I2 under the heading "Avg. Weight." Therefore, the formula for cell I2 is =AVERAGE(F2:H2); in other words, $(.6316 + .6923 + .5000)/3 = .608$.

After obtaining the average percentages for each criterion, multiply the pairwise comparison matrix with the average criteria percentage (labeled as "Avg. Weight" in Exhibit 10-9). Since this involves multiplication of two matrices, we utilize the matrix multiplication command in Excel. The command =MMULT(B2:D4, $I$2:$I$4) multiplies the pairwise comparison matrix for criteria with the average criteria percentage. In this formula, B2:D4 represents the pairwise comparison matrix, and $I$2:$I$4 represents the average percentage for each criterion. After specifying the formula, we highlight the cells in which we want the answer to be displayed (cells J2, J3, and J4) in column J of Exhibit 10-9, labeled as column "Sum." We proceed by highlighting the formula we just typed in the formula bar and hit Ctrl-Shift-Enter. The results of 1.9040 .8346, and .3626 are displayed in cells J2, J3, and J4 respectively.

Exhibit 10-9 also contains the calculation of the weighted priorities for the criteria and the calculation of the consistency index and consistency ratio. Weighted priorities are calculated using the ratio of the weighted sum priorities and average criteria percentage. For instance, the weighted sum priority for the criterion price is calculated in cell K2 by the formula = J2/I2. In other words, the weighted sum priority for the price criterion is calculated by 1.904/.608 = 3.1318. After the calculation of the weighted priorities, we proceed to the calculation of the consistency index. The formula for the consistency index is determined in two steps. First, we calculate the average of the weighted sum priorities in cell K5 by using the formula =AVERAGE(K2:K4). In the second step, the consistency index for criteria is calculated by using the following formula: =(K5/COUNT(K2:K4))/((COUNT(K2:K4))−1). In other words, we divide the average weighted priority by n which is equal to the number of observations used to calculate the average. This result is divided by the number of observations minus 1. The COUNT command simply counts the number of observations used to calculate the weighted priorities. Once the consistency index is calculated, it is very easy to calculate the consistency ratio. The consistency ratio is the consistency index divided by the random index. The random index values are given in a table in cells N3:O11. The random index value is chosen with the help of the following VLOOKUP command: = VLOOKUP(COUNT(K2:K4),N3:O11,2). In executing this command, Excel counts the number of observations used to calculate the weighted priorities, COUNT (K2:K4), then goes to a lookup table consisting of cells N3:O11 and chooses the value of the random index based on the count in the second column of the VLOOKUP table. In our example, since the count is three, the Excel program goes to the third value in the second column of the VLOOKUP table and chooses the appropriate entry .58. Therefore, the consistency ratio for criteria is calculated in cell L7 by taking consistency index value and dividing by the random index value (cells L5/O4 = .037/.58 = .064).

Julie's pairwise comparison matrix for price, sound, and options based on the three products (Sharp, Lucidity, and Clarity) are also given in Exhibit 10-9. For these pairwise comparison matrices, we calculate the proportion matrices (normalized matrices) by taking the ratio of the pairwise comparison value in each column and dividing it by the column total, similar to the calculation of the normalized values for the criteria as described above. Exhibit 10-9 also shows the values of the priority percentage for each criterion. Cells I9:I11 display the priority percentage for price, cells I16:I18 display the priority percentage for sound, and cells I22:I24 display the priority percentage values for options. These priority percentages are calculated by simply averaging the respective rows for the proportion (normalized) matrices. The consistency index and the consistency ratio for the products are calculated in the same way that they were calculated for the comparison of criteria. All of the relevant formulas are listed in Table 10-10.

The last step in the analytical hierarchy process is the calculation of the weighted score and the overall priority for each product. The weighted scores are calculated in Exhibit 10-9 in cells F29 through F31. In determining the weighted scores, we multiply the average criteria percentage calculated for each criterion (weight) with the average priority percentage for each product-criterion combination. In other words, we have to calculate another matrix multiplication similar to the matrix multiplication calculation described in the multiplication of the pairwise comparison matrix for criteria with the average criteria percentage described earlier. In this matrix multiplication, simply multiply the average priority percentage matrix (cells B29:D31) with the average criteria percentage matrix (cells E29:E31) to obtain the overall priority percentage given in cells F29 through F31. Another name for overall priority percentage is the weighted criteria scores. The priority percentage values are given in cells F29:F31 in Exhibit 10-9. The results are consistent with the manual calculation results provided earlier; it appears that Julie favors Sharp to Clarity and also favors Clarity to Lucidity. In other words, since .4456 > .3924 > .1621, Julie should choose Sharp.

![] Scoring Models

The **scoring model** is a subjective multicriteria method that enables the decision maker to assign weights to each criterion that describes the importance of the criterion and then assign a rating for each decision alternative on each criterion. The outcome is the sum of the products of the criteria weight with the respective ratings of criteria for that decision alternative. This simplistic selection procedure has many areas of application. The three most common areas of application are (1) facility location, (2) product selection, and (3) job selection.

The scoring model is a very flexible method that considers both tangible and intangible factors. It has the capability to consider multiple decision criteria simultaneously.

The Steps for the Scoring Model

1. Develop a list of (factors) criteria to be considered. The decision maker should consider these factors important in evaluating each decision alternative.
2. Assign a weight to each factor that describes the factor's relative importance.

   Let w_i = the weight for factor i, where $i = 1, 2, \ldots, F$
   F = the number of factors considered

   The higher the weight, the more important the criterion.

   We will use a five-point scale to establish the relative importance of the factors considered. The following table provides an interpretation of the weight scale:

   ### Factor Weight Interpretation Table

Importance	Weight
Very important	5
Somewhat important	4
Average importance	3
Somewhat unimportant	2
Very unimportant	1

   For example, if a factor has a weight of 4, it is somewhat more important than the average factor. If a factor has weight of 1, relative to the other factors being considered, the factor in question is very unimportant.
3. Determine a list of decision alternatives. Let d_j = decision alternative j and assign a rating for each factor/decision alternative combination.

   Let r_{ij} = the rating for factor i and decision alternative j

   where

   $j = 1, 2, \ldots, D$
   D = number of decision alternatives considered

   For the purposes of rating each decision alternative/factor combination, we use the following nine-point scale.

**Decision Alternative Rating
Interpretation Table**

Level of Satisfaction	Rating
Extremely high	9
Very high	8
High	7
Slightly high	6
Average	5
Slightly low	4
Low	3
Very low	2
Extremely low	1

For example, a score of 7 for a given decision alternative would indicate that the decision maker (manager) rates this decision alternative (location) high with respect to a given factor (availability of qualified labor).

4.   Compute the factor score for each decision alternative. Let S_j = factor score for factor j.

$$S_j = \sum_{j}^{D} w_i r_{ij}$$

5.   Sequence the decision alternatives from the highest score to the lowest score. The decision alternative with the highest factor score is the recommended decision alternative. The decision alternative with the second highest factor score is the second-choice decision alternative, and so on.

Product selection and facility location are company-related problems, while job selection is an individualized problem. An example for the product selection problem follows.

Example 10-5

Product Selection
An appliance manufacturing company is considering expanding its product line. It has sufficient capital to introduce only one of the three following products:

1.   Microwave ovens
2.   Refrigerators
3.   Stoves

The management thinks the following decision criteria should be used in selecting the product:

1.   Manufacturing capability/cost
2.   Market demand
3.   Profit margin
4.   Long-term profitability/growth
5.   Transportation costs
6.   Useful life

The company has determined the following weights for the decision criteria:

Factors

Criterion	Weight
Manufacturing capability/cost	4
Market demand	5
Unit profit margin	3
Long-term profitability/growth	5
Transportation costs	2
Useful life	1

The decision factor ratings for each criterion are given in the following table:

Decision Factor Ratings

Factor	Microwave	Refrigerator	Stove
1	4	3	8
2	8	4	2
3	6	9	5
4	3	6	7
5	9	2	4
6	1	5	6

Based on the information provided, determine the factor scores for all three products. What is the best choice for the appliance manufacturing company? What is the second-best choice?

Solution

$S_{micro} = 4(4) + 5(8) + 3(6) + 5(3) + 2(9) + 1(1) = 108$
$S_{refrigerator} = 4(3) + 5(4) + 3(9) + 5(6) + 2(2) + 1(5) = 98$
$S_{stove} = 4(8) + 5(2) + 3(5) + 5(7) + 2(4) + 1(6) = 106$

Therefore, the first choice is the microwave oven and the second choice is the stove.

◼ Summary

This chapter utilizes two multicriteria decision-making models: goal programming and the analytical hierarchy process (AHP). Goal programming is a variation of linear programming that can be used to handle problems that have multiple objectives. AHP is designed to solve complex multicriteria decision-making problems. If we are deciding the quantity of each decision variable, then the goal programming model provides the right solution procedure because it provides the quantity of each decision variable, while taking priorities into account. However, if the goal of the decision maker is to select an alternative from a set of alternatives based on multiple criteria, then AHP is the more appropriate method.

In goal programming, the objectives (goals) are expressed as soft constraints that reflect target levels to be achieved. In addition, some goal programming models also have constraints that specify upper and lower bounds rather than target levels specified in soft constraints. These are referred to as hard constraints and are identical to the constraints of the linear programming models of the previous chapters. This chapter illustrates the

Modern Management Science Application: *Motorola, Inc.*

Motorola, Inc., needed to cut costs and improve operations productivity. Since purchasing materials made up more than 50 percent of Motorola's costs, the company decided to improve its supplier negotiation process. This problem was formulated as a mixed-integer linear programming problem (MILP).

The company hired Emptoris to create an Internet purchasing function with advanced capabilities for the entire company in order to make the bidding and selection process seamless. The results of the pilot program were very good, with final prices averaging 40 to 60 percent lower than the previously contracted prices. By using a pilot program for Internet auctions (e-auctions) among its suppliers, the company was able to save 15 to 20 percent more than it would have through traditional face-to-face negotiations.

However, the program could only be applied under specific conditions and could not be generalized to a complicated negotiation system. Motorola wanted to develop a comprehensive Internet-based negotiation system to handle all material purchases.

The company hired the consulting company Emptoris to provide a complete comprehensive Internet-based negotiation system. The system developed by Emptoris provided Motorola the following functions and capabilities:

1. Integrated work flow that reduces work load during multistage negotiations, so that the bidding and selection process required less time because Motorola and its supplier were able to communicate better.
2. Multiple online negotiation types (e-auctions, online competitive bidding, multistage negotiation, and one-on-one negotiation).
3. The ability to manage thousands of line items and suppliers that have complex pricing schemes.
4. The ability to handle "expressive bidding," where a supplier's bid might include factors (in addition to the price) such as quantity, quality, discounts, and special delivery requirements.

The company implemented a six-step, Internet negotiation process:

Step 1. Motorola determines the total cost of ownership (TCO), which includes price, shipping, and maintenance costs, as well as intangible attributes such as product specifications.

Step 2. Motorola chooses the best negotiation type from the following choices: e-auction or e-RFQ (request-for-quotations).

Step 3. Motorola's purchasing team communicates with the suppliers via MINT (Motorola's Internet Negotiation Tool), exploring various options as to how the supplier can meet Motorola's needs at the lowest cost while providing the greatest service.

Step 4. Suppliers use MINT to submit innovative bids for Motorola to evaluate.

Step 5. Motorola's purchasing team evaluates various purchasing scenarios and determines the effect of policies by considering unlimited what-if scenarios. MINT recommends the optimal line-by-line purchasing decision.

Step 6. Motorola's purchasing team decides on which supplier to award this particular transaction.

The model employed by Motorola allows and encourages split awards and suppliers to compete in various ways. For example, the supplier might offer 30 units of item 1 at $10 and 100 units of item 2 at $30. However, if Motorola decides to purchase both items from this supplier, it will receive a discount of a certain percentage on both items.

This system has many advantages for both Motorola and its suppliers, including decreasing the time spent negotiating as well as the time spent traveling. Emptoris developed a purchasing plan for Motorola that was fast, was easy to understand, and provided Motorola with an optimal solution.

Before MINT was implemented, many of the potential users of the system went through an intensive training program. The number of products covered by MINT has increased considerably, mainly because of MINT's capabilities and user training. MINT provides Motorola with the ability to negotiate over 50 percent of its purchases, and employees find MINT to be user friendly and faster. The company was able to save over $250 million in 2002 and over $300 million in 2003. Motorola suppliers also benefited from the program due to faster negotiations that provided more information, thus giving them a more level playing field. In recent years, the company was able to save $600 million (an average of 5 to 15 percent savings per transaction).

Source: T. Metty, R. Harlan, Q. Samelson, T. Moore, T. Morris, R. Sorenson, A. Schneur, O. Raskina, R. Schneur, J. Kanner, K. Potts, and J. Robbings, "Reinventing the Supplier Negotiation Process at Motorola," *Interfaces* 35, no. 1 (January–February 2005), pp. 7–23.

formulation of the various constraints and the associated goal programming models. In a prioritized goal programming model, the focus is on minimizing deviations from the various goals according to a priority ranking established by the decision maker. In the analysis of a goal programming model, the deviation with the highest priority is minimized while disregarding the other goals. After achieving priority goal 1, the deviation with the second highest priority is minimized as long as it does not require any increase or sacrifice in the highest priority deviation. This process continues until all priorities have been attended to.

In a weighted goal programming model, instead of rank-ordering the goals, the decision maker assigns numerical weights to each goal. If a goal has twice the numerical value of another goal, then it is considered to be twice as important as the other goal. The advantage of solving weighted goal programming models using Excel as opposed to solving prioritized goal programming models using Excel is that the weighted goal programming model can be solved in one step, similar to a simple linear programming model with a single objective function. In solving the prioritized goal programming model with Excel, we need to solve a sequence of goal programming problems.

Three solution approaches are demonstrated in the chapter: (1) a graphical approach similar to graphical linear programming (2) use of Excel for the solution of prioritized goal programming problems, and (3) use of Excel for the solution of weighted goal programming problems.

In presenting the AHP model, the chapter demonstrates how judgments concerning the relative importance of criteria or decision alternatives are converted into pairwise comparisons. A consistency ratio is computed to determine the consistency of the pairwise comparisons provided by the decision maker. The solution procedure for AHP is described and finally the priority levels for each decision alternative are multiplied by the criteria weights reflecting the importance of the criteria. The sum of the products of the criteria weights and priority levels provides the overall priority level for each decision alternative.

The chapter concludes with a discussion and demonstration of scoring models. The objective of the scoring model is very similar to AHP. The scoring model is very simplistic and tend to be subjective. The scoring model is a multicriteria method that enables the decision maker to assign weights to each criterion and then assign a rating for each alternative on each criterion.

◼▶ Glossary

Analytical Hierarchy Process (AHP) An approach to multicriteria decision making based on pairwise comparisons.

Consistency A concept that compares the quality of pairwise comparisons made by the decision maker. It measures how consistent the decision maker is regarding the values he or she assigns to the pairwise comparisons.

Consistency Ratio A numerical measure of the consistency of pairwise comparisons made by the decision maker. A ratio of less than .10 is considered acceptable.

Deviation Variable A variable used to account for the amount by which a solution to a goal programming problem overachieves or underachieves a goal.

Goal A target level of performance (e.g., a profit of $30,000).

Goal Constraint A constraint equation whose right-hand-side value is the target for the goal; the left-hand side of the equation represents the decision and the deviation variables and the level of the goal achieved.

Goal Programming A variation of linear programming that allows multiple objectives.

Hard Constraint A nongoal constraint; equal-to, less-than-or-equal-to, or greater-than-or-equal-to constraint that does not involve deviation variables. Specifies upper and lower bounds that cannot be exceeded, or an equality that must be exactly met.

Hierarchy Diagram A diagram that shows the level of hierarchies in AHP problems in terms of the overall objective, the decision criteria, and the decision alternatives.

Normalized Pairwise Comparisons Numerical values obtained by dividing each pairwise comparison value by its column total. The normalized pairwise comparisons are also referred to as proportions.

Objective Function In priority and goal programming models, this indicates which deviation variables will be minimized and their order of importance.

Pairwise Comparisons A paired, relative comparison of the criteria or decision alternatives that consist of preference of relative importance.

Prioritized Goal Programming Model A goal programming model that ranks the deviation variables according to their relative importance based on the decision maker's judgment.

Satisficing An analytical process in which trade-offs are made in order to find a satisfactory solution.

Scoring Model A subjective multicriteria method that enables the decision maker to assign weights to each criterion that describes the importance of the criterion and then assign a rating for each decision alternative on each criterion. The outcome is a score for each decision alternative.

Soft Constraint A goal constraint that involves the deviation variables.

Weighted Goal Programming Model A goal programming model that assigns weights to the deviation variables according to their relative importance based on the decision maker's judgment. These weights serve as the objective function coefficients for the associated goal programming problem.

Weighted Product Score In AHP for each decision alternative, the sum of the products of priority percentage values and the criteria weight percentages.

Solved Problems

Problem 1

a. Formulate a goal programming model and solve it graphically, given the following information:

The manager of a company that makes quilted material that is sold by the yard wants to determine the mix of products to make during a week shortened by a holiday. Material supplies are plentiful, but labor is not. There are 24 hours of labor available; each yard of Colonial quilt requires 2 hours of labor and each yard of Southern Comfort quilt requires 3 hours of labor.

The manager's priorities, is order of importance, are

1. Minimize the underutilization of labor.
2. If there is any overtime, try to keep it to 12 hours or less.
3. Try to avoid making less than 10 yards of Southern Comfort.
4. Avoid using any overtime, if possible.

b. Solve the problem you formulated in part a using Excel.

Solution

a. Start by identifying the decision variables:

x_1 = amount of Colonial quilt to produce
x_2 = amount of Southern Comfort quilt to produce

Begin formulation by listing the *names* of the constraints or goals. Thus, the constraints relate to

1. Labor.
2. Overtime.
3. Amount of Southern Comfort.
4. Overtime (same as z).

This suggests that there are three constraints.

For the labor constraint, apparently, it is possible to be either under ("minimize underutilization") or over ("avoid overtime if possible"). Hence, the labor constraint is a goal constraint:

$$2x_1 + 3x_2 + u_1 - v_1 = 24 \text{ hours}$$

The overtime constraint is a bit unusual because it pertains only to a deviation variable (being over on the labor goal). The overtime goal is

$$v_1 + u_2 - v_2 = 12 \text{ hours}$$

The manager has listed as the third priority to try to avoid making less than 10 yards of Southern Comfort; it would seem that deviations in either direction are possible. That goal constraint is

$$x_2 + u_3 - v_3 = 10 \text{ yards}$$

Next, the priorities can be arranged into the objective function:

$$P_1 u_1, P_2 v_2, P_3 u_3, P_4 v_1$$

where

u_1 = amount of underutilization of labor
v_2 = amount of overtime above 12 hours of overtime
u_3 = amount of Southern Comfort under 10 yards
v_1 = amount of overtime

In summary, the model is

minimize $P_1 u_1, P_2 v_2, P_3 u_3, P_4 v_1$

subject to

Labor	$2x_1 + 3x_2 + u_1 - v_1 = 24$ hours	
Overtime	$v_1 + u_2 - v_2 = 12$ hours	
Southern	$x_2 + u_3 - v_3 = 10$ yards	
	All variables ≥ 0	

In order to solve this graphically, because there are no hard constraints, begin by plotting the goal constraint that contains the deviation variable with the highest priority (u_1) and indicate the direction of the priority (see Figure 10-9).

Next, add the goal constraint containing the deviation variable (v_2) that has the second highest priority and indicate the direction of the priority (see Figure 10-10). In order to plot a deviation goal, set $v_1 = 12$, then add the amount of overtime to the right-hand-side of the labor constraint (because v_1 is in that constraint). The result is

$$2x_1 + 3x_2 + u_1 - v_1 = 36 \text{ hours}$$

Figure 10–9 Identifying the Feasible Solution Space for Solved Problem 1

Figure 10–10 Identifying the Feasible Solution Space for Solved Problem 1

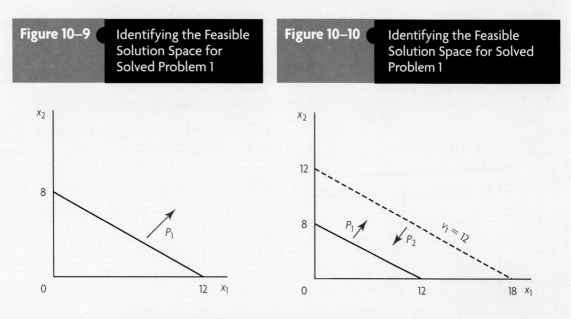

Plotting this line produces the dashed line in Figure 10-10. The dashes differentiate this *deviation constraint* from the other constraints.

At this point, any combination of x_1 and x_2 that lies on or between the two goal constraints would be acceptable.

The third priority refers to u_3. Hence, we add the third goal constraint to the plot (see Figure 10-11). The shaded region indicates the area of acceptability.

The fourth priority refers to v_1 and, thus, to the first goal constraint, which is already on the graph. Therefore, the only addition is an indication of the direction of P_4 (see Figure 10-12). This makes the optimum point the point that is in the acceptable area that is closest to the first goal constraint (i.e., $x_2 = 10$).

In terms of the deviations, we see in Figure 10-12 that the optimum point lies in the area that is acceptable for the first three priorities. Hence, only the fourth will be nonzero. We can determine its value by submitting the optimal values of the

Figure 10–11 Identifying the Feasible Solution Space for Solved Problem 1

Figure 10–12 Identifying the Feasible Solution Space for Solved Problem 1

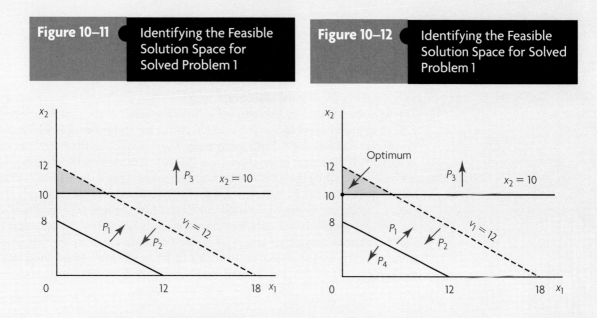

Exhibit 10-10 Excel Worksheet for Solved Problem 1, Goal Programming Problem, Considering Only Priority 1 (Minimizing Labor Underutilization) Goal

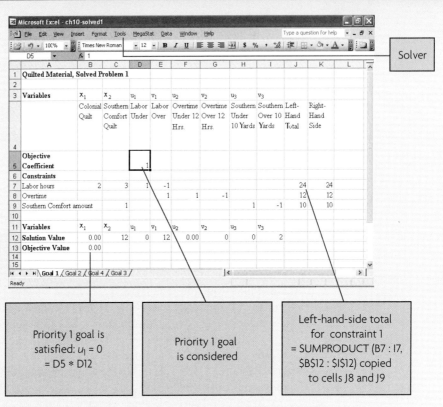

Priority 1 goal is satisfied: $u_1 = 0$ = D5 * D12

Priority 1 goal is considered

Left-hand-side total for constraint 1 = SUMPRODUCT (B7 : I7, $B$12 : $I$12) copied to cells J8 and J9

decision variables (i.e., $x_1 = 0$, $x_2 = 10$) into the labor goal, omitting the deviation variables:

$$2(0) + 3(10) = 30$$

This is 6 above the original 24; hence, $v_1 = 6$.

b. The worksheet shown in Exhibit 10-10 shows the result of the first iteration of the goal programming problem. The worksheets for iterations 2 and 3, which involve the objective of meeting priority goals 2 and 3, are identical to the worksheet shown in Exhibit 10-10, except in iteration 2, the objective function coefficient for v_2 in cell G5 becomes 1 while the objective function coefficient for u_1 in cell D5 is changed from 1 to 0. Likewise in iteration 3, the objective coefficient for u_3 in cell H5 becomes 1 while the objective function coefficient for u_1 in cell D5 remains at 0 and the objective function coefficient for v_2 in cell G5 is changed from 1 to 0. Exhibit 10-11 shows the Solver Parameters screen for the first iteration involving the first goal. The value of "zero" in the objective value in cell B13 in Exhibit 10-10 indicates that the first priority goal is met. Exhibit 10-12 shows the Solver Parameters screen for

Exhibit 10-11 Excel Solver Parameters Screen for Solved Problem 1, Goal Programming Problem Considering Only Priority 1 (Minimizing Labor Underutilization) Goal

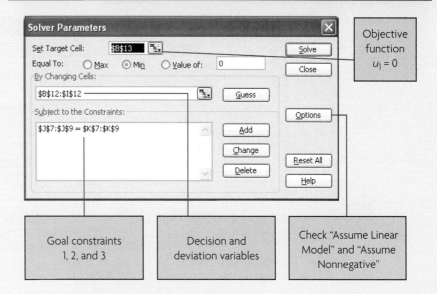

Exhibit 10-12 Excel Solver Parameters Screen for Solved Problem 1, Goal Programming Problem Considering Priority 2 Goal Given That Priority 1 Goal Is Met

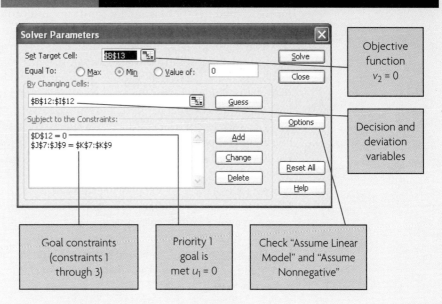

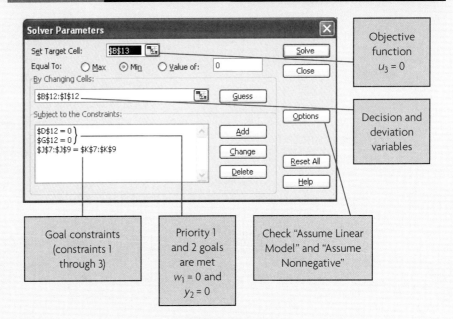

Exhibit 10-13 Excel Solver Parameters Screen for Solved Problem 1, Goal Programming Problem Considering Priority 3 Goal Given That Priority 1 and Priority 2 Goals Have Been Met

the second iteration, where we keep all of the goal constraints in Exhibit 10-11 and for the second iteration, we add a constraint indicating that the first priority goal has been met: $u_1 = 0$ ($D$12 = 0$).

Exhibit 10-13 shows the Solver Parameters screen associated with the third iteration of the Excel solution. We keep all of the goal constraints in Exhibit 10-12. In Exhibit 10-12, we indicated that the first priority goal had been met: $u_1 = 0$ ($D$12 = 0$). In Exhibit 10-13, for the third iteration, we add the constraint indicating that the second priority goal has been met: $v_2 = 0$ ($G$12 = 0$).

The worksheet shown in Exhibit 10-14 shows the result of the fourth and final iteration of the goal programming problem. Note that the objective coefficient for v_1 in cell E5 is equal to one, indicating that we are solving the fourth iteration of the goal programming problem. Exhibit 10-15 shows the Solver Parameters screen associated with the fourth and final iteration of the Excel solution. In Exhibit 10-15, we keep all of the goal constraints in Exhibit 10-13, and in addition, we have three constraints reflecting the fact that the first, second, and third priority goals have been met: $u_1 = 0$ ($D$12 = 0$), $v_2 = 0$($G$12 = 0$), $u_3 = 0$ ($H$12 = 0$).

The same solution as indicated by the graphical solution is obtained, where $x_2 = 10$, $v_1 = 6$, and $u_2 = 6$. This indicates that we were not able to satisfy the fourth priority goal ($v_1 = 6$, $v_1 \neq 0$)

Problem 2

a. Graphically solve the following goal programming model for the optimal values of the decision variables and determine the optimal values of the deviation variables that are specified in the objective function.

b. Solve the following problem using Excel.

$$\text{minimize} \quad P_1 u_1, P_2 u_2$$

subject to

$$
\begin{array}{rlll}
4x_1 + x_2 & & \le 40 & \text{(1)} \\
x_1 + 2x_2 & & \le 24 & \text{(2)} \\
x_1 + 2x_2 + u_1 - v_1 & = 30 & \text{(3)} \\
x_1 \quad + u_2 - v_2 & = 15 & \text{(4)}
\end{array}
$$

All variables ≥ 0

Exhibit 10-14   Excel Worksheet for Solved Problem 1, Goal Programming Problem, Considering Priority 4 (Minimizing Labor Overutilization) Goal Given That Priority 1, 2, and 3 Goals Have Been Met

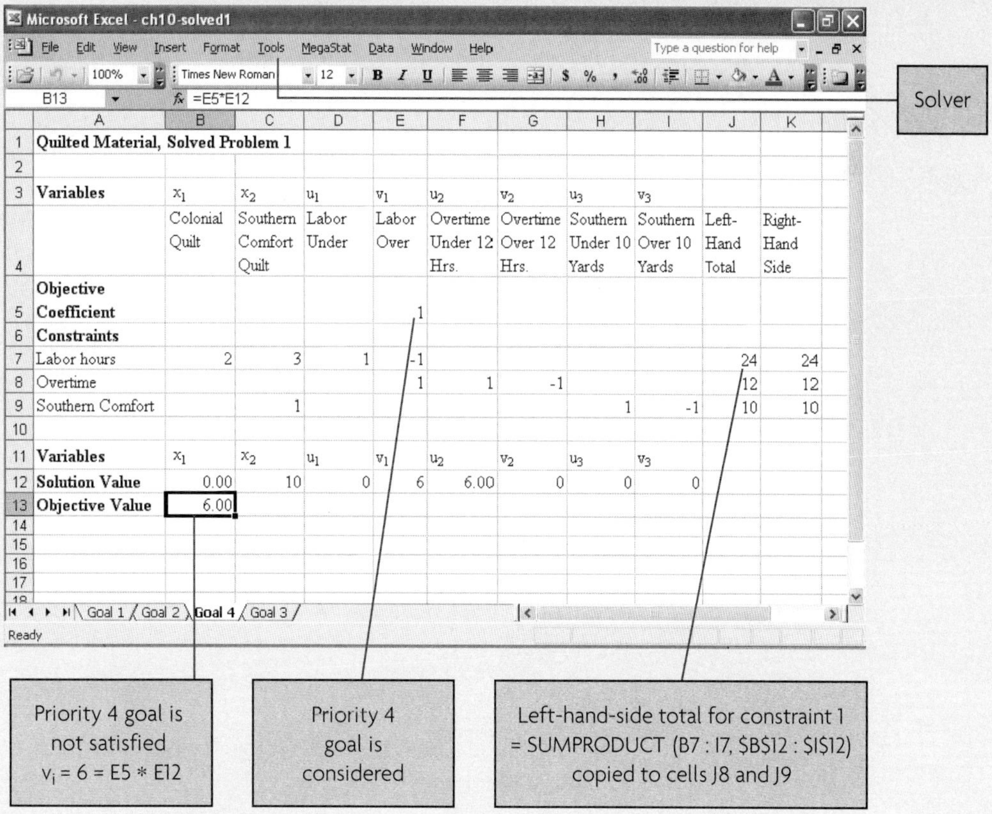

Priority 4 goal is not satisfied
$v_i = 6 = E5 * E12$

Priority 4 goal is considered

Left-hand-side total for constraint 1
= SUMPRODUCT (B7 : I7, $B$12 : $I$12)
copied to cells J8 and J9

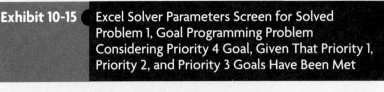

Exhibit 10-15 Excel Solver Parameters Screen for Solved Problem 1, Goal Programming Problem Considering Priority 4 Goal, Given That Priority 1, Priority 2, and Priority 3 Goals Have Been Met

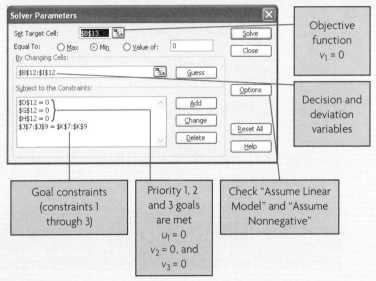

Solution   a.   We first note which ones are hard constraints: the first two because they do not have any deviation variables. These are plotted, and the feasible solution space is identified (see Figure 10-13(a)).

Next, we see that the highest priority is to minimize being under on the first goal. We add this to the graph and see that some amount of underdeviation is unavoidable because the goal does not have any points in common with the feasible solution space. In addition, note that the goal constraint is *parallel* to one of the hard constraints. Therefore, the portion of the feasible solution space that minimizes the underdeviation on the first goal is the line segment indicated in Figure 10-13(b).

The other priority is to minimize being under on the second goal. Adding that goal to the graph (see Figure 10-13(c)) reveals that the best part of the line segment from Figure 10-13(b) is the point where the two hard constraints intersect (point A). Hence, point A is the optimum. Solving for point A using simultaneous equations as follows:

$$4x_1 + x_2 = 40$$
$$-\tfrac{1}{2}(x_1 + 2x_2 = 24)$$

$$4x_1 + x_2 = 40$$
$$-\tfrac{1}{2}x_1 - x_2 = -12$$

$$\tfrac{7}{2}x_1 = 28, x_1 = 8$$

This yields $x_1 = 8, x_2 = 8$

Substituting these values into the first goal constraint (omitting v_1 because it is obviously zero) and solving for u_1 yields

$$x_1 + 2x_2 + u_1 = 30$$

Figure 10-13   Identifying the Feasible Solution Space for Solved Problem 2

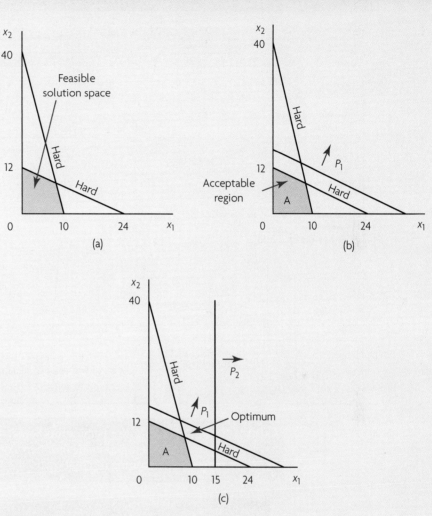

(a)

(b)

(c)

and becomes

$$8 + 2(8) + u_1 = 30$$

Thus, $u_1 = 6$.

Doing the same for the second constraint yields

$$x_1 + u_2 = 15$$

and becomes

$$8 + u_2 = 15$$

Thus, $u_2 = 7$.

b. The worksheet shown in Exhibit 10-16 shows the result of the first iteration of the goal programming problem. The value of 6 in the objective function value in cell B13 in Exhibit 10-16 indicates that the result of the first priority goal is $u_1 = 6$ and $u_1 \neq 0$. Therefore, the first priority goal has not been met. Exhibit 10-17 shows the Solver Parameters screen for the first iteration involving the first goal. In Exhibit 10-17, the first set of constraints,

Exhibit 10-16 Excel Worksheet for Solved Problem 2, Goal Programming Problem, Considering Only Priority 1 (Minimizing u_1) Goal

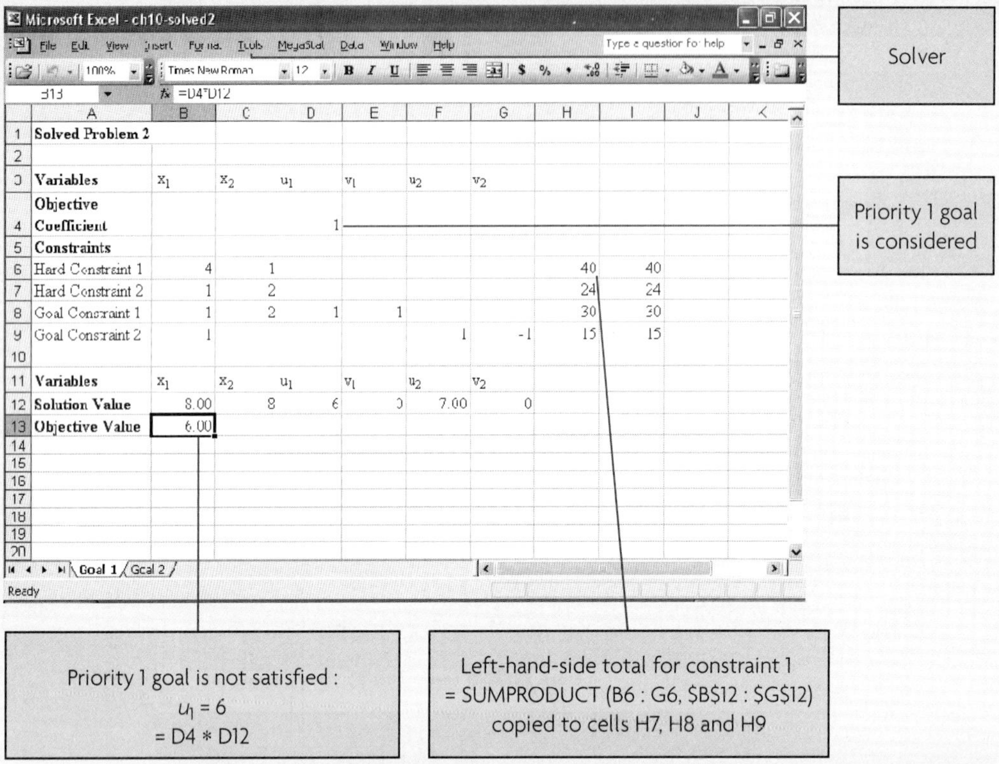

Microsoft Excel - ch10-solved2
Solver
=D4*D12
Solved Problem 2
Variables x1 x2 u1 v1 u2 v2
Objective Coefficient 1
Constraints
Hard Constraint 1 4 1 40 40
Hard Constraint 2 1 2 24 24
Goal Constraint 1 1 2 1 1 30 30
Goal Constraint 2 1 1 -1 15 15
Variables x1 x2 u1 v1 u2 v2
Solution Value 8.00 8 6 0 7.00 0
Objective Value 6.00
Goal 1 Goal 2
Ready
Priority 1 goal is considered
Priority 1 goal is not satisfied : u_1 = 6 = D4 * D12
Left-hand-side total for constraint 1 = SUMPRODUCT (B6 : G6, $B$12 : $G$12) copied to cells H7, H8 and H9

Exhibit 10-17 Excel Solver Parameters Screen for Solved Problem 1, Goal Programming Problem Considering Only Priority 1 (Minimizing u_1) Goal

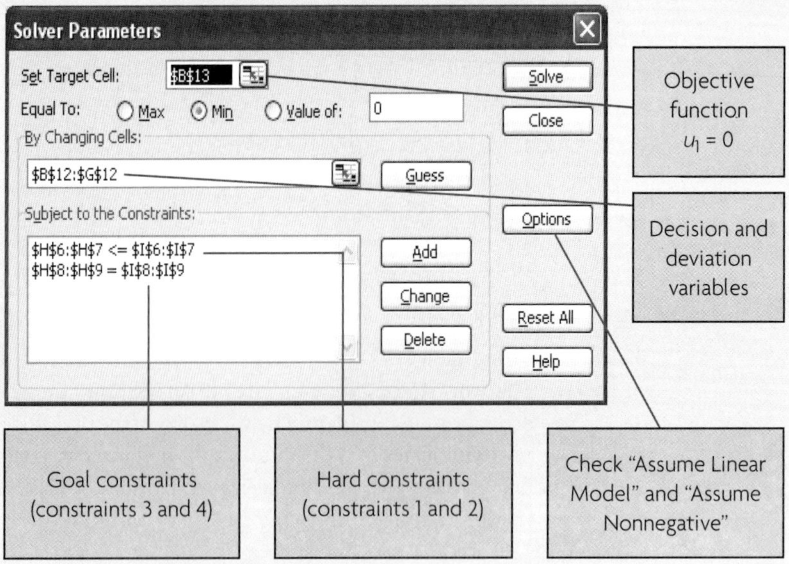

Solver Parameters
Set Target Cell: $B$13
Equal To: Max Min Value of: 0
By Changing Cells:
$B$12:$G$12
Subject to the Constraints:
$H$6:$H$7 <= $I$6:$I$7
$H$8:$H$9 = $I$8:$I$9
Solve
Close
Guess
Options
Add
Change
Delete
Reset All
Help
Objective function u_1 = 0
Decision and deviation variables
Goal constraints (constraints 3 and 4)
Hard constraints (constraints 1 and 2)
Check "Assume Linear Model" and "Assume Nonnegative"

Exhibit 10-18 Excel Worksheet for Solved Problem 2, Goal Programming Problem, Considering Priority 2 (Minimizing u_2) Goal Given That Priority 1 Goal Has Not Been Met: $u_1 = 6$

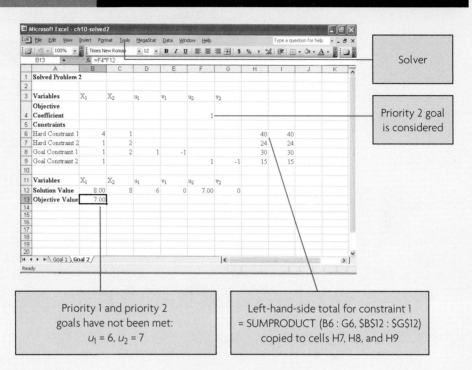

Solver

Priority 2 goal is considered

Priority 1 and priority 2 goals have not been met: $u_1 = 6$, $u_2 = 7$

Left-hand-side total for constraint 1 = SUMPRODUCT (B6 : G6, $B$12 : $G$12) copied to cells H7, H8, and H9

$H$6:$H$7 <= $I$6:$I$7, represents the two hard constraints. The second set of constraints, $H$8:$H$9=$I$8:$I$9, represents the two goal constraints.

The worksheet shown in Exhibit 10-18 shows the result of the second and final iteration of the goal programming problem. Note the objective function coefficient for u_2 in cell F4 is equal to one, indicating that we are solving the second iteration of the goal programming problem with $u_2 = 1$. Exhibit 10-19 shows the Solver Parameters screen associated with the second and final iteration. In Exhibit 10-19, we keep all of the hard constrains and goal constraints stated in Exhibit 10-17, and in addition, we add a constraint reflecting the fact that the first priority goal has not been met: $u_1 = 6$ ($D$12 = 6). The same solution indicated by the graphical solution is obtained, where $x_1 = 8$, $x_2 = 8$, $u_1 = 6$, and $u_2 = 7$. This indicates that we were not able to satisfy either the first or the second priority goal ($u_1 = 6$, $u_1 \neq 0$, $u_2 = 7$, $u_2 \neq 0$).

Problem 3

Acorn University is in the process of searching for a head coach for its Division I men's basketball program. It has narrowed the field of candidates to two: (1) Byron Duclos and (2) Eric Meyer. The search committee is split as to whom to select for the position. The committee has been recommended to use AHP to assist in the selection process. The committee feels that the following three factors are the most important qualities needed from a Division I basketball coach: (1) coaching experience (preferably head coaching experience) at the Division I level; (2) coaching ability and interpersonal skills: and (3) recruiting skills and potential.

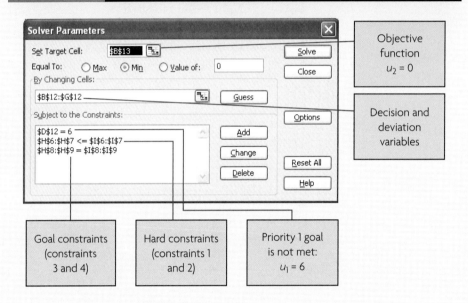

Exhibit 10-19   Excel Solver Parameters Screen for Solved Problem 2, Goal Programming Problem Considering Priority 2 (Minimizing u_2) Goal Given That Priority 1 (Minimizing u_1) Goal Has Not Been Met: $u_1 = 6$

The search committee is asked to perform pairwise comparisons of the criteria and the pairwise comparison of each candidate relative to each criterion. The following results are obtained:

Criteria Pairwise Comparisons

	Experience	Ability	Recruiting
Experience	1	3	5
Ability	1/3	1	2
Recruiting	1/5	1/2	1
Σ	1.53333	4.5	8

Pairwise Comparisons—Experience

	Duclos	Meyer
Duclos	1	2
Meyer	1/2	1
Σ	1.5	3

Pairwise Comparisons—Ability

	Duclos	Meyer
Duclos	1	1/6
Meyer	6	1
Σ	7	1.16667

Pairwise Comparisons—Recruiting

	Duclos	Meyer
Duclos	1	1/3
Meyer	3	1
Σ	4	1.3333

a.   Determine if the criteria pairwise comparisons established by the search committee are acceptable.

b.   Calculate the priority percentage for each candidate on each criterion.

c.   Determine the overall priority for each candidate.

d.   Solve this problem using Excel to decide which coach should be hired.

Solution

a.   To determine if the criteria pairwise comparisons are acceptable, first, normalize the pairwise comparisons by dividing each pairwise comparison value by its column total.

Normalized Criteria Pairwise Comparisons

	Experience	Ability	Recruiting
Experience	0.6521753	.66667	0.625
Ability	0.2173892	.22222	0.250
Recruiting	0.1304348	.11111	0.125
Σ	1.0	1.0	1.0

Average criteria percentages for the three factors are calculated by averaging the normalized criteria priority percentages for each row:

Experience: $(0.6521753 + .66667 + 0.625)/3 = .6479474$

Ability: $(0.2173892 + .22222 + 0.25)/3 = .22986973$

Recruiting: $(0.1304348 + .11111 + 0.125)/3 = .122182$

Then multiply the pairwise comparison matrix by the average criteria percentages calculated above to obtain the weighted sums for each criterion.

$$\begin{bmatrix} 1 & 3 & 5 \\ 1/3 & 1 & 2 \\ 1/5 & 1/2 & 1 \end{bmatrix} \begin{bmatrix} .6479474 \\ .22986973 \\ .122182 \end{bmatrix} = \begin{bmatrix} 1.9484625 \\ 0.6902162 \\ 0.36671 \end{bmatrix}$$

The weighted-sum values are divided by their respective priority percentages for each criterion to obtain the weighted sum percentages.

Criterion (1)	Weighted Sum (2)	Priority % (3)	Weighted Sum (4) = (2) * (3)
Experience	1.9484625	.6479474	3.00713067
Ability	0.6902162	.22986973	3.00264067
Recruiting	0.36671	.122182	3.00134226

These weighted-sum values displayed in the above table are averaged to obtain λ_A (average ratio).

$$\lambda_A = \frac{3.00713067 + 3.00264067 + 3.00134226}{3} = 3.0037045$$

Using the value of λ_A calculated above, we calculate the value of the consistency index (CI).

$$CI = \frac{\lambda_A - 3}{n - 1} = \frac{3.0037045 - 3}{3 - 1} = .00185227$$

In the CI equation, $n = 3$ because there are three criteria being compared. Using the CI value, we proceed to calculate the consistency ratio (CR) using the following equation:

$CR = CI/RI$. In this equation, RI = random index (value of the consistency index if each pairwise comparison is randomly generated. The RI values are displayed in Table 10-5. Since $n = 3$, RI = .58; therefore, CR = (0.00185227)/.58 = 0.0031936

   Since the CR value of 0.0031936 < .10, the consistency of the pairwise comparison of the criteria is at an acceptable level.

b.   The totals for the pairwise comparisons of each candidate on each criterion are given in the problem. We simply normalize these pairwise comparisons by dividing each pairwise comparison by its column total to obtain the following proportion matrices.

Proportion Matrix—Experience

	Duclos	Meyer	Average
Duclos	0.66667	0.66667	0.66667
Meyer	0.33333	0.33333	0.33333
Σ	1	1	1

Proportion Matrix—Ability

	Duclos	Meyer	Average
Duclos	.14285714	.14285714	.14285714
Meyer	.85714286	.85714286	.85714286
Σ	1.0	1.0	1.0

Proportion Matrix—Recruiting

	Duclos	Meyer	Average
Duclos	0.25	0.25	0.25
Meyer	0.75	0.75	0.75
Σ	1.0	1.0	1.0

The average priority percentage for each criterion, for each candidate, is shown in the rightmost column of each proportion matrix.

c.   The overall priority for each candidate is calculated by multiplying the criteria weights (percentages) by the average priority percentage for each candidate on each criterion. The resulting values are called the weighted scores for each candidate. These weighted scores are calculated in the following table.

Calculation of the Overall Priority (Weighted Scores)

	Byron Duclos		
Criterion (1)	Weight (%) (2)	Priority % (3)	(2) * (3)
Experience	.6479474	0.66667	0.43196495
Ability	.22986973	0.14285714	0.03283853
Recruiting	.122182	0.25	0.0305455
Weighted score for Mr. Duclos			0.49535

Exhibit 10-20 Analytical Hierarchy Process for Solved Problem 3 (Selection of the Head Coaching Job)

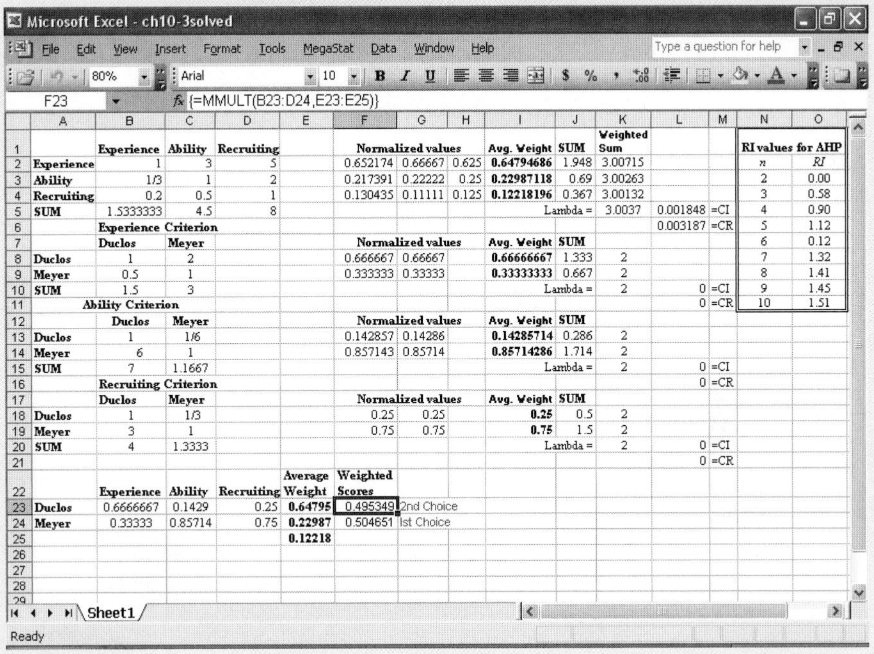

Eric Meyer

Criterion (1)	Weight (%) (2)	Priority % (3)	(2) * (3)
Experience	.6479474	0.33333	0.21598245
Ability	.22986973	.85714286	0.19571766
Recruiting	.122182	0.75	0.0916365
Weighted score for Mr. Meyer			0.504651

Since .49535 < .5033366, the committee should recommend to offer the Acorn University's men's basketball head coaching job to Mr. Eric Meyer.

d. When solving this problem using Excel, we prepare the worksheet shown in Exhibit 10-20. The formulas for this worksheet are shown in Table 10-11. As can be seen from this worksheet, the same results are obtained as in parts a, b, and c of this problem and the committee should offer the Acorn University's men's basketball head coaching job to Mr. Eric Meyer.

Discussion and Review Questions

1. Describe how goal programming differs from linear programming.
2. Discuss what the deviation variable u_i means and how we would go about formulating a goal constraint when we have two products: x_1 and x_2 and the total demand for both products equals 200 units.
3. The per-unit profit margin for product 1 is 5 and the per-unit profit margin for product 2 is 8. The company's goal is to earn a profit of $2,000 per day. Assume that this is

Table 10-11	Excel Formulas for the AHP Worksheet in Exhibit 10-20	
Cell	**Copied to**	**Formula**
B5	C5:D5	=SUM(B2:B4)
B3		=1/C2
B4		=1/D2
C4		=1/D3
F2	F3:F4	=B2/B$5
G2	G3:G4	=C2/C$5
H2	H3:H4	=D2/D$5
I2	I3:I4	=AVERAGE(F2:H2)
J2	J3:J4	=MMULT(B2:D4,I2:I4)
K2	K3:K4	=J2/I2
K5		=AVERAGE(K2:K5)
L5		=((K5−COUNT(K2:K4)))/((COUNT(K2:K4))−1)
L6		=L5/VLOOKUP(COUNT(K2:K4),$N$3:$O$11,2)
F23	F30:F31	=MMULT(B23:D24,E23:E25)
B29	B30:B31	=I9
C29	C30:C31	=I16
D29	D30:31	=I23
E29	E30:E31	=I2

the first of a few goal constraints. Formulate a goal constraint utilizing the deviation variable u_1 only. Indicate why it would not be necessary to utilize v_1.

4. When solving a goal programming problem, we try to reach a satisficing solution. When solving a linear programming problem, we attempt to find an optimal solution. Explain the difference between optimizing and satisficing.

5. In solving a goal programming problem, we can use one of two approaches. In utilizing the first approach, we can assign weights to goals, and in utilizing the second approach, we can rank the goals in order of importance. Explain the difference between these two approaches.

6. What are the differences between goal programming and the analytical hierarchy process?

7. Explain the circumstances in which the pairwise comparisons have to be utilized.

8. Explain how the numerical values are assigned in making pairwise comparisons. Describe the scale.

9. Explain the meaning of the reciprocal rating approach with an example.
10. In AHP, why is it important to use the consistency ratios?
11. In calculating the consistency ratio, explain the calculation of the weighted sum and weighted sum priority.
12. What is the procedure for computing the proportion matrix from the pairwise comparison matrix?
13. Once we calculate the proportion matrix for a given criterion, explain the procedure for calculating the priority percentage.
14. Explain the procedure for calculating the weighted scores (overall priority) for each option considered.

Problems

1. Manager Barney Bidwell has formulated the following LP model:

x_1 = amount of Product 1
x_2 = amount of Product 2
x_3 = amount of Product 3

maximize $Z = 4x_1 + 2x_2 - 3x_3$

subject to

Labor	$2x_1 + x_2 + 4x_3 \leq 160$ hours
Storage	$x_1 + 2x_2 + 3x_3 \leq 150$ square feet
Product 1	$x_1 \geq 10$ units

$$x_1, x_2, x_3 \geq 0$$

After discussions with several colleagues, Barney now believes that a goal programming model would be more appropriate. Accordingly, the manager has decided on these priorities, which are listed in order of importance.

a. Minimize the underutilization of labor.
b. Achieve a satisfactory profit level of $300.
c. Try to avoid making less than 10 units of x_1.

Reformulate this as a goal programming model.

2. For the preceding problem, incorporate one additional priority:

One more term added
$P_4 v_4$
Another goal constraint
added-overtime $v_1 + u_4$
$- v_4 = 10$

d. If overtime is used, try to avoid using more than 10 hours.
   Indicate how the model of the previous problem would *change*.

3. Given this goal programming model:

minimize $P_1 u_2, P_2 v_1$

subject to

Labor	$10x_1 + 10x_2 + u_1 - v_1 = 600$ hours
Product 1	$x_1 + u_2 - v_2 = 80$ units

All variables ≥ 0

a. Is the first constraint a hard or a soft constraint? How do you know?
b. What is the highest priority in this model?

    c. Solve the problem graphically for the optimal solution. What are the optimal values of the decision variables? What are the optimal values of the deviation variables u_2 and v_1?

    d. Suppose that the objective had been $P_1 v_1$, $P_2 u_2$. What would your answers to the question posed in part c be?

4. Given this goal programming problem:

    minimize $P_1 u_1$, $P_2 v_2$, $P_3 u_3$

    subject to

Newspaper advertising	$8x_1 + 15x_2 + u_1 - v_1 = 120$ lines	
Budget	$2x_1 + 3x_2 + u_2 - v_2 = 12$	($000)
Direct marketing	$6x_1 + 18x_2 + u_3 - v_3 = 54$ hours	

                          All variables ≥ 0

a. See the IM

b. See the IM

c. $x_1 = 0, x_2 = 8$
d. Does not alter solution

e. $u_1 = 0, v_2 = 12, u_3 = 0$

    a. Plot the first constraint and indicate the direction that will satisfy the highest priority.

    b. Plot the second constraint and indicate the direction that will satisfy the second highest priority.

    c. What is the optimal solution at this point?

    d. Add the third constraint and indicate the direction that will satisfy the third priority. Does the addition of the third constraint and the third priority alter the solution? Why? Would changing the third priority to $P_3 v_3$ alter the solution? Why?

    e. Compute the values of the deviation variables u_1, v_2, and u_3 for the optimal solution.

5. Find the values of the decision variables that will minimize the objective function for the following goal programming model and also find the resulting values of each of the deviation variables that are listed in the objective function:

    minimize $P_1 v_1$, $P_2 v_3$, $P_3 u_2$, $P_4 u_4$

    subject to

Plastic	$2x_1 + 4x_2 + u_1 - v_1 = 80$ pounds	
Cloth	$3x_1 + 6x_2 + u_2 - v_2 = 180$ square yards	
Product 1	$x_1 \qquad + u_3 - v_3 = 30$ units	
Painting	$5x_1 \qquad + u_4 - v_4 = 250$ minutes	

                          All variables ≥ 0

6. Given the following goal programming model:

    minimize $P_1 v_1$, $P_2 u_2$, $P_3 u_3$

    subject to

Budget	$2A + 4B + u_1 - v_1 = 80$	($000)
Profit	$2A + 4B + u_2 - v_2 = 120$	($000)
Product A	$A \qquad + u_3 - v_3 = 30$ barrels	

                          All variables ≥ 0

a. $x_1 = 30, x_2 = 5$
b. $v_1 = 0, u_4 = \$40, u_3 = 0$

    a. Find the values of the decision variables that minimize the objective function.

    b. Determine the values of the deviation variables that are in the objective function that will result from your solution.

7. Given this goal programming model:

   minimize $P_1u_1, P_2u_2, P_3(u_3 + v_3)$

   subject to

Sodium	$8N + 6L$	≤ 48 grams
Carbohydrate	$N + 6L + u_1 - v_1$	$= 24$ grams
Protein	$5N + L + u_2 - v_2$	$= 10$ grams
Input L	$L + u_3 - v_3$	$= 3$ cubic centimeters
	All variables ≥ 0	

   a. Find the best values of the decision variables.
   b. Find the values of all deviation variables that are listed in the objective function.

8. Given this goal programming model:

   minimize P_1v_1, P_2u_2

   subject to

Product A	A	≤ 30 units
Budget	$3A + 5B + u_1 - v_1 = 300$	($)
Revenue	$9A + 10B + u_2 - v_2 = 900$	($)
	All variables ≥ 0	

   a. $A = 30, B = 42,$
   $v_1 = 0, u_2 = \$210$
   b. $A = 100, B = 0,$
   $v_1 = 0, u_2 = 0$

   a. Determine the optimal values of the decision variables and the resulting values of v_1 and u_2.
   b. How would your answers change if the first constraint was $A \geq 30$?

9. Solve this goal programming problem for the optimal solution.

   minimize $P_1v_1, P_2u_2, P_3u_3, P_4u_4$

   subject to

Profit	$9S + 5T$	≥ 45	($000)
Budget	$8S + 9T + u_1 - v_1 = 72$		($000)
Material	$S + 5T + u_2 - v_2 = 5$		
T	$T + u_3 - v_3 = 10$		
S	$S + u_4 - v_4 = 9$		
	All variables ≥ 0		

   Then, indicate the optimal values of the decision variables *and* the values of each of the deviation variables that are listed in the objective. Solve using the graphical method.

10. Given this goal programming model, determine the optimal values of the decision variables and the resulting values of the deviation variables that are listed in the objective function:

    minimize $P_1v_1, P_2v_2, P_3u_2, P_4v_3, P_5u_3$

    subject to

Product 1	x_1	≤ 100 units
Storage	$x_1 + x_2 + u_1 - v_1 = 80$ square feet
Product 1	$x_1 + u_2 - v_2 = 40$ units
Material	$2x_1 + 4x_2 + u_3 - v_3 = 320$ pounds
	All variables ≥ 0	

    $x_1 = 40,$
    $x_2 = 40,$
    $u_1 = u_2 = v_1 = v_2 = 0,$
    $u_3 = 80$

11. Solve this goal programming problem for the optimal solution using Excel:

minimize $P_1 v_1, P_2 u_2, P_3 v_3$

subject to

Material	$5x_1 + 4x_2 + u_1 - v_1 = 200$ pounds
Profit	$2x_1 + x_2 + u_2 - v_2 = 40$ $000)
Machine	$2x_1 + 2x_2 + u_3 - v_3 = 30$ minutes
	All variables ≥ 0

(This problem was solved in the chapter (Example 10-2) using the graphical approach. It would be helpful to compare the Excel solution and the graphical solution.)

$x_1 = 30, x_2 = 5,$
$v_1 = 0, u_2 = 40, u_3 = 0$

a. $x_1 = x_2 = 3.43$
b. $u_1 = u_2 = u_3 = u_4 = .43$

12. Solve Problem 6 using Excel.
13. Solve Problem 9 using Excel.
14. Solve Problem 7 using Excel.
15. Solve Problem 10 using Excel.
16. A plastics manufacturer is experiencing sustained increase in the demand for its products. The demand has been substantially exceeding capacity. The company has decided to build a new manufacturing facility. The committee responsible for the new facility has narrowed its choices to three locations: (1) Memphis, Tennessee; (2) Cleveland, Ohio, and (3) Ft. Lauderdale, Florida. The management has decided to utilize AHP in order to decide where the facility should be located. The management feels that there are three dominating factors in making this decision: (1) construction and land costs, (2) proximity to suppliers and customers, and (3) labor relations/availability of qualified labor in the region.

The management has provided the following pairwise comparisons for the criteria and for the locations on each criterion. These matrices are presented below:

Criteria Pairwise Comparisons

	Construction/Land Cost	Transportation Cost	Labor
Construction/Land Cost	1	1/3	2
Transportation Cost	3	1	6
Labor	1/2	1/6	1
Σ	4.5	1.5	9

Pairwise Comparisons—Construction/Land Cost

	Memphis	Cleveland	Ft. Lauderdale
Memphis	1	3	6
Cleveland	1/3	1	2
Ft. Lauderdale	1/6	1/2	1
Σ	1.5	4.5	9

Pairwise Comparisons—Transportation Cost

	Memphis	Cleveland	Ft. Lauderdale
Memphis	1	1/4	2
Cleveland	4	1	7
Ft. Lauderdale	1/2	1/7	1
Σ	5.5	1.393	10

a. Yes.

b.

	Cons-truction	Transpor-tation	Labor
Memphis	.6667	.1871	.3077
Cleveland	.2222	.7151	.0769
Ft. Lauderdale	.1111	.0978	.6154

c. Memphis = .3071
   Cleveland = .5346
   Ft. Lauderdale = .1583

Pairwise Comparisons—Labor

	Memphis	Cleveland	Ft. Lauderdale
Memphis	1	4	1/2
Cleveland	1/4	1	1/8
Ft. Lauderdale	2	8	1
Σ	3.25	13	1.625

a. Determine if the criteria pairwise comparisons established by the search committee are acceptable.
b. Calculate the priority percentage for each location on each criterion.
c. Determine the overall priority for each location.

17. Solve Problem 16 using Excel.

18. A manufacturer of cleaning products (Top-to-Bottom-Clean) is interested in knowing the market response towards one of the laundry detergents it manufactures. In order to assess the effectiveness of this laundry detergent, the company has selected a number of volunteers to participate in a market study. In this study, each participant is given a small bottle of this detergent (Brand A) and, further, they are asked to wash a similar load of laundry with brand A, brand B, and brand C. Brand A is manufactured by Top-to-Bottom-Clean, while brand B and brand C are manufactured by the competition. There are three criteria to evaluate these detergents: (1) cleanliness, (2) brightness, and (3) price.

    Regarding the cleanliness criterion, the first respondent stated the following:

    - Brand A is moderately preferred to brand B.
    - Brand A is strongly preferred to brand C.
    - Brand B is equally to moderately preferred to brand C.

    Regarding the brightness criterion, the first respondent stated the following:

    - Brand B is moderately preferred to brand A.
    - Brand A is moderately preferred to brand C.
    - Brand B is strongly preferred to brand C.

    Regarding the price criterion, the first respondent stated the following:

    - Brand A is very strongly preferred to brand B.
    - Brand A is moderately preferred to brand C.
    - Brand C is equally to moderately preferred to brand B.

    The respondent also provided the following pairwise ratings in comparing the criteria:

    - Price is strongly to very strongly preferred to brightness.
    - Price is moderately preferred to cleanliness.
    - Cleanliness is equally to moderately preferred to brightness.

a. See the IM
b. See the IM
c. See the IM

a. Set up the cleanliness pairwise comparison matrix for this respondent.
b. Set up the brightness pairwise comparison matrix for this respondent.
c. Set up the price pairwise comparison matrix for this respondent.

d. Use Excel and determine if the cleanliness, brightness, and price pairwise comparisons established by the respondent are consistent.

e. Set up the criteria pairwise comparison matrix for this respondent.

f. Use Excel and determine if the criteria pairwise comparisons established by the respondent are consistent.

g. Use Excel and calculate the priority percentage for each brand of detergent on each criterion.

h. Use Excel and determine the overall priority for each brand of detergent.

i. Which detergent does the respondent prefer?

19. In the upcoming election, there are three candidates running for the governor's position (Mr. Leach, Ms. Borck, and Mr. Thompson). State taxes happen to be an important issue for the election. Each candidate has his or her own tax proposal. Individuals are asked to compare the fairness and effectiveness of the three tax proposals. A potential voter provides the following pairwise comparisons of the three tax proposals.

- Mr. Thompson's plan is extremely preferred to Mr. Leach's plan.
- Mr. Thompson's plan is equally to moderately preferred to Ms. Borck's plan.
- Ms. Borck's plan is moderately preferred to Mr. Leach's plan.

a. Prepare the pairwise comparison matrix for this voter.

b. Are his pairwise comparisons consistent?

20. An individual is interested in investing his money in one of two stocks; stock 1, ALO; stock 2: PHI stock. ALO stock has higher expected returns but is also more risky. The investor cannot decide which stock to invest in. The stockbroker has decided to utilize AHP in the decision-making process. There are two relevant criteria: risk and return. The investor is risk averse and therefore, views return moderately preferred to risk.
    In addition, the stockbroker provides the following additional information:

- In terms of risk, PHI is strongly to very strongly preferred to ALO.
- In terms of return, ALO is moderately preferred to PHI.

a. Determine the values of all the pairwise comparison matrices.

b. Determine the overall priority for the two stocks. Which investment should the investor undertake?

21. Complete the following partially completed pairwise comparisons matrix and normalize the pairwise comparisons.

	Criterion A	Criterion B	Criterion C
Criterion A		5	4
Criterion B			3
Criterion C			

22. Compute the proportion (normalized) matrix from the following pairwise comparison matrix.

	Option A	Option B	Option C
Option A	1	5	3
Option B	1/5	1	1/2
Option C	1/3	2	1

23. Use the following proportion matrix for a given criterion and calculate the priority percentage for options A, B, and C.

	Option A	Option B	Option C
Option A	.6	.5	.4
Option B	.3	.3	.3
Option C	.1	.2	.3

24. The weight percentages for criteria X, Y, and Z are .55, .25, and .20 respectively. The priority percentages for options A, B, and C on criteria X, Y, and Z are given in the following table:

Priority %
A = .5350   1st choice
B = .2675   2nd choice
C = .1975   3rd choice

	Criterion X	Criterion Y	Criterion Z
Option A	.5	.60	.55
Option B	.3	.25	.20
Option C	.2	.15	.25

Calculate the priority percentage for each option.

25. A company is in the process of deciding among three different advertising media: (1) television, (2) radio, and (3) newspaper. The company feels that three criteria are very important in making this decision: (1) cost, (2) audience exposure and (3) flexibility (ability to cancel or change contracts quickly and without penalty). The associated pairwise comparison matrices are given below.

Criteria Pairwise Comparisons

	Cost	Audience Exposure	Flexibility
Cost	1	1/2	4
Audience Exposure	2	1	7
Flexibility	1/4	1/7	1

Pairwise Comparisons—Cost

	Television	Radio	Newspaper
Television	1	1/5	1/8
Radio	5	1	1/3
Newspaper	8	3	1

Pairwise Comparisons—Audience Exposure

	Television	Radio	Newspaper
Television	1	5	7
Radio	1/5	1	3
Newspaper	1/7	1/3	1

Pairwise Comparisons—Flexibility

	Television	Radio	Newspaper
Television	1	1/5	1/8
Radio	5	1	2
Newspaper	8	1/2	1

a. Use Excel and determine if the criteria pairwise comparisons established by management are acceptable.
b. Calculate the priority percentage for each medium, or each criterion.
c. Determine the overall priority for each medium. Which medium should the company select?

26. Due to a significant sustained increase in demand, the ITM fastener manufacturing company has decided to build a new plant. After an initial study, it has narrowed its choices to four locations: (1) Albany, New York; (2) Indianapolis, Indiana; (3) Akron, Ohio; and (4) Mason, Georgia.

    ITM also identified the following as being important factors in terms of the facility location decision:

    a. Transportation costs
    b. Construction/land costs
    c. Labor climate
    d. Availability of qualified labor
    e. Production costs

    On a five-point scale, the company has determined the following weights for these factors:

    ### Factor Weights

Factor	Weight
Transportation costs	5
Construction/land costs	3
Labor climate	1
Availability of qualified labor	2
Production costs	4

    The decision factor ratings for each criterion are given in the following table:

    ### Decision Factor Ratings

Factor	Albany	Indianapolis	Akron	Mason
1	3	8	6	1
2	5	4	7	8
3	3	5	2	9
4	8	7	6	2
5	4	5	6	7

    $S_{Albany} = 65$,
    $S_{Indianapolis} = 91$,
    $S_{Akron} = 89$,
    $S_{Mason} = 70$;
    Indianapolis is the First choice; Akron is the second choice

    Determine the factor scores for all four locations. What is the recommended site? If the first site is not available, what is the second choice?

27. Assume that you are a senior student majoring in marketing. You have been involved in the job search process for the last few months. At this time you have three job offers from three different firms. Your potential job titles and the locations of the jobs are presented below:

    a. Pharmaceutical sales—Chicago
    b. Marketing research—St. Louis
    c. Advertising promotions—San Diego

The salaries of the jobs are as follows:

a. Chicago, $37,000
b. St. Louis, $30,000
c. San Diego, $40,000

The following table provides additional information about each job and company:

Company/Job Characteristics

Characteristic	Chicago	St. Louis	San Diego
Culture	Formal	Mix	Informal
Job Security	High	Medium	Low
Future earnings and advancement potential	Limited	Medium	High
Job expectations	Reasonable	Medium	Very high

a. Determine the weights for all the listed factors (5 being very important and 1 being very unimportant) and rate the importance of the factors from one to five.

Factor #	Factor	Weight
1	Salary and benefits	
2	Type of job	
3	Location: social/cultural	
4	Location: climate	
5	Location: proximity to family and friends	
6	Type of company	
7	Opportunities for advancement	

b. Complete the following table indicating your decision factor ratings for each criterion.

Factor	Chicago	St. Louis	San Diego
1			
2			
3			
4			
5			
6			
7			

c. Determine the factor score for each location.
d. Based on your answer to part c, indicate the best choice and the second best choice.

28. X-Tech Inc. is interested in determining the best location of a new plant it plans to open up in a year. After a detailed analysis, the company was able to come up with

three choices. Three final choices are Akron, Ohio; Elmhurst, Illinois; and Fort Wayne, Indiana. The facility location project team studied these three sites and rated them with respect to six criteria. The following table indicates those ratings on a 9-point scale as well as the criteria importance weights on a 5-point scale. Use a scoring model and select the best location of the new plant for X-Tech Inc.

Criterion	Weight	Akron, OH	Ft. Wayne, IN	Elmhurst, IL
Labor cost	4	6	7	8
Labor availability	3	7	6	8
Labor climate	2	5	8	4
Land cost	5	7	9	3
Transportation—outbound	4	8	6	4
Transportation—inbound	5	5	8	7
Construction cost	3	7	8	6

$S_{Akron} = 168$,
$S_{Ft. Wayne} = 195$,
$S_{Elmhurst} = 145$;
$195 > 168 > 145$, choose
Ft. Wayne

Chapter 10 Case   Hi-Tech Incorporated

Hi-Tech Incorporated is a small company that produces three products daily: (1) CD players, (2) cell phones, and (3) photograph cameras. The company has a limited amount of resources used in the production of these products. The limited resources are labor, machine hours, and inventory space allocated to all products. Hi-Tech has 1,560 labor hours per day, 1,900 machine hours per day, and 1,400 square feet of storage space capacity availability to store the three different products each day. In addition, the management policies of the company dictate the following:

- The minimum number of cell phones produced needs to be at least 20 percent of all units produced for all three products.
- The minimum number of CD players produced needs to be at least 40 percent of all units produced for all three products.

Given the above resource requirements, Hi-Tech Incorporated has the following resource requirements for production and profit for each product being produced.

Resource Requirements

Product	Labor Hours	Machine Hours	Storage Space (square feet)	Profit per Unit
CD players	1	1.25	.5	27
Cell phones	5	5.00	4.5	55
Photograph cameras	3	3.50	2.5	80

a. If Hi-Tech's goal is to maximize the profit, what would be the production quantity of each product and the total profit?
b. Instead of a single objective of maximizing profit, the company has listed the following objectives in order of importance:

1. The owner of Hi-Tech, Donald Schroeder, wants to be able to provide a stable environment for his employees. In order to accomplish his goal of having a stable workforce, he does not want to use fewer than 1,560 hours of labor per day.

2. Hi-Tech would like to achieve a satisfactory daily profit level of $32,000.
3. Donald Schroeder also is concerned about the machine utilization at his company. He wants to be able to effectively utilize the machine hours. In order to reach his goal of high machine utilization, he would like a utilization of at least 1,900 machine hours.
4. Hi-Tech does not want to utilize more than 1,400 square feet of inventory space available.
5. Because Mr. Schroeder has to pay overtime, and due to high overhead costs when the plant is kept open past the normal operating hours, he wants to minimize the amount of overtime by its employees.
6. Due to warehouse space regulations, the company cannot produce more than 180 cell phones per day.
7. If the company can meet the restrictions on manufacturing cell phones specified in objective 6, the company also would like to limit the production of cameras in the following way: Due to warehouse space regulations, the company wants to limit the production of photograph cameras to 220 units per day.

Formulate and solve the goal programming problem and comment on the goals achieved and the goals not achieved.

c. Mr. Schroeder has accepted the fact that some overtime may be unavoidable. He revised the fifth priority goal such that overtime may be limited to 20 hours per day. How will the formulation in part b change? Solve the resulting goal programming problem. How is the solution different than the solution in part b?

## Part 3

Probabilistic Decision Models

Part II studied deterministic models where the assumption is made that the parameters and variable values are known with certainty. However, in the real world, organizations and individuals face many uncertainties, which make the use of deterministic models unrealistic and unsuitable.

Part III discusses probabilistic decision models, which, unlike deterministic models, can be used when the value of the variable(s) are uncertain. Probabilities must be incorporated into the models to account for randomness. The solutions to probabilistic models take the form of expected values, which can be thought of as an approximate average.

Chapter 11 will investigate the decision theory models. Decision theory models require a decision maker to choose one alternative from a list of alternatives. In making that choice, he or she will consider the uncertainty using probabilities, then choose the alternative that will result in the best outcome.

Chapter 12 discusses Markov analysis, which studies the evolution of a system over repeated time periods. Markov analysis is often used to model probabilistic changeover behaviors in "systems" or cases such as brand switching, machine breakdown, or accounts receivable over time. Steady-state probabilities (long-term average probabilities) are determined by using Markov analysis, which helps decision makers understand how the system behaves over time.

Chapter 13 studies waiting-line models, which are a common occurrence at services such as gas stations, fast food restaurants, post offices, banks, as well in manufacturing and supply chain systems. Waiting-line models can be particularly useful in making capacity decisions, such as how many machines or employees to utilize at a given time. These models must take into account the trade-off between the cost of waiting and the cost and speed of service.

Chapter 14 considers simulation models, which are frequently used when other models cannot deal with the complicated nature of the real world. Simulation models represent a system and can be used to determine the effect that variables, conditions, or changes in parameters would have on that system. An advantage of simulation models is that they do not require the decision maker to experiment with the real world. Simulation models are used to study system outcomes, often with the goal of exploring the "what if . . .?" that affects the behavior of variables.

Part Outline
Chapter   11   Decision Theory
Chapter   12   Markov Analysis
Chapter   13   Waiting Line Models
Chapter   14   Simulation

Decision Theory

Learning Objectives

After completing this chapter, you should be able to:

1. Outline the characteristics of a decision theory approach to decision making.
2. Describe and give examples of decisions under certainty, risk, and complete uncertainty.
3. Make decisions using maximin, maximax, minimax regret, Hurwicz, equally likely, and expected value criteria and use Excel to solve problems involving these techniques.
4. Use Excel to solve decision-making problems under risk using the expected value criterion.
5. Develop decision trees that consist of a combination of decision alternatives and events.
6. Use TreePlan to develop decision trees with Excel.
7. Determine if acquiring additional information in a decision problem will be worth the cost.
8. Calculate revised probabilities manually and with Excel.
9. Analyze the sensitivity of decisions to probability estimates.
10. Describe how utilities can be used in lieu of monetary value in making decisions.

Chapter Outline

Introduction, 540
List of Alternatives, 541
States of Nature, 541
Payoffs, 541
Degree of Certainty, 541
Decision Criterion, 542

The Payoff Table, 542

Decision Making under Certainty, 543

Decision Making under Complete Uncertainty, 544
Maximin, 544
Maximax, 545
Minimax Regret, 545
The Hurwicz (Realism) Criterion, 547
Equal Likelihood Criterion, 548

Using Excel for Decision Making under Complete Uncertainty, 549

Decision Making under Risk, 552
Expected Monetary Value, 552
Expected Opportunity Loss, 553
Expected Value of Perfect Information, 553

Using Excel for Decision Making under Risk, 555

Decision Trees, 556

Using TreePlan to Develop Decision Trees with Excel, 559

Sequential Decision Tree Analysis with Excel and TreePlan, 564

Decision Making with Additional Information, 567
Efficiency of Sample Information, 570
Computing the Probabilities, 571

Computing Revised Probabilities with Excel, 573

Sensitivity Analysis, 573

Utility, 578

Summary, 580

Glossary, 581

Solved Problems, 582

Discussion and Review Questions, 594

Problems, 595

Chapter 11 Case: MKGP Construction Company, 602

Most decision makers are called on to make a variety of decisions. Very often they encounter situations in which they must choose one alternative from a list of alternatives. For instance, the president of a small manufacturing firm may have to select a site for a new warehouse from a list of potential sites. Similarly, a marketing manager may have to select a pricing strategy from a list of strategies.

Let's take a young couple in the process of buying their first home. In the mean time, they must make a decision about buying a car without knowing what house they will end up with. The alternatives are the possible new and used cars they can buy now and future conditions are the house payments for the house they will eventually buy. Alternatives and future conditions are among the characteristics and components discussed in the next section.

Decision theory is important in decisions such as the ones mentioned above because it provides decision makers with a rational way of making a selection: it provides a logical framework for analyzing the situation and coming up with a selection. Unlike optimizing approaches, such as linear programming, decision theory does not guarantee an "optimal" decision. This is because the type of problems that lend themselves to linear programming solutions involve complete *certainty*. Decision theory problems, on the other hand, are characterized by at least some uncertainty, and very often, by a considerable amount of uncertainty. But even though decision theory cannot provide optimal solutions, it can indicate to the decision maker which alternative on a list is most suited to the decision maker's own philosophy, be it optimistic, pessimistic, or somewhere in between.

Applications of decision theory are widespread. They include selection of investment portfolios, oil and gas exploration (to drill or not to drill), contracting (to bid or not to bid), agriculture (which crops to plant, how much acreage, whether to use pest control), manufacturing (which technology to invest in, which machines, how much capacity, maintenance schedules), marketing (introduction of new products, advertising/ trade promotion/couponing strategies), home buying (selection of mortgage type—conventional fixed or adjustable rate), retailing (strategies for buying, pricing, and inventories), and so on. Obviously, decision analysis is an important management science topic.

This chapter introduces the general approach of decision theory and two important tools of analysis: payoff tables and decision trees. These provide structure for organizing relevant information in a format conducive to rational decision making. The chapter begins with a description of the components of a decision model. Later, a variety of methods are illustrated, ranging from situations in which there is complete uncertainty as to how likely the various conditions are, to partial uncertainty, where some assessment of the likelihood of the various conditions is possible. Tabular and graphical methods are illustrated for analyzing decision problems and selecting appropriate alternatives.

◼◖ **Introduction**

Decision theory problems are characterized by the following:

1. A list of alternatives.
2. A list of possible future states of nature.
3. Payoffs associated with each alternative/state of nature combination.
4. An assessment of the degree of certainty of possible future events.
5. A decision criterion.

Let's examine each of these.

List of Alternatives

The list of alternatives must be a set of mutually exclusive and collectively exhaustive decisions that are available to the decision maker. (Sometimes, but not always, one of these alternatives will be to "do nothing.")

Suppose that a real estate developer must decide on a plan for developing a certain piece of property. After careful consideration, the developer has ruled out "do nothing" and is left with the following list of acceptable alternatives:

1. Residential proposal.
2. Commercial proposal #1.
3. Commercial proposal #2.

States of Nature

States of nature refer to a set of possible future conditions, or *events*, beyond the control of the decision maker that will be the primary determinants of the eventual consequence of the decision. The states of nature, like the list of alternatives, must be mutually exclusive and collectively exhaustive. Suppose, in the case of the real estate developer, the main factor that will influence the profitability of the development is whether or not a shopping center is built, and the size of the shopping center, if one is built. Suppose that the developer views the possibilities as:

1. No shopping center.
2. Medium-sized shopping center.
3. Large shopping center.

Payoffs

In order for a decision maker to be able to rationally approach a decision problem, it is necessary to have some idea of the payoffs that would be associated with each decision alternative and the various states of nature. The payoffs might be profits, revenues, costs, or other measure of value. Usually the measures are financial. They may be weekly, monthly, or annual amounts, or they might represent *present values* of future cash flows.[1] Usually, payoffs are estimated values. The more accurate these estimates, the more useful they will be for decision-making purposes and the more likely it is that the decision maker will choose an appropriate alternative.

The number of payoffs depends on the number of alternative/state of nature combinations. In the case of the real estate developer, there are three alternatives and three states of nature, so there are $3 \times 3 = 9$ possible payoffs that must be determined.

Degree of Certainty

The approach used by a decision maker often depends on the degree of certainty that exists. There can be different degrees of certainty. One extreme is complete **certainty** and the other is complete **uncertainty.** The latter exists when the likelihood of the various states of nature are unknown. Between these two extremes is **risk,** a term that implies that probabilities are known for the states of nature.

---

[1]A *present value* is a lump-sum payment that is the current equivalent of one or a set of future cash amounts using an assumed interest rate.

Knowledge of the likelihood of each of the states of nature can play an important role in selecting a course of action. Thus, if a decision maker feels that a particular state of nature is highly likely, this will mean that the payoffs associated with that state of nature are also highly likely. This enables the decision maker to focus more closely on probable results of a decision. Consequently, probability estimates for the various states of nature can serve an important function *if they can be obtained.* Of course, in some situations, accurate estimates of probabilities may not be available, in which case the decision maker may have to find a way to estimate the probabilities or select a course of action without the benefit of probabilities.

Decision Criterion

The process of selecting one alternative from a list of alternatives is governed by a **decision criterion,** which embodies the decision maker's attitudes toward the decision as well as the degree of certainty that surrounds a decision. For instance, some decision makers tend to be optimistic, whereas others tend to be pessimistic. Moreover, some want to maximize gains, whereas others are more concerned with protecting against large losses.

One example of a decision criterion is "Maximize the expected payoff." Another example is "Minimize opportunity cost." A variety of the most popular decision criteria are presented in the remainder of this chapter.

◼ **The Payoff Table**

A **payoff table** is a device a decision maker can use to summarize and organize information relevant to a particular decision. It includes a list of the alternatives, the possible future states of nature, and the payoffs associated with each of the alternative/state-of-nature combinations. If probabilities for the states of nature are available, these also can be listed. The general format of a payoff table is illustrated in Table 11-1.

Table 11-1	General Format of a Decision Table

		State of Nature		
		s_1	s_2	s_3
	a_1	V_{11}	V_{12}	V_{13}
Alternative	a_2	V_{21}	V_{22}	V_{23}
	a_3	V_{31}	V_{32}	V_{33}

where

a_i = the ith alternative
s_j = the jth state of nature (event)
V_{ij} = the value of payoff that will be realized if
     alternative i is chosen and event j occurs

Table 11-2	Payoff Table for Real Estate Developer		
		State of Nature	
	No center	Medium center	Large center
Residential	$400,000	$1,600,000	$1,200,000
Alternative **Commercial #1**	$600,000	$500,000	$1,400,000
Commercial #2	−$100,000	$400,000	$1,500,000

A payoff table for the real estate developer's decision is shown in Table 11-2. The three alternatives under consideration are listed down the left side of the table and the three possible states of nature are listed across the top of the table. The payoffs that are associated with each of the alternative/state-of-nature combinations are shown in the body of the table. Suppose that those values represent profits. Hence, if the residential proposal is chosen and no shopping center is built, the developer will realize a profit of $400,000. Similarly, if the second commercial proposal is selected and no center is built, the developer will lose $100,000.

Decision Making under Certainty

The simplest of all circumstances occurs when decision making takes place in an environment of complete certainty. For example, in the case of the real estate problem, an unexpected early announcement concerning the building of the shopping center could reduce the problem to a situation of certainty.

Thus, if there is an announcement that no shopping center will be built, the developer then can focus on the first column of the payoff table (see Table 11-3). Because the Commercial #1 proposal has the highest payoff in that column ($600,000), it would be selected. Similarly, if the announcement indicated that a medium-sized shopping center is planned, only the middle column of the table would be relevant, and the residential alternative would be selected because its estimated payoff of $1,600,000 is the highest of the

Table 11-3	If It Is Known That No Shopping Center Will be Built, Only the First Column Payoffs Would Be Relevant		
		State of Nature	
	No center	Medium center	Large center
Residential	$400,000	$1,600,000	$1,200,000
Alternative **Commercial #1**	$600,000	$500,000	$1,400,000
Commercial #2	−$100,000	$400,000	$1,500,000

three payoffs for a medium-sized shopping center; whereas if a large center is planned, the developer could focus on the last column, selecting the Commercial #2 proposal because it has the highest estimated payoff of $1,500,000 in that column.

In summary, when a decision is made under conditions of complete certainty, the attention of the decision maker is focused on the column in the payoff table that corresponds to the state of nature that will occur. The decision maker then selects the alternative that will yield the best payoff, given that state of nature.

■■■ Decision Making under Complete Uncertainty

Under complete uncertainty, the decision maker either is unable to estimate the probabilities for the occurrence of the different states of nature, or else he or she lacks confidence in available estimates of probabilities, and for that reason, probabilities are not included in the analysis. Still another possibility is that the decision is a one-shot case, with an overriding goal that needs to be satisfied (e.g., a firm may be on the verge of bankruptcy and this might be the last chance to turn things around).

Decisions made under these circumstances are at the opposite end of the spectrum from the certainty case just mentioned. We shall consider five approaches to decision making under complete uncertainty:

1. Maximin.
2. Maximax.
3. Minimax regret.
4. Hurwicz.
5. Equal likelihood.

Maximin

The **maximin** strategy is a conservative approach; it consists of identifying the worst (minimum) payoff for each alternative and then selecting the alternative that has the best (maximum) of the worst payoffs. In effect, the decision maker is setting a floor for the potential payoff; the actual payoff cannot be less than this amount.

For the real estate problem, the maximin solution is to choose the second alternative, Commercial #1, as illustrated in Table 11-4.

Many people view the maximin criterion as pessimistic because they believe that the decision maker must assume that the worst will occur. In fact, if the minimum payoffs are

Table 11-4	Maximin Solution for Real Estate Problem				
		State of Nature			
		No center	Medium center	Large center	Worst payoff	
Residential		$400,000	$1,600,000	$1,200,000	$400,000	
Alternative Commercial #1		$600,000	$500,000	$1,400,000	$500,000	← Maximum of the worst payoffs
Commercial #2		−$100,000	$400,000	$1,500,000	−$100,000	

Table 11-5 Maximax Solution for Real Estate Problem

	State of Nature				
	No Center	Medium center	Large center	Best payoff	
Residential	$400,000	$1,600,000	$1,200,000	$1,600,000	← Maximum
Alternatives Commercial #1	$600,000	$500,000	$1,400,000	$1,400,000	
Commercial #2	−$100,000	$400,000	$1,500,000	$1,500,000	

all negative, this view is accurate. Others view the maximin strategy in the same light as a decision to buy insurance: Protect against the worst possible events, even though you neither expect them nor want them to occur.

Maximax

The **maximax** approach is the opposite of the previous one: The best payoff for each alternative is identified, and the alternative with the maximum of these is the designated decision.

For the real estate problem, the maximax solution is to choose the residential alternative, as shown in Table 11.5.

Just as the maximin strategy can be viewed as pessimistic, the maximax strategy can be considered optimistic: that is, choosing the alternative that could result in the maximum payoff.

Minimax Regret

Both the maximax and maximin strategies can be criticized because they focus only on a single, extreme payoff and exclude the other payoffs. Thus, the maximax strategy ignores the possibility that an alternative with a slightly smaller payoff might offer a better overall choice. For example, consider the payoff given in Table 11-6. The maximax criterion would lead to selecting alternative a_1, even though two out of the three possible states of nature will result in negative payoffs. Moreover, both other alternatives will produce a payoff that is nearly the same as the maximum, regardless of the state of nature.

Table 11-6 Payoff Table with Similar Maximum Payoffs

	State of Nature		
	s_1	s_2	s_3
a_1	−$500,000	$1,600,000	−$1,000,000
Alternative a_2	$1,500,000	$1,500,000	$1,500,000
a_3	$1,500,000	$1,500,000	$1,500,000

Table 11-7   Opportunity Loss Table for Real Estate Problem

Original Payoff Table

		State of Nature	
	No center	Medium center	Large center
Residential	$400,000	$1,600,000	$1,200,000
Alternatives Commercial #1	$600,000	$500,000	$1,400,000
Commercial #2	−$100,000	$400,000	$1,500,000
Best Payoff in Column	$600,000	$1,600,000	$1,500,00

Opportunity Loss Table

		State of Nature	
	No center	Medium center	Large center
Residential	$200,000	0	$300,000
Alternatives Commercial #1	0	$1,100,000	$100,000
Commercial #2	$700,000	$1,200,000	0

A similar example could be constructed to demonstrate comparable weakness of the maximin criterion, which is also due to the failure to consider all payoffs.

An approach that does take all payoffs into account is **minimax regret.** In order to use this approach, it is necessary to develop an o*pportunity loss* table. The **opportunity loss** reflects the difference between each payoff and the best possible payoff in a column (i.e., given a state of nature). Hence, opportunity loss amounts are found by identifying the best payoff in a column and then subtracting each of the other values in the column from that payoff. For the real estate problem, the conversion of the original payoffs into an opportunity loss table is shown in Table 11-7.

Hence, in column 1, the best payoff is $600,000; therefore, all payoffs are subtracted from $600,000 to determine the amount of payoff the decision maker would miss by not having chosen the alternative that would have yielded the best payoff *if that state of nature* (no center) occurs. Of course, there is no guarantee that it will occur. Similarly, the best payoff in column 2 is $1,600,000, and all payoffs are subtracted from that number to reflect the opportunity losses that would occur if a decision other than Residential was selected *and* a medium-sized shopping center turned out to be the state of nature that comes to pass. And, for column 3, the opportunity costs evolve by subtracting each payoff from $1,500,000. Note that for every column, this results in a value of zero in the opportunity loss table in the same position as the best payoff for each column. For example, the best payoff in the last column of the payoff table is $1,500,000, and the corresponding position in the last column of the opportunity loss table is 0.

The values in an opportunity loss table can be viewed as potential **regrets** that might be suffered as the result of choosing various alternatives. A decision maker could select an alternative in such a way as to minimize the maximum possible regret. This requires identifying the maximum opportunity loss in each row and then choosing the alternative that

Table 11-8	Identifying the Minimax Regret Alternative

Opportunity Losses

	States of Nature				
	No center	Medium center	Large center	Maximum loss	
Residential	$200,000	0	$300,000	$300,000	← Minimum
Alternatives Commercial #1	0	$1,100,000	$100,000	$1,100,000	
Commercial #2	$700,000	$1,200,000	0	$1,200,000	

would yield the best (minimum) of those regrets. As illustrated in Table 11-8, for the real estate problem, this leads to selection of the residential alternative.

Although this approach has resulted in the same choice as the maximax strategy, the reasons are completely different; therefore, it is merely coincidence that the two methods yielded the same result. Under different circumstances, each can lead to selection of a different alternative.

Although this approach makes use of more information than either maximin or maximax, it still ignores some information and, therefore, can lead to a poor decision. Consider, for example, the opportunity loss table illustrated in Table 11-9. Using minimax regret, a decision maker would be indifferent between alternatives a_2 and a_3, although a_1 would be a better choice because for all but one of the states of nature there would be *no* opportunity loss, and in the worst case, a_1 would result in an opportunity loss that exceeded the other worst cases by $1.

The Hurwicz (Realism) Criterion

Still another approach is to use the **Hurwicz criterion,** also referred to as weighted average or realism criterion, which offers the decision maker a compromise between the maximax and the maximin criteria. This approach requires the decision maker to specify a degree of optimism, in the form of a **coefficient of optimism, α.** Possible values of α range from 0 to 1.00. The closer the selected value of α is to 1.00, the more optimistic the decision maker is, and the closer the value of α is to 0, the more pessimistic the decision maker is. Note that a

Table 11-9	Minimax Regret Can Lead in a Poor Decision

Opportunity Loss Table

	States of Nature					
	s_1	s_2	s_3	s_4	s_5	Worst in Row
a_1	0	0	0	0	24	24
Alternatives a_2	23	23	23	23	0	23 ← Minimum regret
a_3	23	23	23	23	0	23 ←

Table 11-10 Equal Likelihood Criterion

Payoff Table
States of Nature

	s_1	s_2	s_3	s_4	s_5	Row Average	
a_1	28	28	28	28	4	23.2	← Maximum
Alternatives a_2	5	5	5	5	28	9.6	
a_3	5	5	5	5	28	9.6	

value of 1.00 would be equivalent to using the maximax criterion, while a value of 0 would be equivalent to using the maximin criterion.

In order to use the Hurwicz criterion, for each alternative, the best payoff is multiplied by α and the worst payoff is multiplied by $1 - \alpha$, and the results are added. The totals for all alternatives are then compared, and the alternative that has the best overall result (maximum payoff) is selected.

For instance, suppose the decision maker in the real estate example elects to use the Hurwicz criterion. And suppose the decision maker feels somewhat pessimistic and chooses a coefficient of optimism equal to .30 (hence, $1 - \alpha = .70$). Using the following format,

α(Best payoff) + $(1 - \alpha)$ (Worst payoff)

the decision maker would choose Commercial #1:

Alternative:	Best payoff	Worst payoff		
Residential	.30($1,600,000) + .70($400,000)	= $760,000	
Commercial #1	.30($1,800,000) + .70($500,000)	= $890,000	(best)
Commercial #2	.30($1,500,000) + .70(−$100,000)	= $380,000	

Equal Likelihood Criterion

The minimax regret criterion weakness is the inability to factor row differences. Hence, sometimes the minimax regret strategy will lead to a poor decision because it ignores certain information.

The **equal likelihood criterion** offers a method that incorporates more of the information. It treats the states of nature as if each were equally likely, and it focuses on the average payoff for each row, selecting the alternative that has the highest row average.

The payoff table from which the opportunity losses of Table 11-9 were computed is shown in Table 11-10, along with the row averages. Note how a_1 now stands out compared to the others. In fact, we could have obtained a similar result by finding the row averages for the opportunity loss table and then choosing the alternative that had the lowest average. Thus, the row averages for the opportunity losses presented in Table 11-9 are

Alternative	Row Average	
a_1	24/5 = 4.8	← Minimum
a_2	92/5 = 18.4	
a_3	92/5 = 18.4	

Table 11-11	Summary of Methods for Decision Making under Complete Uncertainty
Method	**Description of the Decision-Making Criteria**
Maximax	Choose the maximum of the largest payoffs from the payoff table (optimistic)
Maximin	Choose the maximum of the smallest payoffs from the payoff table (pessimistic)
Minimax regret	Choose the minimum of the maximum losses from the opportunity loss table (loss oriented)
Hurwicz	Weighted-average approach where the largest payoff for an alternative is weighted with the coefficient of optimism (α) and the smallest payoff is weighted with $1 - \alpha$, and the largest weighted average is chosen
Equal likelihood	Weighted-average approach where each decision alternative is weighted equally and the largest average is chosen

Note that in both cases, the difference between the average of a_1 and the average of the other two is the same ($23.2 - 9.6 = 13.6$ or $18.4 - 4.8 = 13.6$). Hence, we could obtain the same result from *either* the payoff table *or* the opportunity loss table; they will both always lead to the same decision.

The basis for the equal likelihood criterion is that under complete uncertainty, the decision maker should not focus on either high or low payoffs, but should treat all payoffs (actually, all states of nature) as if they were *equally likely*. Averaging row payoffs accomplishes this.

Table 11-11 provides a summarization of methods used in decision making under complete uncertainty.

Using Excel for Decision Making under Complete Uncertainty

In the previous section, we demonstrated how to use five different types of criteria for decision making under complete uncertainty. Excel worksheets also can be prepared to solve decision-making problems given complete uncertainty. Exhibit 11-1 shows the Excel worksheet that includes all five criteria using the real estate example that was discussed earlier in the chapter. Note that the values in Exhibit 11–1 are truncated by 100,000 to make the exhibit fit into one screen.

The upper-right-hand side of the worksheet shows the payoff table for this problem. Next to the payoff table, on the left side, are the calculations and the results of the maximax and the maximin approaches. The equations associated with both approaches are given at the bottom of Exhibit 11-1. In cells E4 through E6, we simply record the maximum payoff for each row or decision alternative. For example, the maximum value for the residential alternative is given in cell E4 by specifying the equation =MAX(B4 : D4). In cell F4, under the column heading Criterion Choice, the following IF statement is provided:

=IF(D4=MAX(D$4 : D$6), "Select", " ")

Exhibit 11-1	Using Excel to Make Decisions under Complete Uncertainty

Cell	Copied to cells	Formula
E4	E5, E6	= MAX (B4 : D4)
F4	F5, F6	= IF (E4 = MAX ($E$4 : $E$6), "Select", " ")
G4	G5, G6	= MIN (B4 : D4)
H4	H5, H6	= IF (G4 = MAX (G$4 : G$6), "Select", " ")
E10	E11, E12	= AVERAGE (B10 : D10)
F10	F11, F12	= IF (E10 = MAX ($E$10 : $E$12), "Select", " ")
G10	G11, G12	= $H$13 * (MAX (B10 : D10) + (1 − $H$13) * MIN (B10 : D10))
H10	H11, H12	= IF (G10 = MAX ($G$10 : $G$12), "Select", " ")
E17	E18, E19	= MAX (B17 : D17)
F17	F18, F19	= IF (E17 = MIN ($E$17 : $E$19, "Select", " ")

Note: The values in Exhibit 11–1 are truncated by $100,000. For example, the value of 4 in cell B4 is actually $400,000.

In this IF statement, we simply state that if D4 is the maximum value of the cells D4, D5, and D6, then we select the residential decision alternative. However, if D4 is not the maximum value of the cells D4, D5, and D6, then we include two quotation marks to prevent the cell returning a FALSE answer. If the condition is not met, and the two quotation marks are not included at the end of the IF statement, then the cell would include a FALSE statement. The equation from cell E4 is copied to cells E5 and E6, and likewise the equation from cell F4 is copied to cells F5 and F6 to complete the maximax rule for the Commercial #1 and

Commercial #2 options. In completing the section of the worksheet in Exhibit 11-1 concerning the maximin method (cells G2 : H6), in cells G4 through G6, we simply record the minimum payoff for each row or decision alternative. For example, the minimum value for the Residential alternative is given in cell G4 by specifying the equation =MIN(B4 : D4). In cell H4, under the column heading Criterion Choice, the following IF statement is provided:

=IF(G4=MAX(G$4 : G$6), "Select", " ")

We can interpret this IF statement as follows: If G4 is the maximum value of the minimum values given in cells G4, G5, and G6, then we select the residential decision alternative. In completing the maximin rule for the Commercial #1 and Commercial #2 options, we copy the equation from cell G4 to cells G5 and G6, and likewise the equation from cell H4 is copied to cells H5 and H6.

The payoff table is repeated in cells A9 : D12 to simplify the formulas that will need to be prepared to demonstrate the equal likelihood and Hurwicz criteria. The equal likelihood criterion is displayed in cells E8 : F12. The formulas for the equal likelihood criterion in cells E10 : E12 and F10 : F12 are shown at the bottom of Exhibit 11-1. Note that using the equal likelihood criterion we choose the residential alternative. The Hurwicz criterion is displayed in cells G8 : H13 in Exhibit 11-1. The formulas for the Hurwicz criterion in cells G10 : G12 and H10 : H12 are shown at the bottom of Exhibit 1-1. In using the Hurwicz criterion, we need to utilize the coefficient of optimism (α), which is displayed in cell H13. In cell G10 we utilize the following equation:

=$H$13*(MAX(B10 : D10)+(1−$H$13)*MIN(B10 : D10))

In interpreting this equation, we multiply the coefficient of optimism specified in cell H13 by the maximum payoff for the residential row (B10 : D10) and add to it

1 − α or (H13) multiplied by the minimum payoff for the residential row (B10 : D10).

At the bottom of Exhibit 11-1, we show how to use the minimax regret criterion with Excel. In using the minimax regret criterion, first we need to develop the opportunity loss table from the payoff table. In determining the opportunity loss table given in cells B17 : D19 in Exhibit 11-1, we subtract each cell value from the maximum value in given column. For example, in determining the opportunity loss for the residential alternative and no center, we use the following formula:

=MAX($C$10 : $C$12)−C10

In other words, we simply subtract the payoff associated with this decision alternative/state-of-nature combination from the maximum payoff for that column, or state of nature. The formulas for selected cells in the opportunity loss matrix are given at the bottom of Exhibit 11-1. After determining the opportunity loss matrix, we proceed to calculate the maximum regret (opportunity loss) values by simply choosing the maximum opportunity loss in each row. For instance, in determining the maximum regret for the residential decision alternative, the following Excel formula in cell E17 is used:

=MAX($B$17 : $D$17)

This formula is copied to cells E18 and E19. We simply select the minimum of the maximum regrets, as shown in the formulas for cells F17 : F19 at the bottom of Exhibit 11-1. Most of the formulas used to develop the worksheet shown in Exhibit 11-1 are given at the bottom of the exhibit.

■ Decision Making under Risk

The essential difference between decision making under complete uncertainty and decision making under partial uncertainty is the presence of *probabilities* for the occurrence of the various states of nature under partial uncertainty. The term *risk* is often used in conjunction with partial uncertainty.

The probabilities may be subjective estimates from managers or from experts in a particular field, or they may reflect historical frequencies. If they are reasonably correct, they provide a decision maker with additional information that can dramatically improve the decision-making process.

The sum of the probabilities for all states of nature must be 1.00. Thus, the real estate developer might estimate the probability of no shopping center being built at .2, the probability of a medium-sized shopping center at .5, and the probability of a large shopping center at .3. (Note that .2 + .5 + .3 = 1.0.)

Expected Monetary Value

The **expected monetary value** (**EMV**) approach provides the decision maker with a value that represents an *average* payoff for each alternative. The best alternative is, then, the one that has the highest expected monetary value.

The average or expected payoff of each alternative is a weighted average: the state of nature probabilities are used to weight the respective payoffs. Thus, the expected monetary value for each alternative is

$$EMV_i = \sum_{i=1}^{k} P_j V_{ij} \qquad (11\text{-}1)$$

where

EMV_i = the expected monetary value for the ith alternative
P_j = the probability of the jth state of nature
V_{ij} = the estimated payoff for alternative i under state of nature j

For example, using the figures in Table 11-12, we can compute the expected payoffs for the real estate developer's alternatives. The expected monetary value of the residential alternative is

$$EMV_R = .2(\$400,000) + .5(\$1,600,000) + .3(\$1,200,000) = \$1,240,000$$

Similarly, the expected monetary values of the other alternatives are

$$EMV_{C1} = .2(\$600,000) + .5(\$500,000) + .3(\$1,400,000) = \$790,000$$
$$EMV_{C1} = .2(-\$100,000) + .5(\$400,000) + .3(\$1,500,000) = \$630,000$$

Because the residential alternative has the largest expected monetary value, it would be selected using this criterion.

Note that it does *not* necessarily follow that the developer will actually realize a payoff equal to the expected monetary value of a chosen alternative. For example, note that the possible payoffs for the residential proposal are $400,000, $1,600,000, and $1,200,000, whereas the expected payoff is $1,240,000, which is not equal to any of the payoffs. Similarly, the expected payoffs for either of the other alternatives do not equal any of the payoffs in those rows. What, then, is the interpretation of the expected payoff? Simply a long-run average amount; the approximate average amount one could reasonably anticipate for a large number of identical situations.

| Table 11-12 | Real Estate Payoff Table with Probabilities | | | | |

		States of Nature			
Probabilities		.2	.5	.3	
		No center	Medium center	Large center	Expected payoff
	Residential	$400,000	$1,600,000	$1,200,000	$1,240,000 ← Maximum
Alternatives	Commercial #1	$600,000	$500,000	$1,400,000	790,000
	Commercial #2	−$100,000	$400,000	$1,500,000	630,000

In contrast to the strategies outlined for decision making under complete uncertainty, which are realistically best used for one-time major decisions, the expected value approach is more suited to an ongoing decision strategy. Over the long run, taking probabilities into account will yield the highest payoff, even though in the short run actual payoffs will tend to be higher or lower than the expected amounts. Conversely, over the long run, a strategy that failed to take probabilities into account would tend to yield lower payoffs than one that does take the probabilities into account.

Expected Opportunity Loss

An alternate method for incorporating probabilities into the decision-making process is to use **expected opportunity loss (EOL).** The approach is nearly identical to the EMV approach, except that a table of opportunity losses is used rather than a table of payoffs. Hence, the opportunity losses for each alternative are weighted by the probabilities of their respective states of nature to compute a long-run average opportunity loss, and the alternative with the *smallest* expected loss is selected as the best choice.

For the real estate problem, the expected opportunity losses based on the values given in Table 11-8 can be calculated as follows:

$$EOL_R = .2(\$200,000) + .5(0) + .3(\$300,000) = \$130,000 \leftarrow Minimum$$
$$EOL_{C1} = .2(0) + .5(\$1,100,000) + .3(\$100,000) = \$580,000$$
$$EOL_{C1} = .2(\$700,000) + .5(\$1,200,000) + .3(0) = \$740,000$$

Note that the EOL approach resulted in the same alternative as the EMV approach. This is more than coincidence; the two methods will always result in the same choice because they are equivalent ways of combining the values; maximizing the payoffs is equivalent to minimizing the opportunity losses.

Expected Value of Perfect Information

It can sometimes be useful for a decision maker to determine the potential benefit of knowing for certain which state of nature is going to prevail. For instance, a decision maker might have the option of delaying a decision until it is evident which state of nature is going to materialize. The obvious benefit of waiting would be to move the decision into the realm of certainty, thereby allowing the decision maker to obtain the maximum possible payoff. Such delays typically will involve a cost of some sort (e.g., higher prices, the cost of an option, storage costs). Hence, the question is whether the cost of waiting outweighs the potential benefits that could be realized by waiting. Or the decision maker might wonder if it would be worth the cost to refine or eliminate the probabilities of the states of nature (e.g., using marketing research or a better forecasting technique). Although such techniques may not completely eliminate uncertainty, the decision maker often can benefit from knowledge of the upper limit of the potential gain that perfect information would permit.

The **expected value of perfect information (EVPI)** is a measure of the difference between the certain payoff that could be realized under a condition of certainty and the expected payoff under a condition involving risk.

Consider the payoff that the real estate developer could expect under certainty. If the developer knew that no center would be built, the Commercial #1 proposal would be chosen with a payoff of $600,000; if the developer knew a medium-sized shopping center would be built, the residential alternative would be chosen for a payoff of $1,600,000; and if the developer knew that a large center would be built, the Commercial #2 proposal would be chosen for a payoff of $1,500,000. Hence, if it were possible to remove the uncertainty surrounding the states of nature, the decision maker could capitalize on the knowledge. Obviously, before investing time or money in eliminating the possibilities, it is impossible for the decision maker to say which state of nature will turn out to be the one that will occur. However, what can be said is that the probability that perfect information will indicate that no center will be built is .2, that the probability that perfect information will indicate a medium center will be built is .5, and the probability of perfect information indicating a large center is .3. Thus, these probabilities, which are the original state-of-nature probabilities, can be used to weight the best payoffs, one of which will occur under certainty. This is called the **expected payoff under certainty (EPC),** and is computed in the following way for the real estate problem.:

$$EPC = .2(\$600,000) + .5(\$1,600,000) + .3(\$1,500,000) = \$1,370,000$$

The difference between this figure and the expected payoff under risk (i.e., the EMV) is the expected value of perfect information. Thus:

$$EVPI = EPC - EMV \tag{11-2}$$

For the real estate problem, with EPC = $1,370,000 and EMV = $1,240,000, we find

$$EVPI = \$1,370,000 - \$1,240,000 = \$130,000$$

The EVPI represents an *upper bound* on the amount of money the real estate developer would be justified in spending to obtain perfect information. Thus, the real estate developer would be justified in spending up to $130,000 to find out for certain which state of nature will prevail. Of course, it is not always possible to completely remove uncertainty. In such cases, the decision maker must weigh the cost to reduce the uncertainty (i.e., obtain better estimates of the probabilities) against the expected benefits that would yield.

Note that the EVPI is exactly equal to the previously computed EOL. In fact, these two quantities will always be equal. The EOL indicates the expected *opportunity loss* due to imperfect information, which is another way of saying the expected *payoff* that could be achieved by having perfect information. Hence, there are two equivalent ways to determine the expected value of perfect information: subtract the EMV from the expected payoff under certainty or compute the EOL.

The expected value (EMV) approach is particularly useful for decision making when a number of similar decisions must be made; it is a "long-run" approach. For one-shot decisions, where none of the alternatives have very high or very low (extreme) payoffs, the EMV approach may still be preferred to other methods. However, when there are extreme payoffs and/or the decision maker does not have confidence in probabilities, then other methods (perhaps maximax or maximin) may be preferable. In addition, nonmonetary factors, although not included in a payoff table, may be of considerable importance. Unfortunately, there is no convenient way to include them in an expected value analysis.

Using Excel for Decision Making under Risk

Excel can easily be utilized to calculate expected monetary values (EMV), expected opportunity losses (EOL), and the expected value of perfect information (EVPI). Exhibit 11-2 demonstrates how a worksheet is used to calculate EMVs, EOLs, and EVPI.

Exhibit 11-2	Using Excel to Make Decisions under Risk

	A	B	C	D	E	F
1		Payoff Table for Real Estate Developer				
2			State of Nature			
3	Alternatives	No Center	Medium Center	Large Center	EMV	Choice
4	Residential	4	16	12	12.4	Select
5	Commercial #1	6	5	14	7.9	
6	Commercial #2	-1	4	15	6.3	
7	Probability	0.2	0.5	0.3		
8						
9		Opportunity Loss Table for Real Estate Developer				
10			State of Nature			
11	Alternatives	No Center	Medium Center	Large Center	EOL	Choice
12	Residential	2	0	3	1.3	Select
13	Commercial #1	0	11	1	5.8	
14	Commercial #2	7	12	0	7.4	
15	Probability	0.2	0.5	0.3		
16					EPC=	Expected Payoff Under Certainty
17	Payoff decision	6	16	15	13.7	
18	with Perfect Info.					
19						
20		EVPI=	1.3			

Cells	Copied to cells	Formula
E4	E5 : E6	= SUMPRODUCT (B4 : D4, $B$7 : $D$7)
F4	F5 : F6	= IF (E4 = MAX ($E$4 : $E$6)," select," " ")
B12	B13 : B14	= MAX ($B$4 : $B$6) − B4
C12	C13 : C14	= MAX ($C$4 : $C$6) − C4
D12	D13 : D4	= MAX ($D$4 : $D$6) − D4
E12	E13 : E14	= SUMPRODUCT (B12 : D12, $B$7 : $D$7)
F12	F13 : F14	= IF (E12 = MIN ($E$12 : $E$14)," select," " ")
E17		= SUMPRODUCT (B7 : D7, B17 : D17)
B20		= E17 − MAX (E4 : E6)

Note: The numbers in Exhibit 11-2 are truncated by $100,000. For example the value of 16 in cell C4 is actually $1,600,000 and the value of 1.3 in cell B20 is actually $130,000.

First we copy the payoff table from Exhibit 11-1 to Exhibit 11-2. EMV values are computed on the right-hand side of the payoff table in cells E4 through E6. For example, the expected monetary value for the residential alternative in cell E4 is calculated by using the following formula: =SUMPRODUCT(B4 : D4, $B$7 : $D$7). In this formula, first we multiply cells B4 : D4 (residential net returns for each state of nature) by the respective cells B7 : D7 (probabilities of each state-of-nature occurrence) and then sum the products. We repeat this calculation for the Commercial #1 and Commercial #2 options in cells E5 and E6 respectively. In cells F4 through F6, we simply have Excel specify the largest of the values in cells E4, E5, and E6. The following formula is used in cell F4 to determine if the largest value among cells E4, E5, and E6 is in cell E4:

=IF(E4=MAX($E$4 : $E$6), "Select", " ")

Since the largest EMV is for the residential option, cell F4 indicates "Select".

The bottom portion of Exhibit 11-2 contains the opportunity loss matrix used in conjunction with the minimax regret criterion. As you recall, we displayed the opportunity loss table and the minimax regret criterion in Exhibit 11-1. The reason for copying the opportunity loss table from Exhibit 11-1 to Exhibit 11-2 is that in Exhibit 11-2 we demonstrate the calculation of the expected opportunity loss (EOL) values for each decision alternative. As you recall, the calculation of the EOL values requires the use of the opportunity loss table. The expected opportunity loss value for the residential alternative in cell E12 is calculated by using the following formula:

=SUMPRODUCT(B12 : D12, $B$7 : $D$7).

In this formula, first we multiply cells B12 : D12 (opportunity loss for each state of nature for the residential alternative) by the respective cells B7 : D7 (probabilities of each state-of-nature occurrence), and then sum the products. We repeat this calculation for the Commercial #1 and Commercial #2 options in cells E13 and E14 respectively. In cells F12 : F14, we simply have Excel specify the smallest of the values in cells E12, E13, and E14. For instance, for cell F12, we use the following formula:

=IF(E12=MIN($E$12 : $E$14), "Select", " ")

Since the smallest EOL is for the residential option, cell F12 (residential) indicates "Select".

After the computation of the EMV and EOL values in Exhibit 11-2, we compute the expected value of perfect information (EVPI). This calculation is shown at the bottom of Exhibit 11-2. First we compute the expected payoff under certainty (EPC) by using the following formula: =SUMPRODUCT($B$17:$D$17). In this formula, we calculate the sum of the cross products of the probabilities in each state of nature (B7 : D7) with the maximum payoff for each state of nature (B17 : D17). Finally we compute EVPI in cell B20 using the following formula: =E17 −MAX(E4 : E6). As you recall from our earlier discussion, the EVPI represents the difference between the EPC value in cell E17 and the maximum of the EMV values in cells E4, E5, and E6. Most of the formulas used to develop the worksheet shown in Exhibit 11-2 are stated at the bottom of the exhibit.

◼ Decision Trees

Decision trees sometimes are used by decision makers to obtain a visual portrayal of decision alternatives and their possible consequences. The term gets its name from the treelike appearance of the diagram (see Figure 11-1).

Figure 11-1	Decision Tree Format

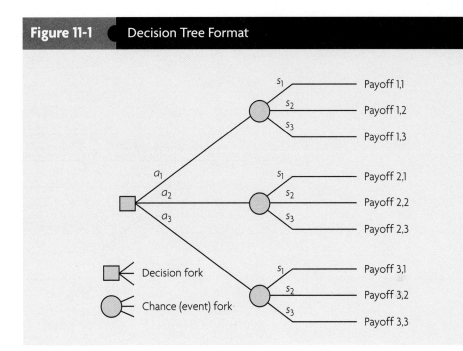

A tree is composed of squares, circles, and lines. The squares indicate decision points while the circles represent chance events. The lines or "branches" that emanate from a square represent alternatives, while the branches that emanate from a circle represent states of nature. The tree is read from right to left.

Decision trees are fairly simple to construct. The decision tree for the real estate developer's problem is shown in Figure 11-2. The dollar amounts alongside each chance node (circle) indicate the expected payoff of the alternative that leads into that particular chance node. The expected payoffs are computed in the same manner as previously described, and, as before, the decision maker will select the alternative with the largest expected payoff if maximizing expected payoff is the decision criterion.

It should be noted that although decision trees represent an alternative approach to payoff tables, they are not commonly used for problems that involve a single decision. Rather, their greatest benefit lies in portraying **sequential decisions** (i.e., a series of chronological decisions). In the case of a single decision, constructing a tree can be cumbersome and time-consuming. For example, imagine the decision tree that would be necessary to portray a decision with 7 alternatives and 10 states of nature; there would be 70 payoffs, and, hence, 70 branch-ends on the right side of the tree. Conversely, situations that involve sequential decisions are difficult to represent in payoff tables.

As an example of a sequential decision, suppose that the real estate developer has several options that might be considered after the initial decision. For instance, regardless of which of the three alternatives he chooses, the worst payoff will result if no shopping center is built. Hence, it might be prudent for the developer to plan for that contingency. Thus, the developer might consider certain options. Suppose the developer states that he would consider

Figure 11-2 — Decision Tree for Real Estate Developer Problem

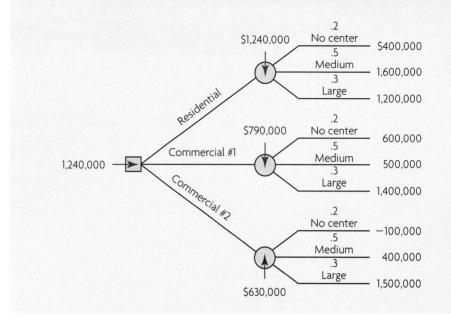

Figure 11-3 — Real Estate Problem with a Second Possible Decision

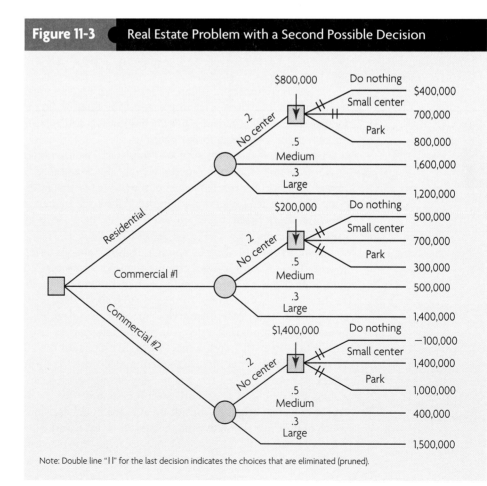

Note: Double line "||" for the last decision indicates the choices that are eliminated (pruned).

these additional alternatives in the event that no center is built:

1. Do nothing.
2. Develop a small shopping center.
3. Develop a park.

The tree diagram of Figure 11-2 has been modified to include these additional options, along with their estimated payoffs as supplied by the real estate developer, and it is shown in Figure 11-3. Note that the payoffs for Do nothing are the same as in the original tree for the event no center is built.

In order to analyze this modified tree (i.e., to make a choice among the alternatives residential, Commercial #1, and Commercial #2), the branches for each possible second decision must be reduced in each instance to a single branch. This is easily accomplished by recognizing that at each of those points, a rational decision maker would simply choose the alternative with the largest payoff. Hence, if residential were chosen initially and no center was built, a park would be selected because it would have the largest payoff. Similarly, if Commercial #1 was chosen and no center was built, the small center option would be chosen because it offers the largest payoff, and if Commercial #2 were initially chosen and no center was built, the developer would choose the option of building a small center because its payoff is greater than either Do nothing or Park. Thus, in each case, the tree is pruned by cutting the undesirable options and keeping the one best option. This also is illustrated in Figure 11-3. Note that the payoff for the best option for each alternative, then, becomes the payoff for each no center branch. The tree would then be analyzed as previously.

◼◼ Using TreePlan to Develop Decision Trees with Excel

We can use an Excel add-in program called TreePlan to develop and solve decision tree problems. Even though we can write the formulas to develop decision trees without TreePlan, it is a very complicated and cumbersome process. TreePlan provides us with a template that significantly simplifies the process of developing decision trees using Excel since it operates in an Excel environment. The first step in using TreePlan is to load TreePlan. The TreePlan program consists of an Excel file, TreePlan.xla. This file is included on the CD-ROM that accompanies this textbook. Loading TreePlan can be accomplished in one of two ways. The first way, which is a temporary manual loading, can be accomplished by the following steps:

1. Open Excel
2. Click **File | Open** and use the Browse button to locate TreePlan.xla on the CD-ROM that accompanies this book.
3. Clicking on Treeplan.xla will open this file. However, opening this file will not change the Excel spreadsheet on the screen.
4. To use TreePlan, click **Tools** and then click **Decision Tree.**

However, loading TreePlan as described above provides only a temporary access to TreePlan. In other words, you would have to repeat the procedure described above each time you run Excel.

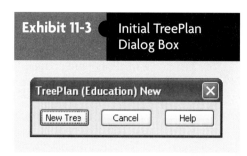

Exhibit 11-3 Initial TreePlan Dialog Box

A permanent loading of TreePlan requires the completion of the loading procedure described below only once.

1. Access the Treeplan.xla file on the CD-ROM that accompanies this book and copy this file to the hard drive.
2. Open Excel.

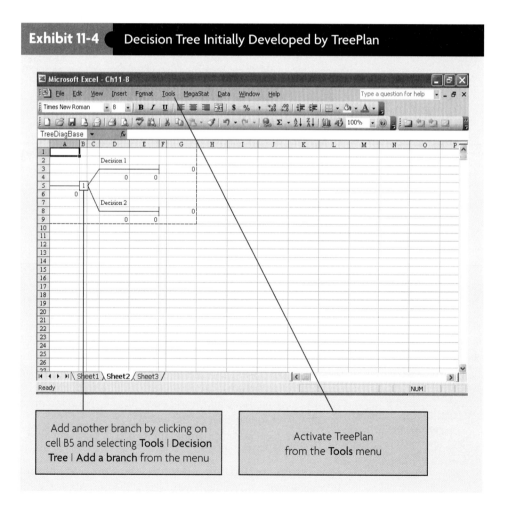

Exhibit 11-4 Decision Tree Initially Developed by TreePlan

Add another branch by clicking on cell B5 and selecting **Tools | Decision Tree | Add a branch** from the menu

Activate TreePlan from the **Tools** menu

Exhibit 11-5   TreePlan Dialog Box to Add Branches, Decision Nodes, or Events

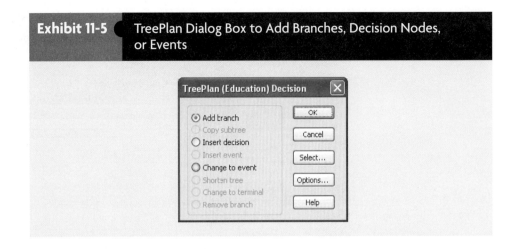

---

3. Click **Tools | Add-Ins;** the Add-in dialog box will appear on the screen. On this dialog box, click on **Browse** and locate the TreePlan.xla file on your hard drive.

4. Click on the TreePlan.xla file. Scroll down the options on the Add-in dialog box, and toward the end of the Add-in options you will see TreePlan. Make sure the box next to TreePlan is checked. If you want to remove Treeplan, simply click **Tools | Add-Ins** and uncheck the Treeplan box.

5. To use TreePlan, click **Tools** and then **Decision Tree.**

Once we load Treeplan, we can utilize it to prepare and solve decision tree problems. Let us consider the real estate example that we have used earlier in the chapter. The decision tree for this real estate developer example is given in Figure 11-2. Now we will develop and solve the same decision tree problem using TreePlan.

We begin utilizing TreePlan by choosing **Tools | Decision Tree,** which brings up the initial TreePlan dialog box shown in Exhibit 11-3. On this initial TreePlan dialog box, if we click on "New Tree," TreePlan will display the initial decision tree shown in Exhibit 11-4.

If we put the cursor on the initial decision node and click on **Tools | Decision Tree,** TreePlan will bring up the dialog box shown in Exhibit 11-5. In the real estate problem, since there are three choices (Residential, Commercial #1, Commercial #2), a new branch needs to be added. After clicking on the Add branch option and clicking OK, the decision tree will be modified from the initial tree with two branches to the modified tree with three branches, as shown in Exhibit 11-6.

After obtaining the tree shown in Exhibit 11-6, we put the cursor at the end of the first branch on cell F3 and click on **Tools | Decision Tree,** and TreePlan will bring up the dialog box shown in Exhibit 11-7. At this stage, we can choose to add another decision node or to add an event (chance) node. In the real estate problem, at this stage the tree contains event nodes; therefore, we click on "Change to event node." On the right side of Exhibit 11-7, the dialog box gives us the option to choose the number of branches emanating from the chance node. Since there are three chance events (no center, medium, and large), click on "Three branches" and click OK. This will result in the partially completed decision tree shown in Exhibit 11-8. Note that since there are three branches coming out

Exhibit 11-6 — Modified Decision Tree with Three Branches

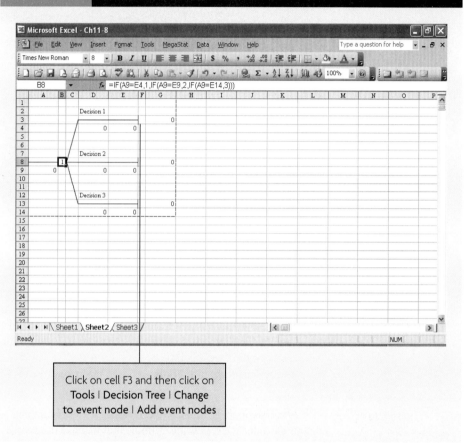

Click on cell F3 and then click on **Tools I Decision Tree I Change to event node I Add event nodes**

Exhibit 11-7 — TreePlan Dialog Box to Add or Change Decision Nodes or Events

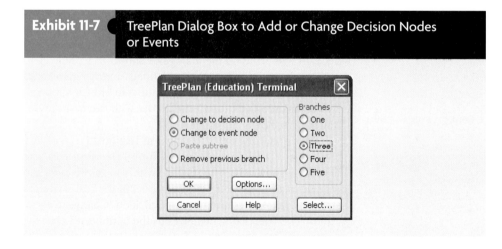

| Exhibit 11-8 | Modified Decision Tree with Three Branches and the Added Event Node with Three Nodes |

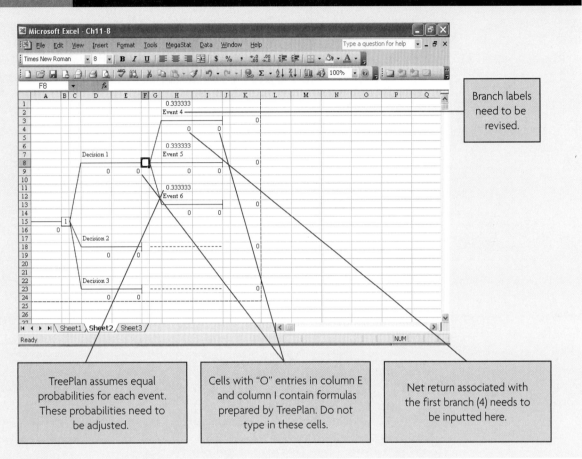

Branch labels need to be revised.

TreePlan assumes equal probabilities for each event. These probabilities need to be adjusted.

Cells with "O" entries in column E and column I contain formulas prepared by TreePlan. Do not type in these cells.

Net return associated with the first branch (4) needs to be inputted here.

of the event node, the default probability on each branch is .3333. Based on Figure 11-2, the other two decisions also have event nodes following them. Therefore, on Exhibit 11-8, we repeat the same process for cell F18 and cell F23 (before we add the event node on cell F18).

After adding the event nodes, we need to change the labels and probabilities on the decision tree. The labels are edited the same way we would edit any label on any spreadsheet. The final step is to add the numerical data at the end of each branch. The revised decision tree is shown in Exhibit 11-9. The numerical values (payoffs for each branch) are changed from 0 to their respective values in Figure 11-2 as shown in cells K2, K6, K10, K14, K18, K22, K26, and K34. The first label in cell D6 was Decision 1. We click on cell D6 and simply relabel it as "Residential". The rest of the numerical values shown as "zeros" in column E and column I in the decision tree represent the formulas for TreePlan. Do not type in these cells. Note that the expected monetary value for the three decision alternatives (Residential, Commercial #1, Commercial #2) are calculated

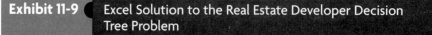

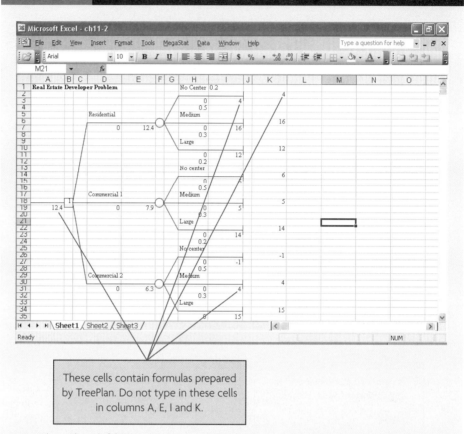

Note: Values at the end of decision tree are truncated. For example, the value in cell K2 is 4, and it can be interpreted as $400,000. Each number in column I and column K are multiplied by $100,000.

by TreePlan and shown in cells E7, E19, and E31. Since the residential alternative results in the largest expected monetary value, the value of 1,240,000 (12.4-EMV associated with the residential option) in cell E7 is repeated in cell A19.

Sequential Decision Tree Analysis with Excel and TreePlan

As we mentioned in the previous section, if a problem involving decision making requires a single decision, then we can utilize either the payoff table or the decision tree to determine the decision for the decision maker. However, as we pointed out in the last section, if a decision-making problem involves a sequence of decisions in combination with various events, then it is not possible to prepare the payoff table, and development of the decision tree is our only option. The following example is used to demonstrate another sequential decision-making problem and the solution of this problem using Excel.

Example 11-1

Unicom Inc. is adding a new product. In order to accommodate the anticipated capacity needs of the new product, the firm believes that a new plant must be built. The firm has to make a decision to build a large plant or a small plant. In either case, demand will be either favorable or unfavorable with probabilities of 0.55 and 0.45 respectively. If a large plant is built and demand is favorable, the net present value of returns is estimated at $1,500,000. If demand is unfavorable, the net loss with the large plant is estimated to be $50,000.

If a small plant is built and demand is unfavorable, the net present value is $700,000. If demand proves to be favorable, the firm can either maintain the small plant or expand it. Maintaining the small plant has a net present value of $950,000. If the firm decides to expand, the firm can expect a high return or a low return. There is a 40 percent change of earning a net present value of $1,330,000 (high return) and a 60 percent chance of earning $720,000 (low return).

a.   Draw a decision tree for this problem
b.   Calculate all of the necessary expected values and determine the best course of action for management.

Solution

The decision tree for this problem is shown in Figure 11-4. After setting up the decision tree, we indicate the net payoffs for each branch and calculate the expected return for each chance event. We start at the end of the tree with the chance event node 1. The expected return (EMV) for this node is calculated as follows:

$$EMV_1 = (.4)(\$1,330,000) + (.6)(\$720,000) = \$964,000$$

We record this value at node 1 and proceed to the decision node 2. At node 2, we can either maintain the size for a net return of $950,000 or expand for a net return of $964,000. Since the expected monetary value of expanding is greater than maintaining the current size (964,000 > 950,000), we choose to expand the plant and we simply write "964,000" on decision node 2. Next we proceed to chance event node 3 and

| Figure 11-4 | Sequential Decision Tree for Unicom Inc. (Example 11-3, part a) |

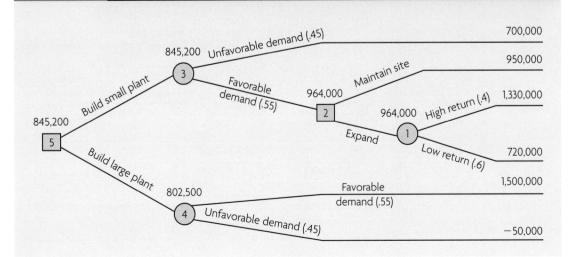

calculate the expected return associated with node 3. This expected monetary value will be the expected value of building a small plant. The expected return (EMV) for this node is calculated as follows:

$$EMV_3 = (.45)(\$700,000) + (.55)(\$964,000) = \$845,200$$

We record this value on node 3 and calculate the expected return associated with chance event node 4. The calculation of the expected value at node 4 provides us with the expected monetary value of the large plant. The expected value at node 4 can be calculated as follows:

$$EMV_4 = (.55)(\$1,500,000) + (.45)(-\$50,000) = \$802,500$$

We record this value on node 4 and at decision node 5, we compare the expected values of nodes 3 and 4. Since the expected value of node 3 is greater than the expected value of node 4 (845,200 > 802,500), we record "845,200" on node 5.

We can summarize the results associated with this sequential decision tree as follows: Unicom Inc. should choose to build a small plant, and if the demand is favorable, the company should choose to expand. The overall expected net return for the company is $842,500.

In the previous section we have already demonstrated in detail how we can use TreePlan to develop and solve a single decision problem. In Exhibit 11-10, we show the decision tree using TreePlan for the sequential decision tree example that we have solved above.

Exhibit 11-10 Excel Solution to the Unicom Inc. Sequential Decision Tree Problem

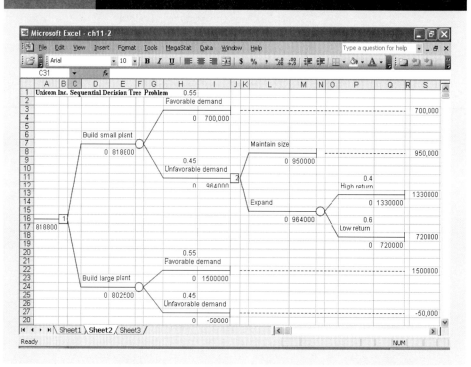

Even though this particular decision tree, shown in Exhibit 11-10, is a little more complicated than the decision tree we developed using TreePlan in the previous section, the decision tree displayed in Exhibit 11-10 was developed in the same way as the decision tree shown in Exhibit 11-9. Therefore, we will not spend any time explaining the development and solution of the decision tree in Exhibit 11-10.

Decision Making with Additional Information

Decision makers can sometimes improve decision making by bringing additional information into the process. The additional information can come from a variety of sources. For example, either a market survey might be used to acquire additional information or a forecasting technique might be employed. In certain situations, it may be possible to delay a decision; the passage of time often allows a decision maker to obtain a clearer picture of the future because it shortens the time horizon the decision maker must deal with. Whatever the source of information, the benefit is that *estimates of probabilities* of possible future events tend to become more accurate.

In general, obtaining additional (sample) information includes an associated cost. Consequently, a key question for a decision maker in such circumstances is whether the value of additional information is worth the cost of obtaining that information. The analysis of that type of problem is the subject of this section.

Let's take a look at an example.

Example 11-2

Suppose an advertising manager is trying to decide which of two advertising proposals to use for an upcoming promotion. The manager has developed the following payoff table:

		Market	
		70	30
		Strong	Weak
Alternative	Print Media	40*	20
	Video media	50	10

*($000)

At this point, the manager simply could make a decision using the expected value criterion with the information given. However, suppose that the manager has the option of testing the market, and this testing will provide *additional information* in the form of revised probabilities on whether the market will be strong or weak. If the manager chooses to test the market, it will cost $1,000; the manager, therefore, must decide whether the expected benefit from the test will offset the cost required to conduct the test.

If the manager conducts the test, this will undoubtedly alter the probabilities of a strong and weak market that were originally estimated. In fact, an integral part of the analysis in assessing the value of this sample information involves computing revised conditional probabilities. However, in order to home in on what we are trying to accomplish, let's suppose that the revised probabilities have been calculated, and consider how the decision maker could use that new information to make a decision.

The market test can show one of two things: a strong market or a weak market. Each result would pertain to the payoff table, but with different probabilities for the states of nature. Suppose these are the two possible results:

If the Market Test Shows a Strong Market		
	.95	.05
	Strong	Weak
Print	40	20
Video	50	10

If the Market Test Shows a Weak Market		
	.34	.66
	Strong	Weak
Print	40	20
Video	50	10

Finally, suppose the manager is able to determine that the probability that the market test will show a strong market is .59 and the probability that it will show a weak market is .41.

Analysis of the problem will result in determining an expected payoff for the two branches at the square node. This will enable the manager to select the branch (i.e., alternative) that has the higher expected payoff. Thus, if "Use market test" has the higher expected payoff, the manager would select that alternative, assuming the difference between its payoff and the payoff for "Don't use market test" is enough to cover the cost ($1,000) of the market test. Of course, if "Don't use market test" has the higher expected payoff, the manager would select that alternative because it would not require the cost of the market test.

The overall problem is shown in the tree diagram of Figure 11-5.

Figure 11-5   Conceptual Portrayal of Market Test Example

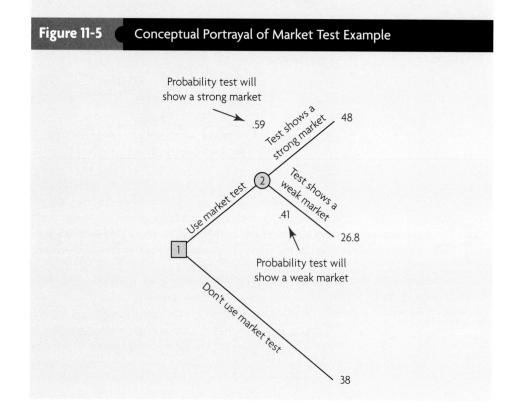

The payoffs for those two branches for "use market test" node (node 2) were determined as follows:

	Market	
	.95	.05
	Strong	Weak
Print	40	20
Video	50	10

$.95(40) + .05(20) = 39$
$.95(50) + .05(10) = 48$ (maximum expected payoff)

	Market	
	.34	.66
	Strong	Weak
Print	40	20
Video	50	10

$.34(40) + .66(20) = 26.8$ (maximum expected payoff)
$.34(50) + .66(10) = 23.6$

The payoff for the bottom branch was determined as follows:

	Market	
	.70	.30
	Strong	Weak
Print	40	20
Video	50	10

$.70(40) + .30(20) = 34$
$.70(50) + .30(10) = 38$ (maximum expected payoff)

Note that in each instance, we want the alternative (either *print* or *video*) that has the higher expected payoff.

The maximum expected payoff for the original table (i.e., the one with probabilities of .70 and .30) is 38 thousand. This, in effect, is the expected value of the branch "Don't use market test."

To find the expected payoff for the "Use market test" branch, we must combine the probability of each possible test result with the expected payoff for that result and then sum these. In other words, there is a probability of .59 that the market test will indicate a strong market, in which case the manager will choose the *video* alternative with an expected payoff of 48. Likewise, there is a probability of .41 that the test will show a weak market, and the manager will choose *print* with an expected payoff of 26.8. Hence, the overall or *combined* expected payoff for using the market test is

$$.59(48) + .41(26.8) = 39.308$$

Thus, our analysis boils down to the results shown in Figure 11-6. Using the market test has an expected value of $39.308 thousand, or $39,308, whereas not using the market test has an expected value of $38,000. We can see that using the market test has an expected value that is $1,308 more than not using the test. Recall, though, that the test will involve an additional cost of $1,000. It would be prudent to spend $1,000 if the additional expected payoff is $1,308. Hence, the manager should use the market test because to do so would lead to an expected gain of $308:

$$\$1,308 - \$1,000 = \$308$$

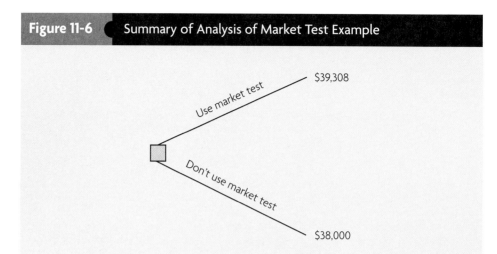

Figure 11-6 • Summary of Analysis of Market Test Example

Use market test — $39,308

Don't use market test — $38,000

The preceding analysis illustrates how a manager can assess the value of additional (sample) information when such information is available. In this instance, we found that the expected gain that would result from using the additional information outweighed the cost that would be needed to acquire that additional information.

In sum, we can compute the **expected value of sample** (additional) **information, or EVSI,** as

$$\text{EVSI} = \begin{matrix}\text{Expected value} \\ \textit{with} \text{ sample} \\ \text{information}\end{matrix} - \begin{matrix}\text{Expected value} \\ \textit{without} \text{ sample} \\ \text{information}\end{matrix} \qquad (11\text{-}3)$$

Then, if the *cost* of obtaining the additional information is less than this amount, it would seem reasonable to spend the money to obtain the information. But if the cost equals or exceeds the expected value of the information, it would seem reasonable to *not* spend the additional money needed to obtain the information.

In order to complete our discussion of decision making using additional information, we need to see how the revised probabilities are computed and how the probabilities for the test results are computed. Before doing that, let's take a brief look at a measure that sometimes is used to express the degree of increase in information from a sample (e.g., test results) relative to perfect information.

Efficiency of Sample Information

One way to judge how much information is generated by a sample is to compute the ratio of EVSI to EVPI. This is known as the *efficiency of sample information.* Thus:

$$\begin{matrix}\text{Efficiency of} \\ \text{sample information}\end{matrix} = \frac{\text{EVSI}}{\text{EVPI}} \qquad (11\text{-}4)$$

For the preceding example, the probabilities *without* additional information were .70 and .30, and the payoff table was

	Market	
	.70	.30
	Strong	Weak
Print	40	20
Video	50	10

The expected monetary value was 38 (i.e., $38,000). The expected profit (EPC) is

.70(50) + .30(20) = 41, or $41,000

(To compute EPC, multiply the best payoff in each column by the column probability and sum the products.)

EVPI is the difference between EPC and EMV. Thus:

EVPI = $41,000 − $38,000 = $3,000

In the preceding example, it was determined that the EVSI = $1,308. Hence, the efficiency of the sample information is

$$\frac{1,308}{3,000} = .436$$

This number is interpreted as follows: The number can range from 0 to 1.00. The closer the number is to 1.00, the closer the sample information is to being perfect; the closer the number is to 0, the less information there is in the sample. Thus, a value such as .436 is mid-range, meaning that relative to perfect information, the information that could be gained from the market test is moderate.

Computing the Probabilities

Two sets of probabilities were used in the analysis of sample information: the probabilities of the test results (.59 and .41) and the revised probabilities for the states of nature (i.e., strong and weak markets) given the test results (i.e., .95, .05 and .34, .66). We now turn our attention to the calculation of those values.

A basic piece of information that is necessary to the procedure is the reliability of the source of sample information (in this case, the market test). In assessing this reliability, the manager might make use of historical data on test results versus actual results, expert opinion, or his or her personal judgment of the probabilities. Let's suppose that in this case, the manager was able to obtain the reliability information from past records. The reliability information pertains to every possible combination of test result and actual result. The reliability figures for the preceding example are shown in Table 11-13.

The figures indicate that in past cases when the market actually was strong, the market test correctly indicated this information 80 percent of the time and incorrectly indicated a weak market 20 percent of the time. Moreover, when a weak market existed, the market test incorrectly indicated a strong market 10 percent of the time, while it correctly indicated a weak market 90 percent of the time. (Note that the probabilities in each *column*

Table 11-13	Reliability of Market Test	
	Actual State of Nature	
Results of Market Test	**Strong Market**	**Weak Market**
Shows strong market	.80	.10
Shows weak market	.20	.90

Table 11-14	Probability Calculations Given the Market Test Indicates a Strong Market			
Actual Market	**Conditional Probabilities**	**Prior Probabilities**	**Joint Probabilities**	**Revised Probabilities**
Strong	.80 ×	.70 =	.56	.56/.59 = .95
Weak	.10 ×	.30 =	.03	.03/.59 = .05
Marginal probability of a strong market		=	.59	

add to 1.00.) These probabilities are known as *conditional* probabilities because they express the reliability of the sampling device (e.g., market test) *given* the condition of actual market type.

In order to calculate the desired probabilities, we must combine these conditional probabilities with the original (*prior*) probabilities (.70 and .30) that were associated with the original payoff table. We must do this for each of the possible test results.

For a strong market test result, the calculations are shown in Table 11-14.

The first column of the table lists the two possible actual market conditions: strong and weak. The next column shows the probability of a market test that will show a strong market, given each possible actual market condition. The prior probabilities are the initial estimates of each type of market condition. Multiplying the prior probabilities by the conditional probabilities yields the *joint* probability of each market condition. The sum of these (e.g., .59) is the marginal probability that a test result will show a strong market. (Note that this one is one of the two types of probabilities we set out to compute.) The last column of the table illustrates the computation of the revised probabilities, given a market test that shows a strong market. The computation involves obtaining the ratio of the joint probability of each market condition to the marginal probability (in this case, .59). The resulting values are .95 and .05. (Note that these are two of the revised probabilities we set out to compute.)

Probabilities for a market test that shows a weak market are computed in a similar way. These are illustrated in Table 11-15. As in the preceding table, the sum of the joint probabilities indicates the marginal probability of this test result (weak market), and the ratios in the last column are the revised probabilities, given this test result.

Table 11-15	Probability Calculations Given the Market Test Indicates a Weak Market			
Actual Market	**Conditional Probabilities**	**Prior Probabilities**	**Joint Probabilities**	**Revised Probabilities**
Strong	.20 ×	.70 =	.14	.14/.41 = .34
Weak	.90 ×	.30 =	.27	.27/.41 = .66
Marginal probability of a weak market		=	.41	

Exhibit 11-11 Calculation of the Revised Probabilities for the Market Test Example

Microsoft Excel - ch11.3.xls

E14 =D14/$D$15

	A	B	C	D	E
1		Market Test Example Calculation of the Revised Probabilities			
2					
3			Condition -- Strong Market		
4	Actual market	Conditional Prob.	Prior Prob.	Joint Prob.	Revised probability
5	(1)	(2)	(3)	(4)=(2)x(3)	
6	Strong	0.8	0.7	0.56	0.949152542
7	Weak	0.1	0.3	0.03	0.050847458
8			Probability of Strong Market =	0.59	
9					
10			Condition -- Weak Market		
11	Actual market	Conditional Prob.	Prior Prob.	Joint Prob.	Revised probability
12	(1)	(2)	(3)	(4)=(2)x(3)	
13	Strong	0.2	0.7	0.14	0.341463415
14	Weak	0.9	0.3	0.27	0.658536585
15			Probability of Weak Market =	0.41	

Revised Probabilities / Solved Problem 5 (a)

Cell	Copied to cells	Formula
D6	D7	= B6 * C6
D8		= SUM (D6 : D7)
E6	E7	= D6 / $D$8
D13	D14	= B13 * C13
D15		= SUM (D13 : D14)
E13	E14	= D13 / $D$15

Computing Revised Probabilities with Excel

The revised probabilities calculated in Tables 11-14 and 11-15 also can be calculated using Excel. The calculation of the revised probabilities is repeated in Exhibit 11-11. The formulas used to calculate the revised probabilities are reported at the bottom of Exhibit 11-11.

Sensitivity Analysis

Analyzing decisions under risk requires working with estimated values: Both the payoffs and the probabilities for the states of nature are typically estimated values. Inaccuracies in these estimates can have an impact on choice of an alternative, and, ultimately, on the outcome of a decision. Given such possibilities, it is easy to see that a decision maker could benefit from an analysis of the *sensitivity* of a decision to possible errors in estimation. If it turns out that a certain decision will be deemed optimal over a wide range of values, the decision maker can proceed with relative confidence. Conversely, if analysis indicates a low tolerance for errors in estimation, additional efforts to pin down values may be needed.

In this section, sensitivity to *probability* estimates is examined. Sensitivity to payoff estimates is not covered; that topic is beyond the scope of this text.

Probability estimates are particularly interesting because it is not unusual to find instances in which managers are reluctant to attempt to pinpoint probabilities. This may stem from a desire to avoid having to justify those estimates, or it may be that certain managers are uncomfortable with making such estimates. The approach described here enables decision makers to identify a *range* of probabilities over which a particular alternative would be optimal. In other words, the manager or decision maker is presented with ranges of probabilities for various alternatives, and he or she need only decide if a probability is within a range, rather than decide on a specific value for the probabilities of a state of nature.

Let's consider an example that has two states of nature. Because only two states of nature can occur, this permits us to use *graphical analysis.* Suppose a decision maker has prepared this profit payoff table:

		State of Nature	
		#1	#2
	a	3	9
Alternative	*b*	12	1
	c	9	6

The analysis is designed to provide ranges for the probability of state of nature #2, merely because it is convenient to do so. Nonetheless, these ranges can easily be converted into ranges for state of nature #1, as you will see. We will use a graph that has two vertical axes and one horizontal axis, as shown in Figure 11-7. The left vertical axis pertains to payoffs if state of nature #1 occurs, whereas the right vertical axis pertains to payoffs if state of nature #2 occurs. The horizontal axis represents the probability of state of nature #2, $P(\#2)$. Each alternative can be represented on the graph by plotting its payoff for state of nature #1 on the left side and its payoff for state of nature #2 on the right side and then connecting

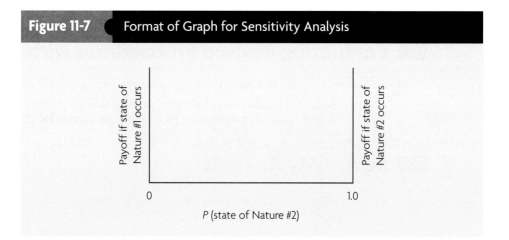

Figure 11-7   Format of Graph for Sensitivity Analysis

Payoff if state of Nature #1 occurs

Payoff if state of Nature #2 occurs

0   1.0

P (state of Nature #2)

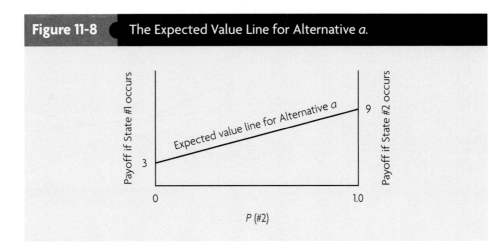

Figure 11-8   The Expected Value Line for Alternative *a*.

those two points with a straight line. This is illustrated for alternative *a* in Figure 11-8. The line represents the expected value of alternative *a* for the entire range of $P(\#2)$. Thus, for any value of $P(\#2)$, the expected value of alternative *a* can be found by running a vertical line from the value of $P(\#2)$ on the horizontal axis up to the point where it intersects the line. By running a horizontal line to either axis from that intersection, the expected value for that probability can be determined. An example is illustrated in Figure 11-9.

Of course, different values of $P(\#2)$ would produce different expected values. In general, you should be able to see from the graph that the nearer $P(\#2)$ is to 0, the closer the expected value of alternative *a* will be to the payoff for state of nature #1, whereas the nearer $P(\#2)$ is to 1.0, the closer the expected value will be to the payoff for state of nature #2.

Our analysis of sensitivity requires that all the alternatives be plotted on the same graph. Adding the other two alternatives produces the graph shown in Figure 11-10. You will recall that plotting the line for an alternative involves connecting its payoff for #1 (left axis) and its payoff for #2 (right axis.)

Because higher expected profits are more desirable than lower expected profits, the highest line for any given value of $P(\#2)$ represents the optimal alternative for that probability. Thus, referring to Figure 11-10, for low values of $P(\#2)$, alternative *b* would give

Figure 11-9   Example of Finding the Expected Value for Alternative *a* when $P(\#2)$ Is .50

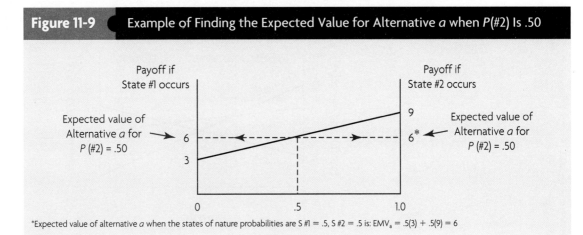

*Expected value of alternative *a* when the states of nature probabilities are S #1 = .5, S #2 = .5 is: $EMV_a = .5(3) + .5(9) = 6$

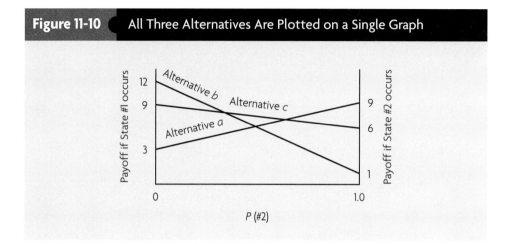

Figure 11-10   All Three Alternatives Are Plotted on a Single Graph

higher expected profits than either alternative a or c. However, for values of $P(\#2)$ close to 1.0, alternative a would have higher expected profits than either b or c, whereas for values of $P(\#2)$ somewhere in the middle, alternative c would yield the highest expected profits. What we want to determine is the *range* of $P(\#2)$ for which each alternative is the best.

We can see in Figure 11-11 that alternative b is best up to the point (probability) where lines b and c intersect because the b line is highest from $P(\#2) = 0$ up to that probability. Then, line c is highest from that point until it intersects with line a; after that, line a is highest all the way to $P(\#2) = 1.0$. Hence, the values of $P(\#2)$ at these intersections are the key values in our analysis because they represent the end points of the ranges. These concepts are illustrated in Figure 11-11.

In order to be able to determine the $P(\#2)$ values at the line intersections, it is necessary to first develop equations of the lines in terms of $P(\#2)$. Typically, the expected value (EV) is computed in the following way:

$$EV = P(\#1) \times \text{Payoff} \#1 + P(\#2) \times \text{Payoff} \#2$$

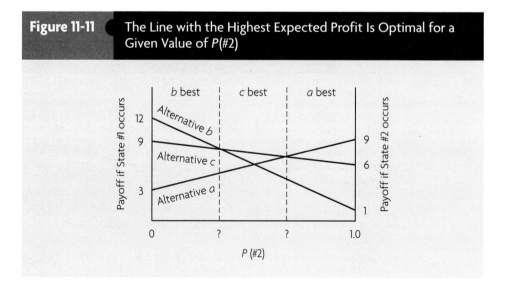

Figure 11-11   The Line with the Highest Expected Profit Is Optimal for a Given Value of $P(\#2)$

Because $P(\#1) + P(\#2) = 1$, $P(\#1) = 1 - P(\#2)$. Substituting $1 - P(\#2)$ in the expected value formula, we can eliminate $P(\#1)$ from the expression:

EV = $(1 - P(\#2)) \times$ Payoff #1 + $P(\#2) \times$ Payoff #2

Expanding the first term, and then rearranging terms, we obtain

EV = Payoff #1 + (Payoff #2 − Payoff #1)$P(\#2)$ (11-5)

Thus, for alternative a, the equation is

$EV_a = 3 + (9 - 3)P(\#2)$,   which is $EV_a = 3 + 6P(\#2)$

Similarly, for b and c we have

$EV_b = 12 + (1 - 12)P(\#2)$,   which is $EV_b = 12 - 11P(\#2)$
$EV_c = 9 + (6 - 9)P(\#2)$,   which is $EV_c = 9 - 3P(\#2)$

Now, to find the values of $P(\#2)$ at the intersections, we can set two equations equal to each other and solve for $P(\#2)$. Thus, for the intersection of lines b and c, we have

$12 - 11P(\#2) = 9 - 3P(\#2)$

Solving for $P(\#2)$ yields

$8P(\#2) = 3$,   so $P(\#2) = 3/8$,   or .375

For the intersection of lines a and c, we set $EV_a = EV_c$:

$3 + 6P(\#2) = 9 - 3P(\#2)$

Solving for $P(\#2)$, we find

$9P(\#2) = 6$,   so $P(\#2) = 6/9$,   or .67

Thus, lines b and c intersect at $P(\#2) = .375$. So, alternative b is best over the range of $P(\#2)$ from 0 to less than .375 (note that for $P(\#2) = .375$, b and c are equivalent). Similarly, alternative c is best from $P(\#2) > .375$ to $P(\#2) < .67$, and from there up to $P(\#2) = 1.0$, alternative a is best.

In sum, the range of $P(\#2)$ over which each alternative is best is

For alternative a: $.67 < P(\#2) \leq 1.0$
For alternative b: $0 \leq P(\#2) < .375$
For alternative c: $.375 < P(\#2) < .67$

These ranges give the decision maker important insight on probability estimates. For example, a decision maker may be reluctant to specify an exact probability for state of nature #2. However, with this information, the decision maker merely has to identify the most appropriate *range* for $P(\#2)$. Thus, if the decision maker believes that $P(\#2)$ is somewhere in the range of, say, .80 to .90, according to the preceding calculations, alternative a would be best. Or, if the decision maker believes that $P(\#2)$ lies close to .50, then alternative c would be best.

A similar analysis can be performed if the payoffs are costs or other values that are to be minimized rather than maximized. In such cases, the *lowest* line for a given value of $P(\#2)$ would be most desirable. An example of this is illustrated in the Solved Problems section at the end of this chapter.

One final comment regarding the use of $P(\#2)$. It was mentioned previously that $P(\#2)$ is used for convenience. It happens that the equations of the lines are a bit easier to develop using $P(\#2)$ rather than $P(\#1)$. However, should a problem refer to $P(\#1)$ ranges rather than

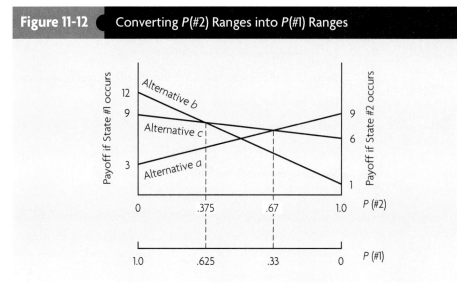

Figure 11-12 Converting *P*(#2) Ranges into *P*(#1) Ranges

P(#2), you can proceed by finding the ranges in terms of P(#2) and then converting these into P(#1) ranges as the final step. This merely involves recognizing that P(#1) and P(#2) are complements. For example, if P(#2) = 0, then P(#1) = 1.0; if P(#2) = .40, then P(#1) = .60; and so on. Hence, if alternative *a* is optimal for the range $0 \leq P(\#2) < .40$, then in terms of P(#1), alternative *a* is optimal for the range $.60 < P(\#1) \leq 1.00$. P(#1) line drawn at the bottom of Exhibit 11-2. Figure 11-12 further illustrates this concept using the previous example.

◤ Utility

Throughout this chapter, decision criteria have been illustrated that use monetary value as the basis of choosing among alternatives. Although monetary value is a common basis for decision making, it is not the only basis, even for business decisions. In certain instances, decision makers use *multiple criteria*, one of which is the potential *satisfaction* or *dissatisfaction* associated with possible payoffs.

For example, a great many people participate in state lotteries. However, the fact is lotteries have a *negative* expected value: the *expected* return is less than the cost of the lottery. If it were not, the states would lose money by running lotteries. Why do people play lotteries, then? The answer is that they are hoping to win a large amount of money, and they are willing to sacrifice a relatively small amount of money to have that chance. In other words, even though their chances of winning are close to zero, they have a greater **utility** for the potential winnings, despite a negative expected value, than for the amount of money they have to give up (pay) to participate in the lottery. Similar arguments can be made for other forms of wagering. People who behave in this fashion, whether for purposes of wagering or in other forms of decision making, are sometimes referred to as **risk takers**.

Just the opposite happens when a person buys insurance, giving up a fixed dollar amount to insure against an event (e.g., a fire) that has very little chance of occurring. Even so, if a fire or other insured event did occur, the consequences would be so catastrophic that an individual would not want to be exposed to that degree of risk. Thus, even though buying

When the cold war ended, the United States and Russia entered into an agreement that was designed to reduce the number of nuclear weapons in their possession. The number of weapons to be destroyed was estimated at over 10,000 for the United States and approximately 20,000 for Russia. The plutonium recovered from these weapons was extremely toxic and considered very dangerous to the environment.

Not only was the plutonium extremely toxic and dangerous, but both countries were concerned that terrorist groups would gain access to the excess plutonium and use it to manufacture nuclear weapons. Therefore, it was very important that the United States and Russia find a safe and secure way to dispose of the plutonium.

On September 2, 1998, the United States and Russia agreed to destroy 50 metric tons of plutonium from their respective weapons program. Both countries wanted to dispose of the excess plutonium at a mutually agreeable rate. Thus, the United States and Russia had to agree on the method of disposal to be used by each country.

In the United States, the Office of Fissile Materials Disposition (OFMD) had been designated to be responsible for the elimination of nuclear weapons. OFMD recognized that some of its decisions would be controversial. Therefore, it hired a team of operations research/management science (OR/MS) consultants to develop a justifiable decision-making process regarding the elimination of these weapons. The team of consultants stated three main objectives:

1. Nonproliferation.
   A. Minimize theft.
   B. Minimize secret diversion of plutonium.
   C. Ensure irreversibility (making it as difficult as possible to recover the actual plutonium to prevent manufacture of nuclear weapons).
   D. Encourage international cooperation with United States for nuclear nonproliferation objective.
   E. Minimize the time required for scheduling the disposition of the plutonium.
2. Operational effectiveness (minimizing investment and cost).
3. Objectives related to the environment, safety, and health.
   A. Maximize human health and safety.
   B. Minimize the negative effects to the environment.
   C. Minimize the negative impact to the local economy.

Plutonium can be disposed using one of three different methods:

1. Reactor options (plutonium is oxidized and converted into reactor fuel, where it is degraded to nonweapon isotopic form).
2. Immobilization option, where plutonium is mixed with glass or ceramics and placed in a protective radiation shield.

This option would have time and cost advantages over the reactor option. However, using this option does not change the isotopic makeup of plutonium, where it would be relatively easy to make nuclear weapons.
3. Direct disposal (plutonium is buried deep into the earth).

Within the three methods for disposal named above, OFMD identified 13 disposition alternatives. These alternatives were analyzed by the U.S. OR/MS team to determine their priority and importance.

The OR/MS team developed a multiattribute utility (MAU) model to evaluate the 13 disposition alternatives. The Russian and American scientists agreed on the use of MAU as a fundamental method to analyze the options regarding the disposition of plutonium. However, Russia and the United States differed in terms of how they viewed the surplus plutonium. The United States considered it to be a liability, while Russia viewed it as a potential asset, a source of energy that could be used to generate electricity.

Russian and American scientists agreed on the criteria that would be used to evaluate the disposition of the plutonium. However, Russian scientists made some changes to the hierarchy of objectives, while maintaining the core of the MAU model. These changes were made to reflect the difference in Russia's position, which viewed plutonium as an asset.

The scope of the disposition was reduced from 50 metric tons to 34 metric tons of excess material because neither country wanted to rely on the immobilization technology. The remaining 16 metric tons of plutonium were unsuitable for use in reactor fuel. To put it into perspective, 34 metric tons are more than sufficient to build thousands of weapons of mass destruction.

Both countries were able to use the recommendation of MAU. The process involving MAU has helped to refine the alternatives and to communicate the results in an organized fashion to all of the stakeholders from both countries so that each country will know where the other one stands in terms of disposition of plutonium. The United States and Russia have continued to use MAU with regards to their plutonium disposition and other nonproliferation issues.

Russia carried out plutonium disposal under ISTC project 369 and ISTC project 1443. These projects assisted Russian scientists to understand and to customize MAU for Russia's needs. Ultimately both countries will dispose of a large part of their surplus plutonium using a reactor approach (fabrication into fuel for existing nuclear reactors). This approach is able to convert the surplus plutonium to a form that cannot be easily altered, thus meeting the object of both countries by making it difficult for terrorists to use the excess plutonium for nuclear weapons.

Source: J. Butler, A. Chebeskov, J. Dyer, T. Edmunds, J. Jia, and V. Oussanov, "The United States and Russia Evaluate Plutonium Disposition Options with Multiattribute Utility Theory," *Interfaces* 35, no. 1 (January–February 2005), pp. 88–101.

insurance carries a negative monetary value, most individuals recognize the merit of doing so. We refer to such individuals as **risk averters.** Of course, some individuals exhibit both forms of behavior in their decision making; they are risk takers for certain kinds of decisions but risk averters for others. A lottery player who owns a life insurance policy would be an example of this.

To get an idea of how a decision maker might use utilities in making a decision, consider a person who buys a lottery ticket. Suppose that each ticket costs $1 and that the chance of winning the $1,000,000 jackpot is 1/10 million. The payoff table would look like this:

| | Dollar Value 999,999 | | |
Alternative	$p = .0000001$ Ticket Wins	$p = .9999999$ Ticket Doesn't Win	Expected Payoff
Buy lottery ticket	$1	−$1	−$.90
Don't buy ticket	0	0	0

Note that the expected payoff from buying a lottery ticket is negative, raising the question of why a person would buy a ticket at all. However, suppose we were to ask such a person his or her subjective assessment of the utilities of the various payoffs. We might discover that winning the lottery would have a disproportionately high utility relative to the cost of a ticket. Hence, if we replace the dollar payoffs with some measure of the utility of that payoff, and then compute the expected *utility,* a somewhat different picture emerges. The expected utility for that person for buying the ticket is *positive:*

| | Utility | | |
Alternative	$p = .0000001$ Ticket Wins	$p = .9999999$ Ticket Doesn't Win	Expected Utility
Buy lottery ticket	100,000,000	−1	9
Don't buy ticket	0	0	0

Thus, *utility* is a measure of the potential satisfaction derived from money. Although utility can be an important factor in certain kinds of decision making, assessing and using utility values can be rather complex. Not only does utility vary within an individual for different types of situations, but it also seems to vary among individuals for the same situations. That is, different people might choose different alternatives in a given instance because of utility considerations.

Summary

Decision theory is a general approach to decision making. It is very useful for a decision maker who must choose from a list of alternatives, knowing that one of a number of possible future states of nature will occur and that this will have an impact on the payoff realized by a particular alternative.

Decision models can be categorized according to the degree of uncertainty that is assigned to the occurrence of the states of nature. This can range from complete knowledge about which state will occur, to partial knowledge (probabilities), to no knowledge (no probabilities, or complete uncertainty). When complete uncertainty exists, the approach a decision maker takes in choosing among alternatives depends on how optimistic or pessimistic he or she is, and it also depends on other circumstances related to the eventual outcome or payoff. Under complete certainty, decisions are relatively straightforward. Under partial uncertainty, expected values often are used to evaluate alternatives. An extension of the use of expected values enables decision makers to assess the value of improved or perfect information about which state of nature will occur.

Problems that involve a single decision are usually best handled through payoff tables, whereas problems that involve a sequence, or possible sequence, of decisions are usually best handled using tree diagrams because payoff tables are difficult to utilize if there are multiple stages to be considered.

Sometimes, decision makers can improve the decision process by taking into account additional (sample) information, which enables them to modify state-of-nature probabilities. Because there is almost always an additional cost associated with obtaining that sample information, the decision maker must decide whether the expected value of that information is worth the cost necessary to obtain it.

Sensitivity analysis can sometimes be useful to decision makers, particularly for situations in which they find it difficult to accurately assess the probabilities of the various states of nature. Sensitivity analysis can help by providing ranges of probabilities for which a given alternative would be chosen, using expected monetary value as the criterion. Hence, the problem of specifying probabilities is reduced to deciding whether a probability merely falls within a range of values.

Although expected monetary value is a widely used approach to decision making, certain individuals and certain situations may require consideration of utilities, which reflect how decision makers view the satisfaction associated with different monetary payoffs.

Glossary

Certainty Refers to a decision problem in which probabilities of occurrence for the various states of nature are known.

Coefficient of optimism, α Used with Hurwicz criterion; ranges from 0 (pessimistic) to 1.0 (optimistic).

Decision Criterion A standard or rule for choosing among alternatives (e.g., choose the alternative with the highest expected profit).

Decision Tree A schematic representation of a decision problem that involves the use of branches and nodes.

Equal Likelihood Criterion A decision criterion that seeks the alternative with the best average payoff, assuming all states of nature are equally likely to occur.

Expected Monetary Value (EMV) For an alternative, the sum of the products of each possible payoff and the probability of that payoff.

Expected Opportunity Loss (EOL) For an alternative, the sum of the products of each possible regret and the probability of that regret.

Expected Payoff under Certainty (EPC) For a set of alternatives, the sum of the products of the best payoff for each state of nature and that state's probability.

Expected Regret See **Expected Opportunity Loss.**

Expected Value of Perfect Information (EVPI) The maximum additional benefit attainable if a problem involving risk could be reduced to a problem in which it was certain which state of nature would occur. Equal to the minimum expected regret. Also equal to EPC minus best EMV.

Expected Value of Sample Information (EVSI) The expected benefit of acquiring sample information. Equal to the difference between the best EMV without information and the best EMV with information.

Hurwicz Criterion A decision criterion that allows the decision maker to incorporate his/her degree of optimism in choosing an alternative.

Maximax A decision criterion that specifies choosing the alternative with the best overall payoff. When costs or times are involved, the term *minimin* is used.

Maximin A decision criterion that specifies choosing the alternative with the best of the worst payoffs for all alternatives. When costs or times are involved, the term *minimax* is used.

Minimax Regret A decision criterion that specifies choosing the alternative that has the lowest regret (opportunity loss).

Opportunity Loss For an alternative given a state of nature, the difference between that alternative's payoff and the best possible payoff for that state of nature.

Payoff Table A table that shows the payoff for each alternative for each state of nature.

Regret See **Opportunity Loss.**

Risk A decision problem in which the states of nature have probabilities associated with their occurrence.

Risk Averters Individuals that avoid taking risks. The decision maker has less utility for greater risk.

Risk Takers Individuals that like taking risks and that have a greater utility for the potential winnings even though their chances of winning are very low.

Sequential Decisions Decisions where the outcome of one decision affects other decisions.

State of Nature Possible future events.

Uncertainty Refers to a decision problem in which probabilities of occurrence for the various states of nature are unknown.

Utility Of a payoff, a measure of the personal satisfaction associated with a payoff.

Solved Problems

Problem 1

Given this *profit* payoff table:

		State of Nature		
		#1	#2	#3
Alternative	a	12	18	15
	b	17	10	14
	c	22	16	10
	d	14	14	14

Determine which alternative would be chosen using each of these decision criteria:

a. Maximax.
b. Maximin.
c. Minimax regret.
d. Equal likelihood.
e. The Hurwicz criterion with $\alpha = .40$.
f. Repeat part *a* through part *e* using Excel.

Solution

a. The maximax approach seeks the alternative that has the best overall payoff. Because these are profits, the best payoff would be the largest value, which is the payoff 22 (row *c*, column #1). Thus, in order to have a chance at that payoff, the decision maker should choose alternative *c*.

b. The maximin approach is to choose the alternative that will provide the best of the worst possible payoffs. To find this, first identify the worst profit possible for each alternative:

Alternative	Worst Payoff	
a	12	
b	10	
c	10	
d	14	(best)

Because alternative *d* has the best of the worst payoffs, it would be chosen using maximin.

c. In order to find the minimax regret decision, we must first obtain the opportunity loss, or regret, table. This is a two-step process. First, identify the best payoff in each *column*. Then subtract every payoff in each column from the best payoff in the column. Hence, the best payoffs are: 22 in column #1, 18 in column #2, and 15 in column #3. The resulting regret (opportunity loss) table is

Opportunity Loss Table
State of Nature

		#1	#2	#3	Worst Regret	
	a	10	0	0	10	
	b	5	8	1	8	
Alternative	c	0	2	5	5	(minimum regret)
	d	8	4	1	8	

(Notice that none of the regrets is negative. This will *always* be the case.) Because alternative *c* has the lowest of the worst regrets, it would be chosen.

d. Using the equal likelihood criterion, we must determine the average payoff for each alternative. We do this by summing the payoffs for each and then dividing by the number of payoffs (three). The resulting averages are

Alternative	Average Payoff
a	15 = (12 + 18 + 15)/3
b	13.67 = (17 + 10 + 14)/3
c	16 (best) = (22 + 16 + 10)/3
d	14 = (14 + 14 + 14)/3

Because alternative *c* yields the highest average profit using the equal likelihood criterion, it would be chosen.

e. For the Hurwicz criterion, identify the best and worst payoffs for each alternative. Then, multiply the best payoff by the coefficient of optimism, α, and the worst payoff by $(1 - \alpha)$ and sum the results. The alternative that has the highest sum (if profits or a similar type payoff is involved would be chosen. For costs, the alternative with the lowest sum would be chosen. Thus,

Alternative a	.40(18) + .60(12) = 14.40	
Alternative b	.40(17) + .60(10) = 12.80	
Alternative c	.40(22) + .60(10) = 14.80	(best)
Alternative d	.40(14) + .60(14) = 14.00	

f. Exhibit 11-12 shows how to solve Solved Problem 1 using Excel. The necessary formulas are exhibited at the bottom of Exhibit 11-12.

Exhibit 11-12   Solved Problem 1: Decision Making under Complete Uncertainty—A Profit Maximization Problem (Part *f*)

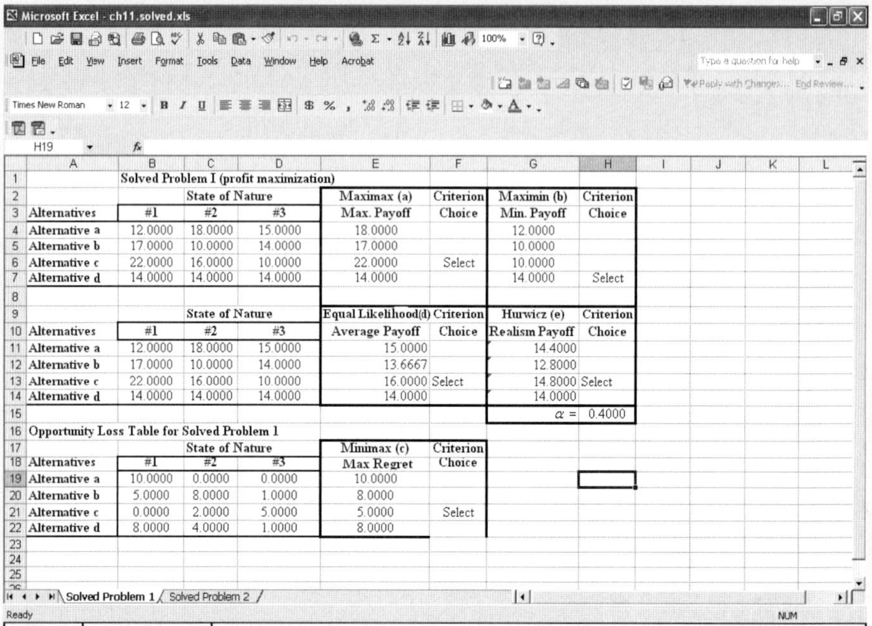

Cell	Copied to	Formula
E4	E5 : E7	= MAX (B4 : D4)
F4	F5 : F7	= IF (E4 = MAX (E\$4 : E\$7), "Select", " ")
G4	G5 : G7	= MIN (B4 : D4)
H4	H5 : H7	= IF (G4 = MAX (G\$4 : G\$7), "Select", " ")
E11	E12 : E14	= AVERAGE (B11 : D11)
F11	F12 : F14	= IF (E11 = MAX (E11 : E14), "Select", " ")
G11	G12 : G14	= \$H\$15 * MAX (B11 : D11) + (1 − \$H\$15) * MIN (B11 : D11)
H11	H12 : H14	= IF (G11 = MAX (G11 : G14), "Select", " ")
E19	E20 : E22	= MAX (B19 : D19)
F19	F20 : F22	= IF (E19 = MIN (E\$19 : E\$22), "Select", " ")
B19	B20 : B22	= MAX (\$B\$11 : \$B\$14) − B11
		The calculations in solved Problem 1 are very similar to formulas in Exhibit 11-1

Problem 2

Suppose the payoffs in the preceding problem had been *costs* rather than profits. Determine which alternative would be chosen, using these decision criteria:

a. Minimin.
b. Minimax.

c. Minimax regret.
d. Equal likelihood.
e. Hurwicz criterion with $\alpha = .4$.
f. Use Excel and solve part *a* through part *e*.

Solution

a. The minimin approach seeks the lowest overall cost. Hence, the smallest value is the best. The smallest value in the table given in Solved Problem 1 is 10. It appears both as a possible cost for alternative *b* and for alternative *c*. Hence, using minimin, the decision maker would be indifferent between those two alternatives.

b. For minimax, we must determine the worst cost for each alternative. Because the values are now *costs*, the *largest* value for each alternative is listed:

Alternative	Worst Cost	
a	18	
b	17	
c	22	
d	14	(lowest cost)

Because alternative *d* has the best of the worst costs, it would be chosen.

c. To obtain the regret table, we must identify the best cost for each column. Because costs are involved, we want the lowest cost in each column. For column #1, 12 is the lowest; for column #2, 10 is the lowest; and for column #3, 10 is the lowest. When costs are involved, the regrets are obtained by subtracting the lowest cost in the column *from* all of the costs in the column. Again, this results in all positive and zero regrets:

		Opportunity Loss Table State of Nature				
		#1	#2	#3	Worst Regret	
	a	0	8	5	8	
	b	5	0	4	5	
Alternative	*c*	10	6	0	10	
	d	2	4	4	4	(minimum regret)

Because alternative *d* had the lowest of the worst regrets, it would be chosen.

d. Using the equal likelihood criterion, we find the average cost for each alternative. These averages are the same as determined in the preceding problem:

Alternative	Average Cost	
a	15	
b	13.67	(best)
c	16	
d	14	

Because alternative *b* has the lowest average cost, it would be chosen.

e. Hurwicz criterion

Alternative *a*	$.4(12) + .6(18) = 15.6$	
Alternative *b*	$.4(10) + .6(17) = 14.2$	
Alternative *c*	$.4(10) + .6(22) = 17.2$	
Alternative *d*	$.4(14) + .6(14) = 14$	(select)

Using the Hurwicz criterion, the best and worst cost would be selected for each alternative. The best (lowest) cost would be multiplied by $\alpha = .4$ and the the worst (highest) cost would be multiplied by $(1 - \alpha)$. The sum of these two cross products would be the total cost for each alternative using the Hurwicz Criterion. For example, for alternative *a*, the lowest cost is 12 and the highest cost is 18. Therefore, $(.4)(12) + (.6)(18) = 15.6$.

Exhibit 11-13   Solved Problem 2: Decision Making under Complete Uncertainty—A Cost Minimization Problem (part *f*)

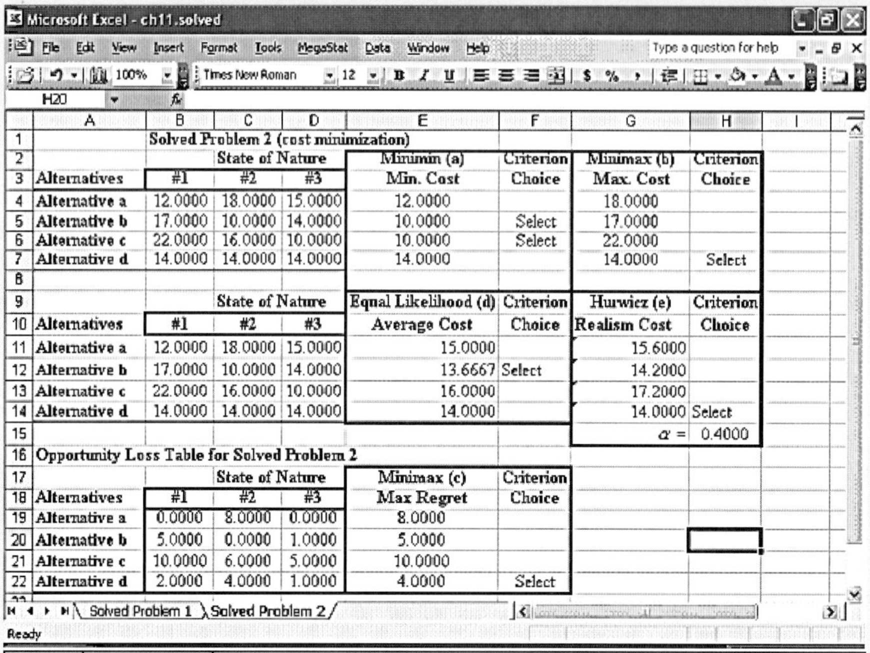

	A	B	C	D	E	F	G	H	I
1		Solved Problem 2 (cost minimization)							
2		State of Nature			Minimin (a)	Criterion	Minimax (b)	Criterion	
3	Alternatives	#1	#2	#3	Min. Cost	Choice	Max. Cost	Choice	
4	Alternative a	12.0000	18.0000	15.0000	12.0000		18.0000		
5	Alternative b	17.0000	10.0000	14.0000	10.0000	Select	17.0000		
6	Alternative c	22.0000	16.0000	10.0000	10.0000	Select	22.0000		
7	Alternative d	14.0000	14.0000	14.0000	14.0000		14.0000	Select	
8									
9		State of Nature			Equal Likelihood (d)	Criterion	Hurwicz (e)	Criterion	
10	Alternatives	#1	#2	#3	Average Cost	Choice	Realism Cost	Choice	
11	Alternative a	12.0000	18.0000	15.0000	15.0000		15.6000		
12	Alternative b	17.0000	10.0000	14.0000	13.6667	Select	14.2000		
13	Alternative c	22.0000	16.0000	10.0000	16.0000		17.2000		
14	Alternative d	14.0000	14.0000	14.0000	14.0000		14.0000	Select	
15								$\alpha =$	0.4000
16	Opportunity Loss Table for Solved Problem 2								
17		State of Nature			Minimax (c)	Criterion			
18	Alternatives	#1	#2	#3	Max Regret	Choice			
19	Alternative a	0.0000	8.0000	0.0000	8.0000				
20	Alternative b	5.0000	0.0000	1.0000	5.0000				
21	Alternative c	10.0000	6.0000	5.0000	10.0000				
22	Alternative d	2.0000	4.0000	1.0000	4.0000	Select			

Cell	Copied to	Formula
E4	E5 : E7	= MIN (B4 : D4)
F4	F5 : F7	= IF (MIN (E$4 : E$7), "Select", " ")
G4	G5 : G7	= MAX (B4 : D4)
H4	H5 : H7	= IF (G4 = MIN (G$4 : G$7), "Select", " ")
E11	E12 : E14	= AVERAGE (B11 : D11)
F11	F12 : F14	= IF (E11 = MIN (E$11 : E$14), "Select", " ")
G11	G12 : G14	= $H$15 * MIN (B11 : D11) + (1 − $H$15) * MAX (B11 : D11)
H11	H12 : H14	= IF (G11 = MIN (G11 : G14), "Select", " ")
B19	B20 : B22	= B11 − MIN ($B$11 : $B$14)
E19	E20 : E22	= MAX (B19 : D19)
F19	F20 : F22	= IF (E19 = MIN (E$19 : E$22), "Select", " ")

f.   Exhibit 11-13 shows how to solve Solved Problem 2 using Excel. The necessary formulas are displayed at the bottom of Exhibit 11-13. Note that the approach is very similar to solving Solved Problem 1. However, instead of maximizing profit, the objective is to minimize cost.

Problem 3

For the payoff table given in Solved Problem 1, suppose the manager has assigned probabilities of .2 to the occurrence of state #1, .5 to the occurrence of state #2, and .3, to the occurrence of state #3.

a.   Which alternative would be chosen using maximum expected value as the criterion, treating the payoffs as profits?
b.   Calculate the expected value of perfect information using (1) the expected payoff under certainty approach and (2) the expected regret approach.
c.   Repeat parts *a* and *b* using Excel.

Solution

a.   Compute the expected value of each alternative:

$$EV_a: .2(12) + .5(18) + .3(15) = 15.9 \quad \text{(best)}$$
$$EV_b: .2(17) + .5(10) + .3(14) = 12.6$$
$$EV_c: .2(22) + .5(16) + .3(10) = 15.4$$
$$EV_d: .2(14) + .5(14) + .3(14) = 14.0$$

Because alternative *a* has the largest expected profit, it would be selected using expected monetary value as the decision criterion.

b.   (1)   The expected payoff under certainty approach is

$$\text{EVPI} = \text{Expected payoff under certainty} - \text{Expected monetary value}$$

The expected payoff under certainty is found by taking the best payoff in each column, multiplying that by the column probability, and summing the results for all columns. Thus:

$$\text{EPC}: .2(22) + .5(18) + .3(15) = 17.9$$

Then:

$$\text{EVPI}: 17.9 - 15.9 = 2.0$$

(2)   Using the regret approach, find the expected regret for each alternative: Using the opportunity loss table obtained in Solved Problem 1*c*, we have

Alternative	Expected Regret	
a	$.2(10) + .5(0) + .3(0) = 2.0$	(lowest)
b	$.2(5) + .5(8) + .3(1) = 5.3$	
c	$.2(0) + .5(2) + .3(5) = 2.5$	
d	$.2(8) + .5(4) + .3(1) = 3.9$	

The lowest expected regret is equal to 2.0. This amount is the expected value of perfect information, EVPI. Note that this agrees with the answer obtained in 1*b*.

c.   For Solved Problem 3, Excel is used to calculate the revised probabilities and EVPI. The bottom of Exhibit 11-14 shows all of the necessary formulas.

Exhibit 11-14   Calculation of the Revised Probabilities and Expected Value of Perfect Information for Solved Problem 3 (part *c*)

	A	B	C	D	E	F	G	H	I	J
1		Payoff Table for Solved Problem 3								
2		State of Nature								
3	Alternatives	#1	#2	#3	EMV	Choice				
4	Alternative a	12.0000	18.0000	15.0000	15.9	Select				
5	Alternative b	17.0000	10.0000	14.0000	12.6					
6	Alternative c	22.0000	16.0000	10.0000	15.4					
7	Alternative d	14.0000	14.0000	14.0000	14					
8	Probability	0.2	0.5	0.3						
9										
10		Opportunity Loss Table for Solved Problem 3								
11		State of Nature								
12	Alternatives	#1	#2	#3	EOL	Choice				
13	Alternative a	10.0000	0.0000	0.0000	0	Select				
14	Alternative b	5.0000	8.0000	1.0000	2					
15	Alternative c	0.0000	2.0000	5.0000	5.3					
16	Alternative d	8.0000	4.0000	1.0000	2.5					
17	Probability	0.2	0.5	0.3						
18						EPC= Expected Payoff Under Certainty				
19	Payoff decision	22	18	15	17.9					
20	with perfect info.									
21	EVPI= 2									
22										

Example 1 / EMV-EOL \ Solved Problem 3 /

Cell	Copied to	Formula
E4	E5 : E7	= SUMPRODUCT (B4 : D4, $B$8 : $D$8)
F4	F5 : F7	= IF (E4 = MAX ($E$4 : $E$7), "Select", " ")
B13	B14 : B16	= MAX ($B$4 : $B$7) − B4
C13	C14 : C16	= MAX ($C$4 : $C$7) − C4
D13	D14 : D16	= MAX ($D$4 : $D$7) − D4
E13	E14 : D16	= SUMPRODUCT (B12 : D12, $B$8 : $D$8)
F13	F14 : F16	= IF (E14 = MIN ($E$14 : $E$16), "Select", " ")
E19		= SUMPRODUCT (B8 : D8, $B$19 : $D$19)
B21		= E19 − MAX (E4 : E7)

Problem 4

Given this table of estimated *costs:*

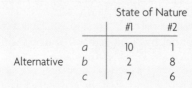

		State of Nature	
		#1	#2
	a	10	1
Alternative	b	2	8
	c	7	6

Find the range of $P(\#2)$ for which each alternative has the best expected value.

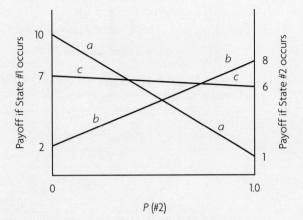

Solution

First, plot each alternative's expected value line on a graph. To do this, mark the payoff for #1 on the left vertical axis and the payoff for #2 on the right vertical axis, then connect these two points with a straight line. Then label each line (e.g., alternative *a*).

Because costs are involved rather than profits, the *lower* the expected value (i.e., the expected *cost*), the better. Consequently, it is the lowest line for given values of $P(\#2)$ that is most desirable. The following figure shows this. We can see, then, that for values of $P(\#2)$ near 0, alternative *b* has the lowest expected cost, whereas for values of $P(\#2)$ close to 1.0, alternative *a* is best. Note that alternative *c* is never best. In order to find the value of $P(\#2)$ for which Alternative *b* and alternative *a* are equivalent, we must formulate equations for lines *a* and *b*. Recall that each line has the form:

$$EV = \text{Payoff \#1} + (\text{Payoff \#2} - \text{Payoff \#1}) \times P(\#2)$$

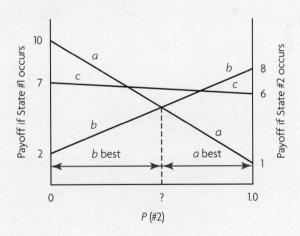

Thus, for line *a* we have

$$EV_a = 10 + (1 - 10)P(\#2), \qquad \text{which reduces to } EV_a = 10 - 9P(\#2)$$

For line *b*, we have

$$EV_b = 2 + (8 - 2)P(\#2), \qquad \text{which reduces to } EV_b = 2 + 6P(\#2)$$

Setting these equal to each other and solving for $P(\#2)$ gives us

$$10 - 9P(\#2) = 2 + 6P(\#2)$$

Rearranging terms produces

$$15P(\#2) = 8$$

Solving for $P(\#2)$:

$$P(\#2) = 8/15 \qquad \text{or } .533$$

Thus, when $P(\#2) = .533$, the decision maker would be indifferent between choosing alternative a or b. For values of $P(\#2)$ from 0 to less than .533, alternative b will give the lowest expected cost, whereas for values of $P(\#2)$ larger than .533, alternative a has the lowest expected cost. Hence, the ranges over which each alternative is best are

Alternative	Best over Range of
b	$0 \leq P(\#2) < .533$
a	$.533 < P(\#2) \leq 1.0$
c	Never

Problem 5

Decision making with sample information A manager has developed a table that shows payoffs ($000) for a future store. The payoffs depend on the size of the store and the strength of demand:

Payoff Table
States of Nature
Demand

		Low	High
	Small	30	50
Alternatives Store Size	Large	10	80

The manager estimates that the probability of low demand is .50, and the probability of high demand is .50.

The manager could request that a local research firm conduct a survey (cost: $2,000) that would better indicate whether demand will be low or high. In discussions with the research firm, the manager has learned the following about the reliability of surveys conducted by the firm:

Actual Result Was

		Low	High
Survey Showed	Low	.90	.30
	High	.10	.70

a. If the manager should decide to use the survey, what would the revised probabilities be for demand, and what probabilities should be used for survey results (i.e., survey shows Low and survey shows High demand)?

b. Construct a tree diagram for this problem.

c. Solve parts a and b using Excel.

d. Determine the EVSI.

e. Would you recommend that the manager use the survey? Explain.

Solution

a. The following are revised probabilities if the survey shows Low demand:

Actual Demand	Conditional Probability		Prior Probability		Joint Probability	Revised Probability
Low	.90	$\times$	.50	$=$	.45	.45/.60 = .75
High	.30	$\times$	.50	$=$	.15	.15/.60 = .25
Marginal probability of low demand				$=$	.60	1.00

The following are revised probabilities if survey shows High demand:

Actual Demand	Conditional Probability		Prior Probability		Joint Probability	Revised Probability	
Low	.10	×	.50	=	.05	.05/.40 =	.125
High	.70	×	.50	=	.35	.35/.40 =	.875
Marginal probability of high demand				=	.40		1.000

Hence, the revised probabilities are $P(\text{Low}) = .75$ and $P(\text{High}) = .25$ if the survey shows Low demand; and $P(\text{Low}) = .125$ and $P(\text{High}) = .875$ if the survey shows High demand. Further, the probability that the survey will show Low demand is .60 (the sum of joint probabilities) and the probability the survey will show High demand is .40.

b.

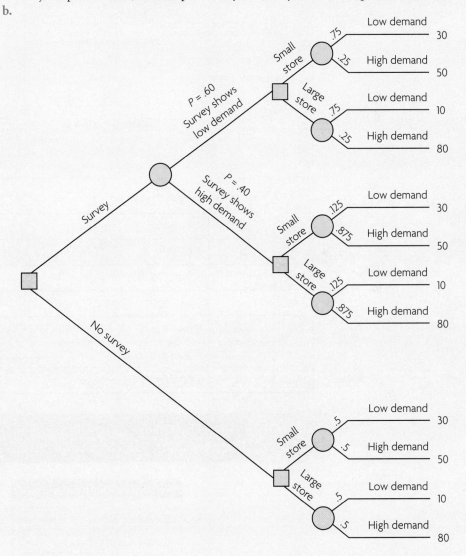

c.   Exhibit 11-15 shows the calculation of the revised probabilities using Excel for Solved Problem 5. The necessary formulas are displayed at the bottom of Exhibit 11-15. Exhibits 11-16, 11-17, and 11-18 demonstrate how to prepare the decision tree of Solved Problem 5. Exhibits 11-16 and 11-17 show how to add a branch. In adding the

Exhibit 11-15   Calculation of the Revised Probabilities for Solved Problem 5 (part *c*)

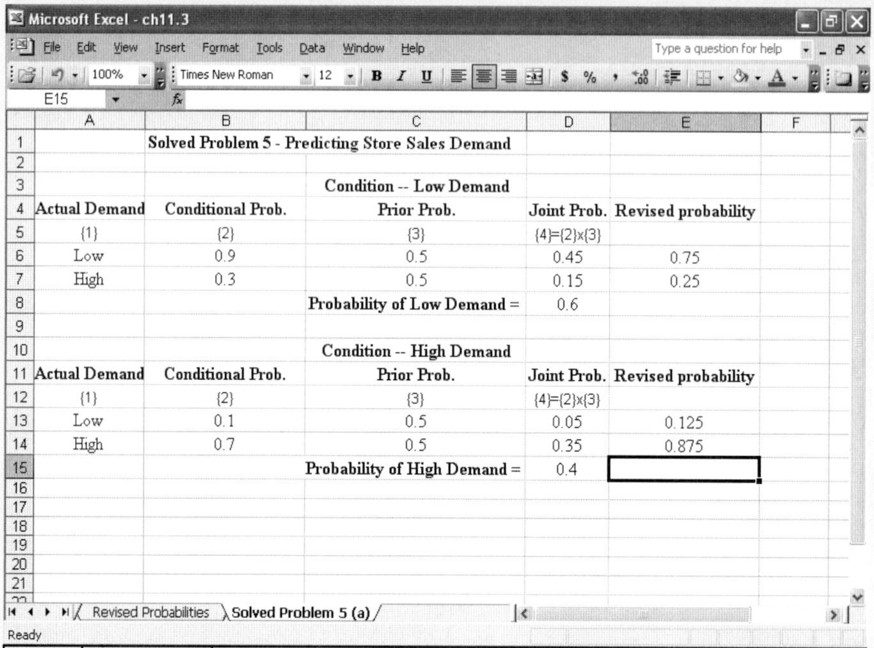

Microsoft Excel - ch11.3

File   Edit   View   Insert   Format   Tools   Data   Window   Help   Type a question for help

E15

	A	B	C	D	E	F
1		Solved Problem 5 - Predicting Store Sales Demand				
2						
3			Condition -- Low Demand			
4	Actual Demand	Conditional Prob.	Prior Prob.	Joint Prob.	Revised probability	
5	{1}	{2}	{3}	{4}={2}x{3}		
6	Low	0.9	0.5	0.45	0.75	
7	High	0.3	0.5	0.15	0.25	
8			Probability of Low Demand =	0.6		
9						
10			Condition -- High Demand			
11	Actual Demand	Conditional Prob.	Prior Prob.	Joint Prob.	Revised probability	
12	{1}	{2}	{3}	{4}={2}x{3}		
13	Low	0.1	0.5	0.05	0.125	
14	High	0.7	0.5	0.35	0.875	
15			Probability of High Demand =	0.4		
16						
17						
18						
19						
20						
21						

Revised Probabilities / Solved Problem 5 (a)

Ready

Cell	Copied to	Formula
D6	D7	= B6 ∗ C6
D8		= SUM (D6 : D7)
E6	E7	= D6 / $D$8
D13	D14	= B13 ∗ C13
D15		= SUM (D13 : D14)
E13	E14	= D13 / $D$15

Exhibit 11-16   TreePlan Dialog Box to Add Branches, Decision Nodes, or Events

TreePlan (Education) Decision

- ⦿ Add branch
- ○ Copy subtree
- ○ Insert decision
- ○ Insert event
- ○ Change to event
- ○ Shorten tree
- ○ Change to terminal
- ○ Remove branch

OK
Cancel
Select...
Options...
Help

Exhibit 11-17   TreePlan Dialog Box to Add or Change Decision Nodes or Events

> **TreePlan (Education) Terminal**   [X]
>
> ⊙ Change to decision node
> ○ Change to event node
> ○ Paste subtree
> ○ Remove previous branch
>
> Branches
> ○ One
> ⊙ Two
> ○ Three
> ○ Four
> ○ Five
>
> [OK]   [Options...]   [Select...]
> [Cancel]   [Help]

branch, make sure TreePlan is activated, then choose **Tools | Decision Tree** and add a branch or change to a decision node or event node as required. Exhibit 11-18 shows the final version of the decision tree prepared using Excel and TreePlan.

Exhibit 11-18   Decision Tree for Solved Problem 5 (part c)

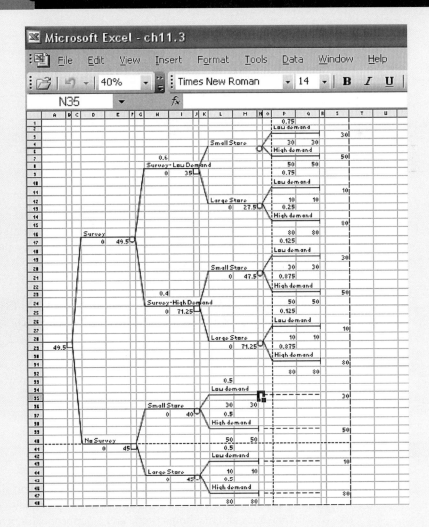

d. In order to find EVSI, first find the expected payoffs for store size for each of the following: Survey shows low demand, Survey shows high demand, and No survey. Thus:

Survey shows low demand:

Small store	.75(30) + .25(50) = 35.00
Large store	.75(10) + .25(80) = 27.50

Survey shows high demand:

Small store	.125(30) + .875(50) = 47.50
Large store	.125(10) + .875(80) = 71.25

No Survey:

Small store	.50(30) + .50(50) = 40.00
Large store	.50(10) + .50(80) = 45.00

These then can be placed on a tree diagram as expected payoffs for store size decisions:

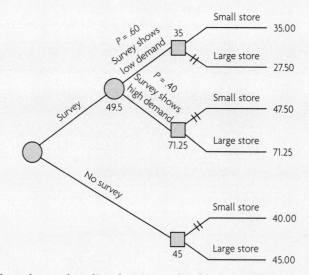

Next, the branch at each ending decision node with the smaller expected payoff can be "cut" or eliminated, as shown by the two slashes on appropriate branches.

Then, the expected payoff for using the survey can be computed using the remaining branches and their expected payoffs. Thus:

.60(35.00) + .40(71.25) = 49.50

The expected payoff for No survey is shown on the tree. It is 45.00.

The expected value of sample information is the difference between these two. Thus:

EVSI = 49.50 − 45.00 = 4.50 thousand, OR $4,500

e. Because the EVSI is $4,500, whereas the cost of the survey is $2,000, it would seem reasonable for the manager to use the survey; the expected gain would be $2,500 ($4,500 − $2,000)

Discussion and Review Questions

1. Describe the difference between a state of nature and decision alternative.
2. Describe the difference between prior and posterior probabilities.
3. Explain maximax and maximin criteria and describe the difference between them.

4. Explain Hurwicz criterion and the relationship between Hurwicz criterion and maximax and maximin criteria.
5. Describe the difference among decision making under certainty, decision making under uncertainty and decision making under risk.
6. Describe the meaning of Expected Monetary Value (EMV).
7. Describe the meaning of Expected Value of Perfect Information (EVPI).
8. Describe the meaning of a circle and a square in developing a decision tree. What is the difference between a single decision and a sequential decision? Describe when it is most useful to utilize the decision tree approach.
9. Describe the difference between risk averters and risk takers by giving examples of both types of behavior from real world.
10. What is utility theory and how does it differ from making decisions based on monetry value?
11. Describe why is it important to perform sensitivity analysis when decisions are made under risk.
12. Describe how to determine the opportunity loss table from the payoff table and the meaning of the minimax regret approach.
13. How does Equally Likely criterion differ from Hurwicz criterion?

◗ Problems

1. Consider the following payoff table (profits in $100,000):

State of Nature

		s_1	s_2	s_3	s_4
	a_1	7	14	13	10
Alternative	a_2	3	6	12	15
	a_3	−8	−1	11	22

Which alternative would be chosen for each of the following decision criteria?
a. Maximin.
b. Maximax.
c. Minimax regret.
d. Equal likelihood.
e. The Hurwicz criterion with $\alpha = .70$.

2. Suppose that probabilities were available for the states of nature in the previous problem. Which alternative would maximize expected payoff if the probabilities were $P(s_1) = .2$, $P(s_2) = .1$, $P(s_3) = .4$, and $P(s_4) = .3$?

$a_1 = \$11.00$

3. Farah Fashion, an assistant buyer of a sportswear department in a New York store, must decide on clothes orders for the winter season. Two new styles of coats were introduced at a recent show. The styles are quite different, and the assistant buyer must decide whether to fill the entire order with one of the styles or to split the order between the two. The profits for various states of nature have been estimated by the head buyer, and are shown in the following payoff table:

Market Acceptance

		Style A	Style B	Split
	Style A	80	30	45
Alternative	Style B	20	90	55
	Split	60	70	96

Use Excel and determine which alternative would be selected for each of these decision criteria:
a. Maximin.
b. Maximax.
c. Minimax regret.
d. Equal likelihood.
e. The Hurwicz criterion using $\alpha = .60$.

4. Suppose that the assistant buyer in the preceding problem is able to estimate that the probability for market acceptance of Style A is .30, the probability for market acceptance of Style B is .20, and the probability of a market split is .50.
a. Which alternative would maximize the expected profit?
b. Determine the expected value of perfect information using the expected payoff under certainty approach.
c. Verify that using the opportunity loss table results in the same expected value of perfect information found in part *b*.
d. Construct a decision tree. Indicate expected branch profits.

5. Suppose that the amounts given in the payoff table of Problem 3 were costs rather than profits. Use Excel and determine the appropriate decision for each of the following criteria:
a. Minimax.
b. Minimin.
c. Minimax regret.
d. Equal likelihood
e. The Hurwicz criterion using $\alpha = .60$.

6. If the data in Problem 3 were costs, and market acceptance probabilities are estimated to be .3 for A, .2 for B, and .5 for split, determine which alternative will minimize expected cost.

7. Anabelle Lee, the director of social services of Down County, has just learned of additional information requirements mandated by the state. This will place an additional burden on the agency. The director has identified three acceptable alternatives to handle the increased workload. One is to reassign present staff members, another is to hire and train two new workers, and the third is to redesign current practice so that workers can readily collect the information with little additional effort. An unknown factor is the caseload for the coming year, during which time the new data will be collected on a trial basis. The estimated costs for various options and caseloads are shown in the table that follows:

Cost Table

	Caseload		
	Moderate	High	Very high
Reassign staff	$50*	60	85
New staff	60	60	60
Redesign collection	40	50	90

*Cost in thousands.

Assuming that probabilities of various caseloads are unreliable, based on past experience, what decision would be appropriate using each of the following criteria?
a. Minimax.
b. Minimin
c. Minimax regret.
d. Equal likelihood.
e. The Hurwicz criterion using $\alpha = .20$.

a. Split = 80
b. 10

c. 10

d. See the IM

Style B = $51.50

8. After contemplating the caseload question, Annabelle (see Problem 7) has decided that reasonable caseload probabilities are .10 for moderate, .30 for high, and .60 for very high.

   a. Which alternative will yield the minimum expected cost?

   b. Construct a decision tree for this problem. Indicate the expected costs for the three decision branches.

   c. Determine the expected value of perfect information using an opportunity loss table.

9. Suppose the director of social services will have the option of hiring an additional staff member if one staff member is hired initially and the caseload turns out to be high or very high. Under that plan, the first entry in row 2 of the cost table (see Problem 7) will be 40 instead of 60, the second entry will be 75 instead of 60, and the last entry will be 80 instead of 60. Assume the caseload probabilities as noted in Problem 8. Construct a decision tree that shows the sequential nature of this decision, and determine which alternative will minimize expected cost.

10. The owner of a small business is considering three options: buying a computer, leasing a computer, or getting along without a computer. Based on the information obtained from the firm's accountant, the following payoff table was developed.

State of Nature

		s_1	s_2
	Do nothing	4	2
Alternative	Buy	8	1
	Lease	5	3

The owner would like to use the expected value criterion to make a decision, but she is hesitant because her probability estimates are quite rough.

   a. Eliminate the alternative that is dominated by another alternative.

   b. Determine $P(s_1)$ and $P(s_2)$ such that the owner would be indifferent between the two remaining alternatives.

   c. For what range of probability would Lease have a higher expected payoff than the other alternative?

   d. If probabilities are ignored, which alternative would offer the more conservative choice in this situation? Why?

   e. Which alternative would the owner choose using the Hurwicz criterion if her degree of optimism is .6?

11. Given the payoff table that follows, determine the value of $P(\text{low})$ and $P(\text{moderate})$ that would make a decision maker indifferent between London and Tokyo.

State of Nature

		Low	Moderate
	London	10	8
Alternative	Tokyo	6	12

12. The owner of the Danish Pastry Baking Company, Fred Butterfield, recently submitted two bids, one to the county to supply baked goods to various county buildings for two years, and the other to supply baked goods to the city school district, again

Margin answers

a. New Staff
b. See the IM

c. 5

a. Eliminate Do nothing because 5 > 4 and 3 > 2
b. $P(s_1) = .4$, $P(s_2) = .6$
   $.6 \le P(s_2) \le 1$
c. Lease (smallest return is 3)
d. Buy = 8(.6) + 1(.4) = 5.2,
e. Lease = 5(.6) + 3(.4) = 4.2;
   Choose Buy: 5.2 > 4.2

for two years. The owner estimates the probabilities of receiving the contracts as follows:

Outcome	Probability
No contracts	.20
City only	.20
County only	.50
City and county	.10

Fred has just learned that a bakery in a nearby county is about to close, and that two delivery trucks will be for sale. These trucks can be bought for a very reasonable price compared to the cost of new trucks, but Fred is unsure of whether to buy one truck, two trucks, or no trucks.

If Fred does not buy any trucks and no contracts are awarded, the net profit will be zero. If the city contract alone is awarded, a profit of $14,000 will be realized even without any trucks because the firm has some excess capacity at present. If the county contract alone is awarded, the profit will be only $10,000. If both contracts are awarded, Fred can buy either one new truck, two new trucks, or no trucks. The estimated profits considering salvage and depreciation are $12,000 for one truck, $15,000 for two trucks, and a loss of $2,000 for no trucks.

If one of the used delivery trucks is purchased, the estimated profits are −$3,000 for No contract, $8,000 for City only, $6,000 for County only, and $11,000 for City and County. However, in the event that both contracts are awarded to the bakery, Fred has the option of buying another truck and realizing a net profit of $16,000.

If two used trucks are initially bought, the estimated profits are −$7,000 for No contract, $9,000 for City only, $5,000 for County only, and $25,000 for both. If No contract is awarded, the owner has the option of selling one or both trucks. For one truck, the net profit would be $3,000, whereas if two are sold, the net profit would be $6,000. If Fred uses maximum expected profits as the decision criterion, use Excel and determine which alternative should be chosen? Explain your reasoning.

See the IM

13. Use Excel and analyze the tree diagram shown in Figure 11-3 using expected monetary value as the decision criterion. What alternative is recommended?

14. A manufacturer produces and sells chilled, ready-to-eat pasta salad in round lots of 50 serving units each. These items have a very limited shelf life; therefore, if items are made but not sold, they have no value. Conversely, if demand exceeds supply during the week (regular production runs are made on Friday of each week for sales the following week), an extra production run can be made. The cost per unit for a regular run is $5 per unit, whereas the cost of an extra production run is $7 per unit. All items are sold for $10 per unit regardless of production cost. Historically, demand has been for 50, 100, or 150 units each week, so the company makes one of those run sizes. In the past, the manager of the department has made 100 units per week for regular production.

a. See the IM

b. 50 units, $355

c. $70

d. See the IM

a. Prepare a payoff table showing profits for each of the lot sizes.
b. If probability of demand for 50 units is .40, probability of demand of 100 units is .50, and probability of demand for 150 units is .10, what lot size would you recommend if the goal is to maximize expected profit?
c. What is the EVPI?
d. Answer question *a*, *b*, and *c* given this additional consideration: Suppose that disposal cost for unsold items is $1 per unit.

15. For Solved Problem 5, determine the EVSI, and decide if you would recommend using the survey if the reliability of surveys conducted by the firm was *changed* to

		Actual Result Was	
		Low	High
Survey Showed	Low	.75	.15
	High	.25	.85

Assume that all other information remains unchanged. What is the efficiency of sample information in this instance?

Don't use the expert

16. An attorney is preparing a case for trial. In an attempt to decide whether to follow an aggressive approach or a conservative approach in presenting his client's case, the attorney has developed this payoff table:

		Case	
		Win	Lose
Approach	Aggressive	$40,000	−10,000
	Conservative	20,000	−6,000

The Attorney believes there is a probability of .30 that he can win the case. However, for a fee of $2,000, he can consult with an expert who is familiar with this type of case and can provide another opinion on whether the case will be won. Previous experience with using that expert can be summarized by the following table:

		Outcome	
		Won	Lost
Expert Predicted	Win	.85	.05
	Lose	.15	.95

Is the expected value of the expert's advice worth the fee? Illustrate your analysis using a decision tree.

17. Barry Greene, the manager of a commercial loan department of a bank, must decide how to allocate loans among various loan proposals. The manager has the following payoff table, which shows profits for various loan strategies and economic scenarios:

		State of Nature Economy	
		Stable	Changing
Alternative	Strategy A	$50,000	20,000
	Strategy B	10,000	80,000

Barry believes that a stable economy is four times as likely as a changing economy. However, the manager is somewhat uncomfortable with this personal assessment and would like to take advantage of a governmental research agency's services regarding the probability of each type of economy.

According to the agency, its reliability for such forecasts in the past has been

		Actual	
		Stable	Changing
Forecast	Stable	.88	.08
	Changing	.12	.92

a. Using the criterion of maximizing expected payoff, what strategy would Barry select without using the agency?
b. If Barry decides to use the agency, what would be the revised probabilities for the economy for each forecast possibility?
c. Prepare a tree diagram that illustrates the problem.
d. Determine the EVSI.
e. If the agency fee is $3,000, would you recommend using the agency? Explain. What is the efficiency of sample information?

18. Annabelle Lee, the director of social services (see Problems 7 and 8), has just learned about a consulting firm that has worked with similar departments throughout the country in making similar assessments. After discussing the matter with a representative of the firm, the following table was produced to summarize the firm's reliability in terms of this problem:

		Actual Caseload		
		Moderate	High	Very high
	Moderate	.80	0	0
Predicted Caseload	High	.10	.90	.10
	Very high	.10	.10	.90

a. EVSI = 2.654, Eff. = .531

b. Don't use consultant
   (2930 < 8,000)

The firm's fee to handle this prediction problem would be $8,000.
a. Determine the EVSI and the efficiency of sample information.
b. Do you recommend that the consulting firm be used? Explain.

19. Given this payoff table:

	Demand low	Demand high
Build small	20	20
Build large	10	40

a. Suppose the values in the table are profits. In terms of the probability that demand will be high, over what range of probability will each alternative action be best?
b. Now suppose that the values in the payoff table are costs. Over what range of values for $P(\text{Demand high})$ will each alternative be best?

20. Manager Sara Stern has compiled estimated profits for various alternative courses of action, but she is reluctant to assign probabilities to the states of nature. The payoff table is

		State of Nature	
		#1	#2
	A	20	140
Alternative	B	120	80
	C	100	40

a. See the IM

b. Alternative C

c. If P(#2) is less than .625

d. If P(#1) is greater
   than .375

a. Plot the expected value lines on a graph.
b. Is there any alternative that would never be appropriate in terms of maximizing expected profit? Explain on the basis of your graph.
c. For what range of $P(\#2)$ would Alternative B be the best choice if the goal is to maximize expected profit?
d. For what range of $P(\#1)$ would Alternative B be the best choice if the goal is to maximize expected profit?

21. Repeat all parts of the preceding question assuming the values in the payoff tables are estimated *costs* and the goal is to minimize expected cost.

22. The research staff of a marketing agency has assembled the following payoff table of estimated profits:

Choose #1
if $0 \leq P < .286$;
choose #2
if $.286 < P < .6$;
choose #3
if $.6 < P < .714$;
choose #4
if $.714 < P \leq 1.0$;

		Receive contract	Not receive contract
Proposal	#1	10	−2
	#2	8	3
	#3	5	5
	#4	0	7

Relative to the probability of not receiving the contract, determine the range of probability for which each of the proposals would maximize expected profit.

23. Although he has prepared a payoff table for a decision problem, manager John Burns is reluctant to assign probabilities to the two states of nature he has determined will occur (i.e., one of these two will definitely occur). Given his payoff table and his feeling that the probability of receiving the job is between .45 and .50, which alternative should John choose if it is his intention to maximize expected profits?

		Receive job	Do not receive job
Alternative	A	90	30
	B	40	70
	C	10	80

a. Choose C
if $0 \leq P(\#1) < .2$;
choose D
if $.2 < P(\#1) < .7$;
choose A
if $.7 < P(\#1) \leq 1.0$

b. Choose A
if $0 \leq P(\#1) < .25$;
choose B
if $.25 < P(\#1) < .583$;
choose C
if $.583 < P(\#1) \leq 1.0$

24. Given this payoff table:

		State of Nature	
		#1	#2
Alternative	A	120	20
	B	60	40
	C	10	110
	D	90	90

a. Determine the range of $P(\#1)$ for which each alternative would be best, treating the payoffs as profits.

b. Answer part *a* treating the payoffs as costs.

25. A manager must decide how many machines of a certain type to buy. The manager has narrowed the decision to two alternatives: (1) buy one machine or (2) buy two machines. If only one machine is purchased and demand is more than the company can handle, then a second machine will be purchased at a later date. However, the cost per machine would be lower if the two machines were to be purchased at the same time. The initial purchase of two machines has a net value of $75,000 if demand is low and $140,000 if demand is high. The probability of low demand is .45. The initial purchase of one machine has a net value of $85,000 if demand is low. If demand is high, and the company decides to purchase one machine initially, the manager has three options. The first option is to do nothing with a net value of $85,000. The second option is to subcontract. If the firm decides to subcontract, there is a 65 percent chance of using vendor X with a net return of $100,000. There is a 35 percent chance of using vendor Y with a net return of $135,000. The third option is to purchase a second machine with a net value of $115,000. How many machines should the firm purchase initially and why? Use a decision tree to analyze the problem.

26. Given the following payoff table:

a. See the IM
b. Choose A
   if .53846 < $P(s_2) \leq$ 1;
   choose B
   if 0 ≤ $P(s_2) \leq$ .53846
c. See the IM
d. Choose A
   if 0 ≤ $P(s_1) \leq$ .46154;
   choose B
   if .46154 ≤ $P(s_1) \leq$ 1
e. Choose B
   if .53846 ≤ $P(s_2) \leq$ 1;
   choose A
   if 0 ≤ $P(s_2) <$ .53846
f. Choose B
   if 0 ≤ $P(s_1) <$ .46154;
   choose A
   if .46154 < $P(s_1) \leq$ 1

		State of Nature	
		#1	#2
Alternative	A	3	8
	B	10	2

a. Plot each alternative's expected value line on a graph. Label the left vertical axis as "Payoff if state #1 occurs"; the right axis as "Payoff state #2 occurs"; and the horizontal axis as $P(\#2)$.

b. Determine the range of $P(\#2)$ for which each alternative would be best

c. Plot each alternative's expected value line on a graph. Label the left vertical axis as "Payoff if state #2 occurs"; the right axis as "Payoff if state #1 occurs"; and the horizontal axis as $P(\#1)$.

d. Determine the range of $P(\#1)$ for which each alternative would be best.

e. Answer part *b* treating the payoffs as costs.

f. Answer part *d* treating the payoffs as costs.

27. Jo-Jo Inc. is a manufacturing firm that produces soap. The company is owned by two brothers, Donald and David Schroeder, and has one plant. The company has experienced significant growth in demand, and the current plant does not appear to have sufficient capacity to meet demand. The company has decided to build a new plant to meet the additional capacity. However, the brothers must decide whether to construct a small, medium, or large plant. The brothers hired a forecasting consultant to predict demand. The consultant's report indicates that there is a 25 percent chance that the demand will be low and a 75 percent chance that the demand will be high. If Jo-Jo Inc. builds a small facility and the demand indeed turns out to be low, the consultant expects net profit of $40 million. If the firm builds a small plant and the demand turns out to be high, then the firm has two options: (1) subcontract or (2) expand the facility. If Jo-Jo Inc. decides to subcontract, the expected net return will be $44 million. If the firm expands the new facility, there is a 40 percent chance that the net return will be $42 million and a 60 percent chance that the net return will be $48 million. If the medium-size facility is constructed and the demand turns out to be low, the net return is estimated at $28 million. However, if the medium-size facility is built and the demand turns out to be high, Jo-Jo Inc. has two options: (1) do nothing, for an expected net return of $48 million, or (2) expand. If the firm decides to expand, there is a 35 percent chance that it will earn a net return of $44 million and a 65 percent chance that it will earn a net return of $54 million. If the firm decides to build a large facility and demand turns out to be low, the net return will be $10 million. However, if the firm decides to build a large plant and the demand turns out to be high, the expected net return is $58 million. Use decision tree analysis and determine the best option for Jo-Jo Inc.

Chapter 11 Case MKGP Construction Company

MKGP has just introduced a new product line. It is considering three options regarding its new product line: (1) subcontract, (2) expand existing facility, or (3) build a new facility. A consultant's report indicates a 30 percent probability that the demand will be low, a

50 percent probability that the demand will be medium, and a 20 percent probability that the demand will be high.

If MKGP decides to subcontract and demand turns out to be low, the net present value of the returns will be $550,000. If the firm decides to subcontract and demand turns out to be medium, the firm has two options available. (1) do nothing, with a net present value of $660,000; or (2) expand its operations. If the firm decides to expand its operations, there is a 35 percent chance of earning a net return of $620,000 and a 65 percent chance of earning a net return of $740,000. If the firm decides to subcontract and demand turns out to be high, then the firm has three options available. (1) do nothing, with a net present value of $620,000; (2) expand, with a net present value of $810,000; or (3) build a new facility, with a net present value of $890,000.

If MKGP decides to expand and the demand turns out to be low, then the company has two choices: (1) do nothing, with an expected net present return of $360,000, or (2) use the expansion for other purposes. Depending on the result of negotiations regarding facilities, there is a 65 percent chance that the firm uses the expansion for manufacturing another product and a 35 percent chance that it will use it for the purposes of warehousing and storage. The net present value of using the expansion for other manufacturing purposes is $700,000, and the net present value of using the expansion as a storage facility is $400,000.

If MKGP decides to expand and the demand is medium, then the expected net return is $510,000. If the firm decides to expand and the demand is high, then the company has the following options available: (1) do nothing (net return of $810,000), (2) subcontract (net return of 740,000), or (3) build a new facility (net return of $840,000).

If MKGP decides to build a new facility and the demand is low, then the company has two choices: (1) do nothing, with an expected net present return of $340,000, or (2) use the new facility for other purposes. Depending on the result of negotiations regarding facilities, there is a 42 percent chance that the firm uses the new building for manufacturing another product and a 58 percent chance that it will use it for the purposes of warehousing and storage. The net present value of using the new building for manufacturing another product is $670,000 and the net present value of using the new building as a storage facility is $490,000. If the firm decides to build a new facility and the demand is medium, then the company has a 35 percent chance of earning a net return of $600,000 and a 65 percent chance of earning a net return of $730,000. If the firm decides to build a new facility and the demand is high, the net present value of the return is $1,200,000. Using decision tree analysis, make a recommendation for MKGP.

Markov Analysis

Learning Objectives

After completing this chapter, you should be able to:

1. Give examples of systems that may lend themselves to be analyzed by a Markov model.
2. Explain the meaning of transition probabilities.
3. Describe the kinds of system behaviors that Markov analysis pertains to.
4. Use a tree diagram to analyze system behavior.
5. Use matrix multiplication to analyze system behavior.
6. Use an algebraic method to solve for steady-state probabilities.
7. Analyze absorbing states, namely accounts receivable, using a Markov model.
8. List the assumptions of a Markov model.
9. Use Excel to solve various problems pertaining to a Markov model.

Chapter Outline

Introduction, 606

Transition Probabilities, 607

System Behavior, 608

Methods of Analysis, 609
Tree Diagram, 609
Matrix Multiplication, 611
Algebraic Solution, 614

Using Excel for Markov Analysis, 616

Analysis of a 3 × 3 Matrix, 621
Tree Diagram, 622
Matrix Multiplication, 623
Algebraic Solution, 624

Using Excel to Solve Three State Problems, 625

Cyclical, Transient, and Absorbing Systems, 630
Analysis of Accounts Receivable, 632

Analysis of Absorbing States Using Excel, 636

Assumptions, 639

Summary, 639

Glossary, 641

Solved Problems, 641

Discussion and Review Questions, 649

Problems, 650

Chapter 12 Case: Memorial Hospital, 657

Introduction

This chapter describes the analysis of *Markov* systems. Markov systems are very useful in studying the development of a system over repeated trials. Repeated trials often involve successive time periods where the state of the system in any particular time period is unknown. Therefore, we are interested in determining the probability of a system being in a particular state at a given time period (trial). A Markov system has these characteristics:

1. It will operate or exist for a number of periods (trials).
2. In each period, the system can assume one of a number of states or conditions.
3. The states are both mutually exclusive and collectively exhaustive.
4. System changes between states from period to period can be described by *transition probabilities*, which remain constant.
5. The probability of the system being in a given state in a particular period depends only on its state in the preceding period and the transition probabilities. It is independent of all earlier periods.

Table 12-1 gives some illustrations of systems that may lead themselves to Markov analysis.[1]

The use of Markov analysis on such systems can help decision makers understand how the systems behave over time. This sort of knowledge can be useful for *short-term* decisions such as scheduling a workforce, stocking inventory, and budgeting, and for *long-term* decisions such as determining locations for new facilities and capacity planning. These decisions may simply involve dealing with expected system behaviors or they may involve strategies for favorably altering the system (e.g., through price changes, advertising, and so on).

The chapter begins with an illustration of transition probabilities, which are the foundation of a Markov analysis. Then, three methods of analysis are illustrated: graphical and matrix, which are useful for describing short-term behavior; and the algebraic method, which is useful for describing long-term behavior patterns.

Table 12-1	Examples of Systems That May Be Described as Markov	
System	**Possible System States**	**Transition Probabilities**
Brand switching	Proportion of customers who buy Brand A, Brand B, Brand C, etc.	Probability that a customer will switch from Brand A to Brand B, etc.
TV market share	Proportion of viewers who watch Channel 8, Channel 10, etc.	Probability that a viewer who watched Channel 8 news will switch to Channel 10 news, etc.
Rental returns	Proportion of renters who return rentals to various locations.	Probability that a renter will return item to a different location than the one it was rented from.
Machine breakdowns	Proportion of machines running, proportion not running.	Probability that a machine's condition—running/not running—will change in the next period.

[1]In order for a system to be considered Markov, it must satisfy certain assumptions that are described later in the chapter.

Transition Probabilities

A system whose behavior can be described as a **Markov process** can be summarized by a set of conditional, or **transition probabilities,** which indicate the tendencies of the system to change from one period to the next. An example will help to clarify this important concept.

Example 12-1

Consider a car rental agency that has rental offices at each of a city's two airports. Customers are allowed to return a rented car to either airport, regardless of which airport they rented from. (It is assumed that this is a closed system: All cars must be returned to one of the two airports.) If some cars will be used for one-way rentals to another city, or if some cars are dropped off from other cities, they can be excluded from the system and treated separately. In addition, it is assumed that all rentals will be for only one day, and that at the end of the day, every car will be returned to one of the two rental offices. Suppose that the manager of the rental agency has made a study of return behavior and has found the following information: 70 percent of the cars rented from Airport A tend to be returned to that airport, and 30 percent of the Airport A cars tend to be returned to Airport B; 10 percent of the cars rented from Airport B are returned to Airport A, and 90 percent of the cars are returned to Airport B. The manager has several questions concerning the system:

1. Prepare the transition matrix.
2. What proportion of cars will be returned to each airport in the *short run* (e.g., over the next several days)? This information will help the manager in scheduling counter help at each location.
3. What proportion of cars will be returned to each location over the *long run*? This information will be helpful in deciding which of the two locations should be chosen for construction of a facility for servicing and repair of the cars.

Solution

This information is summarized in the **transition matrix** illustrated in Table 12-2.

Because it is assumed that all of the rentals will be returned to one of the two airports, the *row* totals are 1.00, or 100 percent. The same does not apply to the column totals, because these *conditional* probabilities are stated in terms of *renting* locations rather than return locations. That is, the first value in the table, .70, represents the proportion of cars that can be expected to be returned to Airport A, *given* that they were rented at Airport A. Similarly, the .30 represents the proportion of cars expected to be returned to Airport B, *given* that they were rented at Airport A.

1.

Table 12-2   Transition Probabilities for Car Rental Example

		Returned to		
		Airport A	Airport B	
Rented from	Airport A	.70	.30	1.00
	Airport B	.10	.90	1.00

Solutions to 2 and 3 will be presented later in the chapter.

In general, managers may be interested in either the short-run or the long-run behavior of a system, or in both. The following section gives an overview of these two behaviors.

System Behavior

Both the long-term behavior and the short-term behavior of a system are completely determined by the system's transition probabilities. Short-term behavior is solely dependent on the system's state in the current period and the transition probabilities. Thus, in the case of the car rental system, it can be seen from the transition matrix that 70 percent of the cars rented at Airport A are expected to be returned to Airport A and that 30 percent are expected to be returned to Airport B. Likewise, 10 percent of the cars rented from Airport B are expected to be returned to Airport A and 90 percent to Airport B. These proportions are expected to remain in effect. Consequently, the *number* of cars returned to each location in any given period is simply a function of the transition probabilities and the number rented from each location in the preceding period. Knowledge of the number of cars at each location at a given point in time can be used to track the short-term behavior of the system. Moreover, the number of cars at each location in the preceding period is normally a significant factor that affects the number of cars at each location in the next several periods. However, the long-term behavior of the system will be unaffected by the initial number of cars at each location; the proportion of cars returned to each location over the long run will be the same, regardless of initial conditions (the number of cars). The long-run proportions are referred to as the **steady-state** proportions, or probabilities, of the system. Not every system has a tendency to stabilize, though. Some tend to cycle back and forth, and some tend to converge on a single state called an *absorbing state*. More will be said about these cases later. Because such systems are less common than steady-state systems, the discussion here will emphasize steady-state systems.

These short-term and long-term tendencies of steady-state systems can be seen in Figure 12-1, which shows the proportion of returns to Airport A as a function of where they were rented in Period 0. Notice that in the first few periods, the original starting point (Airport A or Airport B) has a marked effect on the proportions, but that effect becomes less and less as time goes by, and that after about 10 periods, the original (Period 0) renting location is immaterial. As shown in Figure 12-1, the long-run proportion of those Period 0 rentals ending up at Airport A is 25 percent. A similar graph could be constructed showing

Figure 12-1	Expected Proportion of Period 0 Rentals Returned to Airport A

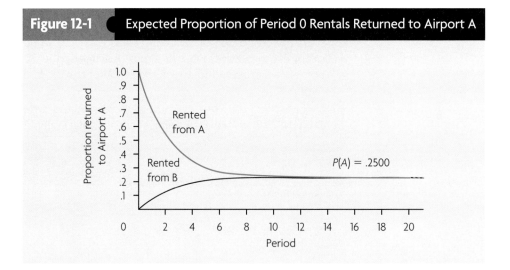

the proportion of original rentals from each location returned to Airport B. It would show a long-run proportion of 75 percent of those Period 0 rentals ending up at Airport B.

◀■ Methods of Analysis

As previously noted, a manager's interest in system behavior can be related to either short-term considerations or long-term considerations, and often it is related to both. Methods for analyzing system behaviors relate to either the short term or the long term. Short-term behavior can be described using either a tree diagram or matrix multiplication. Long-term behavior could theoretically be analyzed by either of those approaches, but for practical reasons related to the amount of effort that would be involved, an algebraic method is used.

Each of these methods is presented below, beginning with a tree diagram for describing short-term system behavior.

Tree Diagram

A **tree diagram** is a visual portrayal of a system's transitions. It is composed of a series of branches, which represent the possible choices at each stage (period) and the conditional probabilities of each choice being selected. For example, a car rented from Airport A can be returned to either Airport A or Airport B. Thus, there are two choices, the first with a probability of .70 and the second with a probability of .30. Similarly, a car rented at Airport B has two possible return locations, Airport A with a probability of .10 and Airport B with a probability of .90. Hence, each possible starting point (rental location) has two possible return locations. Moreover, we can represent the choices for each with separate tree diagrams. The two diagrams are illustrated in Figure 12-2.

Figure 12-2	Tree Diagrams for the Car Rental Example for One Period

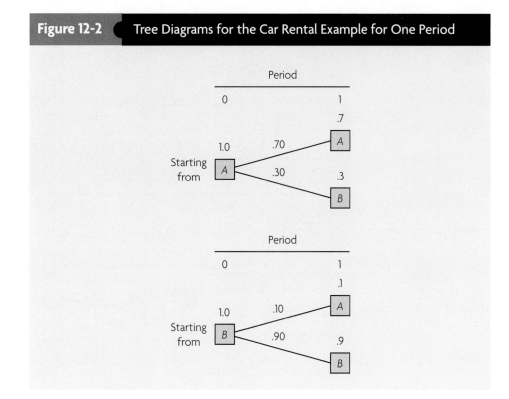

If two or more periods are involved, the tree becomes more involved, but it is also more informative, particularly if the *joint* probabilities are shown for each branch. These reflect the proportion of members of the system (e.g., rental cars) that can be expected to follow a certain path (series of branches) through the tree diagram. The next example illustrates this.

Example 12-2

Prepare a tree diagram that shows the choices for two periods of the car rental system using the information contained in Table 12-2. Then, compute joint probabilities and use them to determine *how many* cars will be at Location A if A originally has 100 cars and Location B has 80 cars. Note that the solution to this problem is also the solution to question 2 in Example 12-1.

Solution

The two tree diagrams (one for a car rented from Airport A and the other for a car rented from Airport B) are shown in Figure 12-3. The joint probabilities are computed by multiplying the probabilities along each particular branch. Therefore, the proportion of cars rented from A in Period 0 that can be expected to be returned to A in

Figure 12-3 Two-Period Tree Diagrams for Car Rental Example

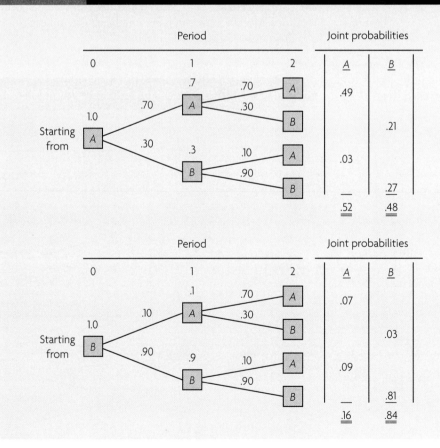

Period 1 and then rented out and returned a second time to A is .70 × .70 = .49. Similarly, the proportion of cars first rented from A in Period 0, then returned to B in Period 1, and finally rented from B in Period 1 and returned to A in Period 2 is .30 × .10 = .03. Then, the *total* proportion of cars rented from A in Period 0 and expected back at A in Period 2 is .49 + .03 = .52, as shown. The other joint probabilities have a similar interpretation.

In effect, the joint probabilities reveal that 52 percent of the cars originally rented from A in Period 0 and 16 percent of the cars originally rented from B in Period 0 will end up at A in Period 2. Multiplying these probabilities by the number of cars originally at each location will yield the *expected number* of cars at Airport A at the end of Period 2. Because Airport A had 100 cars in Period 0 and Airport B had 80 cars, we find:

A   B
100(.52) + 80(.16) = 64.8 cars

The fractional value of .8 does not imply that one of the cars may be returned with a missing door or bumper. The 64.8 represents an *average* number of cars. The actual number of cars would be an *integer* value. For repeated period, the number of cars returned to airport A will average 64.8.

Advantages of a tree diagram are that it is simple to construct and it provides us with a visual model that illustrates how the transition probabilities combine to determine system behavior over the short run. However, as the number of periods covered by a tree increases beyond two or three, the number of branch ends tends to become too large to make this method impractical. For example, to portray 5 periods would require 32 branch ends, and 6 periods would require 64 branch ends.

A more compact method for generating the short-term probabilities involves the use of matrix multiplication, which is covered in the next section.

Matrix Multiplication

A fairly simple method for obtaining expected state proportions over the short run is to use **matrix multiplication.** It is based on state proportions for any period being equal to the product of the proportions in the preceding period multiplied by the matrix of transition probabilities. Because the proportions, at any time, can be expressed in matrix form, this approach involves the multiplication of the "current" proportions, which is referred to as a *probability vector*, by the transition matrix. The vector has one row and the same number of columns as the transition matrix. For instance, the initial "current" vector for a case with two possible states of nature, and starting from State A, would be [1 0]. For the car rentals, this would mean all cars are at Airport A at the start. Conversely, starting in Period 0 from State B would be represented by [0 1]. For the car rentals, this would mean that all cars are at Airport B at the start. If there are three states of nature (location C is added). Period 0 would be expressed in the following way, depending on the starting state:

Starting from	Current Matrix
A	[1 0 0]
B	[0 1 0]
C	[0 0 1]

Matrix multiplication requires that the elements of the row of the first (current) matrix be matched with (multiplied by) the elements of the first column of the transition matrix and summed to obtain the first state proportion for the next period. Then, the elements of the row of the current matrix are matched with the elements of the second column and summed to obtain the second state proportion, and so on. The number of columns for the first matrix must be equal to the number of rows for the second matrix. The multiplication of two matrices, where the first matrix is of the order $K^* M$ and the second matrix is of the order $M^* N$, will result in the following:

$$(K^* M)(M^* N) = (K^* N)$$

For example, we can calculate the state proportions for Period 1 for the car rental example for State (airport) A as follows:

$$[1 \quad 0]\begin{bmatrix} .70 & .30 \\ .10 & .90 \end{bmatrix} = \begin{matrix} 1(.70) & 1(.30) \\ + \ 0(.10) & + \ 0(.90) \\ \hline [.70 & .30] \end{matrix}$$

These values are, of course, simply the elements of the first row of the transition matrix. This is because the transition matrix describes the proportion of system members that are expected to end up in each state in Period 1, given State A start (the first row) and given State B start (the second row). The main point, here, though, is how to complete the matrix multiplication in order to obtain those values, so that values for subsequent periods can be calculated. You might find it helpful to think of the initial matrix as *vertical* rather than horizontal. That is:

Example 12-3

Use matrix multiplication for the car rental example to find the state proportions for Periods 2 and 3, assuming State A start.

Solution
Because Period 1 proportions are .70 and .30, for Period 2 we have:

$$[.70 \quad .30]\begin{bmatrix} .70 & .30 \\ .10 & .90 \end{bmatrix} = \begin{matrix} .70(.70) \ = \ .49 & .70(.30) \ = \ .21 \\ .30(.10) \ = \ .03 & .30(.90) \ = \ .27 \\ \hline .52 & .48 \end{matrix}$$

Thus, the Period 2 matrix is [.52   .48], which means that 52 percent are expected to be in State A and 48 percent are expected to be in State B. Now, we can calculate the proportions for Period 3:

$$[.52 \quad .48]\begin{bmatrix} .70 & .30 \\ .10 & .90 \end{bmatrix} = \begin{matrix} .52(.70) \ = \ .364 & .52(.30) \ = \ .156 \\ .48(.10) \ = \ .048 & .48(.90) \ = \ .432 \\ \hline .412 & .588 \end{matrix}$$

> Note that in each period, the state proportions sum to 1.00, and that the calculation for any period using this approach requires the proportions from the preceding period.

If we continued this sequential multiplication of each period's matrix and the transition matrix, we would discover that after a time the state proportions would not change significantly. That is, multiplying the state proportions by the transition matrix would result in the same state proportions. This condition is referred to as the *steady-state*, and the proportions indicate the expected percentage of system members in each state over the long run. Moreover, these steady-state values will be the same irrespective of which starting state is used, although the number of periods required to reach the steady-state may vary, depending on which state is used as a starting point. Table 12-3 illustrates the results of matrix multiplications from each starting point and the eventual steady-state proportions for each state. Thus, starting from State A, the steady-state values were obtained in approximately 19 periods, while starting from State B, the steady-state proportions were obtained in approximately 17 periods.

As you can surmise, considerable effort would be required to obtain these values manually. A computer could remove this burden. However, the primary concern is with the *values* at steady-state, rather than with how many periods would be required to obtain the values. And for that purpose, there is a much simpler method for deriving these steady-state proportions, which is described in the next section.

Table 12-3	Period-by-Period Proportions for the Rental Example, and the Steady-State Proportions Based on Matrix Multiplications			
	Starting from A		**Starting from B**	
Period	P(A)	P(B)	P(A)	P(B)
0	1.0	0.0	0.0	1.0
1	.70	.30	.10	.90
2	.52	.48	.16	.84
3	.412	.588	.196	.804
4	.3472	.6528	.2176	.7824
5	.3083	.6917	.2306	.7694
6	.2850	.7150	.2384	.7616
7	.2710	.7290	.2430	.7570
8	.2626	.7374	.2458	.7542
9	.2576	.7424	.2475	.7525
10	.2546	.7454	.2485	.7515
11	.2528	.7472	.2491	.7509
12	.2517	.7483	.2495	.7505
13	.2510	.7490	.2497	.7503
14	.2506	.7494	.2498	.7502
15	.2504	.7496	.2499	.7501
16	.2502	.7498	.2499	.7501
17	.2501	.7499	.2500	.7500
18	.2501	.7499		
19	.2500	.7500		

Algebraic Solution

An **algebraic approach** provides the most efficient method for obtaining the steady-state probabilities. The basis for an algebraic solution is a set of equations developed from the transition matrix. Moreover, because the states are mutually exclusive and collectively exhaustive, the sum of the state probabilities must be 1.00, and another equation can be developed from this requirement. The result is a set of equations that can be used to solve for the steady-state probabilities.

We will now develop the equations needed for an algebraic solution to the steady-state of a Markov process and then use the equations to determine the steady-state probabilities.

The steady-state equations for the car rental example can be developed in the following manner. Because the ending states are represented by the *columns* of the transition matrix, the *probabilities in each column* supply the necessary information for that state's long-term probabilities. Thus, the equation for Airport A is

$$P(A) = .70P(A) + .10P(B)$$

where

$P(A)$ = proportion of cars at Airport A
$P(B)$ = proportion of cars at Airport B

In effect, it expresses that the expected proportion of system members (or, equivalently, the proportion of time the system is expected to be in that state) is comprised of 70 percent from *A* and 10 percent from *B*. Similarly, the equation for Airport B is

$$P(B) = .3P(A) + .90P(B)$$

This equation is derived from the fact that the expected proportion in *B* is 30 percent of *A*'s "output" and 90 percent of *B*'s "output." Still a third equation can be developed since the total of the two probabilities must be 1.00:

$$P(A) + P(B) = 1$$

The development of these equations is illustrated in Figure 12-4.
Another way of developing the equations needed for algebraic solution is illustrated below.

In general, from the calculations shown in Table 12-3, we can state that

$$[P(A_{n+1}) \quad P(B_{n+1})] = [P(A_n) \quad P(B_n)] \begin{bmatrix} P_{11} & P_{12} \\ P_{21} & P_{22} \end{bmatrix}$$

$$\updownarrow$$

Transition Matrix

where n = period number.

Figure 12-4	**Development of Algebraic Equations**	
	To:	
	A	*B*
From: A	.70	.30 → $P(A) = .7P(A) + .10 P(B)$
B	.10	.90 → $P(B) = .3P(A) + .90 P(B)$
		$P(A) + P(B) = 1$

However, as shown in Table 12-3, as n gets larger, the difference between $P(A_{n+1})$ and $P(A)$ and the difference between $P(B_{n+1})$ and $P(B)$ become negligible.

After a large number of periods, $P(A_{n+1}) = P(A)$ and $P(B_{n+1}) = P(B)$. Therefore, we can state that:

$$[P(A) \quad P(B)] = [P(A) \quad P(B)] \begin{bmatrix} P_{11} & P_{12} \\ P_{21} & P_{22} \end{bmatrix}$$

or by substituting the transition probabilities, we get

$$[P(A) \quad P(B)] = [P(A) \quad P(B)] \begin{bmatrix} .7 & .3 \\ .1 & .9 \end{bmatrix}$$

After performing matrix multiplication of the right-hand side, we get

$$[P(A) \quad P(B)] = [.70P(A) + .10P(B); .30P(A) + .90P(B)]$$

We can write these equations as

$P(A) = .70P(A) + .10P(B)$
$P(B) = .30P(A) + .90P(B)$

In addition to these equations we have the following equation that specifies the two probabilities for A and B must sum to 1.

$P(A) + P(B) = 1$

Because there are two unknowns and three equations, one of the equations is superfluous and can be eliminated. As a general rule, it will be most efficient to eliminate either of the state equations while retaining the other state equation as well as the last equation. Suppose that we arbitrarily eliminate the equation for B. We are then left with these two equations:

$P(A) = .70P(A) + .1P(B)$
$P(A) + P(B) = 1$

From the second equation, we can express B in terms of A:

$P(B) = 1 - P(A)$

We can then substitute this for B in the equation for A and solve for A:

$P(A) = .70P(A) + .10[1 - P(A)]$
$P(A) = .70P(A) + .10 - .10P(A)$
$P(A) = .60P(A) + .10$

Collecting terms yields:

$P(A) - .60P(A) = .10$
$.40P(A) = .10$

$$P(A) = \frac{.10}{.40} = .25$$

Since $P(B) = 1 - P(A)$,

$P(B) = 1 - .25 = .75$

Taking the example one step further, if there were initially 400 cars at Airport A and 300 at Airport B, we can determine the expected number of cars at each airport once the system has reached steady-state. Assume that all cars remain in the system, no new cars are added, and there is no transporting of cars between locations. The expected number for each airport is the product of the *total* number of cars (i.e., 700) and the steady-state probability of that airport. Thus, for *A* we have 700(.25) = 175 cars, and for *B* we have 700(.75) = 525 cars.

▊◖ **Using Excel for Markov Analysis**

In demonstrating how Excel can be utilized to perform Markov analysis, consider the following example.

Example 12-4

Joe's machine shop is developing a machine maintenance management program. Joe believes that the functioning of a major machine can be explained based on a transition matrix and Markov analysis can be used to analyze it.

Let State 1 (O = Operation) = machine is in operation
     State 2 (B = Broken)   = machine is down and/or is being repaired

p_{ij} = probability of making a transition from state *i* to state *j* in the next period (day)
 P = transition probability matrix

Joe has determined that when the machine was in operation on a given day, it was also in operation on the following day 90 percent of the time. When the machine was in operation on a given day, it was broken on the next day 10 percent of the time. Joe also has estimated that when the machine was down on a given day, it was operational on the following day 70 percent of the time. When the machine was broken on a given day, it remained broken on the next day 30 percent of the time.

a. Determine the transition matrix *P*.
b. Use Excel and determine the probability that the machine is broken two days from today (the second day) given that the machine is in operation today (day zero).
c. Use Excel and determine the probability that the machine is functioning two days from today (the second day) given that the machine is in operation today (day zero).
d. Draw the decision tree associated with parts *b* and *c*.
e. Use Excel and determine the probability that the machine is broken two days from today (the second day) given that the machine is down (broken) today (day zero).
f. Use Excel and determine the probability that the machine is operating two days from today (the second day) given that the machine is down (broken) today (day zero).
g. Draw the decision tree associated with parts *e* and *f*.
h. Use Excel and determine the steady-state probabilities.

Solution

a. Transition probabilities for the machine maintenance example are given in Table 12-4.

Table 12-4   Transition Probabilities for the Machine Maintenance Example

From: \ To:	State 1 (Operating)	State 2 (Broken)
State 1 (Operating)	0.90	0.10
State 2 (Broken)	0.70	0.30

We will answer parts *b, c, e, f,* and *h* utilizing Excel. Exhibit 12-1 includes the Excel worksheet that contains the calculations necessary to answer parts *b, c, e, f,* and *h.* In preparing the worksheet shown in Exhibit 12-1, first we enter the transition matrix and current state matrix in the top portion of the worksheet. The portion labeled as "Daily Probabilities" illustrates the calculation of the probabilities of being in different states based on a given starting state. For example, if the machine is initially operating (during day zero), the probability of it operating and the probability of it being broken during day 1 can be calculated using matrix multiplication. The Excel function MMULT can be utilized to multiply two matrices. In multiplying two matrices, it is required that the number of columns in the first matrix be equal to the number of rows in the second matrix. If the first matrix has an order $M*N$, then the second matrix must be of the order $N*Q$, the resulting matrix will be of the order $M*Q$. In determining the probability of the machine operating and broken on day 1 given that it is currently operating (day 0), we need to multiply the first row of the current state matrix by the probability transition matrix. Multiplication of these two matrices can be accomplished by typing in the following formula in the formula bar: =MMULT(D3 : E3, $B$3 : $C$4). In this formula, D3 : E3 represents the first row of the current state matrix (machine currently operating) and $B$3 : $C$4 represents the probability transition matrix.

After specifying the formula, we highlight the cells in which we want the answer to be displayed (cells B7 and C7). We proceed by highlighting the formula we just typed in the formula bar and press Ctrl-Shift-Enter. The results of .9 and .1 are displayed in cells B7 and C7 respectively. These probabilities represent the machine operating and machine broken, respectively, on day 1.

We proceed in a similar fashion and calculate the probability of the machine operating or broken on day 1 given that it is currently broken. This time, we need to multiply the second row of the current state matrix by the probability transition matrix. Multiplication of these two matrices can be accomplished by typing in the following formula in the formula bar: =MMULT(D4 : E4, $B$3 : $C$4). In this formula, D4 : E4 represents the second row of the current state matrix (machine currently broken) and $B$3 : $C$4 represents the probability transition matrix.

b. The answer to part *b* is given in row 9 of Exhibit 12-1. In answering this part of the problem, we need to determine the probability that the machine is broken two days from today (the second day) given that the machine is in operation today (day zero). We need to multiply matrices again. However, instead of multiplying the part of the current state matrix by the probability transition matrix, we multiply the results we have obtained above in row 7 (B7 : C7) by the transition matrix. We multiply the transition matrix by the row matrix given in B7 : C7 because B7 : C7 contain the probabilities of the two states on day 1 given that the machine is operating on day zero. This can be accomplished by using the following formula: =MMULT(B7 : C7, $B$3 : $C$4). After specifying the formula, we highlight the cells in which we want the answer to be displayed (cells B9 and C9). We proceed by highlighting the formula we just typed in the formula bar

Exhibit 12-1 Worksheet for the Markov Analysis of the Machine Maintenance Problem

Microsoft Excel - Chapter12

B25 =B22+C22

	A	B	C	D	E
1		Transition	Matrix	Current State	Matrix
2		State 1 (Operating)	State 2 (Broken)	To State 1 (Operating)	To State 2 (Broken)
3	State 1 (Operating)	0.9	0.1	1	0
4	State 2 (Broken)	0.7	0.3	0	1
5					
6	Daily Probabilities	State 1 (Operating)	State 2 (Broken)		
7	If starting state = 1 Op, Prob n day 1	0.9	0.1		
8	If starting state = 0 Broken, Prob in day 1	0.7	0.3		
9	If starting state = 1 Op, Prob n day 2	0.88	0.12		
10	If starting state = 0 Broken, Prob in day 2	0.84	0.16		
11	If starting state = 1 Op, Prob n day 3	0.876	0.124		
12	If starting state = 0 Broken, Prob in day 3	0.868	0.132		
13	If starting state = 1 Op, Prob n day 4	0.8752	0.1248		
14	If starting state = 0 Broken, Prob in day 4	0.8736	0.1264		
15	If starting state = 1 Op, Prob n day 5	0.87504	0.12496		
16	If starting state = 0 Broken, Prob in day 5	0.87472	0.12528		
17	If starting state = 1 Op, Prob n day 6	0.875008	0.124992		
18	If starting state = 0 Broken, Prob in day 6	0.874944	0.125056		
19					
20		Steady State	Probabilities		
21		P(Operating)	P(Broken)		
22		0.875000872	0.125000128		
23		0.875000874			
24		0.125000126			
25	P(Operating) + P (Broken)	1.000001			
26					
27					

Example 4 / Example 10 / Example 8-c / Example 8-b / Example 8

Ready

Cells	Formula
B7, C7	= MMULT (D3 : E3, \$B\$3 : \$C\$4)
B8, C8	= MMULT (D4 : E4, \$B\$3 : \$C\$4)
B9, C9	= MMULT (B7 : C7, \$B\$3 : \$C\$4)
B10, C10	= MMULT (B8 : C8, \$B\$3 : \$C\$4)
B11, C11	= MMULT (B9 : C9, \$B\$3 : \$C\$4)
B12, C12	= MMULT (B10 : C10, \$B\$3 : \$C\$4)
B13, C13	= MMULT (B11 : C11, \$B\$3 : \$C\$4)
B14, C14	= MMULT (B12 : C12, \$B\$3 : \$C\$4)
B15, C15	= MMULT (B13 : C13, \$B\$3 : \$C\$4)
B16, C16	= MMULT (B14 : C14, \$B\$3 : \$C\$4)
B17, C17	= MMULT (B15 : C15, \$B\$3 : \$C\$4)
B18, C18	= MMULT (B16 : C16, \$B\$3 : \$C\$4)
B23	= B3 * \$B\$22 + B4 * \$C\$22
B24	= C3 * \$B\$22 + C4 * \$C\$22
B25	= B22 + C22

Figure 12-5	Decision Tree Representation of the Machine Maintenance Problem: Initial State = Operation

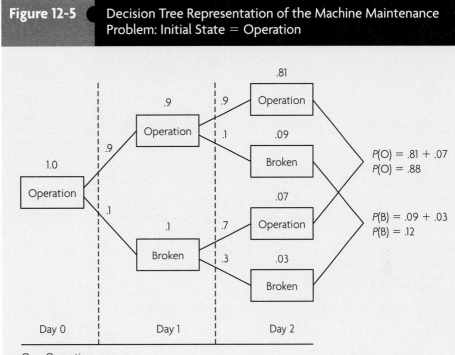

O = Operation
B = Broken

and pressing Ctrl-Shift-Enter. The results (.88 and 12) are displayed in cells B9 and C9 respectively. The answer to part *b* is 12 percent and is given in cell C9. In other words, if the machine is operating on day zero, the probability that it is broken on day 2 is 12 percent.

c.   The answer to part *c* as given in cell B9 is 88 percent. Interpretation of this value is as follows: If the machine is operating on day zero, the probability that it is operating on day 2 is 88 percent.

d.   The decision tree of the machine maintenance problem when the machine is currently operating is given in Figure 12-5.

e.   The answer to this part is given in row 10 of Exhibit 12-1. In answering this part of the problem, we need to determine the probability that the machine is broken two days from today (the second day) given that the machine is broken today (day zero). The answer to this part is found in a similar fashion to the solutions to parts *b* and *c*. The main difference from parts *b* and *c* is that the initial state of the machine is broken. Since the machine is initially broken, we multiply the probabilities from row 8 in cells B8 (Probability of Operating = .70 given that the machine is currently broken) and C8 (Probability of Broken = .30 given that the machine is currently broken) by the transition matrix. This can be accomplished by using the following formula: =MMULT(B8 : C8, $B$3 : $C$4). In this formula B8 : C8 represents the probability of State 1 and State 2 as discussed above and $B$3 : $C$4 is the transition matrix. After specifying the formula, we highlight the cells where we want the answer to be displayed (cells B10 and C10). We proceed by highlighting the formula we just typed in the formula bar and pressing Ctrl-Shift-Enter. The results (.84 and .16) are displayed in cells B10 and C10 respectively. Thus, if the machine is broken on day zero, the probability that it is broken on day 2 is 16 percent.

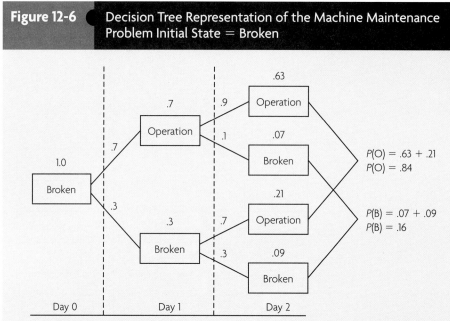

Figure 12-6 Decision Tree Representation of the Machine Maintenance Problem Initial State = Broken

O = Operation
B = Broken

f. The answer to part *f*, given in cell B10, is interpreted as follows: If the machine is broken on day zero, the probability that it is operating on day 2 is 84 percent.

g. The decision tree of the machine maintenance problem when the machine is currently broken is given in Figure 12-6.

h. The steady-state probabilities are calculated at the bottom of the worksheet in Exhibit 12-1. Cells B21 and C21 are set up as the steady-state probabilities for which we will solve. Cells B22, B23, and B24 contain the equations utilized in algebraically solving for steady-state probabilities. These three equations are

$P(O) = .9P(O) + .7P(B)$ (The right-hand side of the equation is contained in cell B22)

$P(B) = .1P(O) + .3P(B)$ (The right-hand side of the equation is contained in cell B23)

$P(A) + P(B) = 1$ (The left-hand side of the equation is contained in cell B24)

The Excel versions of the formulas for these three equations are shown at the bottom of Exhibit 12-1. After entering these three formulas and arbitrary values of 0 for the decision variables, we choose **Tools | Solver** and obtain the Solver parameters screen shown in Exhibit 12-2.

In the Set Target Cell box, we choose cell B24 because the right-hand side of this equation is a numeric value of 1. The right-hand side of the other two equations does not have a numeric value. In the "Equal To" location, we click on the "Value of" button and in the box on the right-hand side of the screen we enter the value of 1, indicating that the sum of the steady-state probabilities stated in cell B24 must add up to 1. In the "By Changing Cells" box, we enter the two unknown variables in cells B21 and C21 that currently have a value of zero assigned to them. In the "Subject to the Constraints" section, we enter the three constraints. Cells B23 and B24 contain the right-hand side of the first two constraints. We set B23 = B22 and

Exhibit 12-2	Solver Parameters Specification Screen of the Machine Maintenance Problem

Solver Parameters

Set Target Cell: `$B$25`

Equal To: ○ Max ○ Min ● Value of: `1`

By Changing Cells:

`$B$22:$C$22`   Guess

Subject to the Constraints:

```
$B$23 = $B$22
$B$24 = $C$22
$B$25 = 1
```

Buttons: Solve, Close, Options, Add, Change, Delete, Reset All, Help

B24 = C22 to complete the specification of the first two equations. In specifying the third and final equation, we let B25 = 1, which indicates that the sum of the probabilities must add up to one. Since we specified this constraint as an objective, entering the third constraint is optional. After specifying the constraints, we simply click on "Options" and check the "Assume Nonnegative" box. Finally we select "Solve" and the Solver provides the values of the steady-state probabilities in cells B22 and C22 in Exhibit 12-1. As can be observed, the steady-state probability for operating is .875 and the steady state probability for broken is .125.

Steady-State Probabilities
$P(O) = .875$
$P(B) = .125$

The remaining entries in rows 11 through 18 continue the short-term calculations for days 5 through 11. In cells A11 through A18 are the descriptions of the probabilities for the respective rows, cells B11 through B18 contain the probability of operating, and cells C11 through C18 contain the probability of broken. The probabilities in cells B11 through C18 are calculated by the matrix multiplication procedure described earlier. The formulas for the various matrix multiplications are given at the bottom of Exhibit 12-1. Note that if the starting (current) state is 1, or operating, the state probability for operating in column B decreases toward the steady-state probability of .875, while the state probability for broken in column C increases toward the steady-state probability of .125.

However, if the starting (current) state is 2, or broken, the state probability for operating in column B increases towards the steady-state probability of .875, while the state probability for broken in column C decreases towards the steady-state probability of .125.

Analysis of a 3 × 3 Matrix

The same methods that were used to analyze a transition matrix with two states can be readily adapted to handle larger problems. The following examples illustrate this. Examples 12-5, 12-6, and 12-7 refer to the transition matrix shown in Table 12-5.

Table 12-5	Transition Matrix for Examples 12-5, 12-6, and 12-7		
		To:	
	X	Y	Z
X	.70	.20	.10
From: Y	.40	.50	.10
Z	.30	.10	.60

Tree Diagram

Example 12-5

Construct two tree diagrams for the transition matrix in Table 12-5, each showing two periods. Have one tree diagram show a starting state of X and the other diagram begin with a starting state of Y. In both cases, use the tree diagram to determine the probability that the system will be in state X, state Y, or state Z given that each tree starts in Period 0.

Solution
See the two tree diagrams and the desired probabilities in Figures 12-7 and 12-8.

Figure 12-7	Tree Diagram for Example 12-5, Starting from X (Initial State = X)

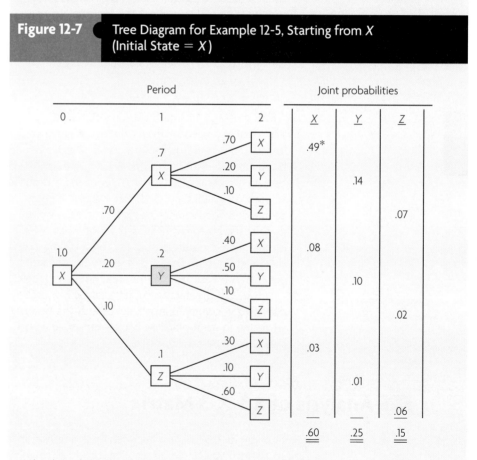

* This value is calculated by multiplying .7 (on the arc between x and x, from period 0 to 1 by the arc between x and x from period 1 to 2.

Figure 12-8	Tree Diagram for Example 12-5, Starting from Y(Initial State = Y)

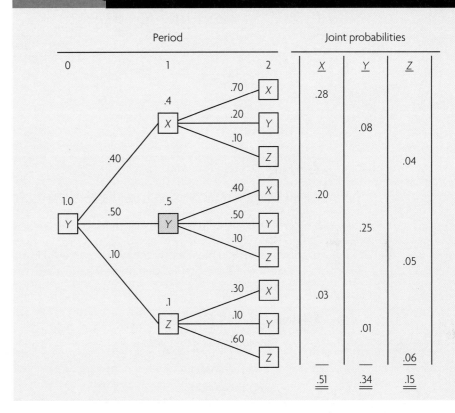

Matrix Multiplication

Example 12-6

Use matrix multiplication to determine the probability that the system described in Table 12-5 will be in each of the various possible states (X, Y, and Z) for Periods 0, 1, 2, and 3, given that the initial state is X in Period 0.

Solution

Period

0     $[1 \quad 0 \quad 0]$

1     $[1 \quad 0 \quad 0]\begin{bmatrix} .70 & .20 & .10 \\ .40 & .50 & .10 \\ .30 & .10 & .60 \end{bmatrix} = \begin{array}{ccc} 1(.70) & 1(.20) & 1(.10) \\ 0(.40) & 0(.50) & 0(.10) \\ \underline{0(.30)} & \underline{0(.10)} & \underline{0(.60)} \\ [.70 & .20 & .10] \end{array}$

2     $[.70 \quad .20 \quad .10]\begin{bmatrix} .70 & .20 & .10 \\ .40 & .50 & .10 \\ .30 & .10 & .60 \end{bmatrix} = \begin{array}{ccc} .70(.70) & .70(.20) & .70(.10) \\ .20(.40) & .20(.50) & .20(.10) \\ \underline{.10(.30)} & \underline{.10(.10)} & \underline{.10(.60)} \\ [.60 & .25 & .15] \end{array}$

(Note that this agrees with the answer for an X start in the preceding example.)

$$3 \qquad [.60 \quad .25 \quad .15] \begin{bmatrix} .70 & .20 & .10 \\ .40 & .50 & .10 \\ .30 & .10 & .60 \end{bmatrix} = \begin{matrix} .60(.70) & .60(.20) & .60(.10) \\ .25(.40) & .25(.50) & .25(.10) \\ \underline{.15(.30)} & \underline{.15(.10)} & \underline{.15(.60)} \\ [.565 & .260 & .175] \end{matrix}$$

Algebraic Solution

Example 12-7

For the transition matrix given in Table 12-5, complete each of the following:

a. Determine the long-run proportions (steady-state probabilities) for each state.
b. If there are 900 members in the system, with 400 in State X in Period 0, 300 in State Y, and 200 in State Z, determine the expected number in each state in the long run.

Solution

a. 1. Develop the state equations:

$$P(X) = .70P(X) + .40P(Y) + .30P(Z)$$
$$P(Y) = .20P(X) + .50P(Y) + .10P(Z)$$
$$P(Z) = .10P(X) + .10P(Y) + .60P(Z)$$
$$P(X) + P(Y) + P(Z) = 1$$

2. Eliminate one of the equations arbitrarily, but not the last one. Suppose the third equation is eliminated. Because it is the state equation for Z, solve for Z in the last equation:

$$P(Z) = 1 - P(X) - P(Y)$$

3. Substitute for Z in the first and second equations:

$$P(X) = .70P(X) + .40P(Y) + .30[1 - P(X) - P(Y)]$$
$$P(Y) = .20P(X) + .50P(Y) + .10[1 - P(X) - P(Y)]$$

4. Simplify each equation with the constant term on the right:

$$.60P(X) - .10P(Y) = .30$$
$$-.10P(X) + .60P(Y) = .10$$

5. Solving, we find

$$P(X) = .543, P(Y) = .257$$

Using $P(Z) = 1 - P(X) - P(Y)$ and these values of $P(X)$ and $P(Y)$, we find

$$P(Z) = .200$$

b.   Using the answers from part *a*, we find the expected number in each state at steady-state, given 900 system members:

$$X = 900(.543) = 488.7$$
$$Y = 900(.257) = 231.3$$
$$Z = 900(.200) = \underline{180.0}$$
$$900.0$$

(It should be noted that the results are independent of the initial conditions.)

Using Excel to Solve Three-State Problems

Consider the following example that demonstrates how a 3*3 Markov analysis problem can be solved.

Example 12-8

At Acorn University students change among the three colleges according to the following transition matrix.

P_{ij} = probability of switching from college *i* to college *j* in the next period (year)

		To		
		Arts and Social Sciences	Engineering	Business
	Arts and Social Sciences	.75	.10	.15
From:	Engineering	.15	.65	.20
	Business	.05	.10	.85

At the beginning of the 2005–2006 academic year, the number of students in each of the three colleges for the incoming freshman class at Acorn University was as follows:

Arts and Social Sciences: 8,000 students
Engineering: 4,000 students
Business: 3,000 students

Use Excel to complete parts *a* through *d*.

a.   Forecast the number of students in each college at the end of the 2006–2007 academic year.
b.   Forecast the number of students in each college at the end of the 2007–2008 academic year.
c.   Determine the steady-state probabilities.
d.   Forecast the number of students in each college in the long run.

Exhibit 12-3	Worksheet for the Markov Analysis of the Acorn University Problem

Microsoft Excel - Chapter12

File Edit View Insert Format Tools MegaStat Data Window Help

Times New Roman ▾ 12 ▾ **B** *I* U

B15 ▾ *fx* {=MMULT(B3:D5, B9:D11)}

	A	B	C	D	E
1		Probability	Transition	Matrix	
2		State 1 (Arts and Soc. Sci.)	State 2 (Engineering)	State 3 (Business)	
3	State 1 (Arts and Soc. Sci.)	0.7500	0.1000	0.1500	
4	State 2 (Engineering)	0.1500	0.6500	0.2000	
5	State 3 (Business)	0.0500	0.1000	0.8500	
6					
7		Probability matrix	at the end of the 2005 - 2006	academic year	
8		State 1 (Arts and Soc. Sci.)	State 2 (Engineering)	State 3 (Business)	
9	State 1 (Arts and Soc. Sci.)	0.7500	0.1000	0.1500	
10	State 2 (Engineering)	0.1500	0.6500	0.2000	
11	State 3 (Business)	0.0500	0.1000	0.8500	
12					
13		Probability matrix	at the end of the 2006 - 2007	academic year	
14		State 1 (Arts and Soc. Sci.)	State 2 (Engineering)	State 3 (Business)	
15	State 1 (Arts and Soc. Sci.)	0.5850	0.1550	0.2600	
16	State 2 (Engineering)	0.2200	0.4575	0.3225	
17	State 3 (Business)	0.0950	0.1550	0.7500	
18					
19					

Sheet1 / Sheet2 / Sheet5 / Sheet4 \ Sheet3 /

Ready   NUM

Cell	Formula
B15 : D17	= MMULT (B3 : D5, B9 : D11)

Solution

In solving this problem, first we have prepared the worksheet shown in Exhibit 12-3. On the top portion of the worksheet shown in Exhibit 12-3, the original probability transition matrix is displayed. In the middle portion of the worksheet, the updated transition probabilities are displayed after one period (year) has gone by. Note that this matrix, which shows the probability of transition from state to state after the first year (end of 2005–2006 academic year), is identical to the original probability transition matrix because the original probability transition matrix is multiplied by the current state matrix, which is an identity matrix. Multiplication of any "initial" transition matrix by the same-size identity matrix will return the original transition matrix.

a. In order to obtain the answer to part *a*, we need to multiply the matrix in the middle of Exhibit 12-3 (probabilities at the end of 2005–2006 academic year) with the original probability transition matrix. In essence, we are multiplying the transition matrix by itself to get the third (bottom) matrix. In order to multiply these two matrices, we enter the formula =MMULT(B3 : D5, B9 : D11). In this formula, B3 : D5 represents the original transition matrix and B9 : D11 represents the probability transition matrix at the end of the 2005–2006 academic year. After specifying the formula, we highlight the cells in which we want the answer to be displayed

Exhibit 12-4	Second Worksheet for the Markov Analysis of the Acorn University Problem

Cell	Formula
B17 : D17	= MMULT (B14 : D14, B9 : D11)

(cells B15 : D17). We proceed by highlighting the formula we just typed in the formula bar and hitting Ctrl-Shift-Enter. The resulting matrix is displayed in cells B15 : D17. This matrix contains the transition probabilities associated with the end of the 2006–2007 academic year. This matrix is repeated in Exhibit 12-4. The answer to part *a* is obtained by multiplying the student population matrix B, shown in cells B14 : D14, by the updated transition matrix stated in cells B3 : D5 in Exhibit 12-4. This matrix multiplication is performed in Exhibit 12-4. In order to multiply these two matrices, we enter =MMULT(B14 : D14, B9 : D11). In this formula, B14 : D14 represents the original population matrix of the students in each of the three respective colleges and B9 : D11 represents the probability transition matrix at the end of the 2005–2006 academic year. After specifying the formula, we highlight the cells in which we want the answer to be displayed (cells B17 : D17). We proceed by highlighting the formula we just typed in the formula bar and hitting Ctrl-Shift-Enter. The resulting matrix is displayed in cells B17 : D17 at the bottom of Exhibit 12-4. The result of this calculation, which states the forecasted number of students in each college at the end of 2006–2007 academic year, is as follows:

College of Arts and Social Sciences: 5,845 students
College of Engineering: 3,535 students
College of Business: 5,620 students

Exhibit 12-5   Third Worksheet for the Markov Analysis and Steady-State Probabilities of the Acorn University Problem

	A	B	C	D	E
		Microsoft Excel - Chapter12			
	B15	fx =0.75*$B$14+0.15*$C$14+0.05*$D$14			
1		State 1 (Arts and Soc. Sci.)	State 2 (Engineering)	State 3 (Business)	
2	B matrix	8000	4000	3000	
3					
4	P(2007-2008)	Probability matrix	at the end of the 2007 - 2008	academic year	
5		State 1 (Arts and Soc. Sci.)	State 2 (Engineering)	State 3 (Business)	
6	State 1 (Arts and Soc. Sci.)	0.47500	0.18525	0.33975	
7	State 2 (Engineering)	0.24975	0.35163	0.39863	
8	State 3 (Business)	0.13200	0.18525	0.68275	
9					
10	B*P(2007-2008)	State 1 (Arts and Soc. Sci.)	State 2 (Engineering)	State 3 (Business)	
11		5195.00	3444.25	6360.75	
12		**Steady State**	**Probabilities**		
13		P(Arts & Social Sciences)	P(Engineering)	P(Business)	
14		0.24074	0.22222	0.53704	
15		0.24074			
16		0.22222			
17		0.53704			
18		1			

Sheet1 / Sheet2 \ **Sheet5** / Sheet4 / Sheet3 /

Cell	Formula
B6 : D8	= MMULT (Sheet 4! B3 : D5, Sheet 4! B9 : D11)
B11 : D11	= MMULT (B2 : D2, B6 : D8)
B15	= 0.75 $*$ $B$14 + 0.15 $*$ $C$14 + 0.05 $*$ $D$14
B16	= 0.1 $*$ $B$14 + 0.65 $*$ $C$14 + 0.1 $*$ $D$14
B17	= 0.15 $*$ $B$14 + 0.2 $*$ $C$14 + 0.85 $*$ $D$14
B18	= B14 + C14 + D14

b.   Once we obtain the answer to part *a*, it is relatively easy to obtain the answer to part *b*. We continue to multiply the most recently calculated probability matrix by the original probability transition matrix. The resulting matrix is given in Exhibit 12-5 in cells B6 through D8.

In executing this multiplication, we utilize the following equation: =MMULT(Sheet4! B3 : D5, Sheet4! B9 : D11). In this formula cells B3 : D5 represent the original transition matrix in sheet 4 and cells B9 : D11 represent in sheet 4 the probability matrix after the 2006–2007 academic year. After obtaining the probability matrix after the 2007–2008 academic year in cells B6 through D8 of Exhibit 12-5, we proceed to multiply this matrix by the initial population matrix of B. This multiplication can be achieved by utilizing the MMULT function again.

More specifically, we specify the following formula in cells B11, C11, and D11 in Exhibit 12-5: =MMULT(B2 : D2, B6 : D8). In this formula, B2 : D2 represents the original population matrix B, which consists of the initial number of students in each of the colleges of Acorn University at the beginning of the academic year 2005–2006. B6 : D8 represents the updated probability matrix calculated earlier, and it represents the updated probabilities of transition from state to state at the end of the academic year 2007–2008. Multiplication of these two matrices results in the answer given in cells B11, C11, and D11 of Exhibit 12-5.

The result of this calculation, which states the forecasted number of students in each college at the end of the 2007–2008 academic year, is as follows:

College of Arts and Social Sciences: 5,195 students
College of Engineering: 3,444 students
College of Business: 6,361 students

c. The steady-state probabilities are calculated in the bottom portion of Exhibit 12-5. Cells B14, C14, and D14 show the steady-state probabilities. In cells B15, B16, B17, and B18 we specify the following steady-state equations.

Let $P(A)$ = probability of the number of students in the College of Arts and Social Sciences
$P(E)$ = probability of the number of students in the College of Engineering
$P(B)$ = probability of the number of students in the College of Business

Cell B15: $P(A) = .75P(A) + .15P(E) + .05P(B)$
Cell B16: $P(E) = .10P(A) + .65P(E) + .10P(B)$
Cell B17: $P(B) = .15P(A) + .20P(E) + .85P(B)$
Cell B18 $P(A) + P(E) + P(B) = 1$

Using Excel, these equations are stated at the bottom of Exhibit 12-5. Initially we let the values of the steady-state probabilities be equal to an arbitrary value (such as zero), and we choose **Tools | Solver;** the Solver parameters specification screen shown in Exhibit 12-6 appears.

In Exhibit 12-6, in the "Set Target Cell" box, we choose cell B18 because the right-hand side of this equation is a numeric value of 1. The right-hand side of the other three equations does not have a numeric value. In the "Equal To" location, we click on the "Value of" button and in the box on the right-hand side of the screen we enter the value of 1, indicating that the sum of the steady-state probabilities in cell B18 must add up to 1. In the "By Changing Cells" box, we enter the three unknown variables in cells B14, C14, and D14 that currently have a value of zero assigned to them. In the "Subject to the Constraints" section, we enter the four constraints. The cells B15, B16, and B17 contain the right side of the first three constraints. We set B15 = B14, B16 = C14, and B17 = D14 to complete the specification of the first three equations. In specifying the fourth and final equation, we simply let B18 = 1, which indicates that the sum of the probabilities must add up to one. Entering the fourth constraint is optional since we already specified this constraint as an objective. After specifying the constraints, we choose "Options" to check the "Assume Nonnegative" box. Finally, we click on "Solve" and the Solver provides the values of the steady-state probabilities in

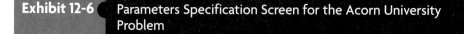

Exhibit 12-6 Parameters Specification Screen for the Acorn University Problem

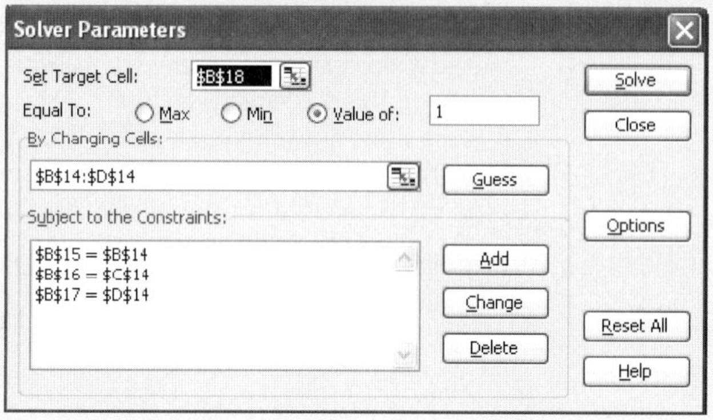

cells B14, C14, and D14 in Exhibit 12-5. As can be observed, the steady-state probability for College of Arts and Social Sciences is .24074, the steady-state probability for the College of Engineering is .22222, and the steady-state probability for the College of Business is .53704.

Steady-State Probabilities
$P(A) = .24074$
$P(E) = .22222$
$P(B) = .53704$

d. Multiplying the steady-state probabilities by the total number of students in the three colleges (8,000 + 4,000 + 3,000) = 15,000 provides the long-term forecast of the students in the three colleges provided that there is no attrition.

College of Arts and Social Sciences: (.24074)* 15,000 = 3,611 students
College of Engineering: (.22222)* 15,000 = 3,333 students
College of Business: (.53704)* (15,000) = 8,056 students

◼ Cyclical, Transient, and Absorbing Systems

Cyclical, transient, and absorbing systems offer a contrast to the ones described so far in this chapter. **Cyclical systems** are those that have a tendency to move from state to state in a definite pattern or cycle. An example of a cyclical system is presented in the transition matrix in Table 12-6.

Let's see why this is a cyclical system. Suppose the system begins in State *A*. Because of the transition probability of 1 for *A* to *B*, the system will be in State *B* in the following period. Then in the next period, it will move from *B* to *C* and then back to *A* and so on. Consequently, we can say with certainty which state the system will be in at any future period (e.g., Period 42) if we know its state in any earlier period (e.g., Period 1).

Table 12-6	An Example of a Cyclical System		

		To:		
		A	B	C
	A	0	1	0
From:	B	0	0	1
	C	1	0	0

Table 12-7	An Example of System with a Transient State		

		To:		
		A	B	C
	A	.4	0	.6
From:	B	0	.65	.35
	C	0	.80	.20

Table 12-8	An Example of a System with Absorbing States		

		To:			
		A	B	C	D
	A	.5	.2	.1	.2
From:	B	.3	.2	.1	.4
	C	0	0	1.0	0
	D	0	0	0	1.0

A **transient system** is a system in which there is at least one state—the transient state—where once a system leaves it, the system will never return to it. In Table 12-7, State A is considered a transient state because if the system is in State A in period 1, the system has a 40 percent chance of returning to State A in period 2. However, if the system leaves State A, the probability of going to State A from State B is zero and the probability of going to State A from State C is zero. Therefore, once the system leaves State A by going to State C, because State A has a 60 percent chance of going to State C and has zero percent chance of going from State C and State B to State C. The system will not be able to return to State A again.

An **absorbing system** is one in which the system gravitates to one or more states. In effect, once a member of such a system enters one of the absorbing states, it becomes trapped and can never exit that state. An example of a transition matrix for an absorbing system is shown in Table 12-8.

States C and D are absorbing states. We can readily observe this by noting that probabilities for exiting to other states from either of these states are equal to zero, whereas the probability of remaining in the state is 1.0, or 100 percent. Note that even though a system

Figure 12-9   Probability Transition Diagrams for the Transition Matrices Given in Tables 12-6, 12-7, and 12-8

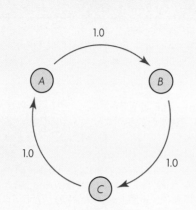

(a) Transition Diagram for Table 12-6

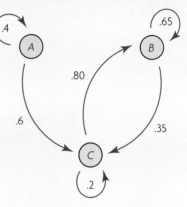

(b) Transition Diagram for Table 12-7

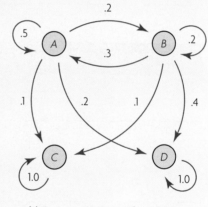

(c) Transition Diagram for Table 12-8

may begin with members in nonabsorbing states such as *A* or *B*, eventually the system will be reduced to members only in the absorbing states.

The transition matrices displayed in Tables 12-6, 12-7, and 12-8 also can be displayed as **probability transition diagrams.** Showing the transition probabilities in the form of a diagram with nodes that represent states and directed branches that show the probability of going from state *i* to state *j* helps in determining whether the transition matrix contains an absorbing or transient state or if the matrix contains a cycle. The probability transition diagrams associated with Tables 12-6, 12-7, and 12-8 are given in Figure 12-9.

Analysis of Accounts Receivable

One example of absorbing states occurs when using Markov analysis for accounts receivable. The states of interest are possible classifications of accounts such as paid, one month overdue, two months overdue, and bad debt. The states paid and bad debt are absorbing states because once an account achieves either status, the passage of time will not change its classification; a paid bill will not become unpaid and a bad debt will be turned over to a collection agency. Even though the bad debt eventually may be collected, the costs associated with collecting it may offset all or a good part of the amount collected. Therefore, it would be misleading to label the bill as "paid" in the sense we are talking about here. Analysis of accounts receivable can provide management with an estimate of the proportion of current accounts receivable that will end up in each of the two absorbing states: *paid* and *bad debt*.

Consider the following example

Example 12-9

A firm has a one-month billing cycle. At the end of each month, outstanding bills are classified into one of the following categories: paid, less than one-month old, more than one-month and less than two-months old, and bad debt. Now, suppose that a transition matrix has been developed that contains probabilities for the accounts:

		Next state			
		Paid	1	2	Bad debt
	Paid	1	0	0	0
Current	1	.80	0	.20	0
state	2	.60	0	0	.40
	Bad debt	0	0	0	1

If there are $30,000 in one-month-old receivables and $45,000 in two-month-old receivables, determine the total amount that will be paid and the total amount that will become a bad debt.

Solution

Let's examine the logic of this matrix. As previously noted, the paid category is an absorbing state. Hence, the probability that an account in this category will move to another category is 0; the probability it will remain as paid is 1. Similarly, *bad debt* is an absorbing state; the probability is 1 that it will retain that classification; any other state (in that row), therefore, has a probability of 0. For an account that is less than one-month old (i.e., State 1), there is some probability that it will be paid. Management may have determined this to be .80. Because the firm is on a one-month billing cycle, though, the accounts in this category must either move to the paid category or move to the one and two-month category; they cannot remain less than one-month old and neither can they become bad debts because the latter category (State 2) is reserved for accounts that are more than one month or less than two months overdue. Therefore, there is a zero probability of staying in State 1 and a zero probability of moving to the *bad debt* state. State 2 accounts, similarly, have a zero probability of remaining there and a zero probability of becoming less than one-month old. Instead either these accounts will end up paid (for which management has assigned a probability of .60) or they will become bad debts (for which management has assigned a probability of .40).

For purposes of analysis, it is desirable to rearrange the matrix so that the extreme states (*paid* and *bad debt*) are listed first, followed by the other two states. Thus:

	Paid	Bad debt	1	2
Paid	1	0	0	0
Bad debt	0	1	0	0
1	.80	0	0	.20
2	.60	.40	0	0

Next, we partition this transition matrix into four parts:

	Paid	Bad debt	1	2
Paid	1	0	0	0
Bad debt	0	1	0	0
1	.80	0	0	.20
2	.60	.40	0	0

We, then, label the parts as follows:

	Paid	Bad debt	1	2
Paid				
Bad debt	1		O	
1				
2	R		Q	

In this way, we can see that

$$I = \begin{array}{c} \\ paid \\ Bad\ debt \end{array} \begin{array}{cc} paid & Bad\ debt \\ \begin{bmatrix} 1 & 0 \\ 0 & 1 \end{bmatrix} \end{array}$$

$$O = \begin{array}{c} \\ paid \\ Bad\ debt \end{array} \begin{array}{cc} 1 & 2 \\ \begin{bmatrix} 0 & 0 \\ 0 & 0 \end{bmatrix} \end{array}$$

$$R = \begin{array}{c} 1 \\ 2 \end{array} \begin{bmatrix} .80 & 0 \\ .60 & .40 \end{bmatrix}$$

$$Q = \begin{array}{c} \\ 1 \\ 2 \end{array} \begin{array}{cc} 1 & 2 \\ \begin{bmatrix} 0 & .20 \\ 0 & 0 \end{bmatrix} \end{array}$$

Matrix 1 is an *identity matrix:* It has 1s on the diagonal and 0s everywhere else. Matrix O is simply a matrix of all 0s. Matrix R contains the transition probabilities of absorptions in the next period, and matrix Q contains the transition probabilities of movement between nonabsorbing states.

Partitioning the matrix in this way allows us to compute the **fundamental matrix,** N:

$$N = (I - Q)^{-1} \tag{12-1}$$

The -1 refers to the *inverse* of a matrix. Hence, to obtain the fundamental matrix, we must subtract matrix Q from matrix I, then find the inverse of the result. Therefore, we subtract Q from I:

$$(I - Q) = \begin{bmatrix} 1 & 0 \\ 0 & 1 \end{bmatrix} - \begin{bmatrix} 0 & .20 \\ 0 & 0 \end{bmatrix}$$

$$= \begin{bmatrix} 1 & -.20 \\ 0 & 1 \end{bmatrix}$$

Then, we find the inverse of this matrix.

In general, the inverse of a matrix is found in the following way. If matrix M is defined as

$$M = \begin{bmatrix} m_{11} & m_{12} \\ m_{21} & m_{22} \end{bmatrix} \tag{12-2}$$

then its inverse is

$$M^{-1} = \begin{bmatrix} m_{22}/d & -m_{12}/d \\ -m_{21}/d & m_{11}/d \end{bmatrix} \tag{12-3}$$

where d is the determinant of a matrix. The determinant of a matrix is calculated in Equational 12-4:

$$d = m_{11}m_{22} - m_{21}m_{12} \tag{12-4}$$

For our accounts receivable problem, the inverse of the matrix $(I - Q)$ is found in the following way:

$$(I - Q) = \begin{bmatrix} 1 & -.20 \\ 0 & 1 \end{bmatrix}$$

Using Equational 12-4, $d = 1(1) - 0(-.20) = 1$. Then

$$N = (I - Q)^{-1} = \begin{bmatrix} 1/1 & -(-.20)/1 \\ -0/1 & 1/1 \end{bmatrix} = \begin{bmatrix} 1 & .20 \\ 0 & 1 \end{bmatrix}$$

Thus, the fundamental matrix, N is

$$N = \begin{array}{cc} & \begin{array}{cc} 1 & 2 \end{array} \\ \begin{array}{c} 1 \\ 2 \end{array} & \begin{bmatrix} 1 & .20 \\ 0 & 1 \end{bmatrix} \end{array}$$

The fundamental matrix indicates the expected probability that the system will be in any of the nonabsorbing states before absorption occurs. Hence, if an account is in State 1, the expected probability that the customer would move to State 2 is .20.

The fundamental matrix can be used to determine the probability that an account eventually will move to the various absorbing states (i.e., paid or bad debt). This can be accomplished by multiplying matrix R by the fundamental matrix. The result in our example is

$$NR = \begin{array}{c} 1 \\ 2 \end{array} \begin{array}{cc} 1 & 2 \end{array} \begin{bmatrix} 1 & .20 \\ 0 & 1 \end{bmatrix} \times \begin{array}{c} 1 \\ 2 \end{array} \begin{array}{cc} \text{Paid} & \text{Bad} \\ \text{debt} \end{array} \begin{bmatrix} .80 & 0 \\ .60 & .40 \end{bmatrix}$$

$$= \begin{array}{c} 1 \\ 2 \end{array} \begin{array}{cc} \text{Paid} & \text{Bad} \\ \text{debt} \end{array} \begin{bmatrix} .92 & .08 \\ .60 & .40 \end{bmatrix}$$

The interpretation of this matrix is that if an account is currently less than one-month overdue (i.e., in State 1), the probability is .92 that it will end up being paid and .08 that it will end up a bad debt. Similarly, if an account is currently in State 2 (more than one month overdue, but less than two months overdue), there is a probability of .60 that it will be paid and a probability of .40 that it will end up a bad debt.

If we know the value of the accounts in each state, we can use the NQ matrix to determine the expected amount that will be paid and the expected amount of bad debt. Since the amount owed for accounts in State 1 is currently $30,000 and the amount owed for accounts in State 2 is currently $45,000 if B = amount-owed matrix, then the expected paid and bad debt amounts can be calculated by multiplying B and NR:

$$B^*NR = \begin{array}{cc} 1 & 2 \end{array} \begin{bmatrix} 30,000 & 45,000 \end{bmatrix} \begin{array}{c} 1 \\ 2 \end{array} \begin{array}{cc} \text{Paid} & \text{Bad} \\ \text{debt} \end{array} \begin{bmatrix} .92 & .08 \\ .60 & .40 \end{bmatrix} = \begin{array}{cc} \text{Paid} & \text{Bad} \\ \text{debt} \end{array} \begin{bmatrix} 54,600 & 20,400 \end{bmatrix}$$

◼️ Analysis of Absorbing States Using Excel

The absorbing states also can be analyzed using Excel. Let's consider the following example.

Example 12-10

Acorn General Hospital is well known for its practice of accepting patients regardless of their ability to pay the medical bills. However, as a result of this practice, the hospital is experiencing accounts receivable problems.

The hospital's accounting department has established the following four categories for all medical accounts.

1. Fully paid.
2. Bad debt, written off.
3. Current and due within 30 days.
4. Delinquent, 31 days to 120 days old.

The above-listed categories will be treated as the states in our Markov analysis. The accounting department has analyzed the past data and came up with the following transition probability matrix, where

p_{ij} = probability of a dollar in a given week in state i moving to state j in the next week.

$$P = \begin{array}{c} 1 \\ 2 \\ 3 \\ 4 \end{array} \begin{bmatrix} 1 & 0 & 0 & 0 \\ 0 & 1 & 0 & 0 \\ .6 & 0 & .2 & .2 \\ .4 & .2 & 0 & .4 \end{bmatrix}$$

Use Excel to answer the following questions:

a. What is the probability that the delinquent accounts (dollars) will be paid?
b. What is the probability that the current accounts (dollars) will be paid?
c. What is the probability that the delinquent accounts (dollars) will be written off?
d. What is the probability that the current accounts (dollars) will be written off?
e. Currently, Acorn General Hospital has a total of $200,000 in total accounts receivable. As was described earlier, the accounts receivable is further classified as either current or delinquent. Of the $200,000 total accounts receivable, $150,000 is in current accounts receivable and $50,000 is delinquent accounts receivable. Determine the amount of the $200,000 accounts receivable that the hospital can expect to be paid.
f. Determine the amount (of the $200,000 accounts receivable) that is expected to turn into bad debts.

Solution
In solving this problem using Excel, we prepare the worksheet shown in Exhibit 12-7. The top portion of the exhibit, in cells B2 through E5, contains the transition matrix. As you may recall in our earlier discussion, we divided the transition matrix into four sub matrices (I, O, R, and Q). Three of the four submatrices are displayed in Exhibit 12-7.

Submatrix I is shown in cells B8 through C9, submatrix Q is shown in cells E8 through F9, and submatrix R is shown in cells B16 through C17. First we subtract the matrix Q from matrix I in cells A12 through B13. Second we find the determinant and the inverse of this matrix. Calculation of the determinant is not necessary because in calculating the inverse, Excel automatically calculates the determinant. However, the calculation of the determinant by Excel is included since we have shown the manual calculation of the determinant in our previous discussion. The value of the determinant is displayed in cell C12 of Exhibit 12-7 and is calculated by the following formula: =MDETERM(A12:B13). The inverse of the I-Q matrix is shown in cells E12 through F13. This inverse is calculated by entering the following formula in cell E12, =MINVERSE(A12 : B13), and highlighting cells E12 through F13. In order to ensure that the entire inverse appears in cells E12 through F13, we need to highlight the formula

Exhibit 12-7   Excel Worksheet for Example 12-10: The Acorn Hospital Absorbing State Problem

Microsoft Excel - Chapter12					
File Edit View Insert Format Tools MegaStat Data Window Help					
C12 ▼ =MDETERM(A12:B13)					
	A	B	C	D	E	F
		State 1 (paid)	State 2 (bad debt)	State 3 (current owed)	State 4 (delinquent)	
1						
2	State 1 (paid)	1.0	0.0	0.0	0.0	
3	State 2 (bad debt)	0.0	1.0	0.0	0.0	
4	State 3 (current owed)	0.6	0.0	0.2	0.2	
5	State 4 (delinquent)	0.4	0.2	0.0	0.4	
6		**I**	**matrix**		**Q**	**Matrix**
7		To State 1	To State 2		To State 3	To State 4
8	From State 1	1.0	0.0	From State 3	0.20	0.20
9	From State 2	0.0	1.0	From State 4	0.00	0.40
10						
11	**I-Q**	**matrix**	**(I-Q) determinant**		**(I-Q) inverse = N**	**matrix**
12		0.800	-0.200	0.480		1.25000	0.41667
13		0.000	0.600			0.00000	1.66667
14		**R**	**matrix**		**N*R**	**matrix**
15		To State 1	To State 2		To State 1	To State 2
16	From State 3	0.600	0.000	From State 3	0.91667	0.08333
17	From State 4	0.400	0.200	From State 4	0.66667	0.33333
18						
19		**B**	**matrix**		**B*(N*R)**	**matrix**
20		State 3 (current owed)	State 4 (delinquent)		State 1 (paid)	State 2 (bad debt)
21		130000.000	30000.000		170833.333	29166.667

Sheet1 \ Sheet2 / Sheet5 / Sheet4 / Sheet3 /   Ready   NUM

Cell	Formula
A12	= B8 − E8
A13	= B9 − E9
C12	= MDETERM (A12 : B13)
E12 : F13	= MINVERSE (A12 : B13)
E16 : F17	= MMULT (E12 : F13, B16 : C17)
E21 : F21	= MMULT (B21 : C21, E16 : F17)
B12	= C8 − F8
B13	= C9 − F9

we just entered in the formula bar for cell E12 and hit Ctrl-Shift-Enter. The resulting matrix is the matrix N (the fundamental matrix).

Next we multiply matrix N and matrix R. In multiplying these two matrices, first we enter the matrix multiplication formula in cell E16 as =MMULT(E12 : F13, B16 : C17). After specifying the formula, we highlight the cells where we want the answer to be displayed (cells E16 through F17). We proceed by highlighting the formula we just typed in the formula bar and pressing Ctrl-Shift-Enter. In this formula, cells E12 : F13 represent the fundamental matrix N, while cells B16 through C17 represent the submatrix R. Multiplication of these two matrices results in the answer given in cells E16, E17, F16, and F17 of Exhibit 12-7.

After finding the N*R matrix, we multiply the B, or "amount-owed," matrix by the N*R matrix. We enter the following formula in cells E21 and F21: =MMULT(B21 : C21, E16 : F17). In this formula, cells B21 : C21 represent the amount-owed matrix B, while cells E16 through F17 represent the N*R matrix. The resulting matrix, given in cells E21 and F21, shows the amount of money that is expected to be eventually paid and the amount of money that has to be written off as bad debt. The formulas for various cells are stated at the bottom of Exhibit 12-7. The answer to the questions in part *a* through part *f* can easily be obtained from Exhibit 12-7. Table 12-9 summarizes the answers along with the cells the answers are displayed in.

Table 12-9   Answers to Example 12-10, Part 1 *a* through *f*

Part	Cell in Exhibit 12-7 Where Answer Is Displayed	Answer
a	E17	.6667
b	E16	.9167
c	F17	.3333
d	F16	.0833
e	E21	$170,833.33
f	F21	$29,166.67

Assumptions

Markov analysis is predicated on a number of important assumptions. These are

1. The probability that an item in the system either will change from one state (e.g., Airport A) to another or remain in its current state is a function of the transition probabilities only.
2. The transition probabilities remain constant.
3. The system is a closed one; there will be no arrivals to the system or exits from the system.

As you might surmise, these assumptions are fairly restrictive; not very many real-life systems completely satisfy them. For this reason, Markov analysis is not as useful, nor as widely used, as most of the other techniques described in this book. Even so, there are some uses of this technique, making the study of Markov analysis worthwhile. Moreover, analysis of systems that can be described in Markov terms can provide some insight into system behaviors, and this knowledge can be generalized to other systems.

Summary

Markov analysis can be useful for describing the behavior of a certain class of systems that change from state to state on a period-by-period basis according to known transition probabilities. Consumer buying patterns, market shares, sporting events, and equipment breakdowns sometimes lend themselves to description in Markov terms.

Markov analysis uses tree diagrams, matrix multiplication, and an algebraic approach. The first two approaches are especially useful for describing short-term system behavior, whereas the third approach is more appropriate for describing long-term, behavior.

Automobile Manufacture

Providing variety in product features is important for manufacturing companies. However, offering additional variety usually results in additional cost to the manufacturer. For that reason, the process employed to provide that variety is critical.

E. K. Pill and M. Holweg studied filling orders in the automobile industry to examine the impact of product variety on the manufacturing strategy. Automobile manufacturers produce automobiles in one of three ways: (1) they build automobiles to put in inventory based on a forecast of demand (make-to-stock), (2) they build automobiles based on individual customer orders (make-to-order), or (3) they assemble automobiles to order (assemble-to-order). The third is a hybrid method where the manufacturer builds the basic automobile for inventory based on forecasted demand and then installs options based on customer specifications.

Product variety in the study was defined in two ways: (1) external variety—the number of choices or options offered to the customer and (2) internal variety—the output of the manufacturing process to meet the needs of the external variety offered to the customer. In the automotive industry, it can be shown that internal and external varieties are independent of each other. For example, the engine compartment of an automobile shell being produced (an internal variable) will not vary depending on the type of engine selected or the color of the automobile (external variables). For purposes of this discussion, the focus will be mainly on internal variety and how it can be achieved.

To reduce internal variety, many companies employ "mutable support structures" where manufacturing components are designed to accommodate multiple product configurations. A mutable component can be used with a variety of options. For example, a mutable automobile body can be used with a variety of options as to engine and transmission types. While "mutable support structures" may cost more than their customized counterparts, the flexibility they provide simplifies the production system. Many production managers consider them to be desirable, especially when manufacturing based on customer orders because they can reduce internal variety as well as improve manufacturing flexibility. While mutability improves production efficiency, when a company is producing

for inventory, the company could save money by using a less mutable system.

"Modularity" is another method used to reduce complexity associated with internal variety. A module represents groupings of component parts into subassemblies. By moving some parts of the production to the subassembly level, variability in options is less important because the main production line is not affected. Modularity allows easy replacement and interchange, so producers can quickly select modules with particular options to be incorporated into a product. Customized products can be manufactured faster because individual parts do not have to be assembled together. The considerable reduction in complexity associated with modularity is a big benefit from a manufacturing standpoint.

"Option bundling" is one way to reduce and manage external variety. Rather than selecting options individually, a customer is only allowed to select certain options that are bundled together as a package. Firms can substantially reduce the choices offered to customers and thereby simplify their distribution systems.

Firms also can use late configuration (also referred to as postponement). Under that method, various components are installed on the product after the majority of the product assembly is completed. For instance, Honda installs various trim accessories at its distribution centers rather than on the assembly line. Late configuration reduces the complexity of the manufacturing process and provides more flexibility to meet customer requirements without increasing fundamental internal variety in the manufacturing process. However, some manufacturers believe late configuration may compromise the quality of the product being produced.

While many solutions have been proposed for dealing with product variety (both internal and external), the effectiveness of the solution depends on whether the firm employs a make-to-stock or make-to-order strategy. For instance, procedures that are helpful in dealing with the impact of variety on a make-to-order system may not be helpful in a make-to-stock system, and vice versa.

Source: F. K. Pill and M. Holweg, "Linking Product Variety and Order Fulfillment Strategies," *Interfaces* 34, no. 5 (September–October 2004), pp. 394–403.

We analyzed absorbing, transient, and cyclical states and provided the accounts receivable example to show an application of two absorbing states, titled as "paid" and "bad debt" categories. The analysis shows how to estimate the dollars in accounts receivable that would be absorbed by each of these two states.

The primary objective of Markov analysis is to estimate the probability of each state after a large number of transitions.

Glossary

Absorbing System A system in which members gravitate to one or a few states; eventually all members end up in those states.

Algebraic Approach Solving the equations developed from the transition matrix simultaneously to obtain the steady-state probabilities.

Cyclical System A system that moves from state to state in a repetitive pattern.

Fundamental Matrix (matrix $N = (I - Q)^{-1}$) A matrix calculated to determine the probabilities associated with problems that have two absorbing states of a Markov process.

Markov Process A closed system that changes from state to state according to stable transition probabilities.

Matrix Multiplication A method of obtaining the short-term state probabilities. It is based on state probabilities being equal to the product of the probabilities in the preceding period multiplied by the matrix of transition probabilities.

Probability Transition Diagrams Showing the transition probabilities in the form of a diagram with nodes that represent states and directed branches that show the probability of going from state i to state j.

State of the System One of a set of mutually exclusive and collectively exhaustive conditions a system can assume.

Steady-State Long-term tendencies of a Markov system to be in its various states.

Transient System A system in which there is at least one state where once a system leaves this particular state, there is no return possible to that state.

Transition Matrix A matrix that shows the probability of a Markov system changing from its current state to each possible state in the next period.

Transition Probability Given that a system is in state i during a given period, the transition probability p_{ij} is the probability that the system will be in state j in the next period. p_{ij} remains constant from period to period.

Tree Diagram A visual portrayal of a system's transitions. It is composed of a series of nodes and branches. The branches represent the possible choices at each stage (period).

Solved Problems

Problem 1

Tree diagram   Given this transition matrix, find the probabilities of the system being in State 1 and State 2 in period 3 if the system begins in State 1 in Period 0:

		To:	
		1	2
From:	1	.80	.20
	2	.40	.60

Solution

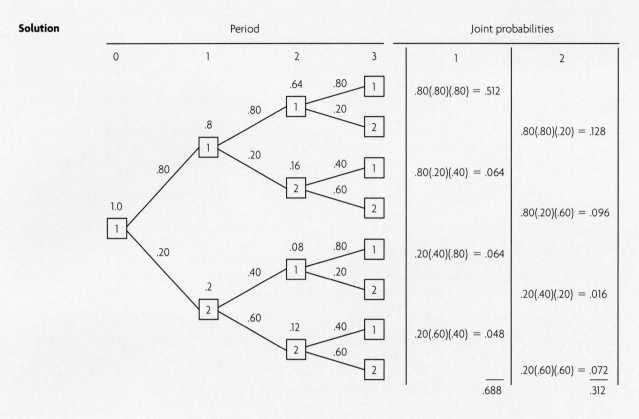

For each branch end, multiply the probabilities of the branches that lead to it, separating by 1 or 2, then add the results as shown. Thus, the probability is .688 that the system will be in State 1 and .312 that it will be in State 2.

Problem 2

Matrix multiplication   For the transition matrix of the previous problem, use matrix multiplication to find the probabilities that the system will be in State 1 and State 2 in Period 3 if the system beings in State 1 at Period 0.

Solution

Period			$P(\text{State 1}) = 1$	$P(\text{State 2}) = 0$
1	$\begin{bmatrix} 1 & 0 \end{bmatrix}$	$\begin{bmatrix} .80 & .20 \\ .40 & .60 \end{bmatrix}$	$\begin{aligned} 1(.80) &= .80 \\ 0(.40) &= .00 \\ \hline &.80 \end{aligned}$	$\begin{aligned} 1(.20) &= .20 \\ 0(.60) &= .00 \\ \hline &.20 \end{aligned}$
2	$\begin{bmatrix} .80 & .20 \end{bmatrix}$	$\begin{bmatrix} .80 & .20 \\ .40 & .60 \end{bmatrix}$	$\begin{aligned} 80(.80) &= .64 \\ 20(.40) &= .08 \\ \hline &.72 \end{aligned}$	$\begin{aligned} 80(.20) &= .16 \\ 20(.60) &= .12 \\ \hline &.28 \end{aligned}$
3	$\begin{bmatrix} .72 & .28 \end{bmatrix}$	$\begin{bmatrix} .80 & .20 \\ .40 & .60 \end{bmatrix}$	$\begin{aligned} .72(.80) &= .576 \\ .28(.40) &= .112 \\ \hline &.688 \end{aligned}$	$\begin{aligned} .72(.20) &= .144 \\ .28(.60) &= .168 \\ \hline &.312 \end{aligned}$

Based on the calculations given in the above table, the probabilities in Period 3 are $P(\text{State 1}) = .688$, $P(\text{State 2}) = .312$.

Problem 3

Matrix multiplication and steady-state probabilities

a.   Given the transition matrix of the previous problem, use matrix multiplication to find the probabilities that the system will be in State 1 and State 2 in Period 3 if the system begins in State 2 in Period 0.

b.   Find the steady-state probabilities for the transition matrix of the previous problem.

Solution   a.

Period			P(State 1) = 0	P(State 2) = 1
1	$[0 \quad 1]$	$\begin{bmatrix} .8 & .2 \\ .4 & .6 \end{bmatrix}$	$\begin{aligned} 0(.8) &= 0 \\ 1(.4) &= \underline{.4} \\ &\quad .4 \end{aligned}$	$\begin{aligned} 0(.2) &= 0 \\ 1(.6) &= \underline{.6} \\ &\quad .6 \end{aligned}$
2	$[.4 \quad .6]$	$\begin{bmatrix} .8 & .2 \\ .4 & .6 \end{bmatrix}$	$\begin{aligned} .4(.8) &= .32 \\ .6(.4) &= \underline{.24} \\ &\quad .56 \end{aligned}$	$\begin{aligned} .4(.2) &= .08 \\ .6(.6) &= \underline{.36} \\ &\quad .44 \end{aligned}$
3	$[.56 \quad .44]$	$\begin{bmatrix} .8 & .2 \\ .4 & .6 \end{bmatrix}$	$\begin{aligned} .56(.8) &= .448 \\ .44(.4) &= \underline{.176} \\ &\quad .624 \end{aligned}$	$\begin{aligned} .56(.2) &= .112 \\ .44(.6) &= \underline{.264} \\ &\quad .376 \end{aligned}$

Based on the calculations given above, if the system begins in State 2 in Period 0, the probabilities in Period 3 are P(State 1) = .624 and P(State 2) = .376.

b.   Calculation of steady-state probabilities:

$$[P(\text{State} = 1) \, P(\text{State} = 2)] = [P(\text{State} = 1) \, P(\text{State} = 2)] \begin{bmatrix} .8 & .2 \\ .4 & .6 \end{bmatrix}$$

After performing matrix multiplication of the right-hand side, we get

$$[P(\text{State} = 1)] = [.80 \, P(\text{State} = 1) + .40 P(\text{State} = 2)]$$
$$[P(\text{State} = 2)] = [.20 \, P(\text{State} = 1) + .60 P(\text{State} = 2)]$$

In addition to these equations, we have the following equation that specifies the two probabilities for State 1 and State 2 must sum to 1.

$$P(\text{State} = 1) + P(\text{State} = 2) = 1$$

In other words, $P(\text{State} = 2) = 1 - P(\text{State} = 1)$
    Substituting $P(\text{State 2}) = 1 - P(\text{State} = 1)$ in equation 1:

$$P(\text{State} = 1) = .80 P(\text{State} = 1) + .40(1 - P(\text{State} = 1))$$

Solving for $P(\text{State} = 1)$:

$$P(\text{State} = 1) = .80 P(\text{State} = 1) + .40 - .40 P(\text{State} = 1)$$
$$.60 P(\text{State} = 1) = .40$$
$$P(\text{State} = 1) = 2/3$$

Since $P(\text{State} = 1) + P(\text{State} = 2) = 1$:

$$^2/_3 + P(\text{State} = 2) = 1$$
$$P(\text{State} = 2) = {}^1/_3$$

Problem 4   Use Excel and provide the solution for Solved Problems 1, 2, and 3.

Exhibits 12-8 and 12-9 show the Excel solution to Solved Problems 1, 2, and 3. Exhibit 12-9 is the Solver parameters screen that shows the necessary formulas for the steady-state computations in the "Subject to the Constraints" box. The necessary formulas for the Excel worksheet are given at the bottom of Exhibit 12-8.

Exhibit 12-8 Worksheet for The Markov Analysis of Solved Problem 4

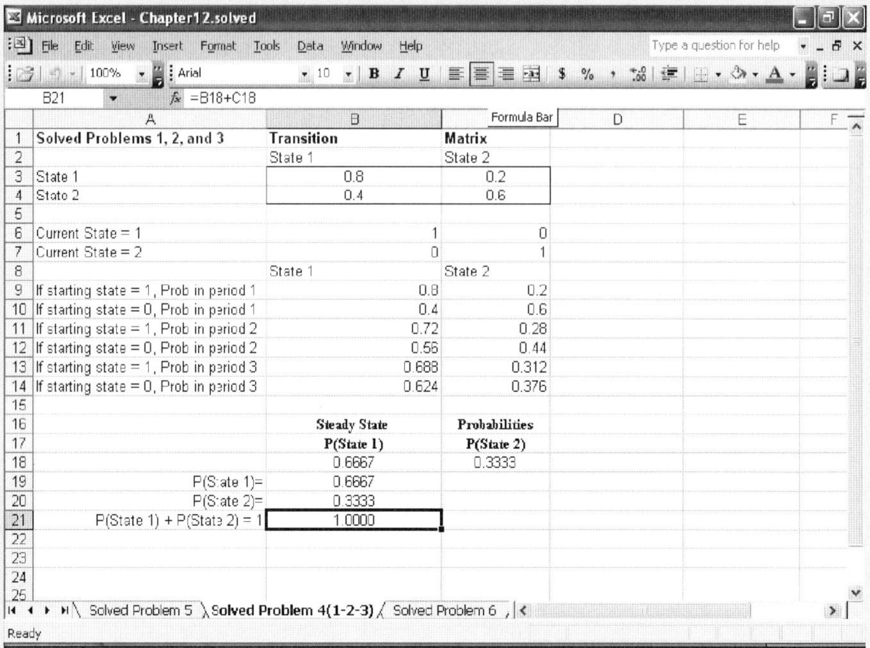

Microsoft Excel - Chapter12.solved

B21 f_x =B18+C18

	A	B	C	D	E	F
1	**Solved Problems 1, 2, and 3**	**Transition**	**Matrix**			
2		State 1	State 2			
3	State 1	0.8	0.2			
4	State 2	0.4	0.6			
5						
6	Current State = 1	1	0			
7	Current State = 2	0	1			
8		State 1	State 2			
9	If starting state = 1, Prob in period 1	0.8	0.2			
10	If starting state = 0, Prob in period 1	0.4	0.6			
11	If starting state = 1, Prob in period 2	0.72	0.28			
12	If starting state = 0, Prob in period 2	0.56	0.44			
13	If starting state = 1, Prob in period 3	0.688	0.312			
14	If starting state = 0, Prob in period 3	0.624	0.376			
15						
16		**Steady State**	**Probabilities**			
17		**P(State 1)**	**P(State 2)**			
18		0.6667	0.3333			
19	P(State 1)=	0.6667				
20	P(State 2)=	0.3333				
21	P(State 1) + P(State 2) = 1	1.0000				

Solved Problem 5 | Solved Problem 4(1-2-3) | Solved Problem 6

Cell	Copied to	Formula
B9	C9	= MMULT (B6 : C6, \$B\$3 : \$C\$4)
B10	C10	= MMULT (B7 : C7, \$B\$3 : \$C\$4)
B11	C11	= MMULT (B9 : C9, \$B\$3 : \$C\$4)
B12	C12	= MMULT (B10 : C10, \$B\$3 : \$C\$4)
B13	C13	= MMULT (B11 : C11, \$B\$3 : \$C\$4)
B14	C14	= MMULT (B12 : C12, \$B\$3 : \$C\$4)
B19		= B3 * B18 + B4 * C18
B20		= C3 * C18 + C4 * C18
B21		= B18 + C18

Problem 5

Steady-state equations

a. Manually find the steady-state probabilities for this transition matrix.
b. Use Excel and find the steady-state probabilities for this problem.

		To: A	B	C
	A	.5	.4	.1
From:	B	.2	.5	.3
	C	.3	.1	.6

Exhibit 12-9   Solver Parameters Specification Screen for the Steady-State Calculations for Solved Problem 4

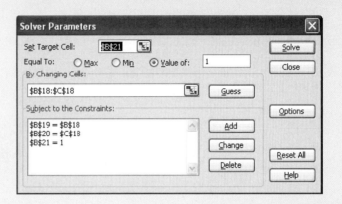

Solution

a. The steady-state equations are derived from *column* probabilities of each state. Thus, we have

$$P(A) = .5P(A) + .2P(B) + .3P(C)$$
$$P(B) = .4P(A) + .5P(B) + .1P(C)$$
$$P(C) = .1P(A) + .3P(B) + .6P(C)$$

In addition, we know that the three probabilities must sum to 1.00:

$$P(A) + P(B) + P(C) = 1$$

We can use this to solve for one of the three probabilities in terms of the other two. For convenience, let's choose C. Then we have

$$P(C) = 1 - P(A) - P(B)$$

With three unknowns, we need only three equations. We can eliminate a steady-state equation for C shown above this paragraph, and then substitute this last equation for C in the first two steady-state equations. That is:

$$P(A) = .5P(A) + .2P(B) + .3[1 - P(A) - P(B)]$$
$$P(B) = .4P(A) + .5P(B) + .1[1 - P(A) - P(B)]$$

Expanding the first of these yields

$$P(A) = .5P(A) + .2P(B) + .3 - .3P(A) - .3P(B)$$

Combining terms and moving the variables to the left side of the equation for A yields

$$.8P(A) + .1P(B) = .3$$

Expanding the steady-state equation for B yields

$$P(B) = .4P(A) + .5P(B) + .1 - .1P(A) - .1P(B)$$

Combining terms and moving the variables to the left side of the equation yields

$$-.3P(A) + .6P(B) = .1$$

Thus, the two resulting equations are

$$.8P(A) + .1P(B) = .3$$
$$-.3P(A) + .6P(B) = .1$$

Solving simultaneously, we find

$$P(A) = .333$$
$$P(B) = .333$$

Given these values and that $P(A) + P(B) + P(C) = 1$, we can determine that

$$P(C) = .333$$

b. The Excel worksheet and the Solver Parameters screen for the steady-state calculations for Solved Problem 5 are given in Exhibits 12-10 and 12-11 respectively. The necessary formulas for this problem are given at the bottom of Exhibit 12-10.

Exhibit 12-10   Worksheet for the Steady-State Calculations of Solved Problem 5

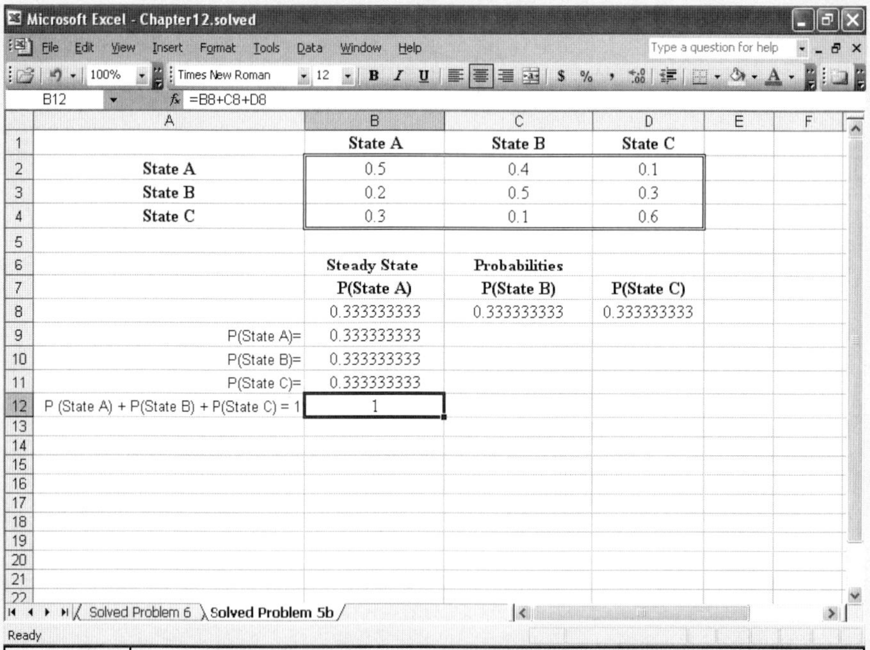

Cell	Formula
B9	= B2 * \$B\$8 + B3 * \$C\$8 + B4 * \$D\$8
B10	= C2 * \$B\$8 + C3 * \$C\$8 + C4 * \$D\$8
B11	= D2 * \$B\$8 + D3 * \$C\$8 + 4 * \$D\$8
B12	= B8 + C8 + D8

Exhibit 12-11   Solver Parameters Specification Screen for the Steady-State Calculations for Solved Problem 5

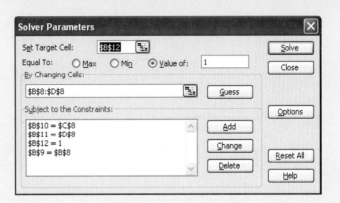

Problems 6

Accounts receivable A manager has developed the following transition matrix for a firm's accounts receivable:

$$
\begin{array}{c c}
 & \begin{array}{c c c c} P & 1 & 2 & b \end{array} \\
\begin{array}{c} p \\ 1 \\ 2 \\ b \end{array} &
\left[\begin{array}{c c c c}
1 & 0 & 0 & 0 \\
.5 & .3 & .2 & 0 \\
.3 & 0 & .4 & .3 \\
0 & 0 & 0 & 1
\end{array}\right]
\end{array}
$$

where

p = paid
1 = 1 to 30 days overdue
2 = 31 to 60 days overdue
b = bad debt

(*Note:* Accounts are billed weekly but classified in terms of months overdue. Consequently, it is possible for an account to remain in either the 1 or 2 category for several periods. Therefore, there is a nonzero probability of remaining in either 1 or 2.)

a. Obtain the fundamental matrix.
b. If there is currently $10,000 in accounts in the 1 category and $6,000 in the 2 category, determine the expected amount of bad debt.
c. Repeat parts *a* and *b* using Excel.

Solution

a. Begin by rearranging the transition matrix so that the two absorbing states (*p* and *b*) are listed first, followed by the two nonabsorbing states. This yields the matrix

$$
\begin{array}{c c}
 & \begin{array}{c c c c} P & b & 1 & 2 \end{array} \\
\begin{array}{c} p \\ b \\ 1 \\ 2 \end{array} &
\left[\begin{array}{c c c c}
1 & 0 & 0 & 0 \\
0 & 1 & 0 & 0 \\
.5 & 0 & .3 & .2 \\
.3 & .3 & 0 & .4
\end{array}\right]
\end{array}
$$

Then, partition the matrix into four parts that are defined as I, O, R, and Q:

$$
\begin{array}{c}
 \\
p \\
b \\
1 \\
2
\end{array}
\left[
\begin{array}{cc|cc}
P & b & 1 & 2 \\
1 & 0 & 0 & 0 \\
0 & 1 & 0 & 0 \\
\hline
.5 & 0 & .3 & .2 \\
.3 & .3 & 0 & .4
\end{array}
\right]
\qquad \text{where} \qquad
\begin{array}{c}
 \\
b \\
1 \\
2
\end{array}
\left[
\begin{array}{cc|cc}
P & b & 1 & 2 \\
I & & O & \\
\hline
R & & Q &
\end{array}
\right]
$$

Next, compute $(I - Q)$:

$$
\begin{bmatrix} 1 & 0 \\ 0 & 1 \end{bmatrix} - \begin{bmatrix} .3 & .2 \\ 0 & .4 \end{bmatrix} = \begin{bmatrix} .7 & -.2 \\ 0 & .6 \end{bmatrix}
$$

Find the inverse of $(I - Q)$. Recall that for matrix M, where M is

$$
\begin{bmatrix} m_{11} & m_{12} \\ m_{21} & m_{22} \end{bmatrix}
$$

the inverse is

$$
\begin{bmatrix} m_{22}/d & -m_{12}/d \\ -m_{21}/d & m_{11}/d \end{bmatrix}
$$

where

$$
\begin{aligned}
d &= m_{11} \cdot m_{22} - m_{12} \cdot m_{21} \\
&= .7(.6) - 0(-.2) = .42
\end{aligned}
$$

Thus:

$$
(I - Q)^{-1} = \begin{bmatrix} .6/.42 & .2/.42 \\ -0/.42 & .7/.42 \end{bmatrix} = \begin{bmatrix} 1.429 & .476 \\ 0 & 1.667 \end{bmatrix}
$$

This is the fundamental matrix, N.

b.   First, multiply matrix R by the fundamental matrix:

$$
NR = \begin{array}{c} 1 \\ 2 \end{array}\begin{bmatrix} 1.429 & .476 \\ 0 & 1.667 \end{bmatrix} \begin{array}{c} 1 \\ 2 \end{array}\begin{bmatrix} .5 & 0 \\ .3 & .3 \end{bmatrix}
$$

$$
NR = \begin{array}{c} 1 \\ 2 \end{array}\begin{bmatrix} .857 & .143 \\ .500 & .500 \end{bmatrix}
$$

Then, find the expected amounts of *paid* and *bad debt* categories:

$$
[10{,}000 \quad 6{,}000]\begin{array}{c} 1 \\ 2 \end{array}\begin{bmatrix} .857 & .143 \\ .500 & .500 \end{bmatrix} = [11{,}570 \quad 4{,}430]
$$

The expected amount of bad debt is \$4,430. Note that in the last matrix the sum of the amounts in the two categories is equal to the amounts currently in the two categories, 1 and 2. Thus, all of the amounts have been accounted for.

Exhibit 12-12	Excel Worksheet for Solved Problem 6: Accounts Receivable—Absorbing State Problem

Cell	Formula
A13	= B9 − E9
B13	= C9 − F9
A14	= B10 − E10
B14	= C10 − F10
C13	= MDETERM (A13 : B14)
E13 : F14	= MINVERSE (A13 : B14)
E18 : F19	= MMULT (E13 : F14, B18 : C19)
E23, F23	= MMULT (B23 : C23, E18 : F19)

c. Exhibit 12-12 shows the worksheet that calculates the fundamental matrix and the expected amount of bad debt. The necessary formulas are stated at the bottom of Exhibit 12-12. The variation from the manual calculation is due to rounding.

Discussion and Review Questions

1. What are the characteristics of Markov systems?
2. Explain the meaning of transition probabilities.

3. Provide two examples of the Markov systems. Explain the possible system states and the possible transition probabilities.
4. Explain the meaning of an absorbing state.
5. Explain the meaning of a transient state.
6. Explain the meaning of cyclical system.
7. What are steady-state proportions?
8. Explain how the tree diagram is structured in solving a Markov analysis problem.
9. Explain the difference between the matrix multiplication approach and the algebraic solution.
10. In the analysis of accounts receivable example, the absorbing states are (1) paid and (2) bad debt. If we formulate a similar problem dealing with a life-threatening hospital surgery, where the ultimate goal is full recovery of the patients and the concern is for the health of the patients, what are the two absorbing states?
11. As the matrix multiplication is performed stage after stage, explain what happens to probabilities of states in comparison to steady-state probabilities.

▶ Problems

1. The following table contains transition probabilities for two products, A and B:

		Next period	
		A	B
This	A	.70	.30
period	B	.20	.80

   a. What percentage of customers who-purchased Product A this period can be expected to purchase Product A next period? What percentage who purchased Product A this period can be expected to purchase Product B next period?
   b. Use a tree diagram to determine the proportion of customers who can be expected to purchase Product A in Period 2, given that they purchased Product B in Period 0.

[.30 .70]

2. Repeat part *b* of the previous problem using matrix multiplication to determine the answer.
3. Find the steady-state proportions for Products A and B in Problem 1 by means of solving simultaneous equations.
4. The weather on an island in the Caribbean can be described by the following transition probabilities:

		Tomorrow	
		Sunny	Cloudy/rainy
Today	Sunny	.90	.10
	Cloudy/rainy	.80	.20

a. See the IM

b. [.888 .112]

c. .889

   a. Use a tree diagram to determine the probability of sunny weather on the third day from now, given that today's weather is cloudy.
   b. Repeat part *a* using matrix multiplication.
   c. Determine the proportion of sunny days using simultaneous equations.

5. After a careful study, an analyst has determined that the probability that a certain machine will have a breakdown is dependent on whether it had a breakdown on the previous day and was repaired. The relevant probabilities are

		Tomorrow	
		No breakdown	Breakdown
Today	No breakdown	.88	.12
	Breakdown	.96	.04

   a. Given that the machine has a breakdown today, what is the probability that it will also experience a breakdown tomorrow?

   b. What is the probability that the machine will experience a breakdown two days in a row?

   c. Use a tree diagram to determine the probability that a machine will have a breakdown on the day after tomorrow, given that no breakdown occurs today.

   d. Repeat part c using matrix multiplication.

   e. Determine the steady-state proportion of days the machine can be expected to experience a breakdown using simultaneous equations.

6. Find the steady-state probabilities for this transition matrix:

A = .615, B = .385

		To:	
		1	2
From:	1	.75	.25
	2	.40	.60

7. A market researcher for Know Your Market, Inc., has studied consumer buying patterns in a situation in which consumers purchase one of three competing brands each week. The researcher found that Brand A retains 50 percent of its customers each week while giving up 30 percent of Brand B and 20 percent to Brand C. The researcher found that B gave up 50 percent to A and 20 percent to C, and that C gave up 50 percent to A and 30 percent to B.

   a. Develop a table of transition probabilities.

   b. What are the steady-state probabilities for the three brands?

8. A bank manager at Country Bank has compiled the following table of transition probabilities for the customers' use of various bank offices:

		Next period		
	Office	Main	East	South
This period	Main	.60	.10	.30
	East	.20	.70	.10
	South	.25	.15	.60

a. East
b. .175
c. [.455 .175 .370]

   a. Which office tends to have the highest "loyalty"? Why?

   b. What proportion of customers who banked at the Main office this time can be expected to bank at the East office two periods later? Solve Using a tree diagram.

   c. Repeat the previous part using matrix multiplication.

9. Determine the steady-state probabilities for the previous problem.

M = .333,
E = .25,
S = .417

10. If the transition probabilities for the South office in Problem 8 change from .25, .15, and .60 to .20 for Main, .10 for East, and .70 for South, what impact will this have on the steady-state probabilities for each office?

11. After studying a brand-switching problem, an analyst concluded that Brand A loses 20 percent of its customers each period to Brand B and 10 percent to Brand C; Brand B loses 10 percent of its customers each period to Brand A and 30 percent to Brand C; and Brand C loses 30 percent to Brand A and 20 percent to Brand B.
    a. Develop a table of transition probabilities for this situation.
    b. If Brand A initially has 400 customers, Brand B has 250 customers, and Brand C has 350, what average number of customers will each brand have in the long run?

12. A small, rural town has two movie theaters. Transition probabilities for weekly attendance for Sunday matinees are shown in the following table:

		Next week	
		Cameo	Strand
This	Cameo	.60	.40
week	Strand	.40	.60

a. C = .50, S = .50

    a. Determine the steady-state probability of theatergoers for each theater.
    b. A group of local investors plans to open a new theater. A consultant has projected transition probabilities for the three theaters for Sunday matinees as follows:

	Next week		
	Cameo	Strand	Cine
Cameo	.50	.30	.20
Strand	.30	.60	.10
Cine	.25	.25	.50

b. Cameo = .361, Strand = .412, Cine = .227

    Use Excel and determine the steady-state probability of customers for each theater.

c. Cameo

    c. Which original theater, the Cameo or the Strand, stands to suffer the greater loss of customers based on the projected probabilities?

13. Residents of a Vermont community buy their Christmas trees from one of three local dealers. The following switching probabilities have been determined:

		This year		
		A	B	C
	A	.65	.25	.10
Last year	B	.35	.60	.05
	C	.40	.30	.30

    a. Use Excel and determine the steady-state probability of customers for each dealer.
    b. Suppose that Dealer C is now considering advertising as a means of increasing his market share, since each customer represents a profit of $4. The dealer projects the following transition probabilities:

		This year		
		A	B	C
	A	.60	.20	.20
Last year	B	.30	.50	.20
	C	.30	.20	.50

If the cost of advertising will be $375, would you recommend that Dealer C advertise? Explain, assuming that there are 800 customers in the "system."

14. A firm that rents video equipment has three stores. Customers are allowed to return rental equipment to any of the stores, regardless of which store they rented the equipment from. A study of rental returns has produced the following probabilities.

		Returned to		
		A	B	C
	A	.84	.09	.07
Rented at	B	.20	.70	.10
	C	.14	.06	.80

a. A = .508,
B = .209,
C = .283

b. See the IM

a. Determine the steady-state probability for the stores.
b. Using Excel and matrix multiplication, determine the expected proportion of customers returning equipment to each store for the next three periods, assuming a rental at store B in the initial period.

15. The following table gives a breakdown of customers staying and switching brands for two periods:

		This period		
		Brand A	Brand B	Brand C
	A	350	80	70
Last Period	B	240	480	80
	C	210	140	350

Assume that these figures accurately reflect period-to-period behaviors of brand switching.
a. Find the transition probabilities.
b. Determine the steady-state probabilities for each brand using Excel.

16. A serviceperson is responsible for handling breakdowns of three robots at Global Mfg. Management is concerned about the number of robots waiting for repair, and the service manager has developed the following table that describes recent experience:

		Number waiting next period		
		0	1	2
	0	.50	.50	0
Number waiting this period	1	.25	.50	.25
	2	.50	.50	.50

a. 50%

b. 50%

c. 75%

a. What is the probability that 1 robot will be waiting for repair next period, given 2 are waiting this period?
b. What is the probability that 1 robot will be waiting for repair in Period 3, given none are waiting this period (Period 0)?
c. What proportion of time will there be a waiting line in this system?

17. A machine breaks down and is repaired according to the following transition matrix:

		Next day	
		Operating	Down
Current	Operating	.85	.15
	Down	.35	.65

The cost for machine downtime is $800 per day. The manager has been presented with a proposal for preventive maintenance that will alter operating transition probabilities from .85 and .15 to .95 and .05. The other probabilities will remain the same. The cost of the preventive maintenance program would be $500 per day. Is the improvement in the steady-state probability of operating enough to justify the cost of the program? Explain.

18. (Refer to Problem 17.) Suppose the manager has a second proposal that relates to repair time. This proposal would change down probabilities from .35 and .65 to .45 and .55, while not affecting the operating probabilities. The cost of this proposal would be $700 per day. If the manager could choose only one proposal, which should it be?

19. Find the determinant and inverse of each matrix.

a.
$$\begin{bmatrix} .6 & -.2 \\ -.3 & .8 \end{bmatrix}$$

b.
$$\begin{bmatrix} .7 & -.1 \\ 0 & 5 \end{bmatrix}$$

c.
$$\begin{bmatrix} .8 & -.1 \\ 0 & .4 \end{bmatrix}$$

20. Given this transition matrix for accounts receivable for GGM, Inc.:

		Next period			
		P	1	2	b
	p	1	0	0	0
Current	1	.7	0	.3	0
	2	.8	0	0	.2
	b	0	0	0	1

where

   p = paid
   1 = 1 to 30 days late
   2 = 31 to 60 days late
   b = bad debt

a. Interpret each of the values in Row 1.
b. Rearrange the matrix so the row and column headings follow the sequence p b 1 2.
c. Partition the new matrix into I, O, R, and Q matrices, and identify each.
d. Obtain the matrix (I − Q) and then find its inverse.
e. What is the fundamental matrix in this problem?
f. Determine the proportion of current accounts receivable that will end up as bad debt.
g. If there is currently $5,000 in category 1 and $8,000 in category 2, what is the expected account that will end up as bad debt? What is the expected amount that will end up as paid?

21. A manager has prepared this transition matrix for the accounts receivable of a firm. However, some of the values are missing.

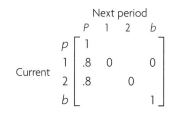

		Next period			
		P	1	2	b
	p	1			
Current	1	.8	0		0
	2	.8		0	
	b				1

where

p = paid
1 = 1 to 30 days late
2 = 31 to 60 days late
b = bad debt

a. Fill in the missing values.
b. Use Excel and obtain the fundamental matrix.
c. Use Excel and determine the proportion of accounts that will end up as paid.
d. If there is currently $50,000 in accounts that are 1 to 30 days late and double that amount that are 31 to 60 days late. Use Excel and determine the expected amount that will end up as paid.

$3,214

22. Suppose the following transition matrix pertains to a food brokerage that has $40,000 in accounts receivable that are 1 to 30 days overdue and $20,000 in accounts receivable that are 31 to 60 days overdue. How much should be allowed for bad debt? (*Note:* Accounts are billed weekly.)

		Next period			
		P	1	2	b
	p	1	0	0	0
	1	.6	.3	.1	0
Current	2	.7	0	.2	.1
	b	0	0	0	1

where

p = paid
1 = 1 to 30 days overdue
2 = 31 to 60 days overdue
b = bad debt

23. A manager has developed the following transition matrix for accounts receivable:

		Next period			
		P	1	2	b
	p	1	0	0	0
	1	.6	.2	.2	0
Current	2	.5	.2	.1	.2
	b	0	0	0	1

where

p = paid
1 = 1 to 30 days overdue
2 = 31 to 60 days overdue
b = bad debt

A typical situation is to have approximately $30,000 in accounts receivable that are 1 to 30 days overdue and $10,000 in accounts receivable that are 31 to 60 days overdue. The manager has received a proposal from the marketing department for increasing the collection rate. Estimated probabilities under the proposal for Row 1 are .7, .2, .1, and 0 and for Row 2, .6, .2, .1, and .1. It will cost $1,000 per period to maintain this new system. Can the proposal be justified on a cost basis? Explain.

24. The local department store's accounting department is trying to determine how much of the accounts receivable will be paid and how much of it will become bad debt. If an account is not paid, it will become delinquent. The manager is trying to predict how much of the outstanding debts will be paid. In order to estimate this correctly, the

manager of the store decided to use Markov analysis and classified the results into one of four states:

1. Paid.
2. Not paid (bad debt).
3. Regular accounts receivable.
4. Delinquent accounts receivable.

The manager has determined the following probabilities for the transition matrix.

To:

		1	2	3	4
	1	1	0	0	0
From:	2	0	1	0	0
	3	.70	0	.17	.13
	4	.30	.40	0	.30

Paid = $324, 578.3;
bad debt = $95, 421.36

Currently there are $300,000 in the regular accounts receivable and $120,000 in the delinquent accounts receivable. How much of the accounts receivable funds (regular and delinquent) will be paid?

25. Draw the probability transition diagrams for the following transition matrices. Then identify the probability transition matrices as
    - Cyclical,
    - Transient, or
    - Absorbing.

    Explain the rationale for your classification.

a.
$$\begin{bmatrix} .3 & .6 & .1 \\ .4 & .3 & .3 \\ 0 & 0 & 1 \end{bmatrix}$$

b.
$$\begin{bmatrix} .25 & .60 & .15 \\ 0 & 1 & 0 \\ .30 & .45 & .25 \end{bmatrix}$$

c.
$$\begin{bmatrix} .2 & .3 & .4 & .1 \\ 0 & 0 & 0 & 1 \\ .5 & .2 & .2 & .1 \\ 0 & 1 & 0 & 0 \end{bmatrix}$$

d.
$$\begin{bmatrix} .4 & .6 & 0 \\ .7 & .3 & 0 \\ .4 & .4 & .2 \end{bmatrix}$$

e.
$$\begin{bmatrix} 0 & 0 & .1 \\ .2 & .5 & .3 \\ 0 & 0 & 1 \end{bmatrix}$$

f.
$$\begin{bmatrix} 0 & 0 & 1 \\ .3 & .4 & .3 \\ 1 & 0 & 0 \end{bmatrix}$$

$$
\text{g.} \quad
\begin{bmatrix}
0 & 0 & .1 \\
.4 & .2 & .4 \\
.5 & 0 & .5
\end{bmatrix}
$$

▶ Chapter 12 Case   Memorial Hospital

The Fort Lauderdale Memorial Hospital has a very successful internationally recognized heart institute. The bypass surgery physicians are very well respected. The director of the heart unit, Dr. Joe Weiss, wants to study the mortality rate of the patients that go through a bypass operation. He just hired Dr. Sandra Strasser as a consultant to analyze the mortality rate of the bypass surgery patients. As a first step, Dr. Strasser decided to use the Markov process and fundamental matrix analysis. In order to implement this method, she classified the patients into four groups (states):

Group 1: Patient dies as a result of the surgery.
Group 2: Patient is in the intensive care unit or in surgery.
Group 3: Patient is in the heart care/rehabilitation unit.
Group 4: Patient is released from the hospital.

States 1 and 4 are considered to be absorbing states. Based on analysis of records and discussions with physicians, Dr. Strasser determined the following probabilities for moving between the four states. (The time period for moving from one state to another is one day.) There is a 10 percent chance that a patient in intensive care will die due to various complications. There is a 50 percent chance that a patient in intensive care will remain in intensive care and a 40 percent chance that the patient will be moved from intensive care to the heart care/heart rehabilitation unit. There is a 2 percent chance that a patient in the heart care/heart rehabilitation unit will die. There is a 10 percent chance that a patient in the heart care unit will become critically ill and will have to be placed in intensive care. There is a 65 percent chance that a patient in the heart care department will remain in the heart care department. There is a 23 percent chance that a patient in the heart care department will be released from the hospital.

Annually, Ft. Lauderdale Memorial Hospital performs an average of 800 bypass surgeries. On the average, at any point in time, 10 percent of the heart patients are in intensive care and 90 percent of them are in the heart care unit. Dr. Weiss wants to know the number of patients expected to die and the number of patients expected to survive annually. Determine the expected mortality rate and the annual expected number of patients surviving/dying as a result of the bypass surgery.

Waiting-Line Models

Chapter 13

Learning Objectives

After completing this chapter, you should be able to:

1. Explain why waiting lines can occur in service systems.
2. Identify typical goals for designing of service systems with respect to waiting.
3. Read the description of the queuing problem and identify the appropriate queuing model needed to solve the problem.
4. Manually solve typical problems using the formulas and tables provided in this chapter.
5. Use Excel to solve typical queuing problems associated with this chapter.
6. Use Excel and perform sensitivity analysis and what-if analysis with the results of various queuing models.
7. Outline the psychological aspects of waiting lines.
8. Explain the value of studying waiting-line models to those who are concerned with service systems.

Chapter Outline

Introduction, 660

Goals of Queuing System Design, 660

Elements and Characteristics of Waiting-Line Systems, 661
Calling Population, 662
Customer Arrivals, 662
Poisson Distribution, 663
Calculation of Poisson Probability Using Excel, 665
The Waiting Line, 667
Processing Order, 667
Service, 667
Exponential Distribution, 668
Calculation of Exponential Probability Using Excel, 672
Exit, 673

Measures of System Performance, 673
Basic Relationships, 674

Queuing Models, 676
Basic Single-Channel (M/M/1) Model, 676
Basic Single-Channel Model with Poisson Arrival and Exponential Service Rate (M/M/1 Model) with Excel, 678
Multiple-Channel Model (M/M/S), 678
Multiple-Channel Model with Poisson Arrival and Exponential Service Rate (M/M/S Model) with Excel, 687
Determining Maximum Length of Waiting Lines, 687

Cost Considerations, 690

Other Queuing Models (Optional Coverage), 692
Model Variation I: Poisson Arrival Rate with Any Service Distribution (M/G/1), 692

Single-Channel Model with Poisson Arrival and Any Service Distribution (M/G/1 Model) with Excel, 693
Model Variation II: Poisson Arrival Rate, Constant Service Time (M/D/1), 695
Single-Channel Model with Poisson Arrival and Constant Service Distribution (M/D/1 Model) with Excel, 695
Model Variation III: Finite Queue Length, 696
Single-Channel Model That Involves a Finite Queue Length with Poisson Arrival and Exponential Service Distribution with Excel, 697
Model Variation IV: Finite Calling Population, 698
Single-Channel Model That Involves a Finite Calling Population with Poisson Arrival and Exponential Service Distribution with Excel, 700
Model Variation V: Multiple-Server, Priority Servicing Model, 702
Revising Priorities, 704
Utilization of Excel's Goal Seek Function, 705

The Psychology of Waiting, 707

The Value of Waiting Line Models, 708

Summary, 710

Glossary, 711

Solved Problem, 711

Discussion and Review Questions, 713

Problems, 713

Chapter 13 Case: Big Bank, 721

Introduction

An important class of management science problems involves situations in which waiting lines occur. Examples abound. In our daily lives, we commonly encounter waiting lines at gas stations, stop signs, supermarkets, restaurants, newsstands, and other places. We often experience waiting lines in transportation systems, such as planes circling an airport awaiting clearance from the control tower, trucks waiting to load or unload cargo, buses backed up waiting to enter a terminal, cabs queuing up at airports, passengers queuing up waiting for cabs, and ferrys queuing up waiting to off-load passengers and autos. Frequently, there are waiting lines at banks and post offices. In factories, jobs queue up awaiting processing, orders need to be filled, machines need repairs or need to be loaded after a job, and employees wait to punch the time clock or to eat in the cafeteria.

Most of these systems are characterized by highly variable arrival and service rates. Consequently, even though overall system capacity exceeds processing requirements, lines tend to form from time to time because of temporary system overloads caused by this variability. At other times, the reverse is true; variability in demand for service results in idle servers or idle service facilities because of a temporary absence of customers.

In general, then, the systems on which our interest centers are *underloaded, highly variable* systems. Waiting lines tend to form in these systems due to temporary overloads created by variability in either the service or the arrival rates or servers may experience idle time. This chapter provides an overview of models that are useful in describing and analyzing such systems. The concept of waiting-line models and queuing analysis can be particularly useful to decision makers who must make *capacity decisions.*

Goals of Queuing System Design

Waiting-line models are *predictive* models of the expected behavior of a **system** in which waiting lines form. As such, queuing analysis forms a basis for the design of system capacity. The **queuing system** might be one that is in existence but is not performing satisfactorily. In this case, the emphasis is on deciding how to modify the system so that it does perform in a satisfactory manner. Also, the system might be in the design stage, in which case the emphasis would be placed on achieving a design that will produce the desired system performance.

A very common goal in queuing design is to attempt to balance the cost of providing service capacity with the cost of customers waiting for service. These two costs are in direct conflict: a decrease in customer waiting cost can be achieved by increasing the amount of capacity (either by increasing the *number* of servers or by increasing the service rate). However, increasing the service capacity means an increase in the cost of the service. The combined cost of service capacity and customer waiting cost is U-shaped because of this trade-off relationship, as depicted in Figure 13-1. The total cost is minimized at the lowest point of the total cost curve. Finding the minimum point often involves successively incrementing service capacity until there are no further decreases. Because increments of service capacity often are discrete (e.g., one server, two servers, etc.), it may be more realistic to represent the cost of service capacity through a series of steps, rather than through a straight line, and, therefore, the total cost curve would not be as smooth as the one shown. Nonetheless, the purpose of the graph is merely to illustrate the general nature of the cost-minimization goal in system design.

Another approach, sometimes called for in designing or redesigning queuing systems, is to satisfy desired specifications. For example, a bank manager may request that the average

Figure 13-1   The Total Cost Curve Is U-Shaped

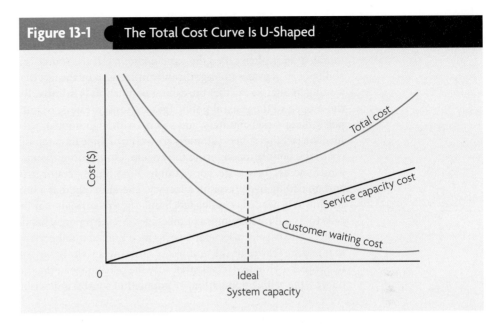

number of customers kept waiting in line should be below seven. In this case, the question would involve determining the number of tellers needed to satisfy that objective. Similarly, the manager of a new restaurant may want to know what size waiting area will be needed to accommodate customers who are waiting to be seated.

Elements and Characteristics of Waiting-Line Systems

Waiting-line systems can be differentiated by certain characteristics, such as the number of servers or whether access to the system is unrestricted or limited. Knowledge of such characteristics can help an analyst first to model the system and then to select an appropriate method for analyzing the system.

The major elements of waiting-line systems are outlined in Figure 13-2. Each of the elements is discussed briefly in this section.

Figure 13-2   Major Elements of Waiting-Line Systems

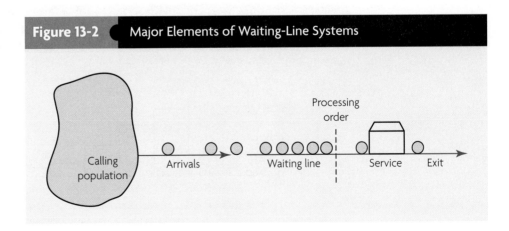

Calling Population

The **calling population** refers to the pool of potential arrivals to the system. In queuing terminology, it is often called the *customer source*. If the source is large enough that the probability of an arrival is not significantly influenced by the fact that some of the customers are waiting in line, we say that the calling population is **infinite.** Examples of such systems are those open to the general public (gas stations, theaters, restaurants, supermarkets, banks, post offices, ticket counters, and so on). Although none of these populations is truly infinite, the fact that some customers are waiting in line does not diminish the potential of others in the population entering the system. On the other hand, there are systems that have limited access for service. For example, a machine operator may be responsible for loading and unloading five presses in a factory. Therefore, there is a limit to the number of presses waiting to be loaded or unloaded. Similarly, a repairman may be responsible for emergency calls to fix a limited number of machines, a sales rep may handle a limited number of customers, and usually, a secretary works for a limited number of people. If the number of jobs that require service or the number of customers waiting for services causes the probability of another arrival to decrease (because the percentage in the population is substantially reduced), the calling population, or population source, is described as **finite** or *limited.*

Customer Arrivals

Customers are considered units that request or require service. In some systems the customers are people, and in others they are not. Examples of nonpeople systems include automobiles arriving at intersections, trucks arriving at a loading dock, machines awaiting repair, orders waiting to be filled, planes waiting to land, animals waiting for veterinarian attention, telephone calls waiting to be answered, and so on.

One key question is whether customers arrive at the system in single units (i.e., one at a time) or whether they arrive in batches. For instance, cars usually arrive at a car wash singly, whereas an entire busload of customers may arrive at a fast-food restaurant. Some situations might be called borderline cases: Theater patrons sometimes arrive in groups of two or more, as do diners at restaurants. For cases in which some arrivals are single units and others are small groups, we often treat them as single-unit arrivals for convenience. In fact, all of the models described in this chapter assume single unit arrivals.

A second key question relates to the distribution of customer arrivals. Generally, the models require that the arrival *rate* variability follow a *Poisson* distribution. A typical distribution is illustrated in Figure 13-3. An equivalent distribution that describes the **interarrival time**

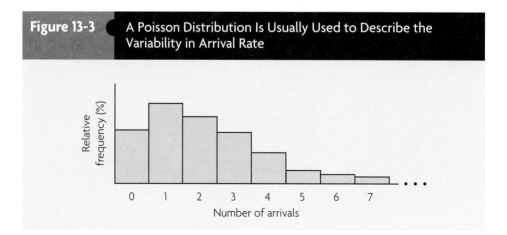

Figure 13-3   A Poisson Distribution Is Usually Used to Describe the Variability in Arrival Rate

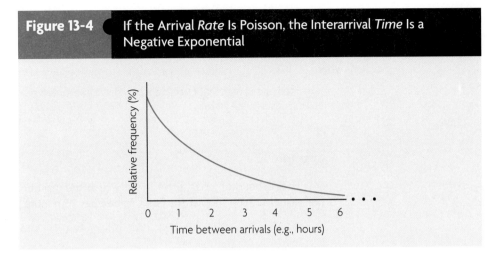

Figure 13-4   If the Arrival *Rate* Is Poisson, the Interarrival *Time* Is a Negative Exponential

(i.e., the average time between arrivals) when the arrival rate is Poisson is the *negative exponential* distribution. A typical distribution is illustrated in Figure 13-4. Note that the Poisson distribution describes a *discrete* random variable, which is the number of customers per unit of time, whereas the exponential distribution describes a *continuous* random variable, which is the time between arrivals. Perhaps the relationship between these two distributions can be understood better through an example. Suppose that the mean arrival rate of cars at a car wash is four cars per hour and this arrival rate can be described by a Poisson distribution. Therefore, the mean time between arrivals is 15 minutes (i.e., the *reciprocal* of the arrival rate of four per hour, which is $1/4$ hour), and this can be described by a negative exponential distribution.

Poisson arrival rates are commonly used in practice, and all of the models described in this chapter assume a Poisson distribution for the arrival rate. In practice, it may be necessary to determine if this assumption is true by using a Chi-square goodness-of-fit test.[1] For cases in which the assumption of a Poisson distribution does not hold, simulation (see the next chapter) may be the most reasonable alternative.

In the next section, we will describe the Poisson distribution in more detail, discuss its assumptions, and demonstrate how to find probabilities using this distribution.

Poisson Distribution

The Poisson distribution enables us to describe the number of times an event (arrival) occurs within an interval of time or space.

The assumptions for using the Poisson distribution are

1. The probability of occurrence of an event (arrival) in a given interval does not affect the probability of occurrence of an event in another nonoverlapping interval.
2. The expected number of occurrences of an event in an interval is proportional to the size of the interval.
3. The probability of occurrence of an event in one interval is equal to the probability of occurrence of the event in another equal-size interval.

If the variable of interest (x) is the number of occurrences of an event within a given interval, then the probability that the event will occur x times within a given interval is specified

---

[1]Although beyond the scope of this text, Chi-square tests are commonly described in most basic statistics textbooks.

by the following probability function.

$$p(x) = \frac{e^{-\mu}\mu^x}{x!}$$

(13-1)

where

μ = expected (mean) number of occurrences within a given interval
e = Euler's constant = 2.71828 . . .

Example 13-1

Machines in need of repair arrive for service at the maintenance and repair shop of the Miller Machine shop at the rate of three per 20-minute period.

a.   What is the probability that there will be six machines arriving in a 20-minute period in need of repair?
b.   What is the probability that there will be 12 machines arriving needing service in one hour?
c.   What is the probability that there will be less than three machines arriving for service in a 20-minute period?

Solution

a.   The parameter associated with the Poisson distribution in this problem is $\mu = 3$ per 20-minute period. Using Equation 13-1, the probability of six arrivals in a 20-minute period is

$$p(x = 6) = \frac{e^{-3}3^6}{6!} = \frac{(.049787)(729)}{720} = .05041$$

b.   In doing this problem, we have to use a value of μ consistent with the time frame. Since there are an average of three arrivals for 20 minutes, then there are nine arrivals in an hour, or $\mu = 9$ per hour. Therefore, the probability of 12 arrivals in an hour can be calculated as follows:

$$p(x = 9) = \frac{e^{-9}9^{12}}{12!} = \frac{(.00012341)(282,429,500,000)}{479,001,600} = .07276516$$

c.   Since $\mu = 3$ per 20 minutes,

$$p(x \le 2) = p(x = 0) + p(x = 1) + p(x = 2)$$

The following probability calculations are based on Equation 13-1:

$$p(x = 0) = \frac{e^{-3}3^0}{0!} = \frac{(.049787)(1)}{1} = .049787$$

$$p(x = 1) = \frac{e^{-3}3^1}{1!} = \frac{(.049787)(3)}{1} = .149361$$

$$p(x = 2) = \frac{e^{-3}3^2}{2!} = \frac{(.049787)(9)}{2} = .2240415$$

$$p(x \le 2) = .049787 + .149361 + .2240415 = .4231895$$

As can be observed in the previous example, the calculation of probabilities using the Poisson distribution can be very cumbersome. Tables have been developed to calculate the probabilities using Poisson distribution.

Using Tables to Calculate Poisson Probabilities The cumulative Poisson probability table is included in Table B in Appendix B.

1. For instance, to obtain the answer to Example 13-1, part *a*, we first locate the mean number of arrivals (μ) on the left column of Table B, labeled as μ/x. Since this is a cumulative table and $\mu = 3$, we find the probability for $x \leq 6$, which is .966, and then we find the probability that $x \leq 5$ (.916). Subtracting $P(x \leq 5)$ from $P(x \leq 6)$, we obtain $P(x = 6) = .966 - .916. = .05$.
2. Since $\mu = 9$, in the row $\mu = 9$, we find the probability of $x \leq 12$, which is .876; we also find the probability that $x \leq 11$ (.803). Subtracting $P(x \leq 11)$ from $P(x \leq 12)$, we obtain $P(x = 12) = .876 - .803 = .073$.
3. We locate $P(x \leq 2)$ in the row $\mu = 3$. Therefore, $P(x \leq 2) = .423$.

Calculation of Poisson Probability Using Excel

It is very easy to calculate a Poisson probability using Excel. First, click on Excel's function wizard labeled as f_x on the worksheet. This will bring up the selection dialog box shown in Exhibit 13-1. At this point, you can either type Poisson on the first line of that dialog box or select the "All" or "Statistical" category and select Poisson distribution from the list by scrolling down.

When you click on Poisson distribution, the dialog screen shown in Exhibit 13-2 will appear.

We will illustrate the use of this Poisson function using Excel by redoing Example 13-1, part *a*. In this example, $X = 6$ arrivals in 20 minutes and $\mu = 3$ arrivals per 20 minutes.

Exhibit 13-1   Selection of a Specified Function from the Function Wizard

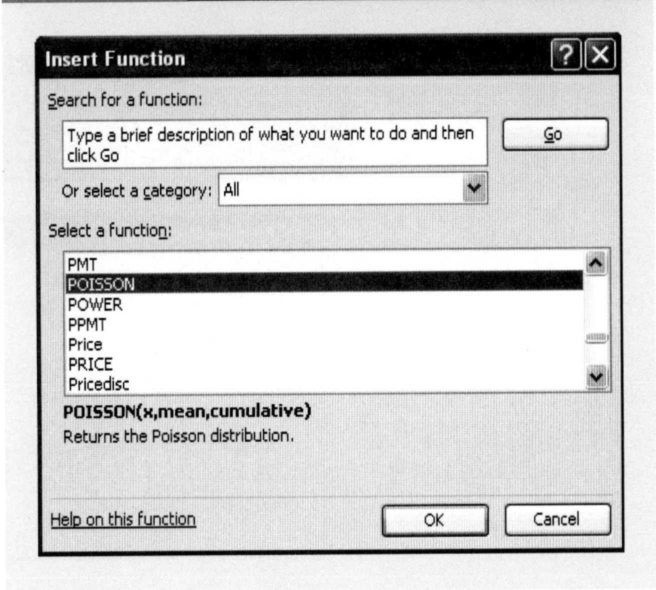

Exhibit 13-2 Calculation of a Probability Using the Poisson Distribution

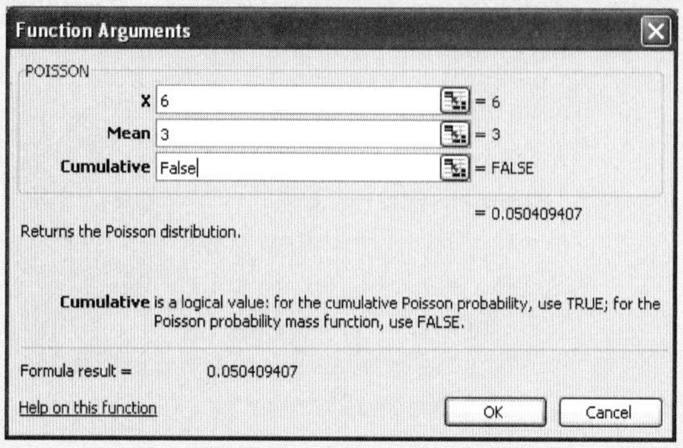

Therefore in Exhibit 13-2, enter 6 for X and 3 for Mean. Since this is not a calculation of a cumulative probability, indicate False in the Cumulative box and then click OK. The Poisson probability of .05041 that we had obtained in answering part *a* of Example 13-1 will appear both in the dialog box and on the worksheet.

Cumulative probabilities can be calculated as well. When there is a need to calculate a cumulative Poisson probability, simply change the response to the Cumulative box to True.

In order to illustrate how we might obtain cumulative probabilities with Excel, we obtain the solution to Example 13-1, part *c*. First we enter 2 for X and 3 for Mean. Since this is a calculation of a cumulative probability, indicate TRUE in the Cumulative box and then click OK. The cumulative Poisson probability of .423190 will appear in the dialog box as well as on the worksheet. This solution is displayed on the dialog box in Exhibit 13-3.

Exhibit 13-3 Calculation of a Cumulative Probability Using the Poisson Distribution

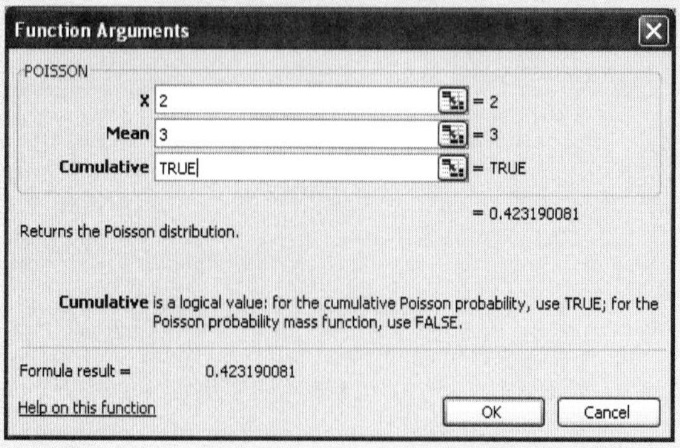

The Waiting Line

The waiting line consists of customers who have been admitted to the system and are awaiting service. In the car wash illustration, the waiting line would consist of cars lined up waiting to be washed. Some key issues are whether arriving customers may refuse to enter the system (**balking**), say, because of a long waiting line; whether customers may arrive, wait for a while, but then leave without being served (**reneging**); or whether customers may switch lines (e.g., checkout lines at supermarkets) in an attempt to lessen waiting time (**jockeying**). The models in this chapter do not deal with these interesting, but somewhat complex, situations. Instead, all models assume that once customers enter the queue, they remain there until they have been served. Moreover, a single waiting line is assumed in which customers are directed to the next available server.

Processing Order

A commonly encountered **queue discipline** (processing order) rule is *first-come, first-served*. When people are involved, this rule is widely perceived as "fair." In some instances, customers take a number when they enter the line (e.g., at a bakery, at a delicatessen take-out counter, or at a catalog sales desk in a department store); in other instances, customers actually wait in a single line (e.g., at many banks and post offices). Another approach is to assign arriving customers a **priority** classification, and process waiting customers according to those priorities. A hospital emergency room is an example of such a system; seriously ill or injured persons are treated before those with lesser illnesses or injuries. Similarly, time-sharing computer systems usually have priority classifications for jobs (e.g., the shortest job first), factories may process rush jobs ahead of routine jobs, and at many firms, orders of important customers may be processed ahead of orders of less important customers.

Both priority and first-come, first-served (FCFS) systems are presented in this chapter; however, most models use the first-come, first-served rule.

Service

The key issues for service concern the number of servers, the number of steps in the service process, and the distribution of service time.

A service center can have one server (**single channel**) or more than one server (**multiple channel**). Unless otherwise specified, we will assume that servers work *independently*, so that if a system has three servers, for example, this implies that as many as three customers could be handled simultaneously. Conversely, if you are told that the three servers work together as a crew, they would be treated as a single-channel system. Both single-channel and multiple-channel models are described in this chapter.

Service may consist of one or a few steps that are handled together (e.g., a banking transaction that consists of making a deposit and cashing a check, or simply making a deposit). This is called **single phase.** Conversely, some systems involve a series of steps (e.g., multiple-step manufacturing processes, registration at a university where students move through a sequence of checkpoints, loan processing that requires multiple steps before final approval or rejection). Such service systems are called **multiple phase.** All models in this chapter assume single-phase systems.

A comparison of single- and multiple-channel, and single- and multiple-phase systems is presented in Figure 13-5. The waiting lines may constitute multiple lines as shown in Figure 13-5. However, in this chapter, we will only discuss models with single lines.

The third important issue is the *distribution* of processing or service time. The most common assumption is that service time can be described by a negative exponential

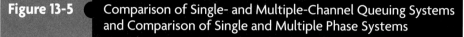

Figure 13-5 Comparison of Single- and Multiple-Channel Queuing Systems and Comparison of Single and Multiple Phase Systems

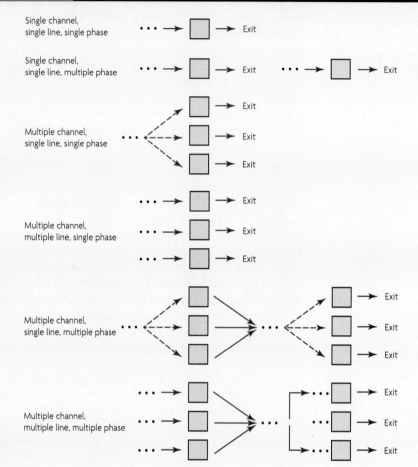

distribution[2] (see Figure 13-6). The implication of this sort of distribution is that most customers require short service times, a small proportion require moderate service times, and a few may require relatively long service times. In practice, exponential service times seem less pervasive than Poisson arrival rates. However, for simplicity, most of the models described in this chapter assume an exponential service time distribution.

Again, testing the assumption of a distribution would involve the use of a Chi-square goodness-of-fit test. If the assumption does not hold, either another queuing model that does not require this assumption should be used, or simulation could be used.

In the following section, we will discuss the exponential distribution and the calculation of probabilities using the exponential distribution.

---

[2]Exponentially distributed service *times* are equivalent to Poisson-distributed service rates. So, if the service rate is Poisson with mean μ, then the service time is exponential with mean $1/\mu$, and vice versa.

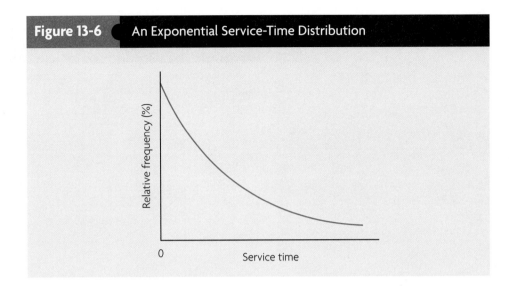

Figure 13-6   An Exponential Service-Time Distribution

Exponential Distribution

In this section we will discuss the exponential distribution in relation to the Poisson distribution. As we discussed earlier, if the Poisson distribution represents the arrival of customers at a grocery store, then the exponential distribution represents the time elapsed between successive customers arriving. Therefore, the exponential distribution is a continuous distribution and is a function of time.

The probability density function of the exponential distribution can be written as follows:

$$f(t) = \begin{cases} \lambda e^{-\lambda t} & \text{for } t, \lambda \geq 0 \\ 0 & \text{elsewhere} \end{cases} \tag{13-2}$$

where

λ = mean number of occurrences of a particular event per time unit

Therefore, for an exponential distribution, the mean and standard deviation are

$$\mu_t = \sigma_t = \frac{1}{\lambda}$$

Integrating this probability density function, it can be shown that

$$P(t \leq a) = 1 - e^{-\lambda a} \tag{13-3}$$

This is the probability of t being at most a. Graphically, this probability can be depicted as the shaded area in Figure 13-7(a).

$$P(t \geq b) = e^{-\lambda b} \tag{13-4}$$

This is the probability of t being at least b. Graphically, this probability can be depicted as the shaded area in Figure 13-7(b).

Based on the above probability formulas, we can also show that

$$P(a \leq t \leq b) = e^{-\lambda a} - e^{-\lambda b} \tag{13-5}$$

This is the probability of t being between a and b. Graphically, this probability can be depicted as the shaded area in Figure 13-7(c).

Figure 13-7 Graphical Depiction of Probabilities Using the Exponential Distribution

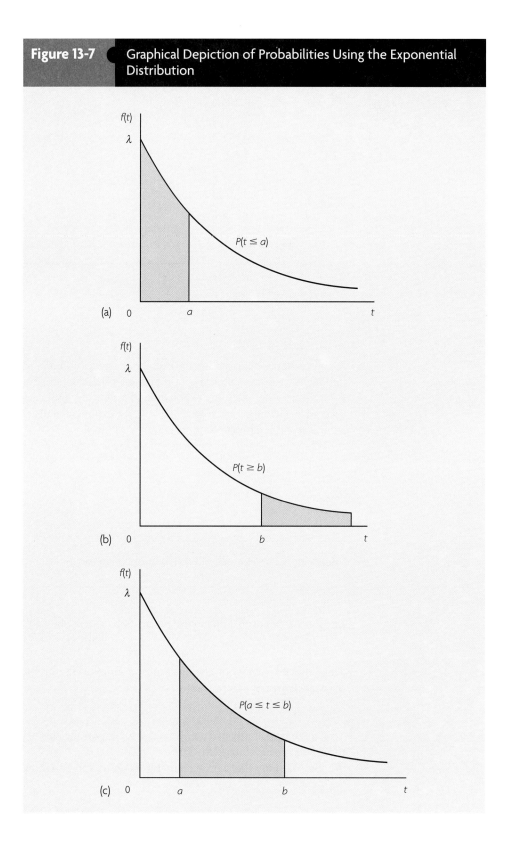

Example 13-2

At the Tip-Top grocery store, time between arrivals is distributed according to the exponential distribution. On the average two customers arrive every four minutes. In addition, the service time is distributed according to the exponential distribution as well, with a mean service rate of 40 customers per hour.

a.   What is the probability that no more than four minutes elapse between successive arrivals of customers.
b.   What is the probability that more than six minutes elapse between successive arrivals of customers.
c.   What is the probability that between four minutes and six minutes elapse between successive arrivals of customers.
d.   What is the expected time between successive arrivals of customers? What is the standard deviation of time between arrivals of customers?
e.   What is the expected service time? What is the standard deviation of service time?
f.   What is the probability that service time is one minute or less?
g.   What is the probability that the service time is more than two minutes?
h.   What is the probability that the service time is between one minute and two minutes?

Solution
Since the question involves a time period of minutes, first we convert λ into number of arrivals per minute. $\lambda = 2/4 = .5$ arrivals per minute.

a.   The probability that no more than four minutes elapse between successive arrivals of customers can be computed using Equation 13-3:

$$P(t \le 4) = 1 - e^{(-.5)(4)} = 1 - e^{-2} = 1 - (.13534) = .86466$$

b.   The probability that more than six minutes elapse between successive arrivals of customers can be computed using Equation 13-4:

$$P(t \ge 6) = e^{(-.5)6} = e^{-3} = .049787$$

c.   The probability that between four minutes and six minutes elapse between successive arrivals of customers can be computed using Equation 13-5:

$$P(4 \le t \le 6) = e^{(-.5)(4)} - e^{(-.5)(6)} = .13534 - .049787 = .085553$$

d.   The mean time between successive arrivals of customers and standard deviation of time.

$$\mu = \sigma = \frac{1}{\lambda} = \frac{1}{.5} = 2$$

In other words, we can say that the mean time between successive arrivals is equal to two minutes, and the standard deviation is also two minutes.

e. The mean service time and standard deviation of service time can be calculated as follows:

$$\lambda = \frac{40}{60} = .6667$$

$$\mu = \sigma = \frac{1}{\lambda} = \frac{1}{.6667} = 1.5 \text{ minutes}$$

In other words, we can say that the mean service time is equal to 1.5 minutes, and the standard deviation of service time is also 1.5 minutes.

f. $P(t \leq 1) = 1 - e^{(-.6667)(1)} = 1 - e^{-.6667} = 1 - .5134 = .486$

g. $P(t \geq 2) = e^{(-.6667)2} = e^{-1.3334} = .2636$

h. $P(1 \leq t \leq 2) = e^{(-.6667)(1)} - e^{(-.6667)(2)} = .5134 - .2636 = .2498$

Calculation of Exponential Probability Using Excel

Calculation of exponential probability is very similar to the calculation of Poisson probability using Excel. First, click on Excel's function wizard labeled as f_x on the worksheet. This will bring up the selection dialog box shown in Exhibit 13-1. At this point, you can either type Exponential on the first line of that dialog box or select "All" or "Statistical" category and select Exponential distribution from the list by scrolling down. When you click on Exponential distribution on the dialog screen in Exhibit 13-1, another dialog screen, shown in Exhibit 13-4, will appear.

We will illustrate the calculation of exponential probability using Excel by redoing Example 13-2, part *a*. In this example, on the dialog screen shown Exhibit 13-4, enter 4 (minutes) for X, .5 (arrivals per minute) for Lambda, and TRUE in the Cumulative box. Entering "true" in the Cumulative box ensures that a less-than-or-equal-to probability is calculated, as required to answer Example 13-2, part *a*. In order to answer Example 13-2, part *b*, we would obtain another cumulative probability in the same way as for part *a* and subtract the answer obtained from 1. Therefore, $1 - .950213 = .049787$. In other words, all greater-than-or-equal-to probabilities are calculated by subtracting the result obtained using Excel (less-than-or-equal-to, or cumulative, probability) from one. Always respond to the Cumulative box as "true" to obtain an exponential

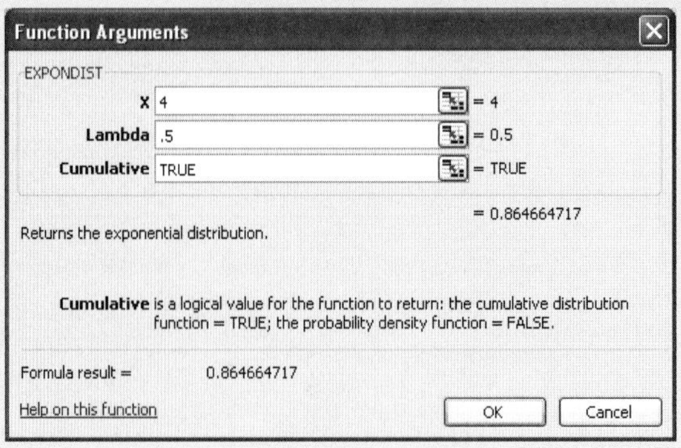

Exhibit 13-4 Calculation of a Probability Using the Exponential Distribution

probability. Answering Cumulative as "false" will calculate the probability density function associated with particular values of X and λ, and will not calculate cumulative probabilities.

Exit

The final consideration is what customers do after leaving the system. For them, possible choices include rejoining the source pool immediately, rejoining the source pool after a delayed interval (e.g., hospital patients recovering at home, car wash customers not immediately returning for another wash, and so on), and permanent departure from the pool (e.g., patients who develop a permanent immunity to a disease). The models presented here assume either an immediate return to the pool (especially with limited calling populations) or a population that is large enough so that delayed returns or permanent departures have almost no impact on the arrival rate.

◼◼ Measures of System Performance

A number of different performance measures can be computed that summarize waiting line behavior given the customer arrival rate, the number of servers, the service rate, and certain other information. Among the most commonly used measures, referred to as operating characteristics, are the following:

L_q = the average number waiting for service
L = the average number in the system (i.e., waiting for service or being served)
P_0 = the probability of zero units in the system
ρ = the system utilization (percentage of time servers are busy serving customers)
W_q = the average time customers must wait for service
W_f = the average time customers spend in the system (i.e., waiting for service and service time)
M = the expected maximum number waiting for service for a given level of confidence

One additional measure is the total cost of the system, which is generally based on the cost of customer waiting time and the cost of server time.

For example, the future owner of a proposed car wash may want to know the following:

1. On the average, how many cars/customers will be waiting for a wash?
2. How long, on the average, will a customer have to wait in line?
3. What proportion of the time will no customers be in the system?
4. What will be the upper limit on the number of cars waiting that will not be exceeded, say, 99 percent of the time?
5. How sensitive are the performance measures to changes in either the number of servers or the service rate? How sensitive is the system to changes in the arrival rate?
6. What level of capacity will minimize the sum of capacity costs and customer waiting costs?

Two key parameters in any waiting line system are the mean arrival rate, which is represented by the Greek letter λ (lambda), and the mean service rate, which is represented by the Greek letter μ (mu). Table 13-1 presents the symbols for number waiting and time waiting in an easy-to-remember format.

In the following pages, models are presented that provide formulas and tables enabling one to determine values for various measures of system performance. All of these formulas and table values pertain to a system that is in a *steady state*. In a steady state, various measures,

Table 13-1	Line and Service Symbols for Average Number Waiting, and Average Waiting and Service Times		
	System		
	In the waiting line	Being served	In the system
Average number	L_q	$\dfrac{\lambda}{\mu}$	$L = L_q + \dfrac{\lambda}{\mu}$
Average time	$W_q = \dfrac{L_q}{\lambda}$	$\dfrac{1}{\mu}$	$W = W_q + \dfrac{1}{\mu}$

where

λ = mean arrival rate
μ = mean service rate

such as the average number waiting in line, or the average waiting time, are *independent* of a particular time. That is not always the case, though. Very often, when a system begins operating after a period of inactivity (e.g., a bank opens in the morning, repair crews arrive for work after a long weekend, and so on), a system goes through a transient state before it settles down. For instance, there may already be a line of customers waiting outside the bank before it opens. Then, too, when human servers are involved, they often go through a warmup period before they reach their usual operating efficiency. Once the system moves into its normal operating pattern, it is usually considered to be in a steady state, and that condition is the one to which the various models apply.

Basic Relationships

There are certain fundamental relationships that hold for all infinite-source models. These relationships can be valuable for converting performance measures from *number* waiting to *time* waiting, and vice versa. The most useful of these relationships are

1. System utilization (percentage of time server is busy) for a single channel system or the average number being served:

$$r = \frac{\lambda}{\mu}$$ where λ = customer arrival rate
μ = service rate   (13-6)

2. The average number in the system:

$$L = L_q + r$$ (13-7)

where

L = average number in the system
L_q = average number in line

3. The average time in line:

$$W_q = \frac{L_q}{\lambda}$$ (13-8)

4. The average time in the system, including service:

$$W_s = W_q + \frac{1}{\mu}$$ (13-9)

5. System utilization (proportion of time servers are busy) for multiple channel systems:

$$\rho = \frac{\lambda}{s\mu} \tag{13-10}$$

where

s = number of channels or servers

In order for a system to be feasible (i.e., underloaded), system utilization must be less than 1.00.

Example 13-3

The owner of a car wash franchise intends to construct another car wash in a suburban location. Based on experience, the owner estimates that the arrival rate for the proposed facility will be 20 cars per hour and the service rate will be 25 cars per hour. (Let's assume, for the sake of illustration, that the arrival rate is Poisson and the service time is exponential). Service time will be variable because all cars are washed by hand rather than by machine. Cars will be processed one at a time (hence, this is a single-channel, or one-servicer, system). Determine the following:

1. The average number of cars being washed.
2. The average number of cars in the system (i.e., either being washed or waiting to be washed), for a case where the average number waiting in line is 3.2.
3. The average time in line (i.e., the average time cars wait to get washed).
4. The average time cars spend in the system (i.e., waiting in line and being washed).
5. The system utilization.

Solution

Arrival rate, λ, = 20 cars per hour
Service rate, μ, = 25 cars per hour
Number of servers, s, = 1
$L_q = 3.2$

1. $r = \dfrac{\lambda}{\mu} = \dfrac{20}{25} = .80$ car being served

2. $L = L_q + r$

    $= 3.2 = .8 = 4.0$ cars

3. $W_q = \dfrac{L_q}{\lambda}$

    $= \dfrac{3.2}{20 \text{ cars per hour}} = .16$ hour, which is .16 hour $\times$ 60 minutes/ hour

    $= 9.6$ minutes

4. $W_s = W_q + \dfrac{1}{\mu}$

    $= .16$ hour $+ \dfrac{1}{25}$ hour $= .20$ hour, which is .20 hour $\times$ 60 minutes/ hour

    $= 12$ minutes

5. $\rho = \dfrac{\lambda}{s\mu} = \dfrac{20 \text{ cars per hour}}{(1)(25 \text{ cars/per hour})} = .80$, or 80 percent

◼ Queuing Models

In this section, the following queuing models are described:

1. Basic single-channel.
2. Multiple-channel.

Basic Single-Channel (M/M/1) Model

This model pertains to situations in which there is one channel or server that processes all customers. Note that if a group of servers works as a single team, that situation would be considered a single-channel system.

A single-channel (M/M/1) model is appropriate when these conditions exist:

1. One server or channel.
2. A Poisson arrival rate.
3. A negative exponential service time.
4. First-come, first-served processing order.
5. An infinite calling population.
6. No limit on queue length.

M/M/1 stands for **M**arkovian (Poisson) arrivals, **M**arkovian (negative exponential) service, and **1** (single) server.

The necessary formulas for the single-server model are presented in Table 13-2. The formulas enable us to compute various measures of system performance. For the most part, the meaning of each measure is readily apparent. One exception may be the last measure: average waiting time for an arrival that is not immediately served.

Let us consider that measure somewhat further. Suppose we observe a system for a period of time, and that during that time, five customers arrive. Suppose, further, that their waiting times (in minutes) are 2.1, 0, 1.4, 0, and .8. We can determine their average waiting time by summing their waiting times and dividing by 5. This would be analogous to W_q. Now suppose we focus on just those who actually waited (the 0 times mean that those customers went directly into service; they did not have to wait in line). Hence, the average time for those who had to wait would be the three nonzero times divided by 3. Note that in both cases, the numerator (the sum of times) would be the same. By eliminating those who did not wait, we obtain a higher average waiting time than we did with all arrivals included. Hence, if we are truly concerned with the waiting times of those who actually wait, we should then focus on W_a rather than on W_q.

With that in mind, let us take a moment to see how the formula for W_a can be derived. We have just seen that W_q is made up of two parts: actual waiting and nonwaiting. In fact, W_q is the *weighted average* of W_a and 0. That is, the proportion of customers that don't wait is $1 - (\lambda/\mu)$ (i.e., P_0), and the proportion that do wait is λ/μ. Therefore, W_a is equal to the proportion that wait multiplied by W_a plus the proportion that don't wait multiplied by 0, divided by the sum of the weights:

$$W_q = \frac{\dfrac{\lambda}{\mu}W_a + \left(1 - \dfrac{\lambda}{\mu}\right)0}{\dfrac{\lambda}{\mu} + \left(1 - \dfrac{\lambda}{\mu}\right) = 1} = \frac{\lambda}{\mu}W_a$$

Now refer to Table 13-2 for the equation for W_q. You can see that it is L_q divided by λ. Referring to Equation 13-11, we can see that $W_q = \lambda/(\mu(\mu - \lambda))$. We just found tha $W_q = (\lambda/\mu)W_a$.

Table 13-2   Formulas for Basic Single Server (M/M/1) Model

Performance Measure	Formula	Formula Number
System utilization	$\rho = \dfrac{\lambda}{\mu}$	(13-11)
Average number in line	$L_q = \dfrac{\lambda^2}{\mu(\mu - \lambda)}$	(13-12)
Average number in system	$L = L_q + \dfrac{\lambda}{\mu}$	(13-13)
Average time in line	$W_q = \dfrac{L_q}{\lambda}$	(13-14)
Average time in system	$W = W_q + \dfrac{1}{\mu}$	(13-15)
Probability of zero units in the system	$P_0 = 1 - \left(\dfrac{\lambda}{\mu}\right)$	(13-16)
Probability of n units in the system	$P_n = P_0\left(\dfrac{\lambda}{\mu}\right)^n$	(13-17)
Probability the waiting line won't exceed k units	$P_{n \leq k} = 1 - \left(\dfrac{\lambda}{\mu}\right)^{k+1}$	(13-18)
Average waiting time for an arrival not served immediately	$W_a = \dfrac{1}{\mu - \lambda}$	(13-19)

Substituting the equation for W_q here, we can solve for W_a:

$$W_q = \frac{\lambda}{\mu(\mu - \lambda)} = \frac{\lambda}{\mu}W_a \quad \text{so} \quad W_a = \frac{\frac{\lambda}{\mu(\mu - \lambda)}}{\lambda/\mu} = \frac{1}{\mu - \lambda}$$

Example 13-4

The mean arrival rate of customers at a ticket counter with one server is 3 per minute, and the mean service rate is 4 customers per minute. Calculate each of the performance measures listed in Table 13-2. Suppose that $n = 2$ and $k = 5$, where $n =$ number of customers in the system, and $k =$ maximum length of the line.

Solution

1. $\rho = \dfrac{3}{4} = .75$, or 75 percent.

2. $L_q = \dfrac{3^2}{4(4 - 3)} = 2.25$ customers.

3. $L = 2.25 + \dfrac{3}{4} = 3.00$ customers.

4. $W_q = \dfrac{2.25}{3} = .75$ minute.

5. $W = .75 + \dfrac{1}{4} = 1.00$ minute.

6. $P_0 = 1 - \frac{3}{4} = .25$. This means that the probability is 25 percent that an arriving unit will not have to wait for service. Hence, the probability that an arrival *will* have to wait for service is 75 percent.

7. $P_{n=2} = .25 \left(\dfrac{3}{4}\right)^2 = .1406$.

8. $P_{n \le 5} = .1 - \left(\frac{3}{4}\right)^{5+1} = .822.$ In other words, there is an 82.2 percent chance that the waiting line won't exceed five customers.

9. $W_a = \frac{1}{4-3} = 1.0$ minute.

Basic Single-Channel Model with Poisson Arrival and Exponential Service Rate (M/M/1 Model) with Excel

Excel spreadsheets can be used to determine the operating characteristics associated with queuing models. The only disadvantage of developing waiting-line models using Excel spreadsheets is that some of the formulas for various operating characteristics can be somewhat complex. However, once the appropriate formulas are entered and the Excel spreadsheet is prepared to model a waiting-line problem, Excel provides tremendous flexibility to do the various calculations. For instance, arrival rate or service rate or other model parameters can be changed to analyze different what-if scenarios. In order to demonstrate preparation of an Excel worksheet for the basic single-server model, we will use Example 13-3.

The Excel worksheet for this model is presented in Exhibit 13-5. The arrival rate is specified in cell D1 and the service rate is specified in cell D2. The basic single-server model formulas specified in the previous section are entered in cells C4 through C12. The Excel formulas for these cells can be observed at the bottom of Exhibit 13.5. For example, cell C9 includes the formula for L_q, which is also displayed on the formula bar at the top of the spreadsheet.

An important characteristic of queuing systems with variable arrival and service rates can be illustrated by noting what happens to the average number waiting for service as the utilization ratio increases. Table 13-3 lists values of L_q for a sequence of increases in **system utilization.** You can see that as utilization increases, the average number waiting in line increases. Note, too, that as the utilization ratio gets closer and closer to the maximum of 100 percent, the average line length increases rapidly, as illustrated in Figure 13-8. The moral is obvious: heavily loaded systems will tend to have a disproportionate amount of waiting time. By the same token, when a system is heavily loaded, a disproportionate reduction in both the average number waiting and the time they wait can be achieved by modest reductions in the utilization (say, by increasing the service rate or, reducing the arrival rate, or diverting the arrivals through other options).

Multiple-Channel Model (M/M/S)

The multiple-server model, or multiple-channel model, as it is sometimes referred to, is very similar to the single-server model, except that the number of servers is not limited to one.

Exhibit 13-5   Basic Single-Channel Model with Poisson Arrival and Exponential Service Rate (M/M/1 Model)

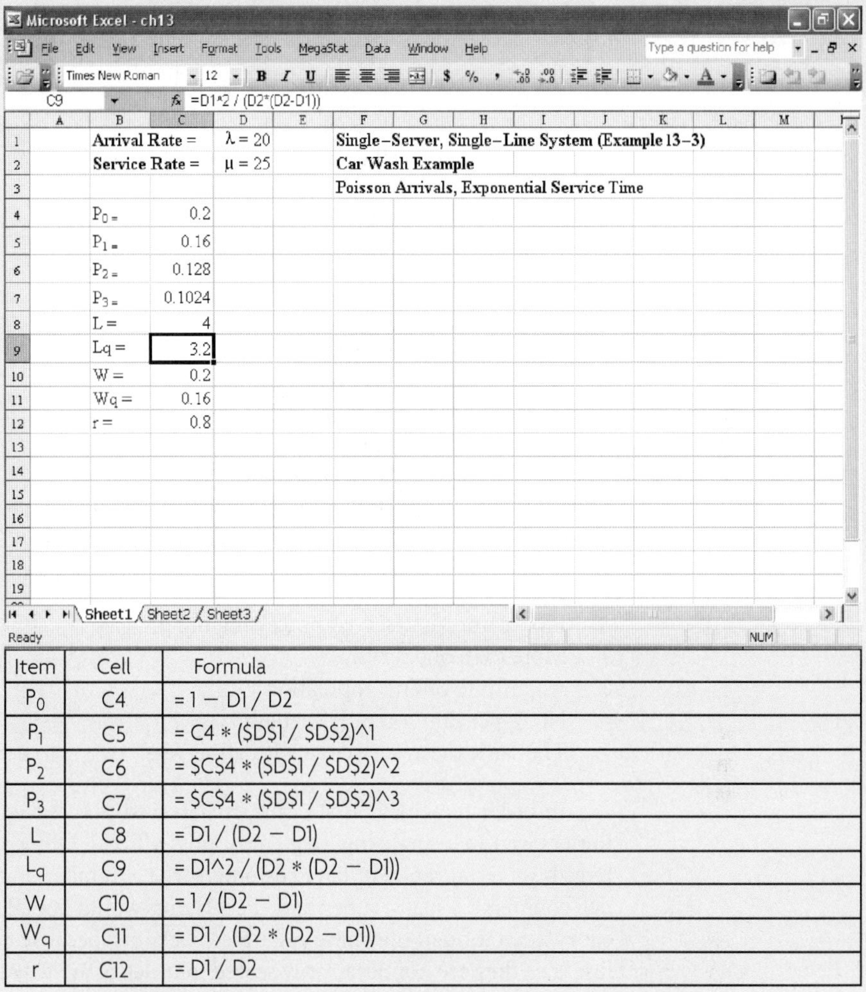

Microsoft Excel - ch13								
File Edit View Insert Format Tools MegaStat Data Window Help							Type a question for help	
Times New Roman ▾ 12 ▾ **B** *I* U ≡ ≡ ≡ ▦ $ % , ⁰⁰ ⁰⁰ ⌂ ⌂ ▦ ▾ ⌂ ▾ **A** ▾								

C9 ▾ f_x =D1^2 / (D2*(D2-D1))

	A	B	C	D	E	F	G	H	I	J	K	L	M
1		Arrival Rate =		$\lambda = 20$		Single–Server, Single–Line System (Example 13–3)							
2		Service Rate =		$\mu = 25$		Car Wash Example							
3						Poisson Arrivals, Exponential Service Time							
4		$P_0 =$	0.2										
5		$P_1 =$	0.16										
6		$P_2 =$	0.128										
7		$P_3 =$	0.1024										
8		L =	4										
9		Lq =	3.2										
10		W =	0.2										
11		Wq =	0.16										
12		r =	0.8										
13													
14													
15													
16													
17													
18													
19													

Sheet1 / Sheet2 / Sheet3 /

Ready   NUM

Item	Cell	Formula
P_0	C4	= 1 − D1 / D2
P_1	C5	= C4 * ($D$1 / $D$2)^1
P_2	C6	= $C$4 * ($D$1 / $D$2)^2
P_3	C7	= $C$4 * ($D$1 / $D$2)^3
L	C8	= D1 / (D2 − D1)
L_q	C9	= D1^2 / (D2 * (D2 − D1))
W	C10	= 1 / (D2 − D1)
W_q	C11	= D1 / (D2 * (D2 − D1))
r	C12	= D1 / D2

Table 13-3

λ	μ	λ/μ	L_q Using Formula 13-12
3.00	5	.60	.900
3.50	5	.70	1.633
4.00	5	.80	3.200
4.50	5	.90	8.100
4.75	5	.95	18.050

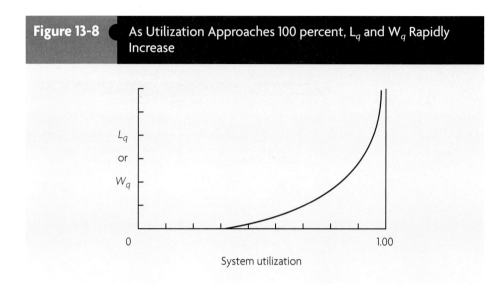

Figure 13-8   As Utilization Approaches 100 percent, L_q and W_q Rapidly Increase

The multiple-channel model is appropriate when these conditions exist:

1. A Poisson arrival rate.
2. A negative exponential service time.
3. First-come, first-served processing order.
4. More than one server.
5. An infinite calling population.
6. No upper limit on queue length.
7. The same mean service rate for all servers.

In order to achieve first-come, first-served processing, some systems may have customers wait in a single line (e.g., most post offices). Other systems record order of arrival (e.g., busy restaurants) or have customers take a number on arrival (e.g., some bakeries and deli counters). Usually, supermarket checkouts would not fall into the multiple-channel category, even though they have multiple checkouts, because customers do not form a single line (i.e., they are not necessarily served in order of arrival at the checkout area).

Note that with the multiple-server model, s must be large enough that the condition $s\mu > \lambda$ is satisfied. Otherwise, the system will not be feasible because it is overloaded.

The multiple-server formulas are presented in Table 13-4.

Similar to the basic single-channel model, this model is referred to as M/M/S. The only difference from M/M/1 Model is that there are $s > 1$ servers.

Example 13-5

The management of a grocery chain plans to open a new store. The store will have a bakery counter with a projected mean arrival rate during the evening hours of 1.2 customers per minute. Three clerks will be employed, and each will have an average service rate of one customer per minute. Compute each of the performance measures listed in Table 13-4 using the formulas. Additional information will be given where necessary in order to illustrate the solution.

Table 13-4	Multiple-Channel Formulas	

Performance Measure	Formula	Formula Number
System utilization	$\rho = \dfrac{\lambda}{s\mu}$	(13-20)
Average number in line	$L_q = \dfrac{\lambda\mu(\lambda/\mu)^x}{(s-1)!(s\mu-\lambda)^2}P_0$	(13-21)
Average number in the system	$L = L_q + \dfrac{\lambda}{\mu}$	(13-22)
Average time in line	$W_q = \dfrac{L_q}{\lambda}$	(13-23)
Average time in the system	$W = W_q + \dfrac{1}{\mu}$	(13-24)
Probability of zero units in the system	$P_0 = \left[\displaystyle\sum_{n=0}^{s-1}\dfrac{(\lambda/\mu)^n}{n!} + \dfrac{(\lambda/\mu)^s}{s!(1-(\lambda/s\mu))}\right]^{-1}$	(13-25)
Probability of n units in the system, where $n \le s$	$P_n = P_0\dfrac{(\lambda/\mu)^n}{n!}$	(13-26)
Probability of n units in the system, where $n > s$	$P_n = \dfrac{P_0(\lambda/\mu)^n}{s!(s^{n-s})}$	(13-27)
Average waiting time for an arrival not immediately served	$W_a = \dfrac{1}{s\mu-\lambda}$	(13-28)
Probability that an arrival will have to wait for service	$P_w = (\lambda/\mu)^s\dfrac{P_0}{s!(1-(\lambda/s\mu))}$	(13-29)

s = number of servers or channels.

Solution

$\lambda = 1.2$ customers per minute

$\mu = 1.0$ customer per minute

$s = 3$ servers

1. $\rho = \dfrac{1.2}{3(1.0)} = .40$

2. $L_q = \dfrac{1.2(1.0)(1.2/1.0)^3}{(3-1)!(3(1.0)-1.2)^2}P_0$

    $= .32P_0$

    $P_0 = \dfrac{1}{\left[\dfrac{(1.2/1.0)^0}{0!} + \dfrac{(1.2/1.0)^1}{1!} + \dfrac{(1.2/1.0)^2}{2!}\right] + \dfrac{(1.2/1.0)^3}{3!(1-(1.2/3(1.0)))}} = .294$

    $L_q = .32(.294) = .094$ customers

3. $L = .094 + \dfrac{1.2}{1.0} = 1.294$.

4. $W_q = \dfrac{.094}{1.2} = .078$ minute.

5. $W = .078 + \dfrac{1}{1.0} = 1.078$ minutes.

6. P_0 (see part 2 above).

7. Suppose $n = 2$.

$$P_2 = \dfrac{.294(1.2/1.0)^2}{2!} = .212$$

8. Suppose $n = 4$.

$$P_4 = \dfrac{.294(1.2/1.0)^4}{3(!3^{4-3})} = \dfrac{.60964}{18} = .034$$

9. $W_a = \dfrac{1}{3(1.0) - 1.2} = .556$ minute.

10. $P_w = \left(\dfrac{1.2}{1.0}\right)^3 \dfrac{.294}{3!(1 - (1.2/3(1.0)))} = .141$

The computations for some of the multiple-server performance measures can be quite formidable, particularly for large values of s. Fortunately, there is an easier method for obtaining values for two key performance measures, L_q and P_0. Table 13-5 contains those values for selected values of λ/μ. The advantage of having a table that can provide values of L_q and P_0 can be seen from these two lists of performance measures that can be computed from them:

L_q: L, W, and W_q
P_0: P_n and P_w

The remaining measures do not involve the computational burden that the listed measures do. Thus, obtaining performance measures for many multiple-channel problems is, indeed, simplified. The exception would be for situations in which the ratio λ/μ is not listed in the table, although, even then, rounding to a listed value is often reasonable.

To use the table, determine the value of λ/μ and read L_q and P_0 for s. For instance, in the preceding example with $\lambda/\mu = 1.2$, we found the value of L_q to be .094 after considerable effort. That same value can be read from Table 13-5. At the same time, we can read the value $P_0 = .294$, which agrees with the previous calculated value. We can further appreciate the value of having this table by considering this question: What are the values of L_q when $\lambda/\mu = 1.2$ for $s = 2$, 3, 4, and 5? We can quickly read all of the values from the table. Thus, we find $L_q = .675$ for $s = 2$, .094 for $s = 3$, and .016 for $s = 4$.

The table also allows us to gain some insight into how sensitive a waiting line system is to changes in the utilization. For example, suppose $\lambda/\mu = 2.9/1 = 2.9$. With three servers, the utilization is $2.9/3 = .967$, a fairly high load. This results in a high average number waiting (27.193). Adding one server reduces the utilization to $2.9/4 = .725$, and the average waiting line is reduced to 1.234. Thus, modest changes to a heavily loaded system can produce rather sizeable improvements in such performance measures as the average number waiting in line and in the system, and the associated average waiting times in line and system. For lighter

Table 13-5				Infinite Source Values for L_q and P_0 given λ/μ and s							
λ/μ	s	L_q	P_0	λ/μ	s	L_q	P_0	λ/μ	s	L_q	P_0
.15	1	.026	.850	.85	1	4.817	.150		4	.060	.199
	2	.001	.860		2	.187	.404		5	.012	.201
.20	1	.050	.800		3	.024	.425	1.7	2	4.426	.081
	2	.002	.818		4	.003	.427		3	.409	.156
.25	1	.083	.750	.90	1	8.100	.100		4	.080	.180
	2	.004	.778		2	.229	.379		5	.017	.182
.30	1	.129	.700		3	.030	.403	1.8	2	7.674	.053
	2	.007	.739		4	.004	.406		3	.532	.146
.35	1	.188	.650	.95	1	18.050	.050		4	.105	.162
	2	.011	.702		2	.277	.356		5	.023	.165
.40	1	.267	.600		3	.037	.383	1.9	2	17.587	.026
	2	.017	.667		4	.005	.386		3	.688	.128
.45	1	.368	.550	1.0	2	.333	.333		4	.136	.145
	2	.024	.633		3	.045	.364		5	.030	.149
	3	.002	.637		4	.007	.367		6	.007	.149
.50	1	.500	.500	1.1	2	.477	.290	2.0	3	.889	.111
	2	.033	.600		3	.066	.327		4	.174	.130
	3	.003	.606		4	.011	.367		5	.040	.134
				1.2	2	.675	.250		6	.009	.135
.55	1	.672	.450		3	.094	.294	2.1	3	1.149	.096
	2	.045	.569		4	.016	.300		4	.220	.117
	3	.004	.576		5	.003	.301		5	.052	.121
.60	1	.900	.400	1.3	2	.951	.212		6	.012	.122
	2	.059	.538		3	.130	.264	2.2	3	1.491	.081
	3	.006	.548		4	.023	.271		4	.277	.105
.65	1	1.207	.350		5	.004	.272		5	.066	.109
	2	.077	.509	1.4	2	1.345	.176		6	.016	.111
	3	.008	.521		3	.177	.236	2.3	3	1.951	.068
.70	1	1.633	.300		4	.032	.245		4	.346	.093
	2	.098	.481		5	.006	.246		5	.084	.099
	3	.011	.495	1.5	2	1.929	.143		6	.021	.100
.75	1	2.250	.250		3	.237	.211	2.4	3	2.589	.056
	2	.123	.455		4	.045	.221		4	.431	.083
	3	.015	.471		5	.009	.223		5	.105	.089
.80	1	3.200							6	.027	.090
	2	.152	.429	1.6	2	2.844	.111		7	.007	.091
	3	.019	.447		3	.313	.187			*(continued)*	

| Table 13-5 | | Infinite Source Values for L_q and P_0 given λ/μ and s *(continued)* | | | | | | | | | |

λ/μ	s	L_q	P_0	λ/μ	s	L_q	P_0	λ/μ	s	L_q	P_0
2.5	3	3.511	.045	3.2	4	2.386	.027		6	.412	.021
	4	.533	.074		5	.513	.037		7	.129	.022
	5	.130	.080		6	.145	.040		8	.041	.022
	6	.034	.082		7	.043	.040		9	.013	.022
	7	.009	.082		8	.012	.041	3.9	4	36.859	.002
2.6	3	4.933	.035	3.3	4	3.027	.023		5	1.830	.015
	4	.658	.065		5	.615	.033		6	.485	.019
	5	.161	.072		6	.174	.036		7	.153	.020
	6	.043	.074		7	.052	.037		8	.050	.020
	7	.011	.074		8	.015	.037		9	.016	.020
				3.4	4	3.906	.019				
2.7	3	7.354	.025		5	.737	.029	4.0	5	2.216	.013
	4	.811	.057		6	.209	.032		6	.570	.017
	5	.198	.065		7	.063	.033		7	.180	.018
	6	.053	.067		8	.019	.033		8	.059	.018
	7	.014	.067	3.5	4	5.165	.015		9	.019	.018
2.8	3	12.273	.016		5	.882	.026	4.1	5	2.703	.011
	4	1.000	.050		6	.248	.029		6	.668	.015
	5	.241	.058		7	.076	.030		7	.212	.016
	6	.066	.060		8	.023	.030		8	.070	.016
	7	.018	.061		9	.007	.030		9	.023	.017
2.9	3	27.193	.008	3.6	4	7.090	.011	4.2	5	3.327	.009
	4	1.234	.044		5	1.055	.023		6	.784	.013
	5	.293	.052		6	.295	.026		7	.248	.014
	6	.081	.054		7	.091	.027		8	.083	.015
	7	.023	.055		8	.028	.027		9	.027	.015
3.0	4	1.528	.038		9	.008	.027		10	.009	.015
	5	.354	.047					4.3	5	4.149	.008
	6	.099	.049	3.7	4	10.347	.008		6	.919	.012
	7	.028	.050		5	1.265	.020		7	.289	.130
	8	.008	.050		6	.349	.023		8	.097	.013
3.1	4	1.902	.032		7	.1099	.024		9	.033	.014
	5	.427	.042		8	.034	.025		10	.011	.014
	6	.120	.044		9	.010	.025	4.4	5	5.268	.006
	7	.035	.045	3.8	4	16.937	.005		6	1.078	.010
	8	.010	.045		5	1.519	.017		7	.337	.012

Table 13-5	Infinite Source Values for L_q and P_0 given λ/μ and s (continued)

λ/μ	s	L_q	P_0	λ/μ	s	L_q	P_0	λ/μ	s	L_q	P_0
	8	.114	.012		8	.279	.006		11	.028	.004
	9	.039	.012		9	.101	.007		12	.010	.004
	10	.013	.012		10	.036	.007	5.6	6	11.519	.001
4.5	5	6.862	.005		11	.013	.007		7	1.944	.003
	6	1.265	.009	5.1	6	3.536	.004		8	.631	.003
	7	.391	.010		7	.936	.005		9	.233	.004
	8	.133	.011		8	.321	.006		10	.088	.004
	9	.046	.011		9	.117	.006		11	.033	.004
	10	.015	.011		10	.042	.006		12	.012	.004
4.6	5	9.289	.004		11	.015	.006	5.7	6	16.446	.001
	6	1.487	.008						7	2.264	.002
	7	.453	.009	5.2	6	4.301	.003		8	.721	.003
	8	.156	.010		7	1.081	.005		9	.266	.003
	9	.054	.010		8	.368	.005		10	.102	.003
	10	.018	.010		9	.135	.005		11	.038	.003
4.7	5	13.382	.003		10	.049	.005		12	.014	.003
	6	1.752	.007		11	.017	.006				
	7	.525	.008	5.3	6	5.303	.003	5.8	6	26.373	.001
	8	.181	.008		7	1.249	.004		7	2.648	.002
	9	.064	.009		8	.422	.005		8	.823	.003
	10	.022	.009		9	.155	.005		9	.303	.003
4.8	5	21.641	.002		10	.057	.005		10	.116	.003
	6	2.071	.006		11	.021	.005		11	.044	.003
	7	.607	.008		12	.007	.005		12	.017	.003
	8	.209	.008	5.4	6	6.661	.002				
	9	.074	.008		7	1.444	.004	5.9	6	56.300	.000
	10	.026	.008		8	.483	.004		7	3.113	.002
4.9	5	46.566	.001		9	.178	.004		8	.939	.002
	6	2.459	.005		10	.066	.004		9	.345	.003
	7	.702	.007		11	.024	.005		10	.133	.003
	8	.242	.007		12	.009	.005		11	.051	.003
	9	.087	.007	5.5	6	8.590	.002		12	.019	.003
	10	.031	.007		7	1.674	.003	6.0	7	3.683	.001
	11	.011	.077		8	.553	.004		8	1.071	.002
5.0	6	2.938	.005		9	.204	.004		9	.392	.002
	7	.810	.006		10	.077	.004			(continued)	

| Table 13-5 | | Infinite Source Values for L_q and P_0 given λ/μ and s (*continued*) |

λ/μ	s	L_q	P_0	λ/μ	s	L_q	P_0	λ/μ	s	L_q	P_0
	10	.152	.002	6.6	7	13.770	.000		11	.238	.001
	11	.059	.002		8	2.420	.001		12	.099	.001
	12	.022	.002		9	.825	.001				
					10	.285	.001	7.2	8	6.314	.000
6.1	7	4.394	.001		11	.130	.001		9	1.729	.001
	8	1.222	.002		12	.052	.001		10	.652	.001
	9	.445	.002						11	.268	.001
	10	.173	.002	6.7	7	19.532	.000		12	.112	.001
	11	.068	.002		8	2.796	.001				
	12	.026	.002		9	.932	.001	7.3	8	7.675	.0003
6.2	7	5.298	.001		10	.363	.001		9	1.963	.0005
	8	1.397	.002		11	.147	.001		10	.732	.0006
	9	.504	.002		12	.060	.001		11	.300	.0007
	10	.197	.002						12	.126	.0007
	11	.078	.002	6.8	7	31.127	.000				
	12	.030	.002		8	3.245	.001	7.4	8	9.511	.0003
					9	1.054	.001		9	2.233	.0005
6.3	7	6.480	.001		10	.409	.001		10	.820	.0006
	8	1.598	.001		11	.167	.001		11	.337	.0006
	9	.571	.002		12	.068	.001		12	.142	.0006
	10	.223	.002								
	11	.089	.002	6.9	7	66.055	.000	7.5	8	12.109	.0002
	12	.035	.002		8	3.786	.001		9	2.546	.0004
6.4	7	8.077	.001		9	1.191	.001		10	.920	.0005
	8	1.831	.001		10	.460	.001		11	.377	.0005
	9	.645	.002		11	.188	.001		12	.160	.0005
	10	.253	.002		12	.077	.001				
	11	.101	.002					7.6	8	16.039	.0002
	12	.040	.002	7.0	8	4.447	.001		9	2.912	.0004
					9	1.347	.001		10	1.031	.0004
6.5	7	10.341	.001		10	.517	.001		11	.421	.0005
	8	2.102	.001		11	.212	.001		12	.179	.0005
	9	.730	.001		12	.088	.001				
	10	.285	.001	7.1	8	5.270	.000	7.7	8	22.636	.0001
	11	.115	.001		9	1.525	.001		9	3.343	.0003
	12	.046	.001		10	.581	.001		10	1.157	.0004

| Table 13-5 | | Infinite Source Values for L_q and P_0 given λ/μ and s (continued) | | | | | | | | | |

λ/μ	s	L_q	P_0	λ/μ	s	L_q	P_0	λ/μ	s	L_q	P_0
	11	.471	.0004	8.0	9	5.227	.00020	8.3	9	8.884	.00011
	12	.201	.0004		10	1.637	.00028		10	2.341	.00019
					11	.653	.00031		11	.903	.00022
7.8	8	35.898	.0001		12	.280	.00033		12	.386	.00024
	9	3.856	.0002								
	10	1.298	.0004	8.1	9	6.161	.00017	8.4	9	10.9960	.00009
	11	.525	.0004		10	1.841	.00025		10	2.647	.00017
	12	.224	.0004		11	.728	.00028		11	1.006	.00020
7.9	8	75.827	.00003		12	.312	.00029		12	.429	.00021
	9	4.474	.00023	8.2	9	7.344	.00014	8.5	9	13.891	.00007
	10	1.457	.00031		10	2.074	.00022		10	3.003	.00015
	11	.586	.00035		11	.811	.00025		11	1.121	.00018
	12	.251	.00036		12	.347	.00026		12	.476	.00019

system loads, the improvements become less and less: Adding a fifth server yields a reduction of about 1.0 in the average number waiting, and adding a sixth server yields a reduction of only about .20.

Finally, note that the single-channel model is a special case of the more general multiple-channel model. Therefore, single-channel problems also can be handled using Table 13-5.

Multiple-Channel Model with Poisson Arrival and Exponential Service Rate (M/M/S Model) with Excel

It is difficult to use Excel to formulate the multiple-channel waiting-line model because the formulas are somewhat cumbersome to prepare. Exhibit 13-6 shows the Excel worksheet for the multiple-channel waiting line model with Poisson arrivals and exponential service times based on Example 13-5. The formulas for this model are given below Exhibit 13-6. As can be observed, some of these formulas can be very complicated. For example, the formula for P_0 in cell B7 is long and complex. The summation terms are directly entered into the formula. Thus, if a problem involved a larger number of servers, additional summation terms would have to be added to the formula in cell B7. As you notice, we have utilized the FACT() term in our formulas. FACT() takes the factorial of a number. For example, the term FACT(4) is $4! = 4 \times 3 \times 2 \times 1 = 24$. Therefore, even though it is difficult to perform sensitivity analysis by changing the number of servers, it is fairly easy to perform what-if analysis assuming different arrival or service rates.

Determining Maximum Length of Waiting Lines

An important issue in waiting line system design relates to the amount of space that will be needed to accommodate waiting customers. This, naturally, is a function of the maximum expected length of the waiting line. Theoretically, for infinite-source systems, the line can be infinitely long. However, in practical terms, it is possible to determine a figure for the number of customers waiting that will not be exceeded a specified percentage of time. For example, we

Exhibit 13-6 Multiple-Channel Model with Poisson Arrival and Exponential Service Rate (M/M/S Model)

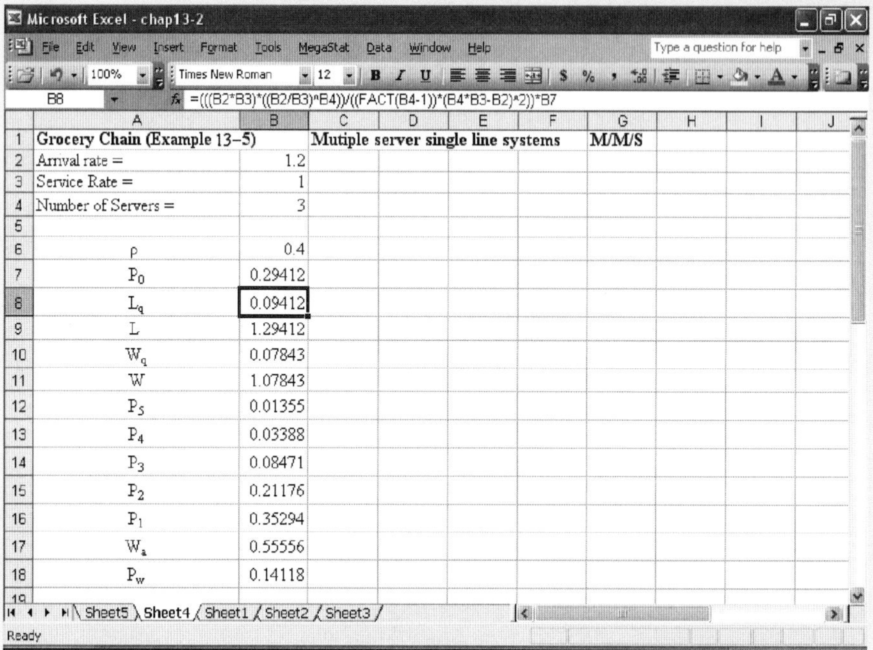

Microsoft Excel - chap13-2			
File Edit View Insert Format Tools MegaStat Data Window Help			Type a question for help
B8	fx =(((B2*B3)*((B2/B3)^B4))/((FACT(B4-1))*(B4*B3-B2)*2))*B7		

	A	B	C	D	E	F	G	H	I	J
1	Grocery Chain (Example 13–5)		Mutiple server single line systems				M/M/S			
2	Arrival rate =	1.2								
3	Service Rate =	1								
4	Number of Servers =	3								
5										
6	ρ	0.4								
7	P_0	0.29412								
8	L_q	0.09412								
9	L	1.29412								
10	W_q	0.07843								
11	W	1.07843								
12	P_5	0.01355								
13	P_4	0.03388								
14	P_3	0.08471								
15	P_2	0.21176								
16	P_1	0.35294								
17	W_a	0.55556								
18	P_w	0.14118								
19										

Sheet5 \ Sheet4 / Sheet1 / Sheet2 / Sheet3 /

Ready

Item	Cell	Formula
λ	B2	= 1.2
μ	B3	= 1
κ	B4	= 3
ρ	B6	= B3 / (B4 * B5)
L_q	B8	= (((B3 * B4) * ((B3 / B4)^B5)) / ((FACT (B5 − 1) * (B5 * B4 − B3)^2)) * B7
L	B9	= B8 + (B3 / B4)
W_q	B10	= B8 / B3
W	B11	= B10 + (1 / B4)
P_5	B12	= ((B7 * ((((B3) / B4)^5)) / ((FACT (B5) * (B5^(5 − B5))))))
P_4	B13	= ((B7 * ((((B3) / B4)^4)) / ((FACT (B5) * (B5^(4 − B5))))))
P_3	B14	= B7 * (((B3 / B4)^3) / FACT (3)
P_2	B15	= B7 * (((B3 / B4)^2) / FACT (2)
P_1	B16	= B7 * (((B3 / B4)^1) / FACT (1)
W_a	B17	= 1 / (B5 * B4) − B3
P_w	B18	= (((B3) / (B4))^B5) * (B7) / (FACT (B5) * (1 − (B3) / ((B5) * (B4))))
P_0	B7	= (1) / ((((((B3 / B4)^0) FACT (0)) + ((B3 / B4)^1 / FACT (1)) + ((B3 / B4)^2 / FACT (2)) + (((((B3) / (B4))^B5) / ((FACT (B5)) * (1 − ((B3) / B5 * B4))))))

could determine the line length that probably will not be exceeded 95 percent of the time or 99 percent of the time.

An approximate line length that will satisfy any stated probability can be determined by solving the following equation for n:

$$\rho^n = K \tag{13-30}$$

where

$$K = \frac{1 - \text{Probability}}{L_q(1 - \rho)}$$

and L_q is from Table 13-5.

The equation can be readily solved using logarithms (either to the base 10 or to the base e):

$$n = \frac{\log K}{\log \rho} \quad \text{or} \quad \frac{\ln K}{\ln \rho} \tag{13-31}$$

The resulting value of n usually will not be an integer. In general, *round up* to the next higher integer and use that value as $n_{\max}$.

Example 13-6

Determine the maximum number of customers waiting in line for probabilities of both 95 percent and 99 percent for this situation:

$s = 1$
$\lambda = 4$ per hour
$\mu = 5$ per hour

Solution

$$\rho = \frac{\lambda}{s\mu} = \frac{4}{1(5)} = .80 \quad \text{and} \quad \frac{\lambda}{\mu} = \frac{4}{5} = .80$$

From Table 13-5 with $\lambda/\mu = .80$ and $s = 1$, $L_q = 3.2$.

For 95 percent, $K = \dfrac{1 - .95}{3.2(1 - .80)} = .078$

$$n = \frac{\log .078}{\log .80} = 11.43 \quad \text{Hence, } n_{\max} = 12$$

For 99 percent, $K = \dfrac{1 - .99}{3.2(1 - .80)} = .0156$

$$n = \frac{\log .0156}{\log .80} = 18.64 \quad \text{Hence, } n_{\max} = 19$$

In some instances, the solution to Equation 13-31 will yield a negative value for n. If that happens, round up to zero. That happens when a system is only very lightly loaded and, in effect, most of the time there will not be a waiting line; hence, the zero.

A related question of interest is the number of channels needed to achieve a specified n_{max}. For example, the platform manager of a commercial bank may want to know how many tellers will be needed to hold the maximum number of waiting customers to 7. The solution to this question requires successively solving Equation 13-31, incrementing s each time, until the desired n_{max} is achieved.

Example 13-7

Suppose that during a noon hour at a bank, the arrival rate is 8 customers per minute and the service rate is 2 customers per minute. This produces λ/μ of $8/2 = 4.0$. Using Table 13-5, we obtain the following:

s	L_q
5	2.216
6	.570
7	.180
8	.059

Using Equation 13-31 with appropriate values of ρ (as shown), n_{max} for, say, 95 percent and 99 percent can be determined:

s	ρ	$n_{.95}$	$n_{.99}$
5	.80	10	17
6	.67	4	8
7	.57	1	4
8	.50	0	

Therefore, 6 servers would achieve a probability of at least 95 percent that the number of waiting customers would not exceed 4, while 7 servers would achieve a probability of at least 99 percent that the line would not exceed 4 waiting customers.

Cost Considerations

The design of a service system often reflects the desire of management to balance the cost of capacity with the expected cost of customers waiting in the system. For example, in designing loading docks for a warehouse, the cost of docks plus loading crews must be balanced against the cost of trucks and drivers that will be in the system, both while waiting to be unloaded and while actually being unloaded. Similarly, the cost of having a mechanic wait for tools at a tool crib must be balanced against the cost of servers at the crib.

The optimal capacity (usually in terms of number of channels) is that which minimizes the sum of customer waiting costs and capacity or server costs. Thus, the goal would be

Minimize Total cost = Customer waiting cost + Capacity (service) cost

The simplest approach to a cost analysis involves computing *system* costs; that is, computing costs for customers in the system and total capacity cost.

In order to identify the capacity size that will minimize total costs, an iterative process is used: Capacity is incremented one unit at a time (e.g., increase the number of channels by one) and the total cost is computed at each increment. Because the total cost curve is U-shaped (see Figure 13-1), usually the total cost will initially decrease as capacity is increased and then it will eventually begin to rise. Once it begins to rise, additional increases in capacity will cause it to continue to rise. Hence, once that occurs, the optimal capacity size can be readily identified.

The computation of customer waiting costs is based on the average *number* of customers in the *system*. This is, perhaps, not intuitively obvious; beginners usually feel that customer waiting *time* in the system would be more appropriate. However, that approach would pertain to only *one* customer—it would not convey information concerning *how many* customers would wait that long. Obviously, an average of 5 customers waiting would involve a lower waiting cost than an average of, say, 10 customers waiting. Therefore, it is necessary to focus on the number waiting. Moreover, if, say, an average of 2 customers are in the system, this is equivalent to having *exactly* two customers in the system at all times, even though in reality there will be times when there are 0, 1, 2, 3, or more customers in the system.

Example 13-8

Trucks arrive at a warehouse at a rate of 15 per hour during business hours. Crews can unload the trucks at a rate of 5 per hour. The high unloading rate is due to cargo being containerized. Recent changes in wage rates have caused the warehouse manager to reexamine the question of how many crews to use. The new rates for crew and dock cost is $100 per hour; truck and driver cost is $120 per hour.

Solution
(L_q values are from Table 13-5 using $\lambda/\mu = 15/5 = 3.0$.)

Note that in Table 13-6, because the total cost will continue to increase once the minimum is reached, it is not really necessary to compute total costs for crew sizes larger than 6, because total cost increased as the crew size was increased from 5 to 6, indicating that a crew size of 5 is optimal.

Table 13-6

Crew Size	Service cat: Crew/Dock Cost	$L = L_q + (\lambda/\mu)$ Average Number in System	Waiting Cost: Driver/Truck Cost @ $120 per Hour	Total Cost = Service Cost + Waiting Cost
4	$400	1.528 + 3.0 = 4.528	$543.36	$943.36
5	500	.354 + 3.0 = 3.354	402.48	902.48 (minimum)
6	600	.099 + 3.0 = 3.099	371.88	971.88
7	700	.028 + 3.0 = 3.028	363.36	1,063.36

One additional point should be made concerning cost analysis. Because both customer waiting costs and capacity costs often reflect estimated amounts, the apparent optimal solution may not, in fact, represent the true optimum. One ramification of this is that when computations are shown to the nearest penny, or even the nearest dollar, the total cost figures may seem to imply a higher degree of precision than is really justified by the cost estimates. This is compounded by the fact that arrival and service rates may either be approximations or not be exactly represented by the Poisson/exponential distributions. Another ramification is that if cost estimates can be obtained as *ranges* (e.g., customer waiting cost is estimated to range between $40 and $50 per hour), total costs should be computed using both ends of the range to see if the optimal solution is affected by this. If it is, management must decide whether additional effort should be expanded to obtain more precise cost estimates or else choose one of the two indicated optimal solutions. For instance, the latter strategy would most likely be employed if there were little disparity between total costs of various capacity levels close to the indicated optimal solutions.

The $40–$50 range of waiting cost is not an out-of-pocket cost. It is a dollar amount to reflect that the revenues and profits will suffer as a result of customer waiting time. Certain customers will choose not to wait and, as a consequence, the company will lose sales revenue and the associated profit. By adding another service line, we can reduce the waiting time (cost) at the expense of higher service cost. The key is to determine the lowest total cost that will minimize the cost of waiting plus cost of service.

Other Queuing Models (Optional Coverage)

The two previously described models (the single-channel and the multiple-channel, infinite-source queuing models) represent what might be thought of as the "mainstream" queuing models. This stems partly from the conceptual understanding of waiting-line systems that they convey and partly from the ease with which system performance measures can be obtained. However, the field of queuing contains a rich variety of models. This section is designed to illustrate some of that richness, and to enhance your appreciation for modeling waiting-line systems.

Each of the models presented in this section offers a slight variation in the assumptions that underlie the two basic models. For example, the first model allows for any service time distribution; the second pertains to constant service time; the third has Poisson arrivals and exponential service times but limits the potential length of the waiting line; the fourth has Poisson arrivals and exponential service but a finite calling population; and the fifth has priority service instead of first-come, first-served. Each of these models is presented briefly. Note that all of the models except the priority service one pertain to a single-server situation.

Model Variation I: Poisson Arrival Rate with Any Service Distribution (M/G/1)

The assumptions of this model are identical to the basic single-server model, except that service time need not be exponential. The service times can be of any distribution. This is indicated by the letter "G" for general in the abbreviated statement of the model. In order to use this model, however, it is necessary to have an estimate of the variance, σ^2, of the service time distribution. Some key formulas are presented in Table 13-7.

Table 13-7	Formulas for Poisson Arrivals, Any Service Distribution	
Performance Measure	**Formula**	**Formula Number**
Average number waiting in line	$L_q = \dfrac{(\lambda/\mu)^2 + \lambda^2\sigma^2}{2(1 - \lambda/\mu)}$	(13-32)
Average number in the system	$L = L_q + \dfrac{\lambda}{\mu}$	(13-33)
Average time waiting in line	$W_q = \dfrac{L_q}{\lambda}$	(13-34)
Average time in the system	$W = W_q + \dfrac{1}{\mu}$	(13-35)
System utilization	$\rho = \dfrac{\lambda}{s\mu}$	(13-36)

Example 13-9

Joe's Tailor Shop is a one-man operation, and owner Fred White does all of the work. The customer arrival rate is Poisson with a mean of .25 per minute. Service time has a mean of 2.0 minutes and a standard deviation of 0.9 minute. Compute each of the performance measures listed in Table 13-7.

Solution

$\lambda = .25$ per minute
$\mu = .50$ per minute
$\sigma = 0.9$ minute

1. $L_q = \dfrac{(.25/.50)^2 + .25^2(0.9)^2}{2(1 - (.25/.50))} = .301$ customer.

2. $L = .301 + (.25/.50) = .801$ customer.

3. $W_q = .301/.25 = 1.203$ minutes.

4. $W = 1.204 + 2.0 = 3.203$ minutes.

5. $\rho = \dfrac{.25}{.50} = .50.$

Single-Channel Model with Poisson Arrival and Any Service Distribution (M/G/1 Model) with Excel

We cannot always assume that the waiting-line model's arrival rate is based on the Poisson distribution and service times are based on the exponential distribution. For example, in many manufacturing situations, due to automation, the service times are constant and not

Exhibit 13-7	Single-Channel Model with Poisson Arrival and Any Service Distribution (M/G/1 Model)

```
Microsoft Excel - chap14-2
File  Edit  View  Insert  Format  Tools  MegaStat  Data  Window  Help          Type a question for help
Times New Roman    12    B  I  U                $  %
    B7          fx  =(((B3/B4)^2)+((B5^2)*(B3^2)))/((2*(1-(B3/B4)))))
         A                    B        C       D       E      F       G      H       I
 1  Joe's Tailor Shop (Example 13–9)       Poisson Arrival Rate, Any Service Distribution  (M/G/1)
 2
 3           Arrival Rate =      0.25
 4           Service Rate =      0.5
 5                0             0.9
 6
 7              Lq =          0.30063
 8               L =          0.80063
 9              Wq =          1.2025
10               W =          3.2025
11               ρ             0.5
12
13
14
15
16
17
18
19
20
21
22
 |< < > >| \ Sheet5 / Sheet4 / Sheet1 / Sheet2 / Sheet3 /          |<                        >|
Ready                                                             NUM
```

Item	Cell	Formula
λ	B3	= .25
μ	B4	= .5
σ	B5	= .9
L_q	B7	= (((B3 / B4)^2) + ((B5^2) * (B3^2))) / (((2 * (1 − B3 / B4)))))
L	B8	= B7 + B3 / B4
W_q	B9	= B7 / B3
W	B10	= B9 + 1 / B4
ρ	B11	= B3 / B4

distributed according to exponential distribution. In some cases, service times are based on an arbitrary distribution; we refer to this as a general service time distribution with a mean of μ and a standard deviation of σ. The utilization of a copy machine at a given office may be distributed according to a general distribution with $\mu = 4$ minutes and $\sigma = 1$ minute. In order to demonstrate the utilization of Excel for a single-channel waiting-line model with Poisson arrivals and general (arbitrary) service times, consider Example 13-9. Exhibit 13-7 illustrates the Excel worksheet for Example 13-9. Similar to Exhibits 13-5 and 13-6, arrival rate (λ) and service rate (μ) are given in cells B3 and B4. The formula bar on top of Exhibit 13-7 as well as at the bottom of Exhibit 13-7 displays the formula for L_q, the average number of customers in the waiting line. At the bottom of Exhibit 13-7 all of the formulas for the main operating characteristics of this problem are shown. We can perform sensitivity analysis by changing the arrival rate, the service rate, or the standard deviation of service time.

Model Variation II: Poisson Arrival Rate, Constant Service Time (M/D/1)

The assumptions of this model are identical to those of the basic single-server model (and the preceding model), except that the service time is constant. This waiting line is described by the M/D/1 model, where D indicates that service times are deterministic.

$$L_q = \frac{(\lambda/\mu)^2}{2(1 - (\lambda/\mu))} = \frac{\lambda^2}{2\mu(\mu - \lambda)} \tag{13-37}$$

The basis for this formula can be seen by referring to the formula for L_q with any service distribution (see Table 13-7). Because the service time is constant, $\sigma^2 = 0$; thus, the second term in the numerator drops out, reducing to the above formula. The formulas for performance measures other than L_q are the same as those shown in Table 13-7.

Example 13-10

A video arcade game is designed to operate for exactly three minutes, during which time a player attempts to capture as many purple monkeys as possible. Customer player arrivals can be described by a Poisson distribution with a mean arrival rate of 12 per hour. Compute each of the performance measures listed in Table 13-7.

Solution

$\lambda = 12$ per hour

$\mu = 20$ per hour

1. $L_q = \dfrac{12^2}{2(20)(20 - 12)} = .45$ customer.

2. $L = .45 + \dfrac{12}{20} = 1.05$ customers.

3. $W_q = \dfrac{.45}{12} = .0375$ hour   or $.0375 \times 60 = 2.25$ minutes.

4. $W = 2.25 + 3.00 = 5.25$ minutes.

5. $\rho = \dfrac{12}{20} = .60$.

Single-Channel Model with Poisson Arrival and Constant Service Distribution (M/D/1 Model) with Excel

Exhibit 13-8 demonstrates an Excel worksheet for Example 13-10 based on a model with Poisson arrivals and constant service times. The formula bar on top of Exhibit 13-8 as well as the bottom of Exhibit 13-8 displays the formula for L_q, the average number of customers in the waiting line. At the bottom of Exhibit 13-8 all of the formulas for the main operating characteristics of this problem are shown. The single-channel model with constant service times is a special case of the single-server model with arbitrary or general service times. As described earlier, the difference between the model with the general service time and the model with constant service time is that in the constant service time model there is no variability, or $\sigma = 0$.

Exhibit 13-8	Single-Channel Model with Poisson Arrival and Constant Service Distribution (M/D/1 Model)

```
Microsoft Excel - chap14-2
File  Edit  View  Insert  Format  Tools  MegaStat  Data  Window  Help          Type a question for help
Times New Roman     12    B  I  U  ≡ ≡ ≡       $  %       ‰ ‰  ≡ ≡      ▯ ▫ ▯ ▯
        B6              fx  =(B3)^2/(2*B4*(B4-B3))
```

	A	B	C	D	E	F	G	H	I	J	K
1	A Video Arcade Game (Example 13–10) Poisson Arrival Rate, Constant Service Times (M/D/1)										
2											
3	Arrival Rate =	12									
4	Service Rate =	20									
5											
6	Lq =	0.45									
7	L =	1.05									
8	Wq =	0.0375									
9	W =	0.0875									
10	ρ	0.6									

Sheet5 / Sheet4 \ Sheet1 / Sheet2 / Sheet3 /

Item	Cell	Formula
λ	B3	= 12
μ	B4	= 20
L_q	B6	= (B3)^2 / (2 * B4 * (B4 − B3))
L	B7	= B6 + (B3 / B4)
W_q	B8	= B6 / B3
W	B9	= B8 + 1 / B4
ρ	B10	= B3 / B4

Model Variation III: Finite Queue Length

This model incorporates all of the assumptions of the basic single-server model. In addition, it allows for a limit on the maximum length of the line. The implication is that once the line reaches its maximum length, no additional customers will be allowed to join the line. New customers will not be allowed on a space-available basis. For instance the drive-through pick-up window at a local fast-food store may exhibit this model, where the number of cars in the waiting line is limited by the size of the parking lot and also the access from the street. The necessary formulas are shown in Table 13-8.

Example 13-11

A single-bay car wash waiting line has a driveway that can only hold 4 cars. Because the car wash is on a busy highway, when there are 5 cars in the system, no additional cars can enter. The arrival and service rates are Poisson, the mean arrival rate is 9 per hour, and the mean service rate is 15 per hour. Compute each of the performance measures listed in Table 13-8.

Table 13-8	Single-Server, Finite Queue Length Formulas	
Performance Measure	**Formula**	**Formula Number**
System utilization	$\rho = \dfrac{\lambda}{\mu}$	(13-38)
Probability of zero units in the system	$P_0 = \dfrac{1 - \rho}{1 - \rho^{m+1}}$	(13-39)
Probability of n units in the system	$P_n = P_0\rho^n$	(13-40)
Average number of units in the system	$L = \dfrac{\rho}{1 - \rho} - \dfrac{(m + 1)\rho^{m+1}}{1 - \rho^{m+1}}$	(13-41)
Average number of units waiting in line	$L_q = L - (1 - P_0)$	(13-42)
Average time in system	$W = \dfrac{L_q}{\lambda(1 - P_m)} + \dfrac{1}{\mu}$	(13-43)
Average time waiting in line	$W_q = W - \dfrac{1}{\mu}$	(13-44)

m = maximum number permitted in the system.

Solution

$\lambda = 9$ per hour
$\mu = 15$ per hour
$m = 5$

1. $\rho = \dfrac{9}{15} = .60.$

2. $P_0 = \dfrac{1 - .6}{1 - .6^{5+1}} = .420.$

3. (Find P_5.) $P_5 = .420(.6^5) = .033.$

4. $L = \dfrac{.6}{1 - .6} - \dfrac{(5 + 1)(.6^{5+1})}{1 - .6^{5+1}} = 1.5 - .294 = 1.206$ cars.

5. $L_q = 1.206 - (1 - .420) = .63$ car.

6. $W = \dfrac{.64}{9(1 - .033)} + \dfrac{1}{15} = .139$ hour.

7. $W_q = .139 - \dfrac{1}{15} = .072$ hour.

Single-Channel Model That Involves a Finite Queue Length with Poisson Arrival and Exponential Service Distribution with Excel

As discussed earlier, for some waiting-line models, the length of the queue may be limited due to the restrictions of the physical area. Consider a drive-up window model near a busy street.

The physical space may only permit five cars to be lined up in the parking lot; the sixth car is not permitted to enter the system because we simply ran out of space in the parking lot and, if allowed, the sixth car would have to wait on a busy street. We can easily modify the basic single-channel system to accommodate a finite queue. It should be noted that for the finite queue model, the service rate does not have to exceed the arrival rate.

Specific assumptions of the model with a finite queue length are presented below:

1. The arrivals are distributed according to the Poisson distribution and the service time distribution is negative exponential. However, the service time distribution assumption can be relaxed to allow any distribution.
2. The system has k channels and the service rate is the same for each channel.
3. The arrival is permitted to enter the system if at least one of the channels is not occupied. An arrival that occurs when all the servers are busy and the waiting line is full (maximum number of cars in the waiting line) is denied service and is not permitted to enter the system.

The Excel worksheet for the single-channel model that involves a finite queue length is demonstrated in Exhibit 13-9, on page 699 using Example 13-11. In this model, arrivals are based on the Poisson distribution and the service time distribution is exponential. At the bottom of Exhibit 13-9, the formulas for L, L_q, W, W_q, and P_0, P_1, P_2, P_3, P_4, and P_5 are shown. We can perform what-if analysis by changing the arrival rate and the service rate or the maximum number of cars in the system.

Model Variation IV: Finite Calling Population

This model has the same assumptions as the basic single-server model except that there is a limited calling population. A typical example of such a waiting line system would be a machine operator who is responsible for loading and unloading five machines. Hence, the calling population if five.

Some appropriate formulas are listed in Table 13-9. Note that λ is defined as the mean arrival rate *per unit*.

Example 13-12

One person handles adjustments for four machines. The machines run an average of 60 minutes before adjustments are needed, and the average adjustment time is 15 minutes. Service time can be described by a negative exponential distribution, and the call rate for each machine can be described by a Poisson distribution. Compute each of the performance measures listed in Table 13-9.

Solution

$\lambda = 1$ call per hour per machine
$\mu = 4$ machines per hour
$N = 4$
$\dfrac{\lambda}{\mu} = \dfrac{1}{4} = .25$

Exhibit 13-9   Single-Channel Model That Involves a Finite Queue Length with Poisson Arrival and Exponential Service Distribution

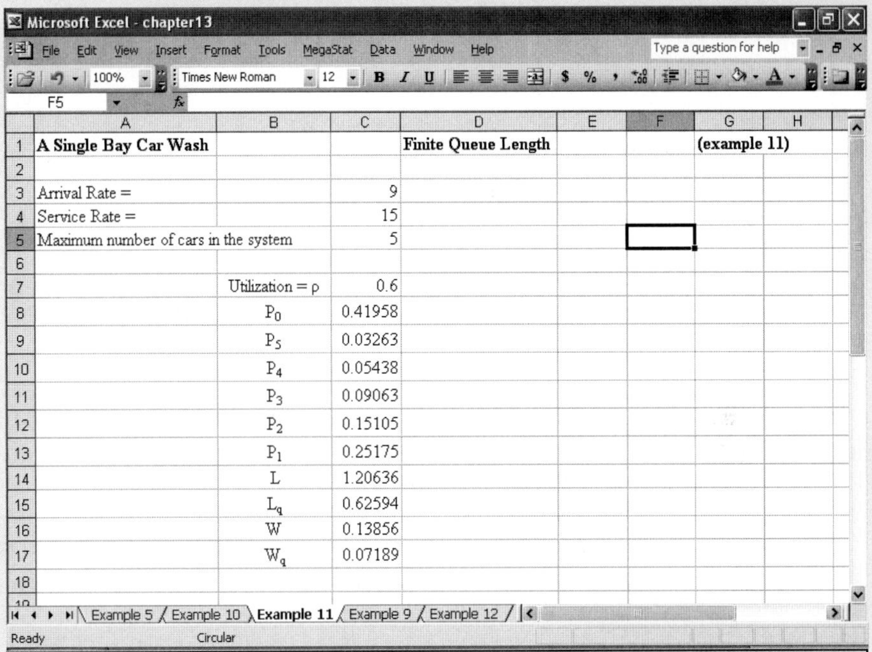

	A	B	C	D	E	F	G	H
1	A Single Bay Car Wash			Finite Queue Length			(example 11)	
2								
3	Arrival Rate =		9					
4	Service Rate =		15					
5	Maximum number of cars in the system		5					
6								
7		Utilization = ρ	0.6					
8		P_0	0.41958					
9		P_5	0.03263					
10		P_4	0.05438					
11		P_3	0.09063					
12		P_2	0.15105					
13		P_1	0.25175					
14		L	1.20636					
15		L_q	0.62594					
16		W	0.13856					
17		W_q	0.07189					
18								

Example 5 / Example 10 \ **Example 11** / Example 9 / Example 12 /

Item	Cell	Formula
λ	C3	9
μ	C4	15
N	C5	5
ρ	C7	= C3/C4
P_0	C8	= (1 − C7) / (1 − (C7^(C5 + 1)))
P_5	C9	= C8 * (C7^5)
P_4	C10	= C8 * (C7^4)
P_3	C11	= C8 * (C7^3)
P_2	C12	= C8 * (C7^2)
P_1	C13	= C8 * C7
L	C14	= (C7 / (1 − C7)) − (((C5 + 1) * ((C7^(C5 + 1))) / (1 − C7^(C5 + 1))))
L_q	C15	= C14 − (1 − C8)
W	C16	= (C15 / (C3 * (1 − C9))) + (1 / C4)
W_q	C17	= C16 − (1 / C4)

1. $$P_0 = \frac{1}{.25^0 \frac{4!}{(4-0)!} + .25^1 \frac{4!}{(4-1)!} + .25^2 \frac{4!}{(4-2)!} + .25^3 \frac{4!}{(4-3)!} + .25^4 \frac{4!}{(4-4)!}}$$

$$= \frac{1}{3.219} = .31068$$

2. (Suppose $n = 4$): $P_4 = \frac{4!}{(4-4)!} .25^4 (.31068) = .02913$

Therefore, it is highly unlikely that no machines will be running (i.e., that all will be awaiting adjustments).

3. $L_q = 4 - \dfrac{1 + 4}{1}(1 - .311) = .555$ machine.

4. $L = .555 + (1 - .311) = 1.244$ machines.

5. $W_q = \dfrac{.555}{1(4 - 1.244)} = .2014$ hour.

6. $W = .2014 + .25 = .4514$ hour.

Single-Channel Model That Involves a Finite Calling Population with Poisson Arrival and Exponential Service Distribution with Excel

The Excel worksheet for the single-channel model that involves a finite calling population is shown in Exhibit 13-10, using Example 13-12. In this model, arrivals are based on the Poisson distribution and the service time distribution is exponential. The formulas for this model are listed at the bottom of Exhibit 13-10. If we are to create the worksheet from scratch, development of this model using Excel spreadsheets could be complicated because of the nature of the formula for P_0. However, if the finite calling population gets to be relatively large, then we can break down the summation formula for the denominator of P_0. We can create an array for the denominator of P_0 and simply enter the cell containing the appropriate finite population. For example, if $N = 2$, the summation component for the denominator of P_0 would be ((B7)^D4)*((FACT(B5)/(FACT(B5 − D4))). If $N = 3$, the summation component

Table 13-9	Finite Calling Population Formulas	
Performance Measure	**Formula**	**Formula Number**
Probability of no units in the system	$P_0 = \dfrac{1}{\sum_{i=0}^{N}(\lambda/\mu)^i\left[\dfrac{N!}{(N-1)!}\right]}$	(13-45)
Probability of n units in the system	$P_n = \dfrac{N!}{(N-n)!}\left(\dfrac{\lambda}{\mu}\right)^n P_0$	(13-46)
Average number waiting in line	$L_q = N - \dfrac{\lambda + \mu}{\lambda}(1 - P_0)$	(13-47)
Average number in the system	$L = L_q + (1 - P_0)$	(13-48)
Average waiting time in line	$W_q = \dfrac{L_q}{\lambda(N - L)}$	(13-49)
Average time in the system	$W = W_q + \dfrac{1}{\mu}$	(13-50)

N = number in calling population.
λ = mean arrival rate *per unit* in the population.

Exhibit 13-10   Single-Channel Model That Involves a Finite Calling Population with Poisson Arrival and Exponential Service Distribution

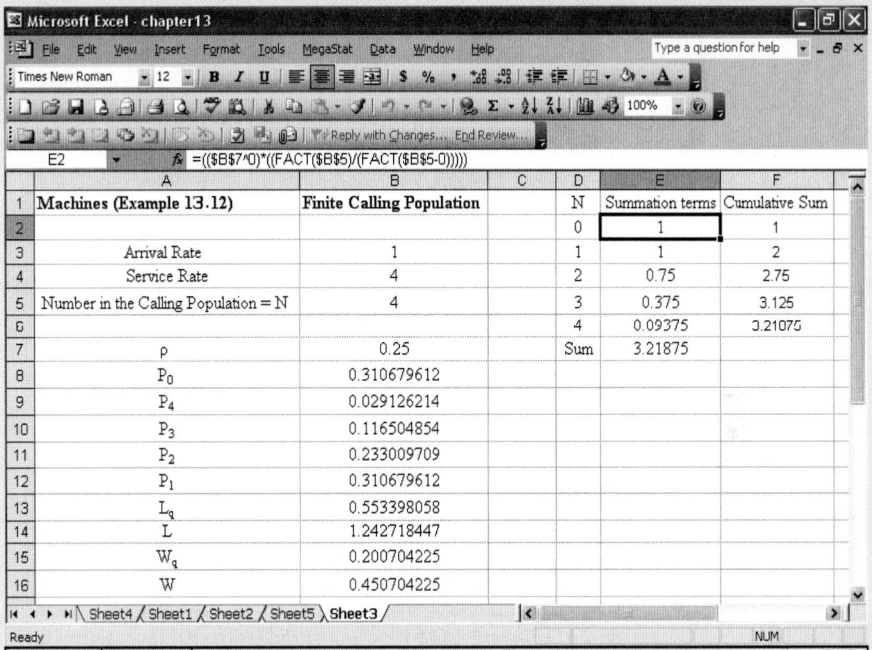

Microsoft Excel - chapter13

File Edit View Insert Format Tools MegaStat Data Window Help   Type a question for help

Times New Roman   12   B I U $ %   100%

E2   =(($B$7^0)*((FACT($B$5)/(FACT($B$5-0)))))

	A	B	C	D	E	F
1	Machines (Example 13.12)	Finite Calling Population		N	Summation terms	Cumulative Sum
2				0	1	1
3	Arrival Rate	1		1	1	2
4	Service Rate	4		2	0.75	2.75
5	Number in the Calling Population = N	4		3	0.375	3.125
6				4	0.09375	3.21875
7	ρ	0.25		Sum	3.21875	
8	P_0	0.310679612				
9	P_4	0.029126214				
10	P_3	0.116504854				
11	P_2	0.233009709				
12	P_1	0.310679612				
13	L_q	0.553398058				
14	L	1.242718447				
15	W_q	0.200704225				
16	W	0.450704225				

Sheet4 / Sheet1 / Sheet2 / Sheet5 \ Sheet3 /

Ready   NUM

Item	Cell	Formula
λ	B3	= 1
μ	B4	= 4
N	B5	= 4
ρ	B7	= B3 / B4
P_0	B8	= 1 / F6
P_4	B9	= (FACT (B5) / FACT (B5 − 4)) * ((B3 / B4)^4) * B8
P_3	B10	= (FACT (B5) / FACT (B5 − 3)) * ((B3 / B4)^3) * B8
P_2	B11	= (FACT (B5) / FACT (B5 − 2)) * ((B3 / B4)^2) * B8
P_1	B12	= (FACT (B5) / FACT (B5 − 1)) * ((B3 / B4)^1) * B8
L_q	B13	= B5 − ((B3 + B4) / B3) * (1 − B8)
L	B14	= B13 + (1 − B8)
W_q	B15	= B13 / (B3 * (B5 − B14))
W	B16	= B15 − (1 / B4)
Sum Tom	E2	= (($B$7^D2) * ((FACT($B$5) / FACT($B$5 − D2)))))
Cum Sum	F3	= E3 + F2

for the denominator of P_0 would be ((B7)^D5)*((FACT(B5))/(FACT(B5 − D5))). We would simply enter the formulas in the array for $N = 0$, $N = 1$, $N = 2$, and so on, all the way up to the finite calling population, and the sum of the values in the array would simply be equal to the denominator of P_0.

Model Variation V: Multiple-Server, Priority Servicing Model

This model incorporates all of the assumptions of the basic multiple-server model except that priority serving is used rather than first-come, first-served. Arrivals to the system are assigned a priority as they arrive (e.g., highest priority = 1, next priority class = 2, next priority class = 3, and so on). An existing queue might look something like this:

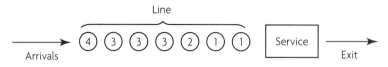

Within each class, waiting units are processed in the order they arrived (i.e., first-come, first-served). Thus, in this sequence, the first #1 would be processed as soon as a server was available. Then, the second #1 would be processed when that server, or another one, became available. If, in the interim, another #1 arrived, it would be next in line *ahead of the first #2.* If there were no new arrivals, the only #2 would be processed by the next available server. At that point, if a new #1 arrived, it would be processed ahead of the #3s and the #4. Similarly, a new #2 would be processed ahead of the #3s and the #4. Conversely, if a new #4 arrived, it would take its place at the end of the line.

Obviously, a unit with a low priority could conceivably wait a rather long time for processing. In some cases, units that have waited more than some specified time are reassigned a higher priority.

This model assumes that service is not **preemptive**. This means that service on a low priority unit is not interrupted even though a higher-priority unit arrives after service has begun.

The appropriate formulas for this multiple-channel, priority service model are given in Table 13-10.

Table 13-10	Multiple-Server, Priority Service Model	
Performance Measure	**Formula**	**Formula Number**
System utilization	$\rho = \dfrac{\lambda}{s\mu}$	(13-51)
Intermediate values: (L_q from Table 13-5)	$A = \dfrac{\lambda}{(1 - \rho)L_q}$	(13-52)
	$B_k = 1 - \displaystyle\sum_{c=1}^{k} \dfrac{\lambda C}{s\mu}$ ($B_0 = 1$)	(13-53)
Average waiting time in line for units in kth priority class	$W_k = \dfrac{1}{A(B_{k-1})(B_k)}$	(13-54)
Average time in the system for units in the kth priority class	$W = W_k + \dfrac{1}{\mu}$	(13-55)
Average number waiting in line for units in the kth priority class	$L_k = \lambda_k \times W_k$	(13-56)

Example 13-13

A machine shop handles tool repairs in a large company. Each job is assigned a priority when it arrives in the shop that is based on the urgency for that tool. Requests for repair can be described by a Poisson distribution. Arrival rates are $\lambda_1 = 2$ per hour, $\lambda_2 = 2$ per hour, and $\lambda_3 = 1$ per hour. The service rate is one tool per hour for each server, and there are six servers in the shop. Determine the following information:

1. The system utilization.
2. The average time a tool in each of the priority classes will wait for service.
3. The average time a tool spends in the system for each priority class.
4. The average number of tools waiting for repair in each class.

Solution

$\lambda = \Sigma \lambda_k = 2 + 2 + 1 = 5$ per hour
$s = 6$ servers
$\mu = 1$ customer per hour

1. $\rho = \dfrac{\lambda}{s\mu} = \dfrac{5}{6(1)} = .833$

2. Intermediate values: $\lambda/\mu = 5/1 = 5$; from Table 13-5, $L_q = 2.938$

$$A = \frac{5}{(1 - .833)2.938} = 10.19$$

$$B_0 = 1$$

$$B_1 = 1 - \frac{2}{6(1)} = \frac{2}{3} = .667$$

$$B_2 = 1 - \frac{2 + 2}{6(1)} = \frac{1}{3} = .333$$

$$B_3 = 1 - \frac{2 + 2 + 1}{6(1)} = \frac{1}{6} = .167$$

$$W_1 = \frac{1}{A(B_0)(B_1)} = \frac{1}{10.19(1)(.667)} = .147 \text{ hour}$$

$$W_2 = \frac{1}{A(B_1)(B_2)} = \frac{1}{10.19(.667)(.333)} = .442 \text{ hour}$$

$$W_3 = \frac{1}{A(B_2)(B_3)} = \frac{1}{10.19(.333)(.167)} = 1.765 \text{ hours}$$

3. Average time in system $= W_k + 1/\mu$. In this case, $1/\mu = 1/1 = 1$.
    Thus, we have

Class	$W_k + 1 = W$ (hours)
1	.147 + 1 = 1.147
2	.442 + 1 = 1.442
3	1.765 + 1 = 2.765

4.   The average number of units waiting in each class is $L_k = \lambda_k \times W_k$. Thus, we have

Class	$\lambda_k \times W_k = L_k$ (units)
1	$2(.147) = .294$
2	$2(.442) = .884$
3	$1(1.765) = 1.765$

Revising Priorities

If any of the waiting times computed in the preceding example are deemed as too long by management (e.g., a waiting time of .147 hour for tools in the first class might be too long), there are several options. One would be to increase the number of servers. Another would be to attempt to increase the service rate, say, by introducing new methods. If such options are not feasible, another approach would be to reexamine the membership of each of the priority classifications. The reason for this is that if some repair requests, say, in the first priority class can be reassigned to the second priority class, this will tend to decrease the average waiting times for repair jobs that retain the highest priority classification simply because the arrival rate of those items will be lower. The repair requests reassigned from the first priority class to the second priority class may be subject to longer waiting times.

Example 13-14

Suppose the manager of the repair shop, after consulting with the managers of the departments that use the shop's services, has been able to revise the list of tools that are given the highest priorities. This would be reflected by revised arrival rates. Suppose that the revised rates are $\lambda_1 = 1.5$, $\lambda_2 = 2.5$, and λ_3 remains unchanged at 1.0. Determine the following information:

1.   The system utilization.
2.   The average waiting time for units in each priority class.

Solution

$\lambda = \Sigma \lambda_k = 1.5 + 2.5 + 1.0 = 5.0$
(Note that in the previous problem (13–13) $\lambda_1 + \lambda_2 = 2 + 2 = 4$ and in this problem $\lambda_1 + \lambda_2 = 1.5 + 2.5 = 4$. Therefore, the total arrival rate is unchanged since $\lambda_3 = 1$ in both problems.
$s = 6$
$\mu = 1$

(Note that these values are the same as in the previous example.)

1. $\rho = 5.0/6(1) = .833$, which is the same as in the previous example.
2.   The value of A, since it is a function of s, μ, and λ, is the same as in the preceding example because these values are the same. Therefore, $A = 10.19$. and

$B_0 = 1$ (always)

$B_1 = 1 - \dfrac{1.5}{6(1)} = .75$

$$B_2 = 1 - \frac{1.5 + 2.5}{6(1)} = .333$$

$$B_3 = 1 - \frac{1.5 + 2.5 + 1.0}{6(1)} = .167$$

Then:

$$W_1 = \frac{1}{10.19(1)(.75)} = .131 \text{ hour}$$

$$W_2 = \frac{1}{10.19(.75)(.333)} = .393 \text{ hour}$$

$$W_3 = \frac{1}{10.19(.333)(.167)} = 1.765 \text{ hours}$$

Here, we find several interesting results. One is that by reducing the arrival rate of the highest priority class, the average waiting time for units in that priority class decreased. Hence, removing some members of the highest class and placing them into the next lower priority class reduced the average waiting time for units that remained in the highest class. Note, though, that the average waiting time for the *second* priority class also was reduced, even though units were added to that class. Although this may appear counterintuitive, it is necessary to recognize that the *total* waiting time (when all arrivals are taken into account) will remain unchanged. We can see this by noting that the average *number* waiting in the preceding example (see part *d*) was .294 + .884 + 1.765 = 2.943. In this example, using the average waiting times just computed, the average number waiting in all three classes is

$$\sum_{k=1}^{3} \lambda_k W_k = 1.5(.131) + 2.5(.393) + 1.0(1.765) = 2.944$$

Aside from a slight difference due to rounding, the totals are the same.

Another interesting observation is that the average waiting time for customers in the third priority class did not change from the preceding example. The reason for this is that the *total* arrival rate for the two higher priority classes did not change, and its own average arrival rate did not change. Hence, units assigned to that lowest class must still contend with a combined arrival rate of 4 for the two higher priority classes.

Utilization of Excel's Goal Seek Function

The goal seek function can be a very useful function to determine the value of a queuing parameter to achieve a specific goal. Let's consider the single-channel car wash example given in Example 13-3. In this problem, assume that the owner of the car wash wants the average customer waiting time not to exceed 6 minutes, or .10 hour. Currently, a customer has to wait an average of .16 hour, or 9.6 minutes, before he or she is served. The owner of the car wash wants to know how much would he have to accelerate the service to reduce the average waiting time from 9.6 minutes to 6 minutes. In the worksheet shown in Exhibit 13-5, we can simply try different values for the service rate and keep track of the W_q value. We can stop the trial-and-error process when the value of W_q falls slightly below .10. However, the trial-and-error approach could be time consuming. An alternative approach that most

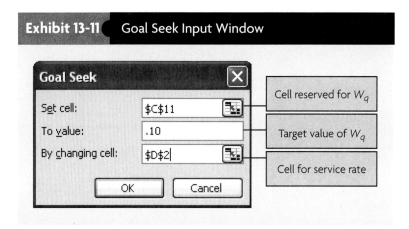

Exhibit 13-11   Goal Seek Input Window

managers would prefer involves the utilization of Excel's goal seek function. We utilize this function by selecting **Tools I Goal Seek** from Excel's main tool bar. The window shown in Exhibit 13-11 shows how we can utilize the goal seek function for Example 13-3 (car wash problem) so that the maximum waiting time is limited to 6 minutes, or .10 hour. The goal seek procedure tries to find the value of the changing cell that will allow the target cell to achieve its desired value. As shown in Exhibit 13-11, in this problem the "Set Cell", or target cell, is $C$11 and its desired value is specified in the "To value" box as .10 hour (6 minutes). The value to be manipulated to achieve the target cell value of .10 hour is the service rate specified in the "By changing cell" box as $D$2.

After clicking OK, the goal seek output window indicating whether the desired goal was achieved is shown in Exhibit 13-12. In addition, the values in the worksheet are updated and the results displaying the updated values are shown in Exhibit 13-13. These results can be interpreted as follows: Instead of .16 hour (9.6 minutes) of waiting time based on a service rate of 25 cars, we can achieve a waiting time of .10 hour (6 minutes) with a service rate of 27.30 cars shown in cell D2 of Exhibit 13-13. In other words, instead of washing a car in 2 minutes and 24 second (60/25), we need to be able to reduce the average time to wash a car to 60/27.301 = 2 minutes and 12 seconds. The manager of the car wash can try to figure out how to improve the system to wash a car on the average 12 seconds faster. This can be accomplished in a number of different ways. The least costly way of reducing the service

Exhibit 13-12   Goal Seek Output Window

Goal Seek Status			Statement indicating targeted value of W_q was achieved
Goal Seeking with Cell C11 found a solution.	OK	
	Cancel	
Target value: 0.1	Step	Showing the target value of W_q and the achieved value of W_q
Current value: 0.10033646	Pause	

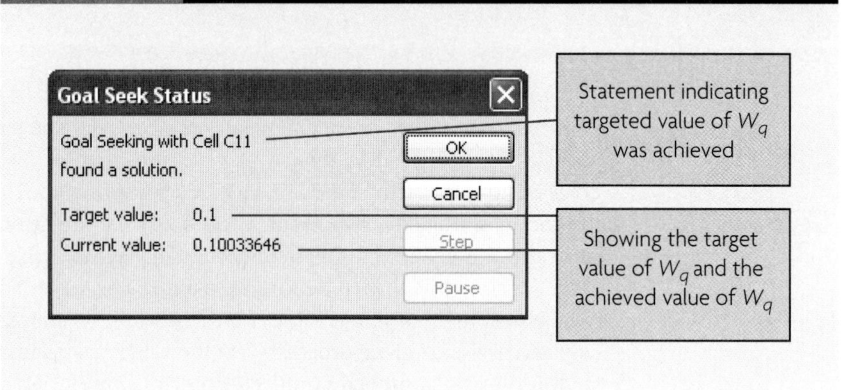

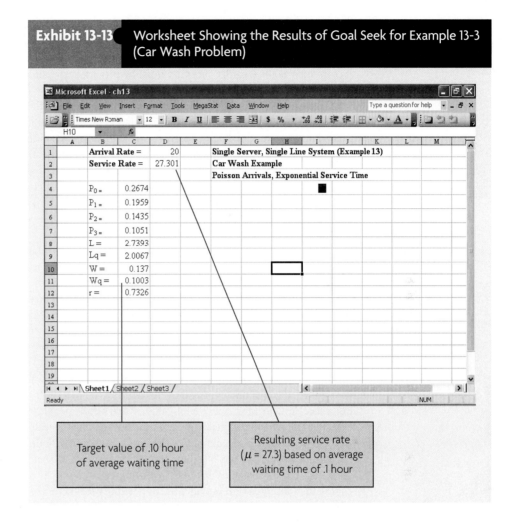

Exhibit 13-13 Worksheet Showing the Results of Goal Seek for Example 13-3 (Car Wash Problem)

Target value of .10 hour of average waiting time

Resulting service rate ($\mu = 27.3$) based on average waiting time of .1 hour

time is by improving the service process without changing the service system. Improving the speed at which the car is washed, faster entry to the system, or faster departure from the system, and so forth, might improve the system or reduce the service time. If reduction in service time cannot be achieved by improving the process, the other alternative is to change the car wash system to improve the service rate, which generally involves higher cost.

The Psychology of Waiting

The emphasis in this chapter has been on mathematical analysis of systems in which waiting lines tend to form. The underlying theme was predicting performance characteristics in order to make decisions relating to system capacity. In certain instances, especially those in which a system is currently in operation and capacity changes would be either difficult or impossible, reduction of waiting times may not be feasible. Nonetheless, in many instances it is possible to diminish the *effects* of waiting, even though the length of a wait cannot be shortened. Some of these approaches are described in this section.

Two costs are generally associated with waiting lines. One is an economic cost, related to factors such as the cost of space that must be provided for potential waiting customers; the cost of employee time spent waiting (e.g., for tools, for repairs); the cost of machines waiting for service (e.g., loading/unloading, repairs); and the cost of idle servers and service capacity. These costs usually can be estimated with a fair degree of accuracy. Another economic cost is related to the potential for lost business due to customers failing to join a line that they perceive as too long. Other customers may wait in line for a while, then leave. In either case, customers may return to the line at a later time, may decide to forgo the service, or may go elsewhere for it. If the customer returns, the impact on profits may be negligible; but if the customer does not return, the loss can be more significant, particularly if potential profit on *additional* products or services the customer may have bought also is taken into account. In other words, the question is: Does the company lose future sales and or goodwill as a result of missing the current sale? However, estimating such additional lost sales or profits may be difficult at best. Consequently, taking such costs into account may be problematic.

A cost that is closely related to customers leaving a line is the *psychological* cost associated with the waiting customer's perception of the waiting time. For example, if customers believe that their time could be better spent elsewhere, they are apt to resent waiting, especially if they feel that management could remedy the length of wait (e.g., simply by adding additional servers). Conversely, if customers are occupied during the waiting period, either in a constructive way or through some form of distraction, they are less likely to resent the waiting experience. Examples of situations in which the psychological aspects of waiting are attended to include doctors' and dentists' offices providing magazines to help patients pass the time; airlines providing music or in-flight movies on long flights; and asking people to fill out forms while waiting (e.g., unemployment office, doctor, dentist), thus making the wait somewhat constructive.

Oddly enough, in certain retail situations, a moderate amount of waiting time is desirable. For instance, supermarkets place an array of impulse-purchase items at checkouts (e.g., candy, gum, cigarettes, magazines, batteries). Waiting customers may add these to their other purchases; the waiting period provides the opportunity for them to consider additional spending.

The Value of Waiting Line Models

Waiting line analysis is sometimes criticized on the grounds that the assumptions required by the models are not satisfied in many real-life situations. Among the more common complaints are the following:

1. Often, service times are not negative exponential.
2. The system is not in steady-state, but tends to be dynamic.
3. "Service" is difficult to define because service requirements can vary considerably from customer to customer.

To be sure, it is important that the assumptions of arrival and service distributions be reasonably satisfied. A Chi-square goodness-of-fit test should be used for that purpose. Note that one of the special-purpose models described in this chapter allows *any* service distribution.

The second criticism is true in many cases. For example, the customer arrival rates at banks, supermarkets, and post offices, and highway and telephone traffic intensities vary by time of day and day of week. In some of these situations, it may be possible to restrict the

Modern Management Science Application: *Routing and Scheduling at CSX Transportation*

Two main goals of a railroad transportation company are routing shipments along its shipping routes and scheduling trains. CSX Railroad Company developed a Computer Aided Routing and Scheduling System (CARS) which enables CSX to bridge the gap between day-to-day scheduling and strategic planning. CSX is one of the largest railroad companies around the world. The railroad network of CSX is one of the biggest around the world as it encompasses well over 20,000 miles covering 19 states in the United States and some territory in Canada. The company has over 35,000 employees, and operates 1,500 trains carrying over 200,000 freight cars per day. Over the last two decades CSX has developed train performance calculators, linear network models, network mapping models and traffic analyzers for improving the operations of the company.

The CARS integrates two separate but related areas of logistics: freight routing and train scheduling. More specifically CSX wanted the system to find a path through a railroad network that also schedule the trains in an optimal fashion. In other words, optimal train scheduling and routing determines the departure and arrival times of trains that pulls the cars through their routes. CARS is a demand driven approach to scheduling and routing of railroads that considers these two functions simultaneously. CARS is an efficient system that transports various goods to the various destinations in a timely fashion. During the fall season the company ships one billion bushels of grain which accounts for a large share of the companies revenues. Even if CARS can provide the company with minor improvements, these improvements can turn into a major source of financial gain. The railroad routing and scheduling is a complex combinatorial optimization problem that is difficult to solve because of the computational complexity involved in solving the problem. However CARS enabled the company to examine various independent performance measures simultaneously. It enables company managers to see the changes in the railroad network structure. It also assists CSX to evaluate the impact on operations of changes in strategy, cost of fuel, track capacity and changes in the labor arrangements. One of the challenges faced by CSX and CARS is the frequency of scheduling. The frequency must be short enough to be customer responsive and long enough to be efficient and cost effective. CARS also serves as an evaluation tool to study marketing strategies such as differential pricing, transportation strategies such as reduction in railroad tracks, service strategy, such as the number and location of warehouses. The CARS impact CSX in the following three major ways: 1. training (estimation of rental car costs and estimation of crew costs based on changes in labor agreements), 2. validation of current plans (this ensures that routing and scheduling are not suboptimal, and 3. evaluation tool for strategic planning. CSX found that CARS was an effective tool for strategic planning. However the major criticism of CARS was that it did not include track depreciation and crew labor costs. However, one of the major benefits of CARS was that it simplified day-to-day operations in terms of routing and scheduling railroad trains and enabled managers to see the problems in scheduling and routing quickly and react to these problems expediently.

Source: C. Huntley, D. Brown, D. Sappington and B. Markowicz "Freight Routing and Scheduling at CSX Transportation" *Interfaces* Vol. 25, No. 3 (May-June 1995), pp. 58–71.

analysis to a narrow time interval for which the system is stable (e.g., for the lunch hour, the morning rush hour, and so on).

The last criticism may or may not be as important. Even if service requirements vary, taken as a whole, those times may exhibit an exponential distribution. Conversely, the times may be so disparate (e.g., some jobs require a few minutes and some a day or more) that two or more distributions are represented. In such cases, more elaborate modeling may be called for.

In any case, in which the assumptions of the basic models are not met, the analyst must decide whether to search for, or develop, a more complex model, whether to use simulation, or whether to simply rely on intuition and experience. The choice will depend on time and cost considerations as well as on the abilities of the analyst.

Certainly the pervasiveness of waiting lines justifies some formal study of queuing systems and their characteristics. The basic models presented here, along with the several tables and Excel models, enable beginners to grasp the important concepts associated with such systems without the need to deal with the fairly complex mathematics that are generally associated with queuing models. Thus, performance measures could be readily calculated, and the sensitivity of those measures to changes in system parameters (arrival and service rates, number of servers) also could be readily assessed.

◼◗ Summary

Waiting-line problems represent an important class of management science models. Waiting lines are commonly found in a wide range of production and service systems that encounter variable arrival rates and service times. Management science interest in these problems centers on predicting system performance for the purpose of capacity design. The most common goal is to design systems that minimize the combined costs of providing capacity and customer waiting. An alternative goal is to design systems that attain specific performance criteria (e.g., keep the average waiting time to under five minutes).

Performance measures for queuing systems include the average number of customers waiting, the average waiting time, system utilization, and the maximum number waiting in line.

Important characteristics of queuing systems in terms of system modeling include the calling population, the arrival distribution, line features, the order of selection for processing, and the service distribution. In general, the models presented in this chapter assumed that there is an infinite calling population; that an arrival rate can be adequately described by a Poisson distribution; that customers arrive individually rather than in batches; that customers funnel into a single waiting line when more than one server is used; that service is on a first-come, first-served basis; and that service time can be adequately described by a negative exponential distribution. The chapter also analyzed models with a finite calling population and service based on priorities rather than first-come-first-serve basis.

The models described in this chapter and some of their main features are summarized in Table 13-11.

Excel worksheets have been illustrated for nearly all types of queuing problems presented in the chapter. All of these Excel worksheets are included on the student CD-ROM.

Table 13-11	Summary of Queuing Models Described in This Chapter					
Model	Number of Servers	Calling Population	Arrival Distribution	Service Distribution	Maximum Queue	Processing Order
Single-channel	1	∞	Poisson	Exponential	∞	FCFS
Multiple-channel	s	∞	Poisson	Exponential	∞	FCFS
Any service	1	∞	Poisson	Any	∞	FCFS
Constant service	1	∞	Poisson	Constant	∞	FCFS
Finite queue	1	∞	Poisson	Exponential	m	FCFS
Priority discipline	s	∞	Poisson	Exponential	∞	FCFS by priority
Limited population	1	N	Poisson	Exponential	N	FCFS

Glossary

Balking Potential customers refuse to enter a waiting line, usually because they feel the line is too long.

Calling Population Pool of potential customers.

Finite Calling Population A system in which the pool of potential customers is limited in size.

Infinite Calling Population A system in which the pool of potential customers is relatively large or unlimited.

Interarrival Time Length of time between customer arrivals.

Jockeying In systems that have multiple waiting lines, when waiting customers switch from one waiting line to another.

Multiple-Channel System A queuing system with more than one server or service facility.

Multiple-Phase System A system with multiple processing steps.

Preemptive Service In a priority service model, this exists if service can be interrupted to handle a customer who has a higher priority than the one who is being served.

Priority Servicing Model Arriving customers are assigned to a priority class according to a predetermined rule and then they are serviced in order of priority class, using first-come, first-served within each class.

Queue Discipline (Processing Order) Order in which waiting customers are served. Usually by order of arrival (first-come-first-serve), except for priority servicing models.

Queuing System System in which waiting lines tend to develop.

Reneging Occurs when a customer, after a period of waiting in line, leaves the waiting line before being serviced.

Single-Channel System A system with one server or one service facility.

Single-Phase System A system with one processing step.

System A waiting line system consists of a waiting line and a service facility.

System Utilization The proportion of time that servers are busy (i.e., serving customers).

Solved Problem

Note: This chapter covers a wide range of queuing models. Rather than attempt to illustrate all of those models and variations, which would merely duplicate the examples presented in the chapter, this section is devoted to emphasizing a few of the basic concepts that underlie applying the queuing models presented in this chapter.

Problem 1

Customers arrive at the checkout area of a large supermarket during the early afternoon hours at the rate of four per minute. Checkout time averages two minutes per customer. There are six cashiers on duty. Assume that the arrival and checkout rates can be modeled by Poisson distributions. After arriving at the checkout area, customers select one of the six checkout lanes by choosing the one that appears to have the shortest line, and they wait in that line.

Answer these questions about this queuing system:

a. What is the significance of the phrase "during the early afternoon hours"?
b. What is the service rate, and why is it necessary to know it?
c. Is the system underloaded? Why is it important for a system to be underloaded?
d. We are told to assume the service rate can be modeled by a Poisson distribution. Is this any different than being told that the service time can be modeled by an exponential distribution?
e. How important is it to be able to assume either that the arrival and service rates are Poisson or that interarrival and service times are exponential? How could these be checked in practice?
f. What requirement of the waiting-line models presented in this chapter is violated if customers can select their own checkout lines? In order for the system to satisfy this requirement, what change would have to be made to the system?

Solution

a. In many waiting-line systems, the average customer arrival rate tends to vary by time of day. For example, lunch-hour demand is higher in restaurants, banks, shops near office buildings, and the like, than during, say, the midmorning hours. Thus, performance measures will differ depending on the time of day. Consequently, performance measures should be related to specific time and/or day intervals.

b. The service rate is the reciprocal of the service time. Here, the service time is 2 minutes. Therefore, the service rate is.

$$\frac{1\ customer}{2\ minutes} = .5\ customer\ per\ minute$$

It is important to know the service rate because many of the formulas in the chapter require the service rate rather than the service time.

c. This question involves the concept of system utilization, which can be calculated as follows:

$$\rho = \frac{\lambda}{s\mu} = \frac{4\ per\ minute}{6(.5\ per\ minute)} = 1.33$$

An underloaded system is one in which the system utilization is less than 1.00. In this case, the system is overloaded. The majority of queuing models require that the system be underloaded. If a system is overloaded, waiting lines will tend to grow longer and longer. Thus, overloaded systems are somewhat unrealistic. The exception would be a finite source system because the arrival rate would decrease as a larger and larger percentage of the population waited in line.

d. No, a Poisson *rate* is equivalent to an exponential *time*.

e. The majority of the models require these assumptions. Hence, if the assumptions are not valid, strictly speaking, the models will not provide results that will be realized (i.e., the calculated values will not reflect reality). Obtaining data (if possible) and using a Chi-square goodness-of-fit test would be a good way to test this.

f. The models require that service be done on a first-come, first-served basis (with the exception of the multiple-priority model). In order to achieve this, customers either could be asked to wait in a single line, as is often done in banks and post offices, or could be given numbers when they arrive and serviced in that order. In this example both would seem to be impractical; some other queuing model (or simulation) would be needed to handle this situation.

Discussion and Review Questions

1. What are the basic characteristics (elements) of a queuing system?
2. What are the basic measures of system performance?
3. First-come, first-served waiting line discipline is assumed in the queuing systems studied in this chapter. Describe two circumstances (business situations) where first-come, first-served discipline is not applicable.
4. In this chapter, one of the waiting line models studied involved a limited or finite waiting line. Provide examples of two situations with finite waiting lines.
5. In studying the basic single-channel waiting line model (M/M/1), what assumptions must be met?
6. What does the three-letter designation for a queuing model stand for? Describe what each position of the three positions such as (M/M/1) entails.
7. In the single-server waiting line models we have studied, the service rate is greater than the arrival rate. Why must this assumption hold for a single-server queuing system?
8. In the study of queuing systems, it is difficult to estimate the cost of waiting. The cost of waiting is generally divided into two components: (1) economic costs and (2) psychological costs. Describe both of these types of waiting costs.
9. One of the main criticisms of waiting line models is that the service times are not distributed according to the negative exponential distribution. In this chapter, we have studied three types of service distributions including the negative exponential distribution. List and briefly describe each type of service distribution that is described in this chapter. Explain when it is appropriate to use the three different service distributions.
10. Provide two examples of when the finite calling population model is applicable.
11. In this chapter, we have studied two versions of multiple-channel waiting line models. The first version involves first-come, first-served service type and the second one involves priority servicing. Explain how the two types of service differ and describe how the priority servicing system works. Explain the meaning that in a priority system, service is not preemptive.
12. In a waiting line system, the total cost is made up of two components: (1) waiting cost and (2) service cost. Discuss these costs in the context of a realistic business example. Which of the two costs is more difficult to estimate? Why?
13. In a waiting line system designed for a grocery store, what is the objective that a grocery store manager is trying to achieve? What specific costs is he/she trying to balance?
14. Certain waiting line systems involve multiple phases. How does a single-phase system compare to a multiple-phase system. Provide a realistic example of a multiple-phase waiting line system.

Problems

1. Relative to waiting line models:
   a. What is meant by the terms *single-channel system* and *multiple-channel system*? If a crew of four workers operates as a team in servicing a customer, how many channels does the system have?
   b. Contrast the terms *service time* and *service rate*. Explain how one can convert from time to rate. Why is this important?
   c. Explain the terms *calling population, infinite source,* and *finite source.*
   d. How does the phrase *first-come, first-served* apply in waiting line? Which models described in the chapter assume this?

e. What does the phrase *the number in the system* refer to?

f. Why do waiting lines form in systems that are underloaded?

g. Which of these are assumptions of most or all of the models presented in this chapter?

(1) Underloaded system.

(2) Variable arrival rate.

(3) Variable service rate.

(4) Processing is first-come, first-served.

h. What are the major elements of a waiting line system?

2. An infinite source queuing system has an arrival rate of 45 customers per hour and an average service time of 2 minutes per customer. The arrival rate can be described as Poisson, and the service time distribution can be described as negative exponential. Suppose it has been determined that the average number of customers waiting for service is 1.929. There are two servers. Determine (*hint*: see Example 13-3):

a. The average number of customers being served.

b. The average number of customers in the system.

c. The average time customers wait in line before being served.

d. The average time customers spend in the system.

e. System utilization.

f. What is the probability that there will be less than six customers arriving in three minutes?

g. What is the probability that there will be two or more customers arriving in three minutes?

h. What is the probability of no more than three minutes elapsing between successive arrivals of customers?

i. What is the probability that the service time is less than three minutes?

j. What is the probability that the service time is more than 2.5 minutes?

k. What is the probability that the service time is between 2.5 and 3 minutes?

a. 1.5

b. 3.429

c. 2.57 minutes

d. 4.57 minutes

e. .75

f. $P(X \le 5) = .975$

g. $P(X \ge 2) = .645$

h. $P(t \le 4) = .98168$

i. $(t \le 3) = .77687$

j. $P(t \ge 2.5) = .2865$

k. $P(2.5 \le t \le 3) = .06337$

3. One clerk is on duty during evening hours at the customer service desk of a supermarket. The clerk can process customer requests in an average time of 3 minutes, and this can be described by a negative exponential distribution that has a mean of 3. Customers arrive at a rate of 15 per hour (Poisson). Find:

a. The expected number of customers waiting to be served.

b. The average time customers spend waiting in line for service.

c. The proportion of time that the clerk is not busy with customers.

d. What is the probability that there will be less than seven customers arriving in a 20-minute period?

e. What is the probability that there will be three or more customers arriving in a 20-minute interval?

f. What is the probability that the service time is less than two minutes?

g. What is the probability that the service time exceeds four minutes?

h. What is the probability that the service time is between two and four minutes?

4. For the preceding question, determine:

a. The probability of no customers in the system.

b. The probability of two customers at the service counter.

c. The probability that a customer will have to wait for service.

a. .25

b. .1406

c. .75

5. Customers in a cafeteria line during lunch on weekdays arrive at the cashier's booth at a mean rate of 2.6 per minute. The cashier can process 4 customers per minute.

Arrival rate is Poisson and service rate is described by one exponential distribution. Compute each of the performance measures listed in Table 13-2 for this system. For Equation 13-17, use $n = 2$, and for Equation 13-18, use $k = 3$.

6. A lawn mower repair service employs one repairperson, who takes an average of one hour to service a lawn mower. A mower is brought in for service on the average of one every 90 minutes. Assume that arrival and service rates can be described by Poisson distributions. Determine the following:

    a. The average number of mowers awaiting service.
    b. The average time a mower waits for service.
    c. The probability that the number waiting for service will exceed 4 mowers.
    d. The probability that the repairperson will be without a mower to service.

a. 1.33 mowers
b. 2 hours
c. .132
d. .33

7. Customers at a bank wait in a single line for the next available teller. Customer arrivals can be modeled by a Poisson distribution that has a mean of 70 per hour during the midmorning hours. A teller can process an average of 100 customers per hour, which also can be modeled by a Poisson distribution. If there is one teller on duty, determine:

    a. The average time a customer must wait in line for the letter.
    b. The average number of customers waiting in line.
    c. Average service time.
    d. System utilization.
    e. The probability of no customers waiting in line.

a. .084 minute
b. .098
c. .6 minute
d. 35%
e. .481

8. What values would be appropriate for the performance measures listed in the preceding problem for the case in which two tellers are available?

9. A supermarket deli counter has a ticket dispenser from which customers take tickets that maintain first-come, first-served processing. The mean arrival rate during the morning hours is 84 per hour. Each server can handle an average of 30 customers per hour. Arrival and service rates can be reasonably well described by Poisson and exponential distributions respectively. Assume that three clerks are on duty. Compute each of the performance measures for this system using the equations listed in Table 13-4. For Equation 13-26, use $n = 2$, and for Equation 13-27, use $n = 4$.

a. 1. $L_q = 12.273$
        customers (13–21)
    2. $L = 15.073$
        customers (13–22)
    3. 8.77 minutes (13–23)
    4. 10.76 minutes
        $W_i =$ (13–24)
    5. $P_0 = .016$
        (13–25)
b. $P(X \leq 6) = .599$
c. $P(X \geq 3) = .918$
d. $P(t \geq 3) = .2231$
e. $P(t \leq 2) = .63212$
f. $P(2 \leq t \leq 3) = .144779$

10. a. For the preceding problem, use Table 13-5 as the basis for determining values of the performance measures represented by Equations 13-21 through 13-25.

    b. What is the probability that there will be less than seven customers arriving in a five-minute period?

    c. What is the probability that there will be three or more customers arriving in a five-minute interval?

    d. What is the probability that the service time exceeds three minutes?

    e. What is the probability that the service time is less than two minutes?

    f. What is the probability that the service time is between two and three minutes?

11. For Problem 9, how many clerks would be necessary to keep the average time customers spend waiting *in line* to no more than 2.5 minutes? How many clerks would be needed to keep the average time customers spend *in the system* to under 2.5 minutes?

a. $L = 19.487$
    customers (13–22)
b. $W = 21.984$ minutes
    (13–23)
c. $W_q = 24.36$ minutes
    (13–24)
d. $P_2 = .047$ (13–26)
e. $P_6 = .038$ (13–27)
f. $W_0 = 23.81$ (13–28)
g. $P_w = .94$ (13–29)

12. The owner of a bakery is thinking about installing a system of poles and chain links that will make customers wait in a single waiting line, instead of having them mill about the store waiting to be served. During evening hours, there are two clerks on duty, and the mean customer arrival rate is .8 per minute. Service time averages 2.375 minutes per customer, and this can be reasonably described by an exponential distribution. The arrival rate can be described by a Poisson distribution. Compute each

of the performance measures in Table 13-4, beginning with Equation 13-22, but omitting Equation 13-25. Use Table 13-5 to find L_q and P_0. For Equation 13-26, assume $n = 2$, and for Equation 13-27, assume $n = 6$.

13. Answer these additional questions concerning the previous problem:
    a. For the information given, what line length will not be exceeded with a probability of 95 percent?
    b. How many servers would be needed to keep the maximum line length to under five with a probability of 95 percent?
    c. How many servers would be needed to keep the average number waiting to be served (line only) to under three?

14. Library users request assistance in locating items at an information desk at a mean rate of 13.8 requests per hour. Each assistant librarian can handle a request in an average of 10 minutes. Suppose that students from a nearby college have studied this system and found arrival rate to be Poisson and service rate to be exponential.
    a. How many assistants would be needed to keep the average time in the system to 16 minutes or less?
    b. Determine the maximum number of persons waiting to submit a request for probabilities of 95 percent and 99 percent if five assistants will be used.
    c. How many assistants would be needed to have a probability of 95 percent that line length would not exceed seven persons?

15. In a large plant, a centralized tool crib is used in order to dispense tools to mechanics on a per-need basis. Mechanics request tools at a mean rate of 40 per hour (Poisson). Clerks can handle requests in a mean time of 4.5 minutes each, including the paperwork that is involved. Service time can be described by an exponential distribution. Mechanics represent a cost of $25 per hour each, and clerks represent a cost of $15 per hour each. Determine the number of clerks that will be needed in order to minimize the total cost of mechanics and clerks in the system.

16. In the parts department of a large automobile dealership, there is a counter that is used exclusively for mechanics' requests for parts. It has been determined that such requests occur once every five minutes, on the average, and the time between the requests can be modeled by a negative exponential distribution that has a mean of five minutes. A clerk can handle requests at a rate of 15 per hour, and this can be modeled by a Poisson distribution that has a mean of 15. Suppose there are two clerks at the counter.
    a. On the average, how many mechanics would be at the counter, including those being served?
    b. What is the probability that a mechanic would have to wait for service?
    c. If a mechanic has to wait, how long, on the average, would the wait be?
    d. If clerks represent a cost of $20 per hour and mechanics represent a cost of $30 per hour, what number of clerks would be optimal in terms of minimizing cost?
    e. What is the probability that there will be less than four requests occurring in a 20-minute period?
    f. What is the probability that there will be two or more requests occurring in a 20-minute interval?
    g. What is the probability that the service time exceeds three minutes?
    h. What is the probability that the service time is less than one minute?
    i. What is the probability that the service time is between one and three minutes?

17. During the daytime hours, calls for paramedics come into an emergency switchboard at the rate of two per hour. The operations chief can schedule two, three, or four crews

a. At least 3

b. 95% = −.125, or 0; 99% = 1.95, or 2

c. $S = 4$

a. .952

b. .229

c. .056 hour

d. 2 clerks

e. $P(X \leq 3) = .333$

f. $P(X \geq 2) = .908$

g. $P(t \geq 3) = .47236$

h. $P(t \leq 1) = .2212$

i. $P(1 \leq t \leq 3) = .30644$

to work this shift. The average time required to complete a trip and return to base is 40 minutes. Arrival rate is Poisson and service rate is exponential.

a. If the chief wants to maintain an average time of no more than 20 minutes between the time a call comes in and the time a crew is dispatched, how many crews should be scheduled?

b. Suppose that two crews are used. What would the average time to dispatch be? What would the system utilization be?

c. Suppose three crews are used. What would the average time to dispatch be? What would the system utilization be?

3 docks

18. One aspect of designing an industrial plant concerns the number of loading docks to include in the design. Driver and truck cost will be $200 per hour, while equivalent dock cost will be $140 per hour. Average loading time is expected to be three hours, and trucks will arrive randomly at a rate of one truck every two hours. Arrival rates can be assumed to be Poisson distributed and service rates are distributed according to exponential distribution. Determine the number of loading docks that will minimize dock and truck/driver costs.

19. Certain automated equipment needs part replacement on a random basis. This can be described by a Poisson distribution that has a mean of one part every other hour. When a break occurs, a technician diagnoses the problem, then goes to the parts counter to obtain the appropriate part. The average time for a clerk to obtain the part is 30 minutes because of the need to check various parts catalogs and retrieve the part from storage. Assume service rates are exponential. Clerk time represents a cost of $30 per hour per clerk. Equipment downtime and technician time represent $400 per hour.

a. If two clerks are used, what would be the average number of machines (i.e., automated equipment) waiting for parts? Assume there are a large number of machines in service (i.e., treat as infinite source calling population)

b. What number of clerks would be optimal for minimizing cost?

20. A clerk in the children's shoes department of a large store waits on customers in the order that they arrive. Each customer signs in when entering the department. A recent study shows that the customer arrival rate on Wednesday mornings can be represented adequately by a Poisson distribution with a mean of 8 per hour. The clerk can handle customers at a mean rate of 12 per hour. Determine the mean number of customers in the system, and the mean time they spend in the system, under each of the following conditions:

a. $L = 2; W = 15$ minutes

b. $L = 1.33; W = 9.96$ minutes

c. $L = 1.66, W = 12.45$ minutes

a. The service rate is exponential.

b. The service rate is constant.

c. The service time is neither exponential nor constant, but it is known that service time has a standard deviation of 3.5 minutes per customer.

21. A vending machine dispenses apples at a constant rate of 4 per minute. Apple eaters arrive to purchase apples at a mean rate of 3.4 per minute during breaks from classes held in the same building. Arrival rates are distributed according to Poisson distribution.

a. Compute the mean number of persons waiting to buy an apple.

b. Compute each of the remaining performance measures using the formulas in Table 13-7.

c. What is the probability that the service time exceeds 30 seconds?

d. What is the probability that the service time is less than 20 seconds?

e. What is the probability that the service time is less than 15 seconds?

f. What is the probability that the service time exceeds 45 seconds?

g. What is the probability that more than four apple eaters arrive in one minute?

h. What is the probability that the number of apple eaters arriving in half a minute will not exceed two?

i. What is the probability that the number of apple eaters arriving in a minute will not exceed two?

a. $L_q = 2.45$

b. $L = 3.30$;
$W_q = .72$ minute;
$W = .97$ minute;
$P = .85$

22. If the apple machine in the previous problem was temporarily out of order and apples were sold by one server who had the same 15-second service time but with a standard deviation of 2 seconds what values would each of the performance measures in Table 13-7 have?

23. Calls come into the reservations desk of a resort motel during the morning hours (weekdays only) at a rate of 15 per hour (Poisson distribution). In this telephone system, as many as two calls can be automatically placed on hold if the reservations clerk is busy with another call. Compute each of the performance measures in Table 13-8 with $\mu = 25$ per hour (Exponential distribution).

24. One librarian is on duty at the reference desk of a branch of the public library during the morning hours. The librarian gets a request for assistance approximately once every four minutes. The time between requests can be modeled using a negative exponential distribution with a mean of four minutes. Each request requires an average of three minutes of the librarian's time. This can be modeled using a normal distribution with a mean of three minutes and a standard deviation of one minute. Determine each of the following performance measures:

a. $L_q = 1.25$

a. The average number of people waiting for the librarian, not including the person being helped.

b. $W = 8$ minutes

b. The average time needed for a person to make a request and to be helped.

c. $P_0 = 25\%$

c. The proportion of time the librarian is not working on requests.

25. Many of a bank's customers use its automatic teller machine to transact business after normal banking hours. During the early evening hours in the summer months, it has been determined that customers arrive at a certain location at the rate of one every other minute. This can be modeled using a Poisson distribution. Each customer spends an average of 90 seconds completing his or her transactions. This time has a standard deviation of 20 seconds. Determine

a. The average time customers spend at the machine, either waiting in line or completing transactions.

b. The probability that a customer will not have to wait upon arriving at the automatic teller machine.

c. The average number waiting to use the machine.

26. In an automatic car wash, it takes four minutes to wash each car. Suppose cars arrive at the car wash at the rate of 12 per hour (Poisson). Hint: Because the carwash uses automatic equipment, it always takes four minutes to wash a car. Determine the following:

a. $L_q = 1.6$

a. The average number of cars waiting to be washed.

b. $W = 12$ minutes

b. The average time between the car's arriving and leaving.

c. $P_0 = 1 - P = .20$

c. The probability that a car will not have to wait in line.

27. The service department of an automobile dealership can handle only six transmission repair jobs per day. Customers who need transmission repairs come in at the rate of one per hour during the morning and early afternoon. Repair time averages 50 minutes. The arrival rate can be modeled by Poisson distribution and service rate is distributed according to exponential distribution. One repair person handles all transmission work. Compute each of the performance measures listed in Table 13-8.

28. A telephone reservation system can accept a maximum of two calls waiting. The reservationist processes calls in an average of four minutes. Average time between calls is five minutes. Service time can be modeled by exponential distribution and arrival rate can be modeled using Poisson distribution. Determine each of the following measures:
    a. The average number of calls waiting.
    b. The probability of two or more calls waiting.
    c. The probability that a caller will not have to wait for the reservationist.

29. An operator handles loading/unloading a group of three machines. The machines operate an average of 30 minutes per job, and loading/unloading time averages 5 minutes. Service time can be modeled by exponential distribution and the arrivals are distributed according to Poisson distribution. Compute each of the performance measures listed in Table 13-9. Use $n = 3$ for Equation 13-46.

30. A repair crew handles equipment breakdowns of construction equipment. There is one piece of equipment at each of five construction sites. When a request for repair comes in, the crew travels to the site, repairs the equipment, and returns to its base. Travel and repair time can be described by an exponential distribution with a mean of 3.5 hours. Equipment breakdowns occur at the rate of one every five hours (Poisson distribution).
    a. What is the probability that at any given instant, none of the equipment is being serviced due to breakdowns?
    b. On the average, how long does it take from the time a call comes in until the crew leaves to repair that piece of equipment?
    c. On the average, how many machines are out of service?
    d. What is the probability that the crew will be idle?
    e. What is the probability of no more than one breakdown in 2.5 hours?
    f. What is the probability that the number of breakdowns will exceed one in a five-hour period?
    g. What is the probability of no breakdowns in an hour?
    h. What is the probability that the service time will exceed four hours?
    i. What is the probability that the service time will be no more than two hours?
    j. What is the probability that the service time will be between two and four hours?

31. Customers arriving at a service center are assigned to one of three categories (1, 2, or 3, with Category 1 given the highest priority) for servicing. Records indicate that an average of nine customers arrive per hour, and that one-third are assigned to each category. There are two servers, and each can process customers at the rate of five per hour. Arrival rate can be described by Poisson distributions and service rate is distributed according to exponential distribution.
    a. What is the utilization rate for this system?
    b. Determine the average waiting time for units in each class.
    c. Find the average number of customers in each class that are waiting for service.

32. A manager must determine requirements for waiting space for customers. A priority system is used to process customers who are assigned to one of two classes when they enter the processing center. The highest priority class has an arrival rate of four per hour, while the other class has an arrival rate of two per hour. Both can be described as Poisson distributed. There are two servers, and each can process customers in an average of six minutes. Service rate is distributed according to exponential distribution.
    a. What is the system utilization?
    b. Determine the number of customers of each class that are waiting for service.

---

a. $L_q = .564$
   $P_n \geq z = .390$
   $P_0 = .339$

a. $P_0 = .012$

b. $W_q = 9.21$ hour

c. $L = 3.588$
d. $P_0 = .012$
e. $P(X \leq 1) = .910$
f. $P(X \geq 2) = .2642$

g. $P(X = 0) = .819$
h. $P(t > 4) = .3189$
i. $P(t \leq 2) = .4353$
j. $P(2 \leq t \leq 4) = .2458$

a. $p = .30$
b. $L_1 = .034, L_2 = .025$

c. $W_1 = .0086$ hours,
$\quad W_2 = .0123$ hour
d. $W_1 = .008$ hour,
$\quad W_2 = .0116$ hour

c.   Determine the average waiting time for each class.

d.   If the manager was able to alter the assignment rules so that arrival rates of the two classes were equal (3 per hour for each priority class), what would be the revised average waiting times for each priority class?

33. A priority waiting system assigns arriving customers to one of four classes. Arrival rates (Poisson) of the classes are shown in the following table:

Class	Arrivals per hour
1	2
2	4
3	3
4	2

Five servers process the customers, and each can handle three customers per hour. Service rate is distributed according to exponential distribution.

a.   What is the system utilization?

b.   On the average, how long do customers in the various classes wait for service? On the average how many are waiting in each class?

c.   If the arrival rate of the second priority class could be reduced to three units per hour by shifting some arrivals into the third priority class, how would your answers to part *b* change?

d.   What observations can you make based on your answers to part *c*?

a. $= .55$
b. $L_1 = .020, L_2 = .056,$
$\quad L_3 = .069, L_4 = .072$
c. $L_1 = .020, L_2 = .039,$
$\quad L_3 = .088, L_4 = .072$
d. See the IM

34. Referring to the preceding problem, suppose that each server could handle four customers per hour. Answer the questions posed in the preceding problem. Explain why the impact of reassigning customers in much less than in the preceding problem.

35. An immigration agent at Heathrow Airport in London could process 120 entrants on average during an eight-hour duty if the agent was busy all the time Assume that time to process each entrant is a random variable with an exponential distribution. On average, an entrant arrives at the agent's station once every six minutes. The number of arrivals is based on a Poisson distribution.

a.   What is the mean service time?

b.   What is the mean service rate?

c.   What is the mean arrival rate?

d.   What is the probability that the service time is more than five minutes?

e.   What is the probability that the service time is between three and five minutes?

f.   Delay problems are expected to occur if more than two entrants arrive during any 10-minute period. What is the probability that a delay problem will occur?

g.   What is the expected number in the system?

h.   What is the expected number in the waiting line?

i.   Determine the amount of time an entrant spends in the system?

j.   What is the expected waiting time in the queue?

a. .25, b. .1406, c. .75

36. Solve Problem 4 using Excel.

37. Solve Problem 7 using Excel.

a. 19.487 customers,
b. 21.984 minutes,
c. 24.36 minutes, d. .047,
e. .038, f. 23.81, g. .94
5 clerks

38. Solve Problem 12 using Excel.

39. Solve Problem 14 using Excel.

40. Solve Problem 15 using Excel.

3 docks

a. $L = 2$, $W = 15$ minutes;
b. $L = 1.33$, $W = .166$ hour;
c. L is 1.66, $W = 12.45$
   minutes

$P = .8333$, $P_0 = .231$, $n = 2$,
$P_1 = .16$, $W = 2.49$ hours,
$W_q = 1.66$ hours,
$L = 2.30$, $L_q = 1.53$

a. 4 entrants/minute,
b. $= .25$ entrant minute,
c. $.167$ arrival/minute,
d. $P = .2865$,
e. $P = .1859$,
f. $P = .2349$,
g. $L = 2.012$ entrants,
h. $L_q = 1.344$ entrants,
i. $W = 12.048$ minutes,
j. $W_q = 8.048$ minutes

41. Solve Problem 17 using Excel.

42. Solve Problem 18 using Excel.

43. Solve Problem 19 using Excel.

44. Solve Problem 20 using Excel.

45. Solve Problem 25 using Excel.

46. Solve Problem 27 using Excel.

47. Solve Problem 30 using Excel.

48. Solve Problem 35 using Excel.

◧ Chapter 13 Case   Big Bank

The operations manager of a soon-to-open branch of a large bank is in the process of configuring teller operations. Currently some branches have a separate teller line for customers who have a single transaction, while other branches don't have separate lines. The manager wants to avoid complaints about long waits that have been received at some branches. Because the demographics differ from location to location, a system that works at one branch won't necessarily work at another.

The manager has obtained data on processing times from the bank's home office, and is ready to explore different options for configuring operations. (Fortunately she has her textbook and CD from when she took management science course at a nearby university.)

One time that will get special attention is the noon hour on Friday. The plan is to have five tellers available. Under consideration are the following options:

1. Have one waiting line and have the first person in line go to the next available teller.
2. Have two waiting lines: one teller for customers who have a single transaction and four tellers who would handle customers who have multiple transactions.

Processing Information

An average of 80 customers are processed during the noon hour. The average processing time for customers with a single transaction is 90 seconds, while the processing time for customers with multiple transactions is 4 minutes. Sixty percent of the customers are expected to have multiple transactions.

Questions

If you were the manager, which option would you select? Why? Explain the disparity between the results for the two options. What assumptions did you make in your analysis?

Simulation

Learning Objectives

After completing this chapter, you should be able to:

1. Explain what the term *simulation* means and how simulation differs from analytical techniques.
2. Explain the difference between discrete and continuous simulations, between fixed-interval and next-event simulations, and between discrete and probabilistic simulations.
3. List and briefly describe the steps in simulation.
4. Use the Monte Carlo method to generate random numbers.
5. Conduct manual simulations using various distributions.
6. Conduct simulation with Excel using various distributions.
7. Conduct simple waiting-line simulation using Excel.
8. Conduct inventory management simulation using Excel.
9. List the advantages and limitations of simulations.

Chapter Outline

Introduction, 724

Replacement Parts Illustration, 725

Types of Simulation, 726
Discrete versus Continuous Simulations, 726
Fixed-Interval versus Next-Event Simulations, 726
Deterministic versus Probabilistic Simulations, 727

Steps in Simulation, 727
Defining the Problem and Setting Objectives, 727
Developing a Model, 729
Gathering Data, 729
Validating the Model, 729
Designing Experiments, 730
Running Simulations, 730
Analyzing and Interpreting the Results, 731

The Monte Carlo Method, 731
Simulation Using a Theoretical Distribution, 735
The Uniform Distribution, 736
The Exponential Distribution, 737
The Normal Distribution, 738

Multiple-Variable Simulations, 739

Computer Simulation, 742

Computer Simulation Using Excel, 742
Random Number Generation with Probability Distributions Using Excel, 743
A Discrete Distribution with Two Outcomes, 746
A Discrete Distribution with More Than Two Outcomes, 747
Simulation of Waiting Lines, 749
Inventory Analysis Using Simulation and Excel, 752

Scenario Manager, 757

Simulation Languages, 759

Pseudo-Random Numbers, 760

Advantages and Limitations of Simulation, 760

When to Use Simulation, 760

Summary, 761

Glossary, 762

Solved Problems, 762

Discussion and Review Questions, 769

Problems, 770

Chapter 14 Case: Krohler Supermarkets, 781

◾◣ **Introduction**

Simulation represents a marked departure from the other tools of analysis described in this book, such as linear programming, inventory analysis, and waiting-line models. All of those other techniques were directed toward helping decision makers to identify an *optimal solution* to a problem. This is not the case with simulation; it is not an optimizing tool. Instead, its purpose is to enable a manager or analyst to *experiment* with a system—to **simulate**—in order to better understand its behavior, and as a result, to make better decisions with regard to the system.

Simulation involves the use of a model that exhibits the important behavioral characteristics of a real system. Studying the behavior of the model under various conditions can lead to tremendous insights with broad applications. Consider these examples:

1. Medical researchers use various animals to *simulate* the effects of certain drugs on human beings.
2. Aircraft designers use wind tunnels to *simulate* the effect of air turbulence on wings and other structural parts of an airplane.
3. NASA trains astronauts in environments that *simulate* the conditions they are likely to encounter on future space missions.
4. Football teams conduct contact drills to prepare their members for upcoming games by *simulating* playing conditions.
5. Training programs for commercial pilots put trainees through a relatively large number of *simulated* takeoffs and landings on the ground before exposing them to the reality of performing actual takeoffs and landings.
6. Automotive safety experts crash test cars to *simulate* accidents.

In each of these examples, an important benefit of simulation is the ability to *experiment* with a situation under *controlled conditions*. Thus, simulation is used to answer "What if . . .?" questions. For example: What if the drug dosage is increased by a factor of two? What if the curvature of the wing is changed slightly? What would happen if a new pass defense is used by the other team? Decision makers can use simulation not only to obtain answers to such questions, but also to redesign a system that will perform in a more desirable way. The redesigned system, then, can be simulated to test its behavior under realistic conditions.

Obviously, there are many different kinds of simulations. One important class of simulation models, especially in business, is *mathematical* simulations. These involve modeling the key aspects of *events* (e.g., use of spare parts, demand for a product, machine breakdowns) in mathematical terms. Then, the model can be studied and modified in roughly the same manner as physical simulations. Because they are mathematical, such simulations lend themselves to computerization. This is important because many simulations are fairly complex and require numerous calculations, and computers offer the only feasible approach to handling such problems.

The simulations that we shall study are mathematical. They can be applied to a wide range of business problems. However, although most real-life simulations tend to be fairly complex, the discussion here will be limited to situations that are not very complex. In fact, many of the problems presented in this chapter lend themselves to *analytical* solutions rather than repeated *simulation runs*, which yield only approximate results. Nonetheless, there are several important reasons for limiting our study to fairly simple problems. One is that such problems lend themselves to *manual* procedures, which will produce identical results across the board. This means that everyone who tries a certain problem will come up with the same result, and this allows for discussion of that result. More important, the simple problems permit illustrating the basic concepts of simulation without being obscured by unnecessary, albeit realistic, complexity.

The discussion begins with a simple example of a simulation that will give you a feel for the descriptive nature of simulation. Next, some of the different types of simulation are outlined, followed by a description of how to actually do a simulation. The remainder of the chapter includes a broader discussion of simulation techniques, validation of simulation models, computer simulation using Excel, and the advantages and limitations of simulation as a management tool.

Replacement Parts Illustration

The manager of a repair shop in a large manufacturing firm had recently been informed that a new type of processing equipment would soon be installed in the plant. The manager was concerned about what level of replacement parts to maintain for a certain vital part that needs frequent replacement. If the part was overstocked, the shop would be needlessly tying up funds and space that could be better used for other purposes. Conversely, understocking the item would have serious consequences in terms of equipment downtime while replacement parts were rush-ordered. Moreover, rush-ordered parts tend to be more costly than those that are not rush-ordered.

In order to better understand the demands this new equipment will put on the shop's inventory, the manager decided to do a simulation analysis of potential usage. Because the equipment was new, there were no historical data on usage. Nonetheless, on the basis of usage of replacement parts for a similar piece of equipment plus discussions with engineers who were familiar with the new equipment, the manager was able to construct a model of usage of replacement parts. The manager then used the model to simulate usage for a 10-day period. The results of the simulation were as follows:

Day	1	2	3	4	5	6	7	8	9	10
Usage	1	0	1	1	0	0	0	2	1	0

Thus, simulated usage was 1 part on Day 1, no parts on Day 2, 1 part on Day 3, and so on. From this, the manager could see that daily usage of spares is typically 0 or 1. Also, a simple computation would show that average daily usage is .60 part.

This example has a relatively small number of simulated days. As a practical matter, the number is too small to enable the manager to gain much insight into the situation. However, the purpose of the example was to illustrate the kind of results one might obtain from a simulation. Had the number of observations been larger, the manager could have learned a number of things about potential usage of replacement parts. For instance, suppose that 10 days constitutes an order cycle. The manager could have run many 10-day simulations. The resulting values could have indicated such information as the average number of parts used over a 10-day cycle as well as information on the *sequence* of daily usage (e.g., the strings of days with no usage, the occurrence of heavy usage on sequential days, and so on). This information would be helpful for establishing a reorder policy and setting stocking levels.

Types of Simulation

There are various ways of classifying simulation types. Some of those ways are presented in this section. The purpose in contrasting the approaches to simulation is to help you gain some additional perspective on simulation.

Simulations can be classified as discrete or continuous, fixed-interval or next-event, and deterministic or probabilistic. Let's take a look at each of these contrasting pairs, beginning with discrete versus continuous simulations.

Discrete versus Continuous Simulations

The replacement parts example involved a variable with integer outcomes: The number of parts used per day could be 0, 1, 2, 3, or 4. Hence, the outcomes were *discrete*. There are many similar situations that involve discrete variables. For the most part, such situations can be described by a *count* of the *number of occurrences* (e.g., number of cars serviced, number of items sold, number of complaints received, and so on).

In certain instances, the variable of interest is *continuous:* It can assume both integer and noninteger values over a range of values. Recall that quantities that are *measured* rather than counted have this characteristic, such as time, weight, distance, and length. The distinction between discrete and continuous variables is important for simulation design. Both cases are illustrated in the following pages.

Fixed-Interval versus Next-Event Simulations

In certain instances, an analyst will be interested in simulating the value of a variable over a given or *fixed interval*. For example, the situation may involve sales of a product, and the analyst may want to simulate the number of units sold *per day*, or *per week*. Hence, the analyst would design the simulation to indicate the sales over one of these intervals. Although time intervals are the most typical intervals, distance and area are two other possible intervals. For instance, a problem may involve the number of defects *per mile* of roadway, or the number of breaks *per square yard* of cloth. In such cases, interest usually centers on *how many* occurrences there are rather than the *where* or *when* of an occurrence. Hence, a manager of an automobile dealership will be mainly concerned with *how many* cars were sold on a particular day rather than whether a car was sold at 1:30 p.m. or 1:40 p.m. Similarly, the superintendent of a mill will often be more concerned with keeping track of the number of defects in cloth that the mill produces rather than exactly where defects occurred; his or her main interest will be deciding if there is a major problem, and the number of defects would be an indicator of a potential problem.

When interest centers on the accumulated value of a variable over a length of time or other interval, we say that the simulation is a **fixed-interval simulation**, and we design the simulation to generate results that correspond to the interval of interest (e.g., sales per day).

Another type of simulation focuses on *when* something happens, or *how much time* is required to perform a task. For instance, a simulation of machine breakdowns may involve information on how long a machine operated before a breakdown and, perhaps, on how much time was required to repair the machine. This sort of information can be very useful for choosing among alternative machines, for deciding how many machines will be needed to meet production quotas, and for scheduling maintenance and repair crews.

When interest centers on *an occurrence* of an event (e.g., a breakdown, a fire alarm, an accident) and, perhaps, how much time or effort is required for the event (e.g., repair time, response time), we refer to the simulation of these situations as **next-event simulations**. Both types of simulations are illustrated in this chapter.

Deterministic versus Probabilistic Simulations

Another important aspect of a simulation is whether it involves a deterministic or a probabilistic situation. The former pertains to cases in which a specific outcome is *certain*, given a set of inputs; the latter pertains to cases that involve *random* variables and, therefore, the exact outcome cannot be predicted with certainty, given a set of inputs.

Consider a case in which an employer is contemplating changes in pay rates and working times for his employees. Although there may be many employees that would be affected, given the pay rates and projected hours of work, the total payroll can be determined right down to the penny. That would not be the case for, say, projecting the amount of time required to repair a complex piece of equipment that has malfunctioned. Because each case would differ somewhat from other cases, the time would be more appropriately modeled as a random variable. The resulting simulation would then have to be *probabilistic* in order to incorporate that feature. This chapter focuses exclusively on probabilistic simulations, which both tend to have broad application and are commonly encountered in managerial environments. This is not to say that deterministic cases are not encountered, but rather that they typically do not involve the level of insight or understanding that probabilistic simulations require.

All probabilistic simulations have a certain feature in common: They incorporate some mechanism for mimicking random behavior in one or more variables.

Steps in Simulation

In designing a simulation, an analyst is typically guided by this basic principle: Of necessity, the simulation model will be a simplification of reality. However, it must be realistic enough to provide meaningful results so that it will be useful for problem-solving and decision making.

Now that we have considered some of the different types of simulations, let us turn our attention to how to conduct a simulation.

Simulation typically involves these steps:

1. Defining the problem and setting objectives.
2. Gathering data.
3. Developing the model.
4. Validating the model.
5. Designing experiments.
6. Performing simulation runs.
7. Analyzing and interpreting the results.

These steps are illustrated in Figure 14-1.

Let's take a brief look at each of these steps.

Defining the Problem and Setting Objectives

The first step in simulation is to clearly define the problem that is to be studied. This involves a determination of what is to be accomplished (i.e., objectives of the simulation) and the

Figure 14-1	Steps in Simulation

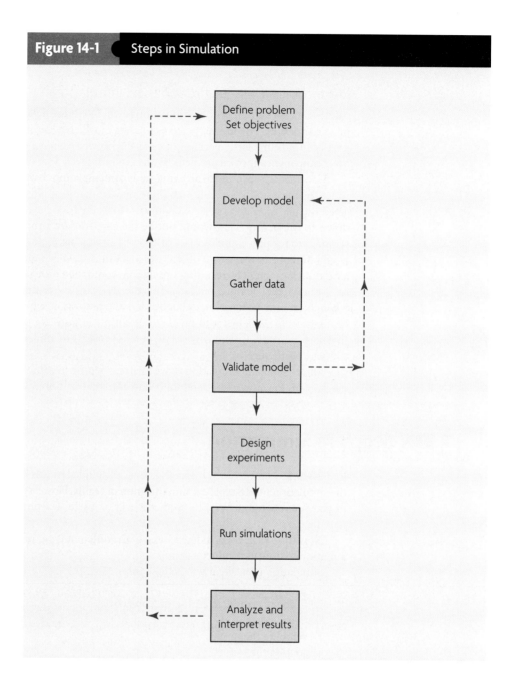

reasons for using simulation. Once the objectives have been established, a means of measuring the degree to which objectives are met by the simulation study must be established. Unless the objectives are determined at the outset, there is the danger that the results of the study will be used to determine them. In general, the goal of a simulation study is to ascertain how a system will behave under certain conditions. However, it is important to specify in as much detail as possible what information is desired. This will help in evaluating the success of the simulation, and it also will provide guidance for model development and the design of simulation experiments.

In the problem definition phase, the *scope* of the study and the *level of detail* that is needed to obtain desired results also must be decided. For example, if a simulation study is to be made of a bus system's passenger ridership patterns, will its scope encompass all routes and all times of the day, or just certain routes and/or certain hours? Will its scope cover all days of the week, or just certain peak days? Will it extend to different seasons, holiday travel, and so on? Will the level of detail include such factors as weather conditions, road conditions, traffic patterns, vehicle breakdowns, department store sales, community events, accidents, and the like? Moreover, will demographic information on riders (e.g., age, income, and occupation) be included? These questions are important because they have a bearing on model design and development, as well as the cost and time needed to accomplish this phase of the simulation.

Developing a Model

The second step in simulation is to develop a model that will accomplish the intended results. Usually, this involves determining the structure of the model, then using computer software such as Excel that will actually perform the simulations. Because manual simulations are employed in the text examples and accompanying chapter problems, using a computer software such as Excel will not be necessary in order to learn the concepts. Nevertheless, most practical applications of simulation do have that requirement. The structure of the model refers to the elements of a problem that are to be included in the model as well as their interrelationships. As in data gathering, capturing those interrelationships is an important aspect of model design, because unless they are realistically portrayed in the model, the results probably will not adequately reflect reality.

Finally, the model must be designed so that it will enable key decision alternatives to be tested. For instance, if bus size or maneuverability have alternatives with related consequences, the model must allow for those possibilities.

Gathering Data

The amount and type of data needed are a function of the scope of the simulation and the level of detail that was decided on in the problem definition stage. The data will be needed both for model development and for evaluating and testing the model. Data may come from direct observation of a system, or they may come from existing historical records. In either case, it is important that the data capture the essence of the system being simulated so they will provide a realistic representation for modeling purposes. Thus, it is usually prudent to verify that this is the case before proceeding with model development. This may involve observation and/or checking with individuals who are knowledgeable about the system.

Validating the Model

This phase of simulation is closely related to model development. The purpose of **validation** is to check to determine if the model adequately reflects real system performance. There are two aspects of the validation procedure. The first is to compare the results of the model with known system performance under identical circumstances. Ideally, the model should generate the same results as the real system. Discrepancies should be noted, and the model should be revised as needed in order to achieve this goal. Naturally, this assumes that there is an existing system that can be used for this purpose. If this is not the case, validation must rely on a second aspect: a test of reasonableness.

The test of reasonableness refers to testing the performance of the model under conditions that relate to questions that are to be answered by the simulation. For instance, in the bus simulation, the question of the impact of different size buses may be important. Presumably, historical data on this are not available, because if they were, there would be no reason to employ simulation. Even though there has been no experience with certain conditions, it should be possible for individuals who are closely associated with the real system, or similar systems, to make meaningful assessments about the reasonableness of simulation results under such modified conditions.

Another aspect of this phase involves careful checking of both the assumptions that underlie the model and the values of the parameters used in the model. The judgment of those who will be using the results of the simulation is a key factor. Not only are those persons apt to be very knowledgeable about such matters, but by being asked for their inputs, they also become an integral part of model design. If those people are not consulted, there is a real possibility that the value of the simulation results will suffer. Either the users will not understand the model and, therefore, will not "buy into" the results, or they will resent having been left out of the development of something that they will be expected to make work.

Notice the feedback loop between validation and model development. The validation phase often uncovers deficiencies in the model that must be corrected, and the ensuing results must then be validated. In fact, it is not unusual to go around this loop a number of times before the final model is obtained.

Designing Experiments

The fifth step in simulation is designing experiments. The experiments are the heart of a simulation study. They are intended to answer the "what if . . .?" questions posed to the model. It is through this process of exploring the model's response to issues of concern that the manager or analyst learns about system behavior. The person who is designing the experiments must look to the objectives of the simulation for guidance. Hence, the more completely those objectives have been spelled out, the better the chances will be for designing experiments that will provide the desired answers to management's questions.

Even though further study of experimental design is beyond the scope of this book, Douglas Montgomery's *Design and Analysis of Experiments*[1] provides an excellent insight in understanding this material.

Running Simulations

The sixth step in the simulation process is actually "running" or performing the simulations. If a simulation is deterministic, runs that are made under identical sets of conditions will produce exactly the same result. Consequently, only one run is required for each set of conditions in a deterministic simulation. Probabilistic simulations, on the other hand, tend to produce different results with successive runs, even though the set of conditions under which the simulations are run are unchanged. Therefore, a probabilistic simulation will require a number of runs—perhaps a large number—in order to "average out" the variability that is inherent in such a simulation.

Probabilistic simulation amounts to a form of sampling, and each run represents one observation. Therefore, the same concepts used in random sampling to determine how large a sample to take, apply to deciding how many simulation runs to make. In general, the higher the amount of variation observed in values of variables of primary interest in repeated runs, the greater the number of runs needed to estimate the expected values of those variables. The higher variability among certain variables, will be the main determinant of the

---

[1]Douglas C. Montgomery, *Design and Analysis of Experiments*, 5th ed., (New York: John Wiley & Sons, 2003).

number of runs needed. Further, the greater the variability obtained during simulation for a particular variable, the greater the likelihood that the behavior exhibited by the real system will differ from the expected value based on the simulation study. If the observed variability is deemed excessive, management may want to devote some effort to redesigning the system to reduce the variability to a more acceptable level or, perhaps, to better cope with the variability. For example, flexible systems due to multipurpose equipment and/or personnel that are capable of performing different tasks can offset some of the effects of variability in demand for services. Flexible scheduling and selective pricing policies also are possible solutions.

Analyzing and Interpreting the Results

The final step in the simulation process is to analyze and interpret the results. Probabilistic simulations tend to require more effort in this phase than deterministic simulations. Due to the presence of random variability, one can never be completely sure that the observed results are completely representative. Statistical analysis of probabilistic simulations provides the key for dealing with random variability; expected values, confidence intervals, and tests of significance are vital tools of analysis. Thus, analysis of simulation results should provide the decision maker with both an expected value for a given variable and a range of values in which the actual value may fall. Moreover, significance tests can be used to help decide whether observed differences among alternatives are indicative of real, or simply chance, factors.

Interpreting simulation results depends to a certain extent on the degree to which the simulation model correctly portrays the real system. Obviously, if the simulation model is a crude approximation of the system, for whatever reason, applying those results to the real system will present a greater challenge, and greater risk, than if the model is a close approximation of reality. Hence, it is essential to take the degree of closeness between the model and the real system into account when interpreting the results.

The Monte Carlo Method

The central feature of probabilistic simulations is the incorporation of *random behavior* for the variable or variables of interest. Random behavior is exemplified by many games of chance, such as drawing cards from a well-shuffled deck, rolling dice, and spinning roulette wheels. In each case, the outcome of a particular draw, or roll, or spin has a *numerical value.* And while the probability of the occurrence of any particular value can be readily computed, it is impossible to predict precisely which value will occur next.

These same characteristics are exhibited in a wide range of situations that are of interest to decision makers, such as the occurrence of accidents, fires, equipment breakdowns, the rate of demand for products and services, and service times. It is convenient to use an approach based on the type of random behavior that games of chance exhibit in order to *simulate* behavior of variables in these other situations because of the ease and simplicity with which randomness can be generated.

A commonly used approach for achieving randomness is **Monte Carlo Simulation,** which derives its name from its similarity to games of chance. Conceptually, this approach is analogous to placing consecutively numbered chips (0, 1, 2, . . .) in a large bowl, mixing the chips, and then drawing a chip from the bowl and recording that number. By returning the chip to the bowl and repeating the process, a series of randomly generated numbers could be obtained. However, the process would be tedious and inefficient. Moreover, there are much better ways of obtaining random numbers. For manual simulation of the sort described in this

Table 14-1   Random Numbers

	1	2	3	4	5	6	7	8	9	10	11	12
1	18	20	84	29	91	73	64	33	15	67	54	07
2	25	19	05	64	26	41	20	09	88	40	73	34
3	73	57	80	35	04	52	81	48	57	61	29	35
4	12	48	37	09	17	63	94	08	28	78	51	23
5	54	92	27	61	58	39	25	16	10	46	87	17
6	96	40	65	75	16	49	03	82	38	33	51	20
7	23	55	93	83	02	19	67	89	80	44	99	72
8	31	96	81	65	60	93	75	64	26	90	18	59
9	45	49	70	10	13	79	32	17	98	63	30	05
10	01	78	32	17	24	54	52	44	28	50	27	68
11	41	62	57	31	90	18	24	15	43	85	31	97
12	22	07	38	72	69	66	14	85	36	71	41	58

chapter, a **random number table** is very useful. Computer simulations generally rely on internally generated random numbers.

Table 14-1 is the table of random numbers that we will use for many of the problems and examples in this chapter. It has been constructed to conform to the following characteristics when numbers are read in any order (e.g., across rows, up or down columns):

1. All numbers are equally likely.
2. No patterns appear in *sequences* of numbers.

The numbers are grouped in sets of two for convenience. However, they can be read in sets of one, two, three, or more as needed. The first characteristic—that the numbers are equally likely—means that if one-digit numbers are read, each number has a probability of one-tenth (there are 10 one-digit numbers, 0 through 9) of occurring at any point. Therefore, knowing that a 3 has just been read has no relevance on predicting the next number; the probability of a 3 or any other number occurring next is still 1 in 10. Similarly, the probability for any two-digit number is one-hundredth because there are one hundred two-digit numbers (00, 01, 02, . . ., 99), and the probability is one-thousandth for any three-digit number.

When we say that no patterns will appear, this means, for example, that high values won't have a tendency to follow high values or low values won't have a tendency to follow high values. In other words, it will not be possible to predict which values will occur next in a sequence of values read from the table on the basis of previous values.

The obvious question at this point is: How can random numbers be used to simulate the behavior of a random variable? The answer lies in the way in which the random numbers are interpreted. How the numbers are interpreted is largely a function of the nature of the variable whose behavior is to be simulated. For instance, consider simulating the results of a series of coin tosses. For each toss, we want to know whether the result is a head or a tail. The values we obtain from the random number table are *numerical*. Consequently, they cannot be used *directly* to generate the desired results. Instead, we must first decide on a plan for transforming the numerical values we obtain from the table into "heads" and "tails." Actually, the approach is quite simple. Suppose we want to simulate results for a fair coin [i.e., $P(\text{heads}) = P(\text{tails}) = .50$]. There are 100 two-digit numbers. If we assign half of those to the result "heads" (say, 01 to 50) and the other half to the result "tails" (i.e., 51 to 00) we can simulate results that will generate "heads" about half the time and "tails" about half the time. Moreover, the sequence of heads and tails will behave in a random manner.

Table 14-2	**Simulating a Coin Toss**

Trial	Random Number*	Simulated Result
1	18	Heads
2	25	Heads
3	73	Tails
4	12	Heads
5	54	Tails
6	96	Tails
7	23	Heads
8	31	Heads

Heads = 01 to 50
Tails = 51 to 00)

*Taken from Table 14-1, column 1.

Example 14-1

Simulate eight flips of a fair coin. Read two-digit numbers from Table 14-1, column 1 going down. Treat the numbers 01 to 50 as "heads" and 51 to 00 as "tails."

Solution

The first random number is 18. Because it falls in the range 01 to 50, it is treated as a head. The next number, 25, also falls in this range, so it too becomes a head. The third number is 73, which falls in the range 51 to 00, so it is treated as a tail. The remaining values are treated similarly. These results are summarized in Table 14-2.

Three out of eight trials produced tails, and five trials produced heads. Although we would expect to get approximately 50 percent of each over the long run, this result seems reasonable for the relatively small number of observations taken.

The essence of using random numbers, then, is to establish a set of rules that can be used to convert the random numbers to simulated results. In general, problems will involve either *theoretical distributions* or *empirical distributions* (i.e., based on historical data). Hence, there will be the need to assign random numbers to outcomes that relate to a specified distribution for the random variable in question.

Consider the replacement parts example that was described at the beginning of this chapter. Demand for spare parts was simulated for a 10-day period. Let's see how that simulation was accomplished. To begin with, the manager needed to obtain a distribution for demand. Recall that the manager did this through consultation with engineers and on the basis of his experience with other equipment. As a result, the manager developed the following distribution for demand frequency:

Parts per Day, x	$f(x)$
0	.60
1	.25
2	.10
3	.04
4	.01
	1.00

Table 14-3	Assigning Random Numbers for the Replacement Parts Example	
Demand per Day, x	**Cumulative $f(x)$**	**Random Ranges**
0	.60	01 to 60
1	.85	61 to 85
2	.95	86 to 95
3	.99	96 to 99
4	1.00	00

In order to assign random numbers to this distribution, it was convenient to first develop the *cumulative* distribution. Thus:

Parts per Day, x	$f(x)$	Cumulative $f(x)$
0	.60	.60
1	.25	.85
2	.10	.95
3	.04	.99
4	.01	1.00

Because the cumulative probabilities are two-digit, it made sense to assign two-digit random number ranges because then there could be exact correspondence between the cumulative frequencies and the random numbers. The assignments for the random numbers are shown in Table 14-3. Note that the assignments begin at the low end of the distribution (i.e., demand of 0), with the smallest possible random number at that end. It will be helpful to note that after the first class, the left (lower) end of each range is equal to 1 more than the cumulative frequency (ignoring the decimal point) of the preceding class, whereas the right (upper) end of each range is equal to the cumulative probability for its class. For instance, for the second class (i.e., demand = 1), the range of two-digit random numbers that will correspond to that class is 61 to 85. Other ranges are similarly determined.

Now, daily usage of replacement parts can be simulated by obtaining a series of random numbers from Table 14-1 and, by noting in which range each random number falls, translating the numbers into number of parts demanded per simulated day. This is illustrated in Table 14-4 using two-digit random numbers from column 10.

These results are identical to those presented in the replacement parts example at the beginning of the chapter, and they illustrate how those results were obtained. Moreover, we

Table 14-4	Simulation of Replacement Parts Usage											
Demand per Day, x	**Random Number Range**	**Day Random Number**	**1** 67	**2** 40	**3** 61	**4** 78	**5** 46	**6** 33	**7** 44	**8** 90	**9** 63	**10** 50
0	01 to 60	⟶		0			0	0	0			0
1	61 to 85	⟶	1		1	1					1	
2	86 to 95	⟶								2		
3	96 to 99											
4	00											

have seen how a random number table can be used in conjunction with a frequency distribution to simulate the behavior of a random variable.

Although Monte Carlo simulation is relatively simple to understand and to use, it provides the manager or analyst with a powerful tool by enabling that person to study the behavior of random variables over any desired number of periods, in a very short "real" time frame. Thus, experience can be quickly built up on paper using simulation, as opposed to going through the process of waiting that would be required if the experience were to come from observing reality.

Simulation Using a Theoretical Distribution

We have seen how frequency distributions based on historical data can be used to conduct a simulation. It is also possible to employ a theoretical distribution, such as a Poisson distribution, exponential distribution, or a normal distribution, for a simulation. In this section, use of a Poisson distribution is demonstrated; in the following section, the use of a normal distribution and an exponential distribution, and a uniform distribution are demonstrated.

Example 14-2

Distress calls are received at a coast guard station at a rate that can be modeled using a Poisson distribution with a mean of .50 call per hour during weekends. Simulate three hours of experience.

Solution

We must first obtain cumulative Poisson probabilities for the stated mean of .50 from Appendix Table B. Those probabilities must then be used to develop ranges for random number interpretation. Thus:

x	Cumulative Probability	Number Ranges
0	.607	001–607
1	.910	608–910
2	.986	911–986
3	.998	987–998
4	1.000	999–000

Note that the number ranges are expressed to three digits. This will make it easier to use the Poisson table, which also is expressed in three-digit numbers. Suppose we want to use numbers from columns 1 and 2 of Table 14-1. We can use the two digits from column 1 plus the first digit from column 2 to obtain a three-digit random number. Thus, reading down the top of columns 1 and 2, we would obtain these three-digit numbers:

182
251
735
124
 .
 .
 .

To simulate three hours of calls, we can use the first three numbers. The first number, 182, falls in the range 001 to 607, so it corresponds to no calls in the first hour. Similarly, the second number, 251, falls in the same range, so it corresponds to no calls in the second hour. The third number, 735, falls in the range 608 to 910, so it corresponds to one call in the third hour. These results can be summarized as follows:

Hour	Random Number	Simulated Number of Calls
1	182	0
2	251	0
3	735	1

In each of the preceding examples, the random variable of interest was discrete: Only certain distinct values were possible. In many cases, the random variable is continuous rather than discrete: It can assume *any* value, integer or noninteger, over some range. Service time would be an example of such a variable. For example, the time to repair a piece of equipment could be 53.28 minutes.

Simulations that involve continuous variables typically are next-event simulations, or they are otherwise concerned with *how much* value (time, distance, area, etc.) a random variable assumes.

Three distributions that are commonly encountered in such simulations are the uniform distribution, the exponential distribution, and the normal distribution. The generation of random numbers based on each of these distributions is described in the following sections, beginning with the uniform distribution.

The Uniform Distribution

In the case of a continuous uniform distribution, a random variable can assume any value over a certain specified range, and all values in that range have an equal probability of being selected. For instance, suppose that service time for a particular process varies uniformly between 2 and 3 minutes. This means that any value in this range is possible, and no value is any more likely than any other.

To simulate values of such a random variable, use the following procedure:

1. Obtain a two-digit random number (RN) from Table 14-1. Place a decimal in front of it (.RN).
2. Treat the lower end of the range as a and the upper end of the range as b. Compute the simulated value using the equation:

   Simulated value $= a + .RN(b - a)$ (14-1)
3. For each simulated value, repeat steps 1 and 2.

Figure 14-2 illustrates this concept.

Figure 14-2	Conversion of a Random Number to a Uniform Distribution

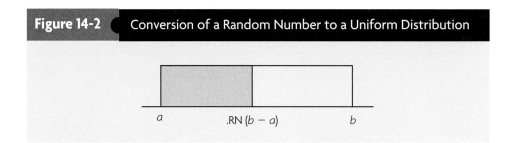

a .RN $(b - a)$ b

> ### Example 14-3
>
> The time needed to process a job order can be modeled using a uniform distribution with endpoints of $a = 2$ minutes and $b = 5$ minutes. Simulate two processing times. Use random numbers from Table 14-1, row 3.
>
> #### Solution
> The random numbers are 73 and 57. The simulated times are
>
> For 73: $2 + .73(5 - 2) = 4.19$ minutes
> For 57: $2 + .57(5 - 2) = 3.71$ minutes

The Exponential Distribution

In the negative exponential distribution, the probability is relatively high that the variable will assume a small value. Moreover, the probability decreases as the value in question increases. The probability that a random variable will take on a value greater than T given that the variable can be described by an exponential distribution with mean equal to $1/\lambda$ is given by the equation

$$P(t > T) = e^{-\lambda T} \tag{14-2}$$

To simulate exponential values, we let the random number serve as this probability, $P(t > T)$, and then solve the equation for T. The result will be a simulated value from the exponential distribution with the given mean, λ. We can obtain an expression for T by taking the natural logarithm (ln) of both sides of the equation. Thus, with $P(t > T) = .RN$, we have

$$\ln(.RN) = \ln(e^{-\lambda T}) = -\lambda T$$

Then $T = -\dfrac{1}{\lambda} \ln(.RN)$

The effect of Equation 14-3 is that small random numbers produce large time values. This concept is illustrated in Figure 14-3.

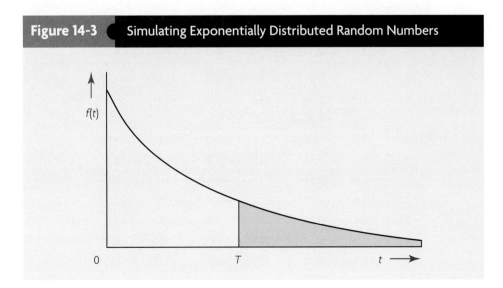

Figure 14-3   Simulating Exponentially Distributed Random Numbers

Example 14-4

An analyst has found that the length of time needed to repair a certain type of equipment when it fails can be described by a negative exponential distribution with a mean of four hours. Simulate two repair times for this type of equipment.

Solution

$$\frac{1}{\lambda} = 4 \text{ hours}$$

Suppose the two random numbers are 45 and 81. Using Equation 14-3, the simulated repair times are,

For 45: $T = -4 \ln(.45) = 3.194$ hours
For 81: $T = -4 \ln(.81) = .843$ hour

The Normal Distribution

It is not unusual to find simulation problems that involve the normal distribution. In fact, the normal distribution is probably the most frequently encountered distribution in practice. This is due, in part, not only to the fact that many natural phenomena can be well-represented by a normal distribution, but also to the fact that the normal distribution is an important theoretical distribution in statistical sampling.

There are a number of different ways to achieve random numbers that are normally distributed. For instance, such random numbers can be easily generated by computers. For hand simulations, an extremely simple approach is to use a special table of normally distributed random numbers. This approach will be demonstrated here.

Table 14-5 contains normally distributed random numbers. Numbers can be obtained from this table in essentially the same manner that we obtained random numbers from

Table 14-5	Normally Distributed Random Numbers								
	1	**2**	**3**	**4**	**5**	**6**	**7**	**8**	**9**	**10**
1	1.46	0.09	−0.59	0.19	−0.52	−1.82	0.53	−1.12	1.36	−0.44
2	−1.05	0.58	−0.67	−0.16	1.39	−1.21	0.45	−0.62	−0.95	0.27
3	0.15	−0.02	0.41	−0.09	−0.61	−0.18	−0.63	−1.20	0.27	−0.50
4	0.81	1.87	0.51	0.33	−0.32	1.19	2.18	−2.17	1.10	0.70
5	0.74	−0.44	1.53	−1.76	0.01	0.47	0.07	0.22	−0.59	−1.03
6	−0.39	0.35	−0.37	−0.52	−1.14	0.27	−1.78	0.43	1.15	−0.31
7	0.45	0.23	0.26	−0.31	−0.19	−0.03	−0.92	0.38	−0.04	0.16
8	2.40	0.38	−0.15	−1.04	−0.76	1.12	−0.37	−0.71	−1.11	0.25
9	0.59	−0.70	−0.04	0.12	1.60	0.34	−0.05	−0.26	0.41	0.80
10	−0.06	0.83	−1.60	−0.28	0.28	−0.15	0.73	−0.13	−0.75	−1.49

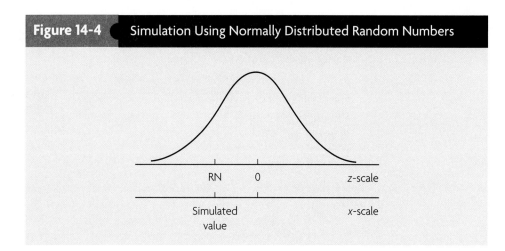

Figure 14-4   Simulation Using Normally Distributed Random Numbers

Table 14-1. Thus, numbers can be read one by one, in either rows or columns. The numbers represent z, which measures the number of standard deviations an observation is from the mean of the normal distribution. For example, a value of -2.13 would indicate a simulated value that is 2.13 standard deviations *below* the distribution mean. This concept is illustrated in Figure 14-4.

In order to determine the value of the observation, the following formula can be applied:

Simulated value = Mean + RN × Standard deviation

Example 14-5

Simulate two values from a normal distribution that has a mean of 200 and a standard deviation of 10. Use the first two random numbers in column 5 of Table 14-5.

Solution
The random numbers are -0.52 and 1.39. Using Equation 14-4, the simulated values are

For -0.52: $200 - 0.52(10) = 194.8$
For 1.39: $200 + 1.39(10) = 213.9$

Multiple-Variable Simulations

The preceding examples illustrate situations in which the behavior of a single variable is being simulated, such as the usage of parts per day, or the length of the repair time. In order to simulate the occurrence of an event, or the experience of one period of time (e.g., a day), in a single-variable problem, one random number is required. Single-variable examples are useful for illustrating important simulation concepts. Moreover, there are many applications of single-variable problems in real life. Nevertheless, there also are many cases in real life that involve *multiple* variables, and we now turn our attention to that class of simulations.

A multiple-variable problem has at least two variables. For example, we might want to simulate a situation in which there are a number of machines that need a variety of services

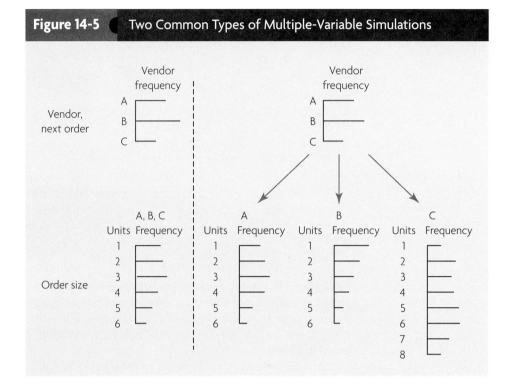

Figure 14-5 Two Common Types of Multiple-Variable Simulations

from time to time. The simulation might involve these phases: which machine needs service, what service is needed, and how much time is required to perform the service. Hence, *three* variables are involved, and *three* sets of random numbers will be needed, one to simulate each of the variables. Another example of a multiple-variable situation would be a case in which the first variable of interest was the type of job to be processed and the second was length of processing time. One set of random numbers would be needed to simulate the type of job and a second set for processing time. Such a simulation may involve two distributions, the first for the type of job and the second for length of processing time. However, if different jobs had processing times that were described by *different* frequency distributions, then simulation of the processing time would depend on which type of job was generated by the simulation of job type.

A similar situation might involve order sizes that were dependent on which vendor was ordering. Figure 14-5 presents a comparison of these two types of multiple-variable simulations using the example stated above.

Example 14-6

An analyst wants to simulate ordering stock from each of three departments, A, B, and C. The percentage of orders by department is shown in the following distribution:

Department	Frequency
A	.35
B	.25
C	.40

The order sizes for these departments can be described by these frequency distributions:

A: Order Size	Frequency		B: Order Size	Frequency		C: Order Size	Frequency
10	.15		20	.20		15	.25
15	.45		25	.25		20	.55
20	.25		30	.30		25	.15
25	.15		35	.15		30	.05
			40	.10			

Simulate four orders. For each order, indicate which department has placed the order and the size of the order. Read two-digit numbers from Table 14-1, column 2 for department and two-digit numbers from column 4 of the same table for order size.

Solution
The first step is to develop ranges for random number interpretations using the frequency distributions. Thus, for department we have

Department	Frequency	Cumulative Frequency	Number Range
A	.35	.35	01–35
B	.25	.60	36–60
C	.40	1.00	61–00

For order size, each department has its individual distribution,

A: Order Size	Frequency	Cumulative Frequency	Number Range	B: Order Size	Frequency	Cumulative Frequency	Number Range
10	.15	.15	01–15	20	.20	.20	01–20
15	.45	.60	16–60	25	.25	.45	21–45
20	.25	.85	61–85	30	.30	.75	46–75
25	.15	1.00	86–00	35	.15	.90	76–90
				40	.10	1.00	91–00

C: Order Size	Frequency	Cumulative Frequency	Number Range
15	.25	.25	01–25
20	.55	.80	26–80
25	.15	.95	81–95
30	.05	1.00	96–00

Next, we obtain random numbers from the specified columns of Table 14-1. Using numbers from column 2 for *departments* and numbers from column 4 for *order size*, we have the following:

Order Number	RN	Simulated Department	RN	Simulated Order Size	
1	20	A	29	15	(Using Department A distribution)
2	19	A	64	20	(Using Department A distribution)
3	57	B	35	25	(Using Department B distribution)
4	48	B	09	20	(Using Department B distribution)

Thus, the first random number in column 2 is 20. Referring to the frequency distribution for departments, this corresponds to Department A. Next, the order size is found by selecting the first random number from column 4 and referring to *Department A's* frequency distribution. Hence, the interpretation of the order size random number is dependent on the department, so we must first determine (simulate) the department and then determine (simulate) order size.

Computer Simulation

Up to this point, the emphasis in this chapter has been on manual simulation. The primary reason for this is to focus on understanding the *concepts* of simulation, and a "hands on" approach is usually the best way to accomplish that goal. Nevertheless, most real-life applications of simulation involve the use of computers. In order to get meaningful results, a large number of runs may have to be made. Sometimes, the required number of runs can be very large, say in the hundreds. This alone would be a reason not to use manual simulation. Beyond that, however, is the fact that many applications involve a great deal of complexity because of the need to simulate the interactions of multiple stages and numerous variables. Again, this is a reason to use computer simulation. In the next section, we will utilize Excel to demonstrate how simulations can be conducted using the computer.

Computer Simulation Using Excel

The manual simulation performed in answering Example 14-5 was manageable because there were not many repetitions as there were only four orders. However, if one were to perform the same simulation for 2,000 orders, the task would quickly become unmanageable. In addition, the simulation performed in Example 14-5 was relatively simple. As simulations get more complex, and as the number of runs increases, it becomes necessary to utilize the computer. In addition, in order for the simulation results to be valid and accepted, it is necessary that we perform many (100s or 1,000s) of repetitions. Since spreadsheets have the ability to generate random numbers from various probability distributions, they provide a convenient tool to develop spreadsheet models.

When starting to develop a simulation model, a random number generator can be used to generate random numbers. Excel uses the **RAND**() function to generate **random numbers**.

We can generate random numbers in a cell when we enter the formula =RAND(). In order to demonstrate this, 60 random numbers are generated in Exhibit 14-1. To do this, enter the formula =RAND() in cell A3 and copy this cell using the right mouse button to cells A3 : F12. The 60 random numbers are provided in Exhibit 14-1.

However, if we attempt to duplicate the table given in Exhibit 14-1, a different set of random numbers would be generated. In fact, any changes made to the spreadsheet will result in the recalculation of the random numbers over and over again. Considering the random numbers in Exhibit 14-1, by hitting F9, one can see that all of the 60 random numbers change. Each time F9 is hit, the random number generator generates a different set of random numbers. However, if it is important to maintain the same set of random numbers, we can freeze the random numbers generated by first highlighting the range of cells to freeze, then hitting the **Copy | Paste Special** commands. Clicking on Paste Special brings up another screen with various options. On this screen choosing "Values" and clicking OK in essence

Exhibit 14-1 60 Random Numbers Generated by the RAND() Function

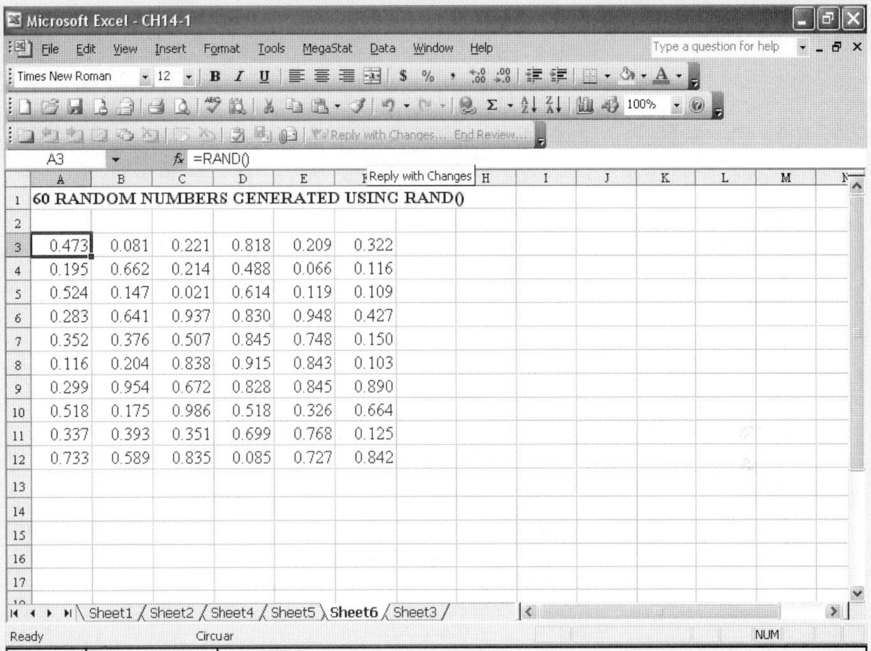
Microsoft Excel - CH14-1

A3 =RAND()

60 RANDOM NUMBERS GENERATED USING RAND()

	A	B	C	D	E	F
3	0.473	0.081	0.221	0.818	0.209	0.322
4	0.195	0.662	0.214	0.488	0.066	0.116
5	0.524	0.147	0.021	0.614	0.119	0.109
6	0.283	0.641	0.937	0.830	0.948	0.427
7	0.352	0.376	0.507	0.845	0.748	0.150
8	0.116	0.204	0.838	0.915	0.843	0.103
9	0.299	0.954	0.672	0.828	0.845	0.890
10	0.518	0.175	0.986	0.518	0.326	0.664
11	0.337	0.393	0.351	0.699	0.768	0.125
12	0.733	0.589	0.835	0.085	0.727	0.842

Cell	Copied to	Formula
A3	A4–F12	= RAND( )

freezes the random numbers already generated in their respective cells. At this point, nothing happens to the random numbers when we hit F9 because they are frozen. Note that in Exhibit 14-1, all of the random numbers are between 0 and 1. Even though it is perfectly okay to utilize random numbers between 0 and 1, if the random numbers need to be converted to values between 0 and 100, simply use the following formula: =100*RAND(). Exhibit 14-2 demonstrates how to generate random numbers between 0 and 100. By entering the formula =100*RAND() in cell A2 and copying this cell using the right mouse button to cells A2 : J21, the 200 random numbers between 0 and 100 in Exhibit 14-2 are generated.

In order for a simulation study to provide valid results, the random numbers generated must be distributed according to the uniform distribution, and the sequence of numbers cannot represent any patterns or trends.

Random Number Generation with Probability Distributions Using Excel

Uniform Distribution There are two types of uniform distributions: continuous and discrete. The formula for a variable distributed according to a continuous uniform distribution is $=c+(d-c)*\text{RAND}()$. According to this formula, the continuous uniform distribution is defined between c and d, where c is the lower limit and d is the upper limit. For example,

Exhibit 14-2	200 Random Numbers Generated Between 0 and 100

Cell	Copied to	Formula
A2	B2–J21 and A3–A21	= 100 * RAND( )

if $c = 20$ and $d = 100$, the formula $=20 + (100 - 20)*RAND()$ will generate random numbers between 20 and 100.

The following built-in formula using Excel's **RANDBETWEEN** function is utilized for the discrete uniform distribution: $=RANDBETWEEN(c,d)$. In other words, if $c = 20$ and $d = 100$, entering the following formula $=RANDBETWEEN(20, 100)$ will generate discrete random numbers between 20 and 100. The outcome associated with generating these random numbers is provided in Exhibit 14-3.

In order to demonstrate that the values in Exhibit 14-3 indeed come from a uniform distribution, we prepare the histogram shown in Exhibit 14-5. In charting this histogram, in Exhibit 14-3 write the values of 30, 40, 50, 60, 70, 80, 90, and 100 in column L labeled "Bin," and then click on **Tools | Data Analysis | Histogram**. The histogram specification screen displayed in Exhibit 14-4 will appear. On this screen, click on the Input Range and highlight all of the 200 values in cells A2 : J21. Then proceed to click on the Bin Range and highlight the values in cells L2 : L9. For example, the value in cell L2 represents all the values that are less than or equal to 30. Cell L3 will include values greater than 30 and less than or equal to 40. In terms of output options, click on "New Worksheet Ply" and "Chart Output" and click OK.

Exhibit 14-3 200 Uniform Discrete Random Numbers Generated Between 20 and 100

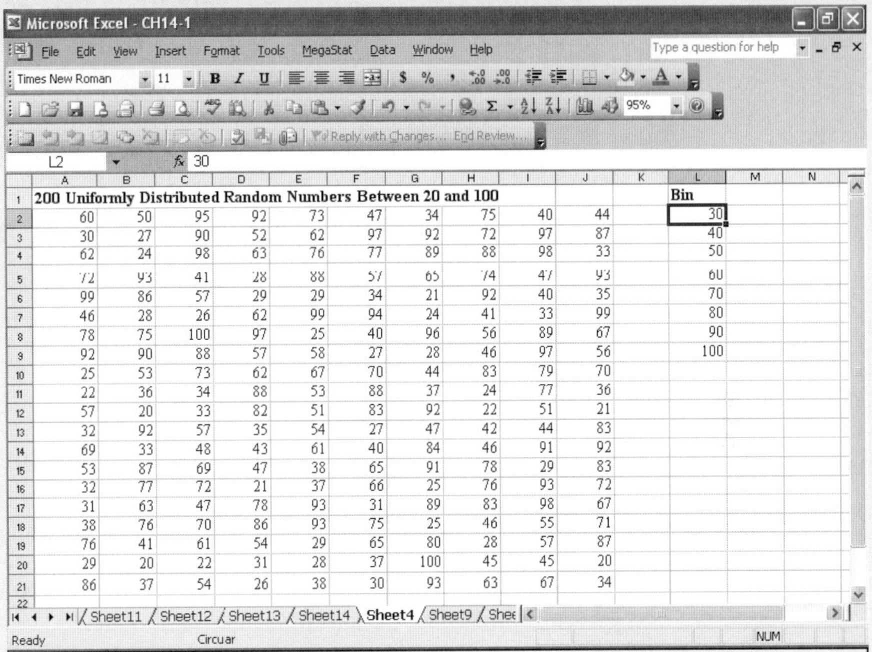

Microsoft Excel - CH14-1

File Edit View Insert Format Tools MegaStat Data Window Help

Times New Roman   11   B I U

L2   30

	A	B	C	D	E	F	G	H	I	J	K	L	M	N
1	200 Uniformly Distributed Random Numbers Between 20 and 100											Bin		
2	60	50	95	92	73	47	34	75	40	44		30		
3	30	27	90	52	62	97	92	72	97	87		40		
4	62	24	98	63	76	77	89	88	98	33		50		
5	72	93	41	28	88	57	65	74	47	93		60		
6	99	86	57	29	29	34	21	92	40	35		70		
7	46	28	26	62	99	94	24	41	33	99		80		
8	78	75	100	97	25	40	96	56	89	67		90		
9	92	90	88	57	58	27	28	46	97	56		100		
10	25	53	73	62	67	70	44	83	79	70				
11	22	36	34	88	53	88	37	24	77	36				
12	57	20	33	82	51	83	92	22	51	21				
13	32	92	57	35	54	27	47	42	44	83				
14	69	33	48	43	61	40	84	46	91	92				
15	53	87	69	47	38	65	91	78	29	83				
16	32	77	72	21	37	66	25	76	93	72				
17	31	63	47	78	93	31	89	83	98	67				
18	38	76	70	86	93	75	25	46	55	71				
19	76	41	61	54	29	65	80	28	57	87				
20	29	20	22	31	28	37	100	45	45	20				
21	86	37	54	26	38	30	93	63	67	34				
22														

Sheet11 Sheet12 Sheet13 Sheet14 Sheet4 Sheet9 Shee

Ready   Circuar   NUM

Cell	Copied to	Formula
A2	B2–J21 and A3–A21	= RANDBETWEEN (20, 100)

Exhibit 14-4 Histogram Specification Screen

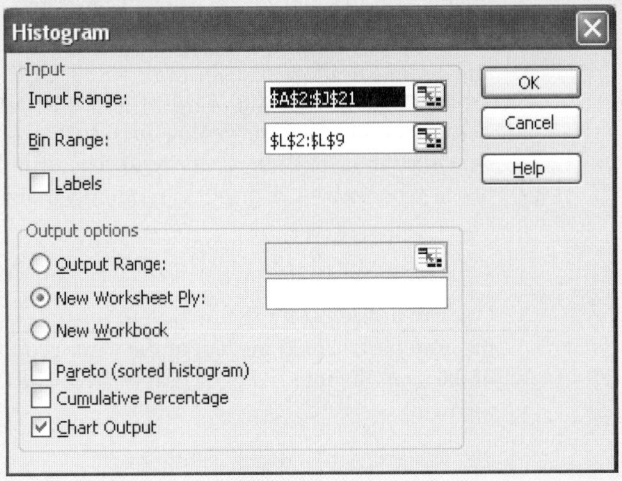

Histogram

Input

Input Range: $A$2:$J$21

Bin Range: $L$2:$L$9

☐ Labels

Output options

○ Output Range:

⦿ New Worksheet Ply:

○ New Workbook

☐ Pareto (sorted histogram)
☐ Cumulative Percentage
☑ Chart Output

OK   Cancel   Help

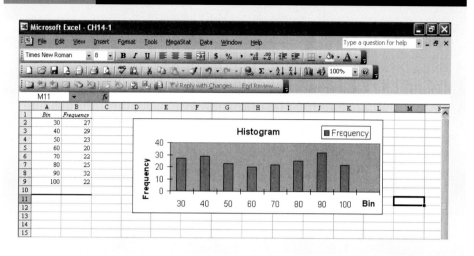

Exhibit 14-5   Histogram of the Values in Exhibit 14-3

Clicking OK will show the worksheet displayed in Exhibit 14-5. The cells A2 : B9 show the frequency table where 30, 40, 50, 60, 70, 80, 90, and 100 serve as the class limits. In this particular problem, 27 (cell B2 in Exhibit 14-5) of the 200 values fall in the range between 20 and 30. The histogram chart shown in Exhibit 14-5 verifies that the numbers in Exhibit 14-3 do come from a uniform distribution because the bars have approximately equal heights. The variation in the frequencies is as a result of random variation in the data. Collecting a larger sample will eliminate the random variation. Histograms also can be graphed to see if other distribution assumptions hold in a simulation study.

Normal Distribution   The normal distribution is frequently used in simulation studies. In order to simulate a normally distributed random variable with two parameters, μ (mean) and σ (standard deviation), Excel's **NORMINV** function is used with the following formula: =NORMINV(RAND(), μ, σ). If $\mu = 100$ and $\sigma = 10$, then =NORMINV(RAND(),100, 10) will generate a normally distributed random variable with a mean of 100 and a standard deviation of 10.

Exponential Distribution   As illustrated in Chapter 13, the exponential distribution is commonly used in analyzing waiting lines. To generate random numbers based on an exponential distribution, one can use the following formula: $= \mu * \mathrm{LN}(\mathrm{Rand}())$, where μ is the mean of the exponentially distributed random variable.

A Discrete Distribution with Two Outcomes

One can utilize Excel's IF function to separate two distinct outcomes. Consider the following example where 35 percent of the items produced need to be heat treated and 65 percent of the items do not need to be heat treated. The IF function can be utilized in one of the two following ways:

IF(RAND() <0.35,"heat treat", "no heat treat")
IF(RAND() <0.65,"no heat treat", "heat treat")

A Discrete Distribution with More Than Two Outcomes

If the number of outcomes is more than two, then a nested IF statement can be utilized. However, setting up IF statements when there are more than two outcomes is much more complicated. In this case, instead of using IF statements, we should utilize the VLOOKUP function.

Example 14-7

The number of cars arriving at Andersen Quick Oil and Lube during the last 200 hours of operations, which uses a single waiting line, is observed to be the following:

Number of Cars Arriving	Frequency
3 or less	0
4	10
5	30
6	70
7	50
8	40
9 or more	0

Estimated revenue for car arrivals is given in the following table:

Number of Cars Arriving	Revenue
3 or less	0
4	100
5	125
6	150
7	175
8	200
9 or more	0

a. Determine the probability distribution of car arrivals.
b. Use Excel and simulate 10 hours of car arrivals and compute the average number of arrivals per hour.
c. Based on the simulated 10 hours of car arrivals, determine the estimated average revenue for the Andersen Quick Oil and Lube.

The information given in Example 14-7 is repeated in the top portion of Exhibit 14-6. The bottom portion of Exhibit 14-6 provides the simulation of 10 hours of car arrivals. In cells B10 through B19, random numbers are generated, using the RAND() command. To control the random numbers generated, one can have the random numbers generated manually. To generate the numbers manually, choose **Tools | Options | Calculation** and click on Manual rather than Automated. Remember, to regenerate the random numbers, one must now hit F9. If the calculation option is left on automated, then it will recalculate a new set of random numbers any time a change is made to the worksheet. Using these random numbers, utilize the **VLOOKUP** command in cells C10 through C19 to determine the number of cars arriving. To generate the number of arrivals in cells C10 through C19, do the following: First indicate the cumulative probabilities and the associated number of arrivals in cells E3 through F7. In creating the VLOOKUP formula, first state the cell where the number of arrivals will be specified, then

Exhibit 14-6   Excel Worksheet and the Results Associated with the Andersen Quick Oil and Lube Example

	A	B	C	D	E	F	G	H	I	J
1	Number of Cars Arriving	Frequency (X)	Random Number (RN) for Arrivals	P(X)	Cumulative Probability	Number of Cars Arriving	Revenue			
2	3 or less	0	None	0	0	3 or less	0			
3	4	30	01 to 15	0.15	0	4	100			
4	5	40	15 to 35	0.2	0.15	5	125			
5	6	50	35 to 60	0.25	0.35	6	150			
6	7	40	61 to 80	0.2	0.6	7	175			
7	8	40	81 to 00	0.2	0.8	8	200			
8	9 or more	0	None	0		9 or more	0			
9	Simulation	RN	Number of Arrivals	Revenue						
10	Week 1	0.703	7	175						
11	Week 2	0.994	8	200						
12	Week 3	0.544	6	150						
13	Week 4	0.917	8	200						
14	Week 5	0.735	7	175						
15	Week 6	0.116	4	100						
16	Week 7	0.490	6	150						
17	Week 8	0.026	4	100						
18	Week 9	0.453	6	150						
19	Week 10	0.883	8	200						
20	Averages		6.4	160						

Cell	Copied to	Formula
D2	D3 : D8	= B2 / SUM ($B$2 : $B$8)
E2		= D2
E3	E4 : E7	= D2 + E2
B10	B11 : B19	= RAND( )
C10	C11 : C19	= VLOOKUP (B10, $E$3 : $F$7, 2)
D10	D11 : D19	= VLOOKUP (B10, $E$3 : $G$7, 3)
C20		= AVERAGE (C10 : C19)
D20		= AVERAGE (D10 : D19)

specify the range of columns used to look up the particular value of arrivals ($E$3 : $F$7). In this range, column E contains the cumulative probabilities (input column) and column F contains the number of arrivals (output column). The final statement can be stated as follows: =VLOOKUP(B10, $E$3 : $F$7, 2). In this statement, the probability value in cell B10 will be compared against the cumulative probabilities in cell E3 through E7. The output value in the second column, specified as 2, will indicate the number of arrivals in the first hour. Since the first random number in cell B10 is .703, which is less than .8 in the cumulative probability column, 7 car arrivals are chosen by the VLOOKUP function. Once all of the car arrivals in cells B10 : B19 are determined, we utilize the VLOOKUP function once again to determine the revenue associated with the number of arrivals. Again in this new VLOOKUP statement, the random number value in cell B10 will be compared against the cumulative probabilities in cell E3 through E7. However, instead of the output values being the number of car arrivals, the output value is the estimated revenue based on arrivals. Therefore in cells D10 : D19, the revenue based on the number of car arrivals has been estimated. The statement is as follows: =VLOOKUP(B10, $E$3 : $G$7, 3). Note that compared to the VLOOKUP statement written for cells C10 : C19, this statement has two major differences:

1. The range of values specified is $E$3 : $G$7, and not $E$3 : $F$7. In other words, the additional cells G3 through G7 are specified.
2. The last observation in the statement is a value 3 instead of 2. This indicates that the output column is the third column (column G), consisting of the revenue values, instead of the second column (number of car arrivals) specified in the range of columns.

The first random number in cell B10 is .703, which is less than .8 in the cumulative probability column. Therefore, based on 7 car arrivals, a revenue value of $175 is chosen by the VLOOKUP function.

According to the results provided in Exhibit 14-6, the average number of arrivals per hour is 6.4 and the estimated average revenue is $160. In order for the simulation to provide valid and reliable results, this simulation study needs to include a very large number of hours.

Simulation of Waiting Lines

Waiting lines are covered extensively in Chapter 13. In this section of the chapter, a simulation model of a waiting-line model with a single server will be built. In order to illustrate the simulation of waiting lines, consider the following example.

Example 14-8

George Nanchoff owns a gas station. The cars arrive at the gas station according to the following interarrival-time distribution. The time to service a car is given by the following service-time distribution. Simulate the arrival and service times of 11 cars at the gas station. Estimate the average customer waiting time, average server idle time, and average time a car spends in the system.

Interarrival Time (Minutes)	$P(X)$	Service Time (Minutes)	$P(X)$
4	.35	2	.30
7	.25	4	.40
10	.30	6	.20
20	.10	8	.10

Exhibit 14-7 demonstrates how a discrete event simulation for the waiting-line problem described in Example 14-8 can be shown. The top part of Exhibit 14-7

Exhibit 14-7 The Excel Worksheet for the Simulation of the Gas Station Waiting-Line Problem

Microsoft Excel - chap14

F19 =AVERAGE(F8:F18)

	A	B	C	D	E	F	G	H	I	J
1		P(X)	Cumulative Probability	Interarrival Time	RN for Arrivals	P(X)	Cumulative Probability	Service Time	RN for Service	
2		0.2	0	1	01 to 20	0.2	0	2	01 to 20	
3		0.25	0.2	4	21 to 45	0.3	0.2	4	21 to 50	
4		0.3	0.45	7	46 to 75	0.15	0.35	6	51 to 65	
5		0.1	0.75	10	76 to 85	0.2	0.55	8	66 to 85	
6		0.15	0.85	13	86 to 00	0.15	0.7	10	86 to 00	
7	Person	RN 1	Arrival Time	Cumulative arrival time	Entering Time	Waiting Time	RN 2	Service Time	Departure Time	Time in the System
8	1	0.451	7	7	7	0	0.358	6	13	6
9	2	0.285	4	11	13	2	0.634	8	21	10
10	3	0.513	7	18	21	3	0.959	10	31	13
11	4	0.197	1	19	31	12	0.119	2	33	14
12	5	0.365	4	23	33	10	0.256	4	37	14
13	6	0.389	4	27	37	10	0.267	4	41	14
14	7	0.663	7	34	41	7	0.122	2	43	9
15	8	0.72	7	41	43	2	0.024	2	45	4
16	9	0.689	7	48	48	0	0.562	8	56	8
17	10	0.953	13	61	61	0	0.577	8	69	8
18	11	0.594	7	68	69	1	0.627	8	77	9
19					Averages	4.273		5.636		9.909

Sheet1 Sheet2 Sheet3

Ready Circuar NUM

Cell	Copied to	Formula
C2		= 0
C3	C4 : C6	= B2 + C2
G2		= 0
G3	G4 : G6	= F2 + G2
B8	B9 : B18	= RAND( )
C8	C9 : C18	= VLOOKUP (B8, $C$2 : $D$6, 2)
D9	D10 : D18	= C 9 + D8
E8		= D8
E9	E10 : E18	= MAX (D9, I8)
F8	F9 : F18	= E8 − D8
G8	G9 : G18	= RAND( )
H8	H9 : H18	= VLOOKUP (G8, $G$2, $H$6, 2)
I9	I10 : I18	= E9 + H9
J8	J9 : J18	= I8 − D8
F19	H19, J19	= AVERAGE (F8 : F18)

repeats the input information given in Example 14-8, while the bottom part of Exhibit 14-7 shows the simulation of the waiting line at the gas station. Cells A8 through D18 show the simulation of the arrivals at the gas station. Cells A8 through A18 indicate the number of people served, while cells B8 through B18 indicate the value of the random number generated using the RAND() command. Based on the random number values in cells B8 : B18, use the =VLOOKUP(B8, $C$2 : $D$6, 2) command. This command uses the random number value in cell B8 and looks up the value of the arrival time based on the random number in cell B8 and the cumulative probability values of interarrival times in cells C2 through C6. It assigns an interarrival time based on the cumulative probability distribution of interarrival times. For example, the value in cell B8 is .451; therefore, from the cumulative probability distribution, this value is greater than the cutoff value for the class whose cumulative probability values start with .45. This corresponds to an interarrival time of 7 minutes. The value in cell B9 is .285; since the cumulative probability distribution value is greater than the cutoff value of .20, the resulting interarrival time is 4 minutes. The arrival of the first person took place in 7 minutes, and the interarrival time for the second person is 4 minutes. The arrival time of each person is shown in cells D8 : D18. For example, since the first person arrived 7 minutes after the store opened up, the second person's arrival time is given in cell D9. The arrival time of the second customer is calculated by the formula =C9 + D8. In other words, the arrival time of the second customer is going to take place 4 minutes after the arrival of the first customer. Since the first customer arrived on the seventh minute and the second customer arrives 4 minutes after the arrival of the first customer, the second customer arrives 11 (7 + 4) minutes after the store opens up.

The columns E through J demonstrate the simulation of service based on the arrivals and the associated arrival times. For example, column E determines when the customer actually enters the system to be served. In order to determine the values in column E, we need to determine the service time. The service time is determined based on the generation of random numbers using the RAND() function in cells G8 : G18. In cells H8 : H18, the following VLOOKUP function is utilized: =VLOOKUP(G8,$G$2 : $H$6,2). This command looks up the value of the service time based on the random number in cell G8 and the cumulative probability values for service in cells G2 through G6. Then, it assigns a service time based on the cumulative probability distribution of service times. For example, the value in cell G8 is .358; therefore, from the cumulative probability distribution, this value is greater than the cutoff value for the class whose cumulative probability values are greater than or equal to .35, but less than the cumulative probability of .55. Since .358 falls between .35 and .55, the service time for the first customer is 6 minutes. Since the VLOOKUP function designates H2 : H6 as the output column values, the remainder of the service times are looked up from the values shown in cells H2 : H6. The departure times in cells I8 : I18 are calculated by adding the service times determined in cells H8 : H18 to the entering time given in cells E8 : E18. The entry time for the first customer is simply the cumulative arrival time given in cell D8. Thus, the formula for cell E8 is =D8. The departure time of the first customer in cell I8 is simply the sum of the arrival time for the first customer in cell E8 and the service time of the first customer in cell H8. Thus, the formula for the departure time of the first customer in cell I8 is =E8 + H8, or 7 + 6 = 13. The acceptance of the arrival of the second customer is the maximum value of the arrival time of the second customer and the departure time of the first customer.

In other words, the value of cell E9 is given by the following formula: =MAX(D9, I8). Since the value of cell D9 is 11 and the value of cell I8 is 13, 13 is chosen as the time of entry into the service system. The second customer's waiting time is 2 minutes before the service begins. In other words, the waiting-time values in cells F8 : F18 are calculated by taking the difference between the entering time in cells E8 : E18 and the arrival time in cells D8 : D18. For example, the formula for cell F8 is =E8 − D8. For the second customer, since the value of cell E9 is 13 and the value of cell D9 is 11, the waiting-time value of cell F9 is equal to 2. In other words, the second customer had to wait for two minutes. However, let's consider customer zero. Likewise, the third customer arrives on 18th minute and is not served until the 21st minute; thus, this customer had to wait for 3 minutes. In other words, E10 − D10 = 21 − 18 = 3. The time spent by a customer in the system is the sum of the waiting time and the service time. This value can be calculated in several different ways. The first way is to add the waiting time and the service time. For instance, observing customer three, since the waiting time is 3 and the service time is 10, this customer spends 13 minutes in the system. However, alternatively, the time in the system also can be calculated by subtracting the cumulative arrival time from the departure time. If we use the first option, the formula for cell J10 is =F10 + H10, or 3 + 10 = 13. If we use the second option, the formula for cell J10 is I10 − D10, or 31 − 18 = 13.

Row 19 depicts basic statistics about the gas station. On average customers wait 4.273 minutes, and the average time it takes to serve a customer is 5.636 minutes. A customer (or a car) takes about 9.909 minutes (4.273 + 5.636) in the system, which includes waiting as well as service times. Again, in order for the simulation to provide valid and reliable results, this simulation study needs to include a very large number of repetitions or a large number of customers.

Inventory Analysis Using Simulation and Excel

When studying inventory management, an analyst is concerned with answering two questions, (1) when to reorder and (2) how much to order. However, in traditional inventory analysis, most of the time, it is assumed that the models are deterministic. In other words, assume that demand is known with certainty and the lead time (time between placing an order and receiving that order) is fixed and known. In some circumstances, it is assumed that the demand and lead time are not known with certainty, but the demand distribution can be defined by a theoretical probability distribution. If there is no theoretical distribution (i.e., normal) that can be used to define the probability distribution of demand or lead time, simulation can be used. Even if the demand can be defined based on a theoretical probability distribution, the analysis can be very complicated and the analyst may choose to utilize simulation. The following example is used to illustrate a problem where demand is a random variable defined by the empirical probability distribution and the lead time is also a random variable defined by a discrete uniform distribution.

Example 14-9

Golden Eagle Plumbing Company installs plumbing for new constructions and existing buildings. Over the past 400 days, the company has observed the following demand pattern for the PVC Couplings.

Daily Demand for PVC Couplings	Frequency	Probability
0	20	20/400 = .05
1	50	50/400 = .125
3	80	80/400 = .20
5	100	100/400 = .25
7	60	60/400 = .15
9	60	60/400 = .15
11	30	30/400 = .075
Totals	400	1.0

In addition, the company also observed that the lead time is distributed according to the uniform distribution, where the maximum lead time is 3 days and the minimum lead time is 1 day. The management of Golden Eagle Plumbing Company wants to identify the reorder point (ROP) and the fixed order quantity (Q) that will result in low monthly total cost.

The total cost has three components:

1. Cost of carrying inventory ($.50 per unit per day).
2. Cost of stockout ($15 per unit).
3. Cost of ordering ($25 per order).

Currently the company has 6 units of PVC couplings in its inventory. In order to get a feel for which combination of reorder point and order quantity will result in a lower cost, we simply try different combinations of order quantity and reorder points. Exhibit 14-8 illustrates the Excel worksheet that employs an order quantity of 12 and reorder point of 5 units. Exhibit 14-9 demonstrates the Excel worksheet with an order quantity of 10 and reorder point of 7 units.

The Excel worksheet in Exhibit 14-8 shows the layout for the Golden Eagle Plumbing Company inventory problem. The demand distribution is given in cells A3 : C9. Other relevant information includes order quantity (cell H1), reorder point (cell H2), carrying cost per unit per year (cell H3), ordering cost (cell H4), and shortage cost per unit (cell H5). Hence, as can be observed form Exhibit 14-8, all input parameters of this model (order quantity, reorder point, carrying cost per unit per year, etc.) are stated in separate cells. All of the formulas in this simulation model utilize these cell references rather than the values associated with these parameters. To perform what-if analysis by changing the values of some of the parameters, we don't need to change the equations that involve those parameters; instead, just change the cell references stated in cells H1 : H5.

In the bottom portion of Exhibit 14-8, we perform the simulation for the inventory example involving Golden Eagle Plumbing Company. Column A indicates the number for the day simulated. Column B shows the beginning inventory. In other words, the beginning inventory is the inventory at the beginning of the day. On day 1, the beginning inventory value is given. For the rest of the days, the beginning inventory is equal to the ending inventory from the day before. For example, the beginning inventory in day 2 is the ending inventory of day 1. Therefore, if the ending inventory of day 1 is 1 unit (cell J11), then the beginning inventory of day 2 is 1 unit. The equation for the beginning inventory in day 2 in cell B12 is =J11. Column C (C11 : C25), column D (D11 : D25), and column E (E11 : E25) are dedicated to the units received Column C is used if the lead time is one day. Column D is used if the lead time is two days. Column E is

Exhibit 14-8   Excel Worksheet and the Results for the Golden Eagle Plumbing Company Inventory Problem Where Quantity = 12, ROP = 5

Microsoft Excel - chap14

H3   fx 0.5

	A	B	C	D	E	F	G	H	I	J	K	L	M	N	O	P
1	Distribution of demand.					Quantity		12.000						Carrying Cost	60.00	
2	Prob.	Cum. Probability	Demand			Reorder Point		5.000						Shortage Cost	210.00	
3	0.050	0.000	0.000			CarryingCost		0.500 per unit/day						Order Cost	175.00	
4	0.125	0.050	1.000			Ordering Cost =		25.000								
5	0.200	0.175	3.000			Shortage Cost -		15.000								
6	0.250	0.375	5.000			Lead Time =		Uniform between 1 and 3 days								
7	0.150	0.625	7.000			F9 to recalulate										
8	0.150	0.775	9.000													
9	0.075	0.925	11.000													
10	Day	Beginning Inventory	Units Rec. 1 day	Units Rec. 2 days	Units Rec. 3 days	Available Units	Demand	Demand Satisfied	Lost Sales	Ending Inventory	Order Placed	Lead Time	Carrying Cost	Shortage Cost	Order Cost	Total Cost
11	1	6	0	0	0	6	7	6	1	0	12	1.0	0.00	15.00	25.00	40.00
12	2	0	12	0	0	12	7	7	0	5	12	3.0	2.50	0.00	25.00	27.50
13	3	5	0	0	0	5	3	3	0	2	12	2.0	1.00	0.00	25.00	26.00
14	4	2	0	0	0	2	7	2	5	0	12	3.0	0.00	75.00	25.00	100.00
15	5	0	0	12	12	24	5	5	0	19	0	0.0	9.50	0.00	0.00	9.50
16	6	19	0	0	0	19	11	11	0	8	0	0.0	4.00	0.00	0.00	4.00
17	7	8	0	0	12	20	0	0	0	20	0	0.0	10.00	0.00	0.00	10.00
18	8	20	0	0	0	20	7	7	0	13	0	0.0	6.50	0.00	0.00	6.50
19	9	13	0	0	0	13	3	3	0	10	0	0.0	5.00	0.00	0.00	5.00
20	10	10	0	0	0	10	5	5	0	5	12	1.0	2.50	0.00	25.00	27.50
21	11	5	12	0	0	17	7	7	0	10	0	0.0	5.00	0.00	0.00	5.00
22	12	10	0	0	0	10	7	7	0	3	12	2.0	1.50	0.00	25.00	26.50
23	13	3	0	0	0	3	11	3	8	0	12	1.0	0.00	120.00	25.00	145.00
24	14	0	12	12	0	24	7	7	0	17	0	0.0	8.50	0.00	0.00	8.50
25	15	17	0	0	0	17	9	9	0	8	0	0.0	4.00	0.00	0.00	4.00
26														Total Cost =		445.00

Cell	Copied to	Formula
B3	—	= 0
B4	B5 : B9	= A3 + B3
B12	B13 : B25	= J11
C11	—	= 0
C12	C13 : C25	= IF (L11 = 1, K11, 0)
D13	D14 : D25	= IF (L11 = 2, K11, 0)
E14	E15 : E25	= IF (L11 = 3, K11, 0)
F11	F12 : F25	= SUM (B11 : E11)
G11	G12 : G25	= VLOOKUP (RAND ( ), $B$3 : $C$9, 2)
H11	H12 : H25	= MIN (F11, G11)
I11	I12 : I25	= MAX (G11 − F11, 0)
J11	J12 : J25	= MAX (F11 − G11, 0)
K11	K12 : K25	= If (T11 <= $H$2, $H$1, 0)

Exhibit 14-9 Excel Worksheet and the Results for the Golden Eagle Plumbing Company Inventory Problem Where Quantity = 10, ROP = 7

Microsoft Excel - chap14

File   Edit   View   Insert   Format   Tools   MegaStat   Data   Window   Help   Type a question for help

Quantity	10.000	Carrying Cost 54.50
Reorder Point	7.000	Shortage Cost 90.00
CarryingCost	0.500 per unit/day	Order Cost 225.00
Ordering Cost =	25.000	
Shortage Cost =	15.000	
Lead Time =	Uniform between 1 and 3 days	
F9 to recalculate		

Distribution of demand.

Prob.	Cum. Probability	Demand
0.050	0.000	0.000
0.125	0.050	1.000
0.200	0.175	3.000
0.250	0.375	5.000
0.150	0.625	7.000
0.150	0.775	9.000
0.075	0.925	11.000

Day	Beginning Inventory	Units Rec. 1 day	Units Rec. 2 days	Units Rec. 3 days	Available Units	Demand	Demand Satisfied	Lost Sales	Ending Inventory	Order Placed	Lead Time	Carrying Cost	Shortage Cost	Order Cost	Total Cost
1	6	0	0	0	6	1	1	0	5	10	3.0	2.50	0.00	25.00	27.50
2	5	0	0	0	5	7	5	2	0	10	1.0	0.00	30.00	25.00	55.00
3	0	10	0	0	10	7	7	0	3	10	1.0	1.50	0.00	25.00	26.50
4	3	10	0	10	23	7	7	0	16	0	0.0	8.00	0.00	0.00	8.00
5	16	0	0	0	16	3	3	0	13	0	0.0	6.50	0.00	0.00	6.50
6	13	0	0	0	13	9	9	0	4	10	2.0	2.00	0.00	25.00	27.00
7	4	0	0	0	4	0	0	0	4	10	1.0	2.00	0.00	25.00	27.00
8	4	0	10	0	24	5	5	0	19	0	0.0	9.50	0.00	0.00	9.50
9	19	0	0	0	19	3	3	0	16	0	0.0	8.00	0.00	0.00	8.00
10	16	0	0	0	16	3	3	0	13	0	0.0	6.50	0.00	0.00	6.50
11	13	0	0	0	13	5	5	0	8	0	0.0	4.00	0.00	0.00	4.00
12	8	0	0	0	8	7	7	0	1	10	2.0	0.50	0.00	25.00	25.50
13	1	0	0	0	1	1	1	0	0	10	3.0	0.00	0.00	25.00	25.00
14	0	0	10	0	10	3	3	0	7	10	3.0	3.50	0.00	25.00	28.50
15	7	0	0	0	7	11	7	4	0	10	2.0	0.00	60.00	25.00	85.00
												Total Cost =			369.50

Cell	Copied to	Formula
L11	L12 : L25	= IF (K11 > 0, RANDBETWEEN (1, 3), 0)
M11	M12 : M25	= $H$3 * J11
N11	N12 : N25	= $H$5 * I11
O11	O12 : O25	= IF (K11 > 0, $H$4, 0)
P11	P12 : P25	= SUM (M11 : O11)
P26	—	= SUM (P11 : P25)
O1	—	= SUM (M11 : M25)
O2	—	= SUM (N11 : N25)
O3	—	= SUM (O11 : O25)

used if the lead time is three days. The lead time distribution specified in column L (L11 : L25) is as follows: =IF(K11 > 0, RANDBETWEEN(1, 3), 0). In other words, if there is an order (an order quantity value appears in column K), then use the discrete uniform distribution via the RANDBETWEEN command to generate lead time values between one day and three days. However, if the order is not present, then we simply use a lead time of 0 days. In cells C12 : C25, if the lead time is one day, then an order quantity was received from the previous day. Therefore, the formula for cell C12 is =IF(L11 = 1, K11, 0): If the lead time is one day, choose the quantity specified in cell K11. Cells K11 : K25 represent the values of order quantities. However, if the lead time is not one or two or three, then no orders are received in column C. Similarly, cells D13 : D25, involve receiving orders when the lead time is two days. In cells D13 : D25, receive an order quantity from two days ago. Therefore, the formula for cell D13 is =IF(L11 = 2, K11, 0): If the lead time is two days, choose the quantity specified in K11. However, if the lead time is not two, simply do not receive any orders in column D. Repeat a similar procedure for cells E14 : E25, where these cells are dedicated to receiving orders with a lead time of three days. Therefore, the formula for cell E14 is =IF(L11=3, K11, 0): If the lead time is three days, choose the quantity specified in K11. However, if the lead time is not three, do not receive any orders in column E. The values in cells F11 : F25 represent the available units. The calculation of the available units is relatively easy. It involves the summation of the beginning inventory and three possible receipts: the first one a for lead time of one day, the second one for a lead time of two days, and the third one for a lead time of three days. For example, we can calculate the available units on day seven in Exhibit 14-8 as follows: =SUM(B17 : E17). Since the beginning inventory in day seven is eight units and three-day lead time receipt is 12 units, the available units for day seven are calculated as follows: $8 + 0 + 0 + 12 = 20$.

Column G shows the demand for each day. The demand values are generated from a general discrete probability distribution specified in cells A3 through C9. A3 : A9 indicate the probability of various demand values. B3 : B9 display the cumulative probabilities, and C3 : C9 show the demand values. The values in cells G11 through G25 are generated using a VLOOKUP function. This function for cell G11 is as follows: =VLOOKUP(RAND(), $B$3 : $C$9 ,2). Based on the random number generated and the cumulative probabilities given in cells B3 : B9, demand values in cells G11 : G25 are generated. After determining the demand value, the next task is to determine if demand specified in cells G11 : G25 are satisfied. In order to determine if the demand is satisfied, compare the value of demand against the value of the available units calculated in cells F11 : F25. The minimum of these two values is the amount of demand satisfied. Therefore, the formula for demand satisfied in cell H11 is =MIN(F11, G11). Since the value of available inventory in cell F11 is 6 and the value of demand in cell G11 is 7, the minimum of these values is 6; therefore, six units of demand are satisfied and one unit of demand is shown as a lost sale. In cases where the value of demand is greater than the value of available units, the company experiences lost sales. The lost sales are shown in cells I11 : I25. The formula for lost sales in cell I11 is given by =MAX(G11 − F11, 0). In other words, the company experiences lost sales equal to the difference between demand and available units when the demand is greater than the available units. However, if the demand is less than or equal to the available units, the company does not experience any lost sales, based on the 0 at the end of the MAX statement. Finally, calculate the ending inventory value in cell J11 and copy it to cells J12 : J25 as follows: =MAX(F11 − G11 ,0). In determining the ending inventory value, take the difference between the available units and the demand. If the difference is negative, choose 0 (the last value in the MAX statement) as the ending inventory value. This is because when the available units are less than demand, the company actually experiences lost sales.

The formulas for the cost calculations as well as the lead time also are given at the bottom of Exhibit 14-8. The inventory carrying cost is calculated in cells M11 : M25 by multiplying the inventory carrying cost per unit specified in cell H3 by the value of ending inventory in cells J11 : J25. The carrying cost formula for the first day in cell M11 is =$H$3 * J11. In this formula, use absolute references for carrying cost per unit per day so that the formula can be copied to cells M12 : M25. The shortage cost values are displayed in cells N11 : N25. These values are calculated by multiplying the per-unit shortage cost with the lost sales values for each day. The shortage cost formula for cell N11 is =$H$5 * I11. Note that cells I11 : I25 contain the number of units of lost sales and H5 is the shortage cost per unit. Again, the absolute reference values are used to enable us to copy the formula to other cells. Cells O11 : O25 display the order cost values. The order cost is a fixed cost; however, it only occurs if there is an order placed during that period. Therefore, at the bottom of Exhibit 14-9, the order cost is stated as the following IF statement for cell O11: =IF(K11 > 0, $H$4, 0). This IF statement results in the order cost only if an order is placed during that period (K11 > 0). Otherwise, the order cost is zero, as specified by the 0 at the end of the IF statement.

The total carrying costs, total order costs, and total shortage costs are given in cells O1, O2, and O3, respectively, as SUM functions. Overall total cost is also given in cell P26 as a SUM function. The formulas for these cells are presented at the bottom of Exhibit 14-9.

Exhibit 14-9 demonstrates a different order quantity (10 instead of 12) and different reorder point (7 instead of 5). Observe the differences in various cost values. However, one may also want to try different shortage, carrying, and ordering cost values to see how sensitive the solution is to the changes in various cost values.

We can try different combinations of order quantities and reorder points to determine which combination of order quantity and reorder point provides the lowest cost. However, due to space restrictions in Exhibits 14-8 and 14-9, only 15 days are simulated. In order to get a much better feel for the problem, it is very important to simulate many more days. For example, simulation of 360 days would give more validity and confidence regarding the results, in comparison to simulating only 15 days. Nevertheless, based on 15 days of simulation using an order quantity of 12 and a reorder point of 5 resulted in a total cost of $445, while the order quantity of 10 and a reorder point of 7 resulted in a total cost of $369.50. (See cell P26 in Exhibits 14-8 and 14-9). Therefore, based on the limited information, an order quantity of 10 and a reorder point of 7 is preferred to an order quantity of 12 with a reorder points of 5. The question still remains as to what the best combination of order quantity and reorder point is. In order to answer this question, many more combinations of order quantity and reorder point must be attempted, and many more days of simulation should be used.

Scenario Manager

Scenario manager can be used with any spreadsheet model to compare the affect of several different combinations of parameters (scenarios) on results. The analyst can select from the menu Tools/Scenarios/Add to define scenarios. For instance, refer to example 14-9.

We choose cell H1 (order quantity) and cell H2 (reorder point) as scenarios in the "changing cells" box, then we choose the appropriate names: order quantity and reorder point for cell H1 and H2 respectively. Exhibit 14-10 provides the dialog box that shows the specification of scenarios. In this exhibit, we only show the specification of H2 (reorder point), but preparation of the scenario dialog box for order quantity (Q) is done in a very similar way.

Since we are trying to estimate the most appropriate values of quantity and reorder point, we can try various values of Q and ROP and chose the values of ROP and Q that gives

Exhibit 14-10 — Add Scenario Dialog Box

the smallest total cost (sum of the costs in cells O1, O2 and O3). Scenario Manager provides a convenient way for Excel to try different values of input parameters. For example, we can try Q = 11 and ROP = 6 in the Scenario Values screen shown in Exhibit 14-11. In order for both of the parameters to be considered simultaneously, we need to specify multiple cells (H1 and H2) in the Add Scenario "Changing Cells" box. Finally, from the scenario dialog box, we click on "Summary," and then we indicate the cells that contain Q and ROP (input parameter cells of H1 and H2) and specify the cells that contain the costs as output in cell O1 (carrying cost), cell O2 (shortage cost), and cell O3 (order cost) and click OK. The model will run the simulation and generate the summary table shown in Exhibit 14-12. This summary

Exhibit 14-11 — Scenario Values

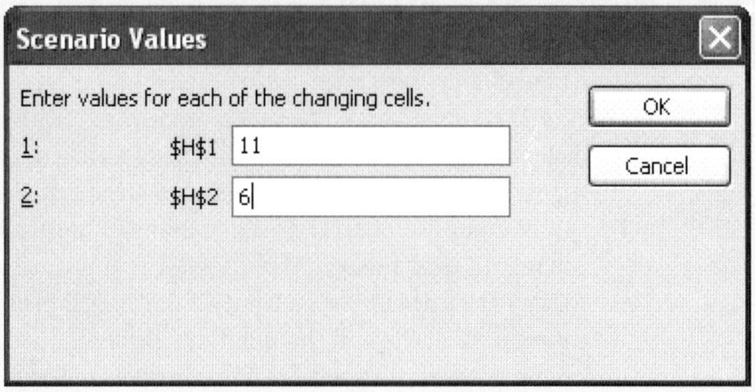

Exhibit 14-12   Scenario Summary Table

	B	C	D	E	F	G
2	Scenario Summary					
3			Current Values:	Q	ROP	
5	Changing Cells:					
6		$H$1	12.000	11.000	12.000	
7		$H$2	5.000	5.000	6.000	
8	Result Cells:					
9		$O$1	92.00	92.50	92.50	
10		$O$2	75.00	210.00	210.00	
11		$O$3	150.00	175.00	175.00	
12	Notes: Current Values column represents values of changing cells at					
13	time Scenario Summary Report was created. Changing cells for each					
14	scenario are highlighted in gray.					

sheet provides a simple way to easily compare different scenarios with different values given to input parameters.

Simulation Languages

Over the years, a number of simulation languages have been developed that make the task of writing simulation programs much more straightforward than working with a standard programming language such as FORTRAN or C++. Some of the most widely used of these specialty languages are SIMSCRIPT II.5, GPSS/H, GASP, SLAM II, and DYNAMO. In addition, there are a number of other simulation languages such as ARENA Extend, Micro Saint, Build Sim, and ProModel, some of which are particularly suited to a narrow application such as simulation of queuing systems or networks.

Most of the simulation packages have certain features in common. In general, they provide for random number generation from different statistical distributions, collection and tabulation of simulation results, time keeping, and printouts of results.

Some managers prefer to write their own simulations, or have their staff do so, using one of the standard programming languages such as FORTRAN, Pascal, or C++ rather than a simulation language. In cases where simulation is used infrequently, this approach may be practical; it may not be worth the time and effort to learn how to use a special simulation language. Conversely, if simulation is used fairly regularly to analyze problems, use of a simulation language is the expedient choice.

Pseudo-Random Numbers

Although computers could be programmed to read random numbers from a table of numbers that has been put into memory, such an approach would not be an efficient use of computer storage. Instead, computer codes usually incorporate a random number generator based on an algorithm that produces a string of digits that exhibit the characteristics of randomness. The resulting numbers, for all practical purposes, can be regarded as random numbers. However, they are referred to as **pseudo-random numbers** because the "next" number at any point in the series can be determined by using the same algorithm used by the computer. In that sense, the numbers are not truly random. Nevertheless, this condition does not impair the usefulness of computer-generated random numbers.

Advantages and Limitations of Simulation

Simulation has proven to be a valuable tool for exploring complex problems. Among the major advantages of simulation are the following:

1. It is particularly well-suited for problems that are difficult or impossible to solve mathematically.
2. It allows an analyst or decision maker to experiment with system behavior in a controlled environment instead of in a real-life setting that has inherent risks.
3. It enables a decision maker to compress time in order to evaluate the long-term effects of various alternatives.
4. It can serve as a mode for training decision makers by enabling them to observe the behavior of a system under different conditions.

Despite the obvious benefits of simulation, decision makers must exercise a certain amount of care in deciding when to use a simulation approach. The reasons for this are varied. Among the main reasons are the following:

1. Probabilistic simulation results are *approximations*, rather than optimal solutions.
2. Good simulations can be costly and time-consuming to develop properly; they also can be time-consuming to run, especially in cases in which a large number of trials are indicated.
3. A certain amount of expertise is required in order to design a good simulation, and this may not be readily available.
4. Analytical techniques may be available that can provide better answers to problems.

When to Use Simulation

Because of the time, effort, and cost associated with simulation studies, and because probabilistic simulations only provide approximate answers to "What if . . .?" questions, simulation is generally not the first choice of a decision maker who is faced with a problem. Instead, other approaches must first be examined; simulation may be used if other approaches are deemed inappropriate. In most instances, an intuitive solution to a problem based on judgment and experience should be considered. If that does not provide a satisfactory solution, suitable analytical techniques should be considered. If none are suitable, simulation may be a reasonable alternative. The decision maker must still weigh the costs and

Modern Management Science Application: *Scheduling the Edmonton Folk Festival*

Edmonton Folk Festival is a four day event, where over 15,000 people attend the various functions of the event. Approximately 1800 volunteers make the Edmonton Folk Festival successful, working over 50,000 hours. In return for their services these volunteers receive free admission, T-shirts, and meals. Edmonton has a population of over 670,000 people and the city is known as "City of Festivals" because it hosts four festivals and a major sporting event over the summer months. Therefore the competition for attracting volunteers is severe.

In past years, the coordinators served as manual schedulers for all volunteers based on given constraints. However manually scheduling the volunteers to the festival activities was very time consuming and making changes to the schedule was very difficult. Even minor changes took considerable time. To reduce the burden on the event coordinators and make this scheduling system as efficient as possible, faculty from the University of Alberta School of Business were asked to develop an efficient volunteer scheduling system that met most of the constraints presented. Integer programming was used to develop an initial schedule that satisfied the constraints that were easy to state. A goal programming model was used to minimize the imbalance between the numbers of shifts scheduled at different functions of the festival.

Once these two programs were working successfully, the consulting team tackled unsolicited volunteer requests. Considering preferences in volunteer scheduling is very important because if volunteers are not satisfied with the schedule, they may decide not to work or they may decide to work in a competing event that requires the services of a volunteer. Even though the policy of the event management team was that no personal preferences would be considered, certain persistent individuals consistently ignored the policy and decided not to work a certain shift that they considered undesirable. The festival management team was indecisive whether to solicit preferences of volunteers, fearing that if the festival solicited the preferences of the volunteers and was not able to accommodate some of those requests this would discourage volunteers because their requests were not met. The consulting team agreed that they could not satisfy all of the requests, but

the schedule would accommodate as many of the requests as possible. Incorporating volunteer requests to the scheduling program had a positive effect on the system by substantially reducing the number of feasible solutions. The consulting team decided to use a point system to satisfy volunteer requests. If a volunteer felt very strongly about their request, then they would assign a very high positive point value (desire to work) or high negative point value (desire not to work) to that event.

After the information was entered for all individual volunteers, the task of the scheduling program was to create a final schedule that the management could distribute to all volunteers. Three different versions of the schedule were completed. The first was a Master schedule with a table of all volunteers scheduled for all shifts. This schedule was developed using integer programming and basic Excel functions. The second showed management that they had assigned an appropriate number of people to each shift and indeed the solution to the problem was feasible. It was prepared with the help of VBA (Visual Basic for Applications), a programming language that offers not only the visual basic programming language but also is extended with Excel functions. The third version provided each volunteer with a list of all of his or her schedule. The program was able to generate these reports very quickly.

In the end, the resulting volunteer schedule accommodated all but one of the volunteer requests, adding the desired consideration of preferences to the scheduling function. The goal was that the festival management team might use this tool independent of the consulting team. This was accomplished by developing a user friendly decision support tool using Excel Solver and VBA, successfully allowing management to use the program on their own. This was a successful application of management science because not only was the consulting team successful in using optimization tools such as integer and goal programming, but also what if features, and successful user interface was developed using Excel and VBA.

Source: L. Gordon, E. Erkut "Improving Volunteer Scheduling for the Edmonton Folk Festival" *Interfaces* 34, no. 5, (September– October 2004) pp. 367–76.

benefits of simulation before using that route, and be fully cognizant that simulation will not guarantee an optimal decision to a problem.

◼ Summary

Simulation can be an important tool for managerial decision making. Unlike analytical techniques such as linear programming, simulation is not an optimizing technique. Instead, simulation is a *descriptive* tool. The goal in simulation is to create a model that will reflect the behavior of some real-life system in order to be able to observe how it may behave when certain inputs or parameters are changed.

The chapter focuses on manual simulations using Monte Carlo simulation. Simulations are illustrated for both fixed-interval and next-event simulations, using a variety of discrete and continuous distributions. In addition, single-variable and multiple-variable simulations are described.

Simulation is useful for problems that are too complex to be handled by either intuitive approaches or analytical models. Simulation models enable decision makers to compress time and to observe system behaviors under a variety of different circumstances (i.e., to answer "What if . . .?" questions). However, simulations sometimes yield only approximate results, they can be costly and/or time-consuming, and they often require considerable expertise to achieve satisfactory models.

▌ Glossary

Fixed-Interval Simulation A simulation in which the value of a variable is counted at the end of an interval.

Monte Carlo Simulation A method for generating random numbers that duplicates chance variability.

Next-Event Simulation A simulation in which the time or distance between event occurrences is simulated.

NORMINV An Excel function used to generate values from a normal probability distribution.

Pseudo-Random Number A random number generated by a computer based on an algorithm.

RAND() An Excel function that generates random numbers ranging from 0 to 1 from a uniform distribution.

RANDBETWEEN An Excel function that generates values between two specified values from a discrete uniform distribution.

Random Number A number typically between 0 and 1 whose value is selected at random.

Random Number Table A table of randomly distributed digits used in Monte Carlo simulations.

Simulate Use a model to obtain observations that represent the behavior of a system.

Simulation A study of the behavior of a system under various conditions.

Validation Checking the output of a simulation model to determine if it approximates the known or expected behavior of its real-life counterpart.

VLOOKUP An Excel function that "looks up" values from a different location on a worksheet.

Solved Problems

Problem 1

a. Simulate the number of calls per day to a fire station for a five-day interval, given the following information that was obtained from station records. Read two-digit numbers across row 11.

b. Use Excel to simulate the number of calls per day for a 10-day interval given the following information.

Calls	Number of Days
0	21
1	15
2	12
3	9
4	3
	60

Solution

a. If the frequency (number of days) is in actual counts rather than relative frequencies (i.e., relative frequencies would add to 1.00), the frequencies must be converted to relative frequencies. To do this, divide each count by the total (e.g., 21/60 = .35, 15/60 = .25, etc.). Next, obtain the cumulative relative frequencies by successively summing the relative frequencies (see the third and fourth columns below). Then, obtain the random number range for each cumulative frequency (see the fifth column below). For example, the first range is 01 to 35. The second range is from 36 to 60, and so on.

Calls	Number of Days	Relative Frequency	Cumulative Relative Frequency	Random Number Range
0	21	.35	.35	01 to 35
1	15	.25	.60	36 to 60
2	12	.20	.80	61 to 80
3	9	.15	.95	81 to 95
4	3	.05	1.00	96 to 00
	60	1.00		

Note: If you look at the numbers on the right-hand side of the Random Number Range column, you will see that they are exactly the same as the numbers in the Cumulative Relative Frequency column (ignoring the decimal points). Therefore, it is entirely possible to omit the Random Number Range column and work directly with the cumulative frequencies when doing a simulation. For instance, looking at the Cumulative Relative Frequency column, it is easy to see that a random number such as 55 falls between 35 and 60, and so would be interpreted as one call. Similarly, the random number 62 would be interpreted as two calls.

The first random number in row 11 is 41. Comparing this to the random number ranges, we can see that it falls in the second range, which corresponds to one call. Hence, the simulated number of calls on the first day is one. The second random number is 62, which falls in the range 61 to 80. This corresponds to two calls on day 2. The third random number is 57. It falls in the range 36 to 60, which corresponds to one call on day 3. The fourth number is 31, which falls in the range 01 to 35. This corresponds to zero calls on day 4. Lastly, the fifth number is 90, which corresponds to three calls on day 5. These results can be summarized as follows:

Day	1	2	3	4	5
Random number	41	62	57	31	90
Simulated number of calls	1	2	1	0	3

b. Exhibit 14-13 shows the Excel worksheet and the associated formulas for Solved Problem 1.

Exhibit 14-13	Excel Worksheet and the Results Associated with Solved Problem 1 (Fire Station)

Microsoft Excel - chap14 (version 1)

File Edit View Insert Format Tools MegaStat Data Window Help

C19   =AVERAGE(C9:C18)

	A	B	C	D	E	F	G	H
1	Number of Calls Arriving	Frequency (X)	Random Number (RN) for Arrivals	P(X)	Cumulative Probability	Number of Calls Arriving		
2	0	21	01 to 35	0.35	0	0		
3	1	15	36 to 60	0.25	0.35	1		
4	2	12	15 to 35	0.2	0.6	2		
5	3	9	35 to 60	0.15	0.8	3		
6	4	3	61 to 80	0.05	0.95	4		
7								
8	Simulation	RN	Number of Arrivals					
9	Day 1	0.23117519	0					
10	Day 2	0.43169206	1					
11	Day 3	0.0665924	0					
12	Day 4	0.33188236	0					
13	Day 5	0.26830544	0					
14	Day 6	0.75973618	2					
15	Day 7	0.93996602	3					
16	Day 8	0.30389053	0					
17	Day 9	0.14858501	0					
18	Day 10	0.81263311	3					
19	Average		0.9					

start   chapt14, 1 - Microsoft...   6 Microsoft Office E...

Cell	Copied to	Formula
E3		= D2
E4		= D3 + E3
E5		= D4 + E4
E6		= D5 + E5
D2	D3 : D6	= B2 / SUM ($B$2 : $B$6)
B9	B10 : B18	= RAND( )
C9	C10 : C18	= VLOOKUP (B9, $E$2 : $F$6, 2)
C19		= AVERAGE (C9 : C18)

Problem 2

a. Travel time to fire calls can be modeled by a normal distribution that has a mean of 6 minutes and a standard deviation of 2 minutes. Simulate travel time for three calls using values from row 2.

b. Use Excel to determine the average travel time for 10 calls.

Solution

a. The random numbers are -1.05, 0.56, and -0.67, Using Equation 14-4 shown at the bottom of Exhibit 14-14 for cells B2 : B11 we obtain the following:

Call	Random Number	Calculation		Simulated Travel Time
1	−1.05	6 − 1.05(2)	=	3.90 minutes
2	0.58	6 + 0.56(2)	=	7.12
3	−0.67	6 − 0.67(2)	=	4.66

Exhibit 14-14	Excel Worksheet and the Results Associated with Solved Problem 2

```
Microsoft Excel - ch14-solved2
File  Edit  View  Insert  Format  Tools  MegaStat  Data  Window  Help
                                                    Arial        10    B  I  U
                    Reply with Changes... End Review
  B11              =NORMINV(RAND(),6,2)
        A              B         C    D    E    F    G    H    I    J
 1  Call Number  TRAVEL TIME
 2  Call 1             9.563
 3  Call 2             2.672
 4  Call 3             7.884
 5  Call 4             8.610
 6  Call 5             4.782
 7  Call 6             5.258
 8  Call 7             4.196
 9  Call 8             4.689
10  Call 9             6.300
11  Call 10            3.044
12  Average            5.700
 start      chopt14.1  Microsoft...       6 Microsoft Office C...
```

Cell	Copied to	Formula
B2	B3 : B11	= NORMINV (RAND( ), 6, 2)
B12	–	= AVERAGE (B2 : B11)

b. Exhibit 14-14 shows the Excel worksheet and the associated formulas for Solved Problem 2. It demonstrates a problem where service times are normally distributed.

Problem 3

Multi-event Telephone company repair trucks require emergency repairs on a random basis. The company has three different types of emergencies, which it has classified as A, B, and C. They occur with these frequencies:

Type	Frequency
A	.35
B	.45
C	.20

Repair times tend to be *uniformly* distributed within these ranges:

Type	Repair Time
A	20 to 40 minutes
B	30 to 60 minutes
C	10 to 50 minutes

a. Simulate repair for five emergencies. Read two-digit numbers across row 2 for type of emergency and two-digit numbers across row 3 for repair time.
b. Use Excel to simulate 12 repairs and find the average repair time.

Solution

a. Prepare a cumulative distribution for type of emergency and establish ranges:

Type	Frequency	Cumulative Frequency	Random Number Ranges
A	.35	.35	01 to 35
B	.45	.80	36 to 80
C	.20	1.00	81 to 00
	1.00		

As specified in the question, obtain random numbers from row 2 for type of emergency and random numbers from row 3 for repair time. These result in the following:

Emergency	Row 2 Random Number	Simulated Type	Row 3 Random Number	Calculation	Simulated Repair Time
1	25	A	73	$20 + .73(40 - 20)$ =	34.6
2	19	A	57	$20 + .57(40 - 20)$ =	31.4
3	05	A	80	$20 + .80(40 - 20)$ =	36.0
4	64	B	35	$30 + .35(60 - 30)$ =	40.5
5	25	A	04	$20 + .04(40 - 20)$ =	20.8

Note that the calculation of simulated repair time *depends* on the simulated type of emergency; each emergency type has a different repair time distribution. In this instance, the first three simulated emergencies involved Type A, the fourth involved Type B, and the fifth involved Type A again. The A calculations are based on a uniform distribution of 20 to 40 minutes, whereas the B calculation is based on its uniform repair distribution of 30 to 60 minutes. And it happened that no Cs occurred, due to the small number of observations.

b. Exhibit 14-15 shows the Excel worksheet and the associated formulas for Solved Problem 3. This demonstrates a problem where there are multiple events. Note the nested "IF" statement in cells D6:D7.

Problem 4

A manager could use simulated repair times to schedule repair personnel and to assess the need to have backup trucks available. A consultant for a regional planning commission has developed a model for the purpose of studying population growth in a certain community. As part of the investigation, the consultant intends to simulate population growth in order to assess community demand for energy. The model to be used is the following:

$$P = 200,000 + 100t + 30e$$

where

P = total population
t = year t
e = error term

The error term, e, is expected to be normally distributed with a mean of zero and a standard deviation of 40. Simulate population totals for years $t = 3$ to $t = 5$, using values from column 2 of Table 14-5, reading down.

Solution

The values from Table 14-5 are

0.09
0.56
−0.02

The first value corresponds to e to $t = 3$, the second corresponds to e for $t = 4$, and the third for e with $t = 5$. Therefore, the simulated population totals are

$$P_{t=3} = 200,000 + 100(3) + 30[40(0.09)] = 200,408$$
$$P_{t=4} = 200,000 + 100(4) + 30[40(0.56)] = 201,072$$
$$P_{t=5} = 200,000 + 100(5) + 30[40(-0.020)] = 200,476$$

Exhibit 14-15 — Excel Worksheet and the Results Associated with Solved Problem 3 (Emergency Repairs)

Microsoft Excel - chap14 (version 1)

File Edit View Insert Format Tools MegaStat Data Window Help

D17   =IF(C17="A",RANDBETWEEN(20,40),IF(C17="B",RANDBETWEEN(30,60),IF(C17="C",RANDBETWEEN(10,50))))

	A	B	C	D	E	F	G	H
1	Type	P(X)	Cumulative Probability	Emergency Type				
2	A	0.35	0	A				
3	B	0.45	0.35	B				
4	C	0.2	0.8	C				
5	Emergency	RN 1	Emergency Type	Repair Time (uniform distr.)				
6	1	0.808	C	27				
7	2	0.591	B	44				
8	3	0.815	C	12				
9	4	0.182	A	23				
10	5	0.533	B	30				
11	6	0.611	B	49				
12	7	0.087	A	40				
13	8	0.602	B	51				
14	9	0.63	B	35				
15	10	0.772	B	42				
16	11	0.094	A	37				
17	12	0.125	A	35				
18			Average Repair Time	35.417				

Cell	Copied to	Formula
C3		= B2 + C2
C4		= B3 + C3
B6	B7 : B17	= RAND( )
C6	C7 : C17	= VLOOKUP (B6, $C$2 : $D$4, 2)
D6	D7 : D17	= IF (C6 = "A," RANDBETWEEN (20, 40), IF (C6 = "B," RANDBETWEEN (30, 60), IF (C6 = "C," RANDBETWEEN (10, 50))))
D18		= AVERAGE (D6 : D17)

The planning commission could use the simulated values to project energy needs for the years covered by this study.

Problem 5

The time between mechanics' requests for tools in a large plant is normally distributed with a mean of 10 minutes and a standard deviation of 1 minute. The time to fill requests is also normal with a mean of 9 minutes per request and a standard deviation of 1 minute. Mechanics' waiting time represents a cost of $2 per minute, and servers represent a cost of $1 per minute.

a. Simulate arrivals for the first nine mechanic requests and their service times, and determine the mechanics' waiting time, assuming one server. Would it be economical to add another server? Explain. Use Table 14-5, column 8 for requests and column 9 for service.

b. Repeat the same analysis for 10 requests using Excel.

Solution   a.   1.   Obtain random numbers and convert to times (see columns a and b in the following table for requests and columns f, g, and h for service).

	Customer Arrivals				Service			
	(a)	(b)	(c)	(d) (e − c)	(e)	(f)	(g)	(h) (e + g)
Customer	Random→ Number	Time between Arrivals	Cumulate Arrival Time	Customer Waiting Time	Service Begins	Random→ Number	Service Time	Service Ends
1	−1.12	8.88	8.88	0.00	8.88	1.36	10.38	19.24
2	−0.62	9.38	18.26	0.98	19.24	−0.95	9.05	28.29
3	−1.20	8.80	27.06	1.23	28.29	0.27	9.27	37.56
4	−2.17	7.83	34.89	2.67	37.56	1.10	10.10	47.66
5	0.22	10.22	45.11	2.55	47.66	−0.59	8.41	56.07
6	0.43	10.43	55.54	0.53	56.07	1.15	10.15	66.22
7	0.38	10.38	85.92	0.30	66.22	−0.04	8.96	75.18
8	−0.71	9.39	75.31	0.00	75.31	−1.11	7.89	83.20
9	−0.26	9.74	85.05	0.00	85.05	0.41	8.59	93.64
				8.26				

2. Determine arrival times (column c) by successive adding to times between arrivals in column b.

3. Use arrival times for service start *unless service is still in progress on a previous request.* In that case, determine how long the arrival must wait (column e − column c). Column e values are the sum of starting time and service time (column g), which is the time service ends (column h). Thus, service on each new request begins (column e) at the same time that service on the previous request ends (column h).

4. The simulation and resulting waiting times for the first nine arrivals are shown in the table. Total waiting time is 8.26 minutes.

5. The total cost for the 93.64 minutes (end of service on the ninth request) of the simulation is

Waiting cost	8.26 minutes at $2 per minute	= $16.52
Server cost	93.64 minutes at $1 per minute	= 93.64
		$110.16

6. Usually, a second simulation with two servers would be needed (but with the same arrival times so that the results would be comparable). However, in this case it is apparent that a second server would increase server cost by about $93 but could not eliminate more than $16.52 of waiting cost. Hence, the second server would not be justified.

Waiting cost	(2.47 minutes) × ($2 per minute) = $4.94
Server cost	(117.3 minutes) × ($1 per minute) = $117.30

Since 117.3 > 4.94, the second server is not justified.

b. Exhibit 14-16 shows the Excel worksheet and the associated formulas for Solved Problem 5. This illustrates a problem where there are multiple events that are normally distributed.

Exhibit 14-16   Excel Worksheet and the Results Associated with Solved Problem 5 (Mechanic)

Microsoft Excel - chap14.3

File Edit View Insert Format Tools MegaStat Data Window Help

Times New Roman   11   **B** *I* U

E13   =AVERAGE(E2:E12)

	Mechanic	Arrival Time	Cumulative arrival time	Entering Time	Waiting Time	Service Time	Departure Time	Time in the system	
1									
2	1	9.215	9.215	9.215	0	10.288	19.503	10.288	
3	2	10.501	19.716	19.716	0	7.651	27.367	7.651	
4	3	10.331	30.047	30.047	0	9.794	39.842	9.794	
5	4	10.383	40.431	40.431	0	10.768	51.198	10.768	
6	5	9.252	49.683	51.198	1.51537	8.320	59.519	9.836	
7	6	9.276	58.959	59.519	0.55976	7.663	67.182	8.223	
8	7	10.795	69.754	69.754	0	7.533	77.286	7.533	
9	8	10.802	80.555	80.555	0	10.479	91.034	10.479	
10	9	11.195	91.750	91.750	0	7.716	99.466	7.716	
11	10	7.511	99.261	99.466	0.20498	9.242	108.708	9.447	
12	11	9.258	108.519	108.708	0.18918	8.591	117.300	8.781	
13				Averages	0.224	8.913		9.138	

Cell	Copied to	Formula
B2	B3 : B12	= NORMINV (RAND( ), 10, 1)
C2		= B2
C3	C4 : C12	= B3 + C2
D2		= C2
D3	D4 : D12	= MAX (C3, G2)
E2	E3 : E12	= D2 − C2
F2	F3 : F12	= NORMINV (RAND( ), 9, 1)
G2		= C2 + F2
G3	G4 : G12	= D3 + F3
H2	H3 : H12	= G2 − C2
E13	F13	= AVERAGE (E2 : E12)
H13		= AVERAGE (H2 : H12)

Discussion and Review Questions

1. What are the advantages and limitations of simulation models?
2. Describe the difference between probabilistic and deterministic simulation.
3. List two applications of simulation.
4. Describe what is meant by discrete event simulation.

5. Why is the utilization of computer software such as Excel to run a medium to large simulation study essential?
6. List the steps involved in performing simulation.
7. What are the two main characteristics of random numbers?
8. List the theoretical distributions used in simulation studies in this chapter.
9. Explain when it is appropriate to use simulation.
10. What is Monte Carlo simulation? In using the Monte Carlo approach, how is randomness achieved?
11. The final step in a simulation study is "analyzing and interpreting the results." Explain this step carefully.
12. The first step in a simulation study is "defining the problem and setting the objectives." Explain this step carefully.

◼▷ Problems

(Unless otherwise specified, read random numbers *down* columns and from left to right *across* rows.)

1. Simulation has proven to be a valuable tool for decision makers over a wide range of problems.
   a. Explain what the term *simulation* means as employed in this chapter.
   b. Explain why simulation usually is the approach of last resort.
   c. What main characteristic did each of the simulation examples in this chapter possess?

2. The cumulative frequency distribution for the number of birthday cakes ordered per day at a bakery is as follows:

Number of Cakes	Cumulative Frequency
0	.01
1	.08
2	.18
3	.32
4	.51
5	.73
6	.89
7	.97
8	1.00

a. # of cakes   RN

# of cakes	RN
0	01
1	02–08
2	09–18
3	19–32
4	33–51
5	52–73
6	74–89
7	90–97
8	98–00

b. 3.667, Average # of orders

c. 4.667, random variability

a. Establish random number ranges for each possible order size.
b. Using two-digit random numbers reading down column 9 of Table 14-1 simulate orders for a six-day period. What is the average number of orders?
c. Simulate a second six-day period, continuing in column 9. What is the average number of orders? How different are these results than those of part *b*? Why are the results different? What is the implication of this?

3. The number of wide-screen television sets sold per day at a department store can be described by this frequency distribution:

Number of Sets	Frequency
0	.16
1	.24
2	.22
3	.15
4	.10
5	.08
6	.05

  a. Indicate how random numbers could be assigned to this distribution.
  b. Simulate the number of sets sold for a five-day period. Use random numbers from Table 14-1, row 2, and determine the average number of sets sold in five days.
  c. Repeat part *b* continuing in row 2 of the random number table.
  d. Why do the weekly averages vary? How do the totals compare to expected sales?

4. The number of typographical errors in letters typed by a certain secretary can be described by this frequency distribution:

Number of Errors per Page	Frequency
0	.75
1	.18
2	.05
3	.02

a. See the IM
b. Average number of errors/per page = .25
c. .5 errors per letter

  a. Indicate how random numbers could be assigned to this distribution.
  b. Simulate the number of errors in four two-page letters, reading two-digit numbers from row 7 of Table 14-1. What is the average number of errors per page?
  c. Based on the results of part *b*, compute the average number of errors per letter.

5. The manager of an auto service center has compiled data on the number of cars per day that need transmission work. The numbers are repeated here:

Number of Cars	Frequency
0	6
1	14
2	18
3	10
4	2

  a. Indicate how random numbers could be assigned to this distribution.
  b. Simulate experience for a five-day period. Read two-digit numbers going down column 8, Table 14-1. What is the average number of cars?

6. The number of days beyond the promised date that customers leave their dry cleaning at a certain store can be summarized by these data, which were obtained from the store's records:

Days beyond Date Promised	Frequency
0	104
1	46
2	16
3	6
4	14
5	10
6	0
7	4

Average = .43

Simulate the days beyond the promised date that the next seven customers leave their clothes. Use two-digit numbers from column 6 of Table 14-1, reading down. Compute the average number of days clothes are left beyond the promised date for the simulation.

7. The night manager of a resort hotel has asked the telephone operator to keep track of the nature of all calls received from outside of the hotel. The results for 100 calls are shown below:

Nature of Call	Number of Calls
R: Make a reservation	42
C: Confirm/cancel	27
A: Check availability	14
P: Price inquiry	7
O: Other	10

The manager knows that the amount of time spent by the operator in responding to the calls differs depending on the nature of the call. The manager is, therefore, particularly interested in getting an idea of the sequence of calls, in order to gain insight into how the operator's time might be spent with the calls. To do this, the manager wants to simulate 10 calls.

  a. Keeping the list of call types in the order shown, indicate how random numbers would be assigned to each call type.
  b. Reading two-digit numbers from row 8 of Table 14-1, simulate the 10 calls. What proportion of calls involve confirming or canceling?
  c. What proportion of calls involve making a reservation? Does this proportion seem reasonable? Explain why it is different than the data collected by the telephone operator.
  d. Repeat parts b and c reading two-digit numbers from row 9 of Table 14-1.

8. A company that sells canoes fills orders from independent retailers from a single warehouse. The manager of the warehouse has collected data on the number of canoes sold per day. The distribution is

Number Sold	Frequency
1	.02
2	.13
3	.20
4	.25
5	.15
6	.10
7	.10
8	.05
	―――
	1.0

The same distribution holds for each day. The warehouse is open five days a week. The manager wants to simulate daily demand for four five-day periods in order to test the merits of beginning each week with 20 canoes on hand. Canoes are received from the factory once a week.

a. See the IM

a. Read two-digit numbers from row 4 and then from row 5 of Table 14-1 to simulate daily demand for the four weeks. Use this format to record your results:

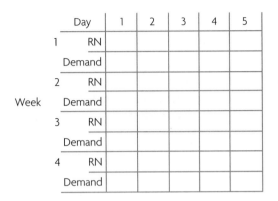

	Day	1	2	3	4	5
1	RN					
	Demand					
2	RN					
Week	Demand					
3	RN					
	Demand					
4	RN					
	Demand					

b. 50%

c. Not accurate, simulate large number of weeks

b. Estimate the proportion of weeks that demand will exceed supply if supply equals 20 canoes.

c. Comment on how accurate you believe your estimate is and why.

9. The managing partner of a construction firm has determined from company records that a certain piece of heavy equipment has a breakdown frequency that can be described by a Poisson distribution with a mean of 2 per month.

a. Simulate one year of breakdown experience for this equipment. Read three-digit numbers from columns 2 and 3 of Table 14-1 (e.g., 208, 190, . . .). What is the average number of breakdowns per year?

b. How many months experienced no breakdowns? Does this result seem reasonable? Explain.

c. There are no instances where there were two months in a row without a breakdown. How plausible is this? Explain.

10. The fire chief in a certain city has been told by a consultant that the occurrence of three-alarm fires can be described by a Poisson distribution that has a mean of 0.4 fire per day. The chief is concerned because it requires approximately two days after fighting a major fire to return equipment to good working order, and she wonders if additional equipment should be requested from the planning board. The consultant has suggested a simulation study of the problem.

a. .291

a. Simulate 24 days of experience using columns 10 and 11 of Table 14-1 (e.g., 675, 407. . . .) for the first 12 days and columns 11 and 12 (e.g., 540, 733, . . .) for the second 12 days. What is the average number of fires in 24 days?

b. No adequate time for fire on day 11, 2nd, 3rd fire on day 19

b. For each fire, determine if there was adequate time to prepare the equipment for the next fire.

c. 3/24 = .125

c. Determine the proportion of fires for which there was not sufficient time to prepare for the next fire.

11. Demand for pineapple juice at a theme park can be described by a uniform distribution that ranges between 50 and 130 gallons per day. Simulate daily demand for pineapple juice for 10 consecutive days. Read two-digit random numbers from column 5 of

Table 14-1. For what proportion of days is simulated demand greater than expected demand? Does this seem reasonable? Explain.

69.467

12. The amount of insecticide dispensed by a crop duster has been found to vary uniformly between 60 and 80 gallons per run. Simulate 12 runs reading two-digit random numbers from row 6 of Table 14-1. Determine the average gallons of insecticide for the 12 runs.

13. A design engineer has estimated that the time to perform a service using state-of-the-art equipment will vary uniformly between five and seven minutes. Simulate service times for eight requests using two-digit random numbers from column 9 of Table 14-1. What is the average time to perform the service for the eight requests?

Mean = .97, .97 ≠ 1.2 due to randomness

14. After reviewing processing times, the manager of a computer service agrees that computer processing times for a certain class of jobs can be described by a negative exponential distribution with a mean of 1.2 minutes of CPU. Using two-digit numbers from row 3 of Table 14-1, simulate the processing times for the next 10 jobs. Then, compute the mean processing time for the simulated jobs. Explain why it does not equal the distribution mean.

15. The manager of a shop that repairs telephone equipment has determined that repair time can be modeled by a negative exponential distribution with a mean repair time of one hour. Simulate repair times for a sequence of seven jobs, using two-digit numbers from column 4 of Table 14-1. Then, compute the mean repair time for the simulated jobs.

Yes, mean = 5.12, 5.12 is close to 5

16. In a study of the length of telephone calls, an analyst found that account representatives in a stockbroker's office spent an average of five minutes per call, and that call length could be modeled using a negative exponential distribution with that mean. Using Table 14-1, row 6, simulate the time for 12 calls. Compute the mean simulated time and compare it to the theoretical mean. Does the difference seem reasonable?

17. A consultant found that the time a doctor spent with a patient who was recovering from major surgery could be modeled by a normal distribution with a mean of 7 minutes and a standard deviation of 2 minutes. Simulate the times doctors might spend with a sequence of five patients using random numbers from row 2 of Table 14-5. Then compute the meantime a doctor spends with a patient.

Total time = 26.41 minutes

18. The time it takes a typist to type a letter in a certain office can be modeled by a normal distribution that has a mean of 4 minutes and a standard deviation of 1 minute. Using values from column 2 of Table 14-5, simulate the times for six letters and then determine the total time required to type those six letters.

19. After careful study of operating room procedures, an analyst concluded that the amount of time required to perform a certain type of surgery could be modeled using a normal distribution with a mean of 120 minutes and a standard deviation of 10 minutes. The analyst wants to simulate times for nine operations. Using random numbers for column 4 of Table 14-5, simulate the times for the nine operations. Compare the average simulated time with the model average. How do they compare?

Average repair time = 3.52 minutes; average waiting time = .176 minutes

20. On the basis of historical data, a manager concluded that the length of time between failures for a certain piece of food-processing equipment could be modeled by an exponential distribution that has a mean of 8 hours. In addition, the manager found that repair times could be modeled by a normal distribution with a mean of 4 hours and a standard deviation of 1.1 hours. For the next five breakdowns, simulate the length of time between breakdowns and the time needed for repairs. Then, find the waiting time for each breakdown (i.e., the length of time equipment waited for repair because the repairperson was busy working on a previous breakdown). Read values from Table 14-1, row 3 for breakdowns and values from Table 14-5, column 6 for repair times. For each breakdown, indicate operating time before breakdown, waiting time, and repair time. What are the average waiting time and repair time for the simulated fire breakdown ?

21. A small supplier receives orders from three different companies for a certain piece of electrical equipment. Forty-five percent of the orders come from Firm A, 35 percent from Firm B, and the remainder from Firm C. Order sizes vary, depending on the firm involved. In the past, orders were as follows:

	Relative Frequency		
Order Size	A	B	C
4	.15	.05	.25
8	.30	.25	.35
12	.40	.35	.25
16	.13	.25	.12
20	.02	.10	.03

Using two-digit numbers from rows 5 and 6 of Table 14-1, simulate the next six orders: For each order, determine which firm ordered (row 5), then the size of the order (row 6). How many of the six simulated orders come from each firm? What is the average order size for time six simulated orders?

22. A firm that replaces windshields receives from 0 to 4 calls per day for a midsized windshield that fits GM cars. The manager of the firm has compiled a frequency distribution for such calls and a distribution of replacement times. The daughter of a friend is currently enrolled in a business program. She examined the replacement time distribution and concluded that a normal distribution with a mean of 1.30 hours and a standard deviation of .20 hour would adequately describe the situation. The distribution of calls for the windshields is

Calls	Frequency
0	7
1	10
2	15
3	10
4	8

Simulate four days' worth of experience. Read two-digit numbers from Table 14-1, column 4 for calls, and values from Table 14-5, column 4 for times for each call. Determine the average time per day for replacements of this type.

23. A recent graduate of a prominent school's college of business encounters six traffic lights on the way to work in the morning. The traffic lights have a two-minute cycle: red for one minute and yellow/green for one minute. This person stops only for a red light. Assume the lights operate independently of each other.
    a. What is the probability that any particular light will be red when the motorist in this problem approaches it?
    b. What probability distribution—normal, exponential, or uniform—would best describe the length of time the motorist would have to wait for a red light? What are the parameters of the distribution?
    c. Simulate four trips for this motorist. For each light's color, use two-digit numbers from Table 14-1, columns 5 and 6. If a light is red (01–50), determine the length of wait the motorist has before the light turns green using two-digit numbers from Table 14-1, column 8. For each light, indicate its condition. For red lights, indicate the amount of waiting time.
    d. Based on the results of part c, compute an estimate of the average amount of time per trip the motorist waits at red lights.

1.85 hours

24. The motorist in the preceding problem wonders if an alternate route would result in a shorter waiting time. The alternate route has only two stoplights with the same two-minute cycle previously described. It also has two stop signs. The number of cars waiting at each stoplight can be described by a Poisson distribution with a mean of 2.0. The wait at a stop sign is approximately 30 seconds, if no cars are waiting. For each car that is waiting, an additional 30 seconds is added to the waiting time of the motorist.

a. See the IM

   a. Simulate four trips on the alternate route. For each light, read a two-digit number from Table 14-1, column 7. For light waiting time, read a two-digit number from column 10 of Table 14-1. For stop signs, read a three-digit number from Table 14-1, columns 5 and 6, to determine the number of cars waiting.

b. 2.8 minutes; no because 1.28 < 2.8

   b. Compute the waiting time for each trip, then the average waiting time. How does this compare to the results of the preceding problem? Which route seems to offer the shorter waiting time? Is that necessarily the better route? Explain.

25. The owner of a firm that installs blacktop driveways wants to simulate weekly revenues. He notes that 70 percent of the jobs the firm receives are for residential work and the rest are for commercial work. The revenue for residential work tends to be uniformly distributed between $400 and $1,000. The revenue for commercial work tends to be normally distributed with a mean of $1,800 and a standard deviation of $500. The number of jobs per week can be modeled by a Poisson distribution with a mean of 2. Simulate total revenue for four weeks using random numbers as follows: For number of jobs per week, read a three-digit random number from Table 14-1, column 7; for type of work, read a two-digit number from Table 14-1, column 8; for residential income, read a two-digit number from row 4 of Table 14-1; and for commercial income, read a number from row 3 of Table 14-5. Indicate the total revenue from each type of work and the total combined weekly revenue.

Cleaning and adjustment = .34 hour; minor repair = .87 hour; major repair = 11.55 hours.

26. A service department in a manufacturing firm handles requests for service from a machine center that has five machines. The service requests can be for cleaning/adjustment, minor repair, or major repair. Records indicate that 25 percent of the requests are for Machine 1, 15 percent for Machine 2, 30 percent for Machine 3, 10 percent for Machine 4, and 20 percent for Machine 5. The nature of the requests is summarized in the following table:

Service	Machine				
	1	2	3	4	5
Cleaning/adjustment	.20	.30	.25	.40	.50
Minor repair	.45	.55	.35	.25	.28
Major repair	.35	.15	.40	.35	.22

Cleaning and adjustment time is uniformly distributed between 20 minutes and 40 minutes for all machines. Minor repair times are exponential with a mean of 30 minutes for all machines, and major repair times are normal with a mean of 5 hours and a standard deviation of 1 hour for all machines. Use random number tables in this way: two-digit numbers from Table 14-1, column 5 for machine, two-digit numbers from Table 14-1, column 7 for type of service, and random numbers from Table 14-5, row 1, for service time. Simulate five requests for service. For each request indicate (*a*) which machine, (*b*) what service is requested, and (*c*) the service time required. Read random numbers from the appropriate tables in order, and simulate each request completely before moving on to the next request. What is the average service time for cleaning/adjustment? Minor repairs? Major repairs?

27. The manager of a building supply company has constructed a model that portrays monthly demand for exterior plywood. The model is

     Total Demand for 4 × 8 sheets = 2,000 + 20t + e

     where

     e = forecast error
     t = period number

     The manager is reasonably comfortable with a forecast error that is normally distributed with a mean of zero and a standard deviation of 100. Using values from Table 14-5, column 5, simulate demand for periods 10 through 15. What is the average simulated demand?

Hillside = $4,622.75
Farmdale = $3,144.75

28. The owner of a fruit farm sells peaches at two roadside stands. Based on past experience and the aid of a retired professor, the owner has developed two models that portray weekly revenue generated by each of the two locations. The models are

     | Hillside location | 4,500 + 80t − 10t^2 + e |
     | Farmdale location | 3,000 + 90t − 10t^2 + e |

     For the Hillside location, e is normally distributed with a mean of zero and a standard deviation of 100; for the Farmdale location, e is uniformly distributed with endpoints of −50 and +50. Simulate the revenue generated at each location for weeks t = 2 through t = 9. For the Hillside simulation, use values from Table 14-5, column 2, reading down. For the Farmdale location, read two-digit numbers from Table 14-1, column 4, reading up from the bottom. What is the average simulated demand for the Hillside location. What is the mean simulated demand for the Farmdale location?

29. John Stewart designs video games for a toy manufacturer. He has recently been working on a video pinball game and has established a set of probabilities for the movements of the "ball" during a game. The player receives points depending on the positions the ball strikes during a game. These are shown below, along with probabilities for ball paths. Simulate the paths for three balls, and determine the number of points received for each ball. Use row 1 of Table 14-1 for ball 1, row 9 for ball 2, and row 3 for ball 3. Read from left to right.

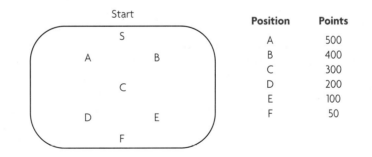

Position	Points
A	500
B	400
C	300
D	200
E	100
F	50

Path	Probability	Path	Probability
S to A	.30	C to A	.10
B	.30	B	.15
C	.25	C	.20
D	.10	D	.10
E	.04	E	.30
F	.01	F	.15

Path	Probability	Path	Probability
A to A	.25	D to A	.10
B	.25	B	.05
C	.25	C	.25
D	.10	D	.15
E	.10	E	.30
F	.05	F	.15
B to A	.30	E to A	.05
B	.20	B	.10
C	.20	C	.15
D	.15	D	.15
E	.10	E	.20
F	.05	F	.35

What are the total simulated points of ball 1, ball 2, and ball 3?

50 bags

30. A distributor supplies pool chemicals to three firms that handle swimming pool maintenance. The distributor maintains an inventory of sodium bisulfate for the three firms. The distributor wants to limit the amount of supplies on hand due to storage problems. Nevertheless, the distributor would like to have a probability of at least 90 percent of not running out of stock during the week. Stocks are replenished every Monday and then picked up during the week by the three firms as needed. The chemicals are sold in multiples of five bags. Historical demand distributions for these firms are

Weekly	Relative Frequency		
Demand	Firm A	Firm B	Firm C
5	.10	.15	.20
10	.20	.25	.30
15	.20	.30	.25
20	.20	.20	.20
25	.30	.10	.05

Simulate demand for 10 weeks. Use row 1 of Table 14-1 for Firm A, row 2 for Firm B, and row 3 for Firm C. Based on your results, how many bags of sodium bisulfate should the distributor plan to have on hand at the beginning of each week to have a probability of 90 percent of satisfying weekly demand? Explain how you arrived at your answer.

31. Jobs are delivered to a workstation at random intervals. The time between job arrivals tends to be normally distributed with a mean of 15 minutes and a standard deviation of 1 minute. Job processing time is also normally distributed with a mean of 14 minutes per job and a standard deviation of 2 minutes.

    a. Using Table 14-5, simulate the arrival and processing of five jobs. Use column 4 of the table for job arrival times and column 3 for processing times. *Start each column at row 4.* Find the total times jobs wait for processing.

    b. The company is considering the use of new equipment that would result in processing time that is normal with a standard deviation of 1 minute. Job waiting represents a cost of $3 per minute, and the new equipment would represent an additional cost of $.50 per minute. Would the equipment be cost justified? (*Note:* Use the same arrival times and the same random numbers for processing times.

32. Customers arrive randomly at a catalog department of a large store. The time between arrivals varies uniformly between 10 and 20 minutes. Service time is normal with a mean of 15 minutes and a standard deviation of 2 minutes.

a. Total waiting time =
4.38 minutes; average
service time = 13.85
minutes

b. Total waiting time =
3.29 minutes

a.   Simulate processing and waiting times for nine customers. Read three-digit numbers going down columns 9 and 10 of Table 14-1 for arrivals (e.g., 156, 884, 576). Use column 8, Table 14-5 for processing time. What are the total waiting time and the average service time?

b.   If management can reduce the range of arrival times to between 13 and 17 minutes, what would the impact be on customer waiting times? (Use the same service times and the same random numbers for arrival times from part *a*.) Round arrival times to two decimal places. What is the total waiting time?

33.   Suppose a manager is concerned about complaints from customers about being out of stock on a certain item. The current policy is to reorder the item when there are four units in stock.

The manager has determined that the time it takes to receive an order (lead time) is from one to three days, with frequencies as shown in the following table:

Lead Time (days)	Relative Frequency
1	.33
2	.45
3	.22

The manager also has determined that daily demand can be modeled using a Poisson distribution that has a mean of 1.9 units per day.

Simulate 10 order cycles (i.e., simulate the number of days needed to receive an order, and the demand for each day during that time, for each cycle). Use random numbers from Table 14-1: For lead times, read two-digit numbers from column 6; for daily demands, read three-digit numbers, starting with the second number of column 2 and both numbers of column 3 (e.g., 084, 905, 780, etc.) and then the first two numbers of columns 4 and the first number of column 5 (e.g., 299, 642, 350, etc.). Then answer these questions:

a.   Assuming there were four units on hand at order time, what percentage of cycles would demand have exceeded stock on hand?

b.   If the manager wants to reduce the stockout percentage to 10 percent, based on this (limited) simulation, how many items should be in stock when new stock is ordered?

See the IM

34.   Refer to Problem 2. Use Excel and simulate the number of cake orders for 360 days. What is the average number of cakes for this problem? What is the difference in the averages between Problem 2 and this problem?

35.   Refer to Problem 3. Use Excel and simulate the number of TV sets sold per day for a 150-day period. What are the average sales and the standard deviation of the sales for the 150-day period.

See the IM

36.   Refer to Problem 4. Use Excel and simulate the number of errors per page for a 180-page book. What is the total number of errors in the book? What is the average number of errors in the book?

37.   Refer to Problem 8. Use Excel and simulate the number of canoes sold per day for a 150-day period. What are the average number of canoes sold and the standard deviation of the sales for the 150-day period?

See the IM

38.   Refer to Problem 11. Use Excel and simulate the amount of pineapple juice sold per day for a 150-day period. What are the average gallons of pineapple juice sold per day and the standard deviation of the sales for the 150-day period?

See the IM

See the IM

See the IM

See the IM

See the IM

39. Refer to Problem 12. Use Excel and simulate the amount of insecticide dispensed by a crop duster for 120 runs. What are the average number of insecticide dispensed and the standard deviation of the insecticide dispensed for 120 runs?

40. Refer to Problem 15. Use Excel and simulate repair times for 130 jobs. What are the average repair time and the standard deviation of repair times?

41. Refer to Problem 16. Use Excel and simulate the length of telephone calls for 150 telephone calls. What is the average length of time of a phone call?

42. Refer to Problem 17. Use Excel and simulate the amount of time a doctor spends with patients recovering from major surgery based on 140 surgeries. Based on the simulated results of the 140 surgeries, what is the average time a doctor spends with a patient recovering from a major surgery?

43. Refer to Problem 18. If there were 120 letters to type, use Excel and simulate the amount of time it takes to type the letters. What is the total estimated typing time for the 120 letters?

44. Refer to Problem 19. Assume that a hospital performs 100 surgeries per day and use Excel to simulate the amount of time it takes to perform 100 surgeries. What is the total estimated time to perform 100 surgeries?

45. Refer to Problem 20. The company wants to simulate the breakdown of the next 100 pieces of equipment. Based on the simulated results of the breakdown of the next 100 pieces of equipment, calculate the time between breakdowns. Assuming there is one repairperson, calculate the average waiting time for repairs and the average time needed for repairs.

46. Repeat the simulation conducted in Problem 31, parts *a* and *b*, for 120 jobs.

47. Refer to Problem 32, part *a*. Simulate the arrival, processing, and waiting times for 120 customers. What is the total waiting time? What is the average processing time?

48. Refer to Problem 32, part *b*. Simulate the arrival, processing, and waiting times for 120 customers. What is the total waiting time? What is the average processing time?

49. The manager of a bank is concerned about the waiting lines forming in front of the two tellers. The bank consists of a single-line system with two servers. Based on historical data, the following empirical distributions on time between arrivals and time to serve the bank customers have been observed. Assume that the second teller serves as a backup teller. In other words, the customers are always assigned to the first teller unless he or she is occupied with another customer. The second teller has other responsibilities; however, if the teller is needed by a customer, he or she will stop and assist the customer.

   a. Simulate the arrival and service of 11 customers. Calculate the average waiting time for the customers, average idle time for the tellers, and average time a customer spends in the bank. Use random numbers from column 3 of Table 14-1 for arrivals (e.g., 84, 05, 80, etc.) and from column 4 of Table 14-1 for service (e.g., 29, 64, 35, etc.).

   b. Use Excel and simulate the arrival and service of 100 customers. Calculate the average waiting time and average time a customer spends in the bank.

Time between Arrivals (minutes)	Probability of Arrivals	Service Time (minutes)	Probability of Service Time
.50	.30	0.5	.25
1.0	.20	1.0	.20
1.5	.15	2.0	.25
2.0	.13	3.0	.15
3.0	.14	4.0	.10
4.0	.08	5.0	.05

◼️▮ Chapter 14 Case   Krohler Supermarkets

The management of Krohler Supermarkets, a national chain, has become aware of decreasing profit margins from its stores during the previous year. Three factors contributed to this earnings decline: (1) rapidly increasing labor costs, (2) increasing costs of wholesale merchandise and inability to increase retail prices because of governmental controls and consumer resistance, and (3) increasing price competition from their major national competitors. Even though earnings have declined significantly, sales volume has been increasing from year to year, but at a lower rate in the immediate past year than in previous years.

Merchandise typically accounted for the largest proportion of a store's operating costs (roughly 80 percent), with the inventory control and stocking functions being critical to this aspect of managing operations. Inventory was ordered each week from a central warehouse by means of a fixed-interval system. Stocking consisted primarily of placing the commodities on display, pricing each item, controlling pilferage, and removing damaged goods.

Labor costs were the second largest factor in supermarket operations (roughly 10 percent). More than 40 percent of the store's wages went to people manning the "front end," which include cashiers and baggers. About 33 percent of the wages went to the stockers, and the balance went to people in the meat, produce, bakery, or deli departments or to the store supervisors. Krohler management personnel felt that a prime area in which to reduce overall operating costs would be the labor requirements, but they were unwilling to reduce their service level to the consumer because of the negative effect it would have on their competitive stance in the supermarket industry.

Krohler's small industrial engineering department had recommended to the management that an investigation be made of the potential savings associated with implementing automatic point-of-sale (APOS) systems at the checkout counters. These APOS systems combined electronic cash registers and optical scanning devices that interact with an in-store minicomputer, and they could substantially boost labor productivity and provide greater control over inventory levels and ordering requirements. Since almost every commodity Krohler carried was labeled with a unique manufacturing code (called the Universal Product Code), the system functioned by having a checker pull an item across the optical scanner so the code could be read. The price of the item would be obtained immediately from the minicomputer's memory, displayed on the register, and tallied into the customer's bill. At the same time, the computer would compute any applicable sales tax and note the sale of all items in its inventory control program for later summarization of daily stock levels and order requirements. If a particular item did not have the code attached to it (for example, a bag of apples, deli specialties, or nonuniform packages of meats), the cashier would enter the price and an item code manually into the register. In addition to the time savings anticipated in checking out individual customers, the industrial engineering department pointed out that a significant amount of time would be saved in closing out a register (counting the cash and reconciling opening and closing balances with the intervening sales) and also in not having to price each item on the shelves.

With the existing manual system in place, the basic functions of front-end personnel, including cashiers and baggers, were (1) enter the merchandise cost into the register, (2) enter applicable sales taxes, (3) total the cost of purchases and taxes, (4) receive payment (cash, check, food stamps, discount coupons, etc.) and make change, (5) bag the items purchased, and (6) assist a customer in removing the bag(s) from the store. Miscellaneous tasks also

Source: James A. Fitzsimmons and Robert S. Sullivan, *Service Operations Management* (New York: McGraw-Hill, 1982). © 1982 by McGraw-Hill, Inc.

included check cashing, looking up prices on unmarked items, weighing and pricing produce, and responding to any customer questions.

In a typical Krohler Supermarket, there would be 10 checkout counters placed in a row at the store front, with one designated as an "express" lane to serve customers with 10 items or less. However, because sales fluctuated greatly by day and by hour, management tried very hard to match the number of counters open with expected demand so that both a high level of customer service and a high level of checkout-counter productivity would be maintained. Customer-service level was defined as the percentage of time that more than a certain number of customers were either being served or waiting in line to be checked out. A general rule of thumb used by Krohler management was that the percentage of time that more than three customers waited in line (including the person being served) should be held to 5 percent or less. Checkout-counter productivity was measured on the basis of sales dollars per manned checkout-counter hour.

As one means of examining the possible savings associated with an APOS system versus the existing manual system, Krohler's industrial engineering department was given the task of simulating the store operations with two systems. Assume you are part of the study team and develop responses to the following questions:

1. What specific questions should a simulation of the two different systems address?
2. What data must be collected before a simulation could be performed?

Discussion Question

Given your responses to the above questions, develop a flowchart of a simulation model that could be used to study the operation of an APOS system at a typical Krohler Supermarket.

Answers to Most Odd-Numbered Problems

Chapter 1 Introduction to Management Science, Modeling, and Excel Spreadsheets

1. a. Profit = $-\$40,000$
   b. Profit = $\$20,000$
   c. $Q_{BEP} = 8,000$ cases
3. a. $TR = \$21,900$; $TC = \$13,000$; $P = \$8,900$
   b. $Q_{BEP} = 2,521$ bottles
5. a. $P = \$79,600$
   b. $Q_{BEP} = 22,271.71$ cases
   c. $P = \$169,400$
7. a. In-house cost = $\$2,900$; Subcontracted cost = $\$2,700$
   b. 10 months

Chapter 2 Forecasting

1. a. Day 12 forecast = 38.5, Day 13 forecast = 34.5
   b. Day 12 forecast = 36.75, Day 13 forecast = 36.75
   c. $F_7 = 35.3$, $F_8 = 35.4$
3. a. Day 15 forecast = 28.7, Day 16 forecast = 30.3
   b. Day 15 forecast = 30.00, Day 16 forecast = 30.00
7. Friday = 163, Saturday = 276, Sunday = 183
9. Wednesday = .60, Thursday = .80, Friday = 1.10, Saturday = 1.20
11. Yes, demand > sales
13. a. Monday = 1.17, Tuesday = .97, Wednesday = .86, Thursday = .80, Friday = 1.19
    b. $Y_t = 8.88 - .147t$
    c. Mon. forecast = 6.77, Tues. forecast = 5.48, Wed. forecast = 4.73, Thurs. forecast = 4.28, Fri. forecast = 6.20
15. a. $Y_t = 44.17 - 2.51t$, $Y_a = 21.58$
    b. February 4th week = TAF = 22.36; $S = 22.89$; $T = -3.47$
17. $Q_1 = .8256$, $Q_2 = .9941$, $Q_3 = .8316$, $Q_4 = 1.3490$
19. $Y_t = 423.87 + 20.51t$; September forecast = 567.5; October forecast = 588.0
23. a. Yes
    b. $r^2 = .854$; fit is good
    c. 687.61 to 745.15

25. a. $y = 3.33 + .0591x$
    b. $r^2 = 59.5\%$
    c. Yes
    d. 7.19 to 9.63
27. a. $y = 68.45 - 8.20x_1 + 2.04x_2 - 4.56x_3$
    b. No, t ratio of x_2 is less than 2.00
29. a. Price is not a valid predictor
    b. All variables invalid
    c. Model 1 $\geq 8.1\%$; Model 2 $\geq 7.8\%$
    d. Model 1
31. a. MAD semester 11 = 5.18; MAD semester 12 = 5.91
    b. All tracking signals within limits of ± 4
33. a. $y_t = 35.8 + 4.02t$; year 13 forecast = 88.04; year 14 forecast = 92.06
    b. $TS_{13} = 2.63$; $TS_{14} = 2.81$
    c. Yes, forecast is in control; $TS_{14} = 2.81$
35. a. MAD week 19 = 2.90; MAD week 20 = 2.63; TS week 19 = 2.41; TS week 20 = 1.90
    All tracking signal values are within the limits of ± 4; conclude forecast is working properly

Chapter 3 Linear Programming: Basic Concepts and Graphical Solution

1. a. Determine the optimal quantity of each decision variable
   b. Quantities of tables, chairs, and bookcases
   c. Labor hours, machine hours, and wood
   d. Each bookcase requires 2.5 hours of labor
   e. At least 10 tables must be produced
   f. Amount of profit from each table
3. a. x_1 = quantity of 3.5-ounce bars; x_2 = quantity of 6-ounce bars
   b. $3.5x_1 + 6x_2 \leq 15,000$; $x_1 \geq 1,000$; $x_2 \geq 1,200$
5. d. $x_1 = 4.71$; $x_2 = 4.12$; $z = 112.94$
   e. $x_1 = 8$; $x_2 = z = 48$
7. b. $x_1 = 45$; $x_2 = 20$; $z = 1,725$
9. b. $x_1 = 60$; $x_2 = 0$; $z = 3,000$

11. a. Yes; $x_1 = 40$; $x_2 = 13.33$
    b. $z = 36$
13. a. Cutting: 110 minutes; frying: 160 minutes; packing: 576 seconds
    b. Cutting: 34 minutes; frying: 0 minutes; packing: 0 seconds
    c. Multiple optimal solutions
15. a. $x_1 = 2$; $x_2 = 9.6$; $z = 27.2$
    b. Constraint C is exceeded by 120 units; $24(2) + 45(9.6) = 480$
17. a. $x_1 = 105$; $x_2 = 25$
    b. $z = \$289.50$
19. coefficient for $x_1 = .6$
21. b. The problem is unbounded.
    c. One or both of the constraints should be I type or the objective should be minimized.
23. The solution is $x_1 = 0$; $x_2 = 0$; $z = 0$
25. a. Let $x_1 =$ # of safety devices for construction worker.
    $x_2 =$ # of safety devices for window washer.
    Max $Z = 60x_1 + 40x_2$
    Subject to: $1/4x_1 + 1/3x_2 \le 75$ (test #1)
    $1/4x_1 + 1/2x_2 \le 50$ (test #2)
    $1/2x_1 + 1/4x_2 \le 40$ (test #3)
    $x_1, x_2 \ge 0$
    b. $x_1 = 40$; $x_2 = 80$; $Z = \$5600$
    c. Test #1, 18.33 minutes
    d. Test #1, constraint is redundant; it does not form a unique boundary of the feasible solution space.
27. a. Let $x_1 =$ pans of ham spread
    $x_2 =$ pans of deli spread
    Min $Z = 3x_1 + 3x_2$ (part b)
    or
    Max $Z = 2x_1 + 4x_2$ (part c)
    Subject to: $1.4x_1 + 1x_2 = 70$ (part b)
    $1.4x_1 + 1x_2 = 112$ (part c)
    $x_1 \ge 20$
    $x_2 \ge 18$
    $x_1, x_2 \ge 0$
    b. $x_1 = 1,818.18$; $x_2 = 5,090.91$; $z = \$414,546$
    c. $S_1 = 0$; $S_2 = 0$; $S_3 = 1,455$
29. $x_1 = 2228.57$; $x_2 = 1200$; $z = \$469.71$
31. a. $A = 7.53$; $B = 3.35$; $z = 42.18$
    b. Constraint 1's surplus is 44.58
    c. No
33. a. Number of bedroom sets and number of living room sets to maximize revenue given the constraints
    b. maximize $Z = 1,000x_1 + 500x_2$
    Subject to $400x_1 + 500x_2 = 40,000$
    $14x_1 + 7x_2 \le 980$

$x_2 \ge 20$
$x_1, x_2 \ge 0$
c. $x_1 = 50$; $x_2 = 40$; $Z = 70,000$

Chapter 4 Applications and Solutions of Linear Programming

1. Minimize $Z = 110x_1 + 120x_2 + 130x_3$
   Subject to: $x_1 + x_2 + x_3 = 15,000$
   $x_1 \ge 1,000, x_1 \le 10,000$
   $x_2 \ge 2,000, x_2 \le 20,000$
   $x_3 \ge 3,000, x_3 \le 30,000$
   $x_1, x_2, x_3 \ge 0$
3. Maximize $Z = 500x_1 + 400x_2$
   Subject to: $8x_1 + 8x_2 \le 720$
   $x_1 \ge 10, x_1 \le 50$
   $x_2 \ge 10, x_1 \le 60$
   $x_1, x_2 \ge 0$
5. Maximize $Z = 45x_1 + 70x_2$
   Subject to: $9x_1 + 12x_2 \le 720, 1x_1 + 1x_2 \le 75$
   $2x_1 + 6x_2 \le 300, x_1, x_2 \ge 0$
7. Maximize $Z = 11x_1 + 4x_2 + 2x_3$
   Subject to: $120x_1 + 52x_2 + 18x_3 = 100,000$
   $120x_1 \le 40,000, 52x_2 \le 40,000$
   $18x_3 \le 40,000, 120x_1 \ge 10,000 \; x_1, x_2, x_3 \ge 0$
9. Minimize $Z = .45A + .55B + .60C, A + B + C = 1$
   Subject to: $-.07A - .04B + .04C = 0$
   $3A - C \ge 0, A, B, C \ge 0$
11. Minimize $Z = 2.50x_1 + 1.80x_2 + 1.00x_3$
    Subject to: $x_1 + x_2 + x_3 = 2,000, x_1 \ge 800$
    $x_3 \le 600, x_2 \ge 300, x_1, x_2, x_3 \ge 0$
13. Cost of mix = \$2.20
    Maximize $Z = 1.80x_1 + .50x_2 + 1.80x_3 + 2.10x_4 + 1.50x_5$
    Subject to: $.40x_1 + x_2 \le 600, .20x_1 + x_3 \le 360,$
    $.20x_1 + x_4 \le 500$
    $.20x_1 + x_5 \le 400, x_1, x_2, x_3, x_4, x_5 \ge 0$
15. Maximize $Z = 7.00x_1 + 3.00x_2 + 2.80x_3 + 3.25x_4 + 3.60x_5 + 3.50x_6 + 5.50x_7$
    Subject to: $.4x_1 + .2x_2 + x_3 \le 400, .4x_1 + x_4 \le 300,$
    $.4x_1 + .2x_2 + x_5 \le 250$
    Subject to: $.4x_1 + .2x_2 + x_6 \le 350, .4x_1 + .4x_2 + x_7 \le 450$
    $1.4x_1 + .7x_2 - .3x_3 - .3x_4 - .3x_5 - .3x_6 - .3x_7 \le 0,$ All variables ≥ 0
17. Maximize $Z = 2.80x_1 + 3.40x_2 + 2.60x_3$
    Subject to: $x_1 + x_2 + x_3 \le 200, -.10x_1 - .10x_2 + .90x_3 \ge 0$
    $x_2 - 2.5x_3 = 0, .80x_1 - .20x_2 - .20x_3 \ge 0$
    $.75x_1 - .25x_2 - .25x_3 \ge 0,$
    All variables ≥ 0

19. Minimize $Z = 4x_1 + 0x_2 + 2x_3 + 0x_4$
    Subject to: $x_1 + x_2 + x_3 + x_4 \leq 350$,
    $2x_1 + 1x_3 + 1x_4 = 276$
    $2x_2 + 1x_3 = 100, x_4 = 250$, All variables ≥ 0

21. Maximize $Z = 4{,}000wo_1 + 1{,}500wo_2 + .3wo_3$
    Subject to: $4{,}000wo_1 + 1{,}500wo_2 + .3wo_3 - 84wi_1 - 6wi_2 - 2{,}000wi_3 \leq 0$
    $3{,}000wo_1 + 1{,}000wo_2 + .2wo_3 - 70wi_1 - 8wi_2 - 4{,}000wi_3 \leq 0$
    $2{,}500wo_1 + 1{,}200wo_2 + .15wo_3 - 88wi_1 - 7wi_2 - 3{,}000wi_3 \leq 0$
    $84wi_1 + 6wi_2 + 2000wi_3 = 1$, All variables ≥ 0

Chapter 4 Supplement (on CD-ROM)   Linear Programming: The Simplex Method

1. a. Both can solve two-variable problems. Simplex can solve problems with more than two variables.
3. a. Corner point is represented by each tableau
   b. The variable with largest C-Z; break ties arbitrarily
   c. Minimum b_i/a_{ij}; break ties arbitrarily
5. a. No, not all basic variables are slack
   b. $s_1 = 30, x_1 = 50, s_3 = 50$
   c. $z = 1{,}000$
   d. No, there is a positive value in the C-Z row
   e. x_2
   f. s_1
   g. $x_2 = 15, x_1 = 50, s_3 = 35, z = \$1{,}180$
7. c. $x_1 = 25, x_2 = 1.5, z = 147.5$
9. $x_1 = 38.57, x_2 = 57.14, s_2 = 1.43, z = 3257.14$
11. $x_1 = 13.33, x_2 = 8.33, s_3 = 11.67, z = 9$
13. $x_2 = 500, s_2 = 110, z = 350$
15. $x_1 = 13, x_2 = 0, x_3 = 0, z = 143$
17. $x_3 = 200, s_1 = 0, s_2 = 50, z = 22{,}000$
19. $x_2 = 1, x_3 = 1, x_4 = 0, s_4 = 0, z = 8$
21. $x_1 = 3, x_2 = 4, z = 39$
23. $x_1 = 24, x_2 = 12, x_3 = 8, s_4 = 2{,}400, z = 108.8$
25. $x_2 = 67{,}500, x_3 = 67{,}500, z = 15{,}525$
27. b. $x_1 = 320, x_2 = 40, x_3 = 20, x_4 = 120, x_5 = 20, x_6 = 60, z = 433$
29. a. Add a slack variable
    b. $2x_1 + 6x_2 + s_1 = 20, 3x_1 + 2x_2 + s_1 = 30$
    c. Add an artificial variable
    d. $3x_1 + 5x_2 + A_2 = 16, 4x_1 - x_2 + A_2 = 18$
    e. Subtract a surplus variable and add an artificial variable
    f. $6x_1 + 4x_2 - s_3 + A_3 = 24, 5x_1 - 2x_2 - s_3 + A_3 = 14$
31. a. No, because a slack variable is only used with a $\leq$ constraint and a surplus variable is only used with a $\geq$ constraint.

b. No, because a slack variable is only used with a $\leq$ constraint and an artificial variable is never used with that type of constraint.

33. b. Maximize $Z = 8x_1 + 5x_2 + 0s_1 + 0s_2 - MA_2$
    Subject to: $4x_1 + 3x_2 + 1s_1 = 240$
    $x_2 - 1s_2 + A_2 = 50$
    All variables ≥ 0

35. $x_1 = 3.6, x_2 = -8, z = 19.6$
    Maximize $Z = x_1 + 2x_2$
    Subject to: $5x_1 + 9x_2 = 90$
    $10x_1 + 3x_2 = 60$

37. a. $x_1 = $ qty. of Style #1, $x_2 = $ qty. of Style #2
    Maximize $Z = 10x_1 + 10x_2$
    Subject to: $5x_1 + 5x_2 \leq 450$ yards
    $x_1 \geq 20$ dresses
    $x_2 \geq 40$ dresses
    b. Maximize $Z = 10x_1 + 10x_2 + 0s_1 + 0s_2 - MA_2 - MA_3$
    Subject to: $5x_1 + 5x_2 + s_1 = 450$
    $x_1 - s_2 + A_2 = 20$
    $x_2 - s_3 + A_3 = 40$
    c. $s_2 = 30, x_1 = 50, x_2 = 40, z = 900$
    d. Style #1 $= 50$, Style #2 $= 40$, Profit $= \$900$

39. $x_3 = 30, s_2 = 5, s_3 = 20, z = 420$
41. Add constraint to previous problem:
    Time: $3x_1 + 2x_2 + 2x_3 \leq 144$ hours
    $x_2 = 72, s_1 = 48, s_2 = 32, z = 360$
43. a. The M coefficients are assigned positive signs instead of negative signs.
    b. The entering variable is the one with the largest negative value in row C-Z.
45. b. Minimize $Z = 8x_1 + 5x_2 + 0s_1 + 0s_2 + 0s_3 + MA_1 + MA_2 + MA_3$
    Subject to: $15x_1 + 6x_2 - s_1 + A_1 = 450$
    $x_1 - s_2 + A_2 = 15$
    $x_2 - s_3 + A_3 = 20$
    c. $x_1 = 22, x_2 = 20, s_2 = 7, z = 276$
    d. s_2 is also in the solution. It tells us that the second constraint is exceeded (surplus) by 7.
47. b. $x_1 = 20, x_2 = 40, z = 240$
49. $x_2 = 36, x_3 = 18, z = 612$

Chapter 5   Linear Programming: Sensitivity Analysis and Duality

1. c. Coefficients of the objective function and RHS values of constraints
3. a. $2.5 \leq C_2 \leq 15$
   b. $3 \leq C_1 \leq 18$

c. Constraint 1 = 1.2, constraint 2 = 2.6

d. $4 \leq b_1 \leq 24.5 \leq b_2 \leq 30$

e. None, new $z = 39.6$

f. Values of the variables stay the same because the change is within the range. However, Z would decrease from 43.2 to 40.4.

5. a. $0 \leq C_1 \leq 5, 6.4 \leq C_2 \leq \infty$

b. No effect on value of x_1, new $z = 24$

c. Shadow price = .8, $20 \leq b_1 \leq \infty$

d. Shadow price = 0, $-\infty \leq b_2 \leq 48$

e. None

7. a. $P = 11, Q = 0, Z = \$132$

b. $10 \leq C_p \leq \infty$

c. 44, new $z = 180$

d. None

e. 1.0909

9. a. Shadow price constraint 1 = 6, constraint 2 = 2, constraint 3 = 0

b. $150 \leq b_1 \leq 252$

c. $26 \leq b_2 \leq 60$

d. $15 \leq b_3 \leq \infty$

e. Option 1

f. $18 \leq C_1 \leq \infty, 0 \leq C_2 \leq 13.33$

11. a. $-\infty \leq C_1 \leq 15, -5.6 \leq C_2 \leq \infty, 9.6 \leq C_3 \leq 25$

b. $-14.4 \leq b_1 \leq 1.44, 0 \leq b_2 \leq \infty, 0 \leq b_3 \leq \infty$

c. 1. x_1 from 13 to 4.4, x_3 from 0 to 10

2. Z from 143 to 188.4

13. a. $F = 0, G = 5, H = 32, Z = 548$

b. $9.4 \leq C_6 \leq 22.4$

c. $Z = 498, Z = 558$

d. $158 \leq b_1 \leq \infty$

e. $50 \leq b_3 \leq 200$

f. $F = 0, G = 1.667, H = 37.333$

g. $Z = 560$

15. a. Assuming sunk cost, labor, $1.3 > .2 > 0$

b. New $Z = 608 [588 + (.2 * 100)]$

c. New $Z = 603 [588 + (.15 * 100)]$

d. No effects, $24 < 36$ (slack)

17. a. Inspection

b. Yes, $10 - 7 = \$3$ of profit

19. a. $x_1 = 0, x_2 = 20, x_3 = 5, Z = 330$

b. $x_1 = 0, x_2 = 10, x_3 = 5, Z = 210$

c. No, because $15 > 12$

d. $C_1 \leq 12 = 20 - 8$

e. No change on quantities, new $Z = 305$

21. Yes, $9 < 12, x_4 = 24, z = 288$

23. Dual: Maximize $Z = 300y_1 + 200y_2$

Subject to: $20y_1 + 40y_2 \leq 5, 10y_1 + 5y_2 \leq 7,$

$$30y_1 + 10y_2 \leq 9$$

All variables ≥ 0; Primal, fewer constraints

25. Dual: Minimize $Z = 180y_1 + 50y_2 + 51y_3$

Subject to: $3y_1 + y_2 \leq 120, 2y_1 + y_3 \leq 12,$

All variables ≥ 0

27. a. 12.8

b. .6, $120 \leq b_2 \leq 270$

c. new $z = 972 + 78 = 10.50(270 - 240) * (4.6 - 2) = \$78$

29. a. No effect because slack = 648 minutes

b. $5

c. Pineapples, shadow price = $1.00/lb

d. $x_1 = 185, x_2 = 265, z = \$2,330$

e. No, since $4 \leq C_3 \leq 12$, yes, z increases by $z * 240$
new $z = \$2,760$

f. Yes, $.5 + .333 < 1.0, \triangle z = \$270$

31. a. Cutting, sewing, and inspecting are binding constraints.

b. Packing, because it has slack.

c. Shadow price = 2.9166, 460 minutes of overtime

d. Sewing $(4.25 > 3)$

e. Within the range of optimality; no change in variables; new $z = \$5,108$

33. a. Protein and fat, zero slack

b. $22 is the amount (cost) that x3 would have to decrease to come into the solution.

c. Amount of surplus of fiber

d. $11.78 \leq C_1 \leq 38, 19 \leq C_2 \leq 60.8$

f. $198.5 \leq b_3 \leq 635.2$

g. Z would decrease by $(19)(25) = \$475$

h. Sum of the percent changes exceeds 100%; obtain new solution.

35. Dual: Minimize $z = 24y_1 + 18y_2 + 32y_3 + 28y_4$

Subject to: $6y_1 + 3y_2 + 2y_3 \qquad \geq 4$

$$2y_1 + \qquad 8y_3 + 4y_4 \geq 3$$

$$y_1, y_2, y_3, y_4 \geq 0$$

Chapter 6 Transportation, Transshipment, and Assignment Problems

1. b. A-2 = 300, A-3 = 400, B-1 = 200, C-1 = 100, C-2 = 100, $z = 35,100$

c. A-1 = 300, A-2 = 400, B-3 = 200, B-2 = 200, $z = 40,200$

3. A-w_4 = 250, B-w_2 = 130, B-w_3 = 140, D_u-w_1 = 340, D_u-w_2 = 10, D_u-w_4 = 200, $z = \$16,910$

5. 1-2 = 15, 1-3 = 75, 2-1 = 105, 3-1 = 45, 3-2 = 60, $z = \$1,050$

7. A-3 = 100, B-3 = 200, C-1 = 50, C-2 = 150, $z = \$3,850$

9. b. R-Co = 90, R-Ci = 70, D-Ch = 75, D-Ci = 50, B-Ci = 30, $z = \$5,690$

c. R-Ch = 70, R-Co = 90, D-Ch = 5, D-Ci = 120,
   B-Ci = 30, z = 5,900, 5,900 − 5,690 = $210 extra

11. b. Ch-De = 48, Ch-Dn = 12, Ch-Kc = 4,
    Sl-Kc = 44, Om-Dn = 36, z = $792

13. a. 1-1 = 35, 2-2 = 45, 3-1 = 15, 3-2 = 5, 3-3 = 40,
    z = $725
    b. Shipment from source 1 to destination 2

15. b. x_{13} = 200, x_{23} = 300, x_{35} = 250, x_{36} = 250,
    z = $7,800

17. For C1: 1-1 = 200
            1-2 = 200
            1-4 = 150
            2-1 = 150
            2-3 = 400
            Z = 18,450
    For C2: 1-1 = 350
            1-2 = 150
            1-4 = 150
            2-2 = 50
            2-3 = 400
            Z = 18,800
    C1 is better than C2 by $350.

19. a. 1-C, 2-B, 3-A
    b. z = 46

21. a. A-Buf, B-Roc, C-Syr, D-Ith
    b. Travel time = 3.9 hours

23. b. A-2, B-1, C-4, D-3; Max z = 1,999

25. a. A-Roc, B-Syr, C-Ith, E-Buf, z = 2.2
    b. D will not be assigned.
    c. No alternate optimal solution

27. 1-C, 2-D, 3-A, 4-B, z = $290

29. a. min $z = 9x_{1A} + 7x_{1B} + 4x_{1C} + 6x_{1D} + 2x_{1E}$
       $+ 7x_{2A} + 4x_{2B} + 5x_{2C} + 2x_{2D} + 1x_{2E}$
       $+ 3x_{3A} + 4x_{3B} + 3x_{3C} + 2x_{3D} + 3x_{3E}$
       $+ 9x_{4A} + 7x_{4B} + 8x_{4C} + 9x_{4D} + 5x_{4E}$
       $+ 3x_{5A} + 2x_{5C} + 4x_{5D} + 3x_{5E}$

    Subject to: $x_{1A} + x_{1B} + x_{1C} + x_{1D} + x_{1E} = 1$
       $x_{2A} + x_{2B} + x_{2C} + x_{2D} + x_{2E} = 1$
       $x_{3A} + x_{3B} + x_{3C} + x_{3D} + x_{3E} = 1$
       $x_{4A} + x_{4B} + x_{4C} + x_{4D} + x_{4E} = 1$
       $x_{5A} + x_{5B} + x_{5C} + x_{5D} + x_{5E} = 1$
       $x_{1A} + x_{2A} + x_{3A} + x_{4A} + x_{5A} = 1$
       $x_{1B} + x_{2B} + x_{3B} + x_{4B} + x_{5B} = 1$
       $x_{1C} + x_{2C} + x_{3C} + x_{4C} + x_{5C} = 1$
       $x_{1D} + x_{2D} + x_{3D} + x_{4D} + x_{5D} = 1$
       $x_{1E} + x_{2E} + x_{3E} + x_{4E} + x_{5E} = 1$
       $x_{1A}, x_{1B}, x_{1C}, x_{1D}, x_{1E}, x_{2A}, x_{2B}, x_{2C}, x_{2D}, x_{2E},$
       $x_{3A}, x_{3B}, x_{3C}, x_{3D}, x_{3E}, x_{4A}, x_{4B}, x_{4C}, x_{4D}, x_{4E},$
       $x_{5A}, x_{5B}, x_{5C}, x_{5D}, x_{5E}$

    b. 1-E, 2-D, 3-C, 4-B, 5-A, z = 14

c. Yes; 1-C, 2-E, 3-D, 4-B, 5-A, z = 14
d. The minimum number of defectives = 14

31. b. 1-G, 2-M, 3-S, 4-J
    c. 21.9 hours

33. b. H-C = 30, H-T = 68, A-C = 5, A-Mi = 50,
    A-Me = 25, z = 851

35. a. $1,860
    b. A-2, A-3, B-2, C-1, C-2

37. Additional cost = $230

Chapter 6 Supplement (on CD-ROM)
Transportation and Assignment Solution
Procedures

1. a. A to 1 = 25, A to 2 = 25, B to 2 = 15, C to 2 = 10,
      C to 3 = 45
      TC = $1465
   b. Not optimal B-3, Reduced cost = −1
   c. e_{A3} = 1, e_{B1} = 5, e_{C1} = 14, e_{B3} = −1
   d. A to 1 = 25, A to 2 = 25, B to 3 = 15, C to 2 = 25,
      C to 3 = 30
   e. TC = $1,450

3. Optimal solution:
   P to C = 40, T to A = 20, T to B = 60, Ph to A = 50,
   Ph to C = 10
   TC = $940
   Alternate optimal solution:
   T to C = 10, T to A = 10, T to B = 60, Ph to A = 40,
   Pi to C = 40
   TC = $940

5. a. O_1 to D_1 = 40, O_1 to D_2 = 80, O_2 to D_4 = 40,
      O_2 to D_5 = 120, O_3 to D_3 = 150,
      O_3 to D_5 = 50, D_u to D_1 = 100, D_u to D_5 = 25
      TC = $4,260
   b. D_1 will be short 100 and D_5 will be short 25.

7. b. ELA to LA = 600, WLA to OC2 = 300,
      WLA to LB = 200, WLA to LA = 300,
      ET to OC1 = 300, ET to OC2 = 100
      TC = $8,000
   c. ELA to OC1 = 300, ELA to LA = 300,
      WLA to LB = 200, WLA to LA = 600,
      ET to OC2 = 400

9. a. A to 1 = 50, A to 2 = 50, B to 3 = 200, C to 2 = 100,
      C to 3 = 100
   b. TP = $3,000

11. A to 2 = 5, A to 3 = 45, B to 2 = 15, C to 1 = 25,
    C to 2 = 30
    TP = $1,860

13. TA to W1 = 300, PA to W2 = 200, PA to W3 = 200,
    PB to W2 = 200, PC to W3 = 200
    Z = TP = $43,800

15. a. 1 to B = 10, 1 to C = 30, 2 to A = 80, 3 to A = 10,
    3 to B = 70, 3 to D = 50
    TC = $6,480
    b. 1 to A = 10, 1 to B = 30, 2 to A = 80, 3 to B = 50,
    3 to C = 30, 3 to D = 50
    TC = $6,310

17. a. TC = $67,800
    b. TC = $67,000
    c. $800

19. a. 1 to D, 2 to C, 3 to B, 4 to A
    b. $240
    c. 1 to D, 2 to C, 3 to A, 4 to B
    TC = $240

21. A to Buf, B to Syr, C to Ith, D to Roc; travel time
    increases 0.1 hour.

23. a. 1 to D, 2 to B, 3 to C, 4 to A
    b. 205
    c. No

25. 1 to A, 2 to B, 3 to C, 4 to D; additional cost = $15

27. a. 1 to E, 2 to D, 3 to C, 4 to F, 5 to A; 10 def.
    b. B
    c. 1 to C, 2 to E, 3 to D, 4 to F, 5 to A; B idle

29. a. A to 2, B to 3, C to 1, D to 4
    b. 7.0
    c. A to 2, B to 3, C to 4, D to 1
    d. No, the objective is still minimization

Chapter 7   Integer Programming

1. $x_1 = 4, x_2 = 0, z = 120$
3. $x_1 = 2, x_2 = 3, z = 24$
5. $x_1 = 1.5, x_2 = 3, z = 28.5$
7. $x_1 = 1, x_2 = 0, x_3 = 1, x_4 = 0, z = \$130$
9. $x_1 = 1, x_2 = 0, x_3 = 1, x_4 = 1, z = 1.05$
11. $x_1 = 0, x_2 = 1, x_3 = 1, x_4 = 1, z = 545$
13. $x_1 = 25, x_2 = 0, x_3 = 0, x_4 = 13, z = 177.5$
15. $x_1 = 2, x_2 = 1, x_3 = 3, z = 30$
17. b. x_1 = number of M_1, x_2 = number of M_2
    y_1 = FC(0-1) for M_1, y_2 = FC(0-1) for M_2
    $x_1 = 9, x_2 = 0, y_1 = 1, y_2 = 0, z = 200$
19. A = number from A, B = number from B, etc.
    y_1 = 0 or 1 for A, y_2 = 0 or 1 for B, etc.
    $A = 100, D = 300, y_1 = 1, y_4 = 1, z = 81$
21. x_1 = location 1, x_2 = location 2, etc.; $x_2 = 1, x_3 = 1,$
    $z = 950$
23. $x_1 = 1, x_2 = 3, x_3 = 0, z = 91$
25. b. $A = 0, B = 450, C = 400, y_A = 0, y_B = 1,$
    $y_C = 1, z = \$10,025$
27. $x_1 = 0, x_2 = 9, x_3 = 0, z = 162$
29. $x_1 = 14, x_2 = x_3 = x_4 = 0, z = 14$

31. b. x_1 = number of lathes, $x_1 = 1$;
    x_2 = number of punch presses = 2, $z = \$67,000$
33. b. $x_{12} = 15,000, x_{13} = 8,000, x_{21} = 3,000,$
    $x_{23} = 16,000, x_{24} = 8,000,$
    $x_{32} = 15,000, x_{51} = 25,000, x_{74} = 24,000,$
    $y_1 = y_3 = y_5 = 1$
    $z = 901,500$ (Iowa City, Springfield, Oklahoma City)
35. a. $2^5 = 32$
    b. $2^{10} = 1024$
    c. $2^{15} = 32,768$
    d. $2^{18} = 262,144$
37. b. $x_{121} = 1, x_{232} = 1, x_{343} = 1, x_{454} = 1, x_{515} = 1$
    Optimal route: $1-2-3-4-5-1$
    Minimum cost = 14 minutes

Chapter 7 Supplement (on CD-ROM)   Methods of Solving Integer Programming Problems

1. b. $x_1 = 3.75, x_2 = 3.5$
    c. $x_1 \le 3, x_1 \ge 4$
    d. $x_1 = 3, x_2 = 4, Z = 350$
3. a. $x_1 = 7, x_2 = 0, Z = 35$
    b. $x_1 = 7, x_2 = .567, Z = 36.7$
5. $x_1 = 2.67, x_2 = 10, Z = 66$
7. $x_1 = 4, x_2 = 0, Z = 120$
9. Minimize $Z = 6x_1 + 4x_2$
    Subject to: $9x_1 + 2x_2 \ge 18$
    $2x_1 + 3x_2 \le 12$
    $x_1, x_2 \ge 0$, and α integer
    $x_1 = 2, x_2 = 3, Z = 24$
11. $x_1 = 2, x_2 = 2.67, z = 22.6$
13. a. $x_1 = 1, x_2 = 0, x_3 = 1, x_4 = 0, z = 130$
    b. $x_1 = 1, x_2 = 0, x_3 = 1, x_4 = 0, z = 130$
    c. Very difficult to solve manually
15. $x_1 = 1, x_2 = 1, Z = 6$
17. $x_1 = 1.5, x_2 = 1, Z = 9$
19. $x_1 = 7, x_2 = 2, Z = 29$
21. $x_1 = 7, x_2 = 2, Z = 29$

Chapter 8   Network Optimization Models

1.
Node	Distance	Shortest Route
2	10	1−2
3	15	1−3
4	14	1−2−4
5	20	1−2−4−5

3.
Node	Distance	Shortest Route
2	14	1−2
3	10	1−3
4	21	1−3−5−4
5	16	1−3−5
6	25	1−3−5−4−6

5. a.
Node	Distance	Shortest Route
2	5	1−2
3	5	1−3
4	11	1−3−4
5	14	1−3−4−5

   b. Round-trip distances are doubled the one-way distances
   c. No

7.
Node	Distance	Shortest Route
2	32	1−2
3	18	1−3
4	46	1−2−4
5	45	1−2−5
6	30	1−3−6
7	57	1−2−5−7
8	60	1−3−6−8
9	66	1−2−5−7−9
10	74	1−2−5−7−9−10
		Or 1−3−6−8−10

9.
Iteration	Connected Nodes
1	1−2
2	2−3
3	1−4
4	3−5
5	5−6
6	6−7
7	6−8
8	6−9

   Minimum = 69

11. Minimum = 96
13. Minimum = 29.5 miles
15. Minimum = $146
17. Total flow = 20
19. a. Total flow = 36
    b. Increase arc 3−5 by 2
21. a. Total flow = 17
    b. Total flow = 17
23. a. Total flow = 50
    b. Total flow = 54

Chapter 9   Nonlinear Optimization Models

1. a. $x = 3.75$
   b. $\dfrac{d^2y}{dx^2} = 8$; $x_2 = 8$, positive $\Rightarrow$ min
3. $x = +8$, $z = 58$, minimum cost is 58 rather than 68
5. Local maximum: $x = 2$, $z = 35$;
   local minimum: $x = 6$, $z = 3$
7. Local maximum: $x = 2$, $z = 40$;
   local minimum: $x = 4$, $z = 32$
9. $x = 14$, $z = 18$

11. Minimum: $x_1 = 2$, $x_2 = 2/3$, $z = -4$
13. Local maximum: $x_1 = 2.343$, $x_2 = 3.138$
15. Maximum: $x_1 = 2$, $x_2 = 3$, $z = 102$
17. Minimum: $x_1 = x_2 = 3.5$, $z = 57.75$
19. $x = 3$, $y = 29$
21. $x = 14$, $y = 18$
23. Maximum: $x_1 = 2$, $x_2 = 3$, $z = 102$
25. Minimum: $x_1 = x_2 = 3.5$, $z = 57.75$
27. b. $m_1 = 66.67$, $m_2 = 40$, $z = \$2,960$

Chapter 10   Multicriteria Models

1. a. Minimize $P_1u_1 + P_2u_2 + P_3u_3$
      Labor: $2x_1 + x_2 + 4x_3 + u_1 - v_1 = 160$ hours
   b. Profit: $4x_1 + 2x_2 + 3x_3 + u_2 - v_2 = \$300$
   c. Product #1: $x_1 + u_3 - v_3 = 10$ units
      Storage: $x_1 + 2x_2 + 3x_3 \leq 150$
      All variables ≥ 0
3. a. Soft, because of presence of deviational variables.
   b. 2nd constraint
   c. $x_1 = 80$, $x_2 = 0$, $u_2 = 0$, $v_1 = 200$
   d. $x_1 = 60$, $x_2 = 0$, $u_2 = 20$, $v_1 = 0$
5. $x_1 = 30$, $x_2 = 5$, $v_1 = 0$, $v_3 = 0$, $u_2 = 60$, $u_4 = 100$
7. a. $x_1 = x_2 = 3.43$
   b. $u_1 = u_2 = u_3 = 0$, $u_4 = .43$
9. $x_1 = 1.1$, $x_2 = 7.02$, $v_1 = 0$, $u_2 = 0$, $u_3 = 2.98$, $u_4 = 7.90$
11. $x_1 = 20$, $x_2 = 0$, $v_1 = 0$, $u_2 = 0$, $v_3 = 10$
13. $x_1 = 1.10$, $x_2 = 7.02$, $v_1 = 0$, $u_2 = 0$, $u_3 = 2.98$, $u_4 = 7.90$
15. $x_1 = 40$, $x_2 = 40$, $u_1 = u_2 = v_1 = v_2 = 0$, $u_3 = 80$
17. Memphis = .3071; Cleveland = .5346; Ft. Lauderdale = .1583
19. b. $.016 < .10$, consistent
21.

	A	B	C
A	1	5	4
B	$1/5$	1	3
C	$1/4$	$1/3$	1

22. $A = .5$; $B = .3$; $C = .2$
25. a. Yes
    b.

	Cost	Audience	Flex.
Television	.0683	.7235	.0764
Radio	.2746	.1932	.5285
Newspaper	.6571	.0833	.3452

   c. Television = .4637; Radio = .2465; Newspaper = .2898
27. a., b., c. and d (Answers will vary)

Chapter 11   Decision Theory

1. a. Max$(7, 8, -8) = 7$; choose a_1
   b. Max$(14, 15, 22) = 22$; choose a_3
   c. Min$(12, 8, 15)$; choose a_2

3. a. Split
   b. Split
   c. Split
   d. Split
   e. Split

5. a. Style A
   b. Style B
   c. Split
   d. Equally likely
   e. Style A

7. a. New staff
   b. Redesign
   c. New staff
   d. New staff or redesign
   e. New staff

9. New staff ($60 < 73 < 74$)

11. P(low) = .5, P(moderate) = .5

13. Residential = $13.2

15. 0.526

17. a. A, EMV$_A$ = $44,000
    b. If stable: P(stable) = .978, P(changing) = .022
       If changing: P(stable) = .343, P(changing) = .657
    d. 7.20
    e. Yes

19. a. If P(high) is less than 1/3, build small;
       if P(high) is greater than 1/3, build large.
    b. If P(high) is less than 1/3, build large;
       if P(high) is greater than 1/3, build small.

21. Alternative B; choose A if P(#2) is less than .444;
    choose A if P(#1) is greater than .556

23. Choose Job A

25. $113,000 > 105,000$; buy 2 machines

27. Choose large plant because 46 million $\geq$ 44.875
    million $\geq$ 44.2 million

Chapter 12   Markov Analysis

1. a. A = 70%, B = 30%
   b. 30%

3. A = .40, B = .60

5. a. .04
   b. .0448
   c. .1104
   d. .8896, .1104
   e. N = .889, B = .111

7. a.

From\To	A	B	C
A	.5	.3	.2
B	.5	.3	.2
C	.5	.3	.2

   b. A = .50, B = .30, C = .20

9. M = .362, E = .293, S = .345

11. a.

From\To	A	B	C
A	.7	.2	.1
B	.1	.6	.3
C	.3	.2	.5

   b. A = 389, B = 333, C = 278

13. a. A = .507, B = .392, C = .101
    b. A = .429, B = .2855, C = .2855.
       Yes, profit of $115.40 = (590.4 - 375)$

15. a. A, A = .70, A, B = .16, A, C = .14
    b. A = .500, B = .300, C = .200

17. Existing = $240/day; proposed = $600/day;
    proposed system would have a higher expected cost.

19. a. $\begin{bmatrix} 1.905 & .476 \\ .714 & 1.429 \end{bmatrix}$

    b. $\begin{bmatrix} .143 & 0 \\ 2.857 & .200 \end{bmatrix}$

    c. $\begin{bmatrix} 1.250 & 0 \\ .313 & .250 \end{bmatrix}$

21. a.
$$\begin{array}{c c} & \begin{array}{cccc} P & b & 1 & 2 \end{array} \\ \begin{array}{c} P \\ b \\ 1 \\ 2 \end{array} & \begin{bmatrix} 1 & 0 & 0 & 0 \\ 0 & 1 & 0 & 0 \\ .8 & 0 & 0 & .2 \\ .8 & .2 & 0 & 0 \end{bmatrix} \end{array}$$

    b. $\begin{bmatrix} 1 & .2 \\ 0 & 1 \end{bmatrix}$

    c. $\begin{bmatrix} .96 & .04 \\ .80 & .20 \end{bmatrix}$

    d. $128,000

23. New system would be justified.
    Expected bad debt (current) = $4,130.
    Expected bad debt (proposed) = $2,560

25. a. Absorbing
    b. Absorbing
    c. Cyclical
    d. Transient
    e. Absorbing
    f. Cyclical
    g. Transient

Chapter 13   Waiting-Line Models

3. a. $L_q = 2.25$
    b. $W_q = 9$ minutes
    c. $P_0 = .25$
    d. $P(x \leq 6) = .762$
    e. $P(x \geq 3) = .875$
    f. $P(t \leq 2) = .48624$
    g. $P(t > 4) = .26363$
    h. $P(2 \leq t \leq 4) = .2501$

5. a. 65%
    b. 1.21 customers
    c. 1.86 customers
    d. .465 minute
    e. .715 minute
    f. .35
    g. .148
    h. .82
    i. .714 minute

7. a. 1.4 minutes
    b. 1.633
    c. .6 minute
    d. 70%
    e. .30

9. a. .933
    b. 12.273
    c. 15.073
    d. 8.77 minutes
    e. 10.76 minutes
    f. .016
    g. .063
    h. .055
    i. .167
    j. .878

11. 4; 5

13. a. 56
    b. 3
    c. 3

15. 5 clerks

17. a. 3 crews
    b. .67
    c. .444

19. a. .004 machine
    b. 3 clerks

21. a. $L_q = 2.41$
    b. $L = 3.26$; $W_q = .71$ minute; $W = .96$ minute; $P = .85$

23. $\rho = .6$
    $P_0 = .460$
    $P_{n=2} = .1656$
    $L = .90$
    $L_q = .36$

$W = 3.98$ minutes
$W_q = 1.62$ minutes

25. a. $L_q = 1.18$; $W = 3.86$ minutes
    b. $P_0 = .25$
    c. $L_q = 1.18$ customers

27. $\rho = 83.8\%$
    $P_0 = .231$
    $P_{n=2} = .16$
    $L = 2.30$
    $L_q = 1.53$
    $W = 2.49$ hours
    $W_q = 1.66$ hours

29. $\rho = .59$
    $P_0 = .016$
    $L_q = .13$
    $L = .54$
    $W_q = 1.58$ minutes
    $W = 6.6$ minutes

31. a. 90%
    b. $A = 11.73$
      $B_0 = 1$
      $B_1 = .7$
      $B_2 = .4$
      $B_3 = .10$
      $W_1 = .12$ hour
      $W_2 = .3045$ hour
      $W_3 = 2.13$ hours
    c. $L_1 = .36$; $L_2 = .91$; $L_3 = 6.39$

33. a. $P = .733$
    b. $A = 32.57$
      $B_0 = 1$
      $B_1 = .87$
      $B_2 = .60$
      $B_3 = .40$
      $B_4 = .27$
      $W_1 = .035$ hour
      $W_2 = .059$ hour
      $W_3 = .128$
      $W_4 = .284$
      $L_1 = .07$
      $L_2 = .236$
      $L_3 = .384$
      $L_4 = .568$
    c. $B_1 = .87$; $W_1 = .035$ hour; $L_1 = .070$
    d. Waiting time in any class is affected by arrival rate of its class and the "B factor" of the immediately higher priority class

35. a. 4 entrants/minute
    b. .25 entrant/minute
    c. .167 arrivals/minute (or 10/hour)

    d. $P > (t > 5) = .2865$
    e. $P = (3 \le t \le 5) = .1859$
    f. $P(t > 2) = .2349$
    g. $L = 2.012$ entrants
    h. $L_q = 1.344$ entrants
    i. $W = 12.048$ minutes
    j. $W_q = 8.048$ minutes

37. a. 1.4 minutes
    b. 1.633
    c. .6 minutes
    d. 70%
    e. .3

39. a. at least 3
    b. 95% $\Rightarrow$ $-.125$ or 0; 99% $= 1.95$ or 2
    c. $s = 4$

41. a. 3 crews
    b. .67
    c. .444

43. a. .004 machine
    b. 3 clerks

45. a. $L_q = 1.18$, $W = 3.86$ minutes
    b. .25
    c. 1.18 customers

47. a. $P_0 = .012$
    b. $W_q = 9.21$ hour
    c. $L = 3.588$
    d. $P_0 = .012$

Chapter 14   Simulation

1. b. Approximate results
    c. Random variability

3. b. Average sets $= 1.2$
    c. Average sets $= 1.8$
    d. Random variation;
       expected weekly sales $= 11.15 > 6$
       (simulated weekly sales)

5. b. .8 car

7. b. 30%
    c. 20%, random variation
    d. Confirming $= 30\%$, reservations $= 40\%$

9. a. 2.166 breakdowns
    b. 1 month; 1 is close to $(.135)(12)$; reasonable
    c. Probability $= (.135)(.135) = .018$, very small

11. 30%

13. 5.855 minutes

15. Mean $= .87$ hour

17. Mean $= 7.03$ minutes

19. Mean $= 116.4$ minutes

21. $2-A$, $3-B$, $1-C$; average order size $= 12.66$ units

23. a. 50%
    b. Uniform; 0 to 1 minute
    d. 1.28 minutes

25. Residential $= \$4,928$, Commercial $= \$3,665$,
    Total $= \$8,593$

27. Average $= 2,230.16$ sheets

29. Ball $1 = 1,550$ points, ball $2 = 2,950$ points,
    ball $3 = 450$ points

31. a. 12.56 minutes
    b. Total cost, original equipment $= \$44.05$; total cost,
       new equipment $= \$37.68$

33. a. 40%
    b. 8 units

Tables

A. Areas under the Normal Curve, 0 to z, 793
B. Cumulative Poisson Probabilities, 794

Table A		Areas under the Normal Curve, 0 to z								

z	.00	.01	.02	.03	.04	.05	.06	.07	.08	.09
0.0	.0000	.0040	.0080	.0120	.0160	.0199	.0239	.0279	.0319	.0359
0.1	.0398	.0438	.0478	.0517	.0557	.0596	.0636	.0675	.0714	.0753
0.2	.0793	.0832	.0871	.0910	.0948	.0987	.1026	.1064	.1103	.1141
0.3	.1179	.1217	.1255	.1293	.1331	.1388	.1406	.1443	.1480	.1517
0.4	.1554	.1591	.1828	.1664	.1700	.1736	.1772	.1808	.1844	.1879
0.5	.1915	.1950	.1985	.2019	.2054	.2088	.2123	.2157	.2190	.2224
0.6	.2257	.2291	.2324	.2357	.2389	.2422	.2454	.2486	.2517	.2549
0.7	.2580	.2611	.2642	.2673	.2703	.2734	.2784	.2794	.2823	.2852
0.8	.2881	.2910	.2939	.2967	.2995	.3023	.3051	.3078	.3106	.3133
0.9	.3159	.3186	.3212	.3238	.3264	.3289	.3315	.3340	.3365	.3389
1.0	.3413	.3438	.3461	.3485	.3508	.3531	.3554	.3577	.3599	.3621
1.1	.3643	.3665	.3686	.3708	.3729	.3749	.3770	.3790	.3810	.3830
1.2	.3849	.3869	.3888	.3907	.3925	.3944	.3962	.3980	.3997	.4015
1.3	.4032	.4049	.4066	.4082	.4099	.4115	.4131	.4147	.4162	.4177
1.4	.4192	.4207	.4222	.4236	.4251	.4265	.4279	.4292	.4306	.4319
1.5	.4332	.4345	.4357	.4370	.4382	.4394	.4405	.4418	.4429	.4441
1.6	.4452	.4463	.4474	.4484	.4495	.4505	.4515	.4525	.4535	.4545
1.7	.4554	.4564	.4573	.4582	.4591	.4599	.4608	.4516	.4625	.4633
1.8	.4641	.4649	.4656	.4664	.4671	.4678	.4686	.4693	.4699	.4706
1.9	.4713	.4719	.4726	.4732	.4738	.4744	.4750	.4756	.4761	.4767

(continued)

z	.00	.01	.02	.03	.04	.05	.06	.07	.08	.09
2.0	.4772	.4778	.4783	.4788	.4793	.4798	.4803	.4808	.4812	.4817
2.1	.4821	.4826	.4830	.4834	.4838	.4842	.4846	.4850	.4854	.4857
2.2	.4861	.4864	.4868	.4871	.4875	.4878	.4881	.4884	.4887	.4890
2.3	.4893	.4896	.4898	.4901	.4904	.4906	.4909	.4911	.4913	.4916
2.4	.4918	.4920	.4922	.4925	.4927	.4929	.4931	.4932	.4934	.4936
2.5	.4938	.4940	.4941	.4943	.4945	.4946	.4948	.4949	.4951	.4952
2.6	.4953	.4955	.4956	.4957	.4959	.4960	.4961	.4962	.4963	.4964
2.7	.4965	.4966	.4967	.4968	.4969	.4970	.4971	.4972	.4973	.4974
2.8	.4974	.4975	.4976	.4977	.4977	.4978	.4979	.4979	.4980	.4981
2.9	.4981	.4982	.4982	.4983	.4984	.4984	.4985	.4985	.4986	.4986
3.0	.4987	.4987	.4987	.4988	.4988	.4989	.4989	.4989	.4990	.4990

Table B   Cumulative Poisson Probabilities

$$P(x \le c) = \sum_{x=0}^{x=c} \frac{\mu^2 \cdot \theta^{-\mu}}{x^1}$$

μ/x	0	1	2	3	4	5	6	7	8	9
0.05	.951	.999	1.000							
0.10	.905	.995	1.000							
0.15	.861	.990	.999	1.000						
0.20	.819	.982	.999	1.000						
0.25	.779	.974	.998	1.000						
0.30	.741	.963	.996	1.000						
0.35	.705	.951	.994	1.000						
0.40	.670	.938	.992	.999	1.000					

Table B	Cumulative Poisson Probabilities (*continued*)								
μ/x	0	1	2	3	4	5	6	7	8	9
0.45	.638	.925	.989	.999	1.000					
0.50	.607	.910	.986	.998	1.000					
0.55	.577	.894	.982	.998	1.000					
0.60	.549	.878	.977	.997	1.000					
0.65	.522	.861	.972	.996	.999	1.000				
0.70	.497	.844	.966	.994	.999	1.000				
0.75	.472	.827	.960	.993	.999	1.000				
0.80	.449	.809	.953	.991	.999	1.000				
0.85	.427	.791	.945	.989	.998	1.000				
0.90	.407	.772	.937	.987	.998	1.000				
0.95	.387	.754	.929	.984	.997	1.000				
1.0	.368	.736	.920	.981	.996	.999	1.000			
1.1	.333	.699	.900	.974	.995	.999	1.000			
1.2	.301	.663	.880	.966	.992	.998	1.000			
1.3	.273	.627	.857	.957	.989	.998	1.000			
1.4	.247	.592	.833	.946	.986	.997	.999	1.000		
1.5	.223	.558	.809	.934	.981	.996	.999	1.000		
1.6	.202	.525	.783	.921	.976	.994	.999	1.000		
1.7	.183	.493	.757	.907	.970	.992	.998	1.000		
1.8	.165	.463	.731	.891	.964	.990	.997	.999	1.000	
1.9	.150	.434	.704	.875	.956	.987	.997	.999	1.000	
2.0	.135	.406	.677	.857	.947	.983	.995	.999	1.000	
2.2	.111	.355	.623	.819	.928	.975	.993	.998	1.000	
2.4	.091	.308	.570	.779	.904	.964	.988	.997	.999	1.000
2.6	.074	.267	.518	.736	.877	.951	.983	.995	.999	1.000
2.8	.061	.231	.470	.692	.848	.935	.976	.992	.998	.999

Table B Cumulative Poisson Probabilities (continued)

μ/x	0	1	2	3	4	5	6	7	8	9	10	11	12	13	14	15	16	17	18	19	20
3.0	.050	.199	.423	.647	.815	.916	.966	.988	.996	.999	1.000										
3.2	.041	.171	.380	.603	.781	.895	.955	.983	.994	.998	1.000										
3.4	.033	.147	.340	.558	.744	.871	.942	.977	.992	.997	.999	1.000									
3.6	.027	.126	.303	.515	.706	.844	.927	.969	.988	.996	.999	1.000									
3.8	.022	.107	.269	.474	.668	.816	.909	.960	.984	.994	.998	.999	1.000								
4.0	.018	.092	.238	.433	.629	.785	.889	.949	.979	.992	.997	.999	1.000								
4.2	.015	.078	.210	.395	.590	.753	.868	.936	.972	.989	.996	.999	1.000								
4.4	.012	.066	.185	.359	.551	.720	.844	.921	.964	.985	.994	.998	.999	1.000							
4.6	.010	.056	.163	.326	.513	.686	.818	.905	.955	.980	.992	.997	.999	1.000							
4.8	.008	.048	.143	.294	.476	.651	.791	.887	.944	.975	.990	.996	.999	1.000							
5.0	.007	.040	.125	.265	.441	.616	.762	.867	.932	.968	.986	.995	.998	.999	1.000						
5.2	.006	.034	.109	.238	.406	.581	.732	.845	.918	.960	.982	.993	.997	.999	1.000						
5.4	.005	.029	.095	.213	.373	.546	.702	.822	.903	.951	.978	.990	.996	.999	1.000						
5.6	.004	.024	.082	.191	.342	.512	.670	.797	.886	.941	.972	.988	.995	.998	.999	1.000					
5.8	.003	.021	.072	.170	.313	.478	.638	.771	.867	.929	.965	.984	.993	.997	.999	1.000					

Table B Cumulative Poisson Probabilities (continued)

μ/x	0	1	2	3	4	5	6	7	8	9	10	11	12	13	14	15	16	17	18	19	20
6.0	.003	.017	.062	.151	.285	.446	.606	.744	.847	.916	.957	.980	.991	.996	.999	.999	1.000				
6.2	.002	.015	.054	.134	.259	.414	.574	.716	.826	.902	.949	.975	.989	.995	.998	.999	1.000				
6.4	.002	.012	.046	.119	.235	.384	.542	.687	.803	.886	.939	.969	.986	.994	.997	.999	1.000				
6.6	.001	.010	.040	.105	.213	.355	.511	.658	.780	.869	.927	.963	.982	.992	.997	.999	.999	1.000			
6.8	.001	.007	.030	.082	.173	.301	.450	.599	.729	.830	.915	.955	.978	.990	.996	.998	.999	1.000			
7.0	.001	.007	.030	.082	.173	.301	.450	.599	.729	.830	.901	.947	.973	.987	.994	.998	.999	1.000			
7.2	.001	.006	.025	.072	.156	.276	.420	.569	.703	.810	.887	.937	.967	.984	.993	.997	.999	.999	1.000		
7.4	.001	.005	.022	.063	.140	.253	.392	.539	.676	.788	.871	.926	.961	.980	.991	.996	.998	.999	1.000		
7.6	.001	.004	.019	.055	.125	.231	.365	.510	.648	.765	.854	.915	.954	.976	.989	.995	.998	.999	1.000		
7.8	.000	.004	.016	.048	.112	.210	.338	.481	.620	.741	.835	.902	.945	.971	.986	.993	.997	.999	1.000		
8.0	.000	.003	.014	.042	.100	.191	.313	.453	.593	.717	.816	.888	.936	.966	.983	.992	.996	.998	.999	1.000	
8.2	.000	.003	.012	.037	.089	.174	.290	.425	.566	.692	.796	.873	.926	.960	.979	.990	.995	.998	.999	1.000	
8.4	.000	.002	.010	.032	.079	.157	.267	.400	.537	.666	.774	.857	.915	.952	.975	.987	.994	.997	.999	1.000	
8.6	.000	.002	.009	.030	.074	.150	.256	.386	.523	.653	.763	.849	.909	.949	.973	.986	.993	.997	.999	1.000	
8.8	.000	.002	.007	.024	.062	.128	.226	.348	.482	.614	.729	.822	.889	.935	.964	.981	.990	.995	.998	.999	1.000
9.0	.000	.001	.006	.021	.055	.116	.207	.324	.456	.587	.706	.803	.876	.926	.959	.978	.989	.995	.998	.999	1.000
9.5	.000	.001	.004	.015	.040	.089	.165	.269	.392	.522	.645	.752	.836	.898	.940	.967	.982	.991	.996	.998	.999

Index

A

Absorbing systems, 631–639, 641
Access, 12
Additivity, 111, 135
Aggregate planning, 294–297
Agricultural problems, 186–189, 194
Akbay, K., 455
Algebraic approach, 614–616, 624–625, 641
Algorithms
  defined, 10, 107, 135
  maximal flow problems, 388–391
  minimum spanning tree problem, 370,
    384–387, 401
  shortest-route problem, 371–384
    defined, 401
    Excel solution, 378–384
    labeling procedure, 371–375
    linear programming and, 376–378
    objective, 370
    procedure for determining, 375–376
Alternatives, list of, 541
American Airlines, 29
Analysis
  break-even, 20–27, 30
  cost-volume, 20
  data envelopment, 189–192, 194
  facility location, 297–298, 341–344, 351
  Markov; *see* Markov analysis
  mathematical, 5
  of models, 10–11
  sensitivity, 208–226
    concept of, 208
    decision theory, 573–578
    defined, 31, 237
    duality, 226–236
    Excel solutions, 219–224
    integer programming and, 329
    minimization problem, 109, 126–129, 219
    multiple changes, 224–226
    objective function coefficient, change in value of,
      209–213
    probability estimates, 573–578
    problems, 246–270

Analysis—*Cont.*
  sensitivity—*Cont.*
    purpose of, 11, 208
    RHS value of a constraint, changes in, 213–219
    shadow price, 214–216, 231, 237
    solved problems, 238–246
    summary of, 226
Analytical hierarchy process (AHP), 493–503
  consistency check, 496–501, 508
  defined, 508
  Excel solutions, 501–503
  pairwise comparisons, 495–501, 509
  proportion matrix, 498–500
  reciprocal rating approach, 496
  when to use, 493
Any service distribution queuing model, 692–694
Arcs, 370, 401
Aronson, Jay, 13
Ashe, M., 302
Assignment problems, 192, 194, 298–303
Assumptions
  of break-even analysis, 24–25
  finite queue length model, 698
  of linear programming models, 111–112
  of Markov analysis, 639
  of models, 7–8
  of Poisson distribution, 662–666
  regression, 71–72
AT&T, 29
Averages, moving
  advantages of, 43
  centered, 61–63, 87
  computation of, 42–43
  defined, 88
  Excel solutions, 45–47
  weighted, 44–45
Averaging techniques
  exponential smoothing
    defined, 88
    double, 55
    Excel solutions, 49–50
    formula for, 47–48
    trend-adjusted, 55, 58–59, 60

Averaging techniques—*Cont.*
   moving averages
      advantages of, 43
      centered, 61–63, 87
      computation of, 42–43
      defined, 88
      Excel solutions, 45–47
      weighted, 44–45
   naive forecasts, 42, 61, 88

B

Backtracking, 375
Balking, 667, 711
Bangash, A., 27
Barkman, M., 193
Bayiz, M., 86
Bell Labs Research and Development, 27
Binary decisions, 325
Binding constraints, 130, 135, 213–219
Blending problems, 164–168, 194
Bollapragada, R., 27
Box-Jenkins technique, 87
Branches, 370
Break-even analysis
   assumptions of, 24–25
   break-even point, 23–24, 30
   components of, 20–23
   defined, 20
   Excel solutions, 25–26
   summary of, 27
Break-even point (BEP), 23–24, 30
Brown, D., 709
Budget constraints, 155–156, 177
Butler, J., 579

C

Calling populations, 662, 711
Canadian Pacific Railway, 28
Capacity, unused, 130
Capacity decisions, 660; *see also* Waiting-line models
Cases
   Big Bank, 721
   Direct Marketing, 204–205
   Furnace County Emergency Response Routes, 420
   Gnomial Functions, Inc., 100–101
   Green Daisy Company, 34
   Hi-Tech Incorporated, 534–535
   Koch International Incorporated, 469–470
   Krohler Supermarkets, 781–782
   Memorial Hospital, 657
   MKGP Construction Company, 602–603
   Red Brand Canners, 270–273
   Son, Ltd., 150–151
   Suburban Suntime, 365–366
   Sunshine Tomato Inc., 321

Cell, 16
Centered moving average, 61–63, 87
Certainty
   decision making under, 543–544
   defined, 581
   degree of, 541–542
Certainty requirement, 112, 135
Chebeskov, A., 579
Chi-square goodness-of-fit test, 663, 668, 708
Chipita International Inc., 28
Chiu, H., 15
Clerkx, M., 400
Coefficient, objective function, 209–213
Coefficient of optimism, 547, 581
Collaborative-planning (CP), 400
Complete uncertainty, decision making under, 544–551
Computer Aided Routing and Scheduling System (CARS), 709
Computer simulation
   discrete distribution with more than two outcomes, 747–749
   discrete distribution with two outcomes, 746
   inventory analysis, 752–757
   random number generation, 743–746
   waiting lines, 749–752
Conditional distributions, 71
Consistency
   checking for, 496–501
   defined, 508
Consistency ratio, 496–497, 508
Constant service time queuing model, 695–696
Constrained optimization, 106, 113, 135, 433; *see also* Linear programming
Constrained problem, one decision variable, 433–439, 458–459
Constraints
   binding, 130, 135, 213–219
   bond, 180
   budget, 155–156, 177
   conflict between, 475
   defined, 106, 135
   demand, 283
   either-or, 331
   elements of, 110–111
   equality, 444–449, 459–463
   global, 474, 476, 487, 508
   goal, 474, 476, 487, 508
   hard, 474–475, 508
   inequality, 449–454
   multiple, 451–454
   nonbinding, 213–214
   nongoal, 474, 476
   nonnegativity, 111, 114, 116, 136
   plotting of, 115–119
   proportionality, 188

Constraints—*Cont.*
redundant, 133, 136
right-hand side, 208, 213–219, 237
soft, 474–475, 509
transition, 182
0-1, 324–325, 329–332, 352
Consumer surveys, 39, 87
Continental Airlines, 28
Continuous distribution, 743
Continuous random variable, 663
Continuous simulation, 726
Control, of forecasts, 76–84
Controlled conditions, 724
Corner points, 125, 135
Correlation coefficient, 67–68
Cost-volume analysis, 20; *see also* Break-even
analysis
Costs
fixed, 20–21, 30
forecast development, 84
total variable, 22–23, 31
variable, 21–22, 31
waiting lines, 660–661, 690–692
CSX Railroad, 709
Customer arrivals, 662–663
Customer source, 662
Cycles, techniques for, 64–65
Cyclical systems, 630–632, 641
Cyclical variation, 40, 87

D

Dantzig, George, 106
Data Analysis, Excel add-in, 16, 19
Data cells, 162
Data envelopment analysis (DEA), 189–192, 194
Database management systems (DBMS), 12
de Blois, Y., 350
de Kok, T., 400
Decision criterion, 542, 581
Decision-making models
analytical hierarchy process (AHP), 493–503
consistency check, 496–501, 508
defined, 508
Excel solutions, 501–503
pairwise comparisons, 495–501, 509
proportion matrix, 498–500
reciprocal rating approach, 496
when to use, 493
under certainty, 543–544
under complete uncertainty, 544–551
goal programming
defined, 474, 508
deviation variables, 475–476, 508
Excel solutions, 482–493
goal constraints, 474, 476, 487, 508

Decision-making models—*Cont.*
goal programming—*Cont.*
graphical solutions, 478–482
introduction to, 474
versus linear programming, 474–475
model formulation, 476–482
no feasible solutions, 132
objectives of, 475
satisficing, 475, 509
weighted goals, 490–493, 509
under risk, 552–556
Decision Sciences, 5
Decision Sciences Institute (DSI), 5, 30
Decision support systems (DSS), 12–13, 27
Decision theory
with additional information, 567–573
applications of, 540
components, 540–542
decision making under certainty, 543–544
decision making under complete uncertainty,
544–551
decision making under risk, 552–556
decision trees, 556–567, 581
Excel solutions, 549–551, 555–556, 559–567
payoff tables, 542–543, 582
problems, 595–602
sensitivity analysis, 573–578
sequential decisions, 557, 559, 564–567, 582
solved problems, 582–594
utility, 578–580, 582
Decision trees, 556–567, 581
Decision variables
defined, 6–7, 30, 135
linear programming and, 109, 113, 125
models with one
constrained problem, 433–439, 458–459
unconstrained problem, 425–432, 457–458
models with two
equality constraints, 444–449, 459–463
multiple constraints, 451–454
single inequality constraint, 449–454
unconstrained problem, 439–443
Deere and Company, 193
Degree of certainty, 8, 541–542
Dell Computers, 28
Delphi technique, 39, 87
Delta Airlines, 29
Demand, 41
Demand constraints, 283
Dependent variables, 65
Derivative, partial, 440, 444–445, 456
Desrosiers, J., 439
Destinations, 276
Deterministic decision models
defined, 30

Deterministic decision models—*Cont.*
  integer programming, 324–366; *see also* Linear
    programming
    case (Suburban Suntime), 365–366
    difficulties in solving problems, 349–350
    divisibility requirements and, 111–112
    Excel solutions, 326–329
    facility location problem, 341–344, 351
    fixed-charge problem, 333–336, 351
    formulating problems with 0-1 constraints,
      324–325, 329–332, 352
    graphical representation of, 325–326
    introduction, 324
    knapsack problem, 340–341, 351
    mixed-integer, 324, 351, 507
    problems, 357–365
    pure-integer, 324, 351
    sensitivity analysis, 329
    set-covering problem, 336–339, 351
    solved problems, 352–356
    traveling salesperson problem, 344–349, 351–352
    types of, 324–325
    0-1 integer problems, 324–325, 329–332, 352
  linear programming; *see* Linear programming
  multicriteria decision-making models; *see* Multicriteria
    decision-making models
  network models; *see* Network models
  nonlinear programming; *see* Nonlinear programming
  when used, 8
Deterministic simulations, 727, 730
Deviation variables, 475–476, 508
Diet problems, 163–164, 194
Discrete distribution, 743, 746–749
Discrete random variable, 663
Discrete simulation, 726
Distributions
  conditional, 71
  continuous, 743
  discrete, 743, 746–749
  empirical, 733
  exponential, 663, 669–672, 737–738, 746
  normal, 738–739, 746
  Poisson, 662–666, 692–701
  theoretical, 733, 735–736
  uniform, 736–737, 743–746
Divisibility assumption, 111, 135
Double exponential smoothing, 55
Double script notation, 166
Double subscript notation, 174, 187
Dual, 226, 237
Duality
  adding another variable, 232
  comparison of the primal and dual solutions, 231
  computational considerations, 232–236

Duality—*Cont.*
  economic interpretation of the dual, 231–232
  formulating the dual, 227–230
Duke, K., 302
Dumas, Y., 439
Dyer, J., 579

E
E-auction, 507
e-RFQ, 507
Economic order quantity, 424
Edmunds, T., 579
Effectiveness, measure of, 11, 31
Efficiency of sample information (EVSI), 570–571
Either-or alternatives, 330
Either-or constraints, 331
Empirical distributions, 733
Emptoris, 507
EOQ, 424
Equal likelihood criterion, 548–549, 581
Equality constraints, 444–449, 459–463
Erkut, E., 761
Errors, in forecasts, 77–82
Excel
  add-ins, 16, 19
  analytical hierarchy process (AHP), 501–503
  assignment problems using, 300–303
  break-even point, 25–26
  computer simulation
    discrete distribution with more than two outcomes,
      747–749
    discrete distribution with two outcomes, 746
    inventory analysis, 752–757
    random number generation, 743–746
    waiting lines, 749–752
  decision making under complete uncertainty, 549–551
  decision making under risk, 555–556
  DSS, used to set up, 12
  estimating trend, 53–57
  explanatory models, 72–76
  exponential probability, 672–673
  exponential smoothing, 49–50
  formulas and functions, 18–19
  goal programming problems, 482–493
  goal-seek function, 25–26, 705–707
  integer programming problems, 326–329
  linear programming, 157–163
  MAD, MSE, MPE, 83–84
  for Markov analysis, 616–621, 625–630, 636–639
  moving averages, 45–47
  multiple-channel model, 687
  one-decision variable
    constrained problem, 435–438
    unconstrained problem, 429–433

Excel—*Cont.*
   Poisson probability using, 665–666
   printing worksheets, 19
   seasonal relatives, 63–64
   sensitivity analysis, 219–224
   set covering problems, 337–339
   shortest-route problem, 378–384
   single-channel model, 678, 693–698, 700–701
   transportation problems, 280–287
   transshipment problems, 291–294
   traveling salesperson problem, 348–349
   trend-adjusted exponential smoothing, 59, 60
   two decision variables
      multiple constraints, 451–454
      single equality constraint, 446–449
      unconstrained problem, 442–443
   using TreePlan, 559–567
   using worksheets, 16–18
Excel 2003 Bible, 20
Executive opinion, 39, 87
Exit, 673
Expected monetary value (EMV), 552–553, 554, 581
Expected opportunity loss (EOL), 553, 554, 581
Expected payoff under certainty (EPC), 554, 581
Expected profit, 571
Expected regret, 581
Expected return, 565–566
Expected value of perfect information (EVPI), 553–554,
     571, 581
Expected value of sample information (EVSI), 570, 581
Experiments, design of, 730
Explanatory forecasting models
   defined, 88
   multiple regression, 66, 72–76, 87
   regression assumptions, 71–72
   simple linear regression, 50, 65–71, 87
Exponential distribution, 663, 669–672, 737–738, 746
Exponential smoothing
   defined, 88
   double, 55
   Excel solutions, 49–50
   formula for, 47–48
   trend-adjusted, 55, 58–59, 60
Extreme point approach, 119–121, 128–129, 135
Extreme point theorem, 119, 135
Extreme points, 125

F

Facility location problem, 297–298, 341–344, 351
Feasibility, range of, 214–219, 237
Feasible solution, 110, 135
Feasible solution space, 119, 135, 433–434
Federal Reserve Bank, 28
Financial planning problems, 176–180, 194

Financial problems for banks, 176–179
Finite calling population, 662, 698–700, 711
Finite queue length model, 696–698
First-come, first-served (FCFS), 667
Fitzsimmons, James A., 781
Fixed-charge problem, 333–336, 351
Fixed costs, 20–21, 30
Fixed-interval simulations, 726–727, 762
Flow capacities, 387
Flow conservation, 387
Flow networks, 370
Focus forecasting, 87
Forecasting, 36–101
   accuracy and control, 76–84
   case (Gnomial Functions, Inc.), 100–101
   costs of developing, 84
   errors, 77–82
   explanatory models
      defined, 88
      multiple regression, 66, 72–76, 87
      regression assumptions, 71–72
      simple linear regression, 50, 65–71, 87
   exponential smoothing
      defined, 88
      double, 55
      Excel solutions, 49–50
      formula for, 47–48
      trend-adjusted, 55, 58–59, 60
   importance of, 38
   judgmental methods, 87
   moving averages
      advantages of, 43
      centered, 61–63, 87
      computation of, 42–43
      defined, 88
      Excel solutions, 45–47
      weighted, 44–45
   problems, 91–99
   qualitative, 39, 87
   quantitative, 87
   selection of approach, 84–85
   solved problems, 89–90
   time series data
      defined, 39, 88
      naive, 42, 61, 88
      techniques for averaging; *see* Techniques for
        averaging
      techniques for cycles, 64–65
      techniques for seasonality, 39–41, 59–64, 88
      techniques for trend; *see* Techniques for trend
   types of, 85
   uses for, 38
Fundamental matrix, 635, 641
Fundamental theorem of linear programming, 125, 135

G

General Electric, 28, 30, 455
Global maximum, 426, 456
Global minimum, 426, 456
Goal constraints, 474, 476, 487, 508
Goal programming; *see also* Linear programming
  defined, 474, 508
  deviation variables, 475–476, 508
  Excel solutions, 482–493
  goal constraints, 474, 476, 487, 508
  graphical solutions, 478–482
  introduction to, 474
  versus linear programming, 474–475
  model formulation, 476–482
  no feasible solution, 132
  objectives of, 475
  satisficing, 475, 509
  weighted goals, 490–493, 509
Goal-seek feature, in Excel, 25–26, 705–707
Goals
  defined, 474, 508
  prioritized, 483
  weighted, 490–493, 509
Gordon, L., 761
Graphical linear programming, 107, 115–119, 135; *see also* Linear programming
Graphical models, 7

H

Hard constraints, 474–475, 508
Harlan, R., 507
Hewlett-Packard, 29
Hicks, R., 439
Hierarchy diagram, 494, 509
Histogram, 744–746
Holweg, M., 640
Homoscedasticity, 71
Hongkong International Terminals, 15
Hsu, C., 350
Huntley, C., 709
Hurwicz criterion, 547–548, 549, 581

I

IBM, 29
Identity matrix, 634
If-then alternatives, 330
Independence, 71
Independent variables, 65
Inequality constraints, 449–454
Infinite calling population, 662, 711
Information technology
  database management systems, 12
  decision support systems, 12–13, 27
  Excel; *see* Excel

Insignificance, range of, 212–213, 237
Institute for Operations Research and the Management Sciences (INFORMS), 5, 30
Integer programming, 324–366; *see also* Linear programming
  case (Suburban Suntime), 365–366
  difficulties in solving problems, 349–350
  divisibility requirements and, 111–112
  Excel solutions, 326–329
  facility location problem, 341–344, 351
  fixed-charge problem, 333–336, 351
  formulating problems with 0-1 constraints, 324–325, 329–332, 352
  graphical representation of, 325–326
  introduction, 324
  knapsack problem, 340–341, 351
  mixed-integer, 324, 351, 507
  problems, 357–365
  pure-integer, 324, 351
  sensitivity analysis, 329
  set-covering problem, 336–339, 351
  solved problems, 352–356
  traveling salesperson problem, 344–349, 351–352
  types of, 324–325
  0-1 integer problems, 324–325, 329–332, 352
Interarrival time, 662–663, 711
Interfaces, 5, 108
Intermediate destinations or nodes, 287
Intersections, 370
Inventory analysis, using simulation, 752–757
Inventory Requirements Planning (IRP), 27
Irregular variations, 40, 88
Iso-profit line, 122–125, 126–128

J

Jansses, F., 400
Java, 12
Jia, J., 579
Jockeying, 667, 711
Joint probabilities, 610
Judgmental forecasting methods, 87

K

k-out-of-n alternatives, 330
Kalish, P., 455
Kanaley, M., 439
Kanner, J., 507
Karmakar's method, 107, 135
Kaya, A., 193
Kim, B., 332
Kim, S., 332
Klein, R., 27
Knapsack problem, 340–341, 351
Knowledge-based systems, 12
Kraas, B., 332

L

Labeling procedure, 371–375
Lacroix, B., 439
Lagrange multipliers, 425, 444–449, 456, 459–463
Lagrangian function, 444–449, 456
Lai, K., 15
Languages, simulation, 759
Late configuration, 640
Leading variable, 65
Least squares regression line, 67
Leung, E., 15
Liang, Ting-Peng, 13
Limited calling population, 662, 698–700
Linear programming; *see also* Goal programming;
     Nonlinear programming
  applications of, 108
    agricultural, 186–189, 194
    assignment problems, 192, 194, 298–303
    blending problems, 164–168, 194
    diet problems, 163–164, 194
    financial planning problems for banks, 176–179
    make-or-buy decisions, 185–186, 194
    marketing research problems, 172–176, 194
    maximal flow problem; *see* Maximal flow problems
    media selection problems, 168–172, 194
    multiperiod production scheduling, 181–183, 194
    portfolio selection problems, 179–180, 194
    product-mix problems, 154–163, 194
    production applications, 180–186
    project management problems, 192, 194
    shortest-route problem, 376–378
    workforce scheduling, 183–184, 194
  assumptions of, 111–112
  cases
    Direct Marketing, 204–205
    Son, Ltd., 150–151
  components of, 109–111
  constrained optimization, 106, 113, 135, 433
  constraints; *see* Constraints
  data envelopment analysis (DEA), 189–192, 194
  decision variables, 109, 113, 125
  defined, 107, 135
  development of, 106
  Excel solutions for, 157–163
  extreme point approach, 119–121, 128–129, 135
  formulating of models, 112–115
  fundamental theorem of, 125, 135
  versus goal programming, 474–475
  graphical method, 107, 115–119, 135
  integer programming; *see* Integer programming
  Karmakar's method, 107, 135
  minimization
    assignment problem, 298–299
    example of, 126–129

Linear programming—*Cont.*
  mixed-integer problem, 324, 351, 507
  multiple optimal solutions, 134
  no feasible solution, 131–132
  objective function approach
    change in coefficients, 209–213
    defined, 110, 136, 509
    plotting, 122–125, 126–128
  problems, 142–150, 196–204
  redundant constraints, 133, 136
  sensitivity analysis, 208–226
    case (Red Brand Canners), 270–273
    concept of, 208
    defined, 31, 237
    duality, 226–236
    Excel solutions, 219–224
    integer programming and, 329
    minimization problem, 109, 126–129, 219
    multiple changes, 224–226
    objective function coefficient, change in value in, 209–213
    probability estimates, 573–578
    problems, 246–270
    purpose of, 11, 208
    RHS value of a constraint, changes in, 213–219
    shadow price, 214–216, 231, 237
    solved problems, 238–246
    summary of, 226
  simplex method, 107, 136
  slack and surplus, 129–131, 136, 214
  solved problems, 136–141, 195–196
  transportation problem, 276–287
    aggregate planning, 294–297
    case (Sunshine Tomato, Inc.), 321
    defined, 194, 303
    equal supply and demand, 279
    examples of, 276
    Excel solution, 280–287, 291–294
    formulating the model, 276–279
    location analysis, 297–298, 341–344, 351
    maximization problems, 109, 126, 279–280
    objective of, 185, 279
    problems, 310–320
    solved problems, 303–309
    transshipment problems, 287–294, 303
    unacceptable routes, 280
    unequal supply and demand, 280
  unbounded problems, 132–133
  verbal model, 107–108
Linear regression models, 50, 65–71, 87
Linear trend equation, 50–52
Linearity, 71, 111
Lines, 370
Liu, J., 15

Liu, Y., 193
Local maximum, 426–427, 456
Local minimum, 426–427, 456
Location analysis, 297–298, 341–344, 351
Lucent Technologies, 27

M

M/M/1, 676–678
M/M/S, 678–687
MAD, 77–78, 83–84, 88
Madrid, R., 439
Make-or-buy decisions, 185–186, 194
Management science
  approach
    implementation and follow-up, 11–12
    model analysis, 10–11
    model construction, 10
    problem definition, 9–10
  defined, 4, 30
  development of, 5
  importance and impact of, 27–30
  models, 6–8
  qualitative approach to, 4–5
  quantitative approach to, 4–5
  role of computers and spreadsheets, 15–16
  successful applications of, 27–29
Management Science, 5
MAPE, 80–81, 83–84, 88
Market research, 87
Marketing applications, of linear programming, 168–176
Marketing research problem, 172–176, 194
Markov analysis, 604–657
  absorbing systems, 631–639, 641
  analysis of a three-state matrix, 621–625
  assumptions, 639
  case (Memorial Hospital), 657
  characteristics of, 606
  cyclical systems, 630–632, 641
  Excel solutions, 616–621, 625–630, 636–639
  methods of analysis
    algebraic solution, 614–616, 624–625, 641
    matrix multiplication, 611–613, 623–624, 641
    tree diagram, 609–611, 622–623, 641
  problems, 650–656
  solved problems, 641–649
  system behavior, 608–609
  systems to analyze using, 606
  transient systems, 631–632, 641
  transition probabilities, 606–608, 641
Markov process, 607, 641
Markovian arrivals, Markovian service, and 1 server, 676–678
Markowicz, B., 709
Marshall, S., 193

Maslin, L., 302
Mathematical analysis, 5
Mathematical models, 6, 31
Mathematical simulation, 724
Matrix multiplication, 611–613, 623–624, 641
Maximal flow problems
  algorithm for, 388–391
  defined, 401
  examples, 370
  linear programming and, 393–399
  objectives of, 387
  reverse flow, 391–393
Maximax, 545, 549, 582
Maximin, 544–545, 549, 582
Maximization (max) problem, 109, 126, 279–280
Mean absolute deviation (MAD), 77–78, 83–84, 88
Mean absolute percentage error (MAPE), 80–81, 83–84, 88
Mean forecast error (MFE), 79
Mean percentage error (MPE), 80–81, 83–84, 88
Mean squared error (MSE), 77–78, 83–84, 88
Measure of effectiveness, 11, 31
Media selection problem, 168–172, 194
Merrill Lynch, 29
Metty, T., 507
Milligan, C., 439
Minimax regret, 545–547, 549, 582
Minimization (min) problem
  assignment problem, 298–299
  linear programming example, 126–129
  sensitivity analysis, 219
Minimum spanning tree problem, 370, 384–387, 401
Mixed-integer linear programming problem (MILP), 324, 351, 507
Model parameters, 110, 136, 208
Models
  analysis of, 10–11
  assumptions of, 7–8
  benefits and risks of using, 7
  construction of, 10
  data collection for, 10
  defined, 6, 31
  deterministic, 8, 30
  graphical, 7
  linear programming; *see* Linear programming
  management science, 6–8
  mathematical, 6, 31
  multicriteria decision-making; *see* Multicriteria decision-making models
  network; *see* Network models
  nonlinear; *see* Nonlinear programming
  with one decision variable
    constrained problem, 433–439, 458–459
    unconstrained problem, 425–432, 457–458

Models—*Cont.*
  probabilistic; *see* Probabilistic models
  qualitative, 4–5, 39, 87
  quantitative, 4–5, 87
  simple linear regression, 50, 65–71, 87
  symbolic, 6, 31
  systems approach to, 10
  with two decision variables
    equality constraints, 444–449, 459–463
    multiple constraints, 451–454
    single inequality constraint, 449–454
    unconstrained problem, 439–443
Modularity, 640
Monte Carlo simulation
  defined, 731, 762
  exponential distributions, 737–738, 746
  normal distributions, 738–739, 746
  random numbers, 732–735, 742–743, 762
  theoretical distributions, 733, 735–736
  uniform distributions, 736–737, 743–746
Montgomery, Douglas C., 730n
Moore, T., 507
Morris, T., 507
Motorola, Inc., 507
Moving average
  advantages of, 43
  centered, 61–63, 87
  computation of, 42–43
  defined, 88
  Excel solution, 45–47
  weighted, 44–45
MPE, 80–81, 83–84, 88
MSE, 77–78, 83–84, 88
Multicriteria decision-making models
  analytical hierarchy process (AHP), 493–503
    consistency check, 496–501, 508
    defined, 508
    Excel solutions, 501–503
    pairwise comparisons, 495–501, 509
    proportion matrix, 498–500
    reciprocal rating approach, 496
    when to use, 493
  case (Hi-Tech Incorporated), 534–535
  goal programming
    defined, 474, 508
    deviation variables, 475–476, 508
    Excel solutions, 482–493
    goal constraints, 474, 476, 487, 508
    graphical solutions, 478–482
    introduction to, 474
    versus linear programming, 474–475
    model formulation, 476–482
    no feasible solutions, 132
    objectives of, 475

Multicriteria decision-making models—*Cont.*
    satisficing, 475, 509
    weighted goals, 490–493, 509
  problems, 525–534
  scoring models, 504–506, 509
  solved problems, 509–523
Multiperiod production scheduling, 181–183, 194
Multiple-channel queuing model, 667–668, 678–687, 711
Multiple constraints, 451–454
Multiple objectives, 474
Multiple optical solutions, 134
Multiple phase system, 667, 711
Multiple regression, 66, 72–76, 87
Multiple-variable simulations, 739–742
Multipliers, Lagrange, 425, 444–449, 456, 459–463
Munshaw, G., 455
Murty, K. T., 15

N

Naive forecasts, 42, 61, 88
National Broadcasting Company, 30
Nearest-neighbor rule, 346, 351
Necessary condition, 426, 440, 450, 456
Negative expected value, 578
Negative exponential distribution, 663
Network, 401
Network flow problems; *see* Assignment problems
Network models, 370–420
  case (Furnace County Emergency Response
    Routes), 420
  defined, 370
  diagram of, 370
  maximal flow problems
    algorithm for, 388–391
    defined, 401
    examples of, 370
    linear programming and, 393–399
    objectives of, 387
    reverse flow, 391–393
  minimum spanning tree problem, 370, 384–387, 401
  problems, 412–419
  shortest-route problem, 371–384
    defined, 401
    Excel solution, 378–384
    labeling procedure, 371–375
    linear programming and, 376–378
    objective, 370
    procedure for determining, 375–376
  solved problems, 401–411
  types of, 370
New York City Police Department, 29
Next-event simulations, 726–727, 762
Nodes, 370, 401
Nonbinding constraints, 213–214

Nongoal constraints, 474, 476
Nonlinear programming, 423–470; *see also* Linear
     programming
  case (Koch International Incorporated), 469–470
  difficulty with, 425
  global maximum, 426, 456
  Lagrange multiplier, 425, 444–449, 456, 459–463
  local maximum, 426–427, 456
  models with one decision variable
    constrained problem, 433–439, 458–459
    unconstrained problem, 425–432, 457–458
  models with two decision variables
    equality constraints, 444–449, 459–463
    multiple constraints, 451–454
    single inequality constraint, 449–454
    unconstrained, 439–443
  necessary conditions, 426, 440, 450, 456
  partial derivative, 440, 444–445, 456
  problems, 466–469
  saddle point, 445, 456
  solved problems, 457–466
  sufficient conditions, 426, 441, 451, 456
Nonnegativity constraints, 111, 114, 116, 136
Normal distribution, 738–739, 746
Normality, 71
Normalized pairwise comparison, 496, 509
NORMINV, 746, 762

O

Objective function
  coefficients, change in, 209–213
  defined, 110, 136, 509
  plotting, 122–125, 126–128
  RHS value of a constraint, changes in, 213–219
100 percent rule, 224, 237
One-period tree diagram, 609
Operating characteristics, 673
Operations Research, 5
Opinions, executive, 39, 87
Opportunity loss, 546–547, 582
Optimal solution, 110, 119–125, 136
Optimality, range of, 209, 237
Optimization, constrained, 106, 113, 135, 433; *see also*
    Linear programming
Option bundling, 640
OR/MS, 5
Original cell values, 280
Origins, 276
Oussanov, V., 579
Output cells, 158, 162
Overachievement, 475

P

p-value, 75, 88
Pairwise comparisons, 495–501, 509

Parameters, 110, 136, 208
Partial derivative, 440, 444–445, 456
Path, 401
Payoff table, 542–543, 582
Payoffs, 541
Peeters, W., 400
Perfect information, expected value of, 553–554, 571, 581
Performance target, 474
Permanently labeled, 371–375
Philips Electronics, 400
Physical simulation, 724
Pill, E. K., 640
Planning, aggregate, 294–297
Planning horizon, 85
Poisson distribution, 662–666, 692–701
Popov, A., Jr., 332
Portfolio selection problems, 179–180, 194
Postoptimality analysis; *see* Sensitivity analysis
Postponement, 640
Potts, K., 507
Preemptive service, 702, 711
Present values, 541
Price, shadow, 214–216, 231, 237
Primal, 226, 237
Prioritized goal programming models, 475, 509
Prioritized goals, 483
Priority percentage, 499–500
Priority servicing model, 702–704, 711
Probabilistic models
  decision theory, 540–603
    with additional information, 567–573
    applications of, 540
    components, 540–542
    decision making under certainty, 543–544
    decision making under complete uncertainty,
      544–551
    decision making under risk, 552–556
    decision trees, 556–567, 581
    Excel solutions, 549–551, 555–556, 559–567
    payoff tables, 542–543, 582
    problems, 595–602
    sensitivity analysis, 573–578
    sequential decisions, 557, 559, 564–567, 582
    solved problems, 582–594
    utility, 578–580, 582
  defined, 31
  versus deterministic models, 8
  markov analysis; *see* Markov analysis
  simulation; *see* Simulation
  waiting-line models; *see* Waiting-line models
Probabilistic simulations, 727, 730
Probabilities
  computing the, 571–573
  estimates of, 567–573

Probabilities—*Cont.*
   joint, 610
   transition, 606–608, 641
Probability density function, 668
Probability estimates, 573–578
Probability transition diagrams, 632, 641
Probability vector, 611
Problem solving, 4–5
Processing order, 667, 711
Procter & Gamble, 29
Product-mix problems, 154–163, 194
Production applications, of linear programming,
      180–186
Production scheduling, 181–183, 194
Profit, 22–23
Profit line approach, 122–125, 126–128
Project management problems, 192, 194
Proportion matrix, 498–500
Proportionality constraints, 188
Proportionality requirement, 111, 136
Pruneau, R., 439
Pseudo-random numbers, 760, 762
Psychology of waiting, 707–708
Purchasing, 507
Pure-integer problems, 324, 351
Pyle, M., 350

Q
Qualitative forecasts, 39, 87
Qualitative models, 4–5
Quantitative models
   break-even analysis
      assumptions of, 24–25
      break-even point, 23–24, 30
      components of, 20–23
      defined, 20
      Excel solutions, 25–26
      summary of, 27
   forecasting, 87
   time series; *see* Time series data
   uses for, 4–5
Queue discipline, 667, 711
Queuing models; *see* Waiting-line models
Queuing system, 660, 711

R
Raman, N., 27
RAND(), 742–743, 762
RANDBETWEEN, 744, 762
Random number tables, 732, 762
Random numbers, 732–735, 742–746, 762
Random variations, 40, 88
Range of feasibility, 214–219, 237

Range of insignificance, 212–213, 237
Range of optimality, 209, 237
Raskina, O., 507
Realism criteria, 547–548, 549
Receiving locations, 276
Reciprocal rating approach, 496
Redundant constraints, 133, 136
Regression
   least squares, 67
   multiple, 66, 72–76, 87
   simple linear, 50, 65–71, 87
Regression assumptions, 71–72
Regression coefficients, 68
Regression line, 50, 67–69
Regrets, 546–547, 582
Reneging, 667, 711
Replacement parts illustration, of simulation, 725
Restrictions, 110; *see also* Constraints
Revenue, 20, 31
Reverse flow, 391–393
Right-hand side (RHS) value of a constraint, 208,
      213–219, 237
Risk
   decision making under, 552–556
   defined, 582
   degree of certainty and, 541
Risk averters, 580, 582
Risk takers, 578, 580, 582
Robbings, J., 507
Routing, 709

S
Saddle point, 445, 456
Sahoo, S., 332
Sales, 41
Sales force composites, 39, 87
Samelson, Q., 507
Samples, 567–573
Sampling, 730
San Francisco Police Department, 29
Sappington, D., 709
Satisficing, 475, 509
Scatter plots, 53, 54, 55, 56
Scenario manager, 757–759
Scheduling
   multiperiod production, 181–183, 194
   transportation, 709
   workforce, 183–184, 194, 761
Schneur, A., 507
Schneur, R., 507
Schulman, H., 27
Scientific approach, 9, 31
Scoring models, 504–506, 509
Search techniques, 11

Seasonal relative, 60, 63–64, 88
Seasonal variations, 39–41, 59–64, 88
Sending locations, 276
Sensitivity analysis, 208–226
    case (Red Brand Canners), 270–273
    concept of, 208
    decision theory, 573–578
    defined, 31, 237
    duality, 226–236
    Excel solutions, 219–224
    integer programming and, 329
    minimization problem, 109, 126–129, 219
    multiple changes, 224–226
    objective function coefficient, change in value,
        209–213
    probability estimates, 573–578
    problems, 246–270
    purpose of, 11, 208
    RHS value of a constraint, change in, 213–219
    shadow price, 214–216, 231, 237
    solved problems, 238–246
    summary of, 226
Sequential decisions, 557, 559, 564–567, 582
Service time, 667–668
Set covering problem, 336–339, 351
Shadow price, 214–216, 231, 237
Shortest-route problem, 371–384
    defined, 401
    Excel solution, 378–384
    labeling procedure, 371–375
    linear programming and, 376–378
    objective, 370
    procedure for determining, 375–376
Simple linear regression models, 50, 65–71, 87
Simplex method, 107, 136
Simulate, 724, 762
Simulation, 722–782
    advantages of, 760
    case (Krohler Supermarkets), 781–782
    computer (using Excel)
        discrete distribution with more than two outcomes,
            747–749
        discrete distribution with two outcomes, 746
        inventory analysis, 752–757
        random numbers, 743–746
        waiting lines, 749–752
    continuous, 726
    defined, 762
    deterministic, 727, 730
    discrete, 726
    fixed-interval, 726–727, 762
    languages, 759
    limitations of, 760
    mathematical, 724

Simulation—*Cont.*
    Monte Carlo method
        defined, 731, 762
        exponential distributions, 737–738, 746
        normal distributions, 738–739, 746
        random numbers, 732–735, 742–743, 762
        theoretical distributions, 733, 735–736
        uniform distributions, 736–737, 743–746
    multiple-variable, 739–742
    next-event, 726–727, 762
    physical, 724
    probabilistic, 727, 730
    problems, 770–780
    pseudo-random numbers, 760, 762
    replacement parts illustration, 725
    scenario manager, 757–759
    solved problems, 762–769
    steps in, 727–731
    types of, 726–727
    when to use, 724, 760–761
Simulation runs, 724
Simultaneous equations, 124, 136
Single-channel queuing model, 667–668, 676–678,
        693–698, 700–701, 711
Single inequality constraint, 449–454
Single phase system, 667, 711
Sink, 387, 401
Slack, 129–131, 136, 214
SmartOp, 193
Smith, D., 27
Smith, J., 193
Smoothing, exponential
    defined, 88
    double, 55
    Excel solution, 49–50
    formula for, 47–48
    trend-adjusted, 55, 58–59, 60
Smoothing constant, 47–48, 88
Soft constraints, 474–475, 509
Solver, 16, 19
Sorenson, R., 507
Soumis, F., 439
Source, 387, 401
Spanning trees, 370, 384–387, 401
Specifications, 660–661
Spreadsheets, 16; *see also* Excel
Standard error of estimate, 69
Standard form, 131, 136
State of nature, 582
State of the system, 641
State properties, 611–613
States of nature, 541–542, 574
Statistical Analysis System (SAS), 74
Statistical Package for the Social Sciences (SPSS), 74

Steady-state, 608, 613–616, 641
Stockouts, 41
Sufficient condition, 426, 441, 451, 456
Sullivan, Robert S., 781
Supply and demand, 279–280
Surplus, 129–131, 136, 214
Surveys, consumer, 39, 87
Swaminathan, J., 302
Symbolic models, 6, 31
System, 711
System behavior, 608–609
System utilization, 674–675, 711
Systems approach to model building, 10

T

Taco Bell, 29
Tang, C. S., 86
Target cells, 159, 162
Tayur, S., 193
Techniques for averaging
    exponential smoothing
        defined, 88
        double, 55
        formula for, 47–48
        trend-adjusted, 55, 58–59, 60
        using Excel, 49–50
    moving averages
        advantages of, 43
        centered, 61–63, 87
        computation of, 42–43
        defined, 88
        Excel solution, 45–47
        weighted, 44–45
    naive forecasts, 42, 61, 88
Techniques for cycles, 64–65
Techniques for seasonality, 39–41, 59–64, 88
Techniques for trend
    defined, 39, 50, 88
    equations for, 50–52
    estimating using Excel, 53–57
    patterns, 40–41
    trend-adjusted exponential smoothing, 55, 58–59, 60
Temporary labels, 371–375
Texas Children's Hospital, 28
Theoretical distributions, 733, 735–736
Time series data, 39–65
    defined, 39, 88
    naive, 42, 61, 88
    techniques for averaging; *see* Techniques for averaging
    techniques for cycles, 64–65
    techniques for seasonality, 39–41, 59–64, 88
    techniques for trend
        defined, 39, 50, 88
        equations for, 50–52

Time series data—*Cont.*
    techniques for trend—*Cont.*
        estimating using Excel, 53–57
        patterns, 40–41
        trend-adjusted exponential smoothing, 55, 58–59, 60
Total cost of ownership (TCO), 507
Total cost of waiting, 660–661
Total revenue, 20, 31
Total variable costs, 22–23, 31
Tracking signal, 82–84, 88
Trade-offs, 475
Transient systems, 631–632, 641
Transition constraints, 182
Transition matrix, 607–608, 621–622, 641
Transition probabilities, 606–608, 641
Transportation problems, 276–287
    aggregate planning, 294–297
    case (Sunshine Tomato Inc.), 321
    defined, 194, 303
    equal supply and demand, 279
    examples of, 276
    Excel solution, 280–287, 291–294
    formulating the model, 276–279
    location analysis, 297–298, 341–344, 351
    maximization problems, 279–280
    objective of, 192, 279
    problems, 310–320
    solved problems, 303–309
    transshipment problems, 287–294, 303
    unacceptable routes, 280
    unequal supply and demand, 280
Transportation table, 294–297
Transshipment problems, 287–294, 303
Traveling salesperson problem, 344–349, 351–352
Tree diagrams, 609–611, 622–623, 641
TreePlan, 559–567
Trend
    defined, 39, 50, 88
    equations for, 50–52
    estimating using Excel, 53–57
    patterns, 40–41
    trend-adjusted exponential smoothing, 55, 58–59, 60
Trend-adjusted exponential smoothing, 55, 58–59, 60
Trend-adjusted forecast (TAF), 55
Troyer, L., 193
Tseng, M., 15
Turban, E., 13
Two-period tree diagrams, 610–611
Tyagi, R., 455

U

Unacceptable routes, 280
Unbounded problems, 132–133

Uncertainty
    decision making under complete, 544–551
    defined, 582
    degree of, 541–542
Unconstrained problem
    models with one decision variable, 425–432, 457–458
    models with two decision variables, 439–443
Uncontrolled variable, 7, 31
Underachievement, 475
Unequal supply and demand, 280
Uniform distributions, 736–737, 743–746
United Parcel Service, 28
Unused capacity, 130
Utility, 578–580, 582

V
Validation, 729, 762
Value of waiting-line models, 708–709
van Doremlen, J., 400
Van Ness, Paul, 366
van Wachem, E., 400
Variable costs, 21–23, 31
Variables
    decision; *see* Decision variables
    defined, 31
    dependent, 65
    deviation, 475–476, 508
    discrete random, 663
    independent, 65
    leading, 65
    slack, 130–131
    uncontrolled, 7, 31
Variation
    cyclical, 40, 87
    irregular, 40, 88
    random, 40, 88
    seasonal, 39–41, 59–64, 88
Verbal mode, 107–108
VLOOKUP, 747, 762
Volume, 20, 31

W
Waiting-line models, 658–721
    case (Big Bank), 721
    cost considerations, 660–661, 690–692
    determining line length, 687–690
    elements of
        calling populations, 662, 711
        customer arrivals, 662–663

Waiting-line models—*Cont.*
    elements of—*Cont.*
        exit, 673
        exponential distribution, 663, 669–672, 737–738, 746
        Poisson distribution, 662–666, 692–701
        processing order, 667
        service, 667–668
        waiting lines, 667, 687–690, 749–752
    Excel solutions, 665–666, 672–673, 678, 687, 693–698, 700–701, 705–707
    goals of queuing systems design, 660–661
    measures of system performance, 673–675
    problems, 713–721
    psychology of waiting, 707–708
    queuing models
        any service distribution, 692–694
        constant service time, 695–696
        finite calling population, 662, 698–700, 711
        finite queue length, 696–698
        infinite calling population, 662, 711
        limited calling population, 662, 698–700
        multiple-channel, 667–668, 678–687, 711
        priority servicing model, 702–704
        single-channel, 667–668, 676–678, 693–698, 700–701, 711
    revising priorities, 704–705
    solved problems, 711–712
    value of, 708–709
Waiting lines, 667, 687–690, 749–752
Walkenbach, John, 20
Wan, Y., 15
Weighted goal programming model, 491–493, 509
Weighted goals, 490–493, 509
Weighted moving averages, 44–45
Weighted product scores, 501, 509
Wilde, L., 302
Workbook, 16
Workers' Compensation of British Columbia, 28
Workforce scheduling problems, 183–184, 194
Worksheets, 16–18
Wright, Robert C., 30

Y
Yaniv, E., 193

Z
0-1 integer problems, 324–325, 329–332, 352

STUDENT CD-Rom

Contents

- **Chapter Quizzes** – self-review, self-grading quizzes for each chapter

- **Excel Templates** – includes text examples and solved problems

- **ScreenCam Tutorials** – seven step-by-step, voiceover video tutorials on how to use Excel for management science

- **Excel Files** – includes many Excel solutions and files from examples and solved problems

- **PowerPoint Slides** – overview lectures for review

- **Software**
  Premium Solver
  TreePlan
  Risksim

- **Chapter Supplements**
  Chapter 4S: Linear Programming: The Simplex Method
  Chapter 6S: Transportation and Assignment Solution Procedures
  Chapter 7S: Methods of Solving Integer Programming Problems
  Chapter 9S: Mini Review of Differential Arithmetic

- **Web Links** (Online Learning Center, Operations Management Center)
  www.mhhe.com/stevensonozgurle
  www.mhhe.com/pom